Concrete Design Handbook

CANADIAN
PORTLAND CEMENT ASSOCIATION

ASSOCIATION
CANADIENNE DU CIMENT PORTLAND

116 ALBERT STREET, OTTAWA, ONTARIO, CANADA   K1P 5G3

Copyright© 1995

by

Canadian Portland Cement Association

All rights reserved. This book or any part thereof
must not be reproduced in any form without the
written permission of the Canadian Portland Cement Association.

Second Edition
First Printing August 1995

ISBN 1-896553-00-1

Printed in Canada

CPCA Concrete Design Handbook

Table of Contents

PART I

PART II

Chapter 1 — General

Chapter 2 — Design for Flexure

Chapter 3 — Development and Splices of Reinforcement

Chapter 4 — Shear and Torsion

Chapter 5 — Slabs

Chapter 6 — Deflections

Chapter 7 — Short Columns

Chapter 8 — Slender Columns

Chapter 9 — Footings

Chapter 10 — Prestressed Concrete

Chapter 11 — Seismic Design

Chapter 12 — Anchorage

Chapter 13 — Tilt-up Concrete Wall Panels

GUIDE TO CHAPTERS

PART I

CSA Standard A23.3-94 — "Design of Concrete Structures"

Explanatory Notes on CSA Standard A23.3-94

Index

PART II

PRÉFACE

L'Association canadienne du ciment portland a décidé de refaire son manuel de calcul des structures de béton, suite à la publication de la norme CSA A23.3-94.

Le manuel contient la norme avec notes explicatives en partie I, suivie des 13 chapitres de la partie II. Chacun de ces chapitres contient des textes explicatifs, des exemples et des graphiques et tableaux couvrant une vaste gamme d'applications pratiques, le tout tenant compte des commentaires reçus de la part des utilisateurs de la version précédente.

Etant donné l'ampleur et la nature de ce document qui est sujet à de fréquentes modifications, et dû au fait que différents auteurs participent à sa rédaction, l'Association canadienne du ciment portland a donné priorité à d'autres documents dans son programme de traduction.

L'association peut toutefois, grâce à son personnel technique, répondre à toutes les questions qui lui seront posées et cela dans les deux langues officielles.

FOREWORD

This Handbook supersedes the first edition of the Concrete Design Handbook, first published by the Canadian Portland Cement Association in 1985.

The Concrete design Handbook addresses analysis and design of reinforced concrete structural elements in accordance with CSA Standard A23.3-94, Design of Concrete Structures. This Standard, henceforth referred to as "CSA Standard A23.3", contains significant revisions to the content of the previous edition. These include:

- New provisions accounting for the features of high strength concrete up to 80 MPa.
- Revised provisions for the design of slender columns.
- The adoption of new concrete stress block factors.
- New expressions for the development of reinforcement to take into account the influence of concrete cover, spacing and transverse reinforcement, and epoxy coating on the reinforcement.
- New seismic design provisions that distinguish ductile coupled wall systems from other ductile wall systems.
- A new Clause 23 dealing with the analysis and design of Tilt-up construction.

Material explaining the intent and application of these revisions is included in this Handbook.

A reproduction of the Standard appears in the Handbook, together with explanatory notes on its provisions. This material is followed by a total of thirteen chapters covering many aspects of the structural design of conventionally reinforced and prestressed concrete buildings. Basic information on design for fire resistance and design recommendations for structures which will be exposed to corrosive environments are also included.

The format of this Handbook was selected to aid designers in a systematic manner. Following the CSA Standard and its explanatory notes, each chapter contains informative text and background information on its subject. Design aids covering a broad range of practical applications are provided for design efficiency. Chapters have been prepared by different authors and therefore differ somewhat in the style of presentation. Some authors emphasize reviews of design requirements or trace the background of new provisions, while others concentrate on numerical examples to illustrate applications. Every effort has been made to ensure that a chapter format which best illustrates practical use of the material under consideration has been adopted in all cases. In all example problems, unless otherwise noted, reference to a 'section', 'table', or 'figure' is an implied reference to the Handbook. A reference to a clause is an implied reference to CSA Standard A23.3.

NOTE

This publication has been prepared by the Canadian Portland Cement Association to aid in the design of reinforced concrete building structures. It has been the intent of CPCA to present information in a manner which will serve as an extension to CSA Standard A23.3-94, Design of Concrete Structures, and the other documents referenced herein. While every attempt has been made to present information that is factual and in a useable format, none of the references to the CSA Standard or the National Building Code should be construed as an endorsement of the material appearing in the Handbook by the agencies responsible for the referenced material. It should also be noted that the published edition of the 1995 National Building Code was not available at the time of printing. As a result, the 1995 NBC material contained in Chapter 1 was obtained from an edited draft of the 1995 NBC shortly before it went to print. Slight editorial differences may exist between the NBC Appendix "D" material appearing the Chapter 1 and the published edition of the 1995 NBC.

This publication is intended for the use of professional personnel competent to evaluate the significance and limitations of its content and recommendations, and who will accept responsibility for the application of the material it contains. The authors and the Canadian Portland Cement Association disclaim any and all responsibility for the application of the stated principles and for the accuracy of any of the material contained herein.

ACKNOWLEDGEMENTS

This Handbook was prepared by a team of authors, many of whom are members of the CSA Technical Committee on Reinforced Concrete Design.

Authors involved in the preparation and review of this publication are:

T.I. Campbell	Queen's University
M.P. Collins	University of Toronto
W. Dilger	University of Calgary
G. Fenton	Technical University of Nova Scotia
J. Fowler	Canadian Prestressed Concrete Institute
J. Gardner	University of Ottawa
R.E. Loov	University of Calgary
J.G. MacGregor	MKM Engineering Consultants
R.J. McGrath	Canadian Portland Cement Association
D. Mitchell	McGill University, Montreal
J. Mutrie	Jones Kwong Kishi Ltd. West Vancouver
P. Paultre	Universite de Sherbrooke
T. Rezansoff	University of Saskatchewan, Saskatoon
M. Saatcioglu	University of Ottawa
A. Scanlon	Pennsylvania State University
S.H. Simmonds	University of Alberta, Edmonton
G.T. Suter	Carleton University
G. Weiler	Weiler, Smith, Bowers

Additonal valuable review work was carried out by:

Perry Adebar	University of British Columbia

The material in Chapter 1 is based on the first edition, which was written by S. Cumming, M. Saatcioglu and J.G. MacGregor.

Chapter 10 is also based on the first edition which was written by P. Breeze, W. Dilger and B. Loov. The listed authors have updated this Chapter to reflect current CSA A23.3 requirements.

Permission has kindly been granted by the Canadian Standards Association to reproduce in this Handbook CSA Standard A23.3-94, Design of Concrete Structures.

The permission of the Canadian Commission on Building and Fire Codes to reproduce portions of Appendix "D", Fire Performance Ratings of the National Building Code of Canada 1995, and other selected extracts from the National Building Code of Canada 1995, is gratefully acknowledged.

PART I

CSA STANDARD A23.3-94

Design of Concrete Structures

with

Explanatory Notes

With the permission of the Canadian Standards Association, material is reproduced from CSA Standard A23.3-94 Design of Concrete Structures, which is copyrighted by CSA and copies of which may be purchased from CSA, 178 Rexdale Boulevard, Rexdale, Ontario, M9W 1R3.

Included in this section are Explanatory Notes on the above standard. Pages containing Explanatory Notes are framed with a black border.

The section concludes with an index.

Note:

This copy of the CSA A23.3 Standard will not be updated to reflect amendments made to the original content by CSA. For up-to-date information, see the current edition of the CSA catalogue of standards.

A23.3-94
Design of Concrete Structures

Structures (Design)

ISSN 0317-5669
Published in December 1994
by
Canadian Standards Association
178 Rexdale Boulevard,
Rexdale (Toronto), Ontario, Canada
M9W 1R3

EXPLANATORY NOTES ON
CSA STANDARD A23.3-94

These Explanatory Notes Were Prepared by:

M.P. Collins	R. McGrath
W. Dilger	D. Mitchell
R. Loov	J. Mutrie
J.G. MacGregor	S. Simmonds

The explanation and opinions expressed in these notes are those of the authors and are not intended to be considered the opinion of the CSA Committee responsible for the preparation of the A23.3 Standard nor to detract from this Committee's duties insofar as interpretation and revision of this Standard is concerned.

Copyright © Canadian Portland Cement Association — 1995

Contents

4

9

CSA Technical Committee on Reinforced Concrete Design

D. Mitchell	*Chair*	McGill University, Montréal, Québec
P.C. Breeze	*Vice-Chair*	Con-Force Structures Limited, Calgary, Alberta
S.H. Simmonds	*Secretary*	University of Alberta, Edmonton, Alberta
W.J. Clark		Morrison Hershfield Limited, North York, Ontario
M.P. Collins		University of Toronto, Toronto, Ontario
W.H. Dilger		The University of Calgary, Calgary, Alberta
J.R. Fowler		Canadian Prestressed Concrete Institute, Ottawa, Ontario
A.J. Kaminker		Carruthers and Wallace Limited, Toronto, Ontario
C.J. Kemp		Dominion Construction Ltd., Vancouver, British Columbia
F. Knoll		Nicolet, Chartrand, Knoll Ltd., Montréal, Québec
R.E. Loov		The University of Calgary, Calgary, Alberta
J.G. MacGregor		University of Alberta, Edmonton, Alberta
R.J. McGrath		Canadian Portland Cement Association, Ottawa, Ontario
J.G. Mutrie		Jones, Kwong, Kishi, Consulting Engineers, North Vancouver, British Columbia

T.R. O'Neill	Alberta Public Works, Edmonton, Alberta
A. Perry	CBCL Limited, Halifax, Nova Scotia
M.J. Prosser	Harris Steel Group Inc., Stoney Creek, Ontario
S.S. Wong	City of Etobicoke, Etobicoke, Ontario
W.L. Glover	Canadian Standards Association, Rexdale, Ontario *Administrator*

In addition to the members of the Committee, the following made valuable contribution to the development of this Standard:

Subcommittee Members

P. Adebar	University of British Columbia, Vancouver, British Columbia
S.D.B. Alexander	University of Alberta, Edmonton, Alberta
W.D. Cook	McGill University, Montréal, Québec
R.H. DeVall	Read Jones Christoffersen Ltd., Vancouver, British Columbia
P. Lam	Choukalos Woodburn McKenzie Maranda Ltd., Vancouver, British Columbia
A. Metten	Bush Bohlman & Partners, Vancouver, British Columbia
D.M. Rogowsky	University of Alberta, Edmonton, Alberta
R. Simpson	Glotman Simpson Consulting Engineers, Vancouver, British Columbia

Preface

This is the fourth edition of CSA Standard A23.3, *Design of Concrete Structures*. It is intended for use in the design of concrete structures for buildings in conjunction with CSA Standards A23.1-94 and A23.4-94. It supersedes previous editions published in 1984, 1977, and 1973.

CSA Standard A23.3-94 differs from the previous edition as follows:

(a) New provisions have been added to take account of some of the features of high-strength concrete up to a compressive strength of 80 MPa. These include new expressions for the modulus of elasticity (Clause 8), revised stress block factors and a new expression for the minimum amount of flexural reinforcement (Clause 10), a new expression for the minimum amount of shear reinforcement (Clause 11), and an upper limit on the value of the concrete compressive strength to be used in determining the development and splice length requirements of reinforcement (Clause 12).

(b) Clauses 8 and 9 have been rearranged.

(c) The load factors in Clauses 8.2 and 8.3 are based on those in the *National Building Code of Canada*, 1995.

(d) Clause 10 on Flexure and Axial Loads contains new expressions for determining stress block factors. The provisions for the design of slender columns have been changed and the transmission of column load through floors has been changed.

(e) Clause 11 on Shear and Torsion contains a new design procedure for beams which is based on the modified compression field theory.

(f) Clause 12 on Development and Splices of Reinforcement has new development length expressions which take into account the influence of concrete cover, spacing and transverse reinforcement, and epoxy coating on the reinforcement.

(g) Clause 13 on Two-Way Slab Systems has been revised to permit the use of elastic plate theory, plasticity, elastic frame analysis, or the direct design method for analysing two-way slab systems. Provisions for the shear design of two-way slab systems have been moved from Clause 11 to Clause 13. Provisions for the minimum thickness of two-way slabs have been modified and moved from Clause 9 to Clause 13.

(h) Clause 16 on Precast Concrete includes new provisions for structural integrity.

(i) Clause 18 on Prestressed Concrete has a new expression for the stress in prestressing tendons at factored resistance. Provisions for the shear design of prestressed two-way slab systems have been moved from Clause 11 to Clause 18.

(j) Clause 21 on Special Provision for Seismic Design now distinguishes between ductile coupled walls and other ductile wall systems to conform to new categories in the *National Building Code of Canada*, 1995. Provisions for structures with nominal ductility have been expanded.

(k) Clause 22 on Structural Plain Concrete has been rearranged and simplified.

(l) Clause 23 on Tilt-Up Wall Panels is a new clause for the analysis and design of tilt-up construction.

This Standard was prepared by the CSA Technical Committee on Reinforced Concrete Design under the jurisdiction of the Standards Steering Committee on Structures (Design), and was formally approved by these Committees.

December 1994

Notes:

(1) *Use of the singular does not exclude the plural (and vice versa) when the sense allows.*

(2) *Although the intended primary application of this Standard is stated in its Scope, it is important to note that it remains the responsibility of the users of the Standard to judge its suitability for their particular purpose.*

(3) *This publication was developed by consensus, which is defined by the CSA Regulations Governing Standardization as "substantial agreement reached by concerned interests. Consensus includes an attempt to remove all objections and implies much more than the concept of a simple majority, but not necessarily unanimity." It is consistent with this definition that a member may be included in the Technical Committee list and yet not be in full agreement with all clauses of the publication.*

(4) *CSA Standards are subject to periodic review, and suggestions for their improvement will be referred to the appropriate committee.*

(5) *All enquiries regarding this Standard, including requests for interpretation, should be addressed to Canadian Standards Association, Standards Development, 178 Rexdale Boulevard, Rexdale, Ontario M9W 1R3.*

Requests for interpretation should

(a) define the problem, making reference to the specific clause, and, where appropriate, include an illustrative sketch;

(b) provide an explanation of circumstances surrounding the actual field condition; and

(c) be phrased where possible to permit a specific "yes" or "no" answer.

Interpretations are published in CSA's periodical Info Update. For subscription details, write to CSA Sales Promotion, Info Update, at the address given above.

A23.3-94
Design of Concrete Structures

1. Scope

1.1 General Requirements

1.1.1 General

This Standard provides requirements for the design and strength evaluation of building structures of reinforced and prestressed concrete in accordance with the *National Building Code of Canada.*

Note: *In addition to the requirements of this Standard, it is necessary that the design be carried out in accordance with the provisions of applicable Building Codes governing fire resistance.*

1.1.2 Plain Concrete Building Elements

Requirements for the design of plain concrete building elements are also included in this Standard.

1.1.3 Structural Equivalents

Designs using procedures not covered by this Standard, which are carried out by a person qualified in the specific methods applied, and which provide a level of safety and performance equivalent to design conforming to this Standard, are acceptable if carried out by one of the following methods:

(a) analysis based on generally established theory;

(b) evaluation of a full-scale structure or a prototype by a loading test; or

(c) studies of model analogues.

1.1.4 Special Structures

For special structures such as parking structures, arches, tanks, reservoirs, bins and silos, towers, water towers, blast-resistant structures, and chimneys, the provisions of this Standard shall govern insofar as they are applicable.

Note: *Special requirements for parking structures are specified in CSA Standard S413.*

1.2 Drawings and Related Documents

In addition to the information required by the applicable Building Codes, the drawings and related documents for structures designed in accordance with this Standard shall include:

(a) size and location of all structural elements, reinforcement, and prestressing tendons;

(b) provision for dimensional changes resulting from prestress, creep, shrinkage, and temperature;

(c) locations and details of expansion or contraction joints and permissible locations and details for construction joints;

(d) magnitude and location of prestressing forces;

(e) specified strength of concrete in various parts of the structure at stated ages or

(f) stages of construction and nominal maximum size and type of aggregate;
(g) required cover;
reinforcing steel standard and specified type and grade of reinforcement;
(h) anchorage length and the location and length of lap splices;
(i) type and location of welded splices and mechanical connections of reinforcement;
(j) type and grade of prestressing steel; and
(k) protective coatings for reinforcement, prestressing tendons, and hardware.

1.3 Reference Publications

This Standard refers to the following publications and where such reference is made it shall be to the edition listed below, including all amendments published thereto:

CSA Standards

A23.1-94,
Concrete Materials and Methods of Concrete Construction;
Note: *Selected excerpts from this Standard are presented in Appendix A.*

A23.2-94,
Methods of Test for Concrete;

A23.4-94,
Precast Concrete—Materials and Construction;

G30.5-M1983(R1991),
Welded Steel Wire Fabric for Concrete Reinforcement;

G30.14-M1983(R1991),
Deformed Steel Wire for Concrete Reinforcement;

G30.15-M1983(R1991),
Welded Deformed Steel Wire Fabric for Concrete Reinforcement;

CAN/CSA-G30.18-M92,
Billet-Steel Bars for Concrete Reinforcement;

G279-M1982,
Steel for Prestressed Concrete Tendons;

CAN/CSA-S16.1-94,
Limit States Design of Steel Structures;

S413-94,
Parking Structures;

W186-M1990,
Welding of Reinforcing Bars in Reinforced Concrete Construction.

National Research Council of Canada
National Building Code of Canada, 1995.

Canadian Geotechnical Society
Canadian Foundation Engineering Manual, 1992.

ACI* Standard
318M-Revised 92,
Building Code Requirements for Reinforced Concrete.

ASTM† Standard
C330-89,
Lightweight Aggregates for Structural Concrete;

C469-87,
Test Method for Static Modulus of Elasticity and Poisson's Ratio of Concrete in Compression;

C567-91,
Test Method for Unit Weight of Structural Lightweight Concrete.

*American Concrete Institute.
†American Society for Testing and Materials.

2. Definitions

2.1 Definition of Terms

The following definitions apply in this Standard. Specialized definitions appear in individual Clauses.

Aggregate, low density — aggregate conforming to the requirements of ASTM Standard C330.

Bonded tendon — prestressing tendon that is bonded to concrete either directly or through grouting.

Column — member with a ratio of height to least lateral dimension of 3 or greater, used primarily to support axial compressive load.

Composite concrete flexural members — concrete flexural members of precast or cast-in-place concrete elements, or both, constructed in separate placements but interconnected so that all elements respond to loads as a unit.

Concrete cover — distance from the concrete surface to the nearest surface of reinforcement or prestressing tendon.

Concrete, structural low density — concrete having a 28 day compressive strength not less than 20 MPa and an air dry density not exceeding 1850 kg/m³.

Concrete, structural semi-low density — concrete having a 28 day compressive strength not less than 20 MPa and an air dry density between 1850 and 2150 kg/m³.

Cross tie — a reinforcing bar which passes through the core and ties together the opposite sides of a member.

Curvature friction — friction resulting from bends or curves in the specified prestressing tendon profile.

Deformed reinforcement — deformed reinforcing bars, bar and rod mats, deformed wire, welded smooth wire fabric, and welded deformed wire fabric conforming to Clause 3.1.3.

Designer — person responsible for the design.

Development length — length of embedded reinforcement required to develop the design strength of reinforcement.

Effective depth of section — distance measured from the extreme compression fibre to centroid of the tension reinforcement.

Effective prestress — stress remaining in prestressing tendons after all losses have occurred.

Embedment length — length of embedded reinforcement provided beyond a critical section.

Helical tie — continuously wound reinforcement in the form of a cylindrical helix enclosing longitudinal reinforcement.

Jacking force — temporary force exerted by the device that introduces tension into prestressing tendons.

Limit states — those conditions of a structure in which it ceases to fulfil the function for which it was designed.

Load, dead — specified dead load as defined in the National Building Code of Canada.

Load factor — factor applied to a specified load which, for the limit state under consideration, takes into account the variability of the loads and load patterns and analysis of their effects.

Load, factored — product of a specified load and its load factor.

Load, live — specified live load as defined in the National Building Code of Canada.

Load, specified — load specified by the National Building Code of Canada without load factors.

Load, sustained — specified dead load plus that portion of the specified live load expected to act over a period of time sufficient to cause significant long-time deflection.

Partial prestressing — prestressing such that the calculated tensile stresses under specified loads exceed the limits specified in Clause 18.4.2(c).

Pedestal — upright compression member with a ratio of unsupported height to least lateral dimension of less than 3.

Plain concrete — concrete containing no reinforcing or prestressing steel or with less than the specified minimum for reinforced concrete.

Plain reinforcement — reinforcement that does not conform to the definition of deformed reinforcement.

Precast concrete — concrete elements cast in a location other than their final position in service.

Prestressed concrete — concrete in which internal stresses have been initially introduced so that the subsequent stresses resulting from dead load and superimposed loads are counteracted to a desired degree. This may be accomplished by:

Post-tensioning — a method of prestressing in which the tendons are tensioned after the concrete has hardened; or

Pretensioning — a method of prestressing in which the tendons are tensioned before the concrete is placed.

Reinforced concrete — concrete reinforced with no less than the minimum amount of reinforcement required by Clauses 7 through 21 and 23 of this Standard and designed on the assumption that the two materials act together in resisting forces.

Reinforcement — non-prestressed steel that conforms to Clauses 3.1.2 and 3.1.3.

Resistance, factored — resistance of a member, connection, or cross section calculated in accordance with the provisions and assumptions of this Standard including the application of appropriate resistance factors.

Resistance, nominal — resistance of a member, connection, or cross section calculated in accordance with the provisions and assumptions of this Standard without the inclusion of any resistance factors (Clause 21).

Resistance factor — factor specified in Clause 8 applied to a specified material property or to the resistance of a member for the limit state under consideration, which takes into account the variability of dimensions, material properties, workmanship, type of failure, and uncertainty in the prediction of resistance.

Spiral — helical tie conforming to Clauses 7.6.4 and 10.9.4 of this Standard.

Spiral column — column in which the longitudinal reinforcement is enclosed by a spiral.

Splitting tensile strength — tensile strength of concrete determined by a splitting test.

Stirrup — reinforcement used to resist shear and torsion stresses in a structural member. (The term "stirrups" is usually applied to lateral reinforcement in flexural members and the term "ties" to those in compression members.)

Strength of concrete, specified — compressive strength of concrete used in the design and evaluated in accordance with the provisions of Clause 4.

Tendon — steel element such as wire, bar, or strand, or a bundle of such elements used to impart prestress to concrete, conforming to Clause 3.1.4.

Tie — loop of reinforcing bar or wire enclosing longitudinal reinforcement. See also Stirrup.

Tilt-up Wall Panels — reinforced concrete panels which are site-cast on a horizontal surface, and subsequently tilted to a vertical orientation to form vertical and lateral load resisting building elements.

Transfer — act of transferring force in prestressing tendons from jacks or the pretensioning anchorage to the concrete member.

Wall — vertical slab element, which may or may not be required to carry superimposed in-plane loads.

Wobble friction — friction caused by unintended deviation of prestressing sheath or duct from its specified profile.

Yield strength — specified minimum yield strength or yield point of reinforcement. See also Clause 8.5.

2.2   Standard Notation for Loads and Resistances
Throughout this Standard the subscript "f" denotes a load effect based on factored loads and the subscript "r" denotes a resistance calculated using factored material strengths.

2.3   Standard Notation for Reinforcing Bar Diameters
The nominal diameter, d_b, of metric reinforcing bars may be taken as the bar designation number.

N2.3   Standard Notation for Reinforcing Bar Diameters
In calculations or spacing limits involving the bar diameter, d_b, it is permissible to take d_b equal to the bar designation number.

N2.4   Units
The equations throughout the standard are consistent with the units listed so that units have been deleted from the remainder of the Standard. A designer may use other units but will then need to revise some of the equations which have units embedded in their constants. An example of this is the equation $\ell_{db} = 0.044 d_b f_y$ in Clause 12.3.2. The constant has units of MPa^{-1} in order to make this equation dimensionally consistent.

2.4 Units

Equations appearing in this Standard are compatible with the following units:

force: N (newtons)
length: mm (millimetres)
moment: N·mm
stress: MPa (megapascals)

Whenever the square root of the concrete strength is determined, the units of both the concrete strength and the square root of the concrete strength are to be in megapascals.

Other dimensionally consistent combinations of units may be used provided appropriate adjustments are made to constants in non-homogeneous equations. Some examples of non-homogeneous equations are found in Clauses 12.3.2 and 12.5.2.

3. Materials

3.1 Reinforcement

3.1.1

Reinforcement and prestressing tendons shall conform to the requirements specified in Clause 7 of CSA Standard A23.1. (See also Clause 8.5.)

Note: *Pretensioned epoxy-coated strands should not be used in building structures because in the event of a fire, heat will cause softening of the coating and a reduction in bond.*

3.1.2

All reinforcement shall be deformed bars except that plain bars may be used for spirals and plain bars smaller than 10 mm in diameter may be used for stirrups or ties.

3.1.3

Deformed reinforcement shall include

(a) reinforcing bars having deformations and conforming to CSA Standard G30.18;

(b) welded wire fabric conforming to CSA Standard G30.5, with welded intersections not farther apart than 200 mm in the direction of the principal reinforcement, and with cross wires having a cross sectional area of not less than 35% of that of the principal reinforcement. (See also Clause 11.2.4(b).);

(c) welded wire fabric conforming to CSA Standard G30.15, with welded intersections not farther apart than 400 mm in the direction of the principal reinforcement, and with cross wires having a cross sectional area of not less than 35% of that of the principal reinforcement. (See also Clause 11.2.4(b).); and

(d) deformed wire for concrete reinforcement conforming to CSA Standard G30.14, and not smaller than size MD25.

3.1.4

Prestressing tendons shall conform to CSA Standard G279.

N3.1.1

Geometric properties of standard prestressing tendons are summarized in Table N3.1.1.

Table N3.1.1
Standard Prestressing Tendons

Tendon Type	Grade f_{pu} MPa	Size Designation	Nominal Dimensions Diameter mm	Nominal Dimensions Area mm^2	Nominal Linear Mass kg/m
Seven Wire Strand	1860	9	9.53	55	0.432
	1860	11	11.13	74	0.582
	1860	13	12.70	99	0.775
	1860	15	15.24	140	1.109
	1760	16	15.47	148	1.173
Pre-stressing Wire	1550	5*	5.00	19.6	0.154
	1720	5	5.00	19.6	0.154
	1620	7	7.00	38.5	0.302
	1760	7	7.00	38.5	0.302
	1080	15	15.0	177	1.44
	1030	26	26.5	551	4.48
Deformed Prestressing Bars	1100	26**	26.5	551	4.48
	1030	32	32.0	804	6.53
	1100	32**	32.0	804	6.53
	1030	36	36.0	1018	8.27

* Available with surface indentation
** Available on special order

3.2 Concrete and Other Materials

3.2.1
Cast-in-place concrete and constituent materials shall conform to CSA Standard A23.1.

3.2.2
Precast concrete and constituent materials shall conform to CSA Standard A23.4, except as set forth in Clause 16.2.2.

4. Concrete Quality

4.0 Notation
f'_c = specified compressive strength of concrete

4.1 General

4.1.1
Concrete shall be proportioned and produced in accordance with CSA Standard A23.1 or A23.4, as applicable.

4.1.2
The compressive strength of concrete, f'_c, shall be determined by testing as prescribed in CSA Standard A23.1 or CSA Standard A23.4, as applicable.

4.1.3
Unless otherwise specified, f'_c shall be based on 28-day tests.

5. Mixing and Placing of Concrete
Concrete shall be mixed, placed, and cured in accordance with CSA Standard A23.1 or A23.4, as applicable.

6. Formwork, Embedded Pipes, and Construction Joints

6.1 General
Forms, falsework, construction joints, and the placement of embedded pipes and hardware shall be in accordance with CSA Standard A23.1 or A23.4, as applicable.

6.2 Embedded Pipes and Openings
Embedded pipes and openings for mechanical and other services shall be so located as not to impair significantly the strength of the construction.

N3.1.3
Reinforcing bars conforming to CSA Standard G30.18 with f_y = 400 MPa (Grade 400) are the most frequently used type of reinforcement. The weldable grade bars conforming to CSA Standard G30.18 have a more closely controlled chemical composition which results in a more predictable and more ductile stress-strain response. Reinforcement for structures subjected to seismic action may need to be weldable grade (see Clause 21.2.5).

The geometric properties of standard reinforcing bars are summarized in Table N3.1.3.

**Table N3.1.3
Standard Deformed Reinforcing Bars**

Bar Number*	Nominal Dimension**			Nominal Linear Mass kg/m
	Area mm²	Diameter mm	Perimeter mm	
10	100	11.3	36	0.785
15	200	16.0	50	1.570
20	300	19.5	61	2.355
25	500	25.2	79	3.925
30	700	29.9	94	5.495
35	1000	35.7	112	7.850
45	1500	43.7	137	11.775
55	2000	56.4	177	19.625

* Bar numbers are based on the rounded off nominal diameter of the bars
** Nominal dimensions are equivalent to those of a plain round bar having the same mass per metre as the deformed bar.

6.3 Construction Joints

Provision shall be made for the transfer of shear and other forces through construction joints.

Note: *Construction joints in floors should generally be located near the midspan of slabs, beams, or girders unless a beam intersects a girder in that location. In such cases, the joint in the girder should be offset a distance at least equal to the depth of the beam.*

7. Details of Reinforcement

Note: *The provisions of CSA Standard A23.1 which are referred to in Clause 7 are reproduced in Appendix A.*

7.0 Notation

A_g = gross area of section
d_b = nominal diameter of bar, wire, or prestressing strand (see Clause 2.3)
f_y = specified yield strength of nonprestressed reinforcement
ℓ_d = development length (see Clause 12)

7.1 Hooks and Bends

Note: *The CSA Standard A23.1 requirements for standard hooks and bends are reproduced in Appendix A.*

7.1.1 General

Standard hooks and bends shall conform to Clause 12.2 of CSA Standard A23.1. Nonstandard hooks or bends shall be detailed on the drawings.

7.1.2 Stirrups and Ties

Stirrups and ties, except cross ties, shall have standard stirrup and tie hooks with a bend of at least 135° unless the concrete cover surrounding the hook is restrained against spalling, in which case a bend of at least 90° is permitted. Standard tie hooks with a bend of at least 90° are permitted for ties in columns having a specified concrete compressive strength equal to or less than 50 MPa. No. 20 and No. 25 stirrups and ties shall have inside bend diameters in accordance with the requirements in Table 5 of CSA Standard A23.1.

7.1.3 Cross Ties

Cross ties shall have a standard tie hook with a bend of at least 135° at one end and a standard tie hook with a bend not less than 90° at the other end. The hooks shall engage peripheral longitudinal bars. The 90° hooks of successive cross ties engaging the same longitudinal bar shall be alternated end for end.

7.2 Placing of Reinforcement

7.2.1 General

Placing of reinforcement shall be shown on the drawings and shall be in accordance with the requirements of CSA Standard A23.1 or A23.4, as applicable.

N7. Details of Reinforcement

N7.1

The CSA Standard A23.1 Clauses concerning hooks and bends are reproduced in Appendix A (see Clause A12.2).

7.2.2 Draped Fabric

When welded wire fabric with wire of 6 mm diameter or less is used for slab reinforcement in slabs not exceeding 3 m in span, the reinforcement may be curved from a point near the top of the slab over the support to a point near the bottom of the slab at midspan, provided such reinforcement is either continuous over or securely anchored at the support.

7.3 Tolerances

7.3.1

The tolerances for placing of reinforcement shall conform to those specified in CSA Standards A23.1 or A23.4, as applicable.

7.3.2

When design requirements necessitate closer tolerances than those specified in Clause 7.3.1, such tolerances shall be clearly indicated on the construction drawings.

7.4 Spacing of Reinforcement and Tendons

7.4.1 Bars

7.4.1.1

The minimum clear distance between parallel bars shall conform to the requirements of CSA Standard A23.1.

Note: *The spacing requirements in CSA Standard A23.1-94 differ from those in previous editions.*

7.4.1.2

In walls and one-way slabs other than concrete joist construction, the principal reinforcement shall be spaced not farther apart than 3 times the wall or slab thickness, nor more than 500 mm.

7.4.1.3

The clear distance between adjacent longitudinal reinforcing bars in compression members shall not be greater than 500 mm.

7.4.2 Bundled Bars

7.4.2.1

Groups of parallel reinforcing bars bundled in contact, assumed to act as a unit, with not more than four in any one bundle, may be used. Bundled bars shall be tied, wired, or otherwise fastened together to ensure that they remain in position.

7.4.2.2

Bars larger than No. 35 shall not be bundled in beams or girders.

N7.3.1

See Clause A12.8 in Appendix A.

N7.4.1.1

See Clause A12.5 in Appendix A.

N7.4.2.1

The phrase "bundled in contact" is intended to preclude bundling more than two bars in the same plane. Fig. N7.4.2.1 illustrates acceptable bar arrangements.

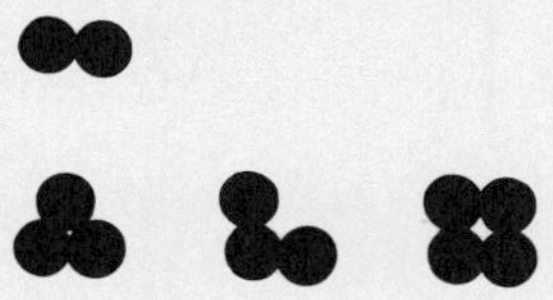

Fig. N7.4.2.1

Bar Arrangements for Bundles

7.4.2.3
Individual bars, in a bundle cut off within the span of flexural members, shall terminate at different points at least 40 bar diameters apart.

7.4.2.4
Where spacing limitations and clear concrete cover are based on bar size, a unit of bundled bars shall be treated as a single bar of a diameter derived from the equivalent total area.

7.4.3 Pretensioning Tendons

7.4.3.1
The clear distance between pretensioning wires or strands at each end of the member shall be not less than $4d_b$ for wire, nor $3d_b$ for strands. Closer vertical spacing and bundling of strands may be permitted in the middle portion of the span.

7.4.3.2
The minimum clear space between groups of bundled strands shall be not less than 1.3 times the nominal maximum size of the coarse aggregate.

7.4.4 Post-tensioning Tendons
The minimum clear distance between post-tensioning tendons and the requirements for bundling of tendons shall conform to CSA Standard A23.1.

7.5 Special Details for Columns and Walls

7.5.1 Offset Bars

7.5.1.1
Where offset bent bars are used, the slope of the inclined portion of the bar with respect to the axis of the column shall not exceed 1:6, and the portions of the bar above and below the offset shall be parallel to the axis of the column. These details shall be shown on the drawings.

7.5.1.2
Adequate horizontal support at the offset bends shall be treated as a matter of design and shall be provided by ties, spirals, or parts of the floor construction; and

(a)   ties or spirals so designed shall be placed not more than 150 mm from the point of the bend;

(b)   horizontal thrust to be resisted shall be assumed as 1.5 times the horizontal component of the factored resistance in the inclined portion of the bar.

7.5.1.3
Where a column or wall face is offset by more than 75 mm, longitudinal bars shall not be offset bent.

N7.4.4
See Clause A25.6.3 in Appendix A.

N7.5.1
The details and design of ties near bends in offset bars are illustrated in Fig. N7.5.1.

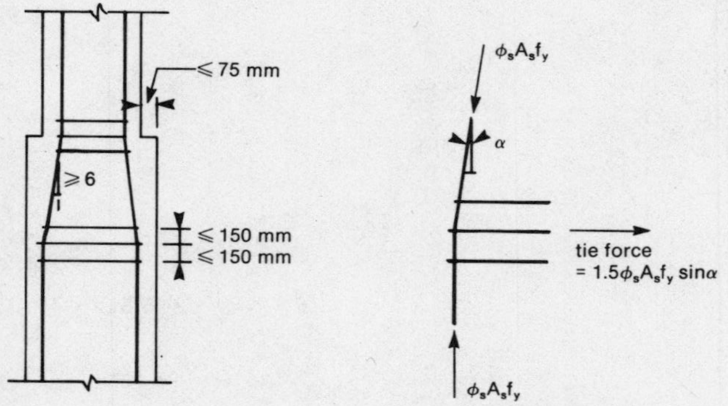

Fig. N7.5.1
Tie Reinforcement Near Offset Bars

7.5.2　Splices and Load Transfer in Metal Cores

In composite columns

(a)　splices of structural steel cores shall be made in accordance with the requirements of CSA Standard CAN/CSA-S16.1; and

(b)　provision shall be made at column bases to transfer the loads to the footings in accordance with Clause 15.8.

7.6　Transverse Reinforcement

7.6.1　General

Transverse reinforcement shall meet the provisions of this Clause and, where shear or torsion reinforcement is required, shall comply with the provisions of Clause 11.

7.6.2　Composite Tied Columns

Transverse reinforcement in composite tied columns shall conform to Clauses 10.18 and 10.19.

7.6.3　Prestressing Tendons

Transverse reinforcement requirements for prestressing tendons shall conform to Clause 18.14.

7.6.4　Spirals for Compression Members

7.6.4.1

Spiral reinforcement for compression members shall conform to Clause 10.9.4 and shall meet the requirements of CSA Standard A23.1, with respect to construction and spacers.

7.6.4.2

Spiral reinforcement shall have a minimum diameter of 6 mm.

7.6.4.3

The pitch or distance between turns of the spirals shall not exceed 1/6 of the core diameter.

7.6.4.4

The clear spacing between successive turns of a spiral shall not exceed 75 mm nor be less than 25 mm.

7.6.5　Ties for Compression Members

7.6.5.1

All nonprestressed bars for tied compression members shall be enclosed by ties having a diameter of at least 30% of that of the largest longitudinal bar when these are No. 30 or smaller, and at least No. 10 in size for No. 35, No. 45, No. 55, and bundled longitudinal bars. Deformed wire or welded wire fabric of equivalent area is allowed.

12

N7.6.4.1
See Clause A12.3 in Appendix A.

7.6.5.2

Tie spacing shall not exceed the smallest of

(a) 16 times the diameter of the smallest longitudinal bars or the smallest bar in a bundle;

(b) 48 tie diameters;

(c) the least dimension of the compression member; and

(d) 300 mm in compression members containing bundled bars.

For specified concrete compressive strengths in excess of 50 MPa, the tie spacing determined above shall be multiplied by 0.75.

7.6.5.3

Ties shall be located not more than 1/2 a tie spacing above the slab or footing and shall be spaced as provided herein to not more than 1/2 a tie spacing below the lowest reinforcement in the slab or drop panel above.

7.6.5.4

Where beams or brackets frame into a column from four directions, the ties may be terminated not more than 75 mm below the lowest reinforcement in the shallowest of such beams or brackets. (See also Clause 7.7.)

7.6.5.5

Ties shall be arranged so that every corner and alternate longitudinal bar shall have lateral support provided by the corner of a tie having an included angle of not more than 135°, and no bar shall be farther than 150 mm clear on either side from such a laterally supported bar.

7.6.5.6

Where the bars are located around the periphery of a circle, a complete circular tie may be used, provided the ends of the ties are lap welded or bent at least 135° around a longitudinal bar, or otherwise anchored within the core of the column.

7.6.5.7

Welded wire fabric of equivalent area may be used if spliced in accordance with Clauses 12.18 and 12.19. The required splice lengths shall be shown on the drawings.

7.6.6   Beams and Girders—Transverse Reinforcement

7.6.6.1

Compression reinforcement in beams and girders shall be enclosed by ties or stirrups satisfying the size and spacing requirements of Clauses 7.6.5.1 and 7.6.5.2 or by welded wire fabric of an equivalent area. Such ties or stirrups shall be provided throughout the distance where compression reinforcement is required.

7.6.6.2

Transverse reinforcement for flexural framing members subject to stress reversals or to torsion at supports shall consist of closed stirrups or spirals extending completely around all main reinforcement.

N7.6.5.2

The purpose of ties is primarily to restrain the longitudinal bars from outward buckling. The diameter and spacing of the ties are therefore related to the diameter of the longitudinal bars with further restrictions relating tie spacing to tie diameter and the least column dimension. For specified concrete strengths greater than 50 MPa, the tie spacings are reduced by 25% to provide more confinement for higher strength concretes.

N7.6.5.5

Fig. N7.6.5.5 illustrates tie arrangements which satisfy the requirements for lateral support of column bars.

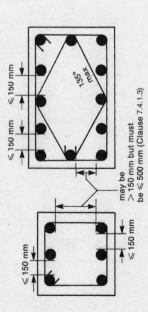

may be
> 150 mm but must
be ≤ 500 mm (Clause 7.4.1.3)

≤ 150 mm

≤ 150 mm

≤ 150 mm

≤ 150 mm

≤ 150 mm

135° max

Fig. N7.6.5.5

Requirements for Lateral Support of Column Bars

N7.6.6.1

Compression reinforcement in beams and girders must be enclosed to prevent buckling.

7.6.6.3

Closed ties or stirrups may be formed in one piece by overlapping standard stirrup or tie end hooks around a longitudinal bar, or they may be formed in one or two pieces, spliced in accordance with the requirements for a Class B splice having a lap of $1.3\ell_d$, or anchored in accordance with Clause 12.13.

7.7   Special Details for Beam-Column Connections

7.7.1

At connections of principal framing elements, such as beams and columns, an enclosure shall be provided for end anchorage of reinforcement terminating in such connections.

7.7.2

Such enclosure may consist of transverse framing members, internal closed ties, spirals, or stirrups.

7.7.3

When gravity load, wind, or other lateral forces cause the transfer of moments from beams to columns, transverse reinforcement (ties), not less than that required by Equation (11-1), shall be provided within connections of framing elements to columns. Except for connections that are part of a primary seismic load-resisting system, this requirement may be waived if the connection is restrained on four sides by beams or slabs of approximately equal depth. (See also Clause 12.11.2.)

7.8   Minimum Reinforcement in Slabs

7.8.1

A minimum area of reinforcement of $0.002A_g$ shall be provided in each direction.

7.8.2

For exposure conditions where crack control is essential, reinforcement in excess of that required by Clause 7.8.1 shall be provided.

7.8.3

Minimum reinforcement shall not be spaced further apart than the smaller of 5 times the slab thickness or 500 mm.

7.8.4

At all sections where it is required, such reinforcement shall be developed for its specified yield strength in conformance with Clause 12.

7.8.5

Prestressing tendons used as minimum reinforcement shall conform to Clause 18.13.

N7.7.3

Edge columns and corner columns and other columns where the connection regions are not restrained by equal depth beams or slabs on all four sides require ties to be placed within the joint region as illustrated in Fig. N7.7.3. These ties will help control diagonal cracking in the joint region, and will improve the anchorage of reinforcement terminating in this region.

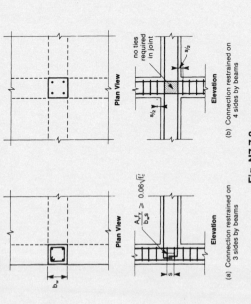

Fig. N7.7.3

Tie Requirements within Connections of Framing Elements

N7.8.1

The purpose of this minimum reinforcement is to provide some control of the cracking caused by shrinkage and temperature effects and to tie the structure together after cracking.

N7.8.2

The amounts of shrinkage and temperature reinforcement given in the previous standards have been found to be inadequate in preventing wide shrinkage and temperature cracks in slabs. In deciding upon appropriate distribution and amounts of reinforcement needed for better crack control the skin reinforcement concept of Clause 10.6.2 provides useful guidance as illustrated in Fig. N7.8.2.

23

7.9 Concrete Protection for Reinforcement

Concrete cover for reinforcement shall be in accordance with the cover requirements of CSA Standard A23.1, A23.4, or S413, as applicable, unless special conditions dictate otherwise.

In all cases concrete cover shall be indicated on the drawings.

Note: *The cover requirements in CSA Standard A23.1-94 differ from those in previous editions.*

8. Design: Limit States, Load Combinations, and Material Properties

8.0 Notation

A_s = area of tension reinforcement

D = dead loads or related internal moments and forces

E = earthquake loads, or related internal moments and forces

E_c = modulus of elasticity of concrete

E_p = modulus of elasticity of prestressing tendons

E_s = modulus of elasticity of reinforcement

f_c' = specified compressive strength of concrete

$\sqrt{f_c'}$ = square root of specified compressive strength of concrete

f_r = modulus of rupture of concrete

f_y = specified yield strength of reinforcement

L = live loads due to intended use and occupancy (includes loads due to cranes); snow, ice, and rain; earth and hydrostatic pressure; static or inertia forces excluding live load due to wind or earthquake

T = cumulative effects of temperature, creep, shrinkage, and differential settlement

W = live loads due to wind, or related internal moments and forces

α_D = load factor on dead loads

α_L = load factor on live loads

α_T = load factor on cumulative effects of temperature, creep, shrinkage, and differential settlement

α_W = load factor on wind loads

ε_s = strain in reinforcement

γ = importance factor

γ_c = density of concrete

λ = factor to account for concrete density

ϕ_a = resistance factor for structural steel

ϕ_c = resistance factor for concrete

ϕ_m = member resistance factor

ϕ_p = resistance factor for prestressing tendons

ϕ_s = resistance factor for reinforcing bars

ψ = load combination factor

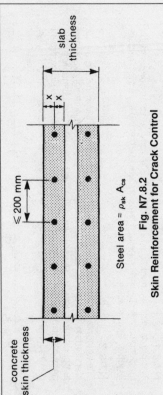

Steel area = $\rho_{sk} A_{cs}$

Fig. N7.8.2
Skin Reinforcement for Crack Control

N8 — Design: Limit States, Load Combinations and Material Properties

Chapters 8 and 9 have been rearranged in this edition of CSA A23.3. Chapter 8 includes general requirements for all structures, limit states, load and resistance factors and properties of steel and concrete for use in design. Chapter 9 deals with structural analysis and computation of deflections.

Sections on structural analysis, formerly in Chapter 8 have been moved to Sections 9.2 and 9.3 and updated. Details of flange widths of T beams and limits on joist dimensions are in the flexural design section of Chapter 10.

N8.1 Limit States

The various limit states to be considered in the design of concrete structures are listed in Sections 8.1.1 through 8.1.5. For specialized structures, such as water tanks, other limit states such as resistance to leaking may also apply.

With the exception of structural integrity, the limit states are listed in the order that they should be considered in a design. First, the concrete strength, water-cement ratio, air entrainment and cement type are chosen to satisfy the intended use and exposure conditions (Section 8.1.1). Second, minimum covers and member sizes are chosen corresponding to the desired fire resistance (Section 8.1.2). Concrete structures are generally proportioned on the basis of the ultimate limit state (8.1.3) and are checked for compliance with various serviceability limit states (Sections 8.1.4.1 through 8.1.4.3). The selection and detailing of the overall structural system should ensure that localized damage will not result in major damage to, or collapse of, the structure as a whole (Section 8.1.5).

8.1 Limit States

8.1.1 Durability

Concrete structures shall satisfy the durability requirements of the applicable CSA Standard, A23.1, A23.4, or S413, for the intended use and exposure conditions.

8.1.2 Fire Resistance

Concrete structures shall satisfy the fire resistance requirements of the applicable Building Code.

8.1.3 Ultimate Limit State

Structures, structural members, and connections shall be designed such that

$$\text{factored resistance} \geq \text{effect of factored loads}$$

where factored resistance is determined in accordance with Clause 8.4 and the effect of factored loads is determined in accordance with Clause 8.3.

Note: *The load factors and load combinations in Clause 8.3 are based on the National Building Code of Canada.*

8.1.4 Serviceability Limit State

8.1.4.1 Deflections

Structures and structural members shall be designed to meet the deflection control requirements of Clause 9.8 with loading in accordance with Clause 8.3.3.

8.1.4.2 Local Damage and Cracking

Structural members and connections shall be designed to meet the requirements of Clauses 10.6, 11.5.5, and 18.4.3 with loadings in accordance with Clause 8.3.3.

8.1.4.3 Vibrations

In the design of structures and structural members, consideration shall be given to controlling vibrations within acceptable limits for the intended use.

Note: *Information on floor vibration and wind vibration can be found in Commentaries A and B in Chapter 4 of the Supplement to the National Building Code of Canada.*

8.1.5 Structural Integrity

Consideration shall be given to the integrity of the overall structural system to minimize the likelihood of a progressive type of collapse.

Note: *Requirements contained in this Standard generally provide a satisfactory level of structural integrity for most concrete structures for buildings. Supplementary provisions for structural integrity may be required for two-way slabs (see Clause 13.11.5), precast concrete structures (see Clause 16.5), tilt-up structures (see Clause 23.3.9), mixed or unusual structural systems, and structures exposed to severe loads such as vehicle impact or chemical explosion. For further guidance see Commentary C in Chapter 4 of the Supplement to the National Building Code of Canada.*

N8.3 Load Combinations

The load factors in this standard are the same as those in the 1995 National Building Code of Canada and are intended for the design of buildings. If other types of structures are designed, such as bridges or tunnel liners, it may be necessary to use load factors derived for such structures.

The 1995 National Building Code of Canada has introduced the three new load combinations for earthquake design given by Equations 8-2, 8-3, and 8-4. There is no load combination factor, ψ, in these equations.

Load factors are intended to account for variability and uncertainty in the magnitude, position and combination of the loads, inaccuracies introduced by the simplified modelling of the loads (e.g. the use of uniform floor loads) and inaccuracies introduced by assumptions made in the structural analysis.

N8.3.2.2 Load Combination Factor

The load combination factor accounts for the reduced probability that two or more independent variable loads would simultaneously reach their full factored values. There is no load combination factor in Equations 8-2, 8-3, and 8-4.

8.2 Loading

8.2.1 Loads

Loads shall be in accordance with Part 4 of the *National Building Code of Canada.*

8.2.2 Imposed Deformations

In addition, consideration shall be given to the effects of forces due to prestressing, temperature, differential settlement, and the forces due to restraint of shrinkage and creep.

8.3 Load Combinations

8.3.1 General

The effect of factored loads acting on a member, its cross section, and its connections to other members in terms of moment, axial load, shear, and torsion shall be computed from factored loads and forces in accordance with the factored load combinations given in Clauses 8.3.2 and 8.3.3 using the values of the load factors, load combination factors, and importance factors given in Clauses 8.3.2.1 to 8.3.2.4.

8.3.2 Load Combinations for Ultimate Limit States

(a) For load combinations not including earthquake the factored load combination shall be taken as:

$$\alpha_D D + \gamma \psi (\alpha_L L + \alpha_W W + \alpha_T T) \qquad (8\text{-}1)$$

(b) For load combinations including earthquake the factored load combinations shall be taken as:

$$1.0D + \gamma(1.0E) \qquad (8\text{-}2)$$

and either:

(i) for storage and assembly occupancies:

$$1.0D + \gamma(1.0L + 1.0E); \quad \text{or} \qquad (8\text{-}3)$$

(ii) for all other occupancies:

$$1.0D + \gamma(0.5L + 1.0E). \qquad (8\text{-}4)$$

8.3.2.1 Load Factors

The load factors, α, shall be equal to

(a) $\alpha_D = 1.25$ except that when the dead load resists overturning, uplift, or reversal of load effect, $\alpha_D = 0.85$;

(b) $\alpha_L = 1.5$;

(c) $\alpha_W = 1.5$; and

(d) $\alpha_T = 1.25$.

Prestressing forces and the effects of prestressing shall have a load factor of 1.0.

8.3.2.2 Load Combination Factor

The load combination factor, ψ, shall be equal to

(a) 1.0 when only one of the loads, L, W, or T is included in Equation (8-1);

(b)   0.70 when two of the loads, L, W, or T are included in Equation (8-1); and
(c)   0.60 when all three of the loads, L, W, or T are included in Equation (8-1).

8.3.2.3 Most Unfavourable Effect

The most unfavourable effect shall be determined by considering the loads, L, W, or T acting alone with $\psi = 1.0$ or in combinations with $\psi = 0.70$ or 0.60.

8.3.2.4 Importance Factor

The importance factor, γ, shall not be less than 1.0 for all buildings, except where it can be shown that collapse is not likely to cause injury or other serious consequences, in which case it shall be not less than 0.8.

8.3.3 Load Combination for Serviceability Checks

The load combination for checking serviceability requirements shall be taken as

$$D + \psi(L + Q + T) \qquad (8\text{-}5)$$

where
ψ is as given in Clauses 8.3.2.2 and 8.3.2.3.

The loads used in Equation (8-5) are the specified loads, except in the case of long time deflection where the sustained loads shall be used. Where applicable, the effects of prestressing shall be included in Equation (8-5).

8.4 Factored Resistance

8.4.1 General

The factored resistance of a member, its cross sections, and its connections shall be taken as the resistance calculated in accordance with the requirements and assumptions of this Standard, using the material resistance factors specified in Clauses 8.4.2 and 8.4.3. In a few cases the factored resistance is the resistance calculated in this way, multiplied by a member resistance factor, ϕ_m, specified in the appropriate Clauses.

Note: *Member resistance factors are used in Clauses 10.15.3, 10.16.3.2, and 23.4.1.3.*

8.4.2 Factored Concrete Strength

The factored concrete strengths used in checking ultimate limit states shall be taken as $\phi_c f'_c$ and $\phi_c \sqrt{f'_c}$, where $\phi_c = 0.60$.

8.4.3 Factored Reinforcement and Tendon Force

The factored force in reinforcing bars, tendons, and structural shapes shall be taken as the product of the resistance factor, ϕ, and the respective steel force as specified in other Clauses of this Standard,
where
$\phi_s = 0.85$ for reinforcing bars
$\phi_p = 0.90$ for prestressing tendons
$\phi_a = 0.90$ for structural steel

N8.3.2.4 Importance Factor

The importance factor is 1.0 unless it can be shown that collapse or structural damage will not have serious consequences. It should be noted that an unmanned building which, for example, houses equipment which is vital to a communications system would have $\gamma = 1.0$.

N8.4 Factored Resistance

Material resistance factors are intended to account for variations in material properties and in section dimensions, to allow for normal inaccuracies in bar placing, and inaccuracies in the design equations. When computing the factored moment resistance, M_r, of a beam, the designer would compute:

$$M_r = \phi_s \left(A_s f_y \right) \left[d - \frac{\phi_s (A_s f_y)}{2 \alpha_1 \phi_c f'_c b} \right]$$

and in the case of factored shear resistance:

$$V_r = 0.2\, \phi_c \sqrt{f'_c}\, b_w d + \frac{\phi_s A_v f_y d}{s}$$

If a plane sections analysis is being employed to determine the factored resistance of a member, an appropriate procedure to account for the material resistance factors is to use the factored stress-strain relationships shown in Fig. N8.4.

Note that ϕ factors are not included in equations giving empirical limits, such as Eq. (10.4) in Clause 10.5.1.2, or in the equations in Clause 12. It was recognized that these empirical equations already included a safety margin.

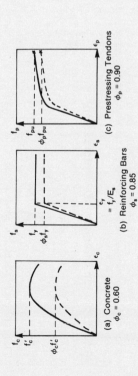

(a) Concrete
$\phi_c = 0.60$

(b) Reinforcing Bars
$= f_y/E_s$
$\phi_s = 0.85$

(c) Prestressing Tendons
$\phi_p = 0.90$

Fig. N8.4
Factored Material Stress-Strain Relationships

8.5 Reinforcement and Tendon Properties for Design

8.5.1 Design Strength for Reinforcement
Design calculations shall be based on the specified yield strength of reinforcement, f_y, which shall not exceed 500 MPa, except for prestressing tendons.

8.5.2 Compression Reinforcement
For compression reinforcement having a specified yield strength exceeding 400 MPa, the value of f_y assumed in design calculations shall not exceed the stress corresponding to a strain of 0.35%.

Note: *CSA Standard G30.18 defines the yield strength of Grade 500 reinforcement at a strain of 0.35%.*

8.5.3 Stress-Strain Curve

8.5.3.1 Reinforcement and Tendon Stress-Strain Curve
The force in the reinforcement shall be calculated as ϕ_s for reinforcing bars and ϕ_p for prestressing tendons, multiplied by the force determined from strain compatibility based on a stress-strain curve representative of the steel.

8.5.3.2 Simplified Reinforcement Stress-Strain Curve
For reinforcement with a specified yield strength of 500 MPa or less, the following assumptions may be used:
(a) for strains less than the yield strain, f_y/E_s, the force in the reinforcement shall be taken as $\phi_s A_s E_s \varepsilon_s$; and
(b) for strains greater than the yield strain, the force in the reinforcement shall be taken as $\phi_s A_s f_y$.

8.5.4 Modulus of Elasticity

8.5.4.1
The modulus of elasticity, E_s, for reinforcement shall be taken as 200,000 MPa.

8.5.4.2
The modulus of elasticity, E_p, for tendons shall be determined by tests or supplied by the manufacturer.

Note: *Typical values of E_p range from 190,000 MPa to 205,000 MPa.*

8.6 Concrete Properties for Design

8.6.1 Design Strength of Concrete

8.6.1.1
Specified concrete compressive strengths used in design shall not be less than 20 MPa nor more than 80 MPa except as allowed in Clause 8.6.1.2

Notes:
(1) *Designers planning to use specified concrete strengths in excess of 50 MPa should*

N8.4.3 Factored Reinforcement and Tendon Force
Clauses 8.4.3 and 8.5.3 require that, when determining the factored resistance of bars and tendons, the resistance factor, ϕ_s, is applied to the bar force, $\phi_s A_s f_y$ or $\phi_s A_s E_s \varepsilon_s$, regardless of whether the steel has yielded or not (see Fig. N8.4). The reason for this is that ϕ_s takes into account deviations in the location of the reinforcement and uncertainty in the prediction of resistances as well as variability in the yield strength.

N8.5.1 Design Strength for Reinforcement
CSA Standard G30.18 specifies requirements for steels with yield strengths of 400 and 500 MPa. Crack widths and deflections may be a problem with f_y in excess of 300 MPa.

N8.5.2
Section 10.1.3 sets the maximum usable concrete compressive strain as 0.0035, up from the 0.003 in previous codes. As a result, the maximum compressive strain which can be developed in reinforcement before the concrete crushes is 0.0035. Steels supplied under a specification which defines the yield strength at strains greater than 0.0035 may not develop their yield strength by the time the concrete crushes. For this reason Section 8.5.2 limits the value of f_y which can be used in design calculations to 400 MPa, which can be achieved by a strain of 0.0035, or to the stress corresponding to that strain.

N8.6.1 Design Strength of Concrete
The strength equations and detailing rules of this standard are applicable for concretes with compressive strengths from 20 to 80 MPa. Section 12.1.1 limits the value of $\sqrt{f'_c}$ for use in bond and anchorage calculations to 8 MPa. This is not intended to imply an upper limit on f'_c of 64 MPa, it merely reflects the upper limit of extensive bond test data. Clauses 21.2.3.1 and 21.2.3.2, respectively, limit the range of strengths in members resisting earthquake-induced forces to 20 to 55 MPa for normal density concretes, and 20 to 30 MPa for structural low density concretes.

Concrete strengths higher than 80 MPa can be used if the designer can establish the structural properties and detailing requirements for the concrete to be used. Major areas requiring documentation are requirements for column ties and confining reinforcement in columns, beams and in beam-column joints.

CSA Standard A23.1-94 defines concretes having compressive strengths of 70 MPa or higher as high-strength concretes and gives special requirements for producing and testing such concretes.

determine whether such concretes are available in their particular locality. Higher strengths may require prequalification of concrete suppliers and contractors, and special construction techniques.

(2) *Additional limitations on concrete strengths are given in Clauses 21.2.3.1 and 21.2.3.2.*

8.6.1.2

The upper limit on specified concrete compressive strength in Clause 8.6.1.1 may be waived if the structural properties and detailing requirements of reinforced concretes having a strength higher than 80 MPa are established for concretes similar to those to be used.

Note: *High-strength concretes vary in their brittleness and need for confinement.*

8.6.1.3

Lower strengths than specified in Clause 8.6.1.1 may be used for mass concrete, plain concrete, or for the strength review of existing structures.

8.6.2 Modulus of Elasticity

8.6.2.1

The modulus of elasticity of concrete in compression, E_c, used in design shall be taken as the average secant modulus for a stress of $0.40f'_c$, determined for similar concrete in accordance with ASTM Standard C469.

Note: *If the modulus of elasticity is critical to the design, a minimum value of E_c shall be specified and shown on the drawings. Before this is done, the designer should establish whether such concrete can be produced in the particular locality.*

8.6.2.2

In lieu of results from tests of similar concrete, it shall be permissible to take the modulus of elasticity, E_c, for concrete with γ_c between 1500 and 2500 kg/m³ as

$$E_c = \left(3300\sqrt{f'_c} + 6900\right)\left(\frac{\gamma_c}{2300}\right)^{1.5} \quad (8\text{-}6)$$

8.6.2.3

In lieu of Clauses 8.6.2.1 and 8.6.2.2 it shall be permissible to take the modulus of elasticity, E_c, of normal density concrete with compressive strength between 20 and 40 MPa as

$$E_c = 4500\sqrt{f'_c} \quad (8\text{-}7)$$

Note: *The value of E_c is affected by the aggregate fraction in the mix, the modulus of elasticity of the aggregates used, and the loading rate. The modulus of elasticity of Canadian concretes will generally be between 80% and 120% of the values given in Clauses 8.6.2.2 and 8.6.2.3.*

8.6.3 Concrete Stress-Strain Relationship

The concrete compressive stress-strain relationship used in design shall conform to Clause 10.1.6.

20

N8.6.2 Modulus of Elasticity

As shown in Figure N8.6.2, the modulus of elasticity is a secant modulus. The modulus of elasticity of Canadian concretes varies considerably as a function of the concrete strength, the density of the concrete and, especially for higher strength concretes, of the type of coarse aggregate. Two new equations are given for the modulus of elasticity. The ten percent reduction in Equation 8-5 reflects experience with Canadian concretes.

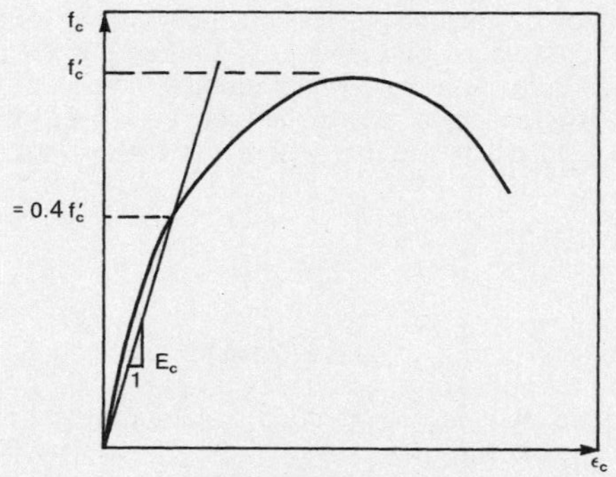

Figure N8.6.2
Modulus of Elasticity of Concrete, E_c

8.6.4 Modulus of Rupture of Concrete

The modulus of rupture, f_r, shall be taken as

$$f_r = 0.6\lambda\sqrt{f'_c} \qquad (8\text{-}8)$$

8.6.5 Modification Factors for Concrete Density

The effect of concrete density on tensile strength and other properties shall be accounted for by the factor λ where

$\lambda = 1.00$ for normal density concrete

$\lambda = 0.85$ for structural semi-low-density concrete in which all the fine aggregate is natural sand

$\lambda = 0.75$ for structural low-density concrete in which none of the fine aggregate is natural sand.

Linear interpolation may be applied based on the fraction of natural sand in the mix.

9. Structural Analysis and Computation of Deflections

9.0 Notation

A'_s = area of compression reinforcement

b = width of compression face of member

c = distance from extreme compression fibre to neutral axis

d = distance from extreme compression fibre to centroid of tension reinforcement

f_r = modulus of rupture of concrete

f_y = specified yield strength of reinforcement

h = overall thickness of member

I_{cr} = transformed moment of inertia of cracked section expressed as the moment of inertia of the equivalent concrete section

I_e = effective moment of inertia for computation of deflection

I_{ec} = value of I_e at continuous end

I_{em} = value of I_e at midspan

I_{e1} = value of I_e at end one of a continuous beam span

I_{e2} = value of I_e at end two of a continuous beam span

I_g = moment of inertia of gross concrete section about centroidal axis, neglecting reinforcement

ℓ_n = (a) length of clear span for positive moment, for negative moment at an exterior support, for shear, or for deflection limits;

(b) the average length of adjacent clear spans for negative moment at interior supports;

(c) length of clear span in long direction of two-way slab construction, measured face-to-face of supports of slabs without beams and face-to-face of beams or other supports of other slabs; or

(d) clear projection of cantilever

M_a = maximum moment in member at load stage at which deflection is computed or at any previous load stage

---

N8.6.5 Modification Factors for Concrete Density

The tensile strength of some low density concretes is lower than that for normal density concrete. This is accounted for by the factor λ which appears in equations for tensile strength of concrete and for shear carried by concrete in Clauses 11, 13, 18, 21, 22 and Appendix D. The governing factor is whether the sand used in the mix is lightweight sand or normal density sand.

N9 Structural Analysis and Computation of Deflections

Chapters 8 and 9 have been rearranged in this edition of CSA A23.3. Chapter 8 includes general requirements for all structures, limit states, load and resistance factors and properties of steel and concrete for use in design. Chapter 9 deals with structural analysis and computation of deflections.

M_{cr} = cracking moment (see Clause 9.8.2.3)
S = factor for creep deflections under sustained loads
w_f = factored load per unit length of beam or per unit area of slab
α_D = load factor on dead loads
y_t = distance from centroidal axis of gross section, neglecting reinforcement, to extreme fibre in tension
γ_c = density of concrete, kg/m³
ρ' = reinforcement ratio for compression reinforcement
= A_s'/bd

9.1 Methods of Analysis

9.1.1
All members of frames or continuous construction shall be designed for the maximum effects of the factored loads as determined by an analysis carried out in accordance with one of the methods of analysis presented in Clauses 9.2 to 9.7.

9.1.2
All structural analyses shall satisfy equilibrium conditions.

9.2 Elastic Frame Analysis
It is permissible to determine load effects by elastic analysis with the assumptions of Clauses 9.2.1 to 9.2.4.

9.2.1 Stiffness

9.2.1.1
Assumptions made for computing the relative flexural and torsional stiffnesses of columns, walls, floors, and roof systems shall be consistent throughout the analysis.

9.2.1.2
Member stiffnesses used in analyses of the lateral deflections of frames or in second-order frame analyses shall be representative of the degree of member cracking and inelastic action at the loading stage for which the analysis is being carried out.

9.2.1.3
The effect of variable cross sections shall be considered both in determining bending moments and in the design of the members.

9.2.2 Span Length

9.2.2.1
In the analysis of continuous frames, the span length shall be taken as the distance from centre-to-centre of supports for the determination of moments using elastic analysis.

N9.1 Methods of Analysis
The section on elastic frame analysis, in Clause 8 of former CSA A23.3 standards has been moved to Clause 9 and expanded to allow other types of analyses. The methods of analyses specified are elastic frame analysis, approximate frame analysis, analysis by strut-and-tie models, elastic stress analysis, elastic plate analysis and plastic analysis.

N9.2.1 Stiffness
As stated in Clause 9.2.1.2, the member stiffnesses used in elastic analyses of lateral deflections of frames, or in second-order frame analyses should be representative of the degree of cracking and inelastic action at the loading stage for which calculations are being carried out. Thus, when computing second-order effects in unbraced or lightly braced structures for use in the design of the columns and beams for strength, the EI assumptions should be representative of the stage just prior to ultimate. The values given in Clause 10.14.1 should be used in such an analysis.

At service loads, member stiffnesses are higher than at ultimate because the cracking and inelastic action are less extensive at service loads. For analyses of lateral frame deflections at service loads the EI of the columns should be taken as 1.0 EI_g (I_g is the gross moment of inertia) or 1.0/0.7 = 1.43 times the value given in Clause 10.14.1. In a similar manner, the service load EI of beams, walls and slabs used in such analyses may be taken as 1.43 times the values given in Clause 10.14.1.

If needed in the analysis, the torsional stiffness may be taken as 0.15 GJ at service loads.

For the analysis of moments in braced frames, where second-order effects are not a problem, it is only necessary that the relative magnitude of the beam and column stiffnesses be modelled in the analysis. Here again, the EI values in Clause 10.14.1 can be used.

Values of E and I for use in the calculation of the gravity load deflection of beams are given in Clauses 9.8.2.3 and 9.8.2.4.

N9.2.2 Span Length
The span lengths used in the analysis of continuous frames should be taken centre-to-centre of joints. Clause 9.2.2.2 allows the moments at the faces of the joints to be used in the design of members. The computation of the moments at the face of the joints should account for the increase in negative moments due to the higher stiffness within the joints. For uniformly loaded prismatic beams it is customary to compute the moment at the face of the joint, M_F as

$$M_F = M_{CL} + Vc/3$$

where M_{CL} is the moment in the beam at the centre of the joint, V is the shear in the beam at the centre of the joint, and c is the width of the column measured parallel to the beam.

9.2.2.2

For beams or one-way slabs built integrally with their supports, or for columns in continuous frames, moments at the faces of the joints may be used for design.

9.2.2.3

The span length of a member that is not built integrally with its supports shall be taken as the clear span plus, at each end, half of its depth, but need not exceed the distance between centres of supports.

9.2.2.4

In the analysis of frames containing shear walls, the effect of the finite width of the wall on the stiffness of the beams framing into the wall shall be considered.

9.2.3   Arrangement of Live Load

9.2.3.1   Continuous Beams and One-Way Slabs

For continuous beams and one-way slabs, the arrangements of live and dead loads may be limited to combinations of

(a)   factored dead load of the structure and factored permanent superimposed dead load on all spans, with factored partition load and factored live load on two adjacent spans;

(b)   factored dead load of the structure and factored permanent superimposed dead load on all spans, with factored partition load and factored live load on alternate spans; and

(c)   factored dead and factored live load on all spans.

Note: *The load factor for the dead load of the structure should be taken as $\alpha_D = 1.25$ in all spans in these loading cases. The superimposed dead load may or may not be patterned with $\alpha_D = 0$ or 1.25, depending on the circumstances.*

9.2.3.2   Two-Way Slabs

Two-way slabs analyzed using the elastic frame method shall be analyzed for the loading patterns specified in Clause 13.9.4.

9.2.4   Redistribution of Moments in Continuous Flexural Members

Except where approximate values for bending moments are used, the negative moments at the supports of continuous flexural members calculated by elastic analysis for any assumed loading arrangement may each be increased or decreased by not more than (30 − 50c/d) per cent, but not more than 20 per cent, and the modified negative moments shall be used for calculation of the moments at sections within the spans.

9.3   Approximate Frame Analysis

9.3.1   General

Except for prestressed concrete, approximate methods of frame analysis may be used for buildings of usual types of construction, spans, and storey heights.

N9.2.2.4

When a structure containing shear walls deflects laterally, the deflections of the walls impose a relative displacement on the ends of the beams as shown in Figure 9.2.2.4. The effect of the width of the shear wall can be accounted by giving the extensions of the beams within the shear walls a very high moment of inertia.

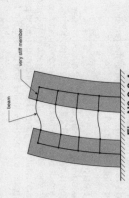

very stiff member

beam

Fig. N9.2.2.4

Idealization of Beams in a Shear-Wall Frame Structure

N9.2.3.1

The Note that follows this clause discusses the load factor for dead load used in analyses involving pattern loads. Self weight dead loads are usually highly correlated from span to span and hence are not patterned. Superimposed dead loads, such as permanent machinery or earth fill may be placed on the structure in a patterned manner.

N9.2.4   Redistribution of Moments in Continuous Flexural Members

Redistribution of elastic bending moments can occur prior to failure as a result of the inelastic deformations in regions with high moments. Sections having low percentages of tension reinforcement or containing compression reinforcement, both of which lead to low c/d ratios, can tolerate larger redistributions. Due to redistribution, the calculated bending moments at a support may be reduced provided that the bending moments in each adjacent span are increased appropriately for the loading case under consideration. Since the loading which causes the highest moment at a support is different from the loading case causing maximum moments in the adjacent spans, allowing for moment redistribution can result in a reduction of required flexural reinforcement at the support and in the spans. This is illustrated in Fig. 9.2.4.

Clause 9.2.4 refers to redistribution of negative moment since this is the normal case in design. Occasionally, as for example, in the case of a continuous inverted T-beam, the amount of redistribution may be limited by the c/d ratio at the point of maximum positive moment.

load case 1 — LL on AB and BC + DL on all spans
load case 2 — LL on BC + DL on all spans
load case 3 — LL on AB and CD + DL on all spans
load case 4 — LL on BC and CD + DL on all spans (not shown)

(a) Moment Diagrams for Pattern Loading

Moment Diagrams Modified as follows:-
(i) load cases 1 and 4 — support moments decreased with corresponding increases made to positive moments
(ii) load cases 2 and 3 — support moments increased with corresponding decreases made to positive moments

(b) Moment Envelopes

Fig. N9.2.4
Illustration of Moment Redistribution

9.3.2 Floor and Roof Loads

It shall be permissible to compute the moments due to floor and roof loads by elastically analysing a portion of the frame consisting of the floor or roof in question, with the columns above and below the floor assumed fixed at their far ends.

9.3.3 Moment and Shear Coefficients

In lieu of a more accurate method of frame analysis, the following approximate moments and shears may be used in the design of continuous beams and one-way slabs (slabs reinforced to resist flexural stresses in only one direction), provided

(a) there are two or more spans;

(b) the spans are approximately equal, with the longer of two adjacent spans not greater than the shorter by more than 20%;

(c) the loads are uniformly distributed;

(d) the factored live load does not exceed 2 times the factored dead load; and

(e) the members are prismatic.

Positive moments

(1) end spans

   (a) discontinuous end unrestrained .... $w_f \ell_n^2/11$

   (b) discontinuous end integral with support .... $w_f \ell_n^2/14$

(2) interior spans .... $w_f \ell_n^2/16$

Negative moments

(1) negative moment at exterior face of first interior support

   (a) two spans .... $w_f \ell_n^2/9$

   (b) more than two spans .... $w_f \ell_n^2/10$

(2) negative moment at other faces of interior supports .... $w_f \ell_n^2/11$

(3) negative moment at interior face of exterior support for members built integrally with supports

   (a) where the support is a spandrel beam or girder .... $w_f \ell_n^2/24$

   (b) where the support is a column .... $w_f \ell_n^2/16$

Shear

(1) shear in end members at face of first interior support .... $1.15 w_f \ell_n/2$

(2) shear at faces of all other supports .... $w_f \ell_n/2$

N9.3 Approximate Frame Analysis

Fig. N9.3.3 summarizes the approximate moments and shears which may be used in lieu of performing a series of frame analyses considering the different live load patterns of Clause 9.2.3.1. It should be noted that Clause 9.3.3(d) is more restrictive than in previous codes.

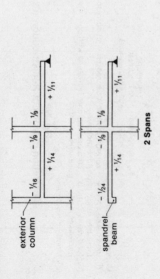

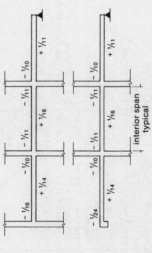

2 Spans

More than 2 Spans

Note: shear force = $1.15 \, w_f \, \ell_n/2$ in end members at face of first interior support and $w_f \, \ell_n/2$ at face of all other supports

moment = coefficient × $w_f \, \ell_n^2$

Fig. N9.3.3
Approximate Moments and Shears for the Design of Flexural Members Satisfying the Conditions of Clause 9.3.3

9.4   Analysis by Strut-and-Tie Models

Strut-and-tie models satisfying the requirements of Clause 11.5 may be used to determine the internal force effects, proportion the reinforcement, and confirm the concrete dimensions.

Note: *Such models are particularly appropriate in regions where engineering beam theory does not apply.*

9.5   Finite Element Analysis

9.5.1

It shall be permissible to use finite element analysis, or other numerical techniques, to determine load effects, provided the differences between the behaviour of the structure and that assumed in the analysis are accounted for.

Note: *The analysis should account for the effects of cracking. If the effects of cracking are not included, the redistribution of stresses due to the anticipated cracking and the effects of this redistribution on the reinforcement layout shall be explicitly considered in the design of the reinforcement.*

9.5.2

Mesh patterns and boundary conditions shall be consistent with geometry, loading, and restraint conditions. Alternative loading cases shall be considered where applicable. Care shall be taken to ensure realistic modelling of the size and stiffness of supporting elements.

9.5.3

Principal reinforcement may be concentrated in bands or tension ties. Anchorage of the reinforcement shall be explicitly considered.

Note: *Principal reinforcement should generally be oriented within ±15° of the direction of the principal tensile stresses. Orthogonal reinforcement may also be provided.*

9.5.4

The analyses shall be checked by independent analyses satisfying equilibrium. If the analysis has not included the effects of cracking of the concrete, this check shall be based on the equilibrium of a system which includes the individual tension tie forces at the force level assumed in the design.

Note: *The strut-and-tie models described in Clauses 9.4 and 11.5 are generally the best way to carry out such a check.*

9.5.5

Crack control and deflections shall be considered.

Note: *Frequently, crack control may be satisfied by the provision of the minimum amounts of distributed reinforcement or skin reinforcement.*

9.6   Elastic Plate Analysis

9.6.1

Analysis of planar structural elements may be based on elastic plate theory (see Clause 13.7).

N9.4   Analysis by Strut and Tie Models

Although strut and tie models can be used to proportion all types of concrete structures, they are generally used in regions where the plane sections theory of flexure is not applicable such as deep beams, discontinuities such as holes, dapped ends, brackets, column-beam joints and prestress anchorage zones.

Clause 9.4 permits the use of strut-and-tie models. Clause 11.5 and the Notes on that clause present design guidance. The most important single requirement of a strut and tie model is that it must be a complete force field which is in equilibrium with the loads and reactions.

N9.5   Finite Element Analysis

Clause 9.5 sets out requirements for the use of finite element analyses in design. Chief among these is the requirement in Clauses 9.5.1 and 9.5.4 that the differences between the idealized finite element model and the reinforced concrete structure be implicitly considered. This is particularly true if an elastic analysis ignoring cracking is used. Clause 9.5.4 requires an independent check of the analysis.

9.7 Plastic Analysis

9.7.1
A plastic analysis shall satisfy either the upper bound theorem or the lower bound theorem of plasticity.

9.7.2
In a plastic analysis it is permissible to assume either a rigid-plastic or elastic-plastic behaviour.

9.7.3
Hinging sections shall be detailed to provide the rotational capacity assumed in the analysis.

9.7.4
Plastic analyses shall not be used for sway frames.

9.8 Control of Deflections

9.8.1 General
Reinforced concrete members subject to flexure shall be designed to have adequate stiffness to limit deflections or any deformations that may adversely affect strength or serviceability of the structure.

9.8.2 One-Way Construction (Nonprestressed)

9.8.2.1 Minimum Thickness
The minimum thickness stipulated in Table 9-1 shall apply to one-way construction not supporting or attached to partitions or other construction likely to be damaged by large deflections, unless computation of deflection indicates a lesser thickness can be used without adverse effects.

9.8.2.2 Immediate Deflections
Where deflections are to be computed, deflections that occur immediately on application of load shall be computed by usual methods or formulae for elastic deflections, considering effects of cracking and reinforcement on member stiffness.
Note: *Deflections may be calculated using formulae for elastic deflections based on effective moments of inertia as specified in Clauses 9.8.2.3 through 9.8.2.5 or by methods based on the integration of curvatures at sections along the span.*

9.8.2.3 E and I
Unless deflections are determined by a more comprehensive analysis, immediate deflection shall be computed using elastic deflection equations, a modulus of elasticity, E_c, for concrete as specified in Clause 8.6.2, and the effective moment of inertia as follows:

$$I_e = I_{cr} + (I_g - I_{cr})\left(\frac{M_{cr}}{M_a}\right)^3 \le I_g \quad (9\text{-}1)$$

N9.7 Plastic Analysis
Braced frames or slabs may be designed using plastic analysis. The use of plastic analysis in two-way slab design is discussed in Clause 13.8.

N9.8 Control of Deflections
This clause deals with gravity-load deflection of beams. The selection of two-way slab thicknesses to control deflection and the computation of slab deflections are considered in Clause 13.3. The control of lateral deflections of frames at service loads is not specifically addressed in this standard. Note N9.2.1 suggests EI values for such an analysis.

N9.8.2.3 E and I
As is illustrated in Fig. N9.8.2.3, the flexural stiffness of a beam decreases after cracking and approaches the fully cracked flexural stiffness, E_cI_{cr}. Equation (9.1) gives an expression for the effective secant stiffness for this case. This equation has been rearranged since the previous code.

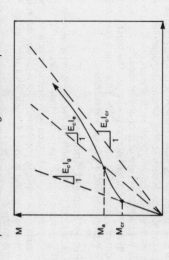

**Fig. N9.8.2.3
Effective Flexural Stiffness**

where

$$M_{cr} = \frac{f_r I_g}{y_t}$$ (9-2)

and f_r is as given in Clause 8.6.4.

Note: *The moment M_a may be due to construction loads.*

9.8.2.4 Moment of Inertia for Continuous Spans

For continuous prismatic members, the effective moment of inertia may be taken as the weighted average of the values obtained from Equation (9-1) for the critical positive and negative moment sections given by:

Two ends continuous:

$$I_{e,avg} = 0.7 I_{em} + 0.15(I_{e1} + I_{e2})$$ (9-3)

One end continuous:

$$I_{e,avg} = 0.85 I_{em} + 0.15 I_{ec}$$ (9-4)

9.8.2.5 Sustained Load Deflections

Unless values are obtained by a more comprehensive analysis, the total immediate, plus long-time deflection for flexural members shall be obtained by multiplying the immediate deflection caused by the sustained load considered, by the factor

$$\left[1 + \frac{S}{1 + 50\rho'}\right]$$ (9-5)

where ρ' shall be the value at midspan for simple and continuous spans and at the support for cantilevers. The time dependent factor, S, for sustained loads may be taken equal to

5 years or more	2.0
12 months	1.4
6 months	1.2
3 months	1.0

9.8.2.6 Deflection Limits

The deflection computed in accordance with Clauses 9.8.2.2 to 9.8.2.5 shall not exceed the limits stipulated in Table 9-2.

9.8.3 Two-Way Construction (Nonprestressed)

Slabs satisfying the minimum thickness given in Clause 13.3 are deemed to satisfy the deflection limit state.

9.8.4 Prestressed Concrete Construction

9.8.4.1 Immediate Deflection

For flexural members designed in accordance with the provisions of Clause 18, immediate deflection shall be computed by usual methods or formulae for elastic deflection.

N9.8.2.5 Sustained Load Deflection

The term $S / (1 + 50 \rho')$ accounts for the long term deflections caused by creep and shrinkage. The total deflection is given by:

$$\Delta_{total} = (\Delta_d + \Delta_{\ell s})\left(1 + \frac{S}{1 + 50\rho'}\right) + (\Delta_\ell - \Delta_{\ell s})$$

The incremental deflection which occurs after partitions are installed is given by:

$$\Delta_{incr.} = (\Delta_d + \Delta_{\ell s})\left(\frac{S}{1 + 50\rho'}\right) + (\Delta_\ell - \Delta_{\ell s})$$

where

Δ_{total} = total immediate and long term deflection
Δ_d = immediate deflection due to dead loads
Δ_ℓ = immediate deflection due to live loads
$\Delta_{\ell s}$ = immediate deflection due to sustained portion of live loads.

If the dead load and the sustained live load are applied at different times it may be desirable to use different values of S for the dead and sustained live load.

N9.8.2.6 Deflection Limits

In checking the limits stipulated in Table 9.2, it is necessary to calculate the long term deflection that will occur after attachment of non-structural elements. In performing these calculations, Fig. N9.8.2.6, which gives the variation of S with load duration, is useful.

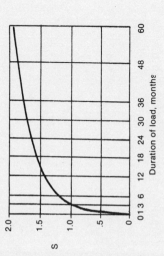

Fig. N9.8.2.6
Variation of Creep Deflection Factor, S, with Load Duration

9.8.4.2 Moment of Inertia

The moment of inertia of the gross concrete section may be used for uncracked sections.

9.8.4.3 Partially Prestressed Members

For partially prestressed members (ie, members not satisfying Clause 18.4.2(c)), the reduction in sectional stiffness caused by cracking shall be taken into account.

9.8.4.4 Sustained Load Deflections

The additional long-time deflection of prestressed concrete members shall be computed taking into account stresses in concrete and steel under sustained load and including effects of creep and shrinkage of concrete and relaxation of steel.

9.8.4.5 Deflection Limits

The computed deflection shall not exceed the limits stipulated in Table 9-2.

9.8.5 Composite Construction

9.8.5.1 Shored Construction

If composite flexural members are supported during construction so that after removal of temporary supports the dead load is resisted by the full composite section, it is permitted to consider the composite member equivalent to a monolithically cast member for the computation of deflection. For nonprestressed composite members containing more than one type of concrete, the portion of the member in compression shall determine whether values in Table 9-1 for normal weight or lightweight concrete shall apply. If deflection is computed, account shall be taken of curvatures resulting from differential shrinkage of precast and cast-in-place components and of axial creep effects in a prestressed concrete member.

9.8.5.2 Unshored Construction

If the thickness of a nonprestressed precast flexural member meets the requirements of Table 9-1, deflection need not be computed. If the thickness of a nonprestressed composite member meets the requirements of Table 9-1, it is not required to compute deflection occurring after the member becomes composite, but the long-term deflection of the precast member should be investigated for magnitude and duration of load prior to beginning of effective composite action.

9.8.5.3 Deflection Limits

Deflection computed in accordance with Clauses 9.8.5.1 and 9.8.5.2 shall not exceed limits stipulated in Table 9-2.

N9.8.4.3

See N18.4.3 for more information.

N Table 9-2 Maximum Permissible Computed Deflections

Ponding may be a problem for medium to long span roofs in regions where snow loads are light. See Commentary I of Chapter 4 of the Supplement to the National Building Code for further guidance. Minor cracking of partitions may occur even if the $\ell / 480$ deflection limit is satisfied.

Table 9-1
Thickness Below Which Deflections Must be Computed for Nonprestressed Beams or One-Way Slabs Not Supporting or Attached to Partitions or Other Construction Likely to be Damaged by Large Deflections
(See Clauses 9.8.2.1 and 9.8.5.)

| | Minimum thickness, h | | | |
	Simply supported	One end continuous	Both ends continuous	Cantilever
Solid one-way slabs	$\ell_n/20$	$\ell_n/24$	$\ell_n/28$	$\ell_n/10$
Beams or ribbed one-way slabs	$\ell_n/16$	$\ell_n/18.5$	$\ell_n/21$	$\ell_n/8$

Note: *Values given shall be used directly for members with normal density concrete, where $\gamma_c > 2150$ kg/m³, and Grade 400 reinforcement. For other conditions the values shall be modified as follows:*

(a) *for structural low-density concrete and structural semi-low-density concrete, the values shall be multiplied by $(1.65 - 0.0003\,\gamma_c)$, but not less than 1.00, where γ_c is the density in kg/m³; and*

(b) *for f_y other than 400 MPa, the values shall be multiplied by $(0.4 + f_y/670)$.*

Table 9-2
Maximum Permissible Computed Deflections
(See Clauses 9.8.2.6, 9.8.4.5, 9.8.5.3, 13.3.2, and 13.3.6.)

Type of member	Deflection to be considered	Deflection limitation
Flat roofs not supporting or attached to nonstructural elements likely to be damaged by large deflections	Immediate deflection due to specified live load, L	$\ell_n/180$ *
Floors not supporting or attached to nonstructural elements likely to be damaged by large deflections	Immediate deflection due to specified live load, L	$\ell_n/360$
Roof or floor construction supporting or attached to nonstructural elements likely to be damaged by large deflections	That part of the total deflection occurring after attachment of nonstructural elements (sum of the long-time deflection due to all sustained loads and the immediate deflection due to any additional live load) ‡	$\ell_n/480$ †
Roof or floor construction supporting or attached to nonstructural elements not likely to be damaged by large deflections		$\ell_n/240$ §

* *Limit not intended to safeguard against ponding. Ponding should be checked by suitable calculations of deflection, including added deflections due to ponded water, and considering long-time effects of all sustained loads, camber, construction tolerances, and reliability of provisions for drainage.*

† *Limit may be exceeded if adequate measures are taken to prevent damage to supported or attached elements.*

‡ *Long-time deflections shall be determined in accordance with Clause 9.8.2.5 or 9.8.4.4 but may be reduced by the amount of deflection calculated to occur before the attachment of nonstructural elements.*

§ *But not greater than the tolerance provided for nonstructural elements. Limit may be exceeded if camber is provided so that total deflection minus camber does not exceed the limit.*

10. Flexure and Axial Loads

10.0 Notation

a = depth of equivalent rectangular stress block as defined in Clause 10.1.7

A = effective tension area of concrete surrounding the flexural tension reinforcement and extending from the extreme tension fibre to the centroid of the flexural tension reinforcement and an equal distance past that centroid, divided by the number of bars or wires. When the flexural reinforcement consists of different bar or wire sizes, the number of bars or wires used to compute A shall be taken as the total area of reinforcement divided by the area of the largest bar or wire used.

A_c = area of core of spirally reinforced compression member measured to outside diameter of spiral

A_{cs} = area of concrete in strips along exposed side faces of beams (Clause 10.6.2)

A_g = gross area of section

A_p = area of prestressing tendons

A_s = area of tension reinforcement

A_{smin} = minimum area of tension reinforcement

A_{st} = total area of longitudinal reinforcement

A_t = area of structural steel shape, pipe, or tubing in a composite section

A_1 = loaded area

A_2 = area of the lower base of the largest frustum of a pyramid, cone, or tapered wedge, contained wholly within the support and having for its upper base the loaded area, and having side slopes of 1 vertical to 2 horizontal (Clause 10.8.1)

b = width of compression face of member

b_t = width of tension zone of section

c = distance from extreme compression fibre to neutral axis

C_m = factor relating actual moment diagram to an equivalent uniform moment diagram

d = distance from extreme compression fibre to centroid of tension reinforcement

d_c = distance from extreme tension fibre to the centre of the longitudinal bar or wire located closest thereto

E_c = modulus of elasticity of concrete (Clause 8.6.2)

E_s = modulus of elasticity of reinforcement (Clause 8.5.4.1)

EI = flexural stiffness of compression member

f'_c = specified compressive strength of concrete

f'_{cc} = specified compressive strength of concrete in columns

f'_{ce} = effective compressive strength of concrete in columns

f'_{cs} = specified compressive strength of concrete in floor slab

f_{pr} = stress in prestressing tendons when concrete reaches limiting compressive strain

f_r = modulus of rupture (Clause 8.6.4)

f_s = calculated stress in reinforcement at specified loads

f_y = specified yield strength of reinforcement

F_y = specified yield strength of structural steel section

---

h = overall thickness of member, or overall depth of beam

I_g = moment of inertia of gross concrete section about centroidal axis, neglecting reinforcement

I_{st} = moment of inertia of reinforcement about centroidal axis of member cross section

I_t = moment of inertia of structural steel shape, pipe, or tubing about centroidal axis of composite member cross section

k = effective length factor for compression members

ℓ_c = length of a compression member in a frame, measured from centre to centre of the joints in the frame

ℓ_u = unsupported length of compression member

M_c = magnified factored moment to be used for design of compression member

M_{cr} = cracking moment

M_f = factored moment

M_r = factored moment resistance

M_s = factored end moment on a compression member due to loads which result in appreciable sway, calculated using a first-order elastic frame analysis

M_1 = smaller factored end moment on a compression member and associated with the same loading case as M_2, positive if member is bent in single curvature, negative if bent in double curvature

M_{1ns} = factored end moment on a compression member at the end at which M_1 acts, due to loads that cause no appreciable sway, calculated using a first order elastic frame analysis

M_{1s} = factored end moment on a compression member at the end at which M_1 acts, due to loads that cause appreciable sway, calculated using a first-order elastic frame analysis

M_2 = larger factored end moment on a compression member, always positive

M_{2ns} = factored end moment on a compression member at the end at which M_2 acts, due to loads that cause no appreciable sway, calculated using a first-order elastic frame analysis

M_{2s} = factored end moment on a compression member at the end at which M_2 acts, due to loads that cause appreciable sway, calculated using a first-order elastic frame analysis

P_c = critical axial load (Equation (10-17))

P_f = factored axial load

P_{ro} = factored axial load resistance at zero eccentricity

P_{rmax} = maximum axial load resistance calculated using Equations (10-8) and (10-9)

Q = stability index for a storey (Clause 10.14.4)

r = radius of gyration of cross section of a compression member

V_f = factored horizontal shear in a storey

z = quantity limiting distribution of flexural reinforcement (Clause 10.6.1)

α_1 = ratio of average stress in rectangular compression block to the specified concrete strength (Clause 10.1.7)

β_1 = ratio of depth of rectangular compression block to depth to the neutral axis (Clause 10.1.7)

β_d = (a) for non-sway frames and for stability checks of sway-frames carried out in accordance with Clause 10.16.5, β_d is the ratio of the maximum

(b)   factored axial dead load to the total factored axial load for sway frames, except as required in Clause 10.16.5, β_d is the ratio of the maximum factored sustained shear within a storey to the maximum total factored shear in that storey

ϵ_s = strain in reinforcement

δ_s = moment magnification factor accounting for second order effects of vertical load acting on a structure in a laterally displaced configuration (Clause 10.16.3)

Δ_o = relative lateral deflection of the top and bottom of a storey due to V_f computed using a first order elastic frame analysis and the stiffness values satisfying Clause 10.14.1

ρ = ratio of tension reinforcement = A_s/bd

ρ_s = ratio of volume of spiral reinforcement to total volume of core (out-out-of spirals) of a spirally reinforced compression member

ρ_{sk} = ratio of area of skin reinforcement to A_{cs}

ρ_t = ratio of total area of reinforcing steel to gross concrete section

ϕ_a = resistance factor for structural steel (Clause 8.4.3)

ϕ_c = resistance factor for concrete (Clause 8.4.2)

ϕ_m = member resistance factor (Clauses 10.15.3 and 10.16.3.2)

ϕ_s = resistance factor for reinforcing bars (Clause 8.4.3)

10.1   General Principles

10.1.1   General

The factored moment and axial load resistance of members shall be based on strain compatibility and equilibrium using material resistance factors and material properties specified in Clause 8 and the additional assumptions in Clause 10.1.2 to 10.1.7.

10.1.2   Plane Sections Assumption

Strain in reinforcement and concrete shall be assumed directly proportional to the distance from the neutral axis, except for unbonded tendons and deep flexural members as defined in Clause 10.7 and in regions of discontinuities.

10.1.3   Maximum Concrete Strain

The maximum strain at the extreme concrete compression fibre shall be assumed to be 0.0035.

10.1.4   Balanced Strain Conditions

Balanced strain conditions exist at a cross section when the tension reinforcement reaches its yield strain just as the concrete in compression reaches its maximum strain of 0.0035.

10.1.5   Tensile Strength of Concrete

The tensile strength of concrete shall be neglected in the calculation of the factored flexural resistance of reinforced and prestressed concrete members.

N10   Flexure and Axial Loads

Clause 10 has been extensively rearranged, incorporating some items formerly in Clause 8. Clause 10.1 presents the basic assumptions for both flexural and axial load resistance. Clauses 10.2 through 10.7 deal with concerns related to flexural members. Items such as T-beam flanges and joist geometry have been relocated here. Clause 10.8 deals with bearing, and Clauses 10.9 through 10.19 deal with columns.

N10.1   General Principles

Fig. N10.1 illustrates the plane section method which uses equilibrium conditions, compatibility conditions and stress-strain relationships for concrete and reinforcement.

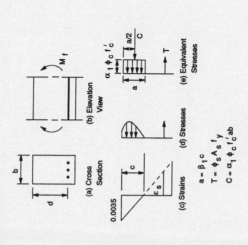

$a = \beta_1 c$

$T = \phi_s A_s f_y$

$C = \alpha_1 \phi_c f'_c ab$

**Fig. N10.1
Plane Sections Method**

N10.1.3   Maximum Concrete Strain

This strain has been increased to 0.0035 because this is more representative of the strain at peak load for the higher strength concretes now being used. This is the value which has been commonly used in Europe for many years.

N10.1.4   Balanced Strain Conditions

The balanced strain condition is illustrated in Fig. N10.1.4.

10.1.6 Concrete Stress-Strain Relationship

The relationship between the compressive stress and concrete strain may be based on stress-strain curves or assumed to be any shape that results in prediction of strength in substantial agreement with results of comprehensive tests.

Note: *To account for differences between the in-place strength and the strength of standard cylinders, stress blocks should be based on stress-strain curves with a peak stress no greater than $0.9f'_c$. The equations in Clause 10.1.7 include this factor.*

10.1.7 Equivalent Rectangular Concrete Stress Distribution

The requirements of Clause 10.1.6 may be satisfied by an equivalent rectangular concrete stress distribution defined by the following:

(a) a concrete stress of $\alpha_1\phi_c f'_c$ shall be assumed uniformly distributed over an equivalent compression zone bounded by edges of the cross section and a straight line located parallel to the neutral axis at a distance $a = \beta_1 c$ from the fibre of maximum compressive strain;

(b) the distance c shall be measured in a direction perpendicular to that axis; and

(c) the factors α_1 and β_1 shall be taken as:

$$\alpha_1 = 0.85 - 0.0015f'_c \geq 0.67 \qquad (10\text{-}1)$$

$$\beta_1 = 0.97 - 0.0025f'_c \geq 0.67 \qquad (10\text{-}2)$$

10.2 Flexural Members—Distance Between Lateral Supports

10.2.1

Unless a stability analysis, including the effects of torsional loading, is carried out, beams shall comply with the limits specified in Clauses 10.2.2 and 10.2.3.

10.2.2

For a simply supported or continuous beam, the distance between points at which lateral support is provided shall not exceed the smaller of 50b or $200b^2/d$.

10.2.3

For a cantilever beam having lateral restraint at the support, the distance between the face of the support and the end of the cantilever shall not exceed the smaller of 25b or $100b^2/d$.

10.3 Flexural Members—T-beams

10.3.1

In T-beams, the flange and web shall be built integrally or otherwise effectively bonded together.

10.3.2

A floor topping shall not be included as part of a structural member unless it is placed monolithically with the floor slab or designed in accordance with the requirements of Clause 17.

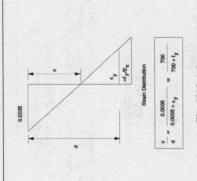

Fig. N10.1.4
Balanced Strain Conditions

N10.1.6 Concrete Stress-Strain Relationship

The concrete in a structure is not expected to be as strong as the control cylinders which are cast from the same batch. This occurs from a variety of causes including bleeding, differences in compaction and differences in loading and restraint.

N10.1.7 Equivalent Rectangular Concrete Stress Distribution

The value of β_1 has been increased and a factor α_1 has been introduced to replace the former constant of 0.85. These changes have been made to take into account the more nearly triangular stress block of higher strengths of concrete. This change will have virtually no effect for lightly loaded beams with small compressive stress blocks. The major change will be a reduction of the predicted strength of columns with large c/d ratios. T-beams with thin flanges and beams with high c/d ratios will have slightly reduced factored resistances. To keep these factors simple, straight-line variations have been assumed that are applicable throughout the range of the current standard (20 MPa to 80 MPa). The minimum values of 0.67 do not apply until $f'_c > 125$ MPa.

N10.2 Flexural Members — Distance Between Lateral Supports

Lateral instability is more critical for narrow deep beams and for beams subjected to eccentric or inclined loads.

10.3.3

The effective flange width of T-beams shall be based on overhanging flange widths on each side of the web which shall not be taken greater than the smallest of:

(a)   1/5 the span length for a simply supported beam;

(b)   1/10 the span length for a continuous beam;

(c)   12 times the flange thickness; or

(d)   1/2 the clear distance to the next web.

10.3.4

For beams with a slab on one side only, the effective overhanging flange width shall not be taken greater than the smallest of:

(a)   1/12 the span length of the beam;

(b)   6 times the flange thickness; or

(c)   1/2 the clear distance to the next web.

10.4   Flexural Members—Joist Construction

10.4.1

Joist construction shall consist of a monolithic combination of regularly spaced ribs and a top slab arranged to span in one direction or two orthogonal directions. Joist construction shall meet the following limits:

(a)   Minimum rib width   . . . .   100 mm;

(b)   Maximum rib depth   . . . .   3.5 times the minimum width of rib;

(c)   Maximum clear distance between ribs   . . . .   800 mm;

(d)   Minimum slab thickness:

      (i)   . . . .   1/12 of clear distance between ribs;

      (ii)   . . . .   50 mm.

10.4.2

Construction not meeting the limitations of Clause 10.4.1 shall be designed as slabs and beams.

10.5   Flexural Members—Reinforcement

10.5.1   Minimum Reinforcement

10.5.1.1

At every section of a flexural member where tensile reinforcement is required by analysis, minimum reinforcement shall be proportioned so that:

$$M_r \geq 1.2 M_{cr} \hspace{3cm} \text{(10-3)}$$

where the cracking moment, M_{cr}, is calculated using the modulus of rupture, f_r, given in Clause 8.6.4.

N10.5.1   Minimum Reinforcement

The provision of a minimum amount of flexural reinforcement is intended to prevent a brittle failure at first cracking by providing adequate post-cracking strength. Footings of uniform thickness can be designed according to Clause 7.8.

10.5.1.2

In lieu of Clause 10.5.1.1, minimum reinforcement may be determined from:

(a) for slabs and footings, the requirements of Clause 7.8;

(b) for other flexural members,

$$A_{smin} = \frac{0.2\sqrt{f'_c}}{f_y} b_t h \tag{10-4}$$

where b_t is the width of the tension zone of the section considered.

10.5.1.3

The requirements of Clauses 10.5.1.1 and 10.5.1.2 may be waived if the factored moment resistance, M_r, is at least one-third greater than the factored moment, M_f.

10.5.2 Limit of c/d for Yielding of Tension Reinforcement

The tension reinforcement in flexural members shall not be assumed to reach yield unless:

$$\frac{c}{d} \le \frac{700}{700 + f_y} \tag{10-5}$$

When c/d exceeds this limit, the stress in the tension reinforcement must be computed based on strain compatibility.

10.5.3 Reinforcement in T-Beam Flanges

10.5.3.1 Flexural Tension Reinforcement

Where flanges are in tension, part of the flexural tension reinforcement shall be distributed over an overhanging flange width equal to 1/20 of the beam span, or the width defined in Clause 10.3, whichever is smaller. The area of this reinforcement shall not be less than 0.004 times the gross area of the overhanging flange.

10.5.3.2 Transverse Reinforcement

Where the principal reinforcement in the slab forming a T-beam flange is parallel to the beam, transverse reinforcement meeting the requirement of Equation (10-4) shall extend past the face of the web a distance of 0.3 times the clear distance between the webs of the T-beams and shall extend at least to the outer bars of the flexural tension reinforcement required in Clause 10.5.3.1.

10.6 Beams and One-Way Slabs—Crack Control

10.6.1 Crack Control Parameter

Bars in flexural tension zones shall be spaced so that the quantity z given by

$$z = f_s (d_c A)^{1/3} \tag{10-6}$$

does not exceed 30 000 N/mm for interior exposure and 25 000 N/mm for exterior exposure. The calculated stress in reinforcement at specified load f_s shall be computed as the moment divided by the product of the steel area and the internal moment arm. In lieu of such computations, f_s may be taken as 60% of the specified yield strength f_y. In calculating d_c and A, the effective clear concrete cover need not be taken greater than 50 mm. If epoxy

---

N10.5.1.2

Eq. (10-4) has been altered so that more reinforcement is required for higher concrete strengths while the requirements for low strength concrete has been slightly reduced.

N10.5.2 Limit of c/d for Yielding of Tension Reinforcement

The strain distribution corresponding to Eq. 10-5 is illustrated in Fig. N10.1.4. The factored concrete strength $\phi_c f'_c$ and the factored bar force $\phi_s A_s f_s$ are used when calculating the neutral axis depth c = a/β_1.

It should be noted that the amount of reinforcement corresponding to c/d = 700/(700 + f_y) is very large and will be difficult to place. Although allowed, it will seldom, if ever, be economical to design beams using amounts of reinforcement which would result in values of c/d larger than this. Columns, on the other hand, frequently have c/d ratios larger than this value. The change of the constant in this equation from 600 to 700 reflects the increased concrete strain assumed at failure.

N10.5.3 Reinforcement in T-Beam Flanges

To help the designer, the required reinforcing has been more explicitly defined. The intent is to ensure sufficient reinforcement in the tension zone of the slab adjacent to the web so that cracks in this region will be adequately controlled.

N10.5.3.2 Transverse Reinforcement

This situation normally occurs when a number of smaller beams supporting a one-way slab are supported by a girder which therefore is parallel to the one-way slab. The transverse reinforcement in the girder is required to extend beyond the web of the girder, a distance equal to 0.3 of the clear spacing between the smaller beams. The purpose of this Clause is to control the cracks which will tend to occur in the flange above the edge of the web, and to avoid the necessity of complex computations to determine a suitable amount of reinforcement.

N10.6.1 Crack Control Parameter

Equation (10-6) is intended to provide a distribution of flexural reinforcement that will provide reasonable control of flexural cracking at specified loads. It is based on Gergely and Lutz's empirical equation. (Gergely, P. and Lutz, L.A. "Maximum Crack Width in Reinforced Concrete Flexural Members," Causes, Mechanisms and Control of Cracking in Concrete, SP-20, American Concrete Institute, Detroit, 1968, pp. 87-117).

$$w = 11 f_s \sqrt[3]{d_c A} \frac{h_2}{h_1} \times 10^{-6} \text{ mm}$$

where, w = crack width at tensile face

h_1 = distance from centroid of tension steel to neutral axis

h_2 = distance from extreme tension fibre to neutral axis.

coated reinforcement is used, the value of z given by Equation (10-6) shall be multiplied by a factor of 1.2.

Note: *The provisions of Clause 10.6.1 may not be sufficient for structures subject to very aggressive exposure or designed to be watertight.*

10.6.2 Skin Reinforcement

For reinforced members with an overall depth, h, exceeding 750 mm, longitudinal skin reinforcement shall be uniformly distributed along the exposed side faces of the member for a distance 0.5h nearest the principal reinforcement. The total area of such reinforcement shall be $\rho_{sk}A_{cs}$, where A_{cs} is the sum of the area of concrete in strips along each exposed side face, each strip having a height of 0.5h and a width of twice the distance from the side face to the centre of the skin reinforcement but not more than half the web width, and where

$$\rho_{sk} = 0.008 \text{ for interior exposure}$$
$$\rho_{sk} = 0.010 \text{ for exterior exposure}$$

The maximum spacing of the skin reinforcement shall be 200 mm. Such skin reinforcement may be included in strength calculations if a strain compatibility analysis is made to determine the stresses in individual bars.

10.7 Deep Flexural Members

10.7.1
Flexural members with clear span to overall depth ratios less than 2 shall be designed as deep flexural members taking into account nonlinear distribution of strain, lateral buckling, and the increased anchorage requirements in such members. In lieu of more accurate procedures, the strut-and-tie model of Clause 11.5 may be used. (See also Clause 12.10.6.)

10.7.2
Minimum horizontal and vertical reinforcement in the side faces of deep flexural members shall satisfy the requirements of Clauses 10.6.2 and 11.5.5.

10.8 Bearing Resistance

10.8.1
The factored bearing resistance of concrete, other than at post-tensioning anchorages, shall not exceed $0.85\phi_c f'_c A_1$, except that when the supporting surface is wider on all sides than the loaded area, the bearing resistance on the loaded area may be multiplied by $\sqrt{A_2/A_1}$, but not more than 2.

10.8.2
Reinforcement shall be provided where required in bearing zones to resist bursting, splitting, and spalling forces.

10.9 Columns—Reinforcement Limits

10.9.1
The area of longitudinal bars for compression members shall be not less than 0.01 times the gross area, A_g, of the section except as permitted in Clause 10.10.5.

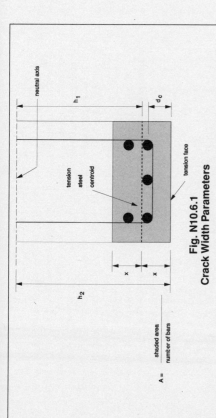

Fig. N10.6.1
Crack Width Parameters

Limiting z to 30 kN/mm and 25 kN/mm corresponds to limiting crack widths to about 0.4 mm and 0.33 mm, respectively.

It may be difficult to satisfy Eq. (10-6) if covers greater than 50 mm are required for durability, fire resistance or in members such as footings. For this reason, it is not necessary to take the cover greater than 50 mm when computing A and d_c.

N10.6.2 Skin Reinforcement

While the main tension reinforcement satisfying Eq. (10-6) should provide adequate crack control in the shaded area shown in Fig. N10.6.1, it is possible that wider cracks may form on the side faces of the beam in the zone between the neutral axis and the main tension reinforcement. For this reason skin reinforcement is needed in the area A_{cs} shown shaded in Fig. N10.6.2.

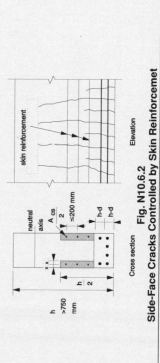

Fig. N10.6.2
Side-Face Cracks Controlled by Skin Reinforcemet

Clause 10.6.2 is based on tests reported in Franz and Breen, "Design Proposal for Side Face Crack Control Reinforcement for Large Reinforced Concrete Beams" Concrete International - Design and Construction, October 1980. The values of ρ_{sk} required by Clause 10.6.2 are, however, somewhat lower than those proposed by Franz and Breen.

N10.7 Deep Flexural Members
The flow of forces in deep flexural members can be investigated with the aid of the truss model described in Clause 11.5.

N10.8 Bearing Resistance
When the loaded area is surrounded on all sides by unloaded concrete, this unloaded concrete confines and hence increases the bearing capacity of the loaded area. Fig. N10.8 illustrates the determination of A_2 for two different situations of bearing and confinement.

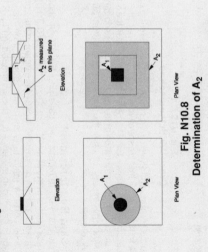

Fig. N10.8
Determination of A_2

See Clause 18.14 for information on bearing stresses associated with tendon anchorage zones.

N10.8.2
In bearing zones the possibility of bursting, splitting or spalling should be considered. If the unconfined concrete cover is directly loaded in bearing it may spall off as shown in Fig. N10.8.2(a). Hence, direct bearing on the concrete cover is undesirable. The dispersion of the bearing stresses under a bearing plate causes transverse tensile stresses which may lead to splitting, particularly in thin members. (see Fig. N10.8.2(b)).

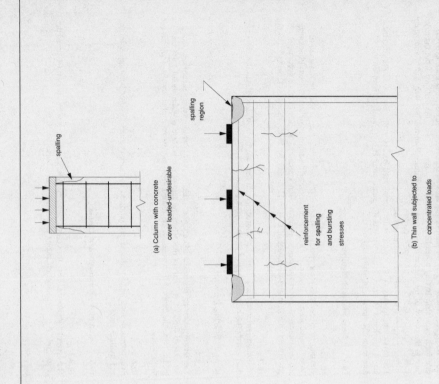

(a) Column with concrete cover loaded-undesirable

(b) Thin wall subjected to concentrated loads

Fig. N10.8.2
Examples of Spalling and Splitting

10.9.2

The area of longitudinal bars for compression members, including regions containing lap splices, shall not exceed 0.08 times the gross area of the section (see Clause 12.17.2).

Note: *The use of more than 4% of reinforcement in a column outside of the region of lap splices can involve serious practical difficulties in placing, compacting the concrete, and placing reinforcement in beam column joints.*

10.9.3

The minimum number of longitudinal reinforcing bars in compression members shall be 4 for bars within rectangular or circular ties, 3 for bars within triangular ties, and 6 for bars enclosed by spirals conforming to Clause 10.9.4.

10.9.4

The ratio of spiral reinforcement shall be not less than the value given by

$$\rho_s = 0.45 \left(\frac{A_g}{A_c} - 1 \right) \frac{f'_c}{f_y}$$ (10-7)

where f_y is the specified yield strength of spiral reinforcement, not to be taken more than 500 MPa.

10.10 Columns—Resistance

10.10.1

Columns shall be designed to have adequate factored resistance under the combinations of factored axial load and moment giving the maximum and minimum ratios of moment to axial load.

10.10.2

Columns supporting two-way slabs shall be designed for the additional requirements of Clause 13.

10.10.3

Slender compression members shall be designed for moments magnified in accordance with Clauses 10.13 to 10.16.

10.10.4 Maximum Axial Load Resistance

The maximum factored axial load resistance, P_{rmax}, of compression members shall be

(a) for spirally reinforced columns

$$P_{rmax} = 0.85 P_{ro}$$ (10-8)

(b) for tied columns

$$P_{rmax} = 0.80 P_{ro}$$ (10-9)

where

$$P_{ro} = \alpha_1 \phi_c f'_c (A_g - A_{st} - A_t - A_p) + \phi_s f_y A_{st} + \phi_a F_y A_t - f_{pr} A_p$$ (10-10)

N10.9.4

The amount of spiral reinforcement given by Eq. (10-7) is intended to provide sufficient confinement to the core concrete so that the capacity lost when the concrete shell spalls can be regained due to the increased capacity of the confined core.

N10.10.1

Due to the non-linear nature of the axial load-moment curvature diagram, it is necessary to check the column for at least two combinations of axial load and moment as shown in Fig. N10.10.1.

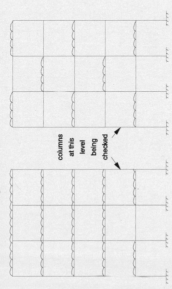

columns at this level being checked

(a) Maximum axial load and corresponding maximum moment

(b) Maximum moment and corresponding axial load

Fig. N10.10.1
Live Load Patterns to be considered for Column Design

N10.10.4 Maximum Axial Load Resistance

Limiting the factored axial load resistance to P_{rmax} is intended to account for eccentricities not considered in the analysis (see Fig. N10.10.4) and for the possibility that the concrete strength may be reduced by sustained high axial loads. Equation 10-10 is a general equation applicable to all types of concrete columns. In the normal case of a non-prestressed column, A_t and A_p are equal to zero. There is no ϕ factor on the final term in Eq. 10-10 because this term reduces the capacity. The computed axial load resistance is reduced from that in the previous Standard by using the factor α_1 instead of 0.85. This reflects the observed reduction in the relative strength of columns made with high strength concrete.

10.10.5

Columns with ρ_t smaller than 0.01 but larger than 0.005 may be used provided the factored axial and moment resistances are multiplied by the ratio $\rho_t/0.01$.

10.11 Columns—Design Dimensions

10.11.1 Equivalent Circular Column

In resistance calculations, in lieu of using the full gross area, a compression member with a square, octagonal, or other regular polygonal shaped cross section may be considered as a circular section with a diameter equal to the least lateral dimension of the actual shape. The gross area considered, the required percentage of reinforcement, and the resistance shall be based on that circular section.

10.11.2 Column Built Monolithically with Wall

The outer limits of the effective cross section of a spirally reinforced or tied reinforced compression member built monolithically with a concrete wall or pier shall be taken at a distance outside of the spiral or tie reinforcement equal to the specified concrete cover at the location with the smallest cover.

10.11.3 Isolated Column with Interlocking Spirals

Outer limits of the effective cross section of a compression member with two or more interlocking spirals shall be taken at a distance outside the extreme limits of the spirals equal to the specified concrete cover at the location with the smallest cover.

10.12 Columns—Transmission of Loads Through Floor System

10.12.1

When the specified compressive strength of concrete in a column is greater than that specified for a floor system, transmission of load through the floor system shall be as provided in Clause 10.12.2 or 10.12.3.

10.12.2

Concrete of the strength specified for the column, f'_{cc}, shall be placed in the floor at the column location. The top surface of the column concrete placed in the floor shall extend at least 500 mm into the floor from the face of the column. The column concrete shall be well integrated with the floor concrete.

10.12.3

The resistance of the column in the joint region shall be based on an effective concrete compressive strength, f'_{ce}, equal to:

(a)   for interior columns:

$$f'_{ce} = 1.05f'_{cs} + 0.25f'_{cc} \le f'_{cc} \tag{10-11}$$

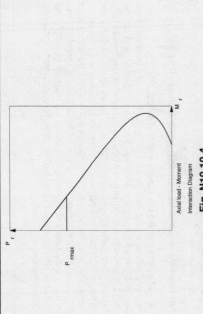

P_r

P_{rmax}

M_r

Axial load - Moment
Interaction Diagram

Fig. N10.10.4
Limiting Factored Axial Load Resistance

N10.10.5

This clause has been revised to make application easier when columns have both axial load and moment.

N10.12 Columns — Transmission of Loads Through Floor System

Application of the concrete placement procedure described in Clause 10.12.2 requires the placing of two different concrete mixes in the floor system. The lower strength mix must be placed while the higher strength concrete is still plastic and must be adequately vibrated to ensure the concretes are well integrated. This requires careful co-ordination of the concrete deliveries and possible use of retarders. It is important that the high strength concrete in the floor in the region of the column be placed before the lower strength concrete in the remainder of the floor to prevent accidental placing of the low strength concrete in the column area. It is the designer's responsibility to indicate on the drawings where the high and low strength concrete are to be placed.

N10.12.3

Recent test results indicate that under some circumstances the code provisions in the 1984 standard were inadequate. For interior columns the new provisions result in an effective strength of column concrete equal to the specified column concrete for $f'_{cc} \le 1.4 f'_{cs}$. For higher ratios of f'_{cc}/f'_{cs}, the effective strength of the column concrete now increases more slowly than predicted by the equation in the 1984 Standard.

(b) for edge columns:

$$f'_{ce} = 1.4f'_{cs} \leq f'_{cc} \qquad \text{(10-12)}$$

(c) for corner columns:

$$f'_{ce} = f'_{cs} \qquad \text{(10-13)}$$

Vertical dowels, spirals, or hoops may be added to increase the effective strength of the floor system.

10.13 Slenderness Effects—General

10.13.1

Except as allowed in Clause 10.13.2, the design of compression members, restraining beams, and other supporting members shall be based on the factored forces and moments from a second-order analysis considering material nonlinearity and cracking, as well as the effects of member curvature and lateral drift, duration of the loads, shrinkage and creep, and interaction with the supporting foundation. The dimensions of the cross sections shown on the design drawings shall be within 10 percent of the dimensions used in the analysis. The analysis procedure shall be shown to result in prediction of strength in substantial agreement with the results of comprehensive tests of columns in indeterminate reinforced concrete structures.

10.13.2

In lieu of the procedure prescribed in Clause 10.13.1, it is permissible to base the design of compression members, restraining beams, and other supporting members on axial forces and moments from the analyses described in Clauses 10.14 to 10.16 provided $k\ell_u/r$ for all compression members is not greater than 100.

10.14 Slenderness Effects—Magnified Moments, General

10.14.1 General

The factored axial forces, P_f, the factored moments, M_1 and M_2, at the ends of the column, and, where required, the first-order lateral storey deflection, Δ_o, shall be computed using an elastic first-order frame analysis with the section properties calculated taking into account the influence of axial loads, the presence of cracked regions along the length of the member, and effects of duration of the loads. Alternatively, it is permissible to use the following properties for the members in the structure:

(a) Modulus of elasticity = E_c from Clause 8.6.2;

(b) Moment of inertia

Beams	$0.35I_g$;
Columns	$0.70I_g$;
Walls — Uncracked	$0.70I_g$;
— Cracked	$0.35I_g$;
Flat plates and flat slabs	$0.25I_g$;

(c) Area = A_g

40

The effective strength of the concrete in edge columns may also remain equal to that of the specified strength of the column concrete for $f'_{cc} \leq 1.4 f'_{cs}$. However, further increases in the specified strength of the column concrete do not further increase the effective strength. Because of the lack of lateral restraint, the effective strength of the concrete in corner columns may not be taken higher than the specified strength of the slab concrete. See Gamble, W.L., and Klinar, J.D., "Tests of High-Strength Concrete Columns with Intervening Floor Slabs," ASCE Journal of Structural Engineering, Vol. 117, No. 5, May 1991, pp. 1462-1476, and Shu, C-C. and Hawkins, N.M.,"Behaviour of Columns Continuous through Concrete Floors," ACI Structural Journal, Vol. 89, No.4, July-August 1992, pp. 405-414.

N10.13 Slenderness Effects — General

A conventional frame analysis (first-order analysis) neglects the influence of the changing geometry caused by deflections. A second-order analysis includes these effects when calculating moments and forces.

The stiffnesses EI used in an elastic analysis for strength design should represent the stiffnesses of the members immediately prior to failure. This is particularly true for second-order analyses which should predict the lateral deflections at loads approaching ultimate. The EI values should not be based totally on the moment-curvature relationship for the most highly loaded section along the length of the member. Instead, they should correspond to the moment-end rotation relationship for a complete member.

In a second-order analysis the axial loads in all columns which are not part of the lateral load resisting system but depend on these elements for stability must be included.

The term "effect of member curvature" refers to amplification of the column moments to account for moments induced by deflection of the column relative to the chord line joining the ends of the column. This is illustrated in Fig. N10.13(a) for a column in a non-sway frame. To account for the deflection between the ends of the column, the maximum moment is taken as the magnified moment M_c.

The term "effect of lateral drift" refers to the additional moments caused by vertical loads acting on a structure which has been displaced laterally. The first order column moments, M_s due to factored lateral loads acting on a frame are shown in Fig. N10.13(b). These cause lateral deflections as shown, and the interaction of these deflections and the gravity loads, P, causes an increase in the column moment from M_s to $\delta_s M_s$ as shown. Lateral drift effects usually result from loadings involving combinations of vertical and lateral loads but can occur due to vertical loads acting on an unsymmetric structure.

The term β_d is defined differently for non-sway and sway frames. See Cl. 10.0. Sway deflections due to short-time loads such as wind or earthquake are a function of the short-time stiffness of the columns following a period of sustained gravity load. For this case $\beta_d = 0$. Sustained lateral loads which result in non-zero values of β_d might exist, for example, if there were permanent lateral loads resulting from unequal earth pressures on opposite sides of a building. Sustained lateral loads should not be resisted by a column-beam frame because excessive lateral deflections may occur.

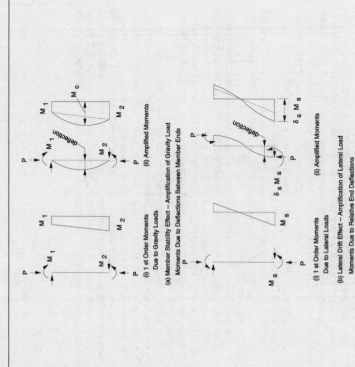

(i) 1 st Order Moments
Due to Gravity Loads

(ii) Amplified Moments

(a) Member Stability Effect – Amplification of Gravity Load Moments Due to Deflections Between Member Ends

(i) 1 st Order Moments
Due to Lateral Loads

(ii) Amplified Moments

(b) Lateral Drift Effect – Amplification of Lateral Load Moments Due to Relative End Deflections

Fig. N10.13
Slenderness Effects

N10.14.1

In lieu of a second order analysis the standard permits an approximate evaluation of the influence of deflection on moments and forces provided the ℓ_u/r ratios for all columns are smaller than the limit.

It is generally sufficiently accurate to take I_g of a T beam as two times the I_g for the web.

If the factored moments from an analysis of a wall based on the moment of inertia taken equal to $0.70I_g$ indicate that the wall will crack in flexure, based on the modulus of rupture, the analysis should be repeated with $I_g = 0.35I_g$ in those storeys where cracking is predicted at factored loads.

The values of EI used in Clauses 10.14.4, 10.16.3.1, and 10.16.5 shall be divided by $(1 + \beta_d)$ when

(i) sustained lateral loads act; or

(ii) stability checks are made according to Clause 10.16.5.

10.14.2 Radius of Gyration

It is permissible to take the radius of gyration, r, equal to 0.30h for rectangular compression members and 0.25 times the diameter for circular compression members. For other shapes, it is permissible to compute the radius of gyration using the gross concrete section.

10.14.3 Unsupported Length of Compression Members

10.14.3.1

The unsupported length, ℓ_u, of a compression member shall be taken as the clear distance between floor slabs, beams, or other members capable of providing lateral support in the direction being considered.

10.14.3.2

Where column capitals or haunches are present, the unsupported length shall be measured to the lower extremity of the capital or haunch in the plane considered.

10.14.4 Designation as Non-Sway

Storeys in structures shall be designated as non-sway if $Q \leq 0.05$ where:

$$Q = \frac{\Sigma P_f \Delta_o}{V_f \ell_c} \qquad (10\text{-}14)$$

where ΣP_f and V_f are the total factored vertical load and the factored storey shear in the storey in question and Δ_o is the first-order relative deflection of the top and bottom of that storey due to V_f. The deflection, Δ_o, shall be determined using the modified value of EI from Clause 10.14.1, with β_d as defined in definition (b) of Clause 10.0, except as required by Clause 10.16.4.

10.14.5 Columns in Non-Sway Frames or Storeys

The design of columns in non-sway frames or storeys shall be based on the analysis given in Clause 10.15.

10.14.6 Columns in Sway Frames or Storeys

The design of columns in sway frames or storeys shall be based on the analysis in Clause 10.16.

Note: *If the value of Q exceeds about 0.2, a more rigid structure may be required to provide stability.*

N10.14.4 Designation as Non-sway

A frame is "non-sway" if the lateral drift effects are resisted by stiff bracing elements such as shear walls, elevator shafts, stairwells and the like. A frame is a "sway frame" if the lateral drift effects are resisted by the frame itself. Generally it will be obvious from inspection whether a frame is sway or non-sway since the lateral stiffness of the bracing elements generally greatly exceeds that of the frame. Eq. (10-14) provides a means for categorizing structures which are not obviously in one class or the other. If the frame is subjected to sustained lateral loads the stiffness EI must be reduced by dividing by $1 + \beta_d$ where β_d is based on definition (b) in Cl. 10.0.

10.15 Slenderness Effects—Non-Sway Frames

10.15.1
For compression members in non-sway frames, the effective length factor, k, shall be taken as 1.0, unless analysis shows that a lower value is justified. The calculation of k shall be based on E and I values in accordance with Clause 10.14.1.

10.15.2
In non-sway frames it is permissible to ignore slenderness effects for compression members which satisfy:

$$\frac{k\ell_u}{r} \le \frac{25 - 10(M_1/M_2)}{\sqrt{P_f/(f'_c A_g)}}$$ (10-15)

where M_1/M_2 is not taken less than -0.5. The term M_1/M_2 is positive if the column is bent in single curvature.

10.15.3 Member Stability Effect
Compression members shall be designed for the effects of member curvature, M_c, as follows:

$$M_c = \frac{C_m M_2}{1 - \dfrac{P_f}{\phi_m P_c}}$$ (10-16)

where $\phi_m = 0.75$ and $C_m M_2$ shall not be taken as less than $P_f(15 + 0.03h)$ about each axis separately.

$$P_c = \frac{\pi^2 EI}{(k\ell_u)^2}$$ (10-17)

EI in Equation (10-17) may be taken as either

$$EI = \frac{0.2E_c I_g + E_s I_{st}}{1 + \beta_d}$$ (10-18)

with β_d as defined in definition (a) of Clause 10.0, except as required by Clause 10.16.3.2; or approximately,

$$EI = 0.25E_c I_g$$ (10-19)

10.15.3.1
For members without transverse loads between supports, C_m shall be taken as

$$C_m = 0.6 + 0.4\frac{M_1}{M_2} \ge 0.4$$ (10-20)

10.15.3.2
For members with transverse loads between supports, C_m shall be taken as 1.0.

42

N10.15.1
The effective length factor, k, is frequently estimated using the Jackson and Moreland Alignment Charts reproduced in Fig. N10.15.1. Because of the assumptions made in deriving these charts they tend to underestimate the value of k. This is unconservative. For this reason it is desirable to err on the high side when computing ψ for use in these charts. It is considered satisfactory to compute ψ using the member stiffnesses given in Clause 10.14.1.

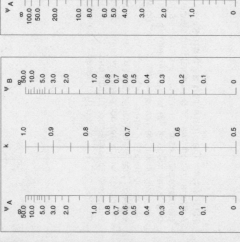

(a) Braced Frames   (b) Unbraced Frames

Fig. N10.15.1
Effective Length Factors

N10.15.2
In evaluating the slenderness limits in Clause 10.15.2, k can be taken as 1.0 or based on Fig. N10.15.2.

Studies of actual structures indicate that slenderness effects can be neglected for about 90 per cent of the columns in non-sway frames (MacGregor, Breen and Pfrang, "Design of Slender Concrete Columns", Journal American Concrete Institute, Vol. 67, No. 1, Jan. 1970, pp 6-28).

TOP	k				BOTTOM
Hinged	0.81	0.91	0.95	1.00	Hinged
Elastic	0.77	0.86	0.90	0.95	Elastic
Elastic	0.74	0.83	0.86	0.91	Elastic
Stiff	0.67	0.74	0.77	0.81	Stiff

Fig. N10.15.2
Effective Length Factors for Non-sway Frames

N10.15.3 Member Stability Effect

The design of columns in a non-sway frame involves the calculation of magnified moments using Eq. (10-16) with M_2 taken as the moments from a conventional frame analysis. A minimum value of $C_m M_2$ is specified in cases where the calculated moments are close to zero. Equation 10-16 gives the magnified M_c for the design of the column. If M_c is less than the maximum end moment, M_2, the maximum moment is at the end of the column and the column should be designed for P_f and M_2. Eqns. (10-18) and (10-19) give approximate expressions for the flexural stiffness of individual columns. Eq. (10-19) does away with the need to evaluate β_d. More accurate values of EI can be used provided they can be shown to give good agreement with tests. For short-time loads the EI calculated from the moment and curvature corresponding to balanced failure has been shown to give such agreement except for low axial loads. See FIP Recommendations, "Practical Design of Reinforced and Prestressed Concrete Structures," Thomas Telford Ltd., London, 1984.

N10.15.3.1

For columns bent in single curvature, the ratio of M_1/M_2 is between 0 and +1.0. For double curvature it is between 0 and −1.0.

10.15.3.3

For compression members subject to bending about both principal axes, the moment about each axis shall be magnified separately based on the conditions of restraint corresponding to that axis.

10.16 Slenderness Effects—Sway Frames

10.16.1

For compression members not braced against sway, the effective length factor, k, shall be determined using E and I values in accordance with Clause 10.14.1 and shall be greater than 1.0.

10.16.2

The moments M_1 and M_2 at the ends of an individual compression member shall be taken as

$$M_1 = M_{1ns} + \delta_s M_{1s} \tag{10-21}$$

$$M_2 = M_{2ns} + \delta_s M_{2s} \tag{10-22}$$

where $\delta_s M_{1s}$ and $\delta_s M_{2s}$ shall be computed according to Clause 10.16.3, with EI divided by $(1 + \beta_d)$ and with β_d as defined in definition (b) of Clause 10.0, except as required by Clauses 10.16.4 and 10.16.5.

10.16.3 Calculation of $\delta_s M_s$

10.16.3.1

The magnified sway moments, $\delta_s M_s$, shall be taken as the column end moments calculated using a second-order analysis based on the member stiffnesses given in Clause 10.14.1.

10.16.3.2

It is permissible to calculate δ_s as

$$\delta_s = \frac{1}{1 - \dfrac{\Sigma P_f}{\phi_m \Sigma P_c}} \tag{10-23}$$

where ΣP_f is the summation for all the vertical loads in a storey and ΣP_c is the summation for all sway-resisting columns in a storey and P_c is computed using Equation (10-17) using k from Clause 10.16.1 and EI from Equation (10-18) with β_d as defined in definition (b) of Clause 10.0 or EI from Equation (10-19).

10.16.3.3

Alternatively, if $Q \leq 1/3$, it is permissible to compute δ_s as

$$\delta_s = \frac{1}{1 - Q} \tag{10-24}$$

N10.16 Slenderness Effects - Sway Frames

Sway-frames are more sensitive to stability problems than braced frames and as a result the design process is considerably more complex.

The effect of lateral drift must be considered for columns in a sway frame as illustrated in Fig. N10.16 for a symmetrical frame subjected to gravity load moments and lateral load moments. The first-order end moments M_{ns} due to gravity loads are shown in Fig. 10.16(a). The moments M_s and $\delta_s M_s$ due to lateral loads are shown in Fig. N10.16(b). The total moments at each end of the columns are obtained by adding the moments M_{ns} and $\delta_s M_s$ at each end, see Fig N10.16(c).

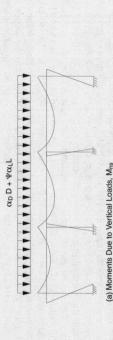

(a) Moments Due to Vertical Loads, M_{ns}

(b) Moments Due to Lateral Loads, M_s and Magnified Lateral Load Moments, $\delta_s M_s$

(c) Vertical Load Moments plus Magnified Lateral Load Moments, $M_{ns} + \delta_s M_s$

**Fig. N10.16
End Moments M_1 and M_2 For Column in Sway Frame**

10.16.4

If an individual compression member has

$$\frac{\ell_u}{r} > \frac{35}{\sqrt{P_f/(f_c' A_g)}} \tag{10-25}$$

it shall also be designed for the factored axial load, P_f, and the moment, M_c, computed using Clause 10.15.3 in which M_1 and M_2 are computed in accordance with Clause 10.16.2, with β_d as defined in definition (a) of Clause 10.0, evaluated for the factored load combination used to compute P_f, and with k in Equation (10-17) as defined in Clause 10.15.1.

10.16.5

In addition to load cases involving lateral loads, the strength and stability of the structure as a whole under factored gravity loads shall be considered using the following criteria:

(a)   When $\delta_s M_s$ is computed from Clause 10.16.3.1, the ratio of second-order lateral deflections to first-order lateral deflections, for loads applied to the structure equal to 1.25 dead load and 1.5 live load plus a lateral load applied to each storey equal to 0.005 multiplied by factored gravity load on that storey, shall not exceed 2.5.

(b)   When δ_s is computed from Clause 10.16.3.2, δ_s computed using ΣP_f and ΣP_c corresponding to 1.25 dead load and 1.5 live load shall be positive and shall not exceed 2.5.

In cases (a) and (b) above, β_d shall be taken as the ratio of the factored sustained axial dead load to the total factored axial load.

10.16.6   Moment Magnification for Flexural Members

Flexural members in sway frames shall be designed for the total magnified end moments of the compression members at the joint.

10.17   Composite Columns—General

10.17.1

Composite compression members shall include all such members reinforced longitudinally with bars and structural steel shapes, pipe, or tubing.

10.17.2

The resistance of a composite member shall be computed for the same limiting conditions applicable to ordinary reinforced concrete members.

10.17.3

In the calculation of factored capacity, the ends of a composite column shall be assumed to be hinged unless definite provisions are made to resist moment at the ends.

10.17.4

Longitudinal bars shall be in accordance with Clauses 10.9.1 and 10.9.2.

10.17.5

The total cross section area of the metal core and reinforcement shall not exceed 20% of the gross area of the column.

44

The standard assumes the analysis will be carried out in the following stages:

(a)   Compute gravity load moments, M_{ns}, due to 1.25D or 1.25D + 0.7(1.5L).

(b)   Compute lateral load moments, M_s, due to 1.5W or 0.7(1.5)W.

(c)   Magnify the lateral load moments according to Clause 10.16.3 to account for the lateral drift effect. This gives $\delta_s M_s$.

(d)   Add the moments, M_{ns}, from step (a) to the magnified lateral load moments, $\delta_s M_s$, from step (c) at both ends of each column to get M_1 and M_2 as shown in Fig. N10.16.

(e)   If ℓ_u/r for any column exceeds the limit given in Eq. (10-25) check whether the moment between the ends of that column exceeds the end moment M_2. This is done using Clause 10.15.3. If M_c is less than M_2, the maximum moment M_2 occurs at the end of the column. If M_c exceeds M_2 the maximum moment M_c will occur between the ends of the column.

If a frame undergoes appreciable lateral deflections under gravity loads, serious consideration should be given to rearranging the frame to make it more symmetrical because with time, creep will amplify these deflections leading to both serviceability and strength problems.

N10.16.3   Calculation of $\delta_s M_s$

Lateral drift effects are considered for frames that undergo appreciable lateral drift due to lateral loads or combined lateral and gravity loads. The standard allows the designer to compute $\delta_s M_s$ using either a second order analysis (Eq. 10.16.3.1) or Eq. (10-23) or Eq. (10-24). The second-order analysis in Clause 10.16.3.1, however, is not the same second-order analysis referred to in Clause 10.13.1. Rather, it is an elastic second-order analysis based on the member stiffnesses prescribed in Clause 10.14.1. The iterative P∆ analysis for second-order moments can be represented by an infinite series. The summation of this series is given by Eq. (10-24). This equation closely approximates the second order moments within the specified limit.

In checking the stability of a storey using 10.16.3.2, δ_s is computed as an average value based on the use of ΣP_f and ΣP_c because the top of the storey moves as a unit relative to the bottom of the storey. This procedure is appropriate when the lateral drifts of all columns in a storey are equal. If significant torsional displacements exist, Eqs. (10-23) and (10-24) may underestimate the magnified moments for columns farthest from the centre of twist. In such cases a second-order analysis is recommended.

10.17.6

The yield strength of the structural steel core used in the design shall be the specified minimum yield strength for the grade of structural steel used but shall not exceed 350 MPa.

10.17.7

The surface of the structural steel member in contact with concrete shall be unpainted.

10.17.8

The axial load resistance assigned to the concrete of a composite member shall be transferred to the concrete by direct bearing or shear.

10.17.9

The axial load resistance not assigned to the concrete of a composite member shall be developed by direct connection to the structural steel.

10.17.10

The structural steel elements shall be designed in accordance with CSA Standard S16.1, for any construction or other load applied prior to the attainment of composite action.

10.17.11

The design of composite columns with a concrete core encased by structural steel shall be in accordance with CSA Standard S16.1.

10.18   Composite Column with Spiral Reinforcement

10.18.1

Spiral reinforcement shall conform to Clause 10.9.4.

10.18.2

For evaluation of slenderness effects, the radius of gyration of a composite section with spiral reinforcement shall not be greater than the value given by

$$r = \sqrt{\frac{(E_c I_g/5) + E_s I_t + E_s I_{st}}{(E_c A_g/5) + E_s A_t + E_s A_{st}}} \qquad (10\text{-}26)$$

For computing P_c in Equation (10-17), EI of the composite section shall not be greater than

$$EI = \frac{0.2E_c I_g}{1 + \beta_d} + E_s I_t + E_s I_{st} \qquad (10\text{-}27)$$

10.19   Composite Column with Tie Reinforcement

10.19.1

Lateral ties shall extend completely around the structural steel core.

10.16.4

Normally the maximum moment in a column in a sway frame is at one end of the column. For very slender columns in sway frames, however, the moment at a point between the ends of the column may exceed the maximum end moment. If ℓ_u/r exceeds the value given by Eq. 10-25, this may occur and it is then necessary to check whether it does. Clause 10.16.4 specifies how this is done:

(a) M_1 and M_2 are computed using Clause 10.16.2.

(b)   The maximum moment along the length of the column is computed using these values of M_1 and M_2 in Eqs. 10-20 and 10-16. The EI values used to compute P_c are those given by Eqs. (10-18) or (10-19). β_d shall correspond to definition (b) in Clause 10.0.

N10.16.5

Because the factored gravity loads (1.25D + 1.5L) are greater in cases not involving lateral loads than they are in cases involving lateral loads (e.g. 1.25D or 1.25D + 1.05L for wind), and because the EI for gravity loads is reduced by dividing by $(1 + \beta_d)$, there is a possibility that a sway frame may buckle under gravity loads alone. Clauses 10.16.5(a) and (b) describe two additional loading cases, one of which may have to be checked, depending on how $\delta_s M_s$ or δ_s was calculated

Clause 10.16.5(a) deals with cases designed using second-order analysis where appreciable lateral deflections occur due to gravity loads (1.25D +1.5L) acting on a symmetrical or unsymmetrical frame, and the factored lateral load. The frame should be analyzed twice, once using a first-order analysis and once using a second order analysis. If one storey is much more flexible than the others, the deflection ratio should be based on that storey. In unsymmetric frames which deflect laterally under gravity loads alone, the lateral load should act in the direction for which it will increase the lateral deflections. Since it is the ratio of the lateral deflections which is determined, the precise value of this load is not important. The factored value has been chosen for convenience.

The limit on δ_s in Clause 10.16.5(b) is intended to prevent instability under gravity loads alone. For values of δ_s above the limit, the frame would be very susceptible to variations in EI, foundation rotations and the like. If δ_s exceeds 2.5 the frame must be stiffened to reduce δ_s.

N10.16.6   Moment Magnification for Flexural Members

The lateral drift of a sway frame will cause the moments in both the columns and the beams to be magnified (see Fig. N10.14.6(b)). The beams must be designed to resist these magnified moments.

10.19.2

No. 10 ties shall be used when the greatest side dimension of a composite column is 500 mm or less.

10.19.3

No. 15 ties shall be used when the greatest side dimension of a composite column is greater than 500 mm.

10.19.4

Vertical spacing of lateral ties shall not exceed the smaller of 16 longitudinal bar diameters, one-half the least side dimension of the composite member, or 500 mm.

10.19.5

Welded wire fabric with an area of horizontal wires per unit length of the column not less than that determined using Clauses 10.19.2 to 10.19.4 may be used.

10.19.6

A longitudinal bar shall be located at every corner of a rectangular cross section, with other longitudinal bars spaced not further apart than one-half of the least side dimension of the composite member.

10.19.7

For evaluation of slenderness effects, the radius of gyration of a composite section with tie reinforcement shall not be greater than the value given by

$$r = \sqrt{\frac{(E_c I_g/5) + E_s I_t}{(E_c A_g/5) + E_s A_t}} \qquad (10\text{-}28)$$

For computing P_c in Equation (10-17), EI of the composite section shall not be greater than

$$EI = \frac{0.2 E_c I_g}{1 + \beta_d} + E_s I_t \qquad (10\text{-}29)$$

11. Shear and Torsion

11.0 Notation

A_c = area enclosed by outside perimeter of concrete cross section including area of holes, if any

A_{cs} = effective cross-sectional area of concrete compressive strut (Clause 11.5.2.2)

A_{cv} = area of concrete section resisting shear transfer

A_g = gross area of section

A_t = total area of longitudinal reinforcement to resist torsion (Clause 11.3.9.5)

A_o = area enclosed by shear flow path including area of holes, if any (Clauses 11.3.9.4 and 11.4.10.3)

A_{oh} = area enclosed by centreline of exterior closed transverse torsion reinforcement including area of holes, if any

A_p = area of tendons in tension zone

A_s = area of reinforcement in tension zone

A_{ss} = area of reinforcement in compression strut

A_{st} = area of reinforcement in tension tie

A_t = area of one leg of closed transverse torsion reinforcement

A_v = area of shear reinforcement perpendicular to the axis of a member within a distance s

A_{vf} = area of shear-friction reinforcement

b_w = minimum effective web width within depth d (Clause 11.2.10)

c = cohesion stress

d = distance from the extreme compression fibre to the centroid of longitudinal tension reinforcement, but need not be less than 0.8h for prestressed members (for circular sections d need not be less than the distance from the extreme compression fibre to the centroid of the tension reinforcement in the opposite half of the member)

d_a = depth of compression strut

d_b = nominal diameter of bar, wire, or prestressing strand (Clause 2.3)

d_v = distance measured perpendicular to the neutral axis between the resultants of the tensile and compressive forces due to flexure, but need not be taken less than 0.9d.

E_p = modulus of elasticity of tendons

E_s = modulus of elasticity of reinforcement

f_{ce} = compressive stress in concrete due to effective prestress only (after allowance for all prestress losses) at extreme fibre of section where tensile stress is caused by externally applied loads

f'_c = specified compressive strength of concrete

$\sqrt{f'_c}$ = square root of specified compressive strength of concrete

f_{cu} = limiting compressive stress in concrete strut (Clause 11.5.2.3)

f_{cp} = compressive stress in concrete (after allowance for all prestress losses) at the centroid of the cross section resisting externally applied loads or at the junction of the web and flange when the centroid lies within the flange (in a composite member, f_{cp} is the resultant compressive stress at the centroid of the composite section or at the junction of the web and flange when the centroid lies within the flange, due to both prestress and moments being resisted by the precast member acting alone)

f_{pe} = effective stress in prestressing tendons after allowance for all prestress losses

f_{po} = stress in prestressing tendons when stress in the surrounding concrete is zero, may be taken as 1.1 times the effective stress, f_{pe}

f_{pr} = stress in prestressing tendons at factored resistance (Clause 18)

f_y = specified yield strength of reinforcement

h = overall height of member

h_a = height of effective embedment of tension tie (see Figure 11-3)

I_g = moment of inertia of gross concrete section about centroidal axis, neglecting reinforcement

l_a = length of effective bearing area

l_b = length of bearing

l_d = development length of reinforcement

M_{cr} = cracking moment

M_f = factored moment at section

N = unfactored permanent compressive load perpendicular to the shear plane (Clause 11.6.4)

N_f = factored axial load normal to the cross section occurring simultaneously with V_f, including effects of tension due to creep and shrinkage, taken as positive for tension and negative for compression

P_c = outside perimeter of the concrete cross section

P_h = perimeter of the centreline of the closed transverse torsion reinforcement

s = spacing of shear or torsion reinforcement measured parallel to the longitudinal axis of the member

s_z = spacing of longitudinal cracks in web of member (Clause 11.4.7)

T_f = factored torsional moment

T_{cr} = pure torsional cracking resistance

T_r = factored torsional resistance provided by circulatory shear flow (Clause 11.3.9)

T_{rg} = factored torsional resistance provided by circulatory shear flow (Clause 11.4.10)

v_f = factored shear stress (Clauses 11.4.5 and 11.4.10.3)

v_r = factored shear stress resistance of shear plane

v_c = factored shear resistance attributed to the concrete, calculated according to Clause 11.3

v_{cg} = factored shear resistance attributed to the concrete, calculated according to Clause 11.4

V_f = factored shear force at section

V_p = component in the direction of the applied shear of the effective prestressing force or for variable depth members, the sum of the component of the effective prestressing force and the components of flexural compression and tension in the direction of the applied shear, positive if resisting applied shear

V_r = factored shear resistance calculated according to Clause 11.3

V_{rg} = factored shear resistance calculated according to Clause 11.4

V_s = factored shear resistance provided by shear reinforcement calculated according to Clause 11.3

V_{sg} = factored shear resistance provided by shear reinforcement calculated according to Clause 11.4

x = anchorage length of tension tie

y_t = distance from centroidal axis of gross section, neglecting reinforcement, to extreme fibre in tension

α = angle between inclined stirrups or bent-up bars and the longitudinal axis of the member

α_f = angle between shear friction reinforcement and shear plane

β = factor accounting for shear resistance of cracked concrete (Clause 11.4.4)

ϵ_s = tensile strain in tensile reinforcement due to factored loads

ϵ_x = longitudinal strain of flexural tension chord of the member, positive when tensile (Clause 11.4.6)

ϵ_1 = principal tensile strain in cracked concrete due to factored loads

σ = effective normal stress

μ = coefficient of friction

ρ_v = ratio of shear friction reinforcement (Clause 11.6.4)

θ = angle of inclination of diagonal compressive stresses to the longitudinal axis of the member

θ_s = smallest angle between compressive strut and adjoining tensile ties

λ = factor to account for low density concrete (Clause 8.6.5)

ϕ_c = resistance factor for concrete (Clause 8.4.2)

ϕ_p = resistance factor for prestressing tendons (Clause 8.4.3)

ϕ_s = resistance factor for reinforcement (Clause 8.4.3)

11.1 Design Procedures

11.1.1 Flexural Regions

Regions of members in which it is reasonable to assume that plane sections remain plane shall be proportioned for shear and torsion using either the general method specified in Clause 11.4 or the strut-and-tie model specified in Clause 11.5. In addition, the applicable requirements of Clause 11.2 shall be satisfied. For members not subjected to significant axial tension, it shall be permissible to base shear design on the simplified method in Clause 11.3 in lieu of Clause 11.4.

11.1.2 Regions Near Discontinuities

Regions of members in which the plane section's assumption of flexural theory is not applicable shall be proportioned for shear and torsion using the strut-and-tie model specified in Clause 11.5. In addition, the applicable provisions of Clause 11.2 shall be satisfied.

11.1.3 Interface Regions

Interfaces between elements such as webs and flanges, between dissimilar materials, and between concretes cast at different times or at existing or potential major cracks along which slip can occur shall be proportioned for shear transfer in accordance with Clause 11.6.

11.1.4 Slabs and Footings

Slab type regions shall be proportioned for punching shear in accordance with Clause 13.

11.1.5 Alternative Methods

In lieu of the methods specified in Clauses 11.1.1 to 11.1.4, the resistance of members in shear or in shear combined with torsion may be determined by satisfying the applicable conditions of equilibrium and compatibility of strains and by using appropriate stress-strain relationships for reinforcement and for diagonally cracked concrete.

11.2 General Requirements

11.2.1 Tension Due to Restraint

In determining shear resistance, the effects of axial tension due to creep, shrinkage, and thermal effects in restrained members shall be considered wherever applicable.

11.2.2 Variable Depth Members

For variable depth members, the components of flexural compression and tension in the direction of the applied shear shall be taken into account if their effect is unfavourable and

N11.1.1

Typical beams, columns or walls can be designed using traditional engineering beam theory, which assumes that plane sections remain plane and that the shear stresses are distributed in a reasonably uniform manner over the depth of the member. Such members can be designed by the simplified method of Clause 11.3, the general method of Clause 11.4, or the strut-and-tie method of Clause 11.5.

N11.1.2

Engineering beam theory studies the response of a member section-by-section and is not concerned with the details of how the forces are introduced into the member. Because of this, the theory is not appropriate for regions of members near static or geometric discontinuities, such as abrupt changes in cross-sectional dimensions or cross-sectional forces. See examples in Fig. N11.1.2(a). Such regions should be designed by the strut-and-tie method of Clause 11.5, which is capable of more accurately modelling the actual flow of forces in these regions.

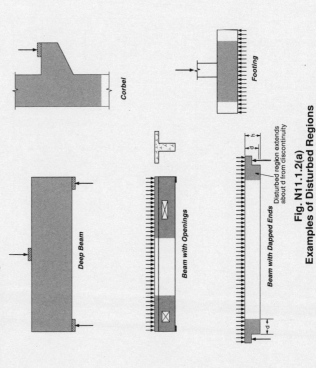

Fig. N11.1.2(a)
Examples of Disturbed Regions

stress-strain relationships. Such an analysis could be a non-linear finite element analysis, which could be used for regions near discontinuities, or a detailed sectional analysis, which could be used for flexural regions.

An example of appropriate stress-strain relationships for cracked concrete are those given by the "modified compression field theory" (F.J. Vecchio and M.P. Collins, "The Modified Compression Field Theory for Reinforced Concrete Elements Subjected to Shear," *Journal of the American Concrete Institute*, Vol. 83, No. 2, March/April 1986, pp. 219-231).

N11.2.1
Axial tension reduces the shear capacity of beams, with the reduction being particularly severe for members containing only small amounts of longitudinal reinforcement and not containing stirrups. In continuous frame structures, which have widely spaced expansion joints and stiff vertical elements, the restraint of shrinkage strains and other volume change effects may result in significant axial tension building up in the beams over time. The detrimental effect of such axial tensions on the shear strength should be taken into account.

An example of applying the strut-and-tie model of Clause 11.5 and the sectional model of Clause 11.4 is illustrated in Fig. N11.1.2(b), which shows how the shear strength of a simply supported reinforced concrete beam loaded with two point loads changes as the "shear span", a, changes. It can be seen that when the load is closer than about 2d to the support, the sectional model is inappropriate. For such "deep beams" the strut-and-tie model should be used.

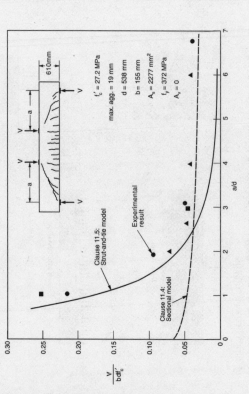

Fig. N11.1.2(b)
Use of Strut-and-Tie Model and Sectional Model to Predict the Strengths of a Series of Beams

N11.1.3
The possibility of a shear failure involving sliding along a defined plane of weakness should be checked by the shear friction procedures of Clause 11.6.

N11.1.4
Shear provisions for slabs are given in Clauses 13.4 and 13.5.

N11.1.5
The resistance of components in shear can be determined by performing a detailed analysis that considers equilibrium, compatibility, and appropriate

may be taken into account if their effect is favourable.

11.2.3   Openings
In determining shear resistance, the effect of any openings in members shall be considered.
Note: *See Clause 11.5.*

11.2.4   Types of Shear Reinforcement
Transverse reinforcement provided for shear may consist of
(a)   stirrups or ties perpendicular to the axis of the member;
(b)   welded wire fabric with wires located perpendicular to the axis of the member, provided that these wires can undergo a minimum elongation of 4% measured over a gauge length of at least 100 mm, which includes at least one cross wire;
(c)   stirrups making an angle of 45° or more with the longitudinal tension reinforcement, inclined to intercept potential diagonal cracks;
(d)   for nonprestressed members, shear reinforcement may consist of No. 35 or smaller longitudinal bars bent to provide an inclined portion having an angle of 30° or more with the longitudinal bars and crossing potential diagonal cracks. However, only the centre three-fourths of the inclined portion of these bars may be considered effective; and
(e)   spirals.

11.2.5   Anchorage of Shear Reinforcement
Stirrups and other bars or wires used as shear reinforcement shall be anchored at both ends according to Clause 12.13 to develop the design yield strength of the reinforcement.

11.2.6   Types of Torsion Reinforcement
Torsional reinforcement shall consist of longitudinal reinforcement and one or more of the following types of transverse reinforcement:
(a)   closed stirrups perpendicular to the axis of the member;
(b)   a closed cage of welded wire fabric with wires meeting the minimum elongation requirements of Clause 11.2.4(b) located perpendicular to the axis of the member; and
(c)   spirals.

11.2.7   Anchorage of Torsion Reinforcement
Transverse torsion reinforcement shall be anchored
(a)   by means of 135° standard stirrup hooks; or
(b)   according to Clause 12.13.2(a) or Clause 12.13.2(b) in regions where the concrete surrounding the anchorage is restrained against spalling.
A longitudinal reinforcing bar or bonded prestressing tendon shall be placed in each corner of closed transverse reinforcement required for torsion. The nominal diameter of the bar or tendon shall not be less than s/16.
Longitudinal torsion reinforcement shall be anchored in accordance with Clause 12.1.

50

N11.2.2
If the member depth increases as the moment increases, the components of the flexural compression and tension forces help to resist the applied shear. These forces can be treated in a similar manner to the component of the prestressing force, V_p.

N11.2.3
Webs with openings need to be designed in a rational manner to ensure that the forces and moments can be adequately transferred in the vicinity of the openings. The strut-and-tie model of Clause 11.5 can be used for the design of these disturbed regions.

N11.2.4
(b)   To effectively increase shear capacity, transverse reinforcement must be capable of undergoing substantial strains prior to failure. Welded wire fabric, particularly if fabricated from small wires and not stress-relieved after fabrication, may fail before the required strain is reached. Such failures may occur at or between the cross-wire intersections.
(c)   There is concern that stirrups inclined at less than 45° to the longitudinal reinforcement will slip along the longitudinal bars.
(d)   In tests, major inclined cracks tend to occur at points where longitudinal reinforcement is bent up. The effective portion of bent-up bars is restricted to 75% of their inclined length due to concern with anchorage conditions at the bends, and because the effectiveness of these bars is sensitive to misplacement.

N11.2.5
To be effective, transverse shear reinforcement must tie together the longitudinal tension reinforcement and the flexural compression zone of the member. Further, the reinforcement must be anchored so that it can develop its yield strength without suffering any significant slip. To this end, the anchorage requirements for stirrups have been made more conservative in this edition of the standard by requiring 135° hooks for most situations. See Clause 7.1.2.

N11.2.7
Diagonal compressive stresses in the concrete due to torsion push outwards at the corners of the beam. The longitudinal corner bars help to support these outward thrusts in the zones between the hoops. Torsion causes tension in the longitudinal reinforcement. Longitudinal torsional reinforcement should be anchored so that it can develop its yield stress in tension at the face of the support.

61

11.2.8 Minimum Shear Reinforcement

11.2.8.1
A minimum area of shear reinforcement shall be provided in all regions of flexural members where the factored shear force, V_f, exceeds $0.5V_c + \phi_p V_p$ or the factored torsion, T_f exceeds $0.25T_{cr}$. This requirement may be waived for
(a) slabs and footings;
(b) concrete joist construction defined by Clause 10.4;
(c) beams with a total depth of not greater than 250 mm; and
(d) beams cast integrally with slabs where the overall depth is not greater than one-half the width of web nor 600 mm.

11.2.8.2
In lieu of more detailed calculations, V_c in Clause 11.2.8.1 may be taken as $0.2\lambda\phi_c\sqrt{f'_c}b_w d$.

11.2.8.3
The requirement for minimum shear reinforcement of Clause 11.2.8.1 may be waived if it can be shown by test that the required flexural and shear resistances can be developed when shear reinforcement is omitted. Such tests shall simulate the effects of differential settlement, creep, shrinkage, and temperature change, based on a realistic assessment of such effects occurring in service.

11.2.8.4
Where shear reinforcement is required by Clause 11.2.8.1 or by calculation, the minimum area of shear reinforcement shall be such that:

$$A_v = 0.06\sqrt{f'_c}\,\frac{b_w s}{f_y} \tag{11-1}$$

11.2.8.5
In calculating the term A_v in Equation (11-1), inclined reinforcement and transverse reinforcement used to resist torsion may be included.

11.2.9 Consideration of Torsion

11.2.9.1
If the magnitude of the torsion, T_f, determined by analysis using stiffnesses based on uncracked sections exceeds $0.25T_{cr}$, then torsional effects shall be considered and torsional reinforcement designed in accordance with Clause 11.3 or 11.4 shall be provided. Otherwise torsional effects may be neglected.

In lieu of more detailed calculations, T_{cr} may be taken as

$$T_{cr} = (A_c^2/p_c)\,0.4\lambda\phi_c\sqrt{f'_c}\sqrt{1+\frac{\phi_p f_{cp}}{0.4\lambda\phi_c\sqrt{f'_c}}} \tag{11-2}$$

N11.2.8.1
Minimum shear reinforcement restrains the growth of inclined cracking, and hence, increases ductility and provides a warning of failure. Such reinforcement can be omitted if there is no significant chance of diagonal cracking. It can also be omitted if the member is of minor importance, or if the member is part of a redundant structural system that allows substantial redistribution of load and hence, will display adequate ductility. Thus, shear reinforcement may be omitted if any one of the items in Clauses 11.2.8.1(a) to (d) is satisfied.

N11.2.8.2
The value of V_c for use in Clause 11.2.8.1 could be determined from Clause 11.3 or from Clause 11.4, with V_c taken equal to V_{cg}. For prestressed concrete sections the procedures of Clause 11.4 would typically lead to higher values of V_c.

N11.2.8.3
In determining "the required flexural and shear resistances" to compare with test results, careful attention must be given to the appropriate treatment of the resistance factors ϕ_c, ϕ_p and ϕ_s. The test results can be taken as corresponding to the case where these factors are all one. Before a comparison with the factored moments and shear forces is made, the test values should be reduced by the appropriate resistance factors.

N11.2.8.4
High-strength concrete members require larger quantities of shear reinforcement to restrain the growth of diagonal cracks.

N11.2.9.1
Torques that do not exceed one-quarter of the pure torsional cracking torque will not cause significant reduction in either flexural or shear strength and hence, can be neglected.

Equation (11-2) is an approximate expression for the torsion causing cracking. The expression has been derived by replacing the actual section with an equivalent thin walled tube with a wall thickness $0.75\,A_c/p_c$ and an area enclosed by the tube centreline of $^2/_3 A_c$. The cracking stress is assumed to be $0.4\lambda\phi_c\sqrt{f'_c}$.

11.2.9.2

In a statically indeterminate structure where reduction of torsional moment in a member can occur due to redistribution of internal forces, the maximum factored torsion, T_f, at the face of the support may be reduced to $0.67T_{cr}$ provided that the corresponding adjustments to torsions, moments, and shears are made in the member and in adjoining members to account for the redistribution. For a spandrel beam where the torsion is caused by a slab, the factored torsion in the spandrel can be assumed to vary linearly from zero at midspan to $0.67T_{cr}$ at the face of the support.

11.2.9.3

For hollow sections in torsion, the distance measured from the centreline of the transverse torsion reinforcement to the inside face of the wall shall be not less than $0.5A_{oh}/p_h$.

11.2.10 Effective Web Width

The effective web width, b_w, shall be taken as the minimum web width within the depth, d. For circular members, b_w may be taken as 0.8 times the diameter. In determining b_w at a particular level, the diameters of ungrouted ducts or one-half the diameters of grouted ducts at that level shall be subtracted from the web width.

11.2.11 Maximum Spacing of Transverse Shear Reinforcement

The spacing of transverse shear reinforcement, s, measured in the longitudinal direction shall not exceed

(a)   600 mm or 0.7d   if $(V_f - \phi_p V_p)/(b_w d) < 0.1\lambda\phi_c f_c'$; or

(b)   300 mm or 0.35d if $(V_f - \phi_p V_p)/(b_w d) \geq 0.1\lambda\phi_c f_c'$.

11.2.12 Reduced Prestress in Transfer Length

In pretensioned members, the reduction in prestress in the transfer length of prestressing tendons shall be considered when computing V_r. The prestress force may be assumed to vary linearly from zero at the point at which bonding commences, to a maximum at a distance from the end of the tendon equal to the transfer length, assumed to be 50 diameters for strand and 100 diameters for single wire.

11.3   Simplified Method for Design for Shear and Torsion in Flexural Regions

11.3.1   Scope

Clause 11.3 shall be permitted for the design for shear of flexural members not subjected to significant axial tension.

11.3.2   Sections Near Supports

Where the reaction force, in the direction of the applied shear, introduces compression into a support region:

(a)   for nonprestressed members, sections located less than a distance d from the face of the support may be designed for the same shear, V_f, as that computed at a distance d; and

---

N11.2.9.2

After cracking, there is a substantial reduction in the torsional stiffness relative to the flexural stiffness. If the torsion in a member is a function of torsional stiffness, the resulting redistribution of internal forces will maintain the maximum torsion in the member at about the cracking torque, even as the loads are increased. This cracking torque will be about two-thirds of the pure torsional cracking load.

N11.2.9.3

For hollow sections with very thin walls, the torsional shear stress expressions in Eqs. (11-4) and (11-26) will be unconservative. Such sections can be treated by replacing the term $\dfrac{T_f p_h}{A_{oh}^2}$ by $\dfrac{T_f}{1.7\, A_{oh}\, t}$ where t is the distance from the centreline of the transverse torsion reinforcement to the inside face of the wall.

N11.2.10

Post-tensioning ducts can act as stress-raisers that will reduce the crushing strength of the concrete web. To account for this, the effective web width is reduced at locations containing ducts.

N11.2.11

The 1984 edition of A23.3 specified different stirrup spacing limits for the "Simplified Method" of Clause 11.3 and for the "General Method" of Clause 11.4. For this latter method, spacings as large as 0.9d were permitted. This edition of the standard requires the same stirrup spacing limits for both design methods. These common limits are typically somewhat more conservative than those previously permitted for the "General Method" but are more liberal than those previously required for the "Simplified Method". See Fig. N11.2.11.

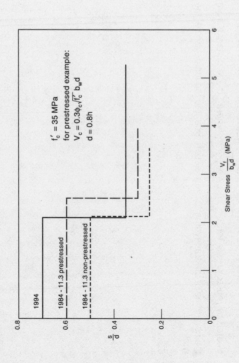

Fig. N11.2.11
Comparison of Stirrup Spacing Limits for 1994 and 1984 Editions of A23.3

N11.3.1

If the axial tension causes a significant increase in the reinforcement stress (say, 50 MPa) at crack locations, its detrimental effect on the shear strength needs to be accounted for by the procedures of Clause 11.4.

N11.3.2

Loads applied in regions near direct supports are carried to the support by strut action [see Fig. N11.1.2(b)] and do not cause additional stresses in the stirrups. Hence, stirrups in these regions may be designed for the shear at some distance from the face of the support. If the support is such that direct strut action will be ineffective, the stirrups must be designed for the shear at the face of the support. See Fig. N11.3.2.

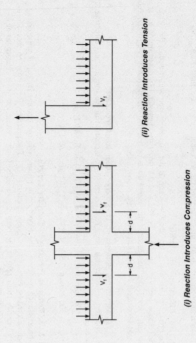

(i) Reaction Introduces Compression

(ii) Reaction Introduces Tension

Fig. N11.3.2
Influence of Support Conditions on Location of Critical Section for Shear

(b) for prestressed members, sections located less than a distance h/2 from the face of the support may be designed for the same shear, V_f, as that computed at a distance h/2.

11.3.3 Required Shear Resistance

Members subjected to shear shall be proportioned so that

$$V_r \geq V_f \tag{11-3}$$

11.3.4 Factored Shear Resistance

The factored shear resistance shall be determined by

$$V_r = V_c + V_s \tag{11-4}$$

but V_r shall not exceed

$$V_r = V_c + 0.8\lambda\phi_c\sqrt{f'_c}\,b_w d \tag{11-5}$$

11.3.5 Determination of V_c—Nonprestressed Members

11.3.5.1

For sections having either

(a) at least the minimum amount of transverse reinforcement given by Equation (11-1);

or

(b) an effective depth not exceeding 300 mm,

the value of V_c shall be computed from

$$V_c = 0.2\lambda\phi_c\sqrt{f'_c}\,b_w d \tag{11-6}$$

11.3.5.2

For sections with effective depths greater than 300 mm and with no transverse reinforcement or less transverse reinforcement than that required by Equation (11-1), the value of V_c shall be computed from

$$V_c = \left(\frac{260}{1000+d}\right)\lambda\phi_c\sqrt{f'_c}\,b_w d \not< 0.10\lambda\phi_c\sqrt{f'_c}\,b_w d \tag{11-7}$$

11.3.6 Determination of V_c—Prestressed Members

11.3.6.1

The shear strength, V_c, may be computed as follows:

$$V_c = 0.06\lambda\phi_c\sqrt{f'_c}\,b_w d + \frac{V_f}{M_f}M_{cr} \tag{11-8}$$

but V_c shall not exceed V_{cw} given in Clause 11.3.6.2 and need not be taken less than $0.17\lambda\phi_c\sqrt{f'_c}b_w d$, where

$$M_{cr} = (I_g/y_t)(0.6\lambda\phi_c\sqrt{f'_c} + \phi_p f_{ce}) \tag{11-9}$$

and V_f/M_f is the factored shear to factored moment ratio at the section under consideration

53

N11.3.4

The upper limit on V_r expressed in Eq. (11-5) is intended to ensure that the stirrups will yield prior to crushing of the web concrete and that diagonal cracking at specified loads is limited.

N11.3.5

Equation (11-6) is identical to the expression for the concrete contribution, V_c, given in the 1984 edition of this standard. This expression had been derived from the traditional ACI expression for V_c, which in psi units is

$$V_c = 2\sqrt{f'_c}\,b_w d$$

A direct conversion to MPa units would have changed the coefficient 2 to 0.167. In 1984, this coefficient was increased to 0.2 (i.e., a 20% increase) to partially offset the conservative decrease in V_c caused by using the value of 0.6 for ϕ_c. This low value of ϕ_c was chosen because of concerns in column design rather than shear design. In comparing the predictions of Eq. (11-6), or the other equations for V_c, where similar modifications were made, with experimental results, this 20% increase in the coefficient must be taken into account.

There is now considerable evidence, see Fig. N11.3.5, that Eq. (11-6) may overestimate the shear strength of large lightly reinforced members that do not contain stirrups. Concern for the safety of such members was raised by Kani about thirty years ago in his paper "How Safe Are Our Large Concrete Beams," ACI Journal, Vol. 64, Mar. 1967, pp. 128-141. Because of this concern, Eq. (11-6) is restricted to members that contain stirrups or that have effective depths not exceeding 300 mm. The concrete contribution, V_c, for larger members with no stirrups is to be determined from Eq. (11-7).

The shear strength of large members with no stirrups is strongly influenced by the amount of longitudinal reinforcement the member contains, see Fig. N11.3.5. In the simplified method this influence is neglected and, hence, Eq. (11-7) can give conservative results for heavily reinforced sections. For such members the general method of Clause 11.4 will give more accurate results.

N11.3.6

This clause gives a somewhat simplified version of the ACI procedure for determining the shear capacity of prestressed concrete sections in which V_c is taken as the lesser of the flexural shear cracking load, given by Eqs. (11-8) and (11-9), and the web shear cracking load, given by Eq. (11-10).

corresponding to the load combination causing maximum moment to occur at the section.

11.3.6.2

V_c shall not exceed V_{cw} where

$$V_{cw} = 0.4\lambda\phi_c\sqrt{f'_c}\ \sqrt{1 + \frac{\phi_p f_{cp}}{0.4\lambda\phi_c\sqrt{f'_c}}}\ b_w d + \phi_p V_p \qquad (11\text{-}10)$$

11.3.7 Determination of V_s

Transverse reinforcement shall be perpendicular to the longitudinal axis of the member. The value of V_s shall be computed from

$$V_s = \frac{\phi_s A_v f_y d}{s} \qquad (11\text{-}11)$$

11.3.8 Longitudinal Reinforcement

11.3.8.1

The flexural tension reinforcement shall be extended a distance of d or $12d_b$, whichever is greater, beyond the location required for flexure alone except at the supports of simple spans, at the free ends of cantilevers, and at the exterior supports of continuous spans.

11.3.8.2

At the supports of simple spans, at the exterior supports of continuous spans, and near the free ends of cantilevers subjected to concentrated loads, the longitudinal reinforcement on the flexural tension side of the member shall be capable of resisting a tensile force of $V_f - 0.5V_s$ at the inside edge of the bearing area where V_s is the value based on the stirrups at that location.

11.3.9 Torsion

11.3.9.1

Where required by Clause 11.2.9, torsion reinforcement shall be provided in addition to the reinforcement required to resist the factored shear, flexure, and axial forces, which act in combination with the torsion.

11.3.9.2

In regions near supports that satisfy the requirements of Clause 11.3.2, nonprestressed sections located less than a distance, d, from the face of the support may be designed for the same torsion, T_f, as that computed at a distance, d, while prestressed sections located less than a distance, h/2, from the face of the support may be designed for the same torsion, T_f, as that computed at a distance, h/2.

11.3.9.3

The transverse reinforcement required for torsion shall be determined from the requirement that $T_r \geq T_f$.

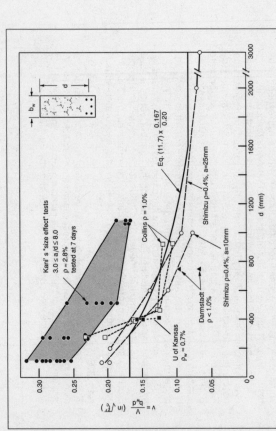

Fig. N11.3.5
Influence of Member Size on Shear Strength at Failure

N11.3.7

The simplified method is restricted to the usual case where the transverse reinforcement is perpendicular to the longitudinal reinforcement. Equation (11-11) is the traditional 45° truss equation for the design of such transverse shear reinforcement.

N11.3.8.1

In a diagonally cracked beam, shear causes tension not only in the stirrups, but also in the longitudinal reinforcement. As shown in Fig. N11.3.8.1, the traditional tension due to shear can be accounted for by "shifting" the moment diagram outwards a distance d.

N11.3.8.2

The tension in the longitudinal reinforcement at the support caused by the shear can be deduced from the free body diagram shown in Fig. N11.3.8.2. Taking moments about point O, and neglecting the turning effect of the aggregate interlock forces on the inclined crack surface, which contribute to V_c, we have

$$V_f \times d_v = T \times d_v + V_s \times 0.5 \, d_v$$

Hence

$$T = V_f - 0.5 \, V_s$$

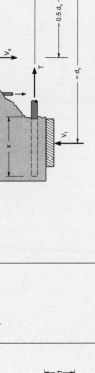

Fig. N11.3.8.1
Variation of Tension Force in Longitudinal Reinforcement along Length of Beam

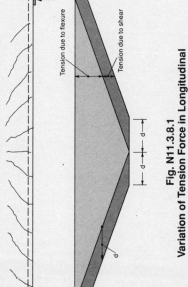

Fig. N11.3.8.2
Tension in Longitudinal Reinforcement at Support

11.3.9.4
The factored torsional resistance shall be computed by

$$T_r = 2A_o \frac{\phi_s A_t f_y}{s}$$ (11-12)

11.3.9.5
The required area, A_t, of longitudinal bars distributed symmetrically around the section, with a spacing not exceeding 300 mm, shall be computed by

$$A_l = \frac{A_t p_h}{s}$$ (11-13)

where A_t/s is the required amount of transverse reinforcement calculated from Equation (11-12).

11.3.9.6
In the flexural compression zone of a member, the area of longitudinal torsion steel required may be reduced by an amount equal to $M_f/(0.9d f_{ly})$ where M_f is the factored moment at the section acting in combination with T_f.

11.3.9.7
The area enclosed by the torsional shear flow, A_o, may be taken as $0.85A_{oh}$.

11.3.9.8
The cross sectional dimensions shall be such that

$$\frac{V_f}{b_w d} + \frac{T_f p_h}{A_{oh}^2} \le 0.25\phi_c f'_c$$ (11-14)

11.4   General Method
Note: *The general method is based on the compression field theory. Further information can be found in "Prestressed Concrete Structures" by M.P. Collins and D. Mitchell, Prentice Hall, Englewood Cliffs, NJ, 1991, 766 pp.*

11.4.1   Sections Near Supports
Where the reaction force, in the direction of the applied shear, introduces compression into the end regions of a member, the critical section for shear shall be located at a distance not greater than d_v from the face of the support.

11.4.2   Required Shear Resistance
Members subjected to shear shall be proportioned so that

$$V_{rg} \ge V_f$$ (11-15)

In evaluating the ability of the longitudinal reinforcement to resist the tensile force, it may be assumed that the bars can develop a tensile stress of $\phi_s f_y (x/\ell_d)$ if the embedment length, x, is less than the development length, ℓ_d.

N11.3.9.4
Equation (11-12) is based on a 45° space truss analogy, see Fig. N11.3.9.4, assuming that the concrete carries no tension and that the reinforcement yields. Transverse reinforcement for torsion is required on all sides of the member and should be in the form of closed hoops.

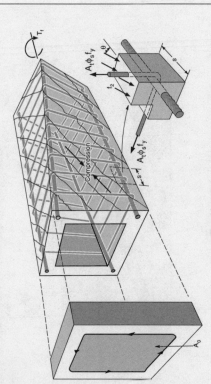

Fig. N11.3.9.4
Design of Transverse Reinforcement for Torsion

N11.3.9.5
The 45° truss analogy requires approximately equal volumes of transverse and longitudinal reinforcement.

N11.3.9.6
Compression due to flexure counteracts the required tension due to torsion.

N11.3.9.8
The purpose of this clause is to avoid diagonal crushing of the web concrete prior to yielding of the reinforcement.

N11.4.1
See explanation under N11.3.2.

11.4.3 Factored Shear Resistance

The factored shear resistance shall be determined by

$$V_{rg} = V_{cg} + V_{sg} + \phi_p V_p \qquad (11\text{-}16)$$

but V_{rg} shall not exceed

$$V_{rg} = 0.25\phi_c f'_c b_w d_v + \phi_p V_p \qquad (11\text{-}17)$$

11.4.3.1 Determination of V_{cg}

The value of V_{cg} shall be computed from

$$V_{cg} = 1.3\lambda\phi_c\beta\sqrt{f'_c}\, b_w d_v \qquad (11\text{-}18)$$

where β is determined in accordance with Clause 11.4.4.

11.4.3.2 Determination of V_{sg}

To determine V_{sg}

(a) For members with transverse reinforcement perpendicular to the longitudinal axis, V_{sg} shall be computed from

$$V_{sg} = \frac{\phi_s A_v f_y d_v \cot\theta}{s} \qquad (11\text{-}19)$$

where θ is given in Clause 11.4.4.

(b) For members with transverse reinforcement inclined at an angle α to the longitudinal axis, V_{sg} shall be computed from

$$V_{sg} = \frac{\phi_s A_v f_y d_v (\cot\theta + \cot\alpha)\sin\alpha}{s} \qquad (11\text{-}20)$$

where θ is given in Clause 11.4.4.

Note: *Members reinforced with appropriately detailed inclined stirrups are capable of resisting higher values of shear stress prior to concrete crushing.*

11.4.4 Determination of β and θ

The values of β and θ, for each design section of a member may be taken from

(a) Table 11-1 or Figure 11-1 for sections containing transverse reinforcement equal to or greater than the amount required by Equation (11-1), or

(b) Table 11-2 or Figure 11-2 for sections with no transverse reinforcement or less transverse reinforcement than that required by Equation (11-1).

Note: *The values of β and θ may change from section to section along the length of the member.*

N11.4.3

The shear resistance of concrete components may be separated into a component, V_{cg}, which relies on tensile stress in the concrete, a component, V_{sg}, which relies on tensile stresses in the transverse reinforcement, and V_p, which relies on the vertical component of the prestressing force. The vertical component of the prestressing force has been multiplied by ϕ_p to allow for possible variations in the prestressing force and in the tendon profile.

The intent of Eq. (11-7) is to ensure that the transverse reinforcement will yield prior to the diagonal crushing of the web concrete.

N11.4.3.1

The coefficient of 1.3 in Eq. (11-18) is to compensate for the low value of ϕ_c, see discussion in N11.3.5, and to make a small allowance (about 10%) for the fact that the general method is typically somewhat more conservative than the simple method.

N11.4.3.2

Equation (11-19) is the expression for the shear contribution of the transverse reinforcement based on a truss model with constant compression diagonals inclined at θ to the longitudinal axis. See Fig. N11.4.3.2.

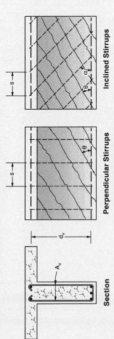

Section Perpendicular Stirrups Inclined Stirrups

Fig. N11.4.3.2

Illustration of Parameters Involved in Determination of V_{sg}

Stirrups inclined to intersect the diagonal cracks, see Fig. N11.4.3.2, are somewhat more effective in resisting shear. This is reflected in Eq. (11-20).

The expression for the shear at which the web concrete will crush, Eq. (11-17), does not distinguish between members with perpendicular stirrups and members with inclined stirrups. For the same shear force, members with inclined stirrups will require smaller values of diagonal compression in the web concrete and hence, can tolerate higher shears prior to web crushing.

N11.4.4

The values of β and θ are based on calculating the stresses that can be transmitted across diagonally cracked concrete. As the cracks become wider,

Figure N11.4.4(b) illustrates the assumptions made concerning the spacing of diagonal cracks.

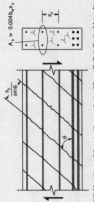

(i) Member with stirrups

(ii) Member without stirrups and with concentrated longitudinal reinforcement

(iii) Member without stirrups but with well distributed longitudinal reinforcement

Fig. N11.4.4(b)
Influence of Reinforcement on Spacing of Diagonal Cracks

the stress that can be transmitted decreases. The expressions for β, based on the modified compression field theory, are

$$\beta = \frac{f_1 \cot \theta}{\sqrt{f'_c}} = \frac{0.33 \cot \theta}{1 + \sqrt{500\,\varepsilon_1}} \leq \frac{0.18}{0.3 + \dfrac{24\,w}{a+16}}$$

where the crack width, w, is taken as the crack spacing, s_θ, times the principal tensile strain, ε_1. See Fig. N11.4.4(a).

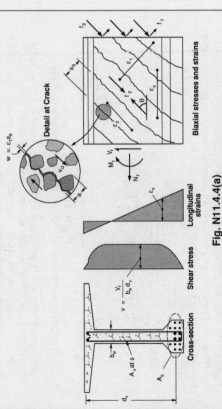

Detail at Crack

Biaxial stresses and strains

Longitudinal strains

Shear stress

$$v = \frac{V_f}{b_w\, d_v}$$

Cross-section

Fig. N11.4.4(a)
Transmission of Forces in Diagonally Cracked Web of Beam

Table 11-1
Values of β and θ for Sections with Transverse Reinforcement
(See Clause 11.4.4.)

$\dfrac{v_f}{\lambda \phi_c f'_c}$		Longitudinal strain, ε_x						
		≤ 0.0000	≤ 0.00025	≤ 0.0005	≤ 0.00075	≤ 0.0010	≤ 0.0015	≤ 0.0020
≤ 0.050	β	0.405	0.290	0.208	0.197	0.185	0.162	0.143
	θ	27.0°	28.5°	29.0°	33.0°	36.0°	41.0°	43.0°
≤ 0.075	β	0.405	0.250	0.205	0.194	0.179	0.158	0.137
	θ	27.0°	27.5°	30.0°	33.5°	36.0°	40.0°	42.0°
≤ 0.100	β	0.271	0.211	0.200	0.189	0.174	0.143	0.120
	θ	23.5°	26.5°	30.5°	34.0°	36.0°	38.0°	39.0°
≤ 0.125	β	0.216	0.208	0.197	0.181	0.167	0.133	0.112
	θ	23.5°	28.0°	31.5°	34.0°	36.0°	37.0°	38.0°
≤ 0.150	β	0.212	0.203	0.189	0.171	0.160	0.125	0.103
	θ	25.0°	29.0°	32.0°	34.0°	36.0°	36.5°	37.0°
≤ 0.200	β	0.203	0.194	0.174	0.151	0.131	0.100	0.083
	θ	27.5°	31.0°	33.0°	34.0°	34.5°	35.0°	36.0°
≤ 0.250	β	0.191	0.167	0.136	0.126	0.116	0.108	0.104
	θ	30.0°	32.0°	33.0°	34.0°	35.5°	38.5°	41.5°

For members that contain at least the minimum amount of transverse reinforcement, the β values given in Table 11-1 and Fig. 11-1 are based on the assumption that the diagonal cracks will be spaced about 300 mm apart. For members with less than the minimum amount of transverse reinforcement, it is assumed that the diagonal cracks will become more widely spaced as the crack inclination, θ, approaches zero. The crack spacing when θ equals 90° is called s_z and this spacing is primarily a function of the maximum distance between reinforcing bars or between reinforcing bars and the flexural compression zone. Note that for members that do not contain stirrups, and that do not contain intermediate layers of crack control reinforcement, the crack spacing parameter, s_z, may be taken as d_v. The β values given in Table 11-2 and Fig. 11-2 are based on the assumption that the spacing of the diagonal cracks for these members is $s_z/\sin\theta$.

In the general method, the "size effect" for members in shear, see Fig. N11.3.5, is accounted for by means of the crack spacing parameter, s_z. Large members that do not contain stirrups or crack control reinforcement will have large values of s_z and hence, low values of β.

It can be seen from Fig. 11-2 and Table 11-2 that members containing large amounts of longitudinal reinforcement or prestressed concrete members (i.e., members with low values of ε_x) will be less sensitive to member size than lightly reinforced members or members subjected to high moments (i.e., members with high values of ε_x). Thus, if ε_x equals 0, the shear stress at failure increases by a factor of 1.3 as the size decreases by a factor of 16, while if ε_x equals 0.002, the shear stress increases by a factor of 3.1.

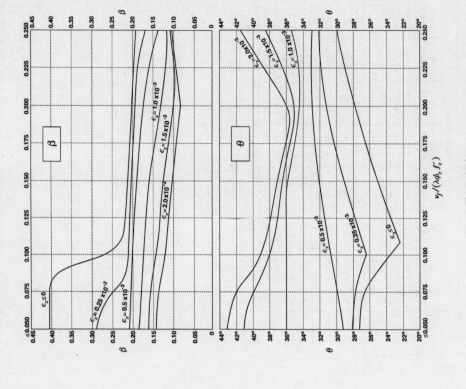

Figure 11-1
Values of β and θ for Sections With Transverse Reinforcement
(See Clause 11.4.4.)

Table 11-2
Values of β and θ for Sections Not Containing Transverse Reinforcement
(See Clause 11.4.4.)

s_z		Longitudinal strain, ϵ_x					
		≤ 0.0000	≤ 0.00025	≤ 0.0005	≤ 0.0010	≤ 0.0015	≤ 0.0020
≤ 125	β	0.406	0.309	0.263	0.214	0.183	0.161
	θ	27°	29°	32°	34°	36°	38°
≤ 250	β	0.384	0.283	0.235	0.183	0.156	0.138
	θ	30°	34°	37°	41°	43°	45°
≤ 500	β	0.359	0.248	0.201	0.153	0.127	0.108
	θ	34°	39°	43°	48°	51°	54°
≤ 1000	β	0.335	0.212	0.163	0.118	0.095	0.080
	θ	37°	45°	51°	56°	60°	63°
≤ 2000	β	0.306	0.171	0.126	0.084	0.064	0.052
	θ	41°	53°	59°	66°	69°	72°

Figure 11-2
Values of β and θ for Sections Not Containing Transverse Reinforcement
(See Clause 11.4.4.)

December 1994

11.4.5 Factored Shear Stress

The factored shear stress shall be computed as

$$v_f = \frac{V_f - \phi_p V_p}{b_w d_v} \qquad (11\text{-}21)$$

11.4.6 Determination of ϵ_x

In lieu of more accurate calculations, the maximum longitudinal strain, ϵ_x, shall be computed from

$$\epsilon_x = \frac{0.5(N_f + V_f \cot\theta) + M_f/d_v - A_p f_{po}}{E_s A_s + E_p A_p} \qquad (11\text{-}22)$$

M_f is taken as positive. However, ϵ_x need not be taken as greater than 0.002.

In lieu of a more accurate determination, the decompression stress, f_{po}, may be taken as 1.1 times the effective stress, f_{pe}.

11.4.7 Determination of s_z

The crack spacing parameter, s_z, shall be taken as d_v or as the maximum distance between layers of crack control reinforcement, whichever is less. Each layer of such reinforcement shall have an area at least equal to $0.004 b_w s_z$. The value of s_z need not be taken greater than 2000 mm.

11.4.8 Proportioning of Transverse Reinforcement

Provided that the cross section does not change within the length of $d_v\cot\theta$, the transverse reinforcement provided within this length may be taken as the average amount calculated for this length.

11.4.9 Proportioning of Longitudinal Reinforcement

11.4.9.1

Longitudinal reinforcement shall be proportioned so that at all sections the factored resistance of the tension reinforcement, taking account of the stress that can be developed in that reinforcement, shall be greater than or equal to

$$\frac{M_f}{d_v} + 0.5N_f + (V_f - 0.5V_{sg} - \phi_p V_p)\cot\theta \qquad (11\text{-}23)$$

11.4.9.2

For members not subject to significant tension, the requirements of Clause 11.4.9.1 may be satisfied by extending the flexural tension reinforcement a distance of $d_v\cot\theta$ beyond the location needed by flexure alone.

11.4.9.3

In regions adjacent to maximum moment locations, the area of longitudinal reinforcement on the flexural tension side of the member need not exceed the area required to resist the maximum moment acting alone. This provision shall only apply if the support or the load at

---

N11.4.6

In the general method, the factors β and θ are functions of the deformations in the diagonally cracked web of the member. See Fig. N11.4.4(a). As an indicator of the magnitude of these deformations, the highest longitudinal strain, ϵ_x, that occurs in the web of the member is used. For simplicity, this strain can be approximated as the strain in the flexural tension chord of an equivalent truss. The determination of ϵ_x, for a non-prestressed beam, is illustrated in Fig. N11.4.6. For a prestressed concrete member, the concrete surrounding the reinforcement will remain in compression until the applied tension exceeds the prestress force, $A_{ps}f_{po}$, where f_{po} is the stress in the tendon when the surrounding concrete is at zero stress.

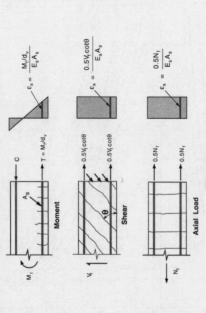

Fig. N11.4.6

Determination of Strain, ϵ_x, for Non-Prestressed Beam

Before ϵ_x can be determined from Eq. (11-22), it is necessary to make an estimate for $\cot\theta$. In this regard, it is useful to evaluate the expression for ϵ_x leaving $\cot\theta$ as an unknown. Thus, for a particular section, subjected to particular loadings, Eq. (11-22) could reduce to

$$\epsilon_x = 0.58 \times 10^{-3} + 0.23 \times 10^{-3} \cot\theta$$

If this section is to contain stirrups, and the shear stress ratio $v_f/(\lambda\, \phi_c\, f'_c)$ equals 0.070, then from Table 11-1, we can see that θ will lie between 30° and 42°. Choosing 36° (i.e., the value listed for ϵ_x less than or equal to 0.0010) we would calculate an ϵ_x value of 0.00090. As the calculated value of ϵ_x is a little less than the assumed value and it is conservative to use larger values of ϵ_x, we can take ϵ_x as 0.0010. That is, for this case use $\theta = 36°$ and $\beta = 0.179$.

In evaluating reinforcement areas at sections near bar cut-off locations, it is appropriate to assume that the effective area of a terminated bar reduces linearly from the full bar area to zero, over the development length of the bar.

N11.4.8

A shear failure caused by yielding of the stirrups involves yielding this reinforcement over a length of beam about $d_v \cot\theta$ long. Hence, a calculation for one section can be taken as representing a length of beam $d_v \cot\theta$ long, with the calculated section being in the middle of this length.

N11.4.9.1

In a diagonally cracked beam, shear causes tension, not only in the stirrups, but also in the longitudinal reinforcement. For a given shear, this tension becomes larger as the inclination of the cracks, θ, becomes smaller, and as the shear carried by the stirrups, V_{sg}, becomes smaller. If, in the free body diagram shown in Fig. N11.3.8.2, the horizontal distances, d_v and $0.5d_v$ are changed to $d_v \cot\theta$ and $0.5d_v \cot\theta$, and V_s is changed to V_{sg}, the tension in the longitudinal reinforcement caused by shear can be deduced to be

$$T = (V_f - 0.5V_{sg}) \cot\theta$$

Shear carried directly by the vertical component of inclined prestressing will not cause tension in the longitudinal reinforcement and hence, for these members

$$T = (V_f - 0.5V_{sg} - \varphi_p V_p) \cot\theta$$

Note that this expression for the tension in the longitudinal reinforcement caused by shear is somewhat different from that implied in Clause 11.4.6 and shown in Fig. N11.4.6. Clause 11.4.9.1 is concerned with the tension in the longitudinal reinforcement at a crack, while Clause 11.4.6 is concerned with the average strain, ε_x, measured over a base length long enough to average out the local influence of the crack. See Fig. N11.4.4(a).

In determining the stress that can be developed in the longitudinal reinforcement at sections near bar cut-off locations, it can be assumed that the tensile capacity of a bar varies linearly from zero at the free end, to a value of $\phi_s A_s f_y$, at a distance of ℓ_d from the free end, where A_b is the bar area and ℓ_d is the development length.

N11.4.9.2

At maximum moment locations, the shear force changes sign and hence, the inclination of the diagonal compressive stresses changes. At direct supports and point loads, this change of inclination is associated with a fan-shaped pattern of compressive stresses radiating from the point load or the direct support, as shown in Fig. N11.4.9.2(a). This fanning of the diagonal stresses reduces the tension in the longitudinal reinforcement caused by shear (i.e., angle θ becomes steeper). Due to this effect, the tension in the reinforcement does not exceed that due to the maximum moment alone, and hence, the longitudinal reinforcement requirements can be met by extending the flexural reinforcement for a distance of $d_v \cot\theta$. See Fig. N11.4.9.2(a).

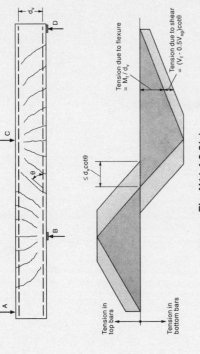

Fig. N11.4.9.2(a)

Influence of Shear on Required Tensile Forces in Longitudinal Reinforcement of Beam on Direct Supports Subjected to Point Loads

If a member is indirectly loaded or supported, then a pattern of parallel diagonal cracks is likely to occur near the maximum moment locations. See Fig. N11.4.9.2(b). In this case, the maximum tension required in the longitudinal reinforcement will be greater than that required for flexure alone and hence, Clause 11.4.9.2 should not be used.

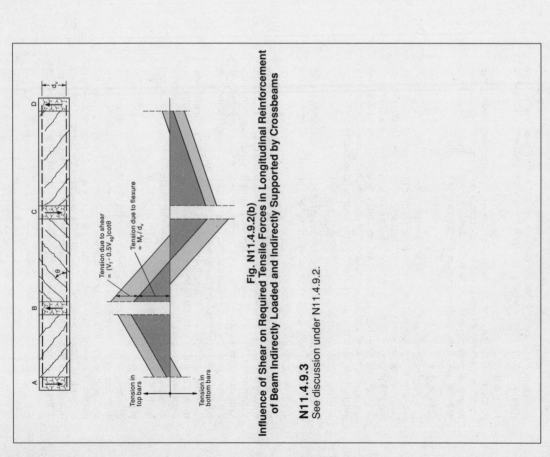

Fig. N11.4.9.2(b)
Influence of Shear on Required Tensile Forces in Longitudinal Reinforcement of Beam Indirectly Loaded and Indirectly Supported by Crossbeams

N11.4.9.3
See discussion under N11.4.9.2.

the maximum moment location introduces direct compression into the flexural compression face of the member.

11.4.9.4

At exterior direct bearing supports, the longitudinal reinforcement on the bottom face of the member shall be capable of resisting a tensile force of $(V_f - 0.5V_{sg} - \phi_p V_p)\cot\theta + 0.5N_f$ at the inside edge of the bearing area, where θ is given in Clause 11.4.4.

11.4.9.5

If longitudinal reinforcement is designed to satisfy Equation (11-23), the requirements of Clause 12.10.5 and 12.11.3 may be waived.

11.4.10 Sections Subjected to Combined Shear and Torsion

11.4.10.1

The transverse reinforcement provided shall be at least equal to the sum of that required for shear and that required for the coexisting torsion.

11.4.10.2

The amount of transverse reinforcement required for torsion shall be such that

$$T_{rg} \geq T_f \tag{11-24}$$

11.4.10.3

The value of T_{rg} shall be computed from

$$T_{rg} = 2A_o \frac{\phi_s A_t f_y}{s} \cot\theta \tag{11-25}$$

where A_o shall be taken as $0.85A_{oh}$ and θ is given in Clause 11.4.4. The factored shear stress, v_f, shall be computed from

(a) for box sections:

$$v_f = \frac{V_f - \phi_p V_p}{b_w d_v} + \frac{T_f p_h}{A_{oh}^2} \tag{11-26}$$

(b) for other sections:

$$v_f = \sqrt{\left(\frac{V_f - \phi_p V_p}{b_w d_v}\right)^2 + \left(\frac{T_f p_h}{A_{oh}^2}\right)^2} \tag{11-27}$$

The longitudinal strain, ϵ_x, shall be taken as 0.002 or shall be computed from

$$\epsilon_x = \frac{0.5N_f + 0.5\cot\theta \sqrt{V_f^2 + \left(\frac{0.9p_h T_f}{2A_o}\right)^2} + \frac{M_f}{d_v} - A_p f_{po}}{E_s A_s + E_p A_p} \geq 0 \tag{11-28}$$

N11.4.9.4

See Fig. N11.3.8.2 and discussion under N11.3.8.2 and N11.4.9.1.

N11.4.9.5

In traditional North American reinforced concrete shear design procedures, and in the simplified method of Clause 11.3, the influence of shear on the longitudinal reinforcement and the influence of the longitudinal reinforcement on the shear strength is accounted for by detailing rules about the flexural reinforcement. These traditional rules can be waived if these influences have been accounted for directly.

N11.4.10.1

The shear stresses due to torsion and shear will add on one side of the section and counteract on the other side. The transverse reinforcement is designed for the side where the effects are additive. Usually the loading that causes the highest torsion differs from the loading that causes the highest shear. While it is conservative to design for the highest torsion combined with the highest shear, it is only necessary to design for the highest torsion and its associated shear and the highest shear and its associated torsion.

N11.4.10.3

Equation (11-25) is based on a space truss analogy, see Fig. N11.3.9.4, assuming that the cracked concrete carries no tension and that the diagonal stresses spiral around the member at an inclination of θ to the longitudinal axis. Transverse reinforcement for torsion is required on all sides of the member and should be in the form of closed hoops.

For a box girder, the shear stress due to shear and the shear stress due to torsion will add together on one side of the box girder. Further, the magnitude of these stresses is largely determined by statics. For other cross-sectional shapes such as a rectangle or an I, there is the possibility of considerable redistribution of shear stresses. To make some allowance for this favourable redistribution, a "root-mean-square" approach is used in calculating the nominal shear stress for these cross-sections.

To account for the fact that on one side of the section the torsional and shear stresses will counteract each other, the required equivalent tension is taken as the square root of the sum of the squares of the individually calculated tensions.

11.4.10.4

The longitudinal reinforcement shall be proportioned so that

$$\phi_s A_s f_y + \phi_p A_p f_{pr} \geq \frac{M_f}{d_v} + 0.5N_f + \cot\theta \sqrt{(V_f - 0.5V_{sg} - \phi_p V_p)^2 + \left(\frac{0.45 p_h T_f}{2A_o}\right)^2} \quad (11\text{-}29)$$

11.5   Strut-and-Tie Model

11.5.1   Structural Idealization

The strength of reinforced concrete structures, members, or regions may be investigated by idealizing the reinforced concrete as a series of reinforcing steel tensile ties and concrete compressive struts interconnected at nodes to form a truss capable of carrying all the factored loads to the supports. In determining the geometry of the truss, account shall be taken of the required dimensions of the compressive struts and tensile ties.

11.5.2   Proportioning of a Compressive Strut

11.5.2.1 Strength of Strut

The dimensions of the strut shall be large enough to ensure that the calculated compressive force in the strut does not exceed $\phi_c A_{cs} f_{cu}$ where A_{cs} and f_{cu} are determined in accordance with Clause 11.5.2.2 and 11.5.2.3, respectively.

11.5.2.2 Effective Cross-Sectional Area of Strut

The value of A_{cs} shall be calculated by considering both the available concrete area and the anchorage conditions at the ends of the strut as given in Figure 11-3.

11.5.2.3 Limiting Compressive Stress in Strut

The value of f_{cu} shall be computed from

$$f_{cu} = \frac{f'_c}{0.8 + 170\epsilon_1} \leq 0.85 f'_c \quad (11\text{-}30)$$

where ϵ_1 is calculated as

$$\epsilon_1 = \epsilon_s + (\epsilon_s + 0.002)\cot^2\theta_s \quad (11\text{-}31)$$

and θ_s is the smallest angle between the compressive strut and the adjoining tensile ties and ϵ_s is the tensile strain in the tensile tie inclined at θ_s to the compressive strut.

11.5.2.4 Reinforced Strut

If the compressive strut contains reinforcement which is parallel to the strut and has been detailed to develop its yield strength in compression, the calculated force in the strut shall not exceed $\phi_c A_{cs} f_{cu} + \phi_s A_{ss} f_y$.

N11.5.1

Cracked reinforced concrete carries load principally by compressive stresses in the concrete and tensile stresses in the reinforcement. After significant cracking has occurred, the principal compressive stress trajectories in the concrete tend towards straight lines and hence, can be approximated by straight compressive struts. Tension ties are used to model the principal reinforcement. The regions of the concrete subjected to multi-directional stresses, where the struts and ties meet (the nodes of the truss) are represented by node regions.

A number of typical strut-and-tie models are shown in Fig. N11.5.1. In sketching such models it should be kept in mind that space must be left to accommodate the required dimensions of the struts and the ties. A second important consideration is to ensure that the angles between the struts and the adjoining tension ties, θ_s, are not too small.

While, for each situation, a number of different strut-and-tie models are feasible, those which involve the most direct path for the loads to travel to the supports will be the most efficient. In visualizing the load path for simple spans subjected to point loads, Fig. N11.5.1(i), it is useful to recall Robert Hooke's dictum, "As the string hangs, so inverted stands the arch." The shape outlined by the struts is geometrically identical to the bending moment diagram.

In some cases it may be appropriate to choose a strut-and-tie model with multiple load paths, e.g., Fig. N11.5.1(v). For these internally statically indeterminate trusses, the load may be assigned between the alternative load paths based on the yield capacity of the tension ties.

N11.5.2.2

The effective cross-sectional area of a strut is typically controlled by the anchorage conditions at the end of the strut. Figure 11-3 suggests that, for a strut anchored by reinforcement, the effective concrete area will extend to a distance of up to six bar diameters from the anchored bar.

N11.5.2.3

This clause requires that, in determining the limiting compressive stress in the concrete, some consideration be given to the strains imposed on the cracked concrete.

If the concrete is not subjected to principal tensile strains greater than about 0.002, it can resist a compressive stress of 0.85 f'_c. This will be the limit for regions of the struts that are not crossed by or joined to tension ties. The reinforcing bars of a tension tie that are bonded to the surrounding concrete. If the reinforcing bars are to yield in tension, there should be significant tensile strains imposed on the concrete. As these tensile strains increase, f_{cu} decreases.

The expression for ϵ_1 is based on the assumption that the principal compressive strain ϵ_2 in the direction of the strut equals 0.002 and that the tensile strain in the direction of the tension tie equals ϵ_s. As the angle between

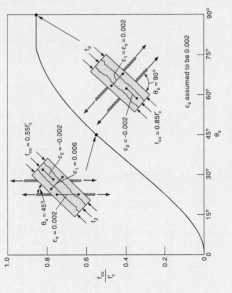

Fig. N11.5.2.3
Crushing Strength of Strut as a Function of Angle between Strut and Adjoining Tie

For a tension tie consisting of reinforcing bars, ε_s can be taken as the tensile strain due to factored loads in the reinforcing bars, or can be taken conservatively as f_y/E_s. For a tension tie consisting of prestressing tendons, ε_s can be taken as zero until the tensile stress in the tendon exceeds the decompression stress f_{po}. For higher stresses, ε_s would equal $(f_{pr} - f_{po})/E_p$.

If the strain, ε_s, varies over the width of the strut, it is appropriate to use the value at the centreline of the strut. Thus, for the situation shown in Fig. 11-3(b), where the tension tie is being developed in the length that crosses the strut, ε_s can be taken as one-half of the tensile strain in the tie at the face of the strut.

Some strut-and-tie models may involve two struts, say "a" and "b", that "share" the same concrete. See example at left support of deep beam in Fig. N11.5.1(v). One approach to check the crushing of the concrete in this situation is to assume that the compressive stresses in the two struts, f_{2a} and f_{2b}, and the limiting compressive stresses for these two struts, f_{cua} and f_{cub}, should satisfy the following limit:

$$\frac{f_{2a}}{f_{cua}} + \frac{f_{2b}}{f_{cub}} \leq 1.0$$

the strut and tie decreases, ε_1 increases and hence, f_{cu} decreases. In the limit, no compressive stresses would be permitted in a strut that is superimposed on a tension tie, i.e., $\theta_s = 0$, a situation that violates compatibility. See Fig. N11.5.2.3.

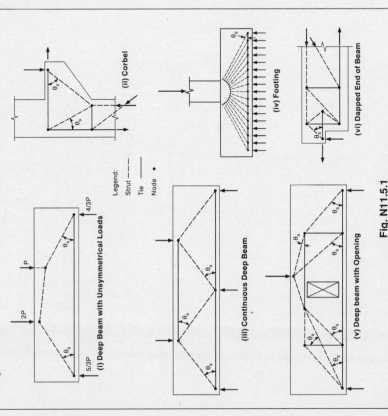

Fig. N11.5.1
Examples of Strut-and-Tie Model

N11.5.2.4

To be effective as compression reinforcement, the bars would have to be enclosed in column ties.

N11.5.3.2

Figure N11.5.3.2 illustrates some aspects of this clause.

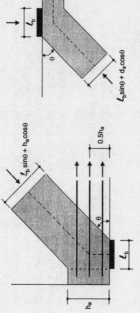

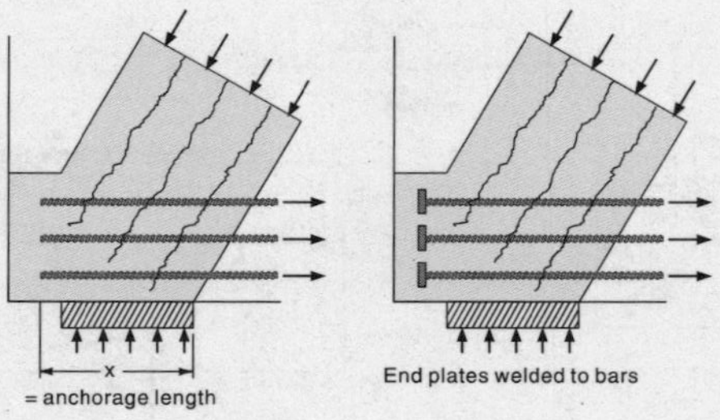

End plates welded to bars

x = anchorage length

Fig. N11.5.3.2
Anchorage of Tension Tie Reinforcement by Straight Embedment or by Mechanical Anchorage

---

(a) Strut anchored by reinforcement

$\ell_a \sin\theta$

θ

$6d_b$

ℓ_a

$6d_b$

d_b

(b) Strut anchored by bearing plate and reinforcement

$\ell_b \sin\theta + h_a \cos\theta$

$0.5h_a$

θ

ℓ_b

h_a

(c) Strut anchored by bearing plate and strut

d_a

ℓ_b

θ

$\ell_b \sin\theta + d_a \cos\theta$

Figure 11-3
Influence of Anchorage Conditions on Effective Cross-Sectional Area of Strut
(See Clause 11.5.2.2.)

11.5.3 Proportioning of a Tension Tie

11.5.3.1 Strength of Tie
The area of reinforcement in the tension tie, A_{st}, shall be large enough to ensure that the calculated tensile force in the tie does not exceed $\phi_s A_{st} f_y$.

11.5.3.2 Anchorage of Tie
The tension tie reinforcement shall be anchored by appropriate development length, hook, or mechanical anchorage, in accordance with Clause 12, so that it is capable of resisting the calculated tension in the reinforcement at the inner edge of the node region. For straight bars extending a distance x beyond the inner edge of the node region where $x < \ell_d$, the

calculated stress shall not exceed $f_y(x/\ell_d)$ where ℓ_d is computed in accordance with Clause 12.

11.5.4 Proportioning of Node Regions

11.5.4.1 Stress Limits in Node Regions

Unless special confinement is provided, the calculated concrete compressive stress in the node regions shall not exceed the following:

(a) $0.85\phi_c f_c'$ in node regions bounded by compressive struts and bearing areas;

(b) $0.75\phi_c f_c'$ in node regions anchoring a tension tie in only one direction; and

(c) $0.65\phi_c f_c'$ in node regions anchoring tension ties in more than one direction.

Note: *The beneficial effects of confinement can be accounted for if substantiated by test results.*

11.5.4.2 Satisfying Stress Limits in Node Regions

The stress limits in node regions may be considered satisfied if the following two conditions are met:

(a) the bearing stress on the node regions produced by concentrated loads or reactions does not exceed the stress limits given in Clause 11.5.4.1; and

(b) the tensile tie reinforcement is uniformly distributed over an effective area of concrete at least equal to the tensile tie force divided by the stress limits given in Clause 11.5.4.1.

11.5.5 Crack Control Reinforcement

Structures, members, or regions which have been designed by the provisions of Clause 11.5 shall contain an orthogonal grid of reinforcing bars near each face. The ratio of reinforcement area to gross concrete area shall not be less than 0.002 in each direction. The spacing of this reinforcement shall not exceed 300 mm. If located within the tension tie, the crack control reinforcement may also be considered as tension tie reinforcement.

11.6 Interface Shear Transfer

11.6.1 General

A crack shall be assumed to occur along the shear plane and relative displacement shall be considered to be resisted by cohesion and friction maintained by the shear friction reinforcement crossing the crack. The factored shear stress resistance of the plane shall be computed from

$$v_r = \lambda \phi_c (c + \mu \sigma) + \phi_s \rho_v f_y \cos \alpha_f \qquad (11\text{-}32)$$

where the expression $\lambda \phi_c (c + \mu \sigma)$ shall not exceed $0.25\phi_c f_c'$ nor $7.0\phi_c$ MPa and α_f is the angle between the shear friction reinforcement and the shear plane.

N11.5.4.1

The allowable concrete compressive stresses in nodal regions, which are illustrated in Fig. N11.5.4.1, are related to the degree of confinement in these regions. The reduced stress limits for nodal regions anchoring tension ties are based on the detrimental effect of the tensile straining caused by these ties. If the ties consist of post-tensioned tendons and the stress in these tendons does not need to exceed f_{se}, no tensile straining of the nodal regions will be required. For this case, the 0.85 $\phi_c f_c'$ limit is appropriate.

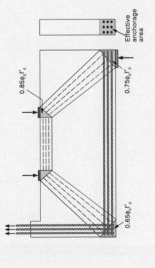

**Fig. N11.5.4.1
Stress Limits in Node Regions**

N11.5.4.2

The stresses in the nodal regions are reduced by increasing the size of the bearing plates, by increasing the dimensions of the compressive struts, and by increasing the effective anchorage area of the tension ties.

N11.5.5

This reinforcement is intended to control the width of the cracks and to ensure a minimum ductility for the member so that, if required, significant redistribution of internal stresses is possible. The 0.002 limit was chosen to be similar to the traditional minimum reinforcement limits used for walls and deep beams.

N11.6.1

Figure N11.6.1(a) illustrates the shear friction concept for the case where the reinforcement is perpendicular to the potential failure plane. Because the interface is rough, shear displacement will cause a widening of the crack. This crack opening will cause tension in the reinforcement balanced by compressive stresses, σ, in the concrete across the crack. The shear resistance of the face is assumed to be equal to the cohesion, c, plus the coefficient of friction, μ, times the compressive stress, σ, across the face. Hence, for this case,

$$v_r = \lambda\, \phi_c\, (C + \mu\, \sigma)$$

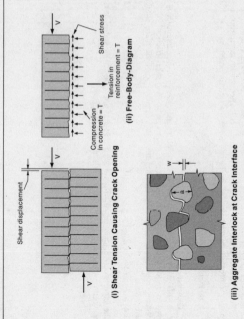

(i) Shear Tension Causing Crack Opening

(ii) Free-Body-Diagram

(iii) Aggregate Interlock at Crack Interface

Fig. N11.6.1(a)
Shear Friction Concept

If inclined reinforcement is crossing the crack, part of the shear can be directly resisted by the component, parallel to the shear plane, of the tension force in the reinforcement. See Fig. N11.6.1(b)

Fig. N11.6.1(b)
Shear-Friction Reinforcement Inclined to Potential Failure Cracks

11.6.2 Values of c and μ

The following values shall be taken for c and μ:

(a) For concrete placed against hardened concrete with the surface clean but not intentionally roughened:
$$c = 0.25 \text{ MPa}$$
$$\mu = 0.60$$

(b) For concrete placed against hardened concrete with the surface clean and intentionally roughened to a full amplitude of at least 5 mm:
$$c = 0.50 \text{ MPa}$$
$$\mu = 1.00$$

(c) For concrete placed monolithically:
$$c = 1.00 \text{ MPa}$$
$$\mu = 1.40$$

(d) For concrete anchored to as-rolled structural steel by headed studs or by reinforcing bars:
$$c = 0.00 \text{ MPa}$$
$$\mu = 0.60$$

11.6.3 Alternative Shear Stress Resistance

For concrete placed monolithically or placed against hardened concrete with the surface clean and intentionally roughened to a full amplitude of at least 5 mm, the factored shear stress resistance may be computed using Equation (11-33) in lieu of Equation (11-32).

$$v_r = \lambda \phi_c k \sqrt{\sigma f_c'} + \phi_s \rho_v f_y \cos \alpha_f \qquad (11\text{-}33)$$

where $k = 0.5$ for concrete placed against hardened concrete
$k = 0.6$ for concrete placed monolithically

where the expression $\lambda \phi_c k \sqrt{\sigma f_c'}$ shall not exceed $0.25 \phi_c f_c'$ nor $7.0 \phi_c$ MPa and α_f is the angle between the shear friction reinforcement and the shear plane.

11.6.4 Values of σ and ρ_v

The value of σ shall be computed as

$$\sigma = \rho_v f_y \sin \alpha_f + \frac{N}{A_g} \qquad (11\text{-}34)$$

where

$$\rho_v = \frac{A_{vf}}{A_{cv}} \qquad (11\text{-}35)$$

and N is the unfactored permanent load perpendicular to the shear plane, positive for compression and negative for tension.

11.6.5 Inclined Shear Friction Reinforcement

In determining the area of inclined shear friction reinforcement to be used in Equation (11-35), only that reinforcement inclined to the shear plane at an angle, α_f, such that the shear force produces tension in the inclined reinforcement shall be included.

The upper limit on the term $\lambda \phi_c (c + \mu \sigma)$ is to avoid concrete crushing failures.

The shear friction formulation in the previous edition of this code, A23.3-M84, did not have a cohesion term. When this formulation was used in the design of concrete members it resulted in some marked discontinuities in the amount of ties required.

N11.6.2

Figure N11.6.2 illustrates that the c and μ values given in this clause result in shear resistances that are somewhat higher than the 1984 values for small amounts of reinforcement and are somewhat lower for large amounts of reinforcement.

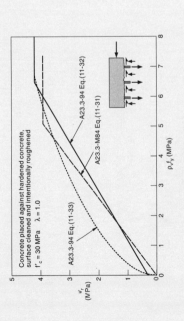

Concrete placed against hardened concrete, surface cleaned and intentionally roughened
$f'_c = 30$ MPa $\lambda = 1.0$

A23.3-94 Eq.(11-33)
A23.3-94 Eq.(11-32)
A23.3-M84 Eq.(11-31)

Fig. N11.6.2
Comparison of Factored Shear Stress Resistance Calculated by Three Different Equations

N11.6.3

The alternative method given in this clause is based on the work of Loov and Patnaik (Loov, R.E. and Patnaik, A.K., "Horizontal Shear Strength of Composite Concrete Beams with a Rough Interface," *PCI Journal*, Vol. 39, no. 1, pp. 48–69). In this method, the shear resistance is a function of both the concrete strength and the amount of reinforcement crossing the failure crack. It can be seen from Fig. N11.6.2 that the method can give values of the factored shear resistance that are considerably higher than those from Eq. (11-32).

11.6.6 Anchorage of Shear Friction Reinforcement

The shear friction reinforcement shall be capable of developing the specified yield strength of the reinforcement on both sides of the shear plane.

11.7 Special Provisions for Brackets and Corbels

11.7.1

Brackets and corbels shall be designed in accordance with the requirements of Clause 11.5 and the additional requirements of this Clause.

11.7.2

The depth, d, at the face of a support shall be not less than the distance between the load and the face of the support.

11.7.3

The depth at the outside edge of the bearing area shall be not less than half of the depth at the face of the support.

11.7.4

The external tensile force, N_f, acting on the bearing area shall not be taken as less than $0.2V_f$ unless special provisions are made to avoid tensile forces.

11.7.5

In place of the crack control reinforcement of Clause 11.5.5, closed stirrups or ties parallel to the primary tensile tie reinforcement, A_{st}, and having a total area of not less than 50% of A_{st}, shall be distributed within two-thirds of the effective depth adjacent to A_{st}.

11.7.6

The ratio, A_{st}/bd, calculated at the face of the support, shall be not less than $0.04(f'_c/f_y)$.

11.7.7

At the front face of the bracket or corbel, the primary tensile tie reinforcement, A_{st}, shall be anchored to develop the required force in the tension tie.

11.7.8

The bearing area of the load on the bracket or corbel shall not project beyond the straight portion of the tension tie bars, nor project beyond the interior face of the transverse anchor bar if one is provided.

11.8 Shear in Joints

When gravity load, wind, earthquake, or other lateral forces cause transfer of moment at connections of framing elements to columns, the shear resulting from moment transfer shall be considered in the design of lateral reinforcement in the columns and joints.

N11.7

Parameters used in this clause are illustrated in Fig. N11.7.

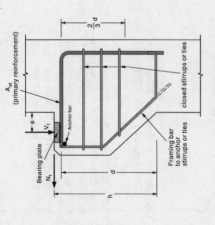

Fig. N11.7
Parameters Used in Corbel Design

N11.7.3

A minimum depth at the outside edge of the bearing area is specified because of concern with failures involving an inclined crack propagating from below the bearing area to the outer sloping face.

N11.7.4

This provision allows for the tension on the corbel caused by the restraint of shrinkage, creep and temperature movements. Connection details shall be such that the tension can be transmitted into the corbel by shear friction or by mechanical anchorage.

N11.7.7

This anchorage may be achieved by welding the tension tie reinforcement to a structural steel plate, bar, or angle, or by bending the tension tie bars into a horizontal loop. Anchorage by means of a vertical hook should be avoided because the concrete outside the hook will tend to split off. If vertical hooks must be used, the outside edge of the bearing plate under the load must not be closer to the edge of the corbel than the point of tangency at the start of the hook, after allowing for tolerances in bar placement.

84

12. Development and Splices of Reinforcement

12.0 Notation

A_b = area of an individual bar

A_s = area of nonprestressed tension reinforcement

A_{tr} = area of reinforcement within ℓ_d which crosses the potential bond splitting crack

A_v = area of shear reinforcement within a distance s

A_w = area of an individual wire to be developed or spliced

b_w = web width or diameter of circular section

d = distance from extreme compression fibre to centroid of tension reinforcement

d_b = nominal diameter of bar, wire, or prestressing strand (Clause 2.3)

d_{cs} = the smaller of (a) the distance from the closest concrete surface to the centre of the bar being developed, or (b) two-thirds the centre-to-centre spacing of the bars being developed

f'_c = specified compressive strength of concrete

$\sqrt{f'_c}$ = square root of specified compressive strength of concrete

f_{pr} = stress in prestressed reinforcement at factored resistance

f_{pe} = effective stress in prestressed reinforcement (after allowance for all prestress losses)

f_y = specified yield strength of nonprestressed reinforcement

f_{yt} = specified yield strength of transverse reinforcement

h = overall thickness of member

k_1 = bar location factor (Clause 12.2.4)

k_2 = coating factor (Clause 12.2.4)

k_3 = concrete density factor (Clause 12.2.4)

k_4 = bar size factor (Clause 12.2.4)

K_{tr} = transverse reinforcement index (Clause 12.2.2)

ℓ_a = additional embedment length at support or at point of inflection

ℓ_d = development length

ℓ_{db} = basic development length

ℓ_{dh} = development length of standard hook in tension, measured from critical section to outside end of hook [straight embedment length between critical section and start of hook [point of tangency] plus radius of bend and one bar diameter], equal to ℓ_{hb} times applicable modification factors

ℓ_{hb} = basic development length of standard hook in tension

M_r = factored moment resistance at section

n = number of bars or wires being developed along potential plane of bond splitting

s = maximum centre-to-centre spacing of transverse reinforcement within ℓ_d

s_w = spacing of wire to be developed or spliced

V_f = factored shear force at section

β_b = ratio of area of cut off reinforcement to total area of tension reinforcement at section

12.1 Development of Reinforcement—General

12.1.1
The calculated tension or compression in reinforcement at each section of reinforced concrete members shall be developed on each side of that section by embedment length, hook, or mechanical device, or by a combination thereof. Hooks may be used in developing bars in tension only.

12.1.2
The maximum permissible value of $\sqrt{f'_c}$ in Clause 12 is 8 MPa.

12.2 Development of Deformed Bars and Deformed Wire in Tension

12.2.1
The development length, ℓ_d, of deformed bars and deformed wire in tension shall be determined from either Clause 12.2.2 or Clause 12.2.3, but ℓ_d shall be not less than 300 mm.

12.2.2
The development length, ℓ_d, of deformed bars and deformed wire in tension shall be

$$\ell_d = 1.15 \frac{k_1 k_2 k_3 k_4}{(d_{cs} + K_{tr})} \frac{f_y}{\sqrt{f'_c}} A_b \tag{12-1}$$

but the term $(d_{cs} + K_{tr})$ shall not be taken greater than $2.5d_b$, where

$$K_{tr} = \frac{A_{tr} f_{yt}}{10.5 \, s \, n}$$

12.2.3
The development length, ℓ_d, of deformed bars and deformed wire in tension may be taken from Table 12-1 provided that the clear cover and clear spacing of the bars or wire being developed are at least d_b and $1.4d_b$, respectively.

N12 Development and Splices of Reinforcement

N12.2.2
Equation (12-1) is a modified form of the general equation for the development length of deformed bars or wires in tension proposed by ACI Committee 408[12.1] which is based on the research carried out by Orangun et al.[12.2]. In the Standard, the term, d_{cs}, is taken as the smaller of the minimum cover measured to the centre of the bar or two-thirds of the centre-to-centre spacing of the bars. The factor, K_{tr}, represents the contribution of transverse reinforcement across potential planes of splitting.

The factor k_1 reflects the adverse effects of top-bar casting position, k_2 is the epoxy-coating factor, k_3 reflects the lower tensile strength of low-density concrete and k_4 is a factor reflecting the more favourable performance of smaller diameter deformed bars and wires (see N12.2.4 for more details).

Equation (12-1) expresses the development length when the bond strength is limited by splitting failures. The term $(d_{cs} + K_{tr})$ is limited to $2.5d_b$ to safeguard against pullout type failures.

N12.2.3
Table 12-1 gives the development length of deformed bars and deformed wires in tension in a simplified format, as a function of the bar diameter, d_b. These simplified expressions have been determined by substituting into Equation (12-1) minimum values of cover and spacing and/or minimum amounts of transverse reinforcement.

For example, consider a case where bars in a slab have a minimum clear cover of $1.0d_b$ and a clear spacing between the bars of $2d_b$. It is assumed that the slab reinforcement perpendicular to the bars being developed serve to control splitting cracks in the cover concrete. Thus the bond strength would be controlled by splitting between the bars in a layer and the value of d_{cs} would be controlled by the bar spacing, giving d_{cs} equal to $2/3 \times 3.0d_b = 2.0d_b$. For this case where K_{tr} equals zero, Equation (12-1) becomes:

$$\ell_d = 1.15 \frac{k_1 k_2 k_3 k_4}{(2 d_b + 0)} \frac{f_y}{\sqrt{f'_c}} \frac{\pi d_b^2}{4}$$

$$= 0.45 k_1 k_2 k_3 k_4 \frac{f_y}{\sqrt{f'_c}} d_b$$

This simplified equation is also used for the case where the minimum clear cover is $1.0d_b$, the minimum clear spacing is $1.4d_b$ and confinement in the form of minimum ties or stirrups is provided.

For the situation where a minimum clear cover of $1.0d_b$ and a minimum clear spacing between bars of $1.4d_b$ are provided, without any transverse reinforcement, then d_{cs} becomes the smaller of $1.5 \, d_b$ or $2/3 \times 2.4 = 1.6d_b$.

Table 12-1
Development Length, ℓ_d, of Deformed Bars and Deformed Wire in Tension
(See Clause 12.2.3.)

Cases	Minimum development length, ℓ_d
Member containing minimum stirrups or ties (Clause 11.2.8.4 or Clause 7.6.5) within ℓ_d or Slabs, walls, shells, or folded plates having clear spacing between bars being developed not less than $2d_b$	$0.45 k_1 k_2 k_3 k_4 \dfrac{f_y}{\sqrt{f'_c}} d_b$
Other cases	$0.6 k_1 k_2 k_3 k_4 \dfrac{f_y}{\sqrt{f'_c}} d_b$

Note: *The clear cover and clear spacing requirements referred to in Clause 12.2.3 are in accordance with the requirements of CSA Standard A23.1-94 (see Appendix A).*

12.2.4 Modification factors
The following modification factors are to be used in calculating the development length from Clauses 12.2.2 and 12.2.3.

Bar location factor, k_1
k_1 = 1.3 for horizontal reinforcement so placed that more than 300 mm of fresh concrete is cast in the member below the development length or splice.
   = 1.0 for other cases.

Coating factor, k_2
k_2 = 1.5 for epoxy-coated reinforcement with clear cover less than $3d_b$, or with clear spacing between bars being developed less than $6d_b$.
   = 1.2 for all other epoxy-coated reinforcement.
   = 1.0 for uncoated reinforcement.

Concrete density factor, k_3
k_3 = 1.3 for structural low-density concrete.
   = 1.2 for structural semi-low-density concrete.
   = 1.0 for normal-density concrete.

Bar size factor, k_4
k_4 = 0.8 for No. 20 and smaller bars and deformed wires.
   = 1.0 for No. 25 and larger bars.

The product k_1k_2 need not be taken greater than 1.7.

Hence the simplified equation for the case labelled "other cases" in Table 12-1 becomes:

$$\ell_d = 1.15 \frac{k_1 k_2 k_3 k_4}{(1.5 d_b + 0)} \frac{f_y}{\sqrt{f'_c}} \frac{\pi d_b^2}{4}$$

$$= 0.6 k_1 k_2 k_3 k_4 \frac{f_y}{\sqrt{f'_c}} d_b$$

The equations in Table 12-1 may be readily evaluated for commonly occurring situations as simple multiples of d_b. For example, for normal density concrete ($k_3 = 1.0$) with $f'_c = 35$ MPa and using uncoated No. 20 or larger bottom bars ($k_2 = k_4 = k_1 = 1.0$) with $f_y = 400$ MPa these expressions, with rounding, reduce to:

$\ell_d = 30d_b$ for the first set of cases
and $\ell_d = 40d_b$ for the others

N12.2.4
The bar location factor, k_1, accounts for the position of the bar in freshly placed concrete. The factor had been reduced from 1.4 in the 1984 Standard to 1.3 to reflect recent research[12.3,12.4].

Studies[12.5,12.6,12.7] of the mechanical anchorage of epoxy-coated bars show that bond strength is reduced because the coating significantly reduces both adhesion and friction between the bar and the concrete. The factor, k_2, reflects the type of anchorage failure likely to occur. When the cover or spacing is small, a splitting failure can occur and the anchorage or bond strength is substantially reduced. If the cover and spacing between bars is large, a splitting failure is precluded and the effect of the epoxy coating on anchorage strength is not as large. Studies[12.2] have shown that although the cover or spacing may be small, the anchorage strength may be increased by adding transverse steel crossing the plane of splitting, and restraining the splitting crack.

Although no studies on the effect of coated transverse steel have been reported to date, the addition of coated transverse steel should improve the anchorage strength of epoxy-coated bars. Since the bond of epoxy-coated bars is already reduced due to loss of adhesion between the bar and the concrete, an upper limit of 1.7 is established for the product of the top reinforcement and epoxy-coated reinforcement factors.

The low-density concrete factor, k_3, has been rounded to reflect the degree of accuracy associated with this factor.

N12.2.5
The reduction factor based on area is not used in those cases where anchorage development for full f_y is required. For example, the excess reinforcement factor does not apply for development of positive moment reinforcement at supports according to Clause 12.11.2, for development of shrinkage and temperature reinforcement according to Clause 7.8.4, or for development of reinforcement provided according to Clause 13.11.5.3.

N12.3.2
Bars in compression have shorter development lengths because the development length is not crossed by cracks due to tension in the concrete and because the end bearing of the bars on the concrete is usually beneficial.

N12.4
An increased development length is required when three or four bars are bundled together. The extra extension is needed because the grouping makes it more difficult to mobilize bond resistance from the "core" between the bars.

The designer should also note Clause 7.4.2.3 relating to the cutoff points of individual bars within a bundle and Clause 12.14.2.2 relating to splices of bundled bars.

N12.5.1
The definition of hook development length is shown in Fig. N12.5.1. This development length is typically controlled by splitting of the concrete in the plane of the hook caused by high local stresses shown.

N12.5.2
Fig. N12.5.2 and Table N12.5.2 gives geometric details for standard hooks and basic hook development length ℓ_{hb} for the case of f_y = 400 MPa.

12.2.5 Excess Reinforcement
The development length, ℓ_d, may be multiplied by the factor (A_s required) / (A_s provided) where reinforcement in a flexural member is in excess of that required by analysis, except where anchorage or development for f_y is specifically required or the reinforcement is designed under the provisions of Clause 21.

12.3 Development of Deformed Bars in Compression

12.3.1 Development Length
The development length, ℓ_d, for deformed bars in compression shall be computed as the product of the basic development length, ℓ_{db}, of Clause 12.3.2 and the applicable modification factors of Clause 12.3.3, but ℓ_d shall be not less than 200 mm.

12.3.2 Basic Development Length
The basic compression development length, ℓ_{db}, shall be $0.24d_b f_y/\sqrt{f'_c}$, but not less than $0.044d_b f_y$.

12.3.3 Modification Factors
The basic development length, ℓ_{db}, may be multiplied by applicable factors, with a cumulative value of not less than 0.5, for
(a) reinforcement in excess of that required by analysis . . (A_s required)/(A_s provided);
(b) reinforcement enclosed within spiral reinforcement of not less than 6 mm diameter and not more than 100 mm pitch or within No. 10 ties in conformance with Clause 7.6.5 and spaced at not more than 100 mm on centre . . . . 0.75.

12.4 Development of Bundled Bars
The development length of individual bars within a bundle, in tension or compression, shall be that for the individual bar, increased by 10% for a 2-bar bundle, 20% for a 3-bar bundle, and 33% for a 4-bar bundle.

12.5 Development of Standard Hooks in Tension

12.5.1 Tension Development Length
Except as provided in Clause 12.13, the development length, ℓ_{dh}, for deformed bars in tension terminating in a standard hook (see Clause 7.1) shall be computed as the product of the basic development length, ℓ_{hb}, of Clause 12.5.2 and the applicable modification factor or factors of Clause 12.5.3, but ℓ_{dh} shall be not less than $8d_b$ or 150 mm, whichever is greater.

12.5.2 Basic Development Length
The basic development length, ℓ_{hb}, for a hooked bar with f_y equal to 400 MPa shall be $100d_b\sqrt{f'_c}$.

12.5.3 Factors Modifying Hook Development Length
The basic development length, ℓ_{hb}, shall be multiplied by the following factor(s), as applicable:
(a) for bars with f_y other than 400 MPa . . . . f_y/400;
(b) for No. 35 or smaller bars, where the side cover (normal to plane of hook) is not

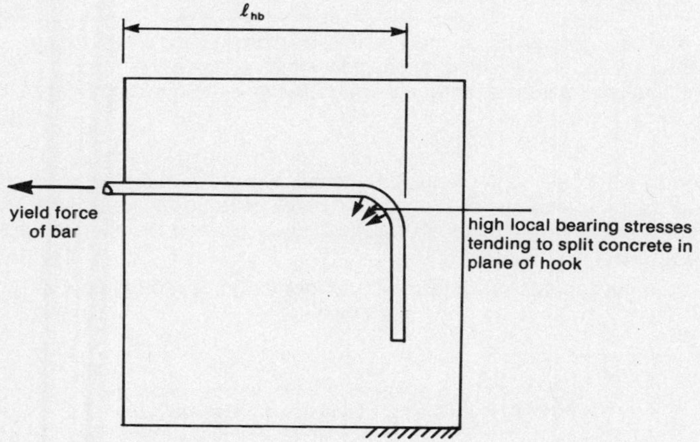

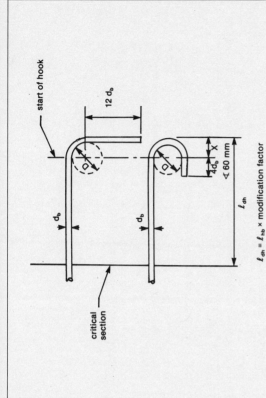

start of hook

12 d_b

critical section

d_b

d_b

X

4d_b

< 60 mm

ℓ_{dh}

$\ell_{dh} = \ell_{hb} \times$ modification factor

**Fig. N12.5.2
Hook Geometry Details**

*X = bend radius + d_b, (values given are for bend radii for Grade 400 R Steel)

N12.5.3

Fig. N12.5.3 illustrates some situations in which the basic hook development length is modified.

ℓ_{hb}

yield force of bar

high local bearing stresses tending to split concrete in plane of hook

**Fig. N12.5.1
Hook Development Length**

Table N12.5.2

Values of Hook Basic Development Length for Grade 400 Bars

Bar No.	X* (mm)	ℓ_{hb} (mm) f'_c (MPa)				
		20	25	30	35	40
10	45	253	226	206	191	179
15	65	358	320	292	270	253
20	80	436	390	356	330	308
25	100	563	504	460	426	398
30	155	669	598	546	505	473
35	185	798	714	652	603	565
45	270	977	874	798	739	691
55	355	1261	1128	1030	953	892

(c) less than 60 mm and for 90° hooks where the cover on the bar extension beyond the hook is not less than 50 mm 0.7;

for No. 35 or smaller bars, where the hook is enclosed vertically or horizontally within at least three ties or stirrup ties spaced along a length at least equal to the inside diameter of the hook, at a spacing not greater than $3d_b$, where d_b is the nominal diameter of the hooked bar 0.8;

(d) where anchorage or development for f_y is not specifically required, for reinforcement in excess of that required by analysis . $(A_s\ \text{required})/(A_s\ \text{provided})$;

(e) for structural low density concrete . . . . 1.3; and

(f) for epoxy-coated reinforcement . . . . 1.2.

12.5.4 Confinement of Hooks

For bars being developed by a standard hook at the ends of members, where both the side cover and the top (or bottom) cover over the hook is less than 60 mm, the hook shall be enclosed within at least three ties or stirrup ties spaced along a length at least equal to the inside diameter of the hook at a spacing not greater than $3d_b$, where d_b is the nominal diameter of the hooked bar. For this case, the factor of Clause 12.5.3(c) shall not apply.

12.5.5 Development of Bars in Compression

Hooks shall not be considered effective in developing bars in compression.

12.6 Mechanical Anchorage

12.6.1
Any mechanical device demonstrated by test to be capable of developing the strength of reinforcement without damage to the concrete may be used.

12.6.2
The development of reinforcement may consist of a combination of mechanical anchorage plus additional embedment length of reinforcement, between the point of maximum bar stress and the mechanical anchorage.

12.7 Development of Welded Deformed Wire Fabric in Tension

12.7.1
The development length, ℓ_d, of welded deformed wire fabric shall be computed as the product of the development length, ℓ_d, of Clause 12.2.2 or 12.2.3 and the applicable wire fabric factor or factors of Clauses 12.7.2 or 12.7.3, but ℓ_d shall be not less than 200 mm except in the computation of lap splices by the method described in Clause 12.18 and in the development of web reinforcement by the method described in Clause 12.13.

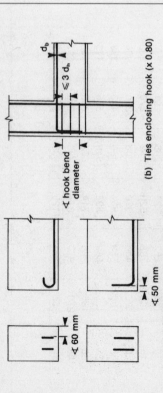

(a) Hooks having extra cover (x 0.70)

(b) Ties enclosing hook (x 0.80)

(c) Stirrups required if both side and bottom cover are less than 60 mm (0.80 factor not applicable)
If side or bottom cover exceeds 60 mm (x 0.80)

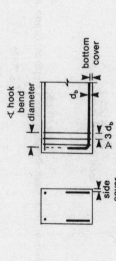

Fig. N12.5.3
Factors Modifying Hook Development Length for No. 35 or Smaller Bars

N12.6.2

Total development of a bar simply consists of the sum of all the parts that contribute to the anchorage. When a mechanical anchorage is not capable of developing the required strength of the reinforcement, additional embedment length of reinforcement must be provided.

N12.7

Fig. N12.7 shows the development requirements for deformed wire fabric with one cross wire within the development length. Some of the development is assigned to the welds and some assigned to the length of deformed wire.

12.7.2

For welded deformed wire fabric with at least one cross wire within the development length and not less than 50 mm from the point of the critical section, the wire fabric factor shall be the greater of

$$\frac{f_y - 240}{f_y} \qquad (12\text{-}2)$$

or

$$\frac{5\,d_b}{s_w} \qquad (12\text{-}3)$$

but need not be taken greater than 1.0.

12.7.3

For welded deformed wire fabric with no cross wires within the development length or with a single cross wire less than 50 mm from the point of the critical section, the wire fabric factor shall be taken as 1.0.

12.8   Development of Welded Smooth Wire Fabric in Tension

The yield strength of welded smooth wire fabric shall be considered to be developed by the embedment of two cross wires with the closer cross wire not less than 50 mm from the critical section. However, the development length, ℓ_d, measured from the critical section to the outermost cross wire shall be not less than

$$\ell_d = 3.3\,k_3 \frac{A_w}{s_w} \frac{f_y}{\sqrt{f_c'}} \qquad (12\text{-}4)$$

If excess reinforcement is present, this length may be reduced in accordance with Clause 12.2.5. ℓ_d shall be not less than 150 mm except in the computation of lap splices by the method described in Clause 12.19.

12.9   Development of Prestressing Strand

12.9.1

Three- or seven-wire pretensioning strand shall be bonded beyond the critical section for a development length, ℓ_d, not less than

$$\ell_d = 0.145(f_{pr} - 0.67f_{pe})d_b \qquad (12\text{-}5)$$

12.9.2

Where bonding of a strand does not extend to the end of a member, and the design includes tension at specified loads in the precompressed tensile zone as permitted by Clause 18.4.2 or 18.4.3, the development length specified in Clause 12.9.1 shall be doubled.

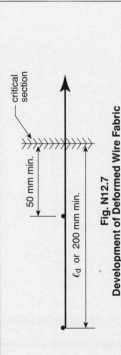

critical
section

50 mm min.

ℓ_d or 200 mm min.

**Fig. N12.7
Development of Deformed Wire Fabric**

N12.8

Fig. N12.8 shows the development requirements for smooth wire fabric with development primarily dependent on properly located cross wires. For fabrics made with the smaller wires, an embedment of at least two cross wires 50 mm or more beyond the point of critical section is adequate to develop the full yield strength of the anchored wires. However, for fabrics made with larger closely spaced wires a longer embedment is required and a minimum development length is provided for these fabrics.

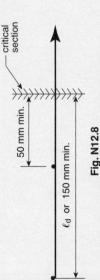

critical
section

50 mm min.

ℓ_d or 150 mm min.

**Fig. N12.8
Development of Welded Smooth Wire Fabric**

N12.9.1

The expression for development length, ℓ_d, may be written as:

$$\ell_d = 0.048 f_{se}\,d_b + 0.145\,(f_{ps} - f_{se})\,d_b$$

The first term represents the transfer length of the strand which is the length over which the prestress, f_{se}, develops. The second term represents the additional length required to increase the stress from f_{se} to f_{ps}. The variation of strand stress along the development length is shown in Fig. N12.9.1.

12.10 Development of Flexural Reinforcement—General

12.10.1

Tension reinforcement may be anchored into the compression zone by bending it across the web and making it continuous with the reinforcement on the opposite face of the member or anchoring it there.

12.10.2

Critical sections for development of reinforcement in flexural members are at points of maximum stress and at points within the span where adjacent reinforcement terminates or is bent. The location of the points of maximum stress and the points at which reinforcement is no longer required to resist flexure shall be derived from the factored bending moment diagram.

12.10.3

Reinforcement shall extend beyond the point at which it is no longer required to resist flexure as required in Clause 11.3.8 or 11.4.9.

12.10.4

Continuing reinforcement shall have an embedment length of not less than the development length, ℓ_d, plus the longer of the effective depth of the member or $12d_b$ beyond the point where bent or terminated tension reinforcement is no longer required to resist flexure.

12.10.5

Flexural reinforcement shall not be terminated in a tension zone unless one of the following conditions is satisfied:

(a) the shear at the cutoff point does not exceed two-thirds of that permitted, including the shear strength of the shear reinforcement provided; or

(b) stirrup area in excess of that required for shear and torsion is provided along each terminated bar or wire over a distance from the termination point equal to three-fourths of the effective depth of the member. The excess stirrup area, A_v, shall be not less than $b_w s/(3f_y)$. The spacing, s, shall not exceed $d/(8\beta_b)$.

12.10.6

Special attention shall be given to the provision of adequate anchorage for tension reinforcement in flexural members such as sloped, stepped, or tapered footings; brackets; deep flexural members; or members in which the tension reinforcement is not parallel to the compression face.

12.11 Development of Positive Moment Reinforcement

12.11.1

At least one-third of the positive moment reinforcement in simply supported members and one-fourth of the positive moment reinforcement in continuous members shall extend along the same face of the member into the support. In beams constructed monolithically with the support, such reinforcement shall extend into the support at least 150 mm, but not less than the requirements of Clause 11.3.8 or 11.4.9.

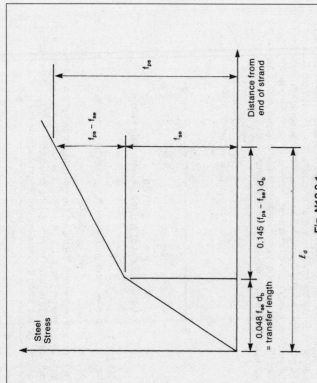

**Fig. N12.9.1
Development of Prestressing Strand**

N12.10.3

The inclined cracking which occurs in regions subjected to shearing forces leads to bar forces which are larger than those calculated from the bending moment diagram. If the Simplified Method of Clause 11.3 is used to design stirrups, the increased tension force in the bars is accounted for by extending the bars at least d past the point where they are no longer needed for flexure. This effect is accounted for directly if both the stirrups and the longitudinal reinforcement are designed using the General Method for shear given in Clause 11.4. If the General Method of shear design (Clause 11.4) has been followed, the requirements of Clause 11.4.9.1 must be met. If the requirements of Clause 11.4.9.1 are satisfied, then the requirements of Clauses 12.10.5 and 12.11.3 may be waived (see Clause 11.4.9.5).

The application of the detailing rules of Clauses 12.10, 12.11 and 12.12, for a beam whose shear reinforcement has been designed by Clause 11.3, is illustrated in Fig. N12.10.3(a).

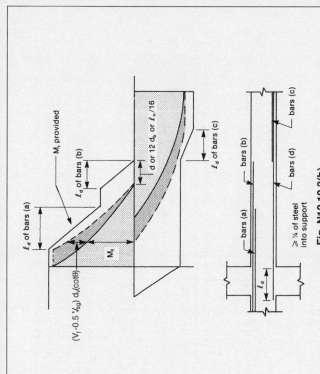

Fig. N12.10.3(b)

Development of Longitudinal Reinforcement in Continuous Beam with Shear Reinforcement Designed by Clause 11.4

N12.11.2

Unexpected loadings such as blasts or earthquakes may cause load reversals. To provide a minimum level of ductility for these situations it is necessary to anchor the required reinforcement so that it can develop its yield stress.

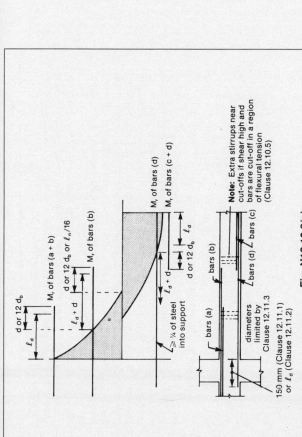

Fig. N12.10.3(a)

Development of Longitudinal Reinforcement in Continuous Beam with Shear Reinforcement Designed by Clause 11.3

If the General Method of shear design, Clause 11.4, is being followed, then the longitudinal reinforcement needs to be designed for the tensions arising from the moment and the shear at every section. Alternatively, each section can be designed for an "equivalent moment" of $M_f + (V_f - 0.5V_{sg})$ $d_v \cot \Theta$. Bar cut-offs are determined to ensure that the M_r provided exceeds the equivalent moments at all sections, see Fig. N12.10.3(b).

N12.10.6

In these types of members the required tension in the reinforcement is not directly proportional to the moment. This is illustrated in Fig. N12.10.6 for a tapered footing. In evaluating the variation of this force, the strut and tie model of Clause 11.5 will often be useful.

N12.11.1

These traditional requirements are intended to give the structure an ability to tolerate some unanticipated actions.

12.11.2

When a flexural member is part of a primary lateral load resisting system, the positive moment reinforcement required by Clause 12.11.1 to be extended into the support shall be anchored to develop the specified yield strength, f_y, in tension at the face of the support.

12.11.3

At simple supports and at points of inflection, the positive moment tension reinforcement shall be limited in diameter or increased in area, such that ℓ_d computed for f_y by the method in Clause 12.2 satisfies Equation (12-6), except that Equation (12-6) need not be satisfied for reinforcement terminating by a standard hook extending ℓ_{dh} beyond the centreline of simple supports or a mechanical anchorage at least equivalent to a standard hook.

$$\frac{M_r}{V_f} + \ell_a \geq \ell_d \qquad (12\text{-}6)$$

where

at a support, ℓ_a shall be the embedment length beyond the centre of the support;

at a point of inflection, ℓ_a shall be limited to the effective depth of the member or $12d_b$, whichever is greater.

The value of M_r/V_f may be increased by 30% when the ends of the reinforcement are confined by a compressive reaction.

12.12 Development of Negative Moment Reinforcement

12.12.1

Negative moment reinforcement in a continuous, restrained, or cantilever member, or in any member of a rigid frame shall be anchored in, or through, the supporting member by embedment length, hooks, or mechanical anchorage.

12.12.2

At least one-third of the total tension reinforcement provided for negative moment at a support shall have an embedment length beyond the point of inflection of not less than the effective depth of the member, $12d_b$, or 1/16 the clear span, whichever is greater.

12.13 Anchorage of Shear Reinforcement

12.13.1

Web reinforcement shall be carried as close to the compression and tension surfaces of a member as cover requirements and proximity of other reinforcement will permit.

12.13.2

Transverse reinforcement provided for shear shall be anchored by one of the following means:

(a) for No. 15 and smaller bars, and for MD200 and smaller wire, by a standard stirrup hook (see Clause 7.1.2) around longitudinal reinforcement;

(b) for No. 20 and No. 25 stirrups by a standard hook (see Clause 7.1.2) around longitudinal reinforcement plus an embedment between mid-depth of the member

---

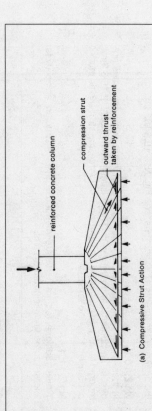

(a) Compressive Strut Action

(b) Required Tensile Force in Reinforcement

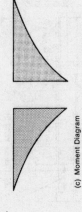

(c) Moment Diagram

Fig. N12.10.6
Required Tension in Reinforcement for Tapered Footing

N12.11.3

In regions of low moment and high shear the tension force in the reinforcing bars will increase rapidly in the direction of increasing moment. This clause is intended to assure that the bond characteristics of such bars will enable this rapid build up of force to occur. As illustrated in Fig. N12.11.3, the "bond" characteristics are considered adequate if the development length of the bars, ℓ_d, is less than $\ell_a + M_r/V_f$. When this requirement is not satisfied, either reduce the bar diameter (ℓ_d reduced) or increase the area of reinforcement at the section (M_r increased).

Note: *If the General Method of shear design (Clause 11.4) has been followed, the rapid build-up of force in the longitudinal reinforcement will have already been accounted for by satisfying the requirements of Clause 11.4.9. Thus Clause 12.11.3 can be waived (see Clause 11.4.9.5).*

(c) and the outside end of the hook equal to or greater than $0.33\ell_d$;
for each leg of welded smooth wire fabric forming simple U-stirrups, either

(i) two longitudinal wires located at a 50 mm spacing along the member at the top of the U; or

(ii) one longitudinal wires located not more than d/4 from the compression face and a second wire closer to the compression face and spaced not less than 50 mm from the first wire. The second wire may be located on the stirrup leg beyond a bend or on a bend with an inside diameter of not less than $8d_b$;

(d) for each end of a single leg stirrup of welded smooth or deformed wire fabric, two longitudinal wires at a minimum spacing of 50 mm, and with the inner wire at least d/4 from the mid-depth of the member. The outer longitudinal wire at the tension face shall not be further from that face than the portion of primary flexural reinforcement closest to the face; or

(e) mechanical anchorage capable of developing the yield strength of the bar.

12.13.3
Between anchored ends, each bend in the continuous portion of a stirrup shall enclose a longitudinal bar.

12.13.4
Longitudinal bars bent to act as shear reinforcement, if extended into a region of tension, shall be continuous with the longitudinal reinforcement and, if extended into a region of compression, shall be anchored beyond the mid-depth, d/2, as specified for development length in Clause 12.2 for that part of f_y required to satisfy Clause 11.3.8 or Clause 11.4.9.

12.13.5
Pairs of U-stirrups or ties so placed as to form a closed unit shall be considered properly spliced when the length of the laps is $1.3\ell_d$. Alternatively, in members at least 450 mm deep and where $A_{b}f_y$ is not more than 40 kN per leg, the splice shall be considered adequate if the stirrup legs extend the full available depth of the member.

12.14 Splices of Reinforcement—General

12.14.1 Limitations on Use
Splices of reinforcement shall be made only as required or permitted on design drawings, in specifications, or as authorized by the designer.

12.14.2 Lap Splices

12.14.2.1
Lap splices shall not be used for bars larger than No. 35 except as provided in Clauses 12.16.2 and 15.8.2.5.

12.14.2.2
Lap splices of bundled bars shall be based on the lap splice length required for individual bars within a bundle, increased by 10% for a 2-bar bundle, 20% for a 3-bar bundle, and 33% for a 4-bar bundle. Individual bar splices within a bundle shall not overlap.

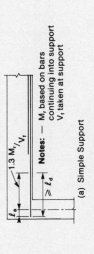

$1.3 M_r/V_f$

ℓ_a $\geq \ell_d$

Notes: — M, based on bars continuing into support
V, taken at support

(a) Simple Support

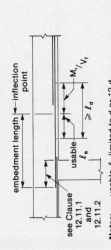

M_r/V_f

$\geq \ell_d$

embedment length — inflection point

usable ℓ_a

see Clause 12.11.1 and 12.11.2

(b) Inflection Point

Notes: — usable ℓ_a limited to d or 12 d_b
— M, based on bars extending past inflection point
— V, taken at inflection point
— Negative moment steel not shown

**Fig. N12.11.3
Development of Positive Moment Reinforcement at Simple Support and Inflection Point**

N12.12
Fig. N12.12 illustrates the development requirements for negative moment reinforcement.

N12.13.1
To be effective, web reinforcement must be capable of tying the main tension reinforcement to the compression zone of the beam.

N12.13.2
For shear reinforcement made with No. 15 and smaller bars or with MD200 and smaller wire there is no need to calculate the straight embedment length in addition to the hook. However, Clause 12.13.1 requires "full-depth" web reinforcement and in addition the web reinforcement must be anchored around longitudinal reinforcement.
Fig. N12.13.2(c) illustrates stirrup anchorage requirements for No. 20 and No. 25 stirrups.

12.14.2.3
Bars spliced by lap splices in flexural members shall not be spaced transversely further apart than 1/5 of the required lap splice length nor 150 mm.

12.14.3 Welded Splices and Mechanical Connections

12.14.3.1
Welded splices and other mechanical connections may be used.

12.14.3.2
Except as provided for in this Standard, all welding shall conform to CSA Standard W186.

12.14.3.3
A full welded splice shall have bars welded to develop, in tension, at least 120% of the specified yield strength, f_y, of the bar, but not less than 110% of the actual yield strength of the bar used in the test of the welded splice.

12.14.3.4
A full mechanical connection shall develop, in tension or compression as required, at least 120% of the specified yield strength, f_y, of the bar, but not less than 110% of the actual yield strength of the bar used in the test of the mechanical connection.

12.14.3.5
Welded splices and mechanical connections not meeting the requirements of Clause 12.14.3.3 or 12.14.3.4 may be used in accordance with Clause 12.15.4.

12.15   Splices of Deformed Bars and Deformed Wire in Tension

12.15.1
The minimum length of lap for tension lap splices shall be as required for a Class A or B splice, but not less than 300 mm, where:
(a)   Class A splice . . . . $1.0\ell_d$; and
(b)   Class B splice . . . . $1.3\ell_d$;
where ℓ_d is the tensile development length for the specified yield strength, f_y, in accordance with Clause 12.2 without the modification factor of Clause 12.2.5.

12.15.2
Lap splices of deformed bars and deformed wire in tension shall be classified according to Table 12-2.

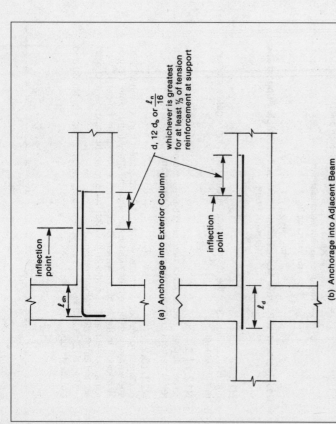

(a) Anchorage into Exterior Column

(b) Anchorage into Adjacent Beam

Fig. N12.12
Development of Negative Moment Reinforcement

N12.13.2.c
Fig. N12.13.2(c) illustrates anchorage details for welded wire fabric stirrups.

N12.13.4
See Fig. N12.13.4.

N12.13.5
See Fig. N12.13.5.

N12.14.2.2
In calculating the lap splice length required for individual bars within a bundle the increases in development length of Clause 12.4 should not be included as these would duplicate the increases required by Clause 12.14.2.2 for the effect of bundling.

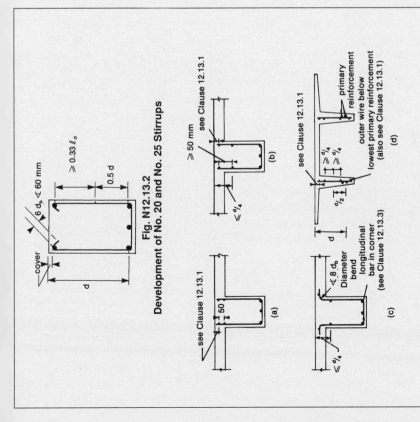

Fig. N12.13.2
Development of No. 20 and No. 25 Stirrups

Fig. N12.13.2(c)
Anchorage of Welded Wire Fabric Stirrups

N12.15.1

In calculating ℓ_d, the modification factor of (A_s required / A_s provided) of Clause 12.2.5 is not to be applied as this factor is already taken into account in the classifications of Table 12-2. Where feasible, splices should be located in regions of low stress in the reinforcement and the splices should be staggered. The classifications for Table 12-2 require longer splice lengths when these conditions cannot be met.

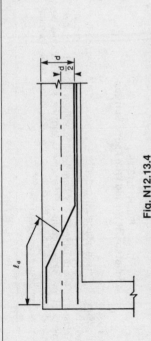

Fig. N12.13.4
Anchorage of Inclined Longitudinal Bars Used as Shear Reinforcement

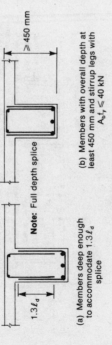

(a) Members deep enough to accommodate $1.3\ell_d$ splice

(b) Members with overall depth at least 450 mm and stirrup legs with $A_b f_y \leq 40$ kN

Fig. N12.13.5
Overlapping U-Stirrups

N12.15.4

This clause describes situations where welded splices or mechanical connections of less strength than 1.25 times the specified yield strength of the reinforcement may be used.

N12.15.5

Lap splices are not permitted in tension tie members. Examples of tension tie members are arch ties, hangers and tension elements in a truss. In determining if a member should be classified as a tension tie, considerations must be given to the importance, function, proportions and stress conditions of the member. For example, a circular tank with many bars and with well-staggered, widely spaced splices should not be classified as a tension tie member.

N12.16

Splice strengths in compression depend considerably on end bearing and hence do not increase proportionally in strength for increasing lap splice length. Table N12.16 gives the minimum lap splice lengths for bars in compression having a yield strength of 400 MPa.

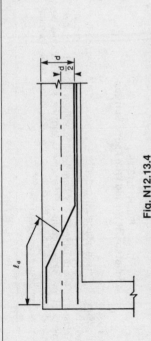

**Table 12-2
Tension Lap Splices
(See Clause 12.15.2.)**

(A_s provided)	Maximum percent of A_s spliced within required lap length	
(A_s required)	50	100
Equal to or greater than 2	Class A	Class B
Less than 2	Class B	Class B

*Ratio of area of reinforcement provided to area of reinforcement required by analysis at splice location.

12.15.3
Welded splices or mechanical connections, used where the area of reinforcement provided is less than 2 times that required by analysis, shall meet the requirements of Clause 12.14.3.3 or 12.14.3.4.

12.15.4
Welded splices or mechanical connections, used where the area of reinforcement provided is at least twice that required by analysis, shall meet the following requirements:
(a)   whenever possible, splices shall be staggered by at least 600 mm and in such a manner as to develop, at every section, at least twice the factored tensile force at that section, but not less than 140 MPa for the total area of reinforcement provided; and
(b)   in computing the tensile resistance developed at each section, spliced reinforcement may be rated at the specified splice strength. Unspliced reinforcement shall be rated at that fraction of f_y defined by the ratio of the shorter actual development length to the development length, ℓ_d, required to develop the specified yield strength, f_y.

12.15.5
Splices in tension tie members shall be made with a full welded splice or a full mechanical connection in accordance with Clause 12.14.3.3 or 12.14.3.4, and splices in adjacent bars shall be staggered by at least 800 mm.

12.16   Splices of Deformed Bars in Compression

12.16.1
The minimum length of the lap for compression lap splices shall be not less than $0.073f_y d_b$, nor $(0.133f_y - 24)d_b$ for f_y greater than 400 MPa, nor 300 mm.

12.16.2

When bars of different sizes are lap spliced in compression, the splice length shall be the larger of the development length of the larger bar or the splice length of the smaller bar. Bar sizes No. 45 and No. 55 may be lap spliced to No. 35 and smaller bars.

12.16.3

Welded splices or mechanical connections used in compression shall meet the requirements of Clause 12.14.3.3 or 12.14.3.4.

12.16.4 End-Bearing Splices

12.16.4.1

In bars required for compression only, the compressive stress may be transmitted by the bearing of square cut ends held in concentric contact by a suitable device.

12.16.4.2

Bar ends shall terminate in flat surfaces within 1-1/2° of a right angle to the axis of the bars and shall be fitted to within 3° of full bearing after assembly.

12.16.4.3

End-bearing splices shall be used only in members containing closed ties, closed stirrups, or spirals.

12.17   Special Splice Requirements for Columns

12.17.1 General

Lap splices, butt-welded splices, mechanical connections, or end-bearing splices shall be used with the limitations of Clauses 12.17.2 through 12.17.5. A splice shall satisfy the requirements for all load combinations for the column.

12.17.2 Reinforcement

Where welded splices, mechanical connections, or end-bearing splices are used, the amount of reinforcement spliced at any one location shall not exceed 0.04 times the gross area of the section. Where the gross area of reinforcement exceeds 0.04 times the gross area of the section, connection or splice locations shall be spaced not less than 750 mm apart (see Clause 10.9.2).

12.17.3 Lap Splices in Columns

12.17.3.1

Where the bar stress due to factored loads is compressive, lap splices shall conform to Clauses 12.16.1, 12.16.2, and, where applicable, to Clause 12.17.3.4 or 12.17.3.5.

Table N12.16
Minimum Compression Lap Splice Lengths Without Special Confinement, f_y = 400 MPa

Bar Size	10	15	20	25	30	35
Splice length	330	467	569	736	873	1049

N12.16.4.1

Experience with end-bearing splices has been almost exclusively with vertical bars in columns. If bars are significantly inclined from the vertical, special attention is required to ensure that adequate end-bearing contact can be achieved and maintained.

N12.17

In columns subject to flexure and axial loads, tension stresses may occur on one face of the column if moderate or large moments must be transmitted. When such tensions occur, Clause 12.17 requires tension splices to be used or an adequate tensile resistance provided. Furthermore, a minimum tension capacity is required in each face of all columns even where analysis indicates compression only. This is achieved by requiring at least compression splices, which give tension capacities of at least one-quarter f_y.

Note that the column splice must satisfy requirements for all load combinations for the column. A load combination, including wind or seismic loads, may induce tensions greater than $0.5f_y$, in some column bars, in which case the column splice must be Class B.

12.17.3.2
Where the bar stress due to factored loads is tensile and does not exceed $0.5f_y$, lap splices shall be Class B if more than one-half of the bars are spliced at any section, or Class A if half or fewer of the bars are spliced at any section and alternate lap splices are staggered by ℓ_d.

12.17.3.3
Where the bar stress due to factored loads is greater than $0.5f_y$ in tension, lap splices shall be Class B.

12.17.3.4
In tied reinforced compression members, where ties throughout the lap splice length have an effective area of not less than $0.0015hs$, the lap splice length as computed by Clauses 12.16.1 and 12.16.2 may be multiplied by 0.83, but the lap splice length shall be not less than 300 mm. Tie legs perpendicular to the dimension, h, shall be used in determining the effective area.

12.17.3.5
In spirally reinforced compression members, the lap splice length of bars within a spiral as computed by Clauses 12.16.1 and 12.16.2 may be multiplied by 0.75, but the lap splice length shall not be less than 300 mm

12.17.4 Welded Splices or Mechanical Connections in Columns
Welded splices or mechanical connections in columns shall meet the requirements of Clauses 12.14.3.3 or 12.14.3.4.

12.17.5 End-Bearing Splices in Columns
End-bearing splices, meeting the requirements of Clause 12.16.4, may be used for column bars stressed in compression provided the splices are staggered or additional bars are provided at splice locations. The continuing vertical bars in each face of the column shall have an area of at least 0.25 of the area of the vertical reinforcement in that face.

12.18 Splices of Welded Deformed Wire Fabric in Tension

12.18.1
The minimum length of lap for lap splices of welded deformed wire fabric, measured between the ends of each fabric sheet, shall be not less than $1.3\ell_d$ nor 200 mm, and the overlap measured between the outermost cross wires of each fabric sheet shall be not less than 50 mm, where ℓ_d shall be the development length for the specified yield strength, f_y, in accordance with Clause 12.7.

12.18.2
The lap splices of welded deformed wire fabric, with no cross wires within the lap splice length, shall be determined as for deformed wire.

N12.17.3.4

To qualify for the 0.83 reduction factor a rectangular column must satisfy the $0.0015hs$ tie area requirement for both directions. As an example, for the column shown in Fig. N12.17.3.4 in the direction perpendicular to h_1 there are 4 legs, hence the required spacing is $(4 \times 100)/(0.0015 \times 800) = 333$ mm. In the direction perpendicular to h_2 there are 2 legs, hence the required spacing is $(2 \times 100)/(0.0015 \times 300) = 444$ mm. Hence ties must be spaced at no greater than 333 mm and must be place throughout the lap splice length to qualify.

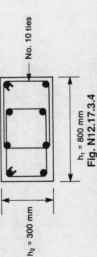

Fig. N12.17.3.4
Rectangular Tied Column for Example Calculation

N12.17.3.5

Spirals meeting the requirements of Clauses 7.6.4 and 10.9.4 increase splitting resistance and hence enable compression lap splice lengths to be reduced.

N12.17.4

The intent of this clause is to avoid excessive congestion at splice locations and to give guidance concerning the staggering of splice locations in very heavily reinforced columns.

N12.18.1

Fig. N12.18.1 illustrates the tension lap splice requirements for welded deformed wire fabric. In computing the ℓ_d from Clause 12.7, the 200 mm minimum length of that clause is neglected. As shown in Fig. N12.18.1, a 200 mm minimum is applied to the overall splice length.

12.19 Splices of Welded Smooth Wire Fabric in Tension

12.19.1
The minimum length of lap for lap splices of welded smooth wire fabric shall be in accordance with Clauses 12.19.2 and 12.19.3.

12.19.2
When the area of reinforcement provided is less than 2 times that required at the splice location, the length of overlap measured between the outermost cross wires of each fabric sheet shall be not less than one spacing of cross wires plus 50 mm, nor less than $1.5\ell_d$, nor 150 mm, where ℓ_d shall be the development length for the specified yield strength, f_y, in accordance with Clause 12.8.

12.19.3
When the area of reinforcement provided is at least twice that required at the splice location, the length of overlap measured between the outermost cross wires of each fabric sheet shall be not less than $1.5\ell_d$ nor 50 mm, where ℓ_d shall be the development length for the specified yield strength, f_y, in accordance with Clause 12.8.

13. Two-Way Slab Systems

13.0 Notation

A_{sb} = minimum area of bottom reinforcement crossing one face of the periphery of a column and connecting the slab to the column or support to provide structural integrity

A_{vs} = cross sectional area of headed shear reinforcement on a line parallel to the perimeter of the column

b_1 = width of the critical section for shear (see Clause 13.4.3.1) measured in the direction of the span for which moments are determined

b_2 = width of the critical section for shear (see Clause 13.4.3.1) measured in the direction perpendicular to b_1

b_o = perimeter of critical section for shear in slabs and footings

c_1 = size of rectangular or equivalent rectangular column, capital, or bracket measured in the direction of the span for which moments are being determined

c_2 = size of rectangular or equivalent rectangular column, capital, or bracket measured in the direction perpendicular to c_1

C = cross sectional constant used in the definition of torsional properties (Equation 13-14)

d = distance from extreme compression fibre to centroid of tension reinforcement

e = distance from centroid of section for critical shear to point where shear stress is being calculated

E_c = modulus of elasticity of concrete

f'_c = specified compressive strength of concrete

f_{py} = specified yield strength of prestressing tendon

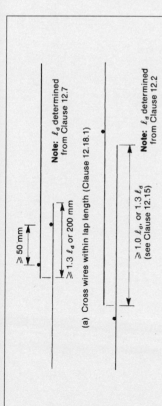

(a) Cross wires within lap length (Clause 12.18.1)

≥ 50 mm

≥ 1.3 ℓ_d or 200 mm

Note: ℓ_d determined from Clause 12.7

≥ 1.0 ℓ_d, or 1.3 ℓ_d (see Clause 12.15)

Note: ℓ_d determined from Clause 12.2

(b) No cross wires in lap length (Clause 12.18.2)

Fig. N12.18.1 Lap Splices of Deformed Fabric

N12.19

The strength of lap splices of welded smooth fabric is dependent primarily on the anchorage obtained from the cross wires, rather than on the length of wire in the splice. Hence the lap is specified in terms of overlap of cross wires (see Fig. N12.19).

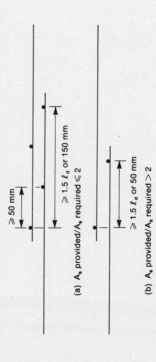

≥ 50 mm

≥ 1.5 ℓ_d or 150 mm

(a) A_s provided/A_s required ⩽ 2

≥ 1.5 ℓ_d or 50 mm

(b) A_s provided/A_s required > 2

Fig. N12.19 Lap Splices of Smooth Fabric

References, Chapter 12

12.1 ACI Committee 408, "Suggested Development, Splice, and Standard Hook Provisions for Deformed Bars in Tension", Concrete International, ACI, V.1, N.7, July 1979, pp. 44-46.

101

f_r	=	modulus of rupture of concrete
f_y	=	specified yield strength of reinforcement
f_{yv}	=	specified yield strength of headed shear reinforcement
h_d	=	overall thickness of drop panel
h_s	=	overall thickness of slab
I_b	=	moment of inertia about centroidal axis of gross section of beam as defined in Clause 13.1
I_e	=	effective moment of inertia for computation of deflection (see Equation (9-1))
I_s	=	moment of inertia about centroidal axis of gross section of slab = $\ell_{2a}b_s^3/12$
J	=	property of the critical shear section analogous to the polar moment of inertia
K_c	=	flexural stiffness of column; moment per unit rotation,
K_{ec}	=	flexural stiffness of equivalent column; moment per unit rotation, (Equation (13-12))
K_t	=	torsional stiffness of member; moment per unit rotation
ℓ_d	=	development length of reinforcing bar
ℓ_n	=	length of clear span in the direction that moments are being determined, measured face-to-face of supports
ℓ_t	=	length of attached torsional member, equal to the smaller of ℓ_{2a} or ℓ_{1a} of spans adjacent to the joint
ℓ_1	=	length of span in the direction that moments are being determined, measured centre-to-centre of supports
ℓ_{1a}	=	average ℓ_1 for spans adjacent to a column
ℓ_2	=	length of span transverse to ℓ_1, measured centre-to-centre of supports
ℓ_{2a}	=	average ℓ_2 for the adjacent spans transverse to ℓ_1
M_a	=	maximum moment in member at load stage at which deflection is computed or at any previous load stage
M_f	=	factored moment at interior support resisted by elements above and below the slab (Equation (13-17))
	=	unbalanced moment about the centroid of the critical shear section (Equation (13-8))
M_o	=	total factored static moment
m_x	=	bending moment per unit length on section perpendicular to the x axis
m_y	=	bending moment per unit length on section perpendicular to the y axis
m_{xy}	=	torsional moment per unit length on section
$\overline{m}_x$	=	total design moment per unit length on section perpendicular to the x axis
$\overline{m}_y$	=	total design moment per unit length on section perpendicular to the y axis
s	=	spacing of headed shear reinforcement or stirrups measured perpendicular to b_o
v_c	=	factored shear stress resistance provided by the concrete
v_f	=	factored shear stress
V_f	=	factored shear force
v_r	=	factored shear stress resistance
v_s	=	factored shear stress resistance provided by shear reinforcement
V_{se}	=	shear transmitted to column or column capital due to specified loads, but not less than the shear corresponding to twice the self-weight of the slab
w_f	=	factored load per unit area

12.2 Orangun, C.O., Jirsa, J.O. and Breen, J.E., "A Reevaluation of Test Data on Development Length and Splices", ACI Journal, Proceedings, V.74, Mar. 1979, pp. 114-122.

12.3 Jirsa, J.O. and Breen, J.E., "Influence of Casting Position and Shear on Development and Splice Length-Design Recommendations", Research Report 242-3F, Center for Transportation Research, Bureau of Engineering Research, The University of Texas at Austin, Nov. 1981.

12.4 Jeanty, P.R., Mitchell, D., and Mirza, M.S., "Investigation of 'Top Bar' Effects in Beams", ACI Structural Journal, V.85, N.3, May-June 1988, pp. 251-257.

12.5 Treece, R.A., "Bond Strength of Epoxy-Coated Reinforcing Bars", Master's thesis, Department of Civil Engineering, The University of Texas at Austin, May, 1987.

12.6 Johnston, D.W., "Bond Characteristics of Epoxy-Coated Reinforcing Bars", Department of Civil Engineering, North Carolina State University, Report No. FHWA/NC/82-002, August, 1982.

12.7 Mathey, R.G. and Clifton, J.R., "Bond of Coated Reinforcing Bars in Concrete", Journal of Structural Division, ASCE, V. 102, N. ST1, Jan., 1976, pp. 215-228.

w_{Df} = factored dead load per unit area

w_{Lf} = factored live load per unit area

x = shorter overall dimension of rectangular part of cross section
= direction of coordinates in elastic plate theory

x_d = dimension from face of column to edge of drop panel

x_1 = direction of one principal axis of critical section for two-way shear

y = longer overall dimension of rectangular part of cross section
= direction perpendicular to coordinate x in elastic plate theory

y_1 = direction of principal axis of critical section for two-way shear, perpendicular to x_1

α = ratio of moment of inertia of beam section to moment of inertia of a width of slab bounded laterally by centrelines of adjacent panels (if any) on each side of the beam = I_b/I_s

α_s = factor which adjusts v_c for support dimensions (Clause 13.4.4)

α_1 = α in direction of ℓ_1

α_2 = α in direction of ℓ_2

α_m = average value of α for beams on the four sides of a panel

β = ratio of clear spans in long to short directions

β_c = ratio of long side to short side of the concentrated load or reaction area

γ_f = fraction of unbalanced moment transferred by flexure at slab-column connections (Clause 13.11.2)

γ_v = fraction of unbalanced moment transferred by eccentricity of shear at slab-column connections (Clause 13.4.5.3)

λ = factor to allow for low density concrete (Clause 8.4.2)

ϕ_c = resistance factor for concrete (Clause 8.4.2)

ψ = adjustment factor for moment of inertia for prismatic modelling of columns (Clause 13.9.3.3)

13.1 Definitions

The following definitions apply in this Clause:

Beam — for monolithic or fully composite construction, a beam includes that portion of slab on each side of the beam extending a distance equal to the projection of the beam above or below the slab, whichever is greater, but not greater than 4 times the slab thickness.

Column Capital — enlargement of the column adjacent to the underside of the slab to improve shear strength of the slab. The dimensions c_1 and c_2 and the clear span ℓ_n shall be based on an effective support area defined by the intersection of the bottom surface of the slab, or of the drop panel if there is one, with the largest right circular cone, right pyramid, or tapered wedge whose surfaces are located within the column and capital or bracket and are oriented no greater than 45° to the axis of the column.

Column Strip — portion of the design strip with a width on each side of a column centre line equal to $0.25\ell_2$ or $0.25\ell_1$, whichever is less. The column strip includes beams, if any.

Design Strip — portion of a slab system including beams and supports along a column line and bounded by the centreline of the panels on each side.

N13 Introduction

Clause 13 of CSA Standard A23.3-94 differs from the previous edition primarily in the grouping of the provisions for two-way slabs. All clauses pertaining to two-way slabs are now contained in Clause 13 and arranged in the order used in design. Provisions for minimum thickness of two-way slabs have been simplified and moved from Clause 9 to Clause 13.3. Similarly, provisions for shear design pertaining to two-way slab systems have been moved from Clause 11 to Clause 13.4 and 13.5. Design provisions for flexure have been rearranged and expanded to include procedures based on elastic plate theory and theorems of plasticity. Slab reinforcement requirements are separated from flexural provisions and arranged in a more logical order.

N13.1 Definitions

This section is new and provides a single location for the definition of terms. Previously, definitions were embedded in clauses of the Standard.

Fig. N13.1(a) illustrates that portion of the slab that is to be included in computing the moment of inertia of a beam. Fig. N13.1(b) illustrates that portion of a capital that qualifies as a support. Fig. N13.1(c) illustrates the definitions of column and middle strips.

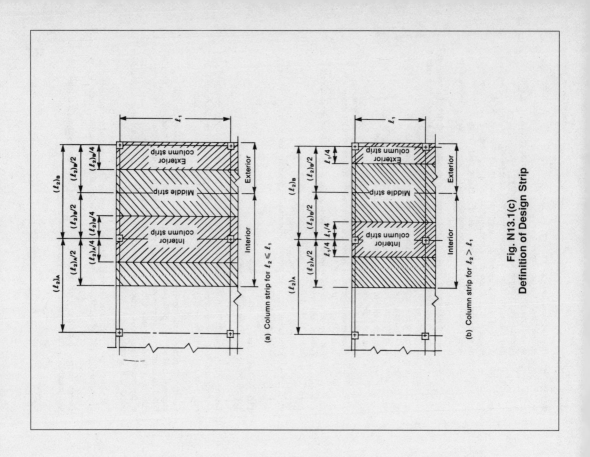

Fig. N13.1(c)
Definition of Design Strip

(a) Column strip for $\ell_2 \leq \ell_1$

(b) Column strip for $\ell_2 > \ell_1$

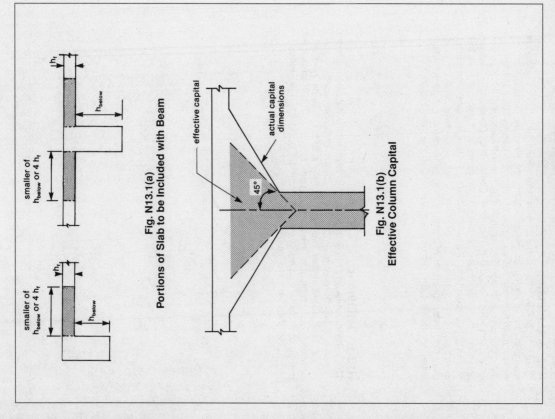

Fig. N13.1(a)
Portions of Slab to be Included with Beam

Fig. N13.1(b)
Effective Column Capital

Drop Panel — thickening of the slab in the area adjacent to a column for deflection control, extra shear strength, or extra flexural depth.

Flat Plate — flat slab without column capitals or drop panels

Middle Strip — portion of the design strip bounded by two column strips.

Panel — slab area bounded by column, beam, or wall centrelines on all sides.

Regular Two-Way Slab Systems — slab systems consisting of approximately rectangular panels and supporting primarily uniform gravity loading. Such systems meet the following geometric limitations:

(a) within a panel, the ratio of longer to shorter span, centre-to-centre of supports, shall not be greater than 2.0;

(b) for slab systems with beams between supports, the relative effective stiffness of beams in the two directions $(\alpha_1 \ell_2^2)/(\alpha_2 \ell_1^2)$ shall not be less than 0.2 or greater than 5.0;

(c) column offsets shall not be greater than 20 percent of the span (in the direction of offset) from either axis between centre lines of successive columns; and

(d) the reinforcement is placed in an orthogonal grid.

13.2 Scope

13.2.1
The provisions of Clause 13 shall apply for the design of slab systems reinforced for flexure in more than one direction with or without beams between supports.

13.2.2
A slab system may be supported on columns or walls.

13.2.3
Solid slabs and slabs with recesses or pockets made by permanent or removable fillers between ribs or joists in two directions are included within the scope of Clause 13.

13.3 Minimum Slab Thickness

13.3.1 General
The minimum slab thickness, h_s, shall be based on serviceability requirements but shall not be less than 120 mm.

13.3.2 Two-Way Slab Systems
For regular two-way slab systems as defined in Clause 13.1, the requirement to show by computation that deflections will not exceed the limits stipulated in Table 9-2 may be waived when slab thicknesses provided are not less than the minimum thicknesses specified in Clauses 13.3.3 to 13.3.5. In Equations (13-1) to (13-3), ℓ_n is the longer clear span.
Note: *The minimum thickness indicated in Clauses 13.3.3 to 13.3.5 may not be adequate for certain sequences of shoring during construction or large live to dead load ratios.*

N13.1 (contd.)

Regular Two-Way Slab Systems — Two-way slabs are slab systems that can deform and carry load in two orthogonal directions. Many of the provisions for their design are based on studies in which the curvatures in the two directions are equal or nearly equal. As the ratio of long to short clear spans increases, there is a tendency for more of the load in the central portion of the panel to be carried in one direction than the other. For slabs without beams this tendency will be in the long span direction whereas for slabs with stiff beams on all sides this tendency will be in the short span direction. The geometric limitations listed are to ensure that the curvatures in the two directions will be approximately equal resulting in two-way behavior. When provisions for regular two-way slab systems are used for slabs not meeting these geometric limitations, care must be taken to account for the manner in which the load is carried.

N13.3 Minimum Slab Thickness

N13.3.1
This clause requires that all slabs designed using the provisions of Clause 13 shall have a thickness sufficient to ensure that slab deflections and crack widths will be satisfactory for the intended use.

N13.3.2
For many commonly occurring slab configurations, detailed deflection computations are not required if the minimum slab thickness is at least as great as that specified in Clauses 13.3.3 to 13.3.5. These are minimum thicknesses based on past experience of slabs with usual values of uniform gravity loading and good construction practice and may not be the most economical or suitable thickness for all applications. For $f_y = 400$ MPa, these expressions result in clear span to overall thickness ratios, ℓ_n/h, in the range of 30 to 46.

13.3.3 Flat Plates and Slabs With Column Capitals

The minimum thickness of flat plates and slabs with column capitals shall be

$$h_s \geq \frac{\ell_n (0.6 + f_y/1000)}{30} \tag{13-1}$$

At discontinuous edges, an edge beam shall be provided with a stiffness ratio, α, of not less than 0.80 or the thickness required by Equation (13-1) shall be multiplied by 1.1 in the panel with the discontinuous edge.

13.3.4 Slabs With Drop Panels

The minimum thickness of slabs with drop panels shall be

$$h_s \geq \frac{\ell_n (0.6 + f_y/1000)}{30\left[1 + \left(\dfrac{2x_d}{\ell_n}\right)\left(\dfrac{h_d - h_s}{h_s}\right)\right]} \tag{13-2}$$

In this Equation $x_d/(\ell_n/2)$ is the smaller of the values determined in the two directions, x_d shall not be taken greater than $\ell_n/4$, and $(h_d - h_s)$ shall not be taken larger than h_s.

13.3.5 Slabs With Beams Between All Supports

The minimum thickness of regular two-way slab systems with beams spanning between supports shall be

$$h_s \geq \frac{\ell_n (0.6 + f_y/1000)}{30 + 4\beta\,\alpha_m} \tag{13-3}$$

where α_m in this Equation shall not be taken greater than 2.0.

13.3.6 Computation of Slab Deflections

A slab thickness less than the minimum thickness required by Clauses 13.3.2 to 13.3.5 may be used if computations show that deflection will not exceed the limits stipulated in Table 9-2. Deflections shall be computed taking into account the size and shape of panel, the conditions of support, and the nature of restraints at the panel edges. For deflection computations, the modulus of elasticity, E_c, for concrete shall be as specified in Clause 8.6.2. The effective moment of inertia shall be that given by Equation (9-1). The moment, M_a, shall take into consideration loads such as construction loads which may extend the cracked region. Other values of I_e may be used if the computed deflection is in reasonable agreement with results of comprehensive tests. The modulus of rupture of the concrete, f_r, shall be taken as one-half the value given by Equation (8-8). Additional long-time deflection shall be computed in accordance with Clause 9.8.2.5.

13.4 Design Procedures for Shear for Slabs Without Beams

13.4.1 General

In the vicinity of concentrated loads or reactions, the factored shear stress resistance, v_r, shall be equal to or greater than the maximum factored shear stress, v_f, due to the factored shear force and unbalanced moments. The stress v_f shall be determined for full load on all spans as well as any other patterns of loading which might result in larger stresses.

N13.3.4 Slabs with Drop Panels

Eqn. (13-2) is a new expression that permits the designer to take advantage of the increased stiffness which results from increasing the thickness or dimensions of the drop panel.

N13.3.6 Computation of Slab Deflections

Clause 13.3.6 gives requirements for the selection of factors to be used in computing deflections of two-way slab systems. It should be noted that in these calculations the modulus of rupture of the concrete, f_r, shall be taken as $0.3\sqrt{f'_c}$ or one-half the value specified in Equation (8-8). The computed deflections must not be greater than those permitted by Clause 9.8.5.3.

N13.4 Design Procedures for Shear for Slabs Without Beams

The provisions of Clause 13.4 are essentially the same as those of Clauses 11.10 and 13.3.3 in the previous edition of the Standard. This consolidates the slab shear provisions and eliminates the cross-referencing between clauses that existed previously.

N13.4.3 Critical Section for Two-way Action

Critical sections that must be investigated for shear are illustrated in Fig. N13.4.3. Expressions for the maximum shear stress resistance to be used when evaluating the punching shear capacity are given in Clause 13.4.4. In checking the capacity of the critical section around a large drop panel such as that shown in Fig. N13.4.3, the maximum shear stress resistance approaches that for one-way shear.

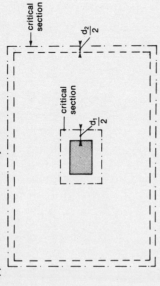
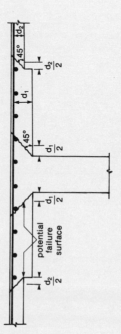

Fig. N13.4.3
Critical Sections for Punching Shear

N13.4.3.4 Openings in Slabs

The reduction in critical shear perimeter to account for the effect of openings located at a distance less than 10 times the slab thickness is shown in Fig N13.4.3.4(a). When the concentrated load or reaction area (column) is located near a free edge, the free edge may be considered as a large opening. Although the Standard is not specific as to the appropriate reduction in the critical section for this case, a procedure suggested by the CEB Code is illustrated in Fig N13.4.3.4(b) and is recommended.

13.4.2 One-Way and Two-Way Shear

Slabs in the vicinity of columns shall be designed for two-way shear in accordance with Clauses 13.4.3 through 13.4.5. Slabs shall also be designed for one-way shear in accordance with Clause 13.4.6.

13.4.3 Critical Shear Section for Two-Way Action

13.4.3.1

The critical section for two-way action shall be a section perpendicular to the plane of the slab and located so that its perimeter, b_o, is a minimum, but the section need not approach closer than d/2 to the perimeter of the concentrated load or reaction area.

13.4.3.2

Where there is any change in slab thickness, a critical section located in the thinner portion at a distance no greater than d/2 from the face of the thicker portion and located such that the perimeter, b_o, is a minimum, must also be investigated.

13.4.3.3

For square or rectangular load or reaction areas, the critical section may be assumed to have four straight sides.

13.4.3.4 Openings in Slabs

When openings in slabs are located at a distance of less than 10 times the slab thickness from a concentrated load or reaction area, or when openings in slabs without beams are located within a column strip, that part of the perimeter of the critical section which is enclosed by straight lines projecting from the centre of the load or reaction area and tangent to the boundaries of the openings shall be considered ineffective.

13.4.4 Maximum Shear Stress Resistance Without Shear Reinforcement

The factored shear stress resistance, v_r, is the smallest of:

(a)

$$v_r = v_c = \left(1 + \frac{2}{\beta_c}\right) 0.2\lambda\phi_c\sqrt{f'_c}$$ (13-4)

where β_c is the ratio of long side to short side of the column, concentrated load, or reaction area.

(b)

$$v_r = v_c = \left(\frac{\alpha_s d}{b_o} + 0.2\right)\lambda\phi_c\sqrt{f'_c}$$ (13-5)

where α_s = 4 for interior columns and 3 for edge columns.

(c)

$$v_r = v_c = 0.4\lambda\phi_c\sqrt{f'_c}$$ (13-6)

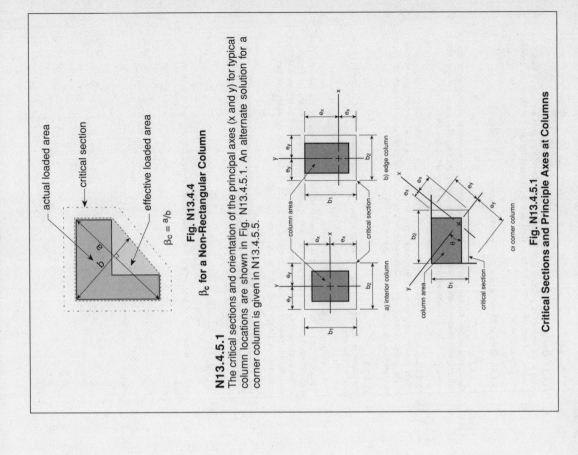

Fig. N13.4.4

β_c for a Non-Rectangular Column

$$\beta_c = a/b$$

actual loaded area

critical section

effective loaded area

N13.4.5.1

The critical sections and orientation of the principal axes (x and y) for typical column locations are shown in Fig. N13.4.5.1. An alternate solution for a corner column is given in N13.4.5.5.

a) interior column

b) edge column

c) corner column

column area

critical section

Fig. N13.4.5.1

Critical Sections and Principle Axes at Columns

---

effective critical section

in-effective critical section

< 10h

(a) Proximity to Openings

free edge

point of tangency

45°   45°   45°

≤ 5d

≤ 5d

> 5d

(b) Proximity to Free Edge

Fig. N13.4.3.4

Effect Of Openings And Free Edges On Critical Sections

N13.4.4   Maximum Shear Stress Resistance Without Shear Reinforcement

This clause reflects the factors that reduce the shear stress resistance of the concrete. The determination of β_c for a non-rectangular column is illustrated in Fig. N13.4.4.

13.4.5 Factored Shear Stress

13.4.5.1

The shear forces and unbalanced moments to be transferred to the support shall be resolved into a single shear force acting at the centroid of the critical section and moments about the centroidal principal axes (x_1 and y_1 directions) of the critical section.

13.4.5.2

The shear stress due to the factored shear force acting at the centroid of the section shall be assumed to be uniformly distributed over the critical shear section.

13.4.5.3

The fraction of the unbalanced moment transferred by eccentricity of shear, γ_v, shall be

$$\gamma_v = 1 - \frac{1}{1 + \frac{2}{3}\sqrt{\frac{b_1}{b_2}}} \qquad (13\text{-}7)$$

13.4.5.4

The shear stress due to moment transfer by eccentricity of shear shall be assumed to vary linearly about the centroid of the critical shear section.

13.4.5.5

The factored shear stress shall be computed from Equation (13-8) where the factored shear force and unbalanced moments about the x_1 and y_1 directions are obtained from a consistent loading.

$$v_f = \frac{V_f}{b_o d} + \left[\frac{\gamma_v M_f e}{J} + \frac{\gamma_v M_f e}{J}\right]_{x_1} + \left[\frac{\gamma_v M_f e}{J} - y_1\right] \qquad (13\text{-}8)$$

13.4.5.6

The fraction of the unbalanced moment not transferred by eccentricity of shear stress shall be transferred by flexure in accordance with Clause 13.11.2.

13.4.6 One-Way Shear

13.4.6.1 General

One-way shear for a slab with a critical section extending in a plane across the entire width and located at a distance, d, from the face of the concentrated load or reaction area shall be in accordance with Clauses 11.1 to 11.4.

13.4.6.2 Corner Columns

The factored shear resistance of slabs in the vicinity of corner columns shall be determined in accordance with Clauses 11.1 through 11.4, along a critical shear section which follows along a straight line of minimum length located not further than d/2 from the corner column. Where the slab cantilevers beyond the face of the corner column, the length of the critical

---

N13.4.5.4

The shear distributions caused by the shear force and the fraction of the unbalanced moment transferred by shear for an interior column are shown in Fig. N13.4.5.4.

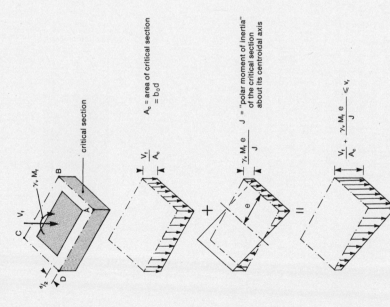

$$A_c = \text{area of critical section} = b_o d$$

$$J = \text{"polar moment of inertia"} \text{ of the critical section about its centroidal axis}$$

$$\frac{V_f}{A_c}$$

$$\frac{\gamma_v M_f e}{J}$$

$$\frac{V_f}{A_c} + \frac{\gamma_v M_f e}{J} \leq v_r$$

Fig. N13.4.5.4

Shear Stress Distributions due to V_f and $\gamma_v M_f$

N13.4.5.5

In Eqn. (13-8), values of M_{fx} and M_{fy} are the factored moments about the x and y axes, respectively. In assigning values of V_f, M_{fx} and M_{fy} some judgement is required as the maximum values for these quantities may not occur simultaneously. For an interior column, the value of V_f occurs with all adjacent panels loaded whereas the maximum values of M_f usually occur with selected pattern loading. It is suggested that a satisfactory value of v_f can be obtained by adding the maximum V_f term to the larger unbalanced moment term using maximum values of M_f. For an edge column, the sum of all three terms is required but the term considering the unbalanced moment about an axis perpendicular to the edge, M_{fy}, must be obtained from an analysis that considers both adjacent panels loaded. This term can be neglected when the spans along the edge are equal. For a corner column, the maximum value for all three terms occurs when the corner panel is loaded.

For a corner column, computing the terms in Eqn. (13-8) when the principal axes are used involves determining the orientation of the axes, θ, and use of the transformation equations (Mohr's Circle) to determine the principal moments of inertia. Alternatively, one can use the orthogonal axes (x' and y') parallel to the column lines shown in Fig. N13.4.5.5 and replace Eqn. (13-8) with the more general expression

$$v_f = \frac{V_f}{b_o d} + \left[\frac{\gamma_{vx} M_{fx} I_{y'} - \gamma_{vy} M_{fy} I_{x'y'}}{I_{x'} I_{y'} - I_{x'y'}^2}\right] e_{x'} + \left[\frac{\gamma_{vy} M_{fy} I_{x'} - \gamma_{vx} M_{fx} I_{x'y'}}{I_{x'} I_{y'} - I_{x'y'}^2}\right] e_{y'}$$

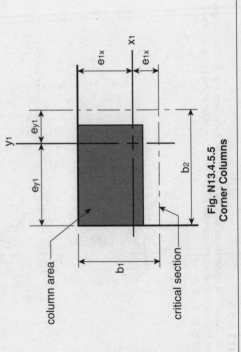

Fig. N13.4.5.5
Corner Columns

N13.4.5.6

See Fig. N13.11.2.

N13.4.6.2 Corner Columns

The critical section for one-way shear at corner columns is illustrated in Fig. N13.4.6.2.

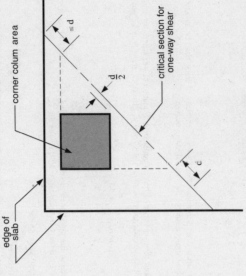

Fig. N13.4.6.2
Critical Section For One-way Shear At Corner Column

shear section may be extended into the cantilevered portion by a length not exceeding d.

13.4.7 Shear Reinforcement for Slabs Without Beams

13.4.7.1

Shear reinforcement consisting of headed shear reinforcement, stirrups, or shearheads may be used to increase the shear capacity of slabs and footings.

Note: *The design of shearheads shall be based on the concepts in the ACI Committee 318 Building Code Requirements for Reinforced Concrete (ACI 318M-89) and Commentary (ACI 318RM-89), American Concrete Institute, Detroit, Michigan, 1989, 351 pp.*

13.4.7.2

The shear resistance shall be investigated at the section defined in Clause 13.4.3.1 and at successive sections more distant from the support.

13.4.7.3

The maximum factored shear stress, v_f, shall not exceed the factored shear stress resistance, v_r.

13.4.7.4

Within the shear reinforced zone, the factored shear stress resistance, v_r, shall be computed as $v_c + v_s$ where v_c and v_s shall be computed in accordance with Clauses 13.4.8.3 and 13.4.8.5 for headed shear reinforcement and in accordance with Clauses 13.4.9.3 and 13.4.9.4 for stirrups.

13.4.7.5

Shear reinforcement shall be extended to the section where $V_f/(b_o d)$ is not greater than $0.2\lambda\phi_c\sqrt{f_c'}$ but at least a distance 2d from the face of the column.

13.4.8 Headed Shear Reinforcement

13.4.8.1

Headed shear reinforcement shall be mechanically anchored at each end by a plate or head bearing against the concrete such that it is capable of developing the yield strength of the bar. The area of the plate or head shall be at least 10 times the cross sectional area of the bar unless a smaller area can be justified experimentally.

13.4.8.2

When headed shear reinforcement is provided, the factored shear stress, v_f, shall not be greater than $0.8\lambda\phi_c\sqrt{f_c'}$.

13.4.8.3

In the zone reinforced by headed shear reinforcement, the factored shear stress resistance of the concrete, v_c, shall be $0.3\lambda\phi_c\sqrt{f_c'}$.

88

N13.4.7 Shear Reinforcement in Slabs Without Beams

Shear reinforcement to increase the punching shear capacity of slabs may consist of either stirrups or headed shear reinforcement. Effective anchorage of stirrups may be difficult to achieve by standard hooks, particularly for thin slabs, and special mechanical anchorage may be required (see Clause 13.4.8.1).

13.4.8.4

Headed shear reinforcement shall be located along concentric lines which parallel the perimeter of the column cross section.

13.4.8.5

The factored shear stress resistance of headed shear reinforcement, v_s, shall be computed as

$$v_s = \frac{\phi_s A_{vs} f_{yv}}{b_o s} \qquad (13-9)$$

where A_{vs} is the cross sectional area of the headed shear reinforcement on a concentric line parallel to the perimeter of the column.

13.4.8.6

The distance between the column face and the first line of headed shear reinforcement shall be s/2. The upper limits for the spacing, s, between lines of headed shear reinforcement shall be based on the value of v_f at a critical section d/2 from the column face and are given by

$$s \leq 0.75d \quad \text{when} \quad v_f \leq 0.61 \lambda \phi_c \sqrt{f_c'}$$

$$s \leq 0.5d \quad \text{when} \quad v_f > 0.61 \lambda \phi_c \sqrt{f_c'}$$

13.4.8.7

Unless the headed shear reinforcement is otherwise protected, the minimum concrete cover over the anchors shall be the same as the minimum cover for the flexural reinforcement in accordance with Clause 7.9. The concrete cover shall not exceed the minimum cover plus one half the bar diameter of the flexural reinforcement.

13.4.9 Stirrup Reinforcement

13.4.9.1

Properly anchored stirrups may be used as shear reinforcement in slabs 300 mm in depth or greater.

13.4.9.2

When stirrups are provided, the factored shear stress, v_f, shall not be greater than $0.6 \phi_c \sqrt{f_c'}$.

13.4.9.3

In the zone reinforced by stirrups, the factored shear stress resistance of the concrete, v_c, shall be $0.2 \lambda \phi_c \sqrt{f_c'}$.

13.4.9.4

The factored shear stress resistance, v_s, shall be computed from Equation (13-9) where A_{vs} is the cross sectional area of the stirrups on a line parallel to the perimeter of the column.

13.4.9.5

The anchorage of stirrup shear reinforcement shall be checked to ensure compliance with the anchorage requirements of Clause 12.13.

13.5 Shear in Slab Systems with Beams

13.5.1

Beams with $(\alpha_1 \ell_2 / \ell_1)$ equal to or greater than 1.0 shall be designed to resist shear caused by factored loads on tributary areas bounded by 45° lines drawn from the corners of the panels and the centrelines of the adjacent panels parallel to the long sides.

13.5.2

Beams with $(\alpha_1 \ell_{2a} / \ell_1)$ less than 1.0 may be designed to resist shear obtained by linear interpolation, assuming beams carry no load at $\alpha_1 = 0$.

13.5.3

In addition to shears calculated according to Clauses 13.5.1 and 13.5.2, beams shall be designed to resist shears caused by factored loads applied directly on the beams.

13.5.4

Slab shears may be computed on the assumption that load is distributed to supporting beams in accordance with Clause 13.5.1 or 13.5.2. Resistance to total shear occurring on a panel shall be provided.

13.5.5

The shear resistance of beams shall satisfy the requirements of Clause 11.

13.6 Design Procedures for Flexure

13.6.1

A slab system may be designed by any procedure satisfying conditions of equilibrium and compatibility with the supports, provided it is shown that the factored resistance at every section is at least equal to the effects of the factored loads, and that all serviceability conditions, including specified limits on deflections, are met.

13.6.2

Requirements and limitations for selected design procedures are given in Clauses 13.7 to 13.13 and Appendix B.

13.6.3

For lateral loads, analysis of unbraced frames shall take into account effects of cracking and reinforcement on stiffness of frame members.

13.6.4

Results of the gravity load analysis shall be combined with results of the lateral load analysis.

N13.5 Shear in Slab Systems with Beams.

N13.5.1

The tributary area used in computing the shear carried by an interior beam is shown in Fig. N13.5.1. For $\alpha_1 \ell_1 / \ell_2 < 1.0$, the beams framing into the column will not account for all of the shear force transferred to the column. The remaining shear force will produce shear stresses in the slab around the column. For these cases the total shear strength of the slab-beam-column connection must be checked.

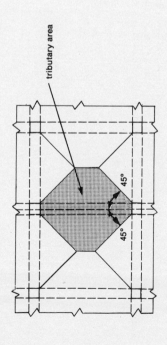

tributary area

45°
45°

Fig. N13.5.1
Tributary Area for Calculating Shear on Interior Beam

N13.6 Design Procedures for Flexure

N13.6.1

This section permits a designer to base a design directly on the fundamental principles of structural mechanics provided it is demonstrated that all safety and serviceability criteria are satisfied. Guidance for applying many of the more commonly used procedures are given in Clauses 13.7 to 13.13.

N13.7 Elastic Plate Theory

N13.7.2
When slab systems are analyzed using classical or numerical techniques based on elastic theory, it is necessary that stiffness assigned to the various slab components reflect the effects of cracking, creep and shrinkage of the concrete. Stiffness based on gross concrete dimensions is not satisfactory.

N13.8 Theorems of Plasticity
The analysis of many slabs with irregular geometry is simplified using techniques based on plasticity. The designer must ensure that when selecting reinforcement the ductility demand requirements are met. For slabs, this can generally be considered satisfied by selecting reinforcement with a failure strain greater than or equal to 0.03. Since the theorems of plasticity only ensure strength requirements, serviceability requirements at service load must be evaluated independently.

13.6.5
Openings of any size may be provided in slab systems if it is shown by analysis that the factored resistance is at least equal to the effects of factored loads considering Clauses 8.3, 8.4, and 13.4.3.4, and that all serviceability conditions, including the specified limits on deflections, are met.

Note: *Clause 13.12.6 provides simple rules for regular slabs without beams.*

13.7 Elastic Plate Theory

13.7.1
Analysis of slab systems for factored loads may be based on elastic plate theory using either classical or numerical techniques.

Note: *The successful application of the results of analysis using elastic plate theory requires proper consideration of factors such as selection of thickness, moment redistribution due to the effects of cracking, creep, and shrinkage effects, and construction loading.*

13.7.2
Care shall be taken to ensure realistic modelling of the size and effective stiffness of the supporting elements including beams, if any.

13.7.3
Appropriate loading patterns shall be considered to ensure determination of maximum values for all stress resultants at each section.

13.7.4
When reinforcement is placed as an orthogonal mat in the x and y directions, the reinforcement may be placed in bands with uniform spacing. The total reinforcement provided within a band shall be sufficient to resist the total factored moment computed for that band. The maximum moment intensity, $\overline{m}_x$ or $\overline{m}_y$, within a band shall not be greater than 1.5 times the average moment in the band where

$$\overline{m}_x = |m_x| + |m_{xy}| \tag{13-10}$$

$$\overline{m}_y = |m_y| + |m_{xy}| \tag{13-11}$$

13.8 Theorems of Plasticity

13.8.1
Analysis of slab systems for factored loads may be based on either the lower bound or upper bound theorems of plasticity.

Note: *The successful application of the results of plastic analysis requires proper assumptions that will ensure that serviceability requirements, including creep and shrinkage effects, are satisfied.*

13.8.2
The size and effective stiffness of the supporting elements shall be considered in the analysis.

13.8.3

When strength design is based on the upper bound theorem (eg, yield line method), the factored moments shall be obtained from calculations based on a need for a mechanism to form over the whole or part of the slab at collapse and the mechanism that is the most critical shall be used for the design of the slab.

13.8.4

Factored moments obtained using lower bound theory (eg, strip method) shall satisfy the requirements of equilibrium and the boundary conditions applicable to the slab.

13.8.5

Reinforcement may be uniformly spaced in bands, with band widths selected to ensure that serviceability requirements are satisfied.

13.9   Slab Systems as Elastic Frames

13.9.1   Definition of Frame Geometry

13.9.1.1

A regular two-way slab system as defined in Clause 13.1 may, for purposes of analysis, be considered as a series of plane frames acting longitudinally and transversely through the building. Each frame shall be composed of equivalent line members intersecting at member centrelines. Each frame shall follow a column line and include the portion of slab bounded laterally by the centreline of the panel on each side.

Note: *Floor systems with beams between supports, not satisfying the limits for regular two-way slab systems contained in Clause 13.1, may be analyzed using the requirements of this Clause but the reinforcing distribution of Clause 13.13 will normally not be applicable.*

13.9.1.2

Each floor and roof slab, with attached columns, may be analyzed separately with far ends of columns considered fixed.

13.9.1.3

Where slab beams are analyzed separately, it may be assumed in determining moment at a given support that the slab-beam is fixed at any support two panels distant therefrom, provided the slab continues beyond that point.

13.9.1.4

The change in length of columns and slabs due to direct stress and deflections due to shear may be neglected.

13.9.1.5

Member stiffness used in the analysis of the elastic frame shall be selected to simulate the behaviour of the slab system.

N13.9   Slab Systems as Elastic Frames

Probably the most frequently used method to determine design moments in regular two-way slab systems is to consider the slab as a series of two-dimensional frames that are analyzed elastically. When using this analogy, it is essential that stiffness properties of the elements of the frame be selected to properly represent the behaviour of the three-dimensional slab system.

In a typical frame analysis it is assumed that at a beam-column connection all members meeting at the joint undergo the same rotation. For slabs supported only by columns the slab will be restrained only locally by the column. For uniform gravity loading this reduced restraint is accounted for by reducing the effective stiffness of the column by either Clause 13.9.2 or Clause 13.9.3.

13.9.2 Nonprismatic Modelling of Member Stiffness

13.9.2.1
When members are modelled as nonprismatic elements, the member stiffness may be as given in Clauses 13.9.2.2 to 13.9.2.10.

13.9.2.2
The moment of inertia of column and slab-beam elements at any cross section outside of joints or column capitals shall be based on the gross area of concrete at that section.

13.9.2.3
The moment of inertia of slab-beams from the centre of the column to the face of the column, bracket, or capital shall be assumed equal to the moment of inertia of the slab-beam at the face of the column, bracket, or capital divided by the quantity $(1 - c_2/\ell_{2a})^2$, where c_2 and ℓ_{2a} are measured transverse to the direction of the span for which moments are being determined.

13.9.2.4
The moment of inertia of column elements from top to bottom of the slab-beam at a joint shall be assumed infinite.

13.9.2.5
An equivalent column shall be assumed to consist of the actual columns above and below the slab-beam plus an attached torsional member transverse to the direction of the span for which moments are being determined.

13.9.2.6
The flexibility of an equivalent column shall be taken as the sum of the flexibilities of the actual columns above and below the slab-beam and the flexibility of the attached torsional member as expressed by

$$\frac{1}{K_{ec}} = \frac{1}{\Sigma K_c} + \frac{1}{K_t} \qquad (13\text{-}12)$$

13.9.2.7
Attached torsional members shall be assumed to have a constant cross section throughout their length consisting of the larger of
(a) a portion of slab having a width equal to that of the column, bracket, or capital in the direction of the span for which moments are being determined;
(b) for monolithic or fully composite construction, the portion of slab specified in Item (a), plus that part of the transverse beam above and below the slab; or
(c) a transverse beam as defined in Clause 13.1

N13.9.2 Non-Prismatic Modelling of Member Stiffness
Examples of the variation in moment of inertia along typical slab-beams and columns are given in Fig. N13.9.2.

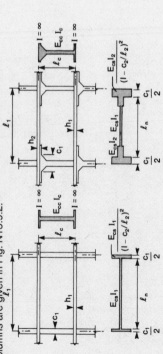

Fig. N13.9.2
Variation of Moment of Inertia for Slab Beams and Columns

N13.9.2.5 and N13.9.2.6
In the non-prismatic modeling procedure, the effective column stiffness is reduced using the attached torsional member concept. The effective column stiffness is a function of the stiffness of the column and the torsional stiffness of the attached members framing into the sides of the column.

13.9.2.8

The stiffness, K_t, of attached torsional members shall be calculated by the following expression:

$$K_t = \sum \frac{9\,E_c\,C}{\ell_t \left(1 - \frac{c_2}{\ell_2}\right)^3}$$ (13-13)

13.9.2.9

The section parameter, C, in Equation (13-13) may be evaluated for the cross section by dividing it into separate rectangular parts and carrying out the following summation:

$$C = \sum \left(1 - 0.63\,\frac{x}{y}\right)\frac{x^3 y}{3}$$ (13-14)

13.9.2.10

Where beams frame into columns in the direction of the span for which moments are being determined, the value of K_t shall be multiplied by the ratio of the moment of inertia of the slab with such beam to the moment of inertia of the slab without such beam.

13.9.3   Prismatic Modelling of Member Stiffness

13.9.3.1

When members are modelled as prismatic elements, the member stiffness may be assigned as given in Clauses 13.9.3.2 and 13.9.3.3.

13.9.3.2

For prismatic modelling of slab-beam elements, the moment of inertia shall be based on the gross area of the concrete outside the joints or column capitals. When the moment of inertia varies outside the joint, as for example drop panels, the slab beam elements may be modelled as a series of prismatic elements with moments of inertia based on the gross concrete dimensions.

13.9.3.3

For prismatic modelling of column elements, the effective moment of inertia shall be taken equal to ψ times the moment of inertia based on the gross area outside the joints, where ψ is given as

$$\psi = \left[0.25 + 0.75\left(\frac{\alpha\,\ell_{2a}}{\ell_1}\right)\right]\left(\frac{\ell_{2a}}{\ell_1}\right)^2$$ (13-15)

but $0.3 \le \psi \le 1.0$

where $\alpha\,\ell_{2a}/\ell_1$ shall not be taken greater than 1.0.

13.9.4   Arrangement of Live Load

13.9.4.1

When the loading pattern is known, the frame shall be analyzed for that load.

N13.9.2.8

The stiffness, K_t, is the sum of the stiffnesses of the attached torsional members perpendicular to the direction in which moments are being computed. Thus for an interior column K_t accounts for the stiffness of two torsional members while for an edge column K_t will account for only one torsional member when moments are being calculated in a direction parallel to the face edge.

N13.9.2.9

The term C is a property of the cross section having the same relationship to the torsional rigidity of a non-circular cross section as does the polar moment of inertia for a circular cross section. The value of C is computed by dividing the cross section of the torsional member into separate rectangles and summing the C-values for each of the component rectangles. Since the value of C obtained by summing the values for each of the component rectangles making up a section will always be less than the theoretically correct value, it is appropriate to subdivide the cross section in such a way as to result in the highest possible value of C.

N13.9.2.10

The stiffening effect on the slab due to the presence of beams between the columns causes the rotation of the slab-beam at a joint to be closer to the rotation of the column at that joint as assumed in a planar frame analysis. This reduces the need to reduce the effective stiffness of the column. Increasing the value of K_t reduces the effect of the attached torsional members.

N13.9.3   Prismatic Modelling of Member Stiffness

When analysis of the elastic frame is performed using a standard frame analysis program based on direct stiffness formulation, the reduced rotational restraint at the joint when the slab is supported on columns can be accounted for by reducing the effective moment of inertia of the column by the factor.

13.9.4.2
When the live load is uniformly distributed and does not exceed three-quarters of the specified dead load or the nature of the live load is such that all panels will be loaded simultaneously, the maximum factored moments may be assumed to occur at all sections with full factored live load on the entire slab system.

13.9.4.3
For loading conditions other that those defined in Clauses 13.9.4.1 and 13.9.4.2, the maximum positive factored moment near midspan of a panel may be assumed to occur with three-quarters of the full factored uniformly distributed live load on the panel and on alternate panels, and the maximum negative factored moment in the slab at a support may be assumed to occur with three-quarters of the full factored uniformly distributed live load on adjacent panels only.

13.9.4.4
Factored moments shall not be taken as less than those occurring with full factored live loads on all panels.

13.9.5 Critical Sections

13.9.5.1
At interior supports, the critical section for the negative factored moment shall be taken at the face of rectilinear supports, but not at a distance greater than $0.175\ell_1$ from the centre of the column.

13.9.5.2
At exterior supports provided with brackets or capitals, the critical section for the negative factored moment in the span perpendicular to an edge shall be taken at a distance from the face of the supporting element not greater than one-half of the projection of the bracket or capital beyond the face of the supporting element.

13.9.5.3
When locating the critical section for the negative design moment, circular or regular polygonal supports shall be treated as square supports with the same area.

13.9.5.4
The selection of reinforcement to resist the moments at the critical sections shall be in accordance with the requirements of Clauses 13.11 to 13.13.

13.10 Direct Design Method

13.10.1 Limitations
Regular two-way slab systems as defined in Clause 13.1 and meeting the following limitations may be designed by the Direct Design Method.

13.10.1.1
There shall be a minimum of three continuous spans in each direction.

N13.9.5

Generally, the output from an elastic frame analysis will give the moments at the ends of the members. From these the moments at the critical sections are calculated. The location of the critical sections for large rectilinear interior supports and for exterior supports with brackets are shown in Fig. N13.9.5.

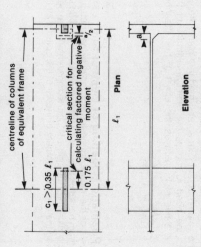

Fig. N13.9.5

Critical Sections for Negative Factored Moment for Cases with Large Rectilinear Interior Supports and Exterior Supports with Brackets

N13.10 Direct Design Method

Although the name has been retained, the Direct Design Method in CSA Standard A23.3-94 has been reduced from a complete design method to a procedure for determining moments at the critical sections and so is essentially a simplified elastic frame analysis. That portion of the design related to the lateral distribution of moments across the critical sections is applicable to all elastic frame solutions and has been incorporated in Clauses 13.12 and 13.13.

N13.10.1.1

When the design strip consists of only two spans the magnitude of the negative moment at the interior support is significantly greater than when there are three or more spans. Distribution coefficients in Table 13-1 are based on three or more spans.

13.10.1.2

Successive span lengths centre-to-centre of supports in each direction shall not differ by more than one-third of the longer span.

13.10.1.3

All loads shall be due to gravity only and uniformly distributed over an entire panel. The factored live load shall not exceed two times the factored dead load.

13.10.1.4

Variations from the limitations of Clauses 13.10.1.1 to 13.10.1.3 may be considered acceptable if it is demonstrated by analysis that the requirements of Clause 13.6.1 are satisfied.

13.10.2 Total Factored Static Moment for a Span

13.10.2.1

The total factored static moment for a span shall be determined in a strip bounded laterally by the centrelines of the panels on each side of the centreline of supports.

13.10.2.2

For each span of each strip the sum of the absolute values of the positive and the average negative factored moments, in each direction, shall be not less than

$$M_o = \frac{w_f \, \ell_{2a} \, \ell_n^2}{8} \qquad (13\text{-}16)$$

13.10.2.3

The clear span, ℓ_n, shall extend from face-to-face of columns, capitals, brackets, or walls. The value of ℓ_n used in Equation (13-16) shall be not less than $0.65\ell_1$.

13.10.3 Negative and Positive Factored Moments

13.10.3.1

In an interior span, the total static moment, M_o, shall be distributed as follows:
(a) negative factored moment at the face of support .... 0.65; and
(b) positive factored moment at midspan .... 0.35.

13.10.3.2

In an end span, the total factored static moment, M_o, shall be distributed as shown in Table 13-1.

N13.10.1.2

The limitation of this clause is to prevent the possibility of developing negative moments beyond the point where the negative moment reinforcement is terminated according to Fig. 13-1.

N13.10.1.3

The distribution coefficients in Table 13-1 are essentially those from an elastic analysis for a uniformly distributed loading on all spans. In the absence of provisions to adequately handle pattern loadings the factored live load is limited to two times the factored dead load.

N13.10.2.1

See Fig. N13.1(c).

N13.10.2.3

When circular or regular polygonal supports are used, it is recommended that the clear span, ℓ_n, be calculated by treating the supports as square sections with the same area as illustrated in Fig. N13.10.2.3.

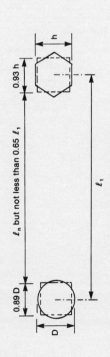

Fig. N13.10.2.3
Examples of Equivalent Square Supports

Table 13-1
Distribution Factors for Total Factored Static Moment
(See Clause 13.10.3.2.)

	Exterior edge unrestrained	Slab with beams between all supports	Slab without beams between interior supports	Exterior edge fully restrained
Interior negative factored moment	0.75	0.70	0.70	0.65
Positive factored moment	0.66	0.59	0.52	0.35
Exterior negative factored moment	0	0.16	0.26	0.65

13.10.3.3
Negative and positive factored moments may be modified by 15% provided the total static moment for a span in the direction considered is not less than that required by Equation (13-16).

13.10.3.4
Negative moment sections shall be designed to resist the larger of the two interior negative factored moments determined for spans framing into a common support; however the moments may first be modified in accordance with Clause 13.10.3.3.

13.10.4 Unbalanced Factored Moments in Columns and Walls
At an interior support, the joint and supporting elements above and below the slab shall resist the factored moment specified in Equation (13-17) in direct proportion to their stiffness.

$$M_f = 0.07\left[(w_{Df} + 0.5w_{Lf})\ell_{2a}\ell_n^2 - w_{Df}'\ell_{2a}'(\ell_n')^2\right] \tag{13-17}$$

where w_{Df}', ℓ_{2a}', and ℓ_n' refer to the shorter span.

13.11 Slab Reinforcement

13.11.1 General
Reinforcement in each direction for two-way slab systems shall be determined from moments at critical sections but shall be not less than that required by Clause 7.8.1

13.11.2 Shear and Moment Transfer
When gravity load, wind, earthquake, or other lateral forces cause transfer of moment between slab and column, a fraction of unbalanced moment given by

$$\gamma_f = 1 - \gamma_v \tag{13-18}$$

shall be transferred by flexural reinforcement placed within a width extending a distance $1.5h_s$ past the sides of the column.

N13.10.3.1 and N13.10.3.2

The total factored static moment for a span, M_o, is distributed between negative and positive moment regions in a manner that reflects the influence of the stiffness of the supporting members. See Fig. N13.10.3 for some examples. The positive factored moments given in this clause are maximum values and do not necessarily occur at mid span.

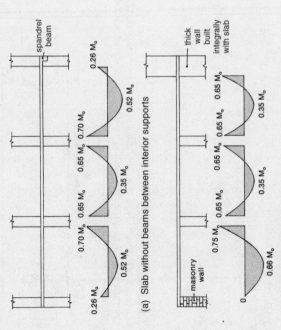

(a) Slab without beams between interior supports

(b) Slab supported on walls

Fig. N13.10.3
Examples of Design Moments for Slabs

N13.10.3.3

This clause reflects the amount of moment redistribution that can occur in regular slab systems. For slabs without beams between interior supports, unless an edge beam is provided, it is recommended that the exterior negative moment not be reduced when calculating maximum factored shear stress due to the moment transfer by eccentricity of shear.

13.11.3 Spacing

Spacing of reinforcement at critical sections shall not exceed the following limits except for portions of slab area that may be of cellular or ribbed construction:

(a) negative reinforcement in the band defined in Clauses 13.12.2.1 and 13.12.2.2: .... $1.5h_s$ but $s \le 250$ mm;

(b) remaining negative moment reinforcement: .... $3h_s$ but $s \le 500$ mm;

(c) positive moment reinforcement: .... $3h_s$ but $s \le 500$ mm.

In the slab over cellular spaces, reinforcement shall be provided as required by Clause 7.8.

13.11.4 Anchorage

13.11.4.1

Positive moment reinforcement perpendicular to a discontinuous edge shall have embedment, straight or hooked, at least 150 mm into the spandrel beams, columns, or walls.

13.11.4.2

Negative moment reinforcement perpendicular to a discontinuous edge shall be bent, hooked, or otherwise anchored, in spandrel beams, columns, or walls, to be developed at the face of support according to the provisions of Clause 12.

13.11.4.3

Where a slab is not supported by a spandrel beam or wall at a discontinuous edge, or where a slab cantilevers beyond the support, both the top and bottom reinforcement shall extend to the edge of the slab.

13.11.5 Minimum Reinforcement for Structural Integrity at Slab-Column Connections

13.11.5.1

The summation of the area of bottom reinforcement connecting the slab to the column or column capital on all faces of the periphery of the column or column capital shall be

$$\Sigma A_{sb} \ge \frac{2V_{se}}{f_y} \qquad (13\text{-}19)$$

Integrity reinforcement is not required if there are beams containing shear reinforcement in all spans framing into the column.

13.11.5.2

The reinforcement provided to satisfy Clause 13.11.5.1 shall consist of at least two bars or two tendons in each span framing into the column.

13.11.5.3

The bottom reinforcement required by Clause 13.11.5.1 must be provided by one or more of the following:

(a) bottom reinforcement extended such that it is lap spliced over a column or column capital with the bottom reinforcement in adjacent spans using a Class A tension lap splice; or

(b) additional bottom reinforcement, passing over a column or column capital, such that

98

N13.11 Slab Reinforcement

N13.11.2 Shear and Moment Transfer

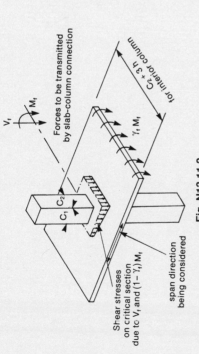

Fig. N13.11.2
Shear and Moment Transfer in Slab-Column Connections

N13.11.3 Spacing

Except in the negative moment regions in the vicinity of the columns, this clause permits a wider spacing of flexural slab reinforcement compared to the previous edition of the Standard.

N13.11.5 Reinforcement for Structural Integrity at Slab-Column Connections

The intent of this clause is to provide a minimum level of structural integrity to the slab system to limit the spread from a local failure that would result in progressive collapse. The provision of properly anchored bottom reinforcing bars or tendons enables the slab to hang from the supports after the initial local failure occurs (see Fig. N13.11.5).

121

(c) an overlap of $2\ell_d$ is provided with the bottom reinforcement in adjacent spans; or at discontinuous edges, bottom reinforcement extended and bent, hooked, or otherwise anchored over the supports such that the yield stress can be developed at the face of the column or column capital according to the provisions of Clause 12;

or

(d) tendons as specified in Clause 13.11.5.4.

13.11.5.4

Continuous tendons, which are draped over columns or column capitals, may be considered effective in satisfying the requirement of Clause 13.11.5.1. The minimum required total area of prestressing steel may be calculated using Equation (13-19) with f_y replaced by f_{py}.

13.11.6 Effective Depth at Drop Panels

Where a drop panel is used to reduce the amount of negative moment reinforcement over the column of a flat slab, the thickness of the drop panel below the slab shall not be assumed greater than one-quarter of the distance from the edge of the drop panel to the edge of the column or column capital.

13.12 Reinforcement for Regular Slabs Without Beams

13.12.1 General

In addition to the requirements of Clauses 13.11, slabs without beams designed in accordance with Clauses 13.9 and 13.10 shall be reinforced for flexure in accordance with Clauses 13.12.2 to 13.12.4.

13.12.2 Factored Moments in Column Strips

The column strip shall be designed to resist the total negative or positive factored moments at the critical sections multiplied by an appropriate factor within the following ranges:

(a) negative moment at an interior column . . . . 0.60 to 1.00;

(b) negative moment at an exterior column 1.00;

(c) positive moment at all spans . . . . 0.50 to 0.70.

13.12.2.1 Interior Columns

At least one-third of the reinforcement for total factored negative moment at interior columns shall be located in a band with a width extending a distance $1.5h_s$ from the sides of the column.

13.12.2.2 Exterior Columns

Reinforcement for the total factored negative moment at exterior columns shall be placed within a band with a width extending a distance $1.5h_s$ from the sides of the column.

13.12.3 Factored Moments in Middle Strips

13.12.3.1

That portion of negative and positive factored moments not resisted by column strips shall be proportionately assigned to corresponding half middle strips.

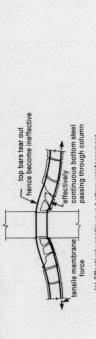

(a) Effectively continuous bottom reinforcement providing post punching failure resistance

top bars tear out hence become ineffective

effectively continuous bottom steel passing through column

tensile membrane force

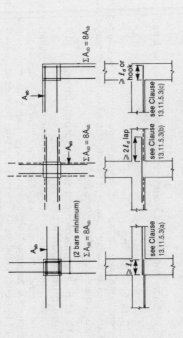

(b) Ways of providing effectively continuous bottom reinforcement

$\Sigma A_{sb} = 8A_{sb}$

A_{sb}

$\geq \ell_d$ or hook

see Clause (13.11.5.3(c))

A_{sb}

$\Sigma A_{sb} = 8A_{sb}$

$\geq 2\ell_d$ lap

see Clause (13.11.5.3(b))

A_{sb}

(2 bars minimum)

$\Sigma A_{sb} = 8A_{sb}$

see Clause 13.11.5.3(a)

$\geq \ell_d$

Fig. N13.11.5
Structural Integrity Requirements for Slabs

N13.11.6 Effective Depth at Drop Panels
See Fig. N13.11.6.

N13.12.2 Factored Moments in Column Strips
A range of values for the portion of the factored moment to be assigned to the column strip gives the designer more freedom in selecting reinforcement placing. For positive moments, a uniform bottom mat is permissible.

N13.12.2.2 Exterior Columns
For slabs with spandrel edge beams only, it is conservative when calculating the torsion in the edge beam to assume that the negative moment is uniformly distributed over the width of the design strip and that the torsion is zero at the panel centrelines (See Fig. N13.12.2(a)). Alternatively, the torsion can be calculated from the distribution of negative moments across the width of the design strip.

If the maximum calculated torque is less than 25% of the cracking torque, T_{cr}, of the spandrel beam, then, from Clause 11.2.9.1, the torsion can be neglected. If the calculated torque exceeds $0.67 T_{cr}$, then, from Clause 11.2.9.2, this maximum torque may be reduced to $0.67 T_{cr}$, to account for the reduction in torsional stiffness that will occur after cracking. If the torsion is reduced, the slab moments must be adjusted accordingly (see Fig. N13.12.2.2(b)).

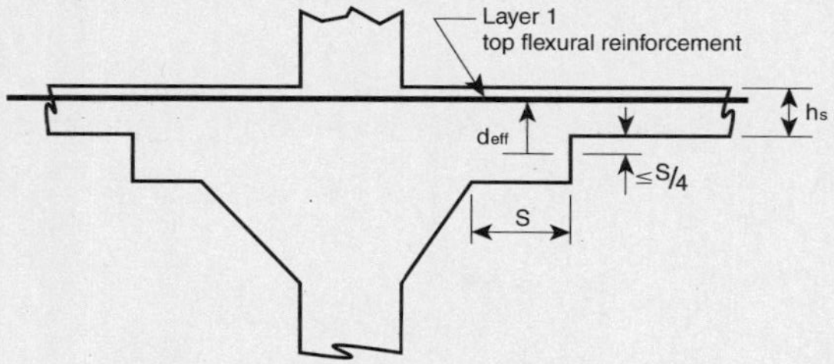

Fig. N13.11.6.
Effective Depth at Drop Panel

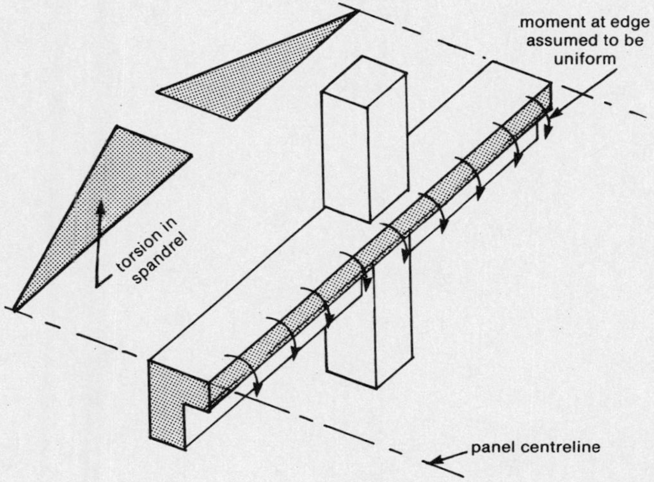

Fig. N13.12.2.2.(a)
Calculation of Torsion at Exterior Edge

13.12.3.2

Each middle strip shall be proportioned to resist the sum of the factored moments assigned to its two half middle strips.

13.12.3.3

A middle strip adjacent to and parallel with an edge supported by a wall shall be proportioned to resist twice the factored moment assigned to the half middle strip corresponding to the first row of interior supports.

13.12.4 Reinforcement for Crack Control

Slabs with drop panels, particularly in a corrosive environment, may require additional reinforcement in the negative middle strip region to limit cracking. This additional reinforcement shall not be included in the calculation of moment resistance.

Note: *Reinforcement required to limit cracking is generally more than that required by Clause 7.8.1.*

13.12.5 Curtailment of Reinforcement

13.12.5.1

For regular slabs, as defined in Clause 13.1 and meeting the additional limitations of Clause 13.10.1, minimum extensions shall be as shown in Figure 13-1. The required extension for slabs not meeting the limitations of Clause 13.10.1 shall meet the requirements of Clauses 12.11 and 12.12 but shall not be less than those shown in Figure 13-1.

13.12.5.2

Where adjacent spans are unequal, the extension of negative reinforcement beyond the face of the support as prescribed in Figure 13-1 shall be based on the longer span.

13.12.6 Openings

13.12.6.1

Openings may be placed in regular two-way slabs without beams as defined in Clause 13.1 without the special analysis required by Clause 13.6.5 provided the requirements of Clauses 13.12.6.1 through 13.12.6.4 are met.

13.12.6.1

Openings of any size may be located in the area common to intersecting middle strips provided the total amount of reinforcement required for the panel without the opening is maintained.

13.12.6.2

In the area common to intersecting column strips, not more than 1/8 of the width of the column strip in either span shall be interrupted by openings. An amount of reinforcement equivalent to that interrupted by an opening shall be added adjacent to the sides of the opening.

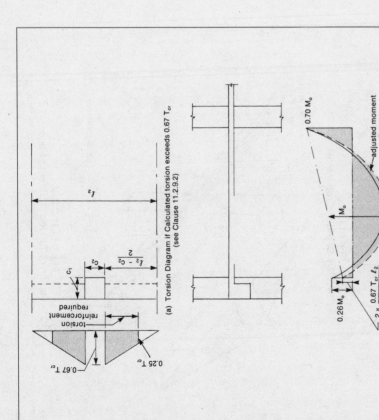

(a) Torsion Diagram if Calculated torsion exceeds $0.67\ T_{cr}$ (see Clause 11.2.9.2)

(b) Adjusted Moment Diagram

Fig. N13.12.2.2(b)
Redistribution of Moments Caused by Reduced Torsional Stiffness of Spandral Beam After Cracking

N13.12.4 Reinforcement for Crack Control

Experience has shown that when stiff drop panels are used there is a greater tendency for the slab to crack in the negative middle strip region. In those applications where crack control is important (i.e. where a brittle topping is used or the slab is located in a corrosive environment) additional reinforcement is required.

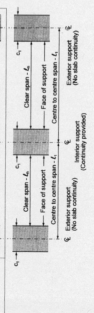

STRIP	LOCATION	MINIMUM PERCENT A_s AT SECTION	WITHOUT DROP PANELS	WITH DROP PANELS
COLUMN STRIP	TOP	50	$0.30\ell_n$	$0.33\ell_n$
		Remainder	$0.20\ell_n$	$0.20\ell_n$
	BOTTOM	50	150 mm	Structural integrity reinforcement (Clause 13.11.5)
		Remainder	75 mm min. — Max. $0.125\ell_n$ — 150 mm	24 d_b or 300 mm min. all bars — 150 mm — Edge of drop — x_d
MIDDLE STRIP	TOP	100	$0.22\ell_n$	$0.22\ell_n$
	BOTTOM	50	150 mm — Max. $0.15\ell_1$ — 150 mm	150 mm — Max. $0.15\ell_1$ — 150 mm

c_1 — Clear span - ℓ_n — c_1 Clear span - ℓ_n c_1
Face of support — Face of support
Centre to centre span - ℓ_1 — Centre to centre span - ℓ_1
Exterior support (No slab continuity) — Interior support (Continuity provided) — Exterior support (No slab continuity)

**Figure 13-1
Minimum Length of Reinforcement for Slabs Without Beams**
(See Clause 13.12.5.)

13.12.6.3
In the area common to one column strip and one middle strip, not more than one-quarter of the reinforcement in either strip shall be interrupted by openings. An amount of reinforcement equivalent to that interrupted by an opening shall be added adjacent to the sides of the opening.

13.12.6.4
Shear requirements of Clause 13.4.3.4 shall be satisfied.

13.13 Reinforcement for Regular Slabs with Beams Between All Supports

13.13.1 General
In addition to the requirements of Clause 13.11, slabs with beams designed in accordance with Clauses 13.9 and 13.10 shall be reinforced for flexure in accordance with Clauses 13.13.2 to 13.13.5.

13.13.2 Factored Moments in Beams

13.13.2.1 Positive and Interior Negative Moment
Beams shall be reinforced to resist the following fraction of the positive or interior factored moments determined by analysis or determined in accordance with Clause 13.10.3:

$$\frac{\alpha_1}{[1 + (\ell_2/\ell_1)^2]} \tag{13-20}$$

In this equation, α_1 shall not be taken larger than 1.0.

13.13.2.2 Exterior Moment
Beams shall be proportioned for 100 per cent of the exterior negative moment

13.13.2.3
In addition to moments calculated for uniform loads applied to the slab according to Clauses 13.13.2.1 and 13.13.2.2, beams shall be proportioned to resist moments caused by concentrated or linear loads applied directly to the beams, including the weight of the beam stem.

13.13.3 Slab Reinforcement for Positive Moment
The slab shall be reinforced to resist the factored positive moments not supported by the beams. This reinforcement may be distributed uniformly over the width of the slab.

13.13.4 Slab Reinforcement for Negative Moment

13.13.4.1 Interior Supports
The slab shall be reinforced to resist the interior negative moments not resisted by the beams. This reinforcement shall be uniformly distributed over the width of the slab.

13.13.4.2 Exterior Supports

The reinforcement for the exterior factored negative moment in the beam shall be placed within a band with a width extending a distance $1.5h_s$ past the sides of the column or the edge of the beam web, whichever is the larger, unless calculations show that reinforcement placed outside this limit can develop its full capacity.

13.13.5 Corner Reinforcement

13.13.5.1

In slabs with beams between supports with a value of α greater than 1.0, top and bottom slab reinforcement shall be provided at exterior corners for a distance, in each direction, equal to 1/5 of the shorter span.

13.13.5.2

The reinforcement shall be sufficient to resist a moment per unit width equal to the maximum positive moment per unit width in the slab.

13.13.5.3

The reinforcement at the top of the slab shall be provided to resist moments about axes perpendicular to the diagonal from the corner. The bottom reinforcement shall be provided to resist moments about axes parallel to the diagonal. The reinforcement may be placed in bands parallel to the sides of the slab.

14. Walls

14.0 Notation

A_g = gross area of section
f'_c = specified compressive strength of concrete
h = overall thickness of member
k = effective length factor
ℓ_c = clear vertical distance between supports
P_r = factored axial load resistance of wall
α_1 = ratio of average stress in rectangular compression block to the specified concrete strength
ϕ_c = resistance factor for concrete (Clause 8.4.2)

14.1 Scope

14.1.1

The provisions of Clause 14 shall apply for the design of walls subjected to axial load with or without flexure.

N13.13.5 Corner Reinforcement

Fig. N13.13.5(a) illustrates the deformation of the slab in the vicinity of a exterior corner due to the high twisting moments present. These result in tension in both the top and bottom of the slab as shown. Fig N13.13.5(b) shows two ways of providing reinforcement to control cracking in these regions. Generally the orthogonal arrangement of bars is used.

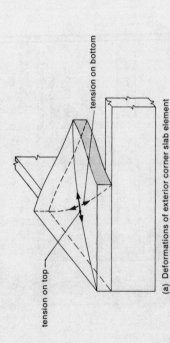

(a) Deformations of exterior corner slab element

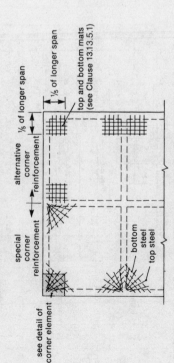

(b) Plan View of slab supported on walls or stiff beams showing reinforcement

Fig. N13.13.5
Special Slab Reinforcement at Exterior Corners

14.1.2
Cantilever retaining walls shall be designed in accordance with the flexural design provisions of Clause 10, with minimum horizontal reinforcement in accordance with Clause 14.3.3.

14.2   General

14.2.1
Walls shall be designed for eccentric loads and any lateral or other loads to which they are subjected.

14.2.2
Walls subject to axial loads shall be designed in accordance with Clauses 14.2, 14.3, and either 14.4 or 14.5.

14.2.3
In lieu of a detailed analysis, the horizontal length of wall to be considered as effective for each vertical concentrated load shall not exceed the centre-to-centre distance between loads, nor the width of bearing plus 4 times the wall thickness.

14.2.4
Compression members built integrally with walls shall conform to Clause 10.11.2.

14.2.5
Walls shall be anchored to intersecting elements such as floors, roofs, columns, pilasters, buttresses, intersecting walls, and footings.

14.2.6
The quantity of reinforcement and the limits of thickness required by Clauses 14.3 and 14.5 may be waived where structural analysis shows adequate strength, ductility, and stability.

14.3   Minimum Reinforcement

14.3.1
Except for walls designed in accordance with Clause 22, minimum reinforcement shall be in accordance with this Clause. Where crack control is critical or where wall geometry or length causes significant restraint of shrinkage or thermal strains, reinforcement additional to that specified in this Clause, or other crack control measures, shall be considered.

14.3.2
The minimum area of vertical reinforcement shall be $0.0015A_g$.

14.3.3
The minimum area of horizontal reinforcement shall be $0.002A_g$.

14.3.4
Walls more than 250 mm thick shall have the reinforcement placed in two layers parallel with the faces of the wall. Each layer shall consist of not less than one-half of the total

104

minimum reinforcement required in each direction, and shall be placed not more than one-third the thickness of the wall from the surface.

14.3.5
The vertical and horizontal reinforcement in each layer shall not be spaced further apart than 3 times the wall thickness nor 500 mm.

14.3.6
Vertical reinforcement need not be enclosed by lateral ties if the vertical reinforcement area is not greater than $0.01A_g$, or where analysis shows that vertical reinforcement is not required as compression reinforcement.

14.3.7
In addition to the minimum reinforcement required by Clauses 14.3.2 and 14.3.3, not less than two No. 15 bars shall be provided around window and door openings. Such bars shall extend at least 600 mm beyond each corner of the opening.

14.4   Walls Designed as Compression Members
Except as provided in Clause 14.5, walls subject to axial load or combined flexure and axial load shall be designed as compression members in accordance with Clauses 10.1, 10.10, 10.13, and 10.14.

14.5   Empirical Design Method

14.5.1
Walls of solid rectangular cross section may be designed by the empirical provisions of Equation (14-1) if the resultant of all factored loads including the effects of lateral loads applied to the wall is located within the middle-third of the overall thickness of the wall.

$$P_r = \frac{2}{3}\,\alpha_1\phi_c f_c' A_g\left[1 - \left(\frac{k\ell_c}{32h}\right)^2\right] \tag{14-1}$$

where the effective length factor, k, shall be:
(a) for walls braced top and bottom against lateral translation and
  (i) restrained against rotation at one or both ends (top or bottom or both) . .   0.8;
  (ii) unrestrained against rotation at both ends 1.0;
(b) for walls not braced against lateral translation . . . .   2.5.

14.5.2
The thickness of bearing walls shall be not less than 1/25 of the unsupported height or length, whichever is shorter, nor less than
(a)   walls which retain earth, and foundation walls . . . .   190 mm;
(b)   cast *in situ* walls . . . .   150 mm;
(c)   precast or tilt-up walls . . . .   100 mm.

N14.3.5
This clause has been revised to clarify that the maximum spacings given apply to the steel in each layer.

N14.5.1
Eccentric loads and lateral forces are used to determine the total eccentricity of the factored axial load, P_f. When the resultant load for all applicable load combinations falls within the middle third of the wall thickness (eccentricity not greater than h/6) at all sections along the length of the undeformed wall, the empirical design method may be used. The design is then carried out considering P_f as a concentric load which must be less than P_r computed by Eq. (14-1). The factored resistance is computed based on an equivalent rectangular stress block equal to 2/3 of the wall thickness. This places the resisting force in line with the assumed load. The capacity based on this equation is reduced slightly compared to that in the 1984 Standard.

In investigating a wall subjected to vertical concentrated loads, A_g in Eq. (14-1) should account for the effective horizontal length of wall defined in Clause 14.2.3.

The effective length factors given in this clause are intended to reflect the general range of end conditions encountered in wall designs. The end condition "restrained against rotation" required for a k factor of 0.8 implies attachment to a member having a flexural stiffness, EI/ℓ, at least as large as that of the wall. Pinned conditions at both ends can occur in some precast and tilt-up applications. The k value of 2.5 must be used when the top of the wall is not effectively braced against translation as occurs with many free-standing walls. A value greater than 2 is used to allow for some rotation of the footing at the base of the wall.

The term in Eq. (14-1) accounting for wall slenderness effects results in relatively comparable strengths by either Clause 14.4 or 14.5 for walls loaded with an eccentricity of h/6.

N14.5.2   Minimum Thickness of Wall Designed by the Empirical Method
The minimum thickness requirements of this clause need not be applied to walls designed according to Clause 14.4.

14.6 Nonbearing Walls

The thickness of nonbearing walls shall be not less than 1/30 of the unsupported height or length, whichever is shorter, nor less than 100 mm.

14.7 Walls as Grade Beams

14.7.1

Walls designed as grade beams shall have top and bottom reinforcement as required for moment in accordance with Clauses 10.5 and 10.6. The design for shear shall be in accordance with Clause 11.

14.7.2

Portions of grade beam walls exposed above grade shall also meet the requirements of Clause 14.3.

15. Footings

15.0 Notation

d_p = diameter of a pile at footing base
β = ratio of long side to short side of footing

15.1 Scope

15.1.1

The provisions of Clause 15 shall apply to the design of isolated footings and, where applicable, to combined footings and mats.

15.1.2

Additional requirements for the design of combined footings and mats are given in Clause 15.10.

15.1.3

Where applicable, strut-and-tie models (see Clause 9.4) may be used in lieu of the provisions of Clause 15.

15.2 Loads and Reactions

15.2.1

Footings shall be proportioned to resist the factored loads and induced reactions in accordance with the appropriate design requirements of this Standard and as provided in Clause 15.

15.2.2

The base area of the footing or the number and arrangement of piles shall be selected based on the principles of soil mechanics. Where the analysis of footings is based on other than

106

N15.2.2

In checking the calculated bearing pressure against the allowable soil pressure specified loads (i.e. unfactored loads) are used. However, in calculating the design moments and shears for the footings, factored loads and their induced reactions are used.

129

linear distributions of soil pressure, the assumed distributions shall be based on an analysis of the interaction of the soil and the footing according to the stiffness of both elements.

15.2.3
For footings on piles, computations for moments and shears, based on the assumption that the reaction from any pile is concentrated at the centre of the pile, shall be acceptable.

15.3 Footings Supporting Circular or Regular Polygon-Shaped Columns or Pedestals
In lieu of detailed analysis, circular or regular polygon-shaped concrete columns or pedestals may be treated as square members, with the same area, for the location of critical sections for moment, shear, and development of reinforcement in the footings.

15.4 Moment in Footings

15.4.1
The external moment on any section of a footing shall be determined by passing a vertical plane through the footing and computing the moment of the forces acting over the entire area of the footing on one side of that vertical plane.

15.4.2
The maximum factored moment for an isolated footing shall be computed as prescribed in Clause 15.4.1 at the critical sections located as follows:

(a) at the face of the column, pedestal, or wall, for footings supporting a concrete column, pedestal, or wall;

(b) halfway between the middle and the edge of the wall for footings supporting a masonry wall; and

(c) halfway between the face of the column and the edge of the steel base for footings supporting a column with steel base plates, unless it is shown through analysis that another position is more appropriate.

15.4.3
In one-way footings and in two-way square footings, reinforcement shall be distributed uniformly across the entire width of the footing.

15.4.4
In two-way rectangular footings, reinforcement shall be distributed as follows:

(a) reinforcement in the long direction shall be distributed uniformly across the entire width of the footing;

(b) for reinforcement in the short direction, a portion of the total reinforcement given by Equation (15-1) shall be distributed uniformly over a band width (centred on the centreline of the column or pedestal) equal to the length of the short side of the footing, or equal to the length of the supported wall or column, whichever is

N15.4.2
Fig. N15.4.2 illustrates the critical locations where flexural resistance and development of reinforcement must be checked.

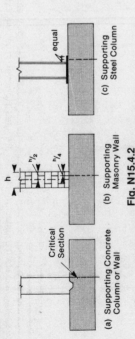

(a) Supporting Concrete Column or Wall

(b) Supporting Masonry Wall

(c) Supporting Steel Column

Fig. N15.4.2
Critical Sections for Moment in Footings

N15.4.4
The total amount of flexural reinforcement in the short direction is determined by considering the total moment acting on the critical section (see Fig. N15.4.4). In recognition of the fact that the moment per unit length will be higher in the vicinity of the column, the flexural reinforcement is concentrated in this region (see Fig. N15.4.4).

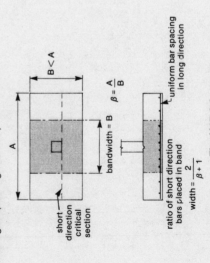

$$\beta = \frac{A}{B}$$

$$\frac{\text{ratio of short direction bars placed in band}}{\text{width}} = \frac{2}{\beta + 1}$$

Fig. N15.4.4
Distribution of flexural Reinforcement in a Rectangular Footing

greater. The remainder of the reinforcement required in the short direction shall be distributed uniformly outside the centre band width.

$$\frac{\text{Reinforcement in band width}}{\text{Total reinforcement in short direction}} = \frac{2}{(\beta + 1)} \tag{15-1}$$

15.5 Shear in Footings

15.5.1
The computation of shear in footings shall be in accordance with Clause 13.4.

15.5.2
The location of the critical section for shear, in accordance with Clause 13.4, shall be measured from the face of the column, pedestal, or wall for footings supporting a column, pedestal, or wall. For footings supporting a column or pedestal with steel base plates, the critical section shall be measured from the location defined in Clause 15.4.2(c).

15.5.3
The computation of shear on any section through a footing supported on piles shall be in accordance with the following:

(a) the entire reaction from any pile, whose centre is located $d_p/2$ or more outside the section, shall be considered as producing shear on that section;

(b) the reaction from any pile, whose centre is located $d_p/2$ or more inside the section, shall be considered as producing no shear on that section; and

(c) for intermediate positions of the pile centre, the portion of the pile reaction to be considered as producing shear on the section shall be based on a straight-line interpolation between the full value at $d_p/2$ outside the section and zero value at $d_p/2$ inside the section.

15.6 Development of Reinforcement in Footings

15.6.1
The computation of the development of reinforcement in footings shall be in accordance with Clause 12.

15.6.2
The calculated tension or compression in the reinforcement at each section shall be developed on each side of that section by proper embedment length, end anchorage, hooks (tension only), or combinations thereof.

15.6.3
The critical sections for development of reinforcement shall be assumed to be at the same locations as defined in Clause 15.4.2 for the maximum factored moment and at all other vertical planes where changes of section or reinforcement occur. (See also Clause 12.10.6.)

N15.5.2
Fig. N15.5.2(a) illustrates the critical sections for which shear resistance must be investigated in accordance with Clause 11.10.

In investigating punching shear for closely spaced piles where the individual critical perimeters overlap, a critical section around the pile group may be more critical (see Fig. N15.5.2(b)).

15.7 Minimum Footing Depth

The depth of the footing above the bottom reinforcement shall be not less than 150 mm for footings on soil, nor less than 300 mm for footings on piles.

15.8 Transfer of Force at Base of Column, Wall, or Reinforced Pedestal

15.8.1 General

15.8.1.1

The forces and moments at the base of a column, wall, or pedestal shall be transferred to the supporting pedestal or footing.

15.8.1.2

Bearing on concrete at the contact surface between the supported and supporting members shall not exceed the factored bearing resistance strength for either surface as given in Clause 10.8.

15.8.1.3

Reinforcement, dowels, or mechanical connectors between supported and supporting members shall be adequate to transfer

(a) all compressive force that exceeds the concrete bearing strength of either member; and

(b) any computed tensile force across the interface.

In addition, reinforcement, dowels, or mechanical connectors shall satisfy Clause 15.8.2.2 or 15.8.3.

15.8.1.4

If the calculated moments are transferred to supporting pedestals or footings, reinforcement, dowels, or mechanical connectors shall be adequate to satisfy Clause 12.17.

15.8.1.5

Lateral forces shall be transferred to the supporting pedestals or footings in accordance with the interface shear transfer provisions of Clause 11.6 or by other appropriate means.

15.8.2 Cast-in-Place Construction

15.8.2.1

In cast-in-place construction, the reinforcement required to satisfy Clause 15.8.1 shall be provided either by extending longitudinal bars into the supporting pedestal or footing or by dowels.

15.8.2.2

For cast-in-place columns and pedestals, the area of reinforcement across the interface shall not be less than 0.005 times the gross area of the supported member.

N15.8

Joints between cast-in-place columns or walls and footings should be designed in accordance with Clauses 15.8.1 and 15.8.2. Joints between precast columns or walls and footings shall satisfy Clauses 15.8.1 and 15.8.3.

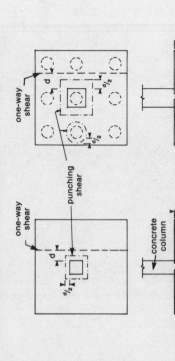

Fig. N15.5.2(a)
Critical Sections for Shear

Fig. N15.5.2(b)
Critical Sections for Groups of Closely Spaced Piles

15.8.2.3

For cast-in-place walls, the area of reinforcement across the interface shall not be less than the minimum vertical reinforcement required by Clause 14.3.

15.8.2.4

The diameter of dowels shall not exceed the diameter of the longitudinal bars by more than one bar size.

15.8.2.5

At footings, No. 45 and No. 55 longitudinal bars, in compression only, may be lap spliced with dowels to provide the reinforcement required to satisfy Clause 15.8.1. Dowels shall not be larger than No. 35 and shall extend into the supported member for a distance of not less than the development length of No. 45 or No. 55 bars, or the splice length of the dowels, whichever is greater, and into the footing for a distance of not less than the development length of the dowels.

15.8.2.6

If a pinned or rocker connection is provided in cast-in-place construction, the connection shall conform to Clauses 15.8.1 and 15.8.3.

15.8.3 Precast Construction

15.8.3.1

In precast construction, the reinforcement required to satisfy Clause 15.8.1 may be provided by anchor bolts or suitable mechanical connectors.

15.8.3.2

Anchor bolts and mechanical connectors shall be designed to reach their factored resistance prior to anchorage failure of the surrounding concrete.

Note: *See Appendix D for more information.*

15.9 Sloped or Stepped Footings

15.9.1

In sloped or stepped footings, the angle of the slope or the depth and location of the steps shall be such that design requirements are satisfied at every section.

15.9.2

Sloped or stepped footings designed as a unit shall be constructed to assure action as a unit.

15.10 Combined Footings and Mats

15.10.1

Footings supporting more than one column, pedestal, or wall (combined footings or mats) shall be proportioned to resist the factored loads and induced reactions in accordance with appropriate design requirements of this Standard.

December 1994

110

N15.8.1

Only the computed end moments that exist at the base of a column (or pedestal) need be transferred to the footing. The minimum eccentricity requirement for slenderness considerations given in Clause 10.11.6.4 need not be considered for transfer of forces and moments to footings.

N15.8.1.2

In investigating the transfer of forces at the base of a column it is necessary to check the bearing stresses in both the column concrete and the footing concrete. The compressive force which exceeds that developed by the permissible concrete bearing stress on the bottom of the column or in the top of the footing must be carried by dowels or column reinforcement extending into the footing (see Fig. N15.8.1.2). It is good practice to use at least four dowels.

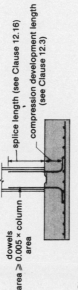

dowels
area ≥ 0.005 × column area

splice length (see Clause 12.16)

compression development length (see Clause 12.3)

Check at contact area:-

$$K = \sqrt{\frac{A_2}{A_1}} \not> 2.0 \text{ (see Clause 10.8)}$$

where

**Fig. N15.8.1.2
Transfer of Compression Force at Column-Footing Interface**

N15.8.1.3

When moments are transferred to footings it is frequently necessary to dowel all the column bars because the column concrete is stressed to 0.85 f'c on one side as shown in Fig. N15.8.1.3.

133

15.10.2
The distribution of soil pressure under combined footings and mats shall be consistent with the properties of the soil and the structure, and with the established principles of soil mechanics.

15.11   Plain Concrete Pedestals and Footings
Plain concrete pedestals and footings shall conform to Clause 22.

16.   Precast Concrete

16.0   Notation
A_g =   gross area of column
R =   force modification factor, as given in the *National Building Code of Canada*, that reflects the capability of a structure to dissipate energy through inelastic behaviour

16.1   Scope

16.1.1
All provisions of this Standard not specifically excluded and not in conflict with the provisions of Clause 16 shall apply to structures incorporating precast concrete elements.

16.1.2
Clauses 7.7, 7.8, 10.4, and 13 do not apply to precast concrete.
Note: *Design responsibility: Information on the suggested division of responsibilities between the designer and the precast concrete manufacturer may be found in CSA Standard A23.4.*

16.1.3
For elements produced in manufacturing plants certified in accordance with Clause 16.2, the concrete material resistance factor, ϕ_c, given in Clause 8.4.2 may be taken as 0.65.

16.2   Prequalification of Manufacturer

16.2.1
All precast concrete elements within the scope of this Standard shall be manufactured and erected in accordance with the requirements of CSA Standard A23.4.
Note: *CSA Standard A23.4 requires that precast concrete be produced in a plant certified in the appropriate categories by a Certification Organization accredited by the Standards Council of Canada in the subject area of building products and structures.*

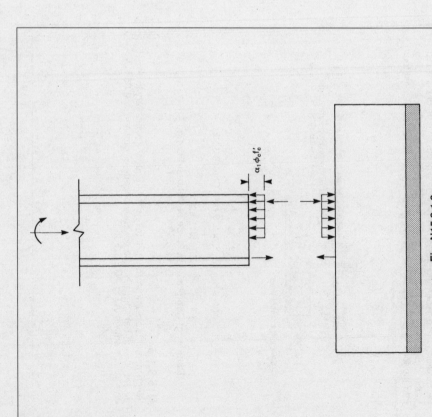

Fig. N15.8.1.3
Transfer of Moment at Column-Footing Interface

$\alpha_1 \phi_c f'_c$

N16.1.3
The ϕ_c factor for precast concrete has been increased to 0.65 to reflect the better quality control in certified plants.

16.2.2

Exemptions to Clause 16.2.1 may be made by the designer of the building for the following reinforced concrete elements:

(a) tilt-up walls;

(b) minor structural elements such as stair flights, stair landings, lintels, and sills; and

(c) lift slab construction.

The designer shall clearly indicate if such reinforced precast elements are to be manufactured in accordance with CSA Standard A23.4, in which case certification shall be required, or in accordance with CSA Standard A23.1, in which case the certification requirement may be waived by the designer.

16.2.3

The exceptions listed in Clause 16.2.2(b) are for building structures. Similar exceptions may apply to other structures.

16.3   Drawings

In addition to the requirements of Clause 1.2, drawings and related documents shall include

(a) sufficient dimensions to permit preparation of the shop drawings;

(b) sufficient indication of the work supporting, or supported by, or attached to the precast concrete to permit preparation of the shop drawings;

(c) the class of surface finish required for structural purposes;

(d) any nonstandard tolerances required for the precast concrete elements or the building structure;

(e) any superimposed loads on the precast concrete elements, the location of connections, and the factored forces to be developed at the connections to the element;

(f) when precast elements are to act as diaphragms, the factored external forces and shears acting on the diaphragms;

(g) the expected deformations of the structure under specified loads, insofar as they affect the design of the precast concrete elements or associated connections. Deformations due to specified earthquake loads shall be shown separately; and

(h) the provisions for stability during construction.

16.4   Design

16.4.1   General

16.4.1.1

The design shall consider loading and restraint conditions from the initial fabrication to the intended use of the structure, including forces from stripping, storage, transportation, and erection.

16.4.1.2

The effects of initial and long-term deformations shall be considered, including the effects on interconnected elements.

N16.4.1

While the design of precast concrete follows the same rules presented for cast-in-place concrete, special considerations are necessary for precast concrete. The use of the strength design method based on 28-day strengths may not be appropriate for the design of elements subjected to the effects of stripping and handling at earlier ages. Cracking of the concrete, although acceptable from structural considerations, may result in unacceptable appearance. Some architectural finishes may tend to exaggerate the effects of early cracking. Further guidance on the design of precast concrete elements and connections can be obtained from the CPCI *Metric Design Manual*.

N16.4.1.1

The loads imposed on precast elements during the period from casting to placement may be greater than the actual service loads.

The behaviour of precast concrete structures may differ substantially from that of monolithic cast-in-place structures. Design of joints to transmit forces due to shrinkage, creep, temperature, elastic deformation, wind forces and earthquake forces requires particular care in precast construction. Details of such joints are especially important for adequate performance of precast construction.

16.4.2 Distribution of Forces Among Elements

16.4.2.1

Distribution of forces that are perpendicular to the plane of the elements shall be established by analysis or test.

16.4.2.2

In-plane forces shall be transferred between the elements of a precast floor or wall system in accordance with the following:

(a)   load paths for in-plane forces shall be transferred through both connections and elements;

(b)   where tension forces occur, a load path of reinforcement or tendons shall be provided;

(c)   the design of joints, connections, and bearings shall include the effects of all forces to be transmitted including the effects of specified loads, tolerances, elastic deformation, temperature, creep, and shrinkage.

16.4.3 Reinforcement of Precast Concrete Elements

16.4.3.1

Elements shall be reinforced in accordance with the requirements of this Standard to meet all conditions of Clauses 16.4.1 and 16.4.2.

16.4.3.2

The minimum reinforcement ratio in each direction shall be not less than 0.0016 for reinforcement or 0.0004 for prestressing tendons except as permitted in Clauses 16.4.3.3 and 16.4.3.4. Additional reinforcement shall be provided at openings and other discontinuities.

16.4.3.3

In one-way floor and roof slabs and in one-way precast, prestressed wall panels, all not exceeding 3000 mm in width, and where elements are not connected to cause restraint in the transverse direction, the minimum transverse reinforcement requirements of Clause 16.4.3.2 can be waived.

16.4.3.4

For nonprestressed walls, the minimum reinforcement ratio shall not be less than 0.001 in each direction. Spacing of reinforcement shall not exceed five times the wall thickness or 500 mm.

16.4.4 Joints and Connections

16.4.4.1

Forces shall be transferred between elements by grouted joints, shear keys, mechanical connectors, reinforcement, topping, or a combination of these means.

N16.4.3.2

The minimum reinforcement ratios of Clause 16.4.3.2 are not sufficient to control the width of full depth cracks caused by the restraint of shrinkage, creep and thermal movements. If it is necessary to limit the width of such cracks, additional reinforcement will be required unless special provisions are made to relieve restraint forces.

N16.4.4

Guidelines summarizing current practice for the design of connections can be found in the CPCI *Metric Design Manual.*

16.4.4.2
Precast segments, when joined and post-tensioned in accordance with CSA Standard A23.1, may be considered as homogeneous structural members.

16.4.4.3
The design of each component of a connection shall be based on the most severe combination of load eccentricities as limited by fabrication and erection tolerances.

16.4.4.4
Special attention shall be given to the design of connections where there is a possibility of corrosion, and in particular those in inaccessible locations in the finished structure.

16.4.4.5
Provision for movement of elements due to earthquake shall accommodate R times the elastic deflection of the lateral force resisting system.
Note: *See the* National Building Code of Canada *for more information.*

16.4.4.6
In the design of connections that accommodate movement by deformation of the connection material, consideration shall be given to the magnitude and frequency of the movement and to the fatigue properties and ductility of the connection.

16.4.4.7
In the design of connections that accommodate movement by sliding, the increase of friction due to the tightness of the fastening, the effects of corrosion, and construction tolerances shall be taken into account.
Note: *For connections whose capacity is sensitive to erection tolerances and for connections in inaccessible locations which may be subject to corrosive conditions, an increase in connection resistance is recommended.*

16.4.5   Bearing
The allowable bearing stress at the contact surface between supported and supporting elements and between any intermediate bearing elements shall not exceed the bearing resistance for either surface, as given in Clause 10.8 or 11.5.4.

16.5   Structural Integrity

16.5.1
In buildings where precast concrete elements constitute a portion of the structural system, all structural elements shall be effectively tied together.

16.5.2
Except as provided in Clause 16.5.3, the provisions for the structural integrity of precast concrete structures shall meet the requirements of Clauses 16.5.2.1 to 16.5.2.5.
Note: *Further guidance on the design for structural integrity of structural systems incorporating precast elements may be obtained from*
(a)   "Design Recommendations for Precast Concrete Structures," ACI-ASCE Joint

---

N16.5
The clauses on Structural Integrity have been expanded to provide specific details to assure structural integrity for precast concrete buildings.

(b)   Committee 550, ACI Structural Journal, January-February 1993, pp.115-121.

(c)   "PCI Design Handbook", fourth edition, Precast/Prestressed Concrete Institute, 1992.

    "Metric Design Manual", second edition, Canadian Prestressed Concrete Institute, 1987.

(d)   "Concrete Design Handbook", Canadian Portland Cement Association, 1985.

16.5.2.1
Longitudinal and transverse tensile tie reinforcement shall be incorporated so as to provide a load path to the lateral load resisting system as specified in Clause 16.4.2.2(b).

16.5.2.2
Where precast elements form floor or roof diaphragms, the connections between the diaphragm and those elements being laterally supported shall be designed for all factored loads but shall have a factored tensile resistance of not less than 5 kN/m.

16.5.2.3
Vertical tension tie requirements shall apply to the horizontal joints in all vertical structural elements, except cladding, and shall be in accordance with the following:

(a)   precast columns shall have a factored tensile resistance of not less than $1.4A_g$ newtons;

(b)   for columns with a larger cross-section than required by analysis, a reduced effective area may be substituted for A_g, but not less than $A_g/2$; and

(c)   precast wall panels shall have a minimum of two ties per panel, with a factored resistance of 30 kN per tie.

16.5.2.4
When factored forces and moments result in compression at the base, the ties required by Clause 16.5.2.3(c) may be anchored to the floor slab on grade.

16.5.2.5
Ties and connections shall be designed such that the resistance is governed by yielding of the steel component.

16.5.3
Structures three or more storeys in height constructed with precast concrete bearing walls shall be tied together in accordance with Clauses 16.5.3.1 to 16.5.3.4.

16.5.3.1
Longitudinal and transverse tension ties shall be incorporated in floor and roof systems to provide a factored resistance of 14 kN per metre of width or length. Tie paths shall be provided over interior wall supports and to exterior walls. Ties shall be located in the floor or roof system or within 600 mm of the plane of the floor or roof system.

16.5.3.2
Longitudinal tension ties parallel to the floor or roof spans shall be spaced not more than 3000 mm on centres.

16.5.3.3
Transverse tension ties perpendicular to the span of the floor or roof shall be spaced not greater than the spacing of the bearing walls.

16.5.3.4
Tension ties around the perimeter of each floor and roof, within 1500 mm of the edge, shall provide a factored tensile resistance of not less than 60 kN.

16.5.3.5
Vertical tension ties shall be provided in all walls and shall be continuous over the full height of the building. They shall provide factored tensile resistance of not less than 40 kN per metre of wall. Not less than two tension ties shall be provided for each precast wall panel.

17.   Composite Concrete Flexural Members

17.0   Notation

A_c =   area of contact surface transmitting transverse shear

b_v =   width of cross section at contact surface being investigated for longitudinal shear

d =   distance from extreme compression fibre to centroid of tension reinforcement for entire composite section

V_{rt} =   factored longitudinal shear resistance

V_f =   factored shear force at section

Note: *The terms transverse shear and longitudinal shear are used in this Clause. For a composite beam with a horizontal axis, transverse shear refers to vertical shear forces and longitudinal shear refers to shear on a horizontal plane.*

17.1   Scope

17.1.1
The provisions of Clause 17 shall apply to the design of composite concrete flexural members defined as precast or cast-in-place concrete elements constructed in separate placements, or both, but so interconnected that all elements act as a unit.

17.1.2
All provisions of this Standard shall apply to composite flexural members except as specifically modified in Clause 17.

17.2   General

17.2.1
An entire composite member or portions thereof may be assumed to resist shear and moment.

17.2.2
Individual elements shall be investigated for all critical stages of loading.

17.2.3
If the specified strength, density, or other properties of the various elements are different, properties of the individual elements or the most critical values shall be assumed for the analysis.

17.2.4
In strength computations of composite members, no distinction shall be made between shored and unshored members.

17.2.5
All elements shall be designed to support all loads introduced prior to full development of the design strength of composite members.

17.2.6
Reinforcement shall be provided as required to control cracking and to prevent separation of individual elements of composite members.

17.2.7
Composite members shall meet the requirements for control of deflections specified in Clause 9.8.

17.3   Shoring
When used, the shoring shall not be removed until the supported elements have developed the design properties required to support all loads and to limit deflections and cracking at the time of shoring removal.

17.4   Transverse Shear Resistance

17.4.1
When an entire composite member is assumed to resist transverse shear, design shall be in accordance with the requirements of Clause 11 for a monolithically cast member of the same cross sectional shape.

17.4.2
Shear reinforcement shall be fully anchored into interconnected elements in accordance with Clause 12.13.

17.5   Longitudinal Shear Resistance

17.5.1
In a composite member, full transfer of the longitudinal shear forces shall be assured at the contact surfaces of the interconnected elements.

N17.2.4
The stresses in, and the deflections of, a composite member at specified loads will be influenced by whether or not the first element cast was shored during casting and curing of the subsequent element(s). However, tests and analysis show that the strength of such a member is not measurably affected by shoring due to the inelastic stress redistributions that occur prior to failure.

N17.2.6
The extent of cracking permitted is dependent on such factors as environment, aesthetics and type of loading. Irrespective of these considerations, cracks wide enough to impair shear transfer cannot be tolerated.

N17.2.7
Premature loading of precast elements can cause excessive deflections as a result of the high creep of young concrete.

17.5.2
Longitudinal shear shall be investigated in accordance with Clause 17.5.3 or 17.5.4.

17.5.3 Values of Factored Shear Resistance

17.5.3.1
Unless calculated in accordance with Clause 17.5.4, the design of cross sections subject to longitudinal shear shall be based on:

$$V_{rl} \geq V_f \qquad (17\text{-}1)$$

17.5.3.2
When contact surfaces are clean, free of laitance, and intentionally roughened the, factored longitudinal shear resistance, V_{rl}, shall not be taken as greater than $0.7\phi_c b_v d$ unless ties are provided to transfer longitudinal shear.

17.5.3.3
When minimum ties are provided in accordance with Clause 17.6, and contact surfaces are clean and free of laitance, but not intentionally roughened, the factored longitudinal shear resistance, V_{rl}, shall not be taken as greater than $0.7\phi_c b_v d$.

17.5.3.4
When the factored shear force, V_f, at the section being considered exceeds $0.7\phi_c b_v d$, the design for longitudinal shear shall be in accordance with Clause 11.6.

17.5.4
Longitudinal shear may be investigated by computing the actual compressive or tensile force in any segment and provisions made to transfer that force as longitudinal shear to the supporting element. The factored longitudinal shear force shall not exceed the factored longitudinal shear resistance, V_{rl}, as given in Clauses 17.5.3.2 to 17.5.3.4 where area of contact surface, A_c, shall be substituted for $b_v d$.

17.5.5
When tension exists across any contact surface between interconnected elements, shear transfer by contact may be assumed only when minimum ties are provided in accordance with Clause 17.6.

17.6 Ties for Longitudinal Shear

17.6.1
When ties are provided to transfer longitudinal shear, the tie area shall be not less than that required by Clause 11.2.8, and the tie spacing shall not exceed 4 times the least dimension of the supported element nor 600 mm.

17.6.2
Ties for longitudinal shear may consist of single bars or wire, multiple leg stirrups, or vertical legs or welded wire fabric (smooth or deformed).

N17.5.3.1
This simplified procedure is based on the assumption that the horizontal shear stress on the interface equals the factored shear force divided by the area, $b_v d$.

N17.5.3.2
Surfaces are intentionally roughened to provide satisfactory interlock. It is noted that in Clauses 11.6 "intentionally roughened" implies an interface roughened to a full amplitude of approximately 5 mm.

N17.5.4
Fig N17.5.4 illustrates the application of this clause. It is conventional to calculate the average longitudinal shear stress between the maximum moment section and the adjacent zero-moment section.

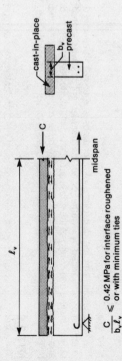

$$\frac{C}{b_v \ell_v} \leq 0.42 \text{ MPa for interface roughened or with minimum ties}$$

$$\leq 1.80 \text{ MPa for interface roughened and with minimum ties}$$

Fig. N17.5.4
Example of Investigating Longitudinal Shear

17.6.3

Ties shall be anchored into the interconnected elements in accordance with Clause 12.13.

17.6.4

Reinforcement for transverse shear that is anchored into the interconnected elements in accordance with Clause 12.13 may be included as ties for longitudinal shear.

18. Prestressed Concrete

18.0 Notation

A = area of that part of cross section between flexural tension face and centroid of gross section

A_s = area of tension reinforcement

A_s' = area of compression reinforcement

A_p = area of prestressing tendons in tension zone

b_o = perimeter of critical section for shear in slabs and footings (see Clause 13.4.3)

c = distance from extreme compression fibre to neutral axis calculated using factored material strengths and assuming a tendon force of $\phi_p A_p f_{pr}$

c_y = distance from extreme compression fibre to neutral axis calculated using factored material strengths and assuming a tendon force of $\phi_p A_p f_{py}$

d = distance from the extreme compression fibre to the centroid of longitudinal tension reinforcement, but need not be less than 0.8h for prestressed members

d_p = distance from the extreme compression fibre to the centroid of the prestressing tendons

f_{ce} = compression stress in the concrete due to effective prestress only (after allowance for all prestress losses) at the extreme fibre of a section where tensile stresses are caused by applied loads

f_{cp} = average compressive stress in concrete due to effective prestress force only (after allowance for all prestress losses). For slabs and footings, f_{cp} is the average of f_{cp} for the two directions

f_c' = specified compressive strength of concrete

$\sqrt{f_c'}$ = square root of specified compressive strength of concrete

f_{ci}' = compressive strength of concrete at time of prestress transfer

$\sqrt{f_{ci}'}$ = square root of compressive strength of concrete at time of prestress transfer

f_{pe} = effective stress in prestressing tendons (after allowance for all prestress losses)

f_{pr} = stress in prestressing tendons at factored resistance

f_{pu} = tensile strength of prestressing tendons

f_{py} = yield strength of prestressing tendons

f_r = modulus of rupture of concrete to be used in deflection and cracking moment calculations

f_y = specified yield strength of tension reinforcement

f_y' = specified yield strength of compression reinforcement

h = overall height or thickness of member

I = moment of inertia of section about centroidal axis

k_p = factor for type of prestressing in Equation (18-1)

ℓ_e = length of tendon between anchors divided by the number of plastic hinges required to develop a failure mechanism in the span under consideration

ℓ_n = length of clear span of two-way slab in direction parallel to that of the reinforcement being determined

M_{dc} = decompression moment. Moment when the compressive stress on the tensile face of a prestressed member is zero

M_f = moment due to factored loads

M_r = factored moment resistance

M_s = moment due to specified loads

N_c = tensile force in concrete

v_c = factored shear stress resistance provided by the concrete

v_f = factored shear stress

V_p = vertical component of all effective prestress forces crossing the critical section

v_r = factored shear stress resistance

y_t = distance from centroidal axis of section to extreme fibre in tension

z = quantity limiting distribution of flexural reinforcement (see Clauses 10.6.1 and 18.9.3)

λ = factor to account for low density concrete (see Clause 8.6.5)

ϕ_c = resistance factor for concrete (see Clauses 8.4.2 and 16.1.3)

ϕ_p = resistance factor for prestressing tendons (see Clause 8.4.3)

ϕ_s = resistance factor for reinforcing bars (see Clause 8.4.3)

18.1 Scope and Definitions

18.1.1

The provisions of Clause 18 shall apply to members prestressed with wires, strands, or bars conforming to the requirements for prestressing steels as specified in CSA Standard A23.1.

Note: *The durability of structures with unbonded prestressing tendons is a function of the environment, occupancy type, and workmanship during construction. Ingress of moisture, chlorides, sulphides, nitrates, or carbonates may cause corrosion of the tendon. Corrosion and failure of unbonded tendons can eventually occur if water accumulates in the tendon sheath. Water, including rainwater, can enter the sheath during tendon shipping, storage, construction, or in some cases after occupancy of the structure if adequate protection is not provided. Materials and workmanship should be in accordance with CSA Standard A23.1.*

18.1.2

All provisions of this Standard not specifically excluded and not in conflict with the provisions of Clause 18 shall apply to prestressed concrete.

18.1.3

The provisions specified in Clauses 10.3.3, 10.3.4, 10.4, 10.5.1, 10.5.2, 10.6.2, 10.9, 13, 14.5, 14.6, and 14.7 of this Standard shall not apply to prestressed concrete, except as specifically noted.

N18.1 Scope and Definitions

N18.1.3

The empirical provisions of Clauses 10.3.3 and 10.3.4 limiting the geometry of T-beams were developed for conventionally reinforced concrete and if applied to prestressed concrete would exclude many standard prestressed products in satisfactory use today (e.g. see standard T-beams in CPCI-Metric Design Manual). Note that when applying Clause 10.5.3 to prestressed T-beams with tapered flanges the spacing limit may be based on the average flange thickness.

The empirical limits for concrete joist construction apply for conventionally reinforced concrete but not for prestressed concrete. Hence Clause 10.4 is excluded. Experience and judgement must be used for prestressed concrete joists.

The limitations on reinforcement amounts given in Clauses 10.5.1, 10.9.1 and 10.9.2 are replaced by those in Clauses 18.9, 18.12.2 and 18.13.4.5.

The skin reinforcement requirements of Clause 10.6.2 were derived for conventionally reinforced concrete members and were not intended to apply to prestressed concrete members.

Many of the design procedures of Clause 13 are not appropriate for prestressed concrete two-way slabs. The prestressed concrete slab design provisions are given in Clause 18.13.

The empirical design method of Clause 14.5 is not applicable to prestressed concrete walls. These elements should be designed by the more general procedures specified in Clause 14.4.

18.2 General

18.2.1
Prestressed members shall meet the strength requirements specified in this Standard.

18.2.2
The effects of the loads at all loading stages that may be critical during the life of the member from the time the prestress is first applied shall be considered.

18.2.3
The stresses in prestressed members at transfer and under specified loads shall satisfy the requirements of Clause 18.4.

18.2.4
Stress concentrations due to prestressing shall be considered, and adequately anchored transverse reinforcement shall be provided to control splitting.

18.2.5
The deflection of prestressed concrete members shall be determined as specified in Clause 9.8.4.

18.2.6
When adjoining parts of the structure can restrain the elastic and long-term deformations (deflections, changes in length, and rotation) of a member caused by prestressing, applied loading, foundation settlement, temperature, and shrinkage, the restraint shall be estimated and its effects both on the member and on the restraining structure shall be considered.

18.2.7
The possibility of buckling in a member between points where concrete and prestressing tendons are in contact and of buckling in thin webs and flanges shall be considered.

18.2.8
In computing section properties, the loss of area due to open ducts or conduits shall be considered.

18.3 Design Assumptions for Flexure and Axial Load

18.3.1
The design of prestressed members for flexure and axial loads shall be based on assumptions given in Clause 10.1.

18.3.2
When investigating the stress limits specified in Clauses 18.4 and 18.5, linear elastic material behaviour may be assumed. Concrete may be assumed to resist tension at sections that are uncracked.

N18.2 General

N18.2.2
Loading stages that are typically considered include:
(1) jacking stage, or transfer of prestress stage - when the prestressing force is high and the concrete strength is normally low
(2) specified load stage - after all prestress losses have occurred and the member is subjected to specified loads,
(3) factored load stage - when the resistance of the member is checked.
  Other load stages that may need to be investigated include: handling, transportation, erection and other construction stages.

N18.3 Design Assumptions for Flexure and Axial Load

N18.3.2
In these stress calculations transformed section properties accounting for the beneficial effects of bonded reinforcement may be used.

18.4 Permissible Stresses in Concrete Flexural Members

18.4.1

Stresses in concrete immediately after prestress transfer due to prestress and the specified loads present at transfer shall not exceed the following:

(a) extreme fibre stress in compression .... $0.6f'_{ci}$;

(b) extreme fibre stress in tension except as permitted in Item (c) .... $0.25\lambda\sqrt{f'_{ci}}$; and

(c) extreme fibre stress in tension at ends of simply supported members ... $0.5\lambda\sqrt{f'_{ci}}$.

18.4.1.1

The stress given in Clause 18.4.1(a) may be exceeded if tests or analyses show that performance will not be impaired.

18.4.1.2

Where computed tensile stresses exceed the values given in Clauses 18.4.1(b) and (c), bonded reinforcement with a minimum area of $A_s = N_c/(0.5f_y)$ shall be provided in the tensile zone to resist the total tensile force, N_c, in the concrete computed on the basis of an uncracked section.

18.4.2

Stresses in concrete under specified loads and prestress (after allowance for all prestress losses) shall not exceed the following:

(a) extreme fibre stress in compression due to sustained loads .... $0.45f'_c$;

(b) extreme fibre stress in compression due to total load .... $0.60f'_c$;

(c) extreme fibre stress in tension in precompressed tensile zone except as specified in Clause 18.4.3 .... $0.5\lambda\sqrt{f'_c}$; and

(d) extreme fibre stress in tension in precompressed tensile zone exposed to corrosive environment .... $0.25\lambda\sqrt{f'_c}$.

18.4.3 Partial Prestressing

18.4.3.1

Partially prestressed members are permitted to exceed the requirements of Clause 18.4.2(c) provided that analysis or tests demonstrate adequate fatigue resistance as well as adequate deflection and crack control under specified loads.

18.4.3.2

Partially prestressed members not subjected to fatigue conditions and not exposed to a corrosive environment may be deemed to have adequate deflection and crack control if the requirements of Clauses 9.8.4 and 18.9 are met.

18.5 Permissible Stresses in Tendons

Tensile stress in tendons shall not exceed the following:

(a) due to tendon jacking force for post-tensioning tendons .... $0.85f_{pu}$;

but not greater than .... $0.94f_{py}$;

(b) due to tendon jacking force for pretensioning tendons .... $0.80f_{pu}$.

The stress in Items (a) and (b) shall not exceed the maximum value recommended by the

---

N18.4 Permissible Stresses in Flexural Members

N18.4.1

These stresses are intended to prevent crushing or cracking of the young concrete due to the high prestress force.

Simply supported beams pretensioned with straight strands will initially have high tensile stresses in the top concrete fibres near the ends of the beams. Experience has shown that a small amount of cracking in these zones can be tolerated and hence higher tensile stresses are permitted.

N18.4.1.2

The tensile stress limits can be exceeded if appropriate reinforcement is provided to control the resulting cracking. This crack control reinforcement should consist of a well distributed array of smaller bars. See Fig. N18.4.1.2.

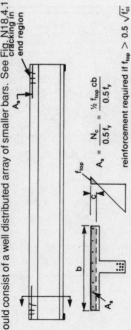

$$A_s = \frac{N_c}{0.5\,f_y} = \frac{\frac{1}{2}\,f_{top}\,cb}{0.5\,f_y}$$

reinforcement required if $f_{top} > 0.5\sqrt{f'_{ci}}$

Fig. N18.4.1.2
Control of Cracking Occurring at Transfer

N18.4.2

The tensile stress limits in this clause are intended to control or avoid cracking after all prestress losses have occurred and the full specified loads have been applied. The tensile zones being investigated are those regions of the member where the prestress causes compressive stresses (precompressed) but are in tension under specified loads.

It is to be noted that the permissible stresses due to total specified load have been increased to $0.6\,f'_c$ in the 1995 edition of the code (from $0.45\,f'_c$ in 1984).

The consequences of cracking for a structure in a corrosive environment (e.g. a parking garage) are much more severe and hence lower tensile stress limits and larger concrete covers should be used.

When low density concrete is used the tensile stress limits should be modified to account for the lower cracking stress of such concretes (e.g. multiply limits by the λ factor of Clause 8.6.5).

N18.4.3. Partial Prestressing

A member is considered to be partially prestressed if the tensile stresses under specified loads exceed the allowable limits of Clause 18.4.2(c). Partially prestressed members are not permitted in corrosive environments.

In checking the deflection of partially prestressed members the reduction in stiffness caused by cracking must be accounted for (see Clause 9.8.4.3). Fig. N18.4.3 illustrates the bi-linear approximation of the load-deflection curve for a simply-supported, partially prestressed, uniformly loaded member. In such calculations the cracking stress may be taken as $0.6 \lambda \sqrt{f'_c}$. The control of crack widths can be investigated by the procedures of Clause 18.9.3. Crack control in situations involving frequently repeated loads requires further investigation.

To investigate fatigue resistance the maximum stress range caused by the repeating loads is calculated and compared to acceptable limits. The allowable stress range is a function of, amongst other things, tendon type and tendon curvature. For strands a limit of 100 MPa will typically be conservative. Anchorages and couplings typically have poor fatigue resistance and hence should not be located in zones subjected to large stress ranges.

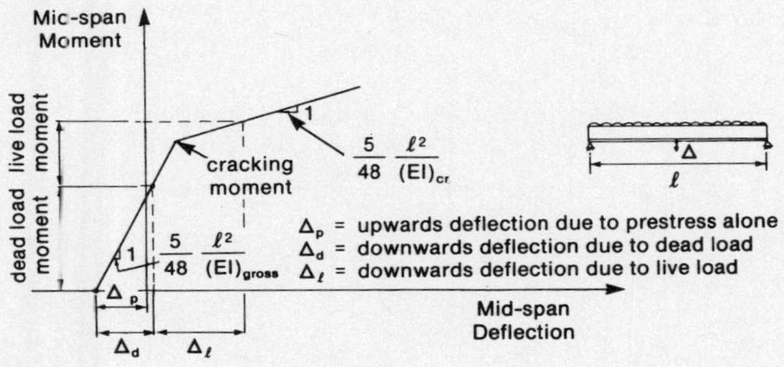

Fig. N18.4.3

Calculating Deflection of a Partially Prestressed Member

N18.5   Permissible Stresses in Tendons

The maximum tensile stress in tendons at jacking and after transfer is limited in order to provide a margin of safety against tendon fracture, to avoid inelastic tendon deformation, and to limit relaxation losses. These stress limits are tabulated below for different types of tendons.

Tendon Type	f'_c	At jacking		After Transfer
		Post-tensioned	Pre-tensioned	
Low relaxation strand or wire	0.90	0.85	0.80	0.74*
Normal stress relieved strand or wire	0.85	0.80	0.80	0.70
Plain Prestressing bars	0.85	0.80	0.80	0.70
Deformed Prestressing bars	0.80	0.75	0.80	0.66

Table N18.5
Stress-Limits in Terms of f_{pu}

* Post-tensioned tendons limited to 0.70 f_{pu} at anchorages and couplers.

N18.6   Prestress Losses

Prestress losses may be expected to vary considerably in different situations. Actual losses will have little effect on member strength but will affect serviceability (deflections, stresses and cracking). Either over-estimating or under-estimating prestress losses may cause serviceability problems (e.g. excessive camber or excessive cracking). Information on calculating prestress losses is given in the CPCA Concrete Design Handbook and the CPCI Metric Design Manual. Comments on the different losses to be considered are given below:

(a) The anchorage seating loss can be determined from the anchorage set characteristic of the post-tensioning system being used (see Fig. N18.6).

(b) The concrete around the tendons shortens as the prestressing force is applied to it. Those tendons which are already bonded to the concrete shorten with it.

(c) During post-tensioning the variation of force along the length of the tendon can be computed by

$$P_x = P_s e^{-(Kx + \mu\alpha)}$$

where

P_x = tendon force at distance x from jacking end

P_s = jacking force

K = wobble friction coefficient accounting for unintended curvature (per metre of tendon)

x = distance from jacking end

μ = friction coefficient accounting for intended curvature

α = accumulated angle change of tendon profile over distance x (radians)

manufacturer of the prestressing tendons or anchorages. If pretensioned tendons are subjected to a temperature drop prior to concreting, the stress at the reduced temperatures shall not exceed the limit specified in Item (b);

(c) immediately after prestress transfer .... $0.82f_{py}$.
but not greater than .... $0.74f_{pu}$; and

(d) post-tensioning tendons, at anchorages and couplers immediately after tendon anchorage .... $0.70f_{pu}$

Note: *The specified yield strength of prestressing tendons is based on the requirements of CSA Standard G279, which specifies the following minimum values for* f_{py}:

(a) *low relaxation strand or wire* .... $0.90f_{pu}$;
(b) *stress relieved strand or wire* .... $0.85f_{pu}$;
(c) *plain prestressing bars* .... $0.85f_{pu}$; and
(d) *deformed prestressing bars* .... $0.80f_{pu}$.

18.6 Loss of Prestress

To determine the effective prestress, f_{pe}, allowance for the following sources of loss of prestress shall be considered:

(a) anchorage seating loss;
(b) elastic shortening of concrete;
(c) friction loss due to intended and unintended curvature in post-tensioning tendons;
(d) creep of concrete;
(e) shrinkage of concrete; and
(f) relaxation of tendon stress.

18.7 Flexural Resistance

18.7.1
Strain compatibility analyses shall be based on the stress-strain curves of the steels to be used.

18.7.2
In lieu of a more accurate determination of f_{pr} based on strain compatibility, the following approximate values of f_{pr} may be used:

(a) for members with bonded tendons, provided c/d_p is not greater than 0.5 and f_{pe} is not less than $0.6f_{py}$.

$$f_{pr} = f_{pu}\left(1 - k_p \frac{c}{d_p}\right) \qquad (18\text{-}1)$$

where $k_p = 2(1.04 - f_{py}/f_{pu})$ and c shall be determined assuming a stress of f_{pr} in the tendons;

Note: *Further information can be found in Loov, R.E., "A General Equation for the Steel Stress for Bonded Prestressed Concrete Members", Precast/Prestressed Concrete Institute Journal, Vol. 13, No. 6, Nov./Dec. 1988, pp. 108-137.*

The use of this equation is illustrated in Fig. N18.6. Values of the friction coefficients, K and μ, to be used for a particular type of tendon and particular types of ducts should be obtained from the manufacturers of the tendons. The

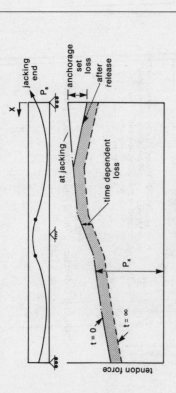

Fig. N18.6
Variation in Tendon Force due to Losses

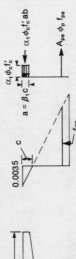

(a) Cross-section

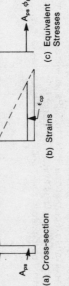

(b) Strains

(c) Equivalent Stresses

$a = \beta_1 c$
$\alpha_1 \phi_c f'_c ab$
$A_{ps} \phi_p f_{ps}$

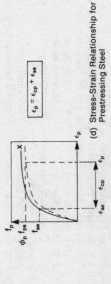

$\epsilon_p = \epsilon_{cp} + \epsilon_{se}$

(d) Stress-Strain Relationship for Prestressing Steel

Fig. N18.7.1
Strain Compatibility Analysis for Prestressed Concrete Members with Bonded Tendons

range of values given in the table below serve as to values that might be expected.

N18.7.2(a)

It can be seen from Fig. N18.7.1 that as the depth of compression increases, the stress in the tendon decreases. For bonded members with $c \leq 0.5\ d_p$ and $f_{pe} \leq 0.6\ f_{py}$ Eq. (18-1) gives a conservative estimate of f_{pr}. The term k_p accounts for the shape of tendon stress-strain curve. Values of k_p are given below:

Tendon Type	k_p
Low relaxation strand or wire	0.28
Normal stress relieved strand or wire	0.38
Plain prestressing bars	0.38
Deformed prestressing bars	0.48

Table N18.7.2
Values of k_p

The value of the neutral axis depth c in Eq. 18-1 can be established by trial and error, or from the equilibrium of internal forces. With $\Sigma T = \Sigma C$ we get for the T-beam of Fig. N18.7.2(a):

$$\phi_p f_{pr} A_p + \phi_s f_y A_s = \alpha_1 \phi_c f_c' b_w \beta_1 c + \alpha_1 \phi_c f_c'(b-b_w)h_f + \phi_s A_s' f_y$$

Substituting $f_{pr} = f_{pu}(1-k_p c/d_p)$ - Eq.(18-1) - and solving for c/d_p we find

$$\frac{c}{d_p} = \frac{\phi_p f_{pu} A_p + \phi_s f_y A_s - \phi_s f_y A_s' - \alpha_1 \phi_c f_c'(b-b_w) h_f}{\alpha_1 \phi_c f_c' \beta_1 b_w d_p + k_p \phi_p f_{pu} A_p}$$

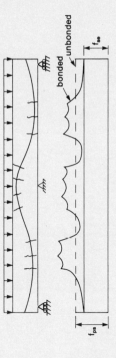

Fig. N18.7.2(a)
Cross-Section of Prestressed Concrete Beam

This equation is general and applies for $A_s = 0$ and/or $A_s' = 0$ and/or $b = b_w$. If $h_f > \beta_1 c$ the beam should be considered to be a rectangular beam of width b and hence

$$\frac{c}{d_p} = \frac{\phi_p f_{pu} A_p + \phi_s f_y A_s - \phi_s f_y A_s - \phi_y A_s'}{\alpha_1 \phi_c f_c' \beta_1 b c_p}$$

After determining f_{pr} from Eq. (18-1) the rectangular stress block depth, a, at factored resistance can be found. Thus, for the beam in Fig. N18.7.2(a) in which $a \leq h_f$

$$a = \frac{\phi_p A_p f_{pr} + \phi_s A_s f_s - \phi_s A_s' f_s'}{\alpha_1 \phi_c f_c' b}$$

where f_s and f_s' are the reinforcing bar stresses determined from strain compatibility for a neutral axis depth of $c = a/\beta_1$.

N18.7.2(b)

While bonded tendons exhibit large stress increases in regions of high moment (particularly at crack locations) unbonded tendons must average out their stress increase over the total length between the anchorages (see Fig. N18.7.2(b)).

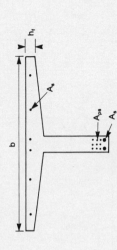

Fig. N18.7.2(b)
Tendon Stress Variation

Eq. (18-2) gives a conservative estimate of the stress in unbonded tendons at the factored resistance. The increase in the constant to 8000 in this code from 5000 reflects better agreement with test results. Variable ℓ_e accounts for the length over which the stress increase is being averaged out and for the number of high moment regions in the span under consideration. The determination of ℓ_e is illustrated in Fig. N18.7.2(b).

(b) for members with unbonded tendons

$$f_{pr} = f_{pe} + \frac{8000}{\ell_e}(d_p - c_y)$$ (18-2)

but shall not exceed f_{py}
where c_y shall be determined assuming a stress of f_{py} in the tendons.

18.7.3
Tension and compression reinforcement may be considered to contribute to the flexural resistance with forces of $\phi_s A_s f_y$ and $\phi_s A'_s f'_y$, provided they are located at least 0.75c from the neutral axis. Other reinforcement may be included in resistance computations provided that a strain compatibility analysis is made to determine the stress in such reinforcement.

18.8 Minimum Factored Flexural Resistance

18.8.1
At every section of a flexural member, except two-way slabs,
$$M_r \geq 1.2 M_{cr}$$ (18-3)
where,
$M_{cr} = I/y_t (f_{ce} + f_r)$ and
$f_r = 0.6\sqrt{f'_c}$
unless the factored flexural resistance at the section is one-third greater than M_f.

18.9 Minimum Bonded Reinforcement

18.9.1
The minimum requirements for bonded reinforcement in beams and slabs shall be as specified in Table 18-1.

18.9.2
The bonded reinforcement required by Table 18-1 shall be uniformly distributed within the precompressed tensile zone as close to the extreme tensile fibre as the cover will permit.

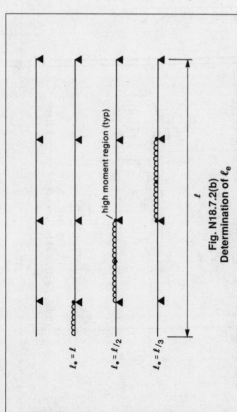

$\ell_e = \ell$

$\ell_e = \ell/2$

high moment region (typ)

$\ell_e = \ell/3$

ℓ

**Fig. N18.7.2(b)
Determination of ℓ_e**

It is to be noted that the reduction of the factored moment resistance required in CSA A23.3-M84 – Clause 18.8 – for c > 0.5 h has been abandoned because of the increase in the factor of safety when concrete compression controls flexural failure.

N18.9 Minimum Bonded Reinforcement

N18.9.1
Table 18-1 summarizes the requirements for minimum amounts of bonded non-prestressed reinforcement. The two columns for tensile stress >0.5λ $\sqrt{f'_c}$ apply to partially prestressed members.

Table 18-1
Minimum Area of Bonded Reinforcement
(See Clauses 18.9.1, 18.9.2, and 18.10.2.)

Type of member	Concrete stress [see Clause 18.4.2(c)]			
	Tensile stress $\leq 0.5\sqrt{f'_c}$		Tensile stress $> 0.5\sqrt{f'_c}$	
	Type of tendon		Type of tendon	
	Bonded	Unbonded	Bonded	Unbonded
Beams	0	0.004A	0.003A	0.005A
One-way slabs	0	0.003A	0.002A	0.004A
Two-way slabs:				
Negative moment regions	0	$0.0006h\ell_n$	$0.00045h\ell_n$	$0.00075h\ell_n$
Positive moment regions, concrete stress $> 0.2\sqrt{f'_c}$	0	0.004A	0.003A	0.005A
Positive moment regions, concrete tensile stress $\leq 0.2\sqrt{f'_c}$	0	0	—	—

18.9.3
For partially prestressed beams and one-way slabs, the distribution of the bonded tendons and reinforcement shall be such that the quantity, z, given by Equation (10-6) does not exceed 20 kN/mm for interior exposure and 15 kN/mm for exterior exposure. In lieu of more detailed analysis, the steel stress, f_s, in Equation (10-6) may be calculated as the difference between the stress in the nonprestressed reinforcement due to the specified load moment, M_s, and the stress due to decompression moment, M_{dc}, defined by Equation (18-4). Only the bonded steel shall be considered for the calculation of A. A bonded post-tensioned cable or a bundle of pretensioned tendons may either be considered as one bar of equal area or may be disregarded in the calculation of z.

$$M_{dc} = f_{ce}\frac{I}{y_t} \qquad (18\text{-}4)$$

18.10   Minimum Length of Bonded Reinforcement

18.10.1
Where bonded reinforcement is provided for flexural resistance, the minimum length shall conform to the provisions of Clause 12.

N18.9.3
For partially prestressed beams and one way slabs, the bonded flexural reinforcement must be distributed to provide adequate crack control. Because of the additional uncertainties in computing crack widths for partially prestressed members and because prestressing steel is more susceptible to corrosion, the z limits for these members are smaller than for reinforced concrete members (see Clause 10.6.1).

N18.11   Frames and Continuous Construction
When a statically indeterminate structure is post-tensioned, the deformation of the structure caused by the prestressing is restrained by the supports. The moments produced in the structure by these restraint reactions are usually referred to as "secondary moments". In design, an elastic analysis is first performed to determine the moments due to factored loads and the secondary moments. The standard then permits a certain amount of redistribution of these elastic moments, provided that minimum bonded reinforcement is present at the supports. See comments for Clause 9.2.4.

N18.13   Two-Way Slab Systems
This clause permits the use of the methods of analysis defined in Clause 13.9 to determine the moments and shears in prestressed concrete two-way slab systems. More detailed procedures such as a finite element analysis are also permitted. Note that the elastic moments must include the restraint effects (i.e. secondary moments).

18.10.2
The minimum length of bonded reinforcement required by Table 18-1 shall be as specified in Clauses 18.10.3 and 18.10.4.

18.10.3
In positive moment areas, the minimum length of bonded reinforcement shall be one-half of the clear span length and shall be centred in the positive moment area.

18.10.4
In negative moment areas, bonded reinforcement shall extend 1/6 of the longer clear span beyond the face of the support, on each side of the support.

18.11 Frames and Continuous Construction
Moments to be used to compute the required strength shall be the sum of the moments due to reactions induced by prestressing (with a load factor of 1.0) and the moments due to factored loads as specified in Clause 18.9. Where a minimum area of bonded reinforcement is provided as specified in Clause 18.9, negative moments may be redistributed according to Clause 9.2.4.

18.12 Compression Members — Combined Flexure and Axial Loads
18.12.1
The design of prestressed concrete members subject to combined flexure and axial load shall be based on the requirements of Clauses 10.9 to 10.16. Effects of prestress, creep, shrinkage, and temperature change shall be included.

18.12.2 Limits for Reinforcement of Prestressed Compression Members
18.12.2.1
Members with average prestress, f_{cp}, less than 1.5 MPa shall have minimum reinforcement in accordance with Clauses 7.6 and 10.9 for columns or Clause 14.3 for walls.

18.12.2.2
Except for walls, members with average prestress, f_{cp}, equal to or greater than 1.5 MPa shall have all prestressing tendons enclosed by spirals or lateral ties in accordance with the following:
(a) spirals shall conform to Clause 7.6.4; and
(b) ties shall conform to Clause 7.6.5, excluding Clauses 7.6.5.2(a) and 7.6.5.5.

18.13 Two-Way Slab Systems
18.13.1 General
Factored moments and shears in prestressed slab systems reinforced for flexure in two directions shall be determined in accordance with the provisions of Clause 13.9 or by more detailed design procedures.

18.13.2 Stresses Under Specified Loads

18.13.2.1
When using the provisions of Clause 13.9, flexural stresses due to unfactored gravity loads in column strips shall be determined by taking 75% of interior negative moments, 100% of exterior negative moments, and 60% of positive moments unless a more detailed analysis is performed.

18.13.2.2
Concrete stresses due to prestressing may be assumed to be uniformly distributed across the slab unless a more detailed analysis is performed.

18.13.2.3
The minimum average compressive stress, f_{cp}, shall be 0.8 MPa.

18.13.2.4
Special attention shall be given to the restraint by walls or stiff columns, which may reduce the effective prestress in the slab (see Clause 18.2.6).

18.13.3 Shear Resistance
In the vicinity of concentrated loads or reactions, the maximum factored shear stress, v_f, calculated in accordance with Clauses 13.4.5 and 13.4.6 shall not exceed v_r.

18.13.3.1
The factored shear stress, v_r, in two-way slabs shall not be greater than the factored shear stress resistance provided by the concrete, v_c, computed in accordance Clauses 13.4.4 or 18.13.3.2 unless shear reinforcement is provided in accordance with Clauses 13.4.7 and 13.4.8 or 13.4.9.

18.13.3.2
At columns of two-way slabs of uniform thickness, the factored shear stress resistance provided by the concrete shall be determined by

$$v_c = 0.41\lambda\phi_c\sqrt{f'_c}\sqrt{1 + \frac{\phi_p f_{cp}}{0.41\phi_c\sqrt{f'_c}}} + \frac{\phi_p V_p}{b_o d} \qquad (18\text{-}5)$$

If the factored shear stress resistance provided by the concrete is computed by Equation (18-5), the following shall be satisfied:
(a) no portion of the cross section of the column shall be closer than 4 times the slab thickness to a discontinuous edge;
(b) f'_c in Equation (18-5) shall not be taken greater than 35 MPa; and
(c) f_{cp} in each direction shall not be greater than 3.5 MPa; otherwise, Equation (13-4), (13-5), or (13-6) shall apply.

18.13.4 Shear and Moment Transfer

18.13.4.1
The fraction of the unbalanced moment transferred by eccentricity of shear shall conform to Clauses 13.4.5.2 and 13.4.5.3.

18.13.5 Minimum Bonded Nonprestressed Reinforcement

18.13.5.1
The minimum requirements for bonded reinforcement in two-way slabs shall be as specified in accordance with Clauses 18.9, 18.10, and 18.13.5.2.

18.13.5.2
In negative moment areas at column supports, the bonded reinforcement, A_s, shall be distributed within a zone equal to the column width plus 1.5 times the slab thickness beyond each side of the column. At least four bars or wires shall be provided in each direction. The spacing of the bonded reinforcement shall not exceed 300 mm.

18.13.6 Spacing of Tendons

18.13.6.1
The spacing of tendons or groups of tendons in one direction shall not exceed 8 times the slab thickness, nor 1500 mm unless adequate additional bonded reinforcement is provided so that the slab has the strength to span between tendons.

18.13.6.2
Tendon spacing shall be given special consideration in slabs supporting concentrated loads.

18.13.6.3
In slabs without beams, a minimum of two tendons or bars shall be provided in each direction over each column. These tendons or bars must satisfy the requirements of Clause 13.11.5.4.

18.14 Tendon Anchorage Zones

18.14.1
Post-tensioning anchorage zones shall be designed to resist the specified tensile strength of the tendons.

18.14.2
One of the following methods shall be used for the design of anchorage zones:
(a) equilibrium based on strut-and-tie models (see Clause 11.5);
(b) elastic stress analysis (finite element methods or equivalent); or
(c) methods based on tests.

N18.13.5 Minimum Bonded Nonprestressed Reinforcement

This clause summarizes the minimum amounts of bonded reinforcement required and the distribution in the negative moment areas.

N18.13.5.1
This Clause provides specific guidance concerning tendon distribution that will permit the use of banded tendon distributions in one direction.

18.14.3
End blocks shall be provided where required for support bearing or for distribution of concentrated prestressing forces.

18.14.4
Regions of stress concentrations due to abrupt changes in section or other causes shall be adequately reinforced.

19.   Shells and Folded Plates

19.0   Notation

f'_c = specified compressive strength of concrete
$\sqrt{f'_c}$ = square root of specified compressive strength of concrete
E_c = modulus of elasticity of concrete (see Clause 8.6.2)
h = thickness of shell or folded plate
ℓ_d = development length (see Clause 12.2)
λ = factor to account for low density concrete (see Clause 8.6.5)
ϕ_c = resistance factor for concrete (see Clause 8.4.2)

19.1   Definitions

The following definitions apply in this Clause:

Auxiliary member — rib or edge beam that serves to strengthen, stiffen, or support the shell. Auxiliary members usually act jointly with the shell.

Elastic analysis — analysis of deformations and internal forces based on equilibrium, compatibility of strains, and assumed elastic behaviour, which suitably approximates the three-dimensional action of the shell together with its auxiliary members.

Experimental analysis — an analysis procedure based on the measurement of deformations and strains of the structure or its model and may be based on either elastic or inelastic behaviour.

Folded plate — a special class of shell structures formed by joining flat, thin slabs along their edges so as to create a three-dimensional spatial structure.

Ribbed shell — spatial structure with material placed primarily along certain preferred rib lines, with the areas between the ribs filled with thin slabs or left open.

Thin shell — three dimensional spatial structure made up of one or more curved slabs or folded plates whose thicknesses are small compared to their other dimensions. Thin shells are characterized by their three dimensional, load-carrying behaviour, which is determined by the geometry of their form, by the manner in which they are supported, and by the nature of the applied load.

19.2 Scope

19.2.1
Provisions of Clause 19 shall apply to thin shell and folded plate concrete structures, including ribs and edge members.

19.2.2
All provisions of this Standard not specifically excluded and not in conflict with the provisions of Clause 19 shall apply to thin shell structures.

19.3 Analysis and Design

19.3.1
Elastic behaviour shall be an accepted basis for determining internal forces and displacements of thin shells. This behaviour may be established by computations based on an analysis of the uncracked concrete structure in which the material is assumed linearly elastic, homogeneous, and isotropic. Poisson's ratio of concrete may be assumed to be equal to zero.
Note: *Further guidance on analysis and design is given in Clause 13.7*

19.3.2
Equilibrium checks of internal resistances and external loads shall be made to ensure consistency of results.

19.3.3
Experimental or numerical analysis procedures may be used where it can be shown that such procedures provide a safe basis for design.

19.3.4
Approximate methods of analysis not satisfying compatibility of strains either within the shell or between the shell and auxiliary members may be used where it can be shown that such methods provide a safe basis for design.

19.3.5
In prestressed shells, the analysis shall also consider behaviour under loads induced during prestressing, at cracking load, and at factored load. Where prestressing tendons are draped within a shell, the design shall take into account the force components on the shell resulting from the tendon profiles not lying in one plane.

19.3.6
The thickness, h, of a thin shell and its reinforcement shall be proportioned for the required strength and serviceability.

19.3.7
The shell designer shall investigate and preclude the possibility of general or local instability.

N19.3.1
Linear elastic theory will usually provide an acceptable analytical model for determining internal forces. Cracking, local yielding of reinforcement under factored loads, and time-dependent effects (e.g., creep, shrinkage, thermal loading and load history) may lead to significant redistribution of the internal forces. This redistribution may be accounted for in the analysis. For shells and folded plates of unusual size, shape or complexity, the analysis should consider the full response of the structure from the elastic, uncracked state up to failure.

N19.3.3
The Finite Element Method is the most widely used numerical analysis procedure. Experience is required in selecting appropriate element types and sizes so that internal forces can be determined to the required degree of accuracy. Note that Clause 19.3.2 requires that the results of the analysis must be checked to ensure that the calculated internal forces are in equilibrium with the external loads.

N19.3.4
Analysis methods satisfying equilibrium and compatibility that include both membrane and bending effects are preferred. Approximate methods which satisfy statics but neglect strain compatibility should only be used when documented evidence exists of the reliability of the given method of analysis for the design of the specific type of shell or folded plate under consideration. Such methods include beam type analyses for barrel shells and folded plates having large ratios of span to either width or radius of curvature and membrane analyses for simple shells of revolution.

N19.3.5
Prestressed shell and folded plate structures must be designed to satisfy the requirements of Clause 18.

N19.3.6
The shell's thickness and reinforcement must be proportioned to resist the internal forces obtained from analysis (i.e. factored resistance ≥ factored load). In choosing shells thickness, attention should also be given to limiting deflections at specified loads, to providing the required concrete cover over reinforcement and to the practicalities of construction.

N19.3.7
The stability of thin shells is influenced by: (1) overall geometry, (2) geometric imperfections, (3) non-linear material properties, (4) creep and shrinkage of concrete (5) cracking, (6) location, amount and orientation of reinforcement, and (7) deformation of supporting elements. Practical procedures for investigating the stability of shells is given in "Recommendations for Reinforced Concrete Shells and Folded Plates" (International Association of Shell and Spatial Structures, Madrid, 1979, 66 pp.), "Design and Construction of Circular Prestressed Concrete Structures (1970 report of ACI Committee 344, also in *ACI Manual of Concrete Practice*, Part 4), and "Concrete Shell Buckling", (SP67, ACI, 1981, 234 pp.).

19.3.8
Auxiliary members shall be designed according to the applicable provisions of this Standard. A portion of the shell equal to the flange width specified in Clause 10.3 may be assumed to act with the auxiliary member. In such portions of the shell, the reinforcement perpendicular to the auxiliary member shall be at least equal to that required for the flange of a T-beam by Clause 10.5.3.2.

19.4 Specified Yield Strength of Reinforcement
For nonprestressed reinforcement, the yield strength used in calculations shall not exceed 400 MPa.

19.5 Shell Reinforcement

19.5.1
Shell reinforcement shall be provided to resist tensile stresses from the internal membrane forces, to resist bending and twisting moments, to control shrinkage and temperature cracking, and as special reinforcement at shell boundaries, load attachments, and shell openings.

19.5.2
Membrane reinforcement shall be provided in two or more directions in all parts of the shell.

19.5.3
The area of shell reinforcement in two orthogonal directions at any section shall be not less than the minimum slab reinforcement required by Clause 7.8, except as given in Clause 19.5.7.

19.5.4
Reinforcement required to resist shell membrane forces shall be provided so that the factored resistance in any direction shall be at least equal to the component of the principal membrane forces in the same direction due to the factored loads.

19.5.5
The area of shell tension reinforcement shall be limited so that the reinforcement will yield before crushing of concrete in compression can take place.

19.5.6
In regions of high tension, membrane reinforcement shall, if practical, be placed in the general directions of the principal tensile membrane forces. Where this is not practical, membrane reinforcement may be placed in two or more directions.
Note: *If the direction of reinforcement varies more than 15° from the direction of principal tensile membrane force, the amount of reinforcement may have to be increased to limit the width of possible cracks under specified loads.*

19.5.7
Where the magnitude of the principal tensile membrane stress within the shell varies greatly over the area of the shell surface, reinforcement resisting the total tension may be

---

N19.3.8
As shown in Fig. N19.2.8, reinforcement should be added near both faces to account for the possibility of moment reversals (see Clause 19.5.8).

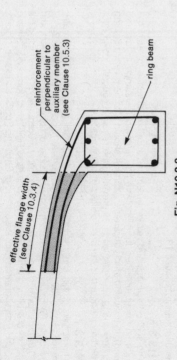

effective flange width (see Clause 10.3.4)

reinforcement perpendicular to auxiliary member (see Clause 10.5.3)

ring beam

Fig. N19.2.8
Auxiliary Member Consisting of Ring Beam Plus Effective Flange Width

N19.5.1
At any point in a shell two different kinds of internal forces may occur simultaneously: those associated with membrane action, and those associated with bending of the shell (see Fig. N19.5.1). The membrane forces are assumed to act in the tangential plane mid-way between the surfaces of the shell, and are the two axial forces N_x and N_y, and the membrane shears, V_{xy}. Flexural effects include bending moments, M_x and M_y, twisting moment, T_{xy}, and the associated transverse shears, V_{xy} and V_{yz}, as shown in Fig. N19.5.1.

N19.5.2
Membrane reinforcement must be provided in at least two approximately orthogonal directions. In some highly stressed regions, it may be appropriate to utilize reinforcement in three directions.

N19.5.3
Minimum reinforcement corresponding to slab shrinkage and temperature reinforcement must be provided even if the calculated membrane forces are compressive. In regions subjected to significant tensile membrane forces the minimum reinforcement ratio of 0.002 traditionally used for slabs in flexure will be insufficient. A minimum ratio of 0.0035 has been suggested for these cases.

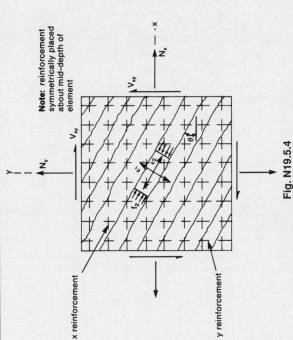

Fig. N19.5.1
Membrane Actions and Bending Actions

N19.5.4

The reinforcement for an element subjected to membrane forces only can be designed using the principles of the Compression Field Theory The two sets of reinforcing bars are designed to carry the forces F_x and F_y, where:

$$F_x = N_x + \frac{|V_{xy}|}{\tan\theta}$$

$$F_y = N_y + |V_{xy}|\tan\theta$$

where all of the above actions are expressed in terms of force per unit length.

More accurate procedures to account for the interaction between the stress resultants acting on a shell element are incorporated into the computer program SHELL 474 described in Adebar, P. and Collins, M.P. "SHELL 474 : Version 5.1" Department of Civil Engineering, University of British Columbia, 1995, 61pp. plus diskette.

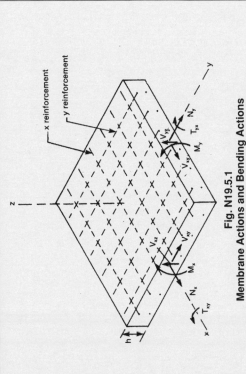

Note: reinforcement symmetrically placed about mid-depth of element

Fig. N19.5.4
Element Subjected to Membrane Forces

N19.5.5

The principal compressive stress in the concrete, f_2, see Fig. N19.5.4, can be computed as:

$$f_2 = (\tan\theta + \frac{1}{\tan\theta})\,\frac{|V_{xy}|}{h}$$

To avoid crushing $f_2 \leq f_{cu}$ given in Clause 11.5.2.3 where f_{cu} is a function of the principal tensile strain ε_1.

N19.5.7

The practice of concentrating tensile reinforcement in the regions of maximum tensile stress has led to a number of successful designs primarily for long folded plates, long barrel vaulted shells and for domes. The requirement of providing the minimum reinforcement in the remaining tensile zone is intended to control cracking.

N19.5.8

One way of accounting for the interaction between bending effects and membrane effects is to model the shell element as a sandwich consisting of 2 outer reinforced concrete layers joined by an unreinforced middle layer acting as a concentrated in the regions of largest tensile stress where it can be shown that this provides a safe basis for design. However, the ratio of shell reinforcement in any portion of the tensile zone shall be not less than 0.0035 based on the overall thickness of the shell.

19.5.8
Reinforcement required to resist shell bending moments shall be proportioned with due regard to the simultaneous action of membrane axial forces at the same location. Where shell reinforcement is required in only one face to resist bending moments, equal amounts shall be placed near both surfaces of the shell even though calculations may not indicate reversal of bending moments.

19.5.9
Where splitting of the shell near its mid-thickness can occur due to transverse tensile stresses, transverse reinforcement shall be provided to prevent the cracks from propagating.

19.5.10 Spacing of Reinforcement
Shell reinforcement in any direction shall not be spaced further apart than 500 mm nor 5 times the shell thickness. Where the principal membrane tensile stress on the gross concrete area due to factored loads exceeds $0.4\lambda\phi_c\sqrt{f'_c}$, reinforcement shall not be spaced further apart than 3 times the shell thickness.

19.5.11
Shell reinforcement at the junction of the shell and supporting members or edge members shall be anchored in or extended through such members in accordance with the requirements of Clause 12, except that the minimum development length shall be $1.2\ell_d$ but not less than 500 mm.

19.5.12 Splices
Splice development lengths of shell reinforcement shall be governed by the provisions of Clause 12, except that the minimum splice length of tension bars shall be 1.2 times the value required by Clause 12, but not less than 500 mm. The number of splices in principal tensile reinforcement shall be kept to a practical minimum. Where splices are necessary, they shall be staggered at least ℓ_d, with not more than one-third of the reinforcement spliced at any section.

19.6   Construction

19.6.1
When removal of formwork is based on a specific modulus of elasticity of concrete because of stability or deflection considerations, the value of the modulus of elasticity, E_c, shall be determined from flexural tests of field-cured beam specimens. The number of test specimens, the dimensions of test beam specimens, and test procedures shall be specified by the designer.
Note: *For guidance see CSA Standard A23.2 - 3C, "Making and Curing Concrete Compression and Flexural Test Specimens".*

132

---

shear connector. The applied forces and moments may be transformed into statically equivalent membrane forces on the outer layers as shown in Fig. N19.5.8. Each layer is then designed for its resulting membrane forces by the procedures described under N19.5.4.

Bending moment diagrams for shells characteristically display a wavelike shape as the moments oscillate between positive and negative values over relatively short lengths of the shell. For this reason, equal amounts of bending reinforcement are to be placed near both outer surfaces of the shell.

N19.5.9
Transverse ties may be required to control splitting of the shell near its centre surface due to high transverse shears and/or transverse tensile stresses (see Fig. N19.5.9). Transverse tensile stresses may be increased by the presence of curved prestressing tendons.

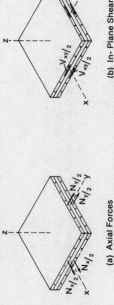

(a) Axial Forces

(b) In- Plane Shear

(c) Bending Moments

(d) Twisting Moments

Fig. N19.5.8
Transforming Sectional Forces into Statically Equivalent Membrane Forces on Outer Reinforced Concrete Layers

**Fig. N19.5.9
Transverse Ties to Control Shell Splitting**

N19.5.11 and N19.5.12
On curved shell surfaces it is more difficult to control the alignment of precut reinforcement. These clauses specify extra reinforcement lengths to maintain sufficient splice and development lengths.

19.6.2
Should a thin shell be constructed with deviations from the shape greater than the tolerances specified by the designer, an analysis of the effect of such deviations shall be made and any required remedial actions shall be taken to ensure its safe behaviour.

20. Strength Evaluation Procedures

20.0 Notation

M_f = the computed or estimated moment due to the factored loads at the section or sections of concern, if moment capacity is in question

V_f = the computed or estimated shear due to the factored loads, at the section or sections of concern, if shear capacity is in question

P_f = the computed or estimated axial force due to the factored loads at the section or sections of concern, if axial force capacity is in question

20.1 Strength Evaluation — General

20.1.1
Where the safety of a structure or structural member is in doubt and a structural strength investigation is required, such evaluation shall be carried out by analysis or by means of load tests, or by a combination of these methods.

20.1.2
This Clause provides requirements and procedures for the evaluation of the strength or safe load rating of structures or structural elements where
(a) doubt exists about the adequacy, due to apparent or suspected deficiencies or defects;
(b) the strength or load bearing capacity is unknown;
(c) a change of function creates different loading characteristics other than the ones provided for in the design of the structure; or
(d) damage has occurred that may have reduced the strength or load-bearing capacity.
Note: *If the structure under investigation does not satisfy the conditions or criteria of Clause 20.2.3, 20.3.9, or 20.4.1, a lower load rating for the structure may be assigned based on the results of the load test or analysis.*

20.2 General Requirements for Analytical Investigation

20.2.1
If the strength evaluation is performed by analytical means, a thorough field investigation shall be made of the dimensions and details of the members, properties of the materials, and other pertinent conditions of the structure as actually built.

N20 Strength Evaluation Procedures

N20.1 Strength Evaluation — General
Load testing is not intended as a method of accepting designs known to be deficient. See also N20.2.3. It is generally preferable to carry out a structural evaluation by analysis rather than load testing.

N20.2.1
Guidance on determining in-situ concrete strength can be found in CSA Standard A23.2 "Methods of Test for Concrete".

20.2.2

If drawings or other documents are used in the evaluation, their completeness and modifications of the structure not reflected on the drawings shall be considered in the evaluation.

20.2.3

The analysis based on this investigation shall satisfy the requirements and intent of the balance of this Standard.

20.3   General Requirements for Load Tests

Notes:

(1)   *Load tests should be conducted in such a manner as to provide for safety of life and structure during the test, but any safety measures should not interfere with the load test procedures or affect results.*

(2)   *Load testing prestressed systems with unbonded tendons where corrosion is suspected is not generally an acceptable method of evaluating the tendons.*

20.3.1

If the strength evaluation is based on load tests, an engineer experienced in such evaluations shall control the tests.

20.3.2

A load test shall generally not be made until the portion of the structure subjected to load is at least 28 days old.

Note: *When the owner of the structures, the contractor, and all involved parties mutually agree, the test may be made at an earlier age.*

20.3.3

The structure or portion of the structure to be load tested shall be loaded in such a manner as to test adequately the suspected weakness and to allow for the characteristics and pattern of the expected loads.

20.3.4

A load to simulate the effect of the portion of the dead loads not already present shall be applied 24 hours prior to the application of the test load and shall remain in place until all testing has been completed.

20.3.5

The superimposed test load shall be applied in not less than four approximately equal increments without shock to the structure and in a manner to avoid arching of the load materials.

20.3.6

When an entire structural system in doubt is load tested or an entire questionable portion of a system is load tested, the test load shall be 90% of the factored loads M_f, V_f, and P_f.

N20.2.3

The analysis must demonstrate that the intent of this Standard and the National Building Code have been satisfied. The intent of this Standard and NBC is to ensure public safety. In general it should be shown that the building will have a strength close to, or in excess of, that envisaged in the original design or as required by this Standard and NBC.

Commentary N of the 1995 National Building Code of Canada discusses the structural evaluation of existing buildings and allows a relaxation in load factors as a function of the completeness of the review process and the risk to human safety if the structure were to fail.

N20.3.1

The selection of the portion of the structure to be tested, pre-test preparation, testing, and the interpretation of the results should be done under the direction of a qualified engineer experienced in structural investigations, field tests, and measurements.

N20.3.3

Tests to investigate the shear resistance of precast members should simulate the effects of differential settlement, creep, shrinkage and temperature change based on a realistic assessment of such effects occurring in service.

When only a portion of the structural system is tested there is a high likelihood that some of the loads will be resisted by structural elements outside the loaded area. This should be considered in the selection of the area to be tested.

20.3.7

Where only a portion of a structural system in doubt is tested and the results of tests are taken as representative of the structural adequacy of other untested portions of the system, the test load shall be equal to the factored loads M_f, V_f, and P_f.

20.3.8

The test load shall be left on the structure for 24 hours.

20.3.9

If the portion of the structure tested fails or shows visible indications of impending failure, it shall be considered to have failed the test.

20.4   Load Tests of Flexural Systems or Members for Moment Resistance

20.4.1

In addition to the requirements of Clause 20.3.9, when flexural systems or members, including beams and slabs, are load tested for moment resistance, they must have a deflection recovery, within 24 hours of removal of the test load, as follows:

(a)   nonprestressed members

    (i)   first test 60%;

    (ii) retest . . . . 75%; and

(b)   prestressed members . . . . 80%.

20.4.2

Deflections of beams, cantilevers, and one-way slabs shall be measured relative to the ends of the span.

20.4.3

In the case of two-way slabs, the central slab deflection shall be measured relative to the deflection at the supporting columns or walls.

20.4.4

Immediately prior to the application of the test load, the necessary initial readings shall be made as datum for the measurements of deflections caused by the application of the test load.

20.4.5

After the test load has been in position for 24 hours, deflection readings shall be taken.

20.4.6

The test load shall then be removed and readings of deflections shall be taken 24 hours after removal of the test load.

20.4.7

Retests of nonprestressed construction shall not be made until 72 hours after removal of the first test load.

N20.3.9

Visible evidence of failure includes spalling, indicative of concrete crushing failure, cracks wide enough to indicate yielding of reinforcement or significant non-linearity in the load-deflection response.

N20.4.1

It is desirable to take deflection readings after each increment of load is added. These will help in assessing the resolution of the data and will make it possible to detect non-linear load-deflection response due to cracking or other causes.

21. Special Provisions for Seismic Design

21.0 Notation

A_{ch} = cross sectional area of the core of a structural member

A_{cv} = net area of concrete section bounded by web thickness and length of section in the direction of lateral forces considered

A_f = area of flange

A_g = gross area of section

A_j = minimum cross sectional area within a joint in a plane parallel to the axis of the reinforcement generating the shear in the joint. It is equal to the lesser of A_g of the column or $(2b_w+h_{col})$

A_s = area of nonprestressed tension reinforcement

A_{sh} = total cross sectional area of transverse reinforcement (including cross ties), within spacing, s, and perpendicular to dimension, h_c

b = width of compression face of member

b_w = beam web width or diameter of circular section or wall thickness

c_c = depth of the neutral axis with the axial loads P_s, P_n, and P_{ns} measured from the compression edge of a wall section

d = distance from extreme compression fibre to centroid of tension reinforcement

d_b = nominal diameter of bar (see Clause 2.3)

d_v = effective shear depth of wall (see Clause 21.7.3.2)

f'_c = specified compressive strength of concrete

f_y = specified yield strength of reinforcement

f_{yh} = specified yield strength of transverse reinforcement

h_{col} = column dimension parallel to shear force in the joint

h_c = cross sectional dimension of column core

h_w = vertical height of wall

ℓ_c = length of the outermost compression segment of a coupled wall

ℓ_d = development length for a straight bar

ℓ_{dh} = development length for a bar with a standard hook as defined in Equation (21-6)

ℓ_j = dimension of joint in the direction of reinforcement passing through the joint

ℓ_o = minimum length measured from the face of the joint along the axis of the structural member, over which transverse reinforcement must be provided

ℓ_u = clear distance between floors or other effective horizontal lines of lateral support or clear span

ℓ_w = horizontal length of wall

M_{nb} = the nominal flexural resistance of a beam (see Clause 21.4.2.2)

M_{rc} = the factored flexural resistance of a column (see Clause 21.4.2.2)

P_n = the earthquake-induced transfer force resulting from interaction between elements of a linked or coupled wall system and shall be taken as the sum of the end shears corresponding to the nominal flexural resistance in the coupling beams above the section

P_{ns} = nominal net force on a cross section for the direction being considered due to yielding in tension or compression of concentrated and distributed reinforcement during plastic hinge formation — positive for tension

P_p = the earthquake-induced transfer force resulting from interaction between elements of a linked or coupled wall system and shall be taken as the sum of the end shears corresponding to the probable flexural resistance in the coupling beams above the section

P_s = axial force at section resulting from specified dead load plus specified live load

Q = stability index for a storey (see Clause 10.14.4)

R = force modification factor, as given in the *National Building Code of Canada*, that reflects the capability of a structure to dissipate energy through inelastic behaviour

s = spacing of transverse reinforcement measured along the longitudinal axis of the structural member

v_f = factored shear stress

V_c = factored shear resistance provided by the concrete (see Clause 11.3.5)

V_{fb} = factored shear force through a beam-column joint acting parallel to beam bars

β = factor accounting for shear resistance of cracked concrete

γ_w = wall overstrength factor equal to the ratio of the load corresponding to nominal moment resistance of the wall system to the factored load on the wall system

Δ_0 = relative deflection of the top and bottom of a storey computed in accordance with Clause 10.

ϵ_v = average vertical strain in wall (see Clause 21.7.3.2)

ϵ_x = longitudinal strain of flexural tension chord of the member, positive when tensile (see Clause 11.4.6)

ρ = ratio of nonprestressed tension reinforcement = A_s/bd

ρ_s = ratio of volume of spiral reinforcement to the core volume confined by the spiral reinforcement (measured out-to-out of spirals)

θ = angle of inclination of the diagonal compressive stresses to the longitudinal axis of the member

λ = a factor to account for low-density concrete (see Clause 8.6.5)

ϕ_c = resistance factor for concrete (see Clause 8.4.2)

ϕ_s = resistance factor for reinforcing bars (see Clause 8.4.3)

21.1 Definitions

The following definitions apply in this Clause:

Base of structure — level at which earthquake motions are assumed to be imparted to a building. This level does not necessarily coincide with the ground level.

Core — that part of the member cross section confined by the perimeter of the transverse reinforcement measured from out-to-out of the transverse reinforcement.

Critical section — section where a plastic hinge may start to form under earthquake loading.

Development length for a bar with a standard hook in tension — length, measured from the critical section to the outside end of the hook (the straight embedment length between the critical section and the start of the hook (point of tangency) plus the radius of the bend and one bar diameter).

Ductile coupled wall — ductile flexural wall system with coupling beams where at least 66% of the base overturning moment resisted by the wall system is carried by axial tension and compression forces resulting from shear in the coupling beams. This structural system qualifies for a force modification factor, R, of 4.0 in the *National Building Code of Canada*.

Ductile flexural wall — structural wall that resists seismic forces and dissipates energy through flexural yielding at one or more plastic hinges. This structural system qualifies for a force modification factor, R, of 3.5 in the *National Building Code of Canada*.

Ductile partially coupled wall — ductile flexural wall system with coupling beams where less than 66% of the base overturning moment resisted by the wall system is carried by axial tension and compression forces resulting from shears in the coupling beams. This structural system qualifies for a force modification factor, R, of 3.5 in the *National Building Code of Canada*.

Factored load effect — effect of factored load combinations as specified in Clause 8.3 which include earthquake load effects as determined in accordance with Clause 4.1.9 of the *National Building Code of Canada*.

Footing — foundation element directly supported on soil.

Hoop — closed tie or continuously wound tie. A closed tie can be made up of several reinforcing elements with seismic hooks at each end. A continuously wound tie shall also have seismic hooks at each end.

Lateral force resisting system — that portion of the structure composed of members proportioned to resist forces related to earthquake effects.

Nominal resistance — resistance of a section calculated using axial loads P_s and P_n where applicable and the specified values of f'_c, f_y, with ϕ_c and ϕ_s taken as 1.0.

Plastic hinge — region of a member where inelastic flexural curvatures occur. Its length extends at least d from a critical section.

Probable moment resistance — moment resistance of a section calculated using axial loads P_s and P_p where applicable and $1.25f_y$ as the stress in the tension reinforcing and the specified values of f'_c with ϕ_c and ϕ_s taken as 1.0.

Seismic cross tie — single bar having a seismic hook at one end and a hook not less than 90° with at least a six-bar-diameter extension at the other end. The hooks shall engage peripheral longitudinal bars. The 90° hooks of successive cross ties engaging the same longitudinal bar shall be alternated end for end.

Seismic hook — hook with at least a 135° bend with a six-bar-diameter extension (but not less than 100 mm) that engages the longitudinal reinforcement and is anchored in the confined core.

Notes on Clause 21

N21.0 Notation

The 1995 NBCC has adopted a new set of load factors for gravity loads when combined with seismic effects. The new factors of 1.0 for Dead Load and 1.0 or 0.5 (depending on the occupancy) for live load effectively give a specified load and as such they should be used whenever the term "specified loads" is used in Clause 21. The figures in these notes use 0.5L for illustration but 1.0L is applicable for some occupancies, see NBCC.

N21.1 Definitions

Seismic cross tie The requirement for 135° hook at each end of a cross tie has been relaxed because there is no evidence of problems with the alternating 90°–135° hooks as used in California.

Seismic hook The hook definition has been changed to ease the placing problems with larger bars. The new definition is the same as the SEAOC seismic hook.

Shell concrete — concrete outside the transverse reinforcement confining the concrete.

Structural diaphragm — structural member, such as a floor or roof slab, that transmits inertial forces to or between lateral force resisting members.

21.2 General Requirements

21.2.1 Scope

21.2.1.1
Clause 21 is intended to apply to structures designed using a force modification factor, R, greater than 1.5.

21.2.1.2
Clause 21 contains special requirements for the design of reinforced concrete members of a structure for which the design forces, related to earthquake motions, have been determined on the basis of energy dissipation in the nonlinear range of response. These structures shall be the subject of capacity design. In the capacity design of structures, energy-dissipating elements or mechanisms are chosen and suitably designed and detailed, and all other structural elements are then provided with sufficient reserve capacity to ensure that the chosen energy-dissipating mechanisms are maintained throughout the deformations that may occur.

21.2.1.3
The provisions of Clauses 1 through 15 shall apply except as modified by the provisions of this Clause. The provisions of Clauses 16 and 18 shall apply only to structural members not considered part of the lateral force resisting system except as permitted in Clause 21.2.1.4.

21.2.1.4
Precast reinforced concrete structural systems shall be allowed as part of the lateral force resisting system provided they emulate the behaviour of a cast in place system. Connections shall be remote from the locations of nonlinear response and proportioned to resist forces due to the probable capacities of the system.

21.2.1.5
A reinforced concrete structural system not satisfying the requirements of this Clause may be used if it is demonstrated by experimental evidence and analysis that the proposed system will have strength and toughness equal to or exceeding those provided by a comparable monolithic reinforced concrete structure satisfying this Clause.

21.2.2 Analysis and Proportioning of Structural Members

21.2.2.1
The linear and nonlinear behaviour and interaction of all structural and nonstructural members, which materially affect the response of the structure to earthquake motions, shall be considered in the analysis.

N21.2.1.2

The design of buildings for earthquake induced loads is fundamentally different than the design for loads which are expected to occur with greater frequency such as dead, occupancy, snow or wind loads. The design equation for all loads is **factored resistance ≥ effect of factored loads (EFL)**. The factored resistance is determined by applying resistance factors (φ values less than 1) in the calculation of the resistance of a member, a cross section or a connection. The effect of factored loads is determined by applying loads and forces to the structure that have been factored up by load factors (α values greater than 1). These resistance and load factors have been selected to reflect the variability of the materials and the loads. The design process set up by this equation allows each and every resistance in a building to be calculated independently since in all cases the nominal resistance will be greater than the specified load by a factor of safety equal to α/ϕ.

In the case of earthquake loads the process on the load side is quite different. The expected load V_E is multiplied by U of 0.6 and then divided by R. The R values range from a low of 1.5 to a high of 4.0 and are a function of the energy absorbing capacity of the selected system. Ignoring the effect of U the factored earthquake loads applied to the building (for R values > 1.5 which this clause covers) range from a high of 50% (1.0/2.0) to a low of 25% (1.0/4.0) of the expected load. The overall factor of safety ranges from a low of 0.29 (α_E / (ϕ_s × R) = 1.0/(0.85 × 4.0)) to a high of 0.83 (α_E / (ϕ_c × R) = 1.0/(0.6 × 2.0)). This illustrates that for earthquake loadings the overall factor of safety is less than 1.0 and the load effects range from 120 % to 340% of the nominal capacity. The structure is expected to go well into the inelastic range to absorb the energy from the earthquake event. This is the fundamental difference between earthquake and all other loadings and why a different approach is needed when designing for earthquake. **The expected loads exceed the capacity of some members.**

To avoid having to design all of the structure to be ductile in all of the possible failure modes the capacity design approach is adopted. Only some elements of the building and locations within these elements which will absorb the energy (fail in the conventional sense) are designed with the necessary ductility. (Fig. N21.2.1.2(a)) The capacity of the selected ductile energy absorber or absorbers is determined and then the non-ductile failure modes and non-yielding locations within the selected elements are designed for capacities higher than the effects of yield of the energy absorbing elements. The structure can be thought of as a chain where all of the non-ductile links are stronger than the ductile link. (Fig. N21.2.1.2(b))

This is the capacity design process which is implicit throughout Clause 21, **factored resistance of non-energy absorbers ≥ effect of development of nominal or probable resistance of energy absorbers**. In addition the rest of the building considered to be not part of the lateral force resisting system must be capable of sustaining the deformations which will occur during the energy absorption process without failure and this is covered in Clause 21.8.

The text "Seismic Design of Reinforced Concrete and Masonry Buildings" by T. Paulay and M. J. N. Priestley published by John Wiley and Sons, Inc. 1992, is a useful reference to the principles contained in Clause 21 even though it is written mainly for the New Zealand code and is therefore not always directly applicable.

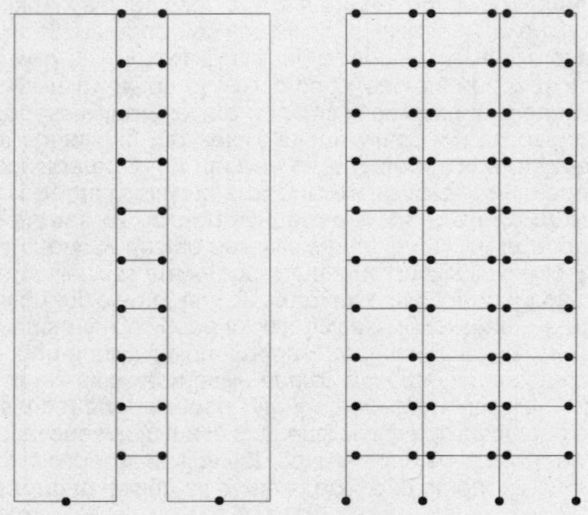

N21.2.1.3

Clause 21 does not have requirements for the use of precast or prestressed concrete systems as primary lateral load resisting systems. Guidance on the seismic design of precast structures is given in the CPCI Design Manual – THIRD EDITION to be published in 1996.

N21.2.2.1 and N21.2.2.2

The forces in the various components of a lateral load resisting system are usually determined by a linear elastic analysis using code equivalent static loads. The section properties used for the elastic model are modified gross section properties and may be taken as:

Structural Type	Element	Effective inertia I_e
Frame	Beams	$0.4\, I_g$
	Columns	$0.7\, I_g$
Walls	Walls	$0.7\, I_g$
	diagonally reinforced coupling beams Cl. 21.5.8.2	$0.4\, k\, I_g$
	traditionally reinforced coupling beams Cl. 21.3	$0.2\, k\, I_g$

These corrections are less than those contained in Clause 10 which include long term effects that do not apply to short term seismic loading. The coefficient 'k' in the effective stiffness equations for coupling beams shall be:

$$k = \frac{1}{[1 + 3\,(h/\ell_n)^2]}$$

where h is the beam depth and ℓ_n is the clear span. This 'k' value is a shear deflection correction which need not be applied if the program elements used for analysis incorporate shear deformation. For coupled walls axial shortening and extension of the individual wall elements is significant and an average effective area A_e of $0.75\, A_g$ may be used.

The stiffness of a wall is significantly affected by the compression stress in the wall. For coupled wall buildings multiple analyses for varying directions of loading may be performed taking $A_e = A_g$ and $I_e = 0.8\, I_g$ for walls under compression and $A_e = 0.5\, A_g$ and $I_e = 0.5\, I_g$ for walls under tension.

Fig. N21.2.1.2 (a)
Plastic Hinge Locations

Shear　Crushing　Stability　Flexure

Fig. N21.2.1.2 (b)
Capacity Design Links

21.2.2.2
Elements assumed not to be a part of the lateral force resisting system shall have the effect of their behaviour on the response of the system considered and accommodated in the structural design. Consequences of failure of structural and nonstructural members which are not part of the lateral force resisting system shall also be considered.

21.2.2.3
The factored resistance of the foundation system and supports of frames or walls, or both, shall be sufficient to develop the nominal moment capacity of the frames or walls and the corresponding shears. Where the factored moment resistance of any wall or any frame significantly exceeds the required factored moment, the factored resistance of unanchored footings supporting those walls or frames need not exceed the maximum factored load effects determined with loads calculated using R equal to 1.3. Where frames or walls are supported by anchored footings or elements other than foundations, the factored resistance of these elements need not exceed the maximum factored load effects determined with loads calculated using R equal to 1.0.

21.2.2.4
In calculation of the slenderness effects for sway frames in accordance with Clause 10.16, Q shall be calculated with Δ_0 multiplied by R. The value of Q shall be limited to 1/3.

21.2.2.5
All structural members assumed not to be part of the lateral force resisting system shall conform to Clause 21.8.

21.2.3 Concrete in Members Resisting Earthquake-Induced Forces

21.2.3.1
The specified compressive strength, f'_c, used in design shall not exceed 55 MPa.

21.2.3.2
The specified compressive strength of structural low-density concrete shall not exceed 30 MPa. A higher compressive strength may be used if it is demonstrated by experimental evidence that structural members made with that structural low-density concrete provide strength and toughness equal to or exceeding those of comparable members made with normal density concrete of the same strength.

21.2.4 Reinforcement in Members Resisting Earthquake-Induced Forces

21.2.4.1
Reinforcement resisting earthquake-induced forces in frame members and walls in lateral load resisting systems designed with force modification factors R greater than 2.0 shall be weldable grade in conformance with CSA Standard G30.18. Lateral load resisting systems designed with force modification factor R of 2.0 or less shall comply with CSA Standard G30.18 but need not be weldable grade.

N21.2.2.3

The intent of this clause is to provide capacity design of the foundation system. The foundation system shall be taken as all portions of the lateral load carrying system below the lowest design plastic hinge. The upper limit on foundation capacity has been introduced to cover situations where the system capacity approaches that of an elastically responding system. This may be encountered when sizes are set by functional requirements and/or the amount of reinforcement in the elements is governed by minimum amounts. The difference between anchored and un-anchored foundations has been introduced to recognize that there is some energy absorption in "stamping" or "rocking" footings even though there is not enough information currently available to allow utilization of these systems without special studies. A description of the type of special study required including inelastic analysis of a building is contained in the paper by A. Filiatrault, D.L. Anderson and R.H. DeVall in the CSCE Journal, Volume 19, Number 3, June 1992.

It can be confusing as to how to apply upper limits on the required capacity of foundation elements when there is more than one element providing the resistance. With one element the concept is clear, the non-ductile links in the chain do not have to be stronger than the maximum expected load on the chain. When there is more than one element resisting the loading the situation is more complicated because there are two ways of considering the problem, looking at displacements or looking at forces. Consider the two element case and think of it as two chains in parallel. Both chairs will contribute to the system resistance in proportion to their stiffness up to the point of yield in one of the chains. From that point on only one chain is capable of providing additional resistance. It is useful to think of the problem in terms of overstrength where overstrength is defined as:

$$\gamma = \frac{Resistance}{Effect\ of\ Factored\ Loads\ (EFL)}$$

and the resistance in this case is the nominal resistance. In other clauses upper limits are framed in terms of probable resistances but the same concepts illustrated here will apply. For a single element the overstrength is:

$$\gamma_1 = \frac{M_{1n}}{M_1\ EFL}$$

For a group of elements the overstrength is:

$$\gamma = \frac{\Sigma M_{in}}{\Sigma M_i\ EFL}$$

In the two element (two chains) example assume that R = 2 and one element carries 10% of the load with an overstrength of 3 and the other carries 90% of the load with an overstrength of 1.0 (Overstrength is always over 1.0 but is useful here for illustration purposes). The group overstrength for this case is:

$$\frac{3*10+1*90}{100} = 1.2$$

For anchored foundations where the upper limit is factored load effects determined with loads calculated using R = 1 this seems to imply that the foundation capacity of the element with a γ = 3 cannot be limited since the group overstrength is less than 2. The force approach applies a load twice the R = 2 EFL to the two chain system and at this force level both chains will yield since the group overstrength is less than 2.

The displacement approach results in a different conclusion. The displacement of the structure calculated with the effects of factored loads determined using loads reduced by R is the assumed structure yield displacement. Displacing the structure R times this factored load effect displacement is equivalent to the elastically responding level or upper limit of the design displacement. Applying this approach to the two chain example the chain carrying 10% of the load is displaced until it carries a load of twice the EFL which is less than its yield level and is in fact the same load that would be determined when calculating factored load effects using R = 1. The chain carrying 90% of the load is displaced twice its yield displacement since γ = 1 and continues to carry the EFL loading. This approach allows us to design the foundation for the 10% element for a factored resistance equal to an overstrength level of two. Which then is the correct approach to the problem? The displacement approach is correct and this can be illustrated by a more extreme example of the two chain problem. Consider the R = 2 problem again where one chain carries 1% of the load with an overstrength of 100 and the other 99% with an overstrength of 1. The combined overstrength is 1.99 and since this is less than 2 the force approach tells us that both chains yield which would require 100 times yield displacement of the element carrying 99% of the load. Since the displacement upper limit for this case is 2 and definitely not 100 it follows that the displacement approach is the correct one. The same principles illustrated here also apply to the upper limits for shear in later clauses.

N21.2.2.4
This clause requires that inelastic deformations be included in the stability design of sway frames.

N21.2.3.1
The upper limit on specified concrete compressive strength has been introduced because of the brittle nature of very high strength concrete and the current lack of research into requirements needed to assure ductile behaviour of high strength concrete members under the action of earthquake forces.

N21.2.4.1
Reinforcement complying with the weldable grade requirements of CSA G30.18 has a more closely controlled chemical composition which results in a more predictable and a more ductile stress-strain response. Use of longitudinal reinforcement with yield strength higher than that assumed in design

will lead to higher shears and higher bond stresses at the time of development of yield moments. This may lead to unexpected brittle failures and hence should be avoided. Increasing the ratio of ultimate strength to yield strength increases the length of plastic hinge regions and hence improves the energy absorbing capabilities of the member.

These more stringent requirements on the properties of the reinforcing steel are not necessary for lateral load resisting systems designed with force modification factors, R, of 2.0 or less.

N21.2.4.2
Welding or tack welding of crossing reinforcing bars can lead to local embrittlement of the steel. If such welding is needed to facilitate fabrication it must be done only on additional bars added specifically for this purpose. Welding performed to splice bars using a controlled procedure with adequate inspection is permitted.

N21.2.4.3
Lateral force resisting elements are expected to develop their yield capacity and deform plastically under the action of seismic forces. Under these circumstances all reinforcement provided is expected to yield and must therefore be spliced for full tension capacity.

N21.3
A ductile moment resisting frame must be capable of sustaining a series of oscillations into the inelastic range of response without critical decay in strength.

N21.3.1(a)
Frame members (beams) subjected to factored axial compressive forces exceeding $A_g f'_c/10$ have different behaviour and must be designed and detailed according to Clause 21.4.

N21.3.2.1 and N21.3.2.2
These Clauses ensure continuity of reinforcement and some positive and negative moment capacity throughout the beam to allow for unexpected deformations and moment redistributions from severe earthquake loading. The reinforcement limits are intended to ensure that the section displays adequate ductility. The upper limit of 0.025 is to avoid excessive steel congestion and excessive joint shear stresses.

N21.3.3.3
Lap splices are unreliable for inelastic cyclic loading and hence are not permitted in the plastic hinge regions of beams.

21.2.4.2

Reinforcement required for the factored load effect including earthquake shall not be welded except as specified in Clauses 21.3.2.4, 21.4.3.4, and 21.5.4.2.

21.2.4.3

The reduction of lap splice length permitted by Clause 12 where the area of reinforcing provided exceeds that required shall not be permitted for members conforming to Clause 21.

21.3   Ductile Frame Members Subjected to Flexure

Note: *This Clause is intended to apply to beams in structures designed using a force modification factor, R, greater than 2.0*

21.3.1   Scope

The requirements of Clause 21.3 apply to ductile frame members that are part of the lateral force resisting system and are proportioned primarily to resist flexure.   These are members that satisfy the following conditions:

(a)   the axial compressive force in the member due to factored load effects shall not exceed ($A_g f_c'/10$);

(b)   the clear span of the member shall be not less than four times its effective depth;

(c)   the width-to-depth ratio of the cross section shall be not less than 0.3; and

(d)   the width shall be not less than 250 mm and not more than the width of the supporting member (measured on a plane perpendicular to the longitudinal axis of the flexural member) plus distances on each side of the supporting member not exceeding three-fourths of the depth of the flexural member.

Note: *Frame members not satisfying Clause 21.3 shall be designed according to Clause 21.8 and shall not be considered part of the lateral force resisting system.*

21.3.2   Longitudinal Reinforcement

21.3.2.1

At any section of a flexural member and for the top as well as for the bottom reinforcement, the area of reinforcement shall each be not less than ($1.4b_w d/f_y$) and the reinforcement ratio, ρ, shall not exceed 0.025.   At least two bars shall be provided continuously both top and bottom.

21.3.2.2

The positive moment resistance at the face of a joint shall be not less than one-half of the negative moment resistance provided at that face of the joint.   Neither the negative nor the positive moment resistance at any section along the member length shall be less than one-fourth of the maximum moment resistance provided at the face of either end joint.

21.3.2.3

Lap splices of flexural reinforcement shall be permitted only if hoop or spiral reinforcement is provided over the lap length.   The maximum spacing of the transverse reinforcement enclosing the lapped bars shall not exceed d/4 or 100 mm.   Lap splices shall not be used

(a)   within the joints;

(b)   within a distance, 2d, from the face of the joint; and

N21.3.3

These hoops are intended to prevent buckling of the longitudinal bars and to provide confinement of the concrete in the compression zone in plastic hinge regions where both the top and bottom reinforcement can be subjected to yielding in tension and compression due to reversed cyclic flexure. See Fig. N21.3.3.

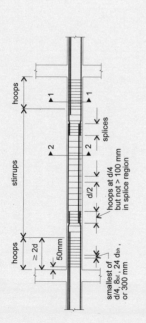

smallest of
d/4, 8b_{f}, 24 d_{bh},
or 300 mm

hoops ≥ 2d

50mm

hoops at d/4
but not > 100 mm
in splice region

splices

stirrups

hoops

Section 2-2

Section 1-1

hoop
diameter
= d_{bh}

stirrup

smallest
longitudinal
bar diameter
= d_{bf}

Note: Transverse reinforcement must also satisfy shear requirements of Clause 21.7

Fig. N21.3.3
Transverse Reinforcement Requirements for Beams in Ductile Moment Resisting Frames

N21.3.3.2(b)

When a plastic hinge region is deliberately relocated away from the column then hoop reinforcement must be provided within and adjacent to the plastic hinge region. See Fig. N21.3.3.2.

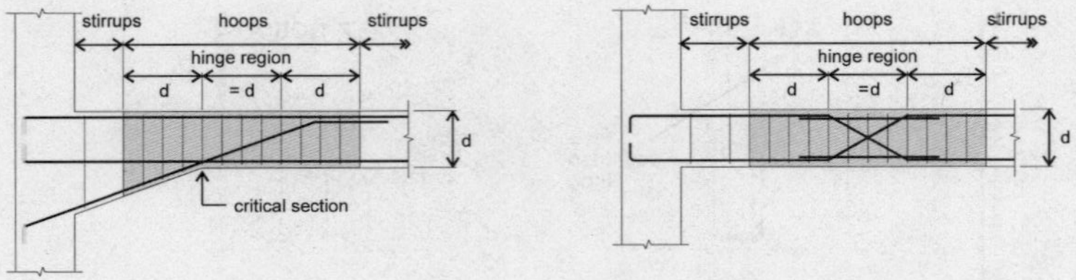

(c)   within a distance, d, from any plastic hinge caused by inelastic lateral displacements.

21.3.2.4

Welded splices and mechanical connections conforming to Clauses 12.14.3.1 to 12.14.3.4 inclusive may be used for splicing, provided not more than alternate bars in each layer of the longitudinal reinforcement are spliced at a section, and the centre-to-centre distance between splices of adjacent bars is 600 mm or more, measured along the longitudinal axis of the frame member. Splices shall not be located within a distance, d, of a plastic hinge caused by inelastic lateral displacements.

21.3.3   Transverse Reinforcement

21.3.3.1

Shear resistance shall satisfy the requirements of Clause 21.7.

21.3.3.2

Hoops shall be provided in the following regions of frame members:

(a)   over a length equal to 2d measured from the face of the joint; and

(b)   over regions where plastic hinges may occur and for a distance, d, on either side of these hinge regions.

21.3.3.3

The first hoop shall be located not more than 50 mm from the face of a supporting member. The maximum spacing of the hoops shall not exceed

(a)   d/4;

(b)   8 times the diameter of the smallest longitudinal bars;

(c)   24 times the diameter of the hoop bars; or

(d)   300 mm.

21.3.3.4

In regions where hoops are required, longitudinal bars on the perimeter shall have lateral support conforming to Clauses 7.6.5.5 and 7.6.5.6.

21.3.3.5

Where hoops are not required, stirrups shall be spaced at no more than d/2 throughout the length of the member.

21.3.3.6

Hoops in flexural members may be replaced by two pieces of reinforcement:

(a)   a U-stirrup enclosing the longitudinal reinforcement with seismic hooks at the ends; and

(b)   a cross tie to make a closed hoop.

If the longitudinal reinforcing bars secured by the cross ties are confined by a slab only on one side of the flexural frame member, the 90° hooks of the cross ties shall all be placed on that side.

142

---

stirrups hoops stirrups

hinge region

d = d d

critical section

(b) Hinge Due to Haunch

stirrups hoops stirrups

hinge region

d = d d

(a) Hinge Due to Special Reinforcement Details

Fig. N21.3.3.2
Plastic Hinges Away From Column Faces

N21.3.3.5

The need for hoops in other regions of the beam where only positive moment hinging can occur is a matter of judgement. In these regions the danger of buckling of the top compression bars is far less since these bars will never have yielded in tension in a previous load cycle. Bottom longitudinal bars which are not subjected to compression need not be laterally supported to prevent buckling.

168

21.4 Ductile Frame Members Subjected to Flexure and Axial Load

Note: *This Clause is intended to apply to columns and similar members in structures designed using a force modification factor, R, greater than 2.0.*

21.4.1 Scope

The requirements of Clause 21.4 apply to ductile frame members that are part of the lateral force resisting system, and are subject to an axial compressive force due to factored load effects which exceeds $(A_g f'_c/10)$ and which satisfy the following conditions:

(a) the shortest cross sectional dimension, measured on a straight line passing through the geometric centroid, shall be not less than 300 mm; and

(b) the ratio of the shortest cross sectional dimension to the perpendicular dimension shall be not less than 0.4.

Note: *Frame members not satisfying Clause 21.4 shall be designed according to Clause 21.8 and shall not be considered part of the lateral force resisting system.*

21.4.2 Minimum Flexural Resistance

21.4.2.1

Flexural resistance shall satisfy Clause 21.4.2.2 or the member shall not be considered to contribute to the lateral resistance of the lateral force resisting system. If the latter is the case, the member shall satisfy the requirements of Clause 21.8.1 and shall be provided with transverse reinforcement as specified in Clause 21.4.4 over its full height.

21.4.2.2

The flexural resistances of the columns and the beams shall satisfy

$$\sum M_{rc} \geq 1.1 \sum M_{nb} \qquad (21\text{-}1)$$

where

$\sum M_{rc}$ = the sum of moments at the centre of the joint, corresponding to the factored resistance of the columns framing into the joint. The factored resistance of the columns shall be calculated for the factored axial force, consistent with the direction of the lateral forces considered, which results in the lowest flexural resistance

$\sum M_{nb}$ = the sum of moments at the centre of the joint, corresponding to the nominal resistance of the beams and girders framing into that joint. The nominal resistance shall also include the effects of slab reinforcement within a distance of 3 times the slab thickness measured from each side of the beam.

Flexural resistances shall be summed such that the column moments oppose the beam moments. Equation (21-1) shall be satisfied for beam moments acting in either direction.

21.4.2.3

Axial design loads in frame columns shall account for beams yielding at levels above the level being considered. The shears from the beams shall be those given by the method of Clause 21.7.2.1 using nominal rather than probable strengths. Allowance may be made for the reduction in accumulated beam shears with increasing numbers of stories.

December 1994

N21.4.2

The energy dissipation necessary for a multi-storey frame to survive a severe earthquake should in general occur by the formation of ductile plastic hinges in beams (see Fig. N21.4.2). Plastic hinges in beams are capable of tolerating larger rotations than hinges in columns. Further, as can be seen from Fig. N21.4.2, mechanisms involving beam hinges cause energy to be dissipated at many locations throughout the frame. An additional consideration is that extensive hinging in columns (see Fig. N21.4.2(a)) may critically reduce the gravity load carrying capacity of the structure.

N21.4.2.2

To achieve the desired beam hinging mechanism, the Standard specifies a "strong column-weak beam" design approach. Eq. (21-1) requires that the total factored resistance of the columns based on $\phi_c = 0.60$ and $\phi_s = 0.85$, must be at least 10% greater than the total nominal resistance, based on ϕ_c and $\phi_s = 1.0$, of the beams framing into the joint.

An approximate procedure for checking this requirement which involves using the moments at the faces of the joint is illustrated in Fig. N21.4.2.2.

(a) Column - Sidesway Mechanism Undesirable

(b) Beam - Hinging Mechanism Desirable

**Fig. N21.4.2
Types of Mechanisms**

21.4.3 Longitudinal Reinforcement

21.4.3.1
The area of longitudinal reinforcement shall be not less than 0.01 nor more than 0.06 times the gross area, A_g, of the section.

21.4.3.2
Lap splices shall be proportioned as tensile splices and are permitted only within the centre half of the member length unless they conform to Clause 21.4.3.3.

21.4.3.3
Tension lap splices with a lap length of 1.3 times that required by Clause 12 may be used at any section, except within the joint, provided they are confined over their full length by transverse steel conforming to Clause 21.4.4 and the bars are not cranked.

21.4.3.4
Welded splices and mechanical connections conforming to Clauses 12.14.3.1 to 12.14.3.4 inclusive may be used for splicing the reinforcement at any section provided not more than alternate longitudinal bars are spliced at a section and the distance between splices is 600 mm or more along the longitudinal axis of the reinforcement.

21.4.4 Transverse Reinforcement

21.4.4.1
Shear resistance shall satisfy the requirements of Clause 21.7.

21.4.4.2
Transverse reinforcement, specified as follows, shall be provided unless a larger amount is required by Clause 21.7:
(a) the volumetric ratio of spiral or circular hoop reinforcement, ρ_s, shall be not less than that given by

$$\rho_s = 0.12 \frac{f'_c}{f_{yh}} \qquad (21\text{-}2)$$

and shall be not less than that required by Equation (10-7);

(b) the total cross sectional area of rectangular hoop reinforcement shall be not less than the larger of the amounts given by Equations (21-3) and (21-4)

$$A_{sh} = 0.3\, s\, h_c \frac{f'_c}{f_{yh}} \left(\frac{A_g}{A_{ch}} - 1 \right) \qquad (21\text{-}3)$$

$$A_{sh} = 0.09\, s\, h_c \frac{f'_c}{f_{yh}} \qquad (21\text{-}4)$$

(c) transverse reinforcement may be provided by single or overlapping hoops. Cross ties of the same bar size and spacing as the hoops may be used; and

---

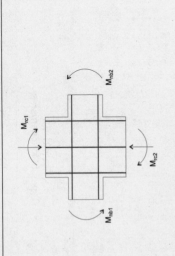

$$M_{rc1} + M_{rc2} \geq 1.1(M_{nb1} + M_{nb2})$$

Fig. N21.4.2.2
Strong Column — Weak Beam Requirement

N21.4.3.1
The lower limit addresses the concern for the effects of time-dependent deformation of columns and the desire to have post-cracking capacity. The upper limit reflects concern for steel congestion.

N21.4.3.2 and N21.4.3.3
Because spalling of the shell concrete in the high moment regions near the ends of columns may reduce the capacity of lap splices, such splices must be located near the mid-height of columns or be increased in length. The lap splices must be confined and have tensile lap splices of length $1.3 \times$ Class B splices unless located at mid-height.

N21.4.4.2
The traditional ratio of spiral reinforcement for columns is given by Eq. (10-7). For large columns the ratio ρ_s given by Eq. (21-2) governs. Rectangular hoop reinforcement is less effective than spirals in confining the concrete, hence Eqns. (21-3) and (21-4) require more transverse reinforcement per unit of length.

The rectangular hoop reinforcement details must satisfy Eqns. (21-3) and (21-4) in both directions. As an example for the column shown in Fig. N21.4.4.2, Eq. (21-3) becomes:

$$A_{sh} = 0.3 \left(sh_c * \frac{25}{400}\right)\left(\frac{300*600}{220*520}-1\right) = 0.0108sh_c$$

while Eq. (21-4) becomes:

$$A_{sh} = 0.09 \left(sh_c * \frac{25}{400}\right) = 0.00563sh_c$$

Hence Eq. (21-3) controls. In the direction perpendicular to h_{c1} there are 3 hoop legs and hence the required spacing is:

$$s = \frac{3*100}{0.0108*220} = 126 \text{ mm}$$

In the direction perpendicular to h_{c2} there are 4 hoop legs and hence the required spacing is:

$$s = \frac{4*100}{0.0108*520} = 71 \text{ mm}$$

Thus a spacing of 71 mm is required.

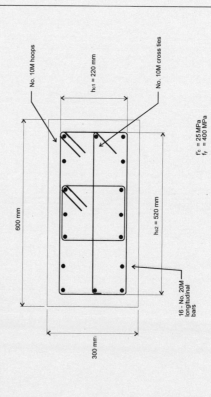

f'_c = 25 MPa
f_y = 400 MPa

Fig. N21.4.4.2
Determination of Required Hoop Spacing

N21.4.4.3

The spacing limits are intended to provide a minimum degree of confinement of the core and also to provide lateral support for the longitudinal reinforcing bars.

N21.4.4.4

Fig. N21.4.4.4 illustrates the requirements of this clause.

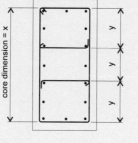

core dimension = x

(a) Overlapping Hoops

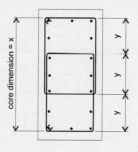

core dimension = x

(b) Cross-ties

If x ≤ 600 mm then y ≤ 200 mm
If x > 600 mm then y ≤ x/3 but ≤ 300 mm

Note: These spacing requirements must be satisfied in both directions

Fig. N21.4.4.4
Spacing Limits for Overlapping Hoops and Cross Ties

(d) if the factored resistance of the member core is greater than the factored load effect including earthquake, then Equations (10-7) and (21-3) need not be satisfied outside the joint.

21.4.4.3

Transverse reinforcement shall be spaced at distances not exceeding

(a) one-quarter of the minimum member dimension;
(b) 100 mm;
(c) 6 times the diameter of the smallest longitudinal bar; or
(d) the requirements of Clause 7.6.

21.4.4.4

In the direction perpendicular to the longitudinal axis of the member, cross ties or legs of overlapping hoops shall not be spaced more than the greater of 200 mm or one-third of the core dimension in that direction, but in any case not more than 300 mm.

21.4.4.5

Transverse reinforcement in the amount specified in Clauses 21.4.4.1 to 21.4.4.3 inclusive shall be provided over a length, ℓ_o, from the face of each joint and on both sides of any section where flexural yielding may occur in connection with inelastic lateral displacements of the frame. The length, ℓ_o, shall be not less than

(a) the depth of the member at the face of the joint or at the section where flexural yielding may occur;
(b) one-sixth of the clear span of the member; or
(c) 450 mm.

21.4.4.6

Where transverse reinforcement, as specified in Clauses 21.4.4.2 through 21.4.4.4, is not provided throughout the length of the column, the remainder of the column length shall contain spiral or hoop reinforcement with centre-to-centre spacing not exceeding the smaller of six times the diameter of the longitudinal column bars or 150 mm.

21.4.4.7

Columns, which due to their connection to rigid members such as discontinued walls or foundations or due to their position at the base of the structure may develop plastic hinges, shall be provided with transverse reinforcement as specified in Clauses 21.4.4.1 to 21.4.4.3 inclusive over their full height. This transverse reinforcement shall extend up into the discontinued member for at least the development length of the largest longitudinal reinforcement in the column in accordance with Clause 21.6.5. If the lower end of the column terminates on a wall, this transverse reinforcement shall extend into the wall for at least the development length of the largest longitudinal reinforcement in the column at the point of termination. If the column terminates on a footing or mat, this transverse reinforcement shall extend at least 300 mm into the footing or mat.

N21.4.4.5

Fig. N21.4.4.5 illustrates the requirements of this clause.

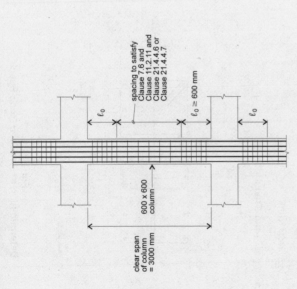

spacing to satisfy
Clause 7.6 and
Clause 11.2.11 and
Clause 21.4.4.6 or
Clause 21.4.4.7

$\ell_o \geq 600$ mm

clear span
of column
= 3000 mm

600 x 600
column

ℓ_o not less than:
(a) column depth = 600 mm
(b) 1/6 of clear span = 500 mm
(c) 450 mm

Fig. N21.4.4.5
Minimum Length ℓ_o

N21.4.4.7

It is important to appreciate that during a severe earthquake some column hinging (e.g. at the base of the column in Fig N21.4.2(b)) and some yielding of columns will occur even if the "strong column-weak beam" philosophy has been followed. For this reason columns need to be detailed for ductility in accordance with the requirement of Clause 21.4.4.7.

21.5 Ductile Flexural Walls

Note: *This Clause is intended to apply to wall systems designed using a force modification factor, R, greater than 2.0.*

21.5.1 Scope

21.5.1.1

The requirements of Clause 21.5 apply to ductile flexural walls serving as parts of the lateral force resisting system.

21.5.1.2

Ductile flexural walls shall not be designed using the provisions of Clause 14.5.

21.5.2 General Requirements

21.5.2.1

Each wall shall be detailed for plastic hinges to occur at any location unless a rational analysis of the structural system shows that plastic hinges will not form in certain regions, in which case these regions need not be detailed for plastic hinges.

21.5.2.2

In the absence of abrupt changes of the strength and stiffness of the lateral load resisting system, the requirements of Clause 21.5.2.1 shall be considered to be satisfied if the walls are detailed for potential plastic hinging over the lower half of their height.

21.5.2.3

Shear resistance shall satisfy Clause 21.7.

Note: *Possible failure mechanisms involving one or more openings shall be investigated.*

21.5.3 Dimensional Limitations

21.5.3.1

The effective flange widths to be used in the design of L-, C-, or T-shaped sections shall not be assumed to extend further from the face of the web than

(a)   half of the distance to an adjacent structural wall web; or

(b)   10% of the total wall height.

21.5.3.2

The wall thickness within a plastic hinge shall be not less than $\ell_u/10$, unless permitted by Clauses 21.5.3.3 to 21.5.3.5.

21.5.3.3

Clause 21.5.3.2 need only apply to those parts of a wall which, under factored vertical and lateral loads, are more than half-way from the neutral axis to the compression face of the wall section.

N21.5.2.1 and N21.5.2.2

One possible approach for determining regions of potential plastic hinging is to compare the distribution of moments over the height of the wall corresponding to the development of the probable moment resistance(s) at locations of known plastic hinging (e.g. at the base of the wall or at abrupt changes of cross-section) with the distribution of the probable moment resistance of the wall over its height. In regions where the resistance considerably exceeds the moment demand it can be assumed that plastic hinging cannot occur. Fig. N21.5.2.1 illustrates a situation for a single wall where hinging will only form at the base of the wall. Some suggestions as to the plastic hinge length are also shown in this figure. Fig. N21.2.1 (a) shows that for coupled systems ductile detailing and capacity design is required over the height of the building. Note, however, that plastic hinges in the walls in this example are limited to the base and principles similar to those illustrated in Fig. N21.5.2.1 may be applied but must be supplemented with consideration of the requirements of Clauses 21.5.8.3 and 21.5.8.5.

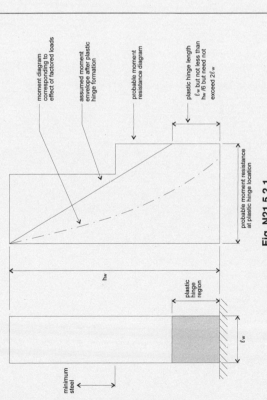

Fig. N21.5.2.1
**Determination of Regions of Potential Plastic Hinging
in a Uniform Uncoupled Wall**

173

N21.5.3

Because wall structures may be relatively thin, care must be taken to prevent possible instability in potential plastic hinge zones. Regions of the walls where yielding of the reinforcement and concrete compressive strains in excess of 0.0015 are expected need to be checked for stability. Fig. N21.5.3(a) illustrates how thickened boundary elements can be used to provide stability in the highly stressed regions of the walls. For simple rectangular walls with low axial compressions the required depth of compression may be small enough to enable the remainder of the wall to provide sufficient restraint to the small highly compressed regions (see Fig. N21.5.3(b)). Certain parts of walls as shown in Fig. N21.5.3(c) provide continuous lateral support of adjacent components. Therefore any part of a wall which is within a distance of 3b' from a line of support is exempted from the slenderness limitation. The shaded part of the flange in Fig. N21.5.3(c) is considered to be too remote to be effectively restrained by the web portion of the wall and hence it needs to comply with the slenderness requirement.

N21.5.2.3

Fig. N21.5.2.3 illustrates possible failure mechanisms involving openings.

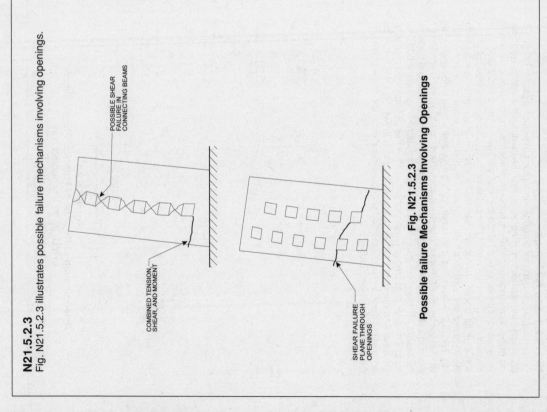

POSSIBLE SHEAR FAILURE IN CONNECTING BEAMS

COMBINED TENSION, SHEAR, AND MOMENT

SHEAR FAILURE PLANE THROUGH OPENINGS

Fig. N21.5.2.3

Possible failure Mechanisms Involving Openings

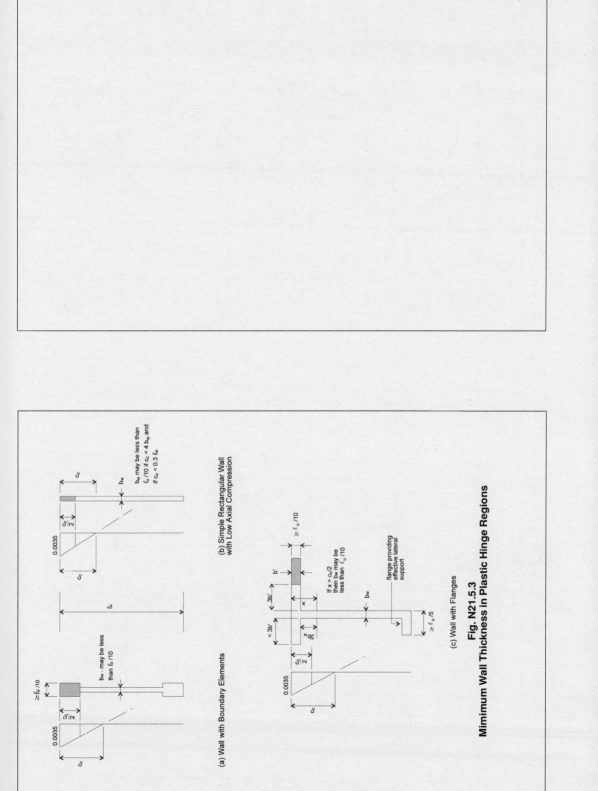

(a) Wall with Boundary Elements

b_w may be less than ℓ_u /10

0.0035

$\frac{c_c}{2}$

c_c

≥ ℓ_u /10

(b) Simple Rectangular Wall with Low Axial Compression

b_w may be less than ℓ_u /10 if c_c < 4 b_w and if c_c < 0.3 ℓ_w

0.0035

c_c

$\frac{c_c}{2}$

c_c

ℓ_u

(c) Wall with Flanges

0.0035

c_c

$\frac{c_c}{2}$

3b'

< 3b'

$3b'$

b_w

If x > c_c/2 then b_w may be less than ℓ_u /10

x

b'

≥ ℓ_u /10

flange providing effective lateral support

≥ ℓ_u /5

Fig. N21.5.3
Mimimum Wall Thickness in Plastic Hinge Regions

21.5.3.4

Clause 21.5.3.2 need not apply to simple rectangular walls when the neutral axis depth computed for the factored load effects is located within a distance of the lesser of

(a) $4b_w$; or
(b) $0.3\ell_w$

from the compression face of the wall section.

21.5.3.5

Clause 21.5.3.2 need not apply to any part of a wall that lies within a distance of $3b_w$ from a continuous line of lateral support provided by a flange or cross wall. The width of the flange providing effective lateral support shall be not less than $\ell_u/5$.

21.5.4   Reinforcement

21.5.4.1

Unless otherwise specified in this Clause, all reinforcement in walls shall be anchored, spliced, or embedded in accordance with the provisions for reinforcement in tension as specified in Clause 12 and modified by Clause 21.5.4.2. All lap splices shall have a minimum length of $1.5\ell_d$.

21.5.4.2

Welded splices and mechanical connections may be used for splicing, provided the connections can develop at least 1.1 times the maximum yield stress of the bar permitted by CSA Standard G30.18. Where such splices and connections are used, not more than alternate bars in each layer of distributed and concentrated longitudinal reinforcement shall be spliced at any section, and the centre-to-centre distance between splices of adjacent bars shall be not less than $40d_b$ measured along the longitudinal axis of the wall.

21.5.4.3

The reinforcement ratio within any region of concentrated reinforcement shall be not more than 0.06.

21.5.4.4

The diameter of the bars used in a wall shall not exceed one-tenth of the thickness of the wall at the bar location.

21.5.5   Distributed Reinforcement

21.5.5.1

Both longitudinal and transverse distributed reinforcement shall be provided such that the reinforcement ratio for this distributed reinforcement is not less than 0.0025 in each direction. The reinforcement spacing in each direction shall not exceed 450 mm. Splices shall conform to Clause 21.5.4.1 or 21.5.4.2. In regions of plastic hinging, the reinforcement spacing in each direction shall not exceed 300 mm.

N21.5.4.2

Fig. N21.5.4.2 illustrates the requirement that if welded splices or mechanical connections are used not more than half the bars be spliced at one section.

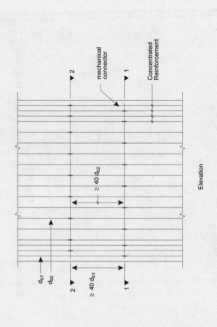

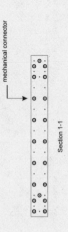

Fig. N21.5.4.2
Locations of Welded Splices or Mechanical Conections

176

N21.5.5

The different requirements for distributed and concentrated reinforcement in plastic hinge regions and other regions of ductile flexural walls are summarized below.

	Plastic Hinge	Other Region
Distributed reinforcement		
Amount	$\rho \geq 0.0025$	$\rho \geq 0.0025$
Spacing	≤ 300 mm	≤ 450 mm
Horizontal reinforcement anchorage	Develop f_y within region of concentrated reinforcement	extend into region of concentrated reinforcement
Concentrated reinforcement		
Where required	at ends of walls and coupling beams, corners, and junctions	at ends of walls and coupling beams
Amount* (at least 4 bars)	$\rho \geq 0.002\, b_w \ell_w$ $\rho \leq 0.06 \times$ area of concentrated reinforcement region	$\rho \geq 0.001\, b_w \ell_w$ $\rho \leq 0.06 \times$ area of concentrated reinforcement region
Hoop requirements	must satisfy Clauses 7.6 and 21.6.5	hoop spacing according to Clause 7.6
Splice requirements	$1.5\,\ell_d$ and not more than 50% at the same location. Unless lap length less than ¼ story height lap alternate floors	$1.5\,\ell_d$ and 100% at the same location.

*Note: *Amount of reinforcement must also satisfy requirements of Clause 21.5.6.2 and 21.5.7.*
Note: *Bar diameters must be less than or equal to 0.1 of the wall thickness.*

N21.5.4.3

This clause is intended to avoid excessive congestion of reinforcement. The reinforcement ratio is calculated using the area of concrete surrounding the concentrated reinforcement. Several such areas are shown shaded in Fig. N21.5.4.3. Note that this limit applies at lap splice locations.

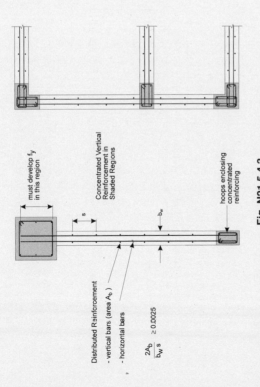

Distributed Reinforcement
- vertical bars (area A_b)
- horizontal bars

$$\frac{2A_b}{b_w\,s} \geq 0.0025$$

must develop f_y in this region

s

Concentrated Vertical Reinforcement in Shaded Regions

b_w

hoops enclosing concentrated reinforcing

Fig. N21.5.4.3
Distributed Reinforcement and Concentrated Reinforcement

21.5.5.2
Horizontal reinforcement shall extend to the ends of the wall and shall be contained at each end of the wall within a region of concentrated reinforcement as specified in Clause 21.5.6.

21.5.5.3
At least two curtains of reinforcement shall be used if, in regions of plastic hinging, the in-plane factored shear force assigned to the wall exceeds $0.2\lambda\phi_c\sqrt{f_c'}A_{cv}$. The vertical reinforcement shall be placed outside the horizontal reinforcement.

21.5.5.4
In regions of plastic hinging, horizontal reinforcement shall be anchored within a region of concentrated reinforcement to develop f_y.

21.5.6   Concentrated Reinforcement

21.5.6.1
Vertical reinforcement shall be concentrated at each end of the wall. Each concentration shall be a minimum of four bars placed in at least two layers. In regions of plastic hinging, such concentration shall also be provided at corners and at junctions of intersecting walls.

21.5.6.2
The concentrated reinforcement shall be proportioned to resist factored load effects including earthquake. Distributed reinforcement shall be taken into account in determining the resistance of the wall.

21.5.6.3
The minimum concentrated reinforcement shall be $0.001b_w\ell_w$ at each end of the wall except as specified in Clause 21.5.6.4.

21.5.6.4
The minimum area of concentrated reinforcement in regions of plastic hinging shall be $0.002b_w\ell_w$ at each end of the wall.

21.5.6.5
The concentrated reinforcement shall be at least tied as a column in accordance with Clause 7.6, and the ties shall be detailed as hoops. In regions of plastic hinging, the spacing between ties shall not exceed the least of
(a)   6 longitudinal bar diameters;
(b)   24 tie diameters;
(c)   one-half of the wall thickness; or
(d)   that required by Clause 21.5.7, if applicable.

21.5.6.6
The concentrated reinforcement shall consist of straight bars with no cranks.

148

N21.5.6.2
The wall moments should be resisted primarily by concentrated reinforcement as walls with just distributed steel often fail by rupture of the edge tension reinforcement prior to developing significant ductility. In calculating the wall resistance the distributed reinforcement is taken into account.

N21.5.6.4
This minimum reinforcement requirement is intended to ensure that the wall possesses post-cracking capacity.

N21.5.6.5
The closer spacing of ties in the plastic hinge region are intended to prevent buckling of bars under compression.

21.5.6.7

In regions of plastic hinging, not more than 50% of the reinforcement at each end of the walls shall be spliced at the same location. In such walls a total of at least half of the height of each storey shall be completely clear of lap splices in the concentrated reinforcement.

21.5.7 Ductility

To ensure ductility in a plastic hinge region of a wall, the distance to the neutral axis, c_c, given either by Equation (21-5) or found by calculating the factored flexural resistance of the wall under the action of the axial loads, P_s, P_n, and P_{ns}, shall not exceed $0.55 \ell_w$. When c_c exceeds $0.14 \gamma_w \ell_w$, the compression region of the wall shall be confined as a column, as specified in Clause 21.4.4, over a distance of not less than $c_c(0.25 + c_c/\ell_w)$ from the compression face of the wall. The minimum vertical reinforcement ratio in any part of this confined region shall be 0.005.

$$c_c = \frac{P_s + P_n + P_{ns} - \alpha_1 \phi_c f'_c A_f}{\alpha_1 \beta_1 \phi_c f'_c b_w} \tag{21-5}$$

21.5.8 Ductile Coupled and Partially Coupled Walls

21.5.8.1

Ductile partially coupled wall systems shall be designed with the limits on c_c calculated taking ℓ_w as the lengths of the individual wall segments. Ductile coupled wall systems shall be designed with the limits on c_c calculated taking ℓ_w as the length of the coupled wall system but c_c shall not exceed $0.5 \gamma_w \ell_w$, unless confinement as a column in accordance with Clause 21.4.4 is provided over the length ℓ_c, in which case c_c shall not exceed ℓ_c.

21.5.8.2

Coupled and partially coupled walls shall be connected by ductile coupling beams. The maximum beam shear stress resulting from factored load effects shall not exceed $1.0\sqrt{f'_c}$. In such coupling beams the entire in-plane factored shear and flexure shall be resisted by diagonal reinforcement in both directions unless the shear stress resulting from the factored load effects is less than $0.1(\ell_u/d)\sqrt{f'_c}$ and the beams satisfy the dimensional requirements of Clause 21.3.1, in which case the beams may instead satisfy the requirements of Clause 21.3. Reinforcement in coupling beams shall be anchored into the wall with a minimum embedment of $1.5\ell_d$. The diagonal reinforcement in each direction shall be interlocked and enclosed by hoops or spirals whose spacing shall not exceed the least of

(a)   6 diagonal bar diameters;

(b)   24 tie diameters; or

(c)   100 mm.

21.5.8.3

Walls at each end of a coupling beam shall be designed such that the factored moment resistance of the wall calculated about its centroid exceeds the moment at its centroid resulting from the nominal resistance of the coupling beams framing into the wall and the factored moment in the wall. The factored capacity shall be calculated using axial loads P_s and P_n.

N21.5.6.7

The requirement to keep at least half the storey height free of lap splices is to provide a height of wall with only the calculated capacity.

N21.5.7

The calculated depth of compression, c_c is used as an indicator of the ductility of the wall. The value of c_c may be determined from Eq. (21-5). Walls in which c_c exceeds $0.55 \ell_w$ have insufficient post yield rotational capacity to be permitted. Walls with very low values of c_c (less than $0.14 \gamma_w \ell_w$) do not require additional measures to improve their ductility. In checking this limit, it is conservative to use a low value of γ_w and hence γ_w can be estimated as $1/\phi_s$ (i.e. $\gamma_w = 1.18$). Fig. N21.5.7 shows the confinement reinforcement required to improve the ductility of walls in which c_c exceeds $0.14 \gamma_w \ell_w$. The definition of γ_w has changed in this edition of the code and is now taken as the individual wall overstrength except for coupled walls where the combined overstrength is used. See clause 21.8.5 for the calculation of γ_w for coupled walls.

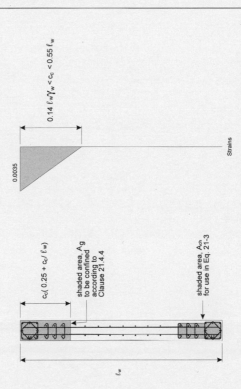

Fig. N21.5.7

Confinement Requirements for Walls with Intermediate Values of C_c

N21.5.8.1

Ductile coupled walls are walls with ductile coupling beams (headers) linking individual wall segments where the primary ductility and energy absorption is in the coupling beam plastic hinges. In order to classify as a coupled wall system with an R of 4.0 a majority of the overturning moment must be carried through axial loads in the wall elements induced by vertical shears in the coupling beams. If this is not the case then a significant proportion of the moment is carried by individual bending in the wall elements with an R of 3.5 as a standard ductile wall. See Figure N21.5.8.1

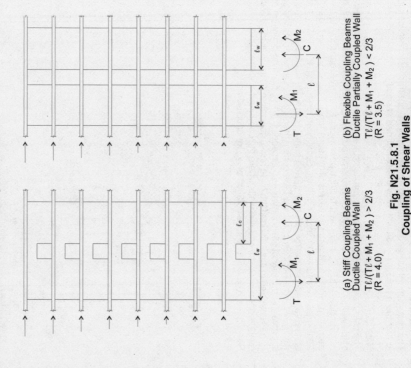

(a) Stiff Coupling Beams
Ductile Coupled Wall
$T\ell/(T\ell + M_1 + M_2) > 2/3$
$(R = 4.0)$

(b) Flexible Coupling Beams
Ductile Partially Coupled Wall
$T\ell/(T\ell + M_1 + M_2) < 2/3$
$(R = 3.5)$

**Fig. N21.5.8.1
Coupling of Shear Walls**

N21.5.8.2

The coupling beam requirements are the same whether a wall is coupled or partially coupled and are selected from two types depending on header proportions and the shear to be carried. The primary system is the diagonally reinforced coupling beam, however if the shears are small and the span to depth ratios large then beams similar to ductile frame beams may be used. X-headers cannot be wider than the wall since the bar anchorage must be contained within the wall. A coupling beam satisfying the requirements of Clause 21.3 can be wider than the wall but if so should be centred on the wall and within the limitations of 21.3.1(d). In the ductile beam case the capacity of the wall to carry the beam moment locally at the beam wall junction and the transfer of the direct shear, torsion and bending forces from the beam to the wall should be checked in addition to the requirements of 21.5.8.3. The limitation on gross shear stress is an attempt to prevent placing problems and is not a limitation of the load carrying system in the case of a diagonally reinforced coupling beam. The practical limit is set by the requirement to have the bars pass through the wall zone at the ends of the beam. The reinforcement centroid of each leg of the cross should be centred in the wall thickness or else secondary moments are developed out of the plane of the wall. Note that the walls must extend a minimum of 1.5 ℓ_d beyond each end of the beam to anchor the reinforcement and in addition must develop the capacity required by 21.5.8.3. Fig. N21.5.8.2(a) illustrates the design and detailing requirements for diagonal reinforcing.

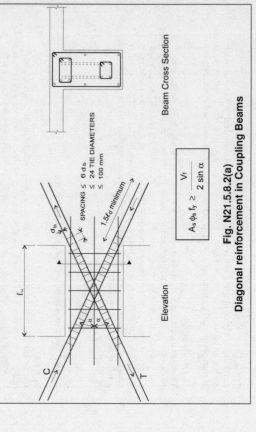

Elevation

SPACING ≤ 6 d_b
≤ 24 TIE DIAMETERS
≤ 100 mm

1.5ℓ_d minimum

Beam Cross Section

$$A_s \phi_s f_y \geq \frac{V_f}{2 \sin \alpha}$$

**Fig. N21.5.8.2(a)
Diagonal reinforcement in Coupling Beams**

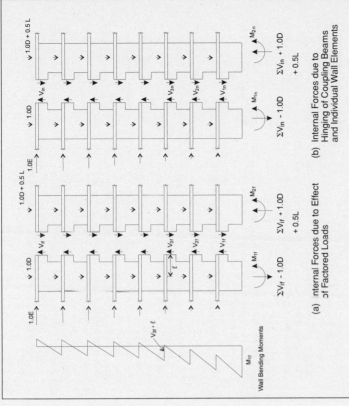

(a) Internal Forces due to Effect of Factored Loads

(b) Internal Forces due to Hinging of Coupling Beams and Individual Wall Elements

Fig. N21.5.8.3
Design Forces for Coupled Walls

The coupling beams may be designed with redistributed shear forces as illustrated in Fig. N21.5.8.2(b). The shear in any individual beam should not be reduced by more than 20% of the elastically determined value. The sum of the resistance over the height of the building must be greater than or equal to the sum of the elastically determined values. For the case where forces are determined using equivalent static loading the design header shears should not be reduced to correspond to the overturning moment calculated using the reduction factor J.

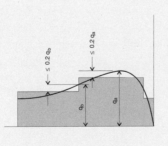

Fig. N21.5.8.2(b)
Design of Coupling Beams Using Redistribution

N21.5.8.3

In order to ensure that the plastic hinges form in the coupling beams (headers), not the walls, the wall at each end of the beam must be stronger than the beams framing into it. This is similar to strong columns weak beams required by Clause 21.4.2.2 for ductile frames. See Figure N21.5.8.3

21.5.8.4
Concentrated vertical reinforcement, as specified in Clause 21.5.6.1, shall be provided in the walls at both ends of the coupling beams.

21.5.8.5
Linked and coupled wall systems shall be designed with factored moment resistance greater than the overturning moment corresponding to the development of the nominal moment resistance of the coupling beams above the level under consideration. The factored capacity shall be calculated using axial loads P_s and P_n.

21.6 Joints of Ductile Frames

21.6.1 Scope and General Requirements
Note: *This Clause is intended to apply to joints between members designed using a force modification factor, R, greater than 2.0.*

21.6.1.1
The requirements of Clause 21.6 apply to joints of ductile frames serving as parts of the lateral force resisting system.

21.6.1.2
Factored forces in joints shall be determined by assuming that the tensile stress in the longitudinal beam reinforcement at the joint is $1.25f_y$.

21.6.1.3
Longitudinal beam reinforcement terminated in a column shall be extended to the far face of the confined column core and anchored in tension according to Clause 21.6.5 and in compression according to Clause 12.

21.6.2 Transverse Reinforcement in Joints

21.6.2.1
Transverse hoop reinforcement, as specified in Clause 21.4.4 and calculated using the larger of f'_c for the column or the joint, shall be provided within the joint, unless the joint is confined by structural members as specified in Clause 21.6.2.2.

21.6.2.2
Within the depth of the shallowest framing member, transverse reinforcement equal to at least one-half of the amount required by Clause 21.6.2.1 shall be provided where members frame into all four sides of the joint and where each member width is at least three-fourths of the column width. At these locations the spacing specified in Clause 21.4.4.3(b) may be increased to 150 mm.

21.6.2.3
Transverse reinforcement, as required by Clause 21.4.4, shall be provided through the joint to provide confinement for longitudinal beam reinforcement located outside the column core, if such confinement is not provided by a beam framing into the joint.

N21.5.8.4
Minimum reinforcing requirements for the intersection of the walls and coupling beams are required. More concentrated reinforcement may be required to develop the required capacities.

N21.5.8.5
The capacity of the tension wall at any level must exceed the sum of the header shear capacities above that level if all the headers are to yield in a push over mechanism. This requirement may be too severe for tall buildings where a significant portion of the header shears come from higher modes. To account for this effect it is suggested that the tension wall be designed for a coupling moment:

$$M_{\gamma coupling} = \gamma_h \times M_{EFL\,coupling}$$

where $M_{EFL\,coupling}$ includes the effect of the 'J' reduction in the case of the equivalent static load approach or is the dynamic moment which includes the effect of higher modes.

The value of γ_h should be the ratio of the sum of the nominal capacities of the coupling beams (designed to include the effects of accidental torsion) to the sum of the effect of factored loads beam forces (without the application of the accidental torsion).

$$\gamma_h = \frac{\Sigma V_{n\,header}}{\Sigma V_{EFL\,header}}$$

The overstrength for coupled walls to be used in the ductility calculation of clause 21.5.7 should be:

$$\gamma_w = \frac{M_{1n} + M_{2n} + M_{\gamma\,coupling}}{M_{EFL\,overturning}}$$

Individual wall moments up to 30% of the elastically determined values may be redistributed from the tension wall to the compression wall. Care must be taken to make sure the requirements of 21.5.8.3 are still satisfied and the shear design is based on the flexural overstrength of the wall elements.

N21.6.1.2
Fig. N21.6.1.2 illustrates the procedure for determining the factored shear in joints of ductile frames. The 1.25 factor is intended to account for the likely stress in the bars when plastic hinges form in the beams.

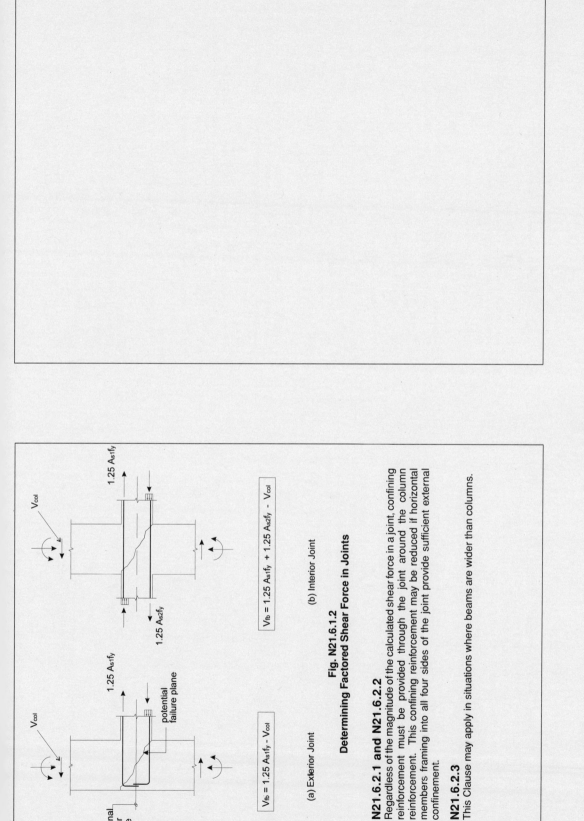

$\boxed{V_{fb} = 1.25\ A_{s1}f_y - V_{col}}$

(a) Exterior Joint

$\boxed{V_{fb} = 1.25\ A_{s1}f_y + 1.25\ A_{s2}f_y - V_{col}}$

(b) Interior Joint

Fig. N21.6.1.2
Determining Factored Shear Force in Joints

N21.6.2.1 and N21.6.2.2
Regardless of the magnitude of the calculated shear force in a joint, confining reinforcement must be provided through the joint around the column reinforcement. This confining reinforcement may be reduced if horizontal members framing into all four sides of the joint provide sufficient external confinement.

N21.6.2.3
This Clause may apply in situations where beams are wider than columns.

N21.6.3

Confinement of the joint core is provided by the cage formed from the longitudinal steel and the corresponding hoops and ties. Depending on the size of the column the maximum spacing between adjacent longitudinal bars is between 200mm (this Clause) and 300mm (Clause 21.4.4.4).

N21.6.4

The shear force is transferred through a joint by diagonal compressive struts in the concrete acting together with tensile forces in the vertical reinforcing bars. Rather than calculating the required amount of joint shear reinforcement this Standard assumes that a joint containing transverse and longitudinal reinforcement satisfying Clauses 21.6.2 and 21.6.3 will have the factored shear resistance given in this clause.

N21.6.5.2

Bars of sizes No. 35 and smaller can be anchored with standard 90 deg. hooks. The development lengths for f_y = 400 MPa are:

Bar No.	X (mm)	ℓ_{dh} (mm) f'_c MPa				
		20	25	30	35	40
10	44	179	160	150	150	150
15	64	268	240	219	203	190
20	80	358	320	292	270	253
25	100	447	400	365	337	316
30	150	537	480	438	406	379
35	216	626	560	511	473	443

These lengths were determined by considering the beneficial effects of confinement which must be present. See Fig. N21.6.5.2 for illustration of the case.

21.6.3 Longitudinal Column Reinforcement

21.6.3.1

Longitudinal column reinforcement in round column cores shall be uniformly distributed around the column core with a centre-to-centre spacing not exceeding the larger of
(a) 200 mm; or
(b) one-third of the column core diameter.

21.6.3.2

Longitudinal column reinforcement in rectangular column cores shall have the reinforcing in each face uniformly distributed along that face with a centre-to-centre spacing not exceeding the larger of:
(a) 200 mm; or
(b) one-third of the core dimension in that direction.

21.6.4 Shear Resistance of Joints

21.6.4.1

The factored shear resistance of the joint shall not be assumed to exceed:
(a) for confined joint, $2.4\lambda\phi_c\sqrt{f'_c}A_j$;
(b) for joints confined on three faces or on two opposite faces, $1.8\lambda\phi_c\sqrt{f'_c}A_j$; and
(c) for others, $1.5\lambda\phi_c\sqrt{f'_c}A_j$
where f'_c is the strength of the concrete in the joint.

A member that frames into a face is considered to provide confinement to the joint if at least three-quarters of the face of the joint is covered by the framing member. A joint is considered to be confined if such confining members frame into all faces of the joint.

21.6.4.2

The shear force, V_{fh}, in the joint determined by using the forces defined in Clause 21.6.1.2 and accounting for other forces on the joint shall not exceed the factored resistance specified in Clause 21.6.4.1.

21.6.5 Development Length for Tension Reinforcement in Joints

21.6.5.1

Hooks, if used, shall be standard 90° hooks and shall be located within the confined column core.

21.6.5.2

For normal density concrete, the development length, ℓ_{dh}, for a bar with a standard 90° hook shall not be less than the greatest of:
(a) $8d_b$;
(b) 150 mm; or

(c) for bar sizes of No. 35 and smaller, the length given by

$$\ell_{dh} = 0.2 \frac{f_y}{\sqrt{f_c}} d_b \qquad (21\text{-}6)$$

21.6.5.3
For structural low-density concrete, the development length for a bar with a standard hook shall be not less than 1.25 times that required by Clause 21.6.5.2.

21.6.5.4
For bar sizes of No. 35 and smaller, the development length, ℓ_d, for a straight bar in a joint shall be not less than
(a) 2.5 times the length required by Clause 21.6.5.2 or 21.6.5.3, if the depth of the concrete cast in one lift beneath the bar does not exceed 300 mm; and
(b) 3.5 times the length required by Clause 21.6.5.2 or 21.6.5.3, if the depth of the concrete cast in one lift beneath the bar exceeds 300 mm.

21.6.5.5
Straight bars terminated at a joint shall pass through the confined core of a column. Any portion of the straight embedment length not within the confined core shall be considered 60% effective.

21.6.5.6
The diameter of straight beam and column bars passing through the joint shall satisfy

$$d_b \leq \lambda \frac{\ell_j}{24} \qquad (21\text{-}7)$$

21.7 Shear Strength Requirements
Note: *This Clause is intended to apply to shear in members designed using a force modification factor, R, greater than 2.0.*

21.7.1 Scope
Unless otherwise specified in Clause 21, the requirements of Clause 21.7 apply to structures designed in accordance with Clauses 21.3 to 21.6, inclusive.

21.7.2 Design Forces

21.7.2.1 Frame Members Subjected Primarily to Bending
Frame members that satisfy Clause 21.3 shall resist a factored shear, determined by assuming that moments equal to the probable moment resistance act at the faces of the joint so as to produce maximum shear in the member, and that the member is then loaded with the specified tributary transverse load along the span. The moments corresponding to probable strength shall be calculated using the properties of the member at the faces of the joint. The factored shear need not exceed that determined from factored load combinations with load effects calculated using R equal to 1.0.

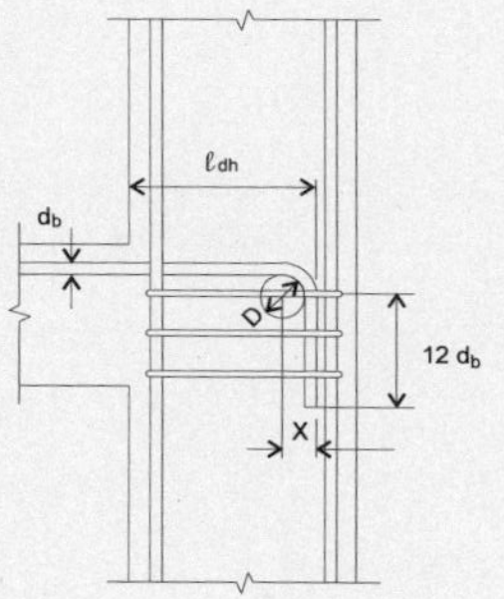

152

Fig. N21.6.5.2
Values of Development Length for Hooked Bars with f_y = 400 MPa Anchored in Confined Column Cores

N21.6.5.6
A straight bar passing through a beam-column joint may be subjected to tension on one side of the joint and compression on the other side of the joint (see Fig. N21.6.1.2). Limiting the bar diameter to 1/24 of the joint length provides some control of the bond stresses.

N21.7.2.1
Fig. N21.7.2.1 illustrates the requirements of this clause which is intended to ensure that the member develops flexural hinging prior to shear failure.

N21.7.2.2

Fig. N21.7.2.2 illustrates an approximate procedure for estimating the column shears corresponding to the development of probable moment resistance in the beams. The column length used should consider the detrimental effects of any infill walls or architectural spandrels.

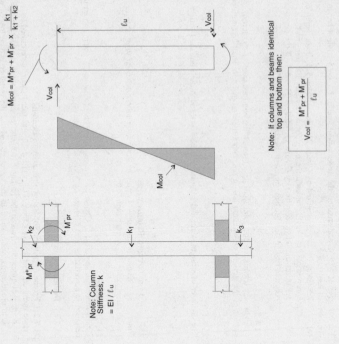

$$M_{col} = M^+_{pr} + M_{pr} \times \frac{k_1}{k_1 + k_2}$$

Note: Column Stiffness, k
$= EI / \ell_u$

Note: If columns and beams identical top and bottom then:

$$V_{col} = \frac{M^+_{pr} + M_{pr}}{\ell_u}$$

Fig. N21.7.2.2
Determination of Column Shears Corresponding to Hinging in the Beams

N21.7.2.3

Fig. N21.7.2.3 illustrates this clause for a single uncoupled wall system. The upper limit on required shear strength is introduced for cases where probable moment strength approaches that of an elastically responding system.

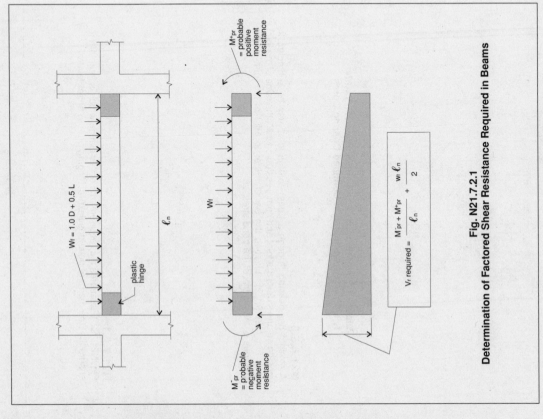

$W_f = 1.0 D + 0.5 L$

plastic hinge

ℓ_n

W_f

M^-_{pr} = probable negative moment resistance

M^+_{pr} = probable positive moment resistance

$$V_r \text{ required} = \frac{M^-_{pr} + M^+_{pr}}{\ell_n} + \frac{w_f \ell_n}{2}$$

Fig. N21.7.2.1
Determination of Factored Shear Resistance Required in Beams

21.7.2.2 Frame Members Subject to Combined Bending and Axial Load

A column that satisfies Clause 21.4 shall have a factored shear resistance that exceeds the greater of

(a) the forces resulting from the development of probable moment resistances of the beams framing into the column; or

(b) shear forces due to the factored load effects.

21.7.2.3 Ductile Flexural Walls

Ductile flexural walls shall have a factored shear resistance not less than the lesser of

(a) the shear corresponding to the development of the probable moment capacity of the wall system at its plastic hinge locations; or

(b) the shear resulting from design load combinations which include earthquake with load effects calculated using R equal to 1.0. Allowance for dynamic magnification of shear forces shall be made where applicable.

21.7.3 Shear Reinforcement in Members

Members subjected to seismic shear shall be designed according to the requirements of Clause 11 but with the following exceptions.

21.7.3.1 Frame Members

(a) For members conforming to Clause 21.3, the values of $\theta=45°$ and $\beta=0$ or $V_c = 0$ shall be used in the regions defined in Clause 21.3.3.2.

(b) For members conforming to Clause 21.4, ϵ_x shall be taken as 0.002 or V_c shall be one-half the value determined from Equation (11-6) in the region defined in Clauses 21.4.4.5 and 21.4.4.7.

(c) Transverse reinforcement required to resist shear shall be hoops over the lengths of members as specified in Clauses 21.3.3, 21.4.4, and 21.6.2.

21.7.3.2 Walls

(a) For regions of walls where the vertical reinforcement is expected to yield, θ shall be taken as 45° and β shall be taken from Table 21-1 or the value $V_c = 0$ may be used.

(b) For ductile flexural walls, the average vertical strain, ϵ_v, shall be calculated using Equation (21-8) for regions required to be detailed for plastic hinging.

$$\epsilon_v = \frac{0.001}{\gamma_w}\left(0.5 - \frac{c_c}{\ell_w}\right)\left(18 + \frac{h_w}{\ell_w}\right) \tag{21-8}$$

where c_c and ℓ_w are given in Clauses 21.5.7 and 21.5.8.1. Alternatively, ϵ_v may be taken as 0.015.

(c) Areas of the wall outside the plastic hinge region, where the vertical reinforcement is expected to remain elastic, shall be designed according to Clause 11.

(d) The effective shear depth, d_v, of a wall shall be calculated as described in Clause 11.0 but need not be taken less than $0.8\ell_w$.

The suggestion that an allowance be made for dynamic magnification of shear forces is intended to refer to both Clauses 21.7.2.3(a) and (b). This requirement is introduced because it is known that shears higher than those determined just by increasing shears based on the ratio of the probable moment resistance to the factored moment are possible. This is partially a result of the **J** factor in NBCC being conservative in predicting the reduction in base moments due to the effects of higher modes and partially due to the fact that accelerations can be transferred to the upper part of a wall through a plastic hinge. All seismic resisting systems except walls absorb their energy in a shear (sway) mode of failure such as, for example, the bending of beams in frames or the tension or compression yielding of braces. For these cases it is important to preclude overturning moment failure before the energy is absorbed by the shear (sway) mechanism and the small **J** value reduction is conservative. In the case of walls the moment yield must take place before the wall fails in shear. For this case the small **J** reduction is not conservative. In addition elasto-plastic time step analysis of wall buildings has shown that the formation of a plastic hinge does not limit the shears induced in the walls.

There are procedures in the New Zealand code which attempt to deal with this problem and there is research currently underway to develop a procedure applicable to Canadian codes. A rational way to deal with this problem in the interim may be to use the New Zealand approach, reduced by **J** since they do not have a **J** in their code, and reduced again by 1/1.25 to account for their use of nominal rather than probable capacity. The reduced value should not be less than 1.0. For the case of dynamic analysis the effective **J** should be used. The New Zealand multiplier is 0.9 + $n/10$ for buildings up to six stories and 1.3 + $n/30$ to a maximum of 1.8 for buildings over six stories where n is the number of stories. This multiplier should be used in addition to the shear overstrength until better values are determined.

N21.7.3

Requirements are given to account for the reduction in shear capacity due to reversed cyclic loading into the yield range of the reinforcement. Modifications to both the simplified and general methods of shear design in Clause 11 are given. Generally the modifications to the general method are less severe.

N21.7.3.1

(a) For the plastic hinge regions of beams a simple conservative approach is used, namely a 45 degree truss model with no concrete contribution.

(b) For columns which are part of a ductile system, a reduction in the shear capacity has been introduced in this standard to reflect the severe consequences of failure of these members.

(c) Because spalling of the concrete cover is expected to occur during a strong earthquake, especially in and near regions of flexural yielding, all transverse reinforcement in these zones must be provided in the form of closed hoops. Note that in determining shear resistance transverse reinforcement provided for confinement and effective in shear can be included.

(b) The parameter ε_v is an indication of the amount of vertical deformation that is expected in the wall. An overstrength of the wall results in a reduction of the ductility demand. The parameter c_c/ℓ_w, which is calculated by the designer in the evaluation of the ductility of the wall (Clause 21.5.7), reflects the magnitude of the axial compression in the wall and the geometry of the wall cross-section. The aspect ratio of the wall (h_w/ℓ_w) influences the rotational ductility demand of the wall.

(e) The maximum factored shear stress in walls depends of the value of the average vertical strain ε_v and is summarized in Fig. N21.7.3.2. If ε_v is not calculated, the maximum factored shear stress shall not exceed $0.10\,\phi_c f'_c$.

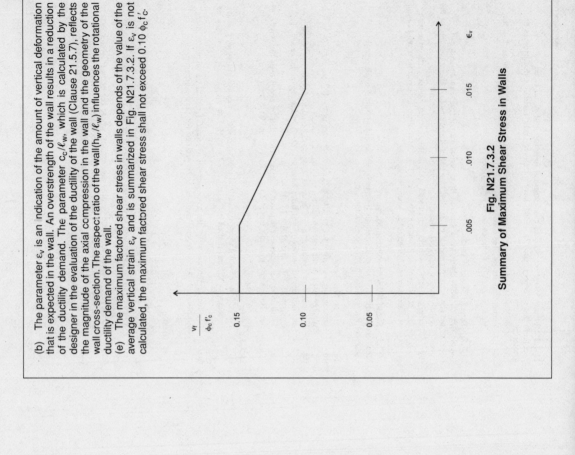

Fig. N21.7.3.2
Summary of Maximum Shear Stress in Walls

(a) Internal Forces due to
Effect of Factored Loads

(b) Internal Forces due
to Wall Hinging

$$\gamma_p = \frac{M_{pw}}{M_f}$$

M_{pw} = probable moment resistance of wall under axial compressive load of 1.0D

Fig. N21.7.2.3
**Calculation of Wall Shear at Occurance of
Plastic Hinge Mechanism**

N21.7.3.2

(a) The designer may use the simple conservative approach of $V_c = 0$ (as in the 1984 code) or make use of the more refined procedures that have been introduced. These refined procedures are particularly valuable for shorter walls with large flexural overstrength.

(e) The wall shall be proportioned so that the factored shear stress, v_f, does not exceed $0.15\phi_c f'_c$ when $\varepsilon_v \leq 0.005$. When $\varepsilon_v > 0.005$ the factored shear stress, v_r, shall be limited to the values given in Table 21-1.

(f) The vertical reinforcement in the plastic hinge region of a wall shall extend vertically beyond the point where yielding will first occur for a minimum distance of the effective shear depth of the wall plus the development length of the bar.

(g) For walls having a ratio of (h_w/ℓ_w) less than 2.0, the minimum vertical reinforcement ratio, ρ_v, is given by Equation (21-9) as a function of the required horizontal reinforcement ratio, ρ_h:

$$\rho_v \geq \left(1 + \frac{2V_c}{V_s}\right)\rho_h \qquad (21\text{-}9)$$

(h) All construction joints in walls shall be clean and free of laitance and shall satisfy the requirements of Clause 11.6.

Table 21-1
Values of β for Walls Subjected to Seismic Shear
(See Clause 21.7.3.2.)

$\dfrac{v_f}{\lambda\,\phi_c f'_c}$	Average vertical strain, ε_v								
	≤ 0.0005	≤ 0.001	≤ 0.0015	≤ 0.002	≤ 0.003	≤ 0.005	≤ 0.010	≤ 0.015
≤ 0.025	0.228	0.195	0.172	0.156	0.133	0.105	0.071	0.054
≤ 0.050	0.222	0.191	0.170	0.154	0.131	0.103	0.069	0.053
≤ 0.075	0.217	0.188	0.167	0.152	0.129	0.101	0.067	0.051
≤ 0.100	0.212	0.184	0.164	0.149	0.127	0.099	0.065	0.047
≤ 0.125	0.207	0.181	0.121	0.147	0.125	0.097	0.063	–
≤ 0.150	0.202	0.177	0.158	0.144	0.122	0.095	–	–

21.7.3.3 Strut-and-Tie Models

Regions near discontinuities, where it is inappropriate to assume that the shear stresses are uniformly distributed over the section, may be designed according to the requirements of Clause 11.5. In plastic hinge regions, the following exceptions shall be satisfied:

(a) The smallest angle between a compression strut and an adjoining tension tie shall not be less than 30°.

(b) The limiting compressive stress in the strut shall be taken as 0.8 times the value determined from Equation (11-30).

(c) A compression strut which during the reverse direction of seismic loading is a tension tie designed to yield, shall contain a minimum of four bars placed in at least two layers. This reinforcement shall be tied as a column in accordance with

154

(f) Fig. N21.5.2.1 suggests a moment envelope which illustrates why extensions are needed beyond the plastic hinge location.

(g) For short walls considerable shear is transmitted directly to the base of the wall by diagonal compression struts. Vertical reinforcement is needed to equilibrate the vertical component of the diagonal compression force. By choosing a smaller V_c a designer can change the relative amounts of horizontal and vertical reinforcement.

(h) These requirements have been introduced because of observations of sliding on construction joints in earthquakes.

N21.7.3.3

Special requirements are introduced for the situation where it is appropriate to design for shear forces by strut and tie methods in a plastic hinge region.

189

Clause 7.6, and the ties shall be detailed as hoops. In addition, the spacing of the ties shall not exceed the least of
(i) 6 longitudinal bar diameters;
(ii) 24 tie diameters; or
(iii) 100 mm.

21.8 Frame Members Not Considered as Part of the Lateral Force Resisting System

Note: *This Clause is intended to apply to members which are not part of the lateral load carrying system in structures designed using a force modification factor, R, greater than 1.5.*

21.8.1 General Requirements

21.8.1.1
The intent of Clause 21.8 is to provide a minimum level of ductility and strength for those members of a structure subject to seismically induced deformations, but not considered as part of the lateral force resisting systems.

21.8.1.2
Unless it can be shown that moments in these members will not exceed their nominal resistance when the complete structure is deformed laterally through R times the deformation calculated for factored loads, these members must be designed to accommodate lateral deflection through the formation of a plastic hinge mechanism

21.8.1.3
The nominal axial, shear, and flexural resistance of each member shall be sufficient to carry all forces due to specified gravity loads and the axial and shear effects generated by the structure undergoing a displacement of R times that calculated for factored seismic loads.

21.8.2 Plastic Hinges in Members

21.8.2.1
Where the formation of plastic hinges is indicated by Clause 21.8.1.2, to ensure adequate rotational capacity when the complete structure is subject to specified gravity loads and lateral deformations, they shall be detailed in accordance with Clauses 21.8.2.2 to 21.8.2.4.

21.8.2.2
Where the member forces calculated at a displacement of the complete structure 1/4 of that determined from Clause 21.8.1.2 are greater than their nominal resistances, then flexural members (beams) shall be detailed to the requirements of Clauses 21.3.2 and 21.3.3 and flexural members with axial loads (columns) shall be detailed to the requirements of Clauses 21.4.4.2 and 21.4.4.3 over their full height.

21.8.2.3
Where the member forces calculated at a displacement of the complete structure 1/2 of that determined from Clause 21.8.1.2 are less than their nominal resistances, then the members need only satisfy the requirements of Clauses 1 to 18.

N21.8

This clause is intended to give guidelines to help ensure that the parts of the structural system designed for gravity loading only will continue to function at the lateral displacements of the frame expected during the earthquake.

Examples of members covered by this clause would include members which by virtue of their flexibility relative to other members are not included in the primary lateral force resisting system. Other examples are beams not satisfying the dimensional limits of Clause 21.3.1 or columns not satisfying the dimensional limits of Clause 21.4.1. The members need to either be strong enough to tolerate the increased deformations in an elastic manner, or the members must be detailed so the plastic hinges can occur without shear or compression failure.

N21.8.1.2

This clause outlines a procedure for determining which structural members in a building in addition to the lateral force resisting system need to be investigated for ductility. It is anticipated that a mathematical model of the complete building structural system is required which will include the lateral force resisting system as well as those portions of the building "going along for the ride". Consideration should also be given to the effects of possible foundation rotation and or "rocking" which may have been a significant factor in the failure of some parking garages in the Northridge earthquake.

N21.8.1.3

The intent of this clause is to prevent a collapse under gravity loads if members develop hinges at their ends when displaced R times the factored seismic deflection. It is important to check both one way and two-way shear capacity as well as induced compressions since flexural hinges in lightly reinforced horizontal members may be tolerable but shear or axial compression failure is not. Columns with more than light axial compression cannot tolerate significant inelastic rotations and deserve special care.

N21.8.2

The intent here is to separate the members of the structure not part of the lateral force resisting system into three detailing categories depending on the level of ductility demand. See Fig. N21.8.2 for a graphical illustration of these clauses.

N21.8.2.2

If plastic hinges start to form at 1/4 of the expected displacement then the element will experience a large ductility demand and must be detailed accordingly.

N21.8.2.3

If plastic hinges have not started at 1/2 of the expected displacement then the element ductility demand will be moderate and the standard detailing inherent in the code is sufficient.

21.8.2.4
Members not satisfying the requirements of Clauses 21.8.2.2 or 21.8.2.3 shall be detailed to the requirements of Clause 21.9.

21.9 Building Members Requiring Nominal Ductility

21.9.1 Scope
The requirements of Clause 21.9 apply to lateral force resisting members designed using a force modification factor, R, of 2.0.

Note: Requirements for the qualification of two-way floor systems without beams are not given. The ability of such structures to sustain their resistance to lateral loads when subjected to deformation reversals in the inelastic range has yet to be established. If used, they must be treated as a system with R equal to 1.5 and be subject to the restrictions of the National Building Code of Canada for such buildings.

21.9.2 Frames

21.9.2.1 Detailing of Beams

21.9.2.1.1
The positive moment resistance at the face of the joint shall be not less than one-third of the negative moment resistance provided at that face of the joint. Neither the negative nor the positive moment resistance at any section along the length of the member shall be less than one-fifth of the maximum moment resistance provided at the face of either joint.

21.9.2.1.2
At both ends of the member, No. 10 or larger stirrups detailed as hoops shall be provided over lengths equal to twice the member depth measured from the face of the supporting member towards midspan. The first stirrup shall be located not more than 50 mm from the face of the supporting member and the spacing along the length of the member shall not exceed
(a) d/4;
(b) 8 times the diameter of the smallest longitudinal bar enclosed;
(c) 24 times the diameter of the stirrup bar; or
(d) 300 mm.

21.9.2.1.3
Stirrups shall be spaced at not more than d/2 throughout the length of the member.

21.9.2.2 Detailing of Columns

21.9.2.2.1
Transverse reinforcement shall be detailed as hoops and cross ties.

21.9.2.2.2
Where plastic hinges are expected to develop in the columns, the tie spacing over a distance of not less than
(a) one-sixth of the clear height of the column;

156

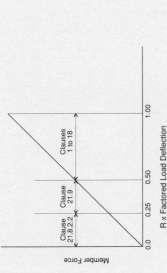

Fig. N21.8.2

Member Force

Clause 21.8.2.2 Clause 21.9 Clauses 1 to 18

0.0   0.25   0.50   1.00

R x Factored Load Deflection

N21.8.2.4
This section covers the intermediate cases.

N21.9.2
This Clause gives the requirements for lateral force resisting frames designed with an R of 2.0.

N21.9.2.1.1
This clause is intended to ensure continuity of reinforcement and some positive and negative moment capacity throughout the beam to allow for unexpected deformations and moment distributions from severe earthquake loading.

N21.9.2.1.2
This clause requires closely spaced stirrups in regions of potential inelastic action to prevent buckling of reinforcing under compression.

N21.9.2.2.2
This clause requires closely spaced column ties in regions of potential inelastic action.

Plastic hinges can be expected to develop in ground floor columns or in columns of storeys adjacent to a substantial change in structural stiffness. At other locations, plastic hinges in columns should be avoided if at all possible and columns should be stronger than adjacent beams (see Clause 21.4.2.2 for guidance).

(b)   the maximum cross sectional dimension of the member; or

(c)   450 mm from the face of each beam column joint

shall not exceed the lesser of one-half of the spacing specified in Clause 7.6.5 or 300 mm and the column reinforcement splices shall be centred at the mid-height of the column.

21.9.2.2.3

The first tie shall be located not more than a half tie space from the joint face.

21.9.2.3 Shear in Frames

The factored shear resistance of beams and columns resisting earthquake effects shall be not less than the lesser of

(a)   the sum of the maximum shear associated with development of nominal moment strengths of the member at each restrained end of the clear span and the shear calculated for specified gravity loads; or

(b)   the maximum shear obtained from design load combinations using specified gravity loads and earthquake loads calculated using R equal to 1.0.

21.9.2.4 Joints in Frames

21.9.2.4.1

The design forces acting on a beam column joint shall be those induced due to the nominal resistance of the beams or the columns framing into the joint, whichever are lesser. Where beams frame into the joint from two directions, each direction may be considered independently.

21.9.2.4.2

Minimum transverse tie reinforcement not less than required by Equation (11-1) shall be provided over the depth of the joint and spaced at 150 mm maximum.

21.9.2.4.3

Longitudinal column reinforcement shall have a centre-to-centre spacing not exceeding 300 mm.

21.9.2.4.4

The diameter of straight beam and column bars passing through the joint shall satisfy

$$d_b \le \lambda \frac{\ell_y}{20}$$

(21-10)

21.9.2.4.5

The maximum joint shear shall not exceed the limits in Clause 21.6.4.1.

21.9.3   Walls

21.9.3.1

The dimensional limitations of Clause 21.5.3 apply, except the limitation of $\ell_u/10$ in Clause 21.5.3.2 shall be taken as $\ell_u/14$.

December 1994

N21.9.2.3

The factored shear resistance for beams and columns shall be based on member flexural capacities as well as factored load effects so that flexural yielding will occur prior to shear failure. An upper limit is introduced corresponding to an elastic response level.

N21.9.2.4

This section on joints in nominally ductile frames is new. The reinforcement required is a minimum. See also clause 11.8 and 21.6.

N21.9.3

The requirements for walls follow the principles of clause 21.5 but are not as stringent.

N21.9.3.1

This clause allows a relaxation in the requirement of the height to thickness requirements for walls of lower ductility demand is suggested in the work of Paulay.

21.9.3.2 Ductility of Walls
To ensure ductility in a plastic hinge region of a wall, the distance to the neutral axis, c_c, determined in accordance with Equation (21-5) shall not exceed $0.33\ell_w\gamma_w$, unless concentrated vertical reinforcement having a minimum reinforcement ratio of 0.005, tied in accordance with Clause 21.4.4, is provided over the outer half of the compression zone.

21.9.3.3 Detailing of Walls

21.9.3.3.1
The distributed reinforcement ratio for walls shall be not less than 0.0025 in the vertical and horizontal directions.

21.9.3.3.2
Concentrated longitudinal reinforcement in plastic hinge regions shall satisfy Clauses 21.5.4.1, 21.5.6.5, and 21.5.6.6 and shall be tied in accordance with Clause 7.6.5 outside these regions.

21.9.3.3.3
Corners and junctions of intersecting walls shall be adequately tied to ensure unity of action. All horizontal bars shall extend to the far face of the joining wall and be bent around a vertical bar with a standard 90° hook.

21.9.3.4 Shear in Walls

21.9.3.4.1
Walls shall have a factored shear resistance not less than the lesser of
(a) the shear corresponding to the development of the nominal moment capacity of the wall system at its plastic hinge locations; or
(b) the shear resulting from design load combinations which include earthquake effect with loads calculated using R equal to 1.0.

21.9.3.4.2
Walls with nominal ductility shall be designed according to either
(a) the requirements of Clause 11.4, except that in plastic hinge regions, θ shall be taken as 45° and β shall be taken as 0.10;
(b) the requirements of Clause 11.3, except that in plastic hinge regions, V_c shall be taken as one-half the value determined from Equation (11-6); or
(c) the requirements of Clause 21.7.3.2, except that ϵ_v calculated by Equation (21-8) may be multiplied by 0.5.

158

N21.9.3.2
The limits in Clause 21.5.7 are relaxed for R = 2.0 walls because of the reduced ductility demand.

N21.9.3.3.2
Concentrated vertical reinforcement needs anti-buckling ties in plastic hinge regions but this requirement can be relaxed elsewhere.

N21.9.3.3.3
The requirements of this clause apply to wall intersections without tied concentrated reinforcement at the intersection. Where tied concentrations exist the horizontal reinforcement shall be anchored within the tied region.

N21.9.3.4
The requirements for shear design are similar to 21.7 but are less stringent reflecting the reduced ductility demand.

22. Plain Concrete

22.0 Notation

A_g = gross area of section

b = width of member

b_o = perimeter of critical section for shear in footings

f'_c = specified compressive strength of concrete

$\sqrt{f'_c}$ = square root of specified compressive strength of concrete

h = overall thickness of member

k = effective length factor (Clause 22.4.1)

ℓ_c = vertical clear distance between supports

P_r = factored axial load resistance of wall

V_f = factored shear force at section

V_r = factored shear resistance of a section

β_c = ratio of long side to short side of concentrated load or reaction area

λ = factor to account for low-density concrete (Clause 8.6.5)

ϕ_c = resistance factor for concrete (Clause 8.4.2)

22.1 Scope

22.1.1

Provisions of Clause 22 are requirements for the design of concrete members containing less reinforcement than the minimum amount specified for reinforced concrete members in the balance of this Standard. The provisions of this Clause shall be limited to pedestals with $\ell_c/h \leq 3$, walls not exceeding 3 m in total height that have continuous vertical support, pad footings, spread footings, deep foundations, and slabs on ground.

Note: *For information on plain concrete deep foundations, refer to the Canadian Foundation Engineering Manual.*

22.1.2

Plain concrete shall not be used for structural members where ductility is required as, for example, for earthquake or blast loads.

22.1.3

Plain concrete shall not be used for footings on piles.

22.2 Control Joints

22.2.1

In plain concrete construction, control joints shall be provided to divide a structural member into flexurally discontinuous elements. The size of each element shall be limited to control stresses caused by restraint to movements from creep, shrinkage, and temperature effects.

N22.1 Scope

Since the structural integrity of plain concrete members depends solely on the properties of the concrete, their use should be limited to: members that are primarily in a state of compression; members that can tolerate random cracks without detriment to their structural integrity; and members where ductility is not an essential feature of design. The standard does not permit the use of plain concrete columns or plain concrete beams.

The minimum concrete strength for plain concrete is not limited to 20 MPa because there is no concern for bond strength and corrosion protection of reinforcement. See Cl. 8.6.1.3. In many circumstances the minimum concrete strength will be governed by the durability provisions of CSA-A23.1. However, even when concrete durability does not restrict the minimum strength it would be normal to use strengths exceeding 15 MPa in order to achieve reasonably homogeneous concrete with adequate cement so that the concrete can be finished satisfactorily. (ACI 318-94 prescribes a minimum of 2500 psi (17 MPa) for plain concrete).

N22.2 Control Joints

Construction joints are a very important design consideration. Control joints are not required if the random cracking resulting from creep, shrinkage and temperature effects will not affect the structural integrity and is otherwise acceptable (e.g., in a continuous wall footing transverse control joints may not be necessary).

Control joints may be made with sheet metal or sheet plastic inserts, "water-stop" inserts, rubber inserts or formed, sawed, or tooled grooves in the concrete surface to cause cracking at the predetermined location. The thickness of the concrete section at these inserts or grooves should be reduced at least 25 percent to make the control joint effective. It is good practice to form joints only part way through the member so that aggregate interlock in the remaining concrete can hold the elements in line. Adjacent elements may be held in line by the use of appropriately aligned, free-sliding dowels protected against corrosion.

22.2.2
In determining the number and location of control joints, consideration shall be given to the influence of climatic conditions, selection and proportioning of materials, mixing, placing, and curing of concrete, the degree of restraint to movement, and stresses due to load. .

22.2.3
Locations and details of control joints shall be indicated on the drawings or in the specifications.

22.2.4
Interruptions of concrete placement shall be made only at control joints.

22.3   Design

22.3.1
The strength design of plain concrete members for factored flexural and axial loads shall be based on a linear stress-strain relationship in both tension and compression.

22.3.2
The flexural tensile strength of concrete may be considered in the design.

22.3.3
No strength shall be assigned to reinforcement that may be present.

22.3.4
The bearing stress on the concrete at the contact surface between supporting and supported members shall not exceed the permissible bearing stress for each surface as given in Clause 10.8.

22.3.5
The entire cross section of a member shall be considered in the design, except for footings cast against soil (see Clause 22.6.3).

22.4   Walls

22.4.1   Design

22.4.1.1
The effective length factor, k, for walls braced at the top and bottom against lateral translation shall be
(a)   if restrained against rotation at one or both ends (top or bottom, or both) 0.8;
(b)   if unrestrained against rotation at both ends . . . . 1.0.

N22.3   Design
Plain concrete members are proportioned for adequate strength by using factored forces and by keeping computed stresses within permissible stress limits for all loading conditions.

N22.4   Walls
Eqs. (22-1) and (22-2) have been revised slightly so that they are consistent with each other. A triangular stress block with a maximum stress of $0.80 \phi_c f'_c$ and a width equal to the wall thickness will have the resistance given by Eq. (22-2) and a force located within the middle third of the wall.

22.4.1.2

Except as provided in Clause 22.4.1.3, walls subject to combined flexure and axial load shall be proportioned so that the maximum compressive stress under factored loads is limited to

$$0.80\phi_c f'_c \left[1 - \left(\frac{k\ell_c}{32h}\right)^2\right]$$ (22-1)

and the maximum tensile stress is less than $0.4\lambda\phi_c\sqrt{f'_c}$. The minimum eccentricity shall be 0.1h.

22.4.1.3

Plain concrete walls of solid rectangular cross section may be designed by Equation (22-2) if the resultant of all factored loads including the effects of lateral loads applied to the wall is located within the middle-third of the overall thickness of the wall.

$$P_r = 0.40\phi_c f'_c A_g \left[1 - \left(\frac{k\ell_c}{32h}\right)^2\right]$$ (22-2)

22.4.2

The horizontal length of wall to be considered effective for each concentrated load or reaction shall not exceed the centre-to-centre distance between loads, nor the width of bearing plus four times the wall thickness.

22.4.3

Plain concrete bearing walls shall have a thickness of not less than 1/20 of the unsupported height or length, whichever is shorter.

22.4.4

Foundation walls, firewalls, party walls, and exterior basement walls shall be not less than 190 mm thick.

22.4.5

Walls shall be braced against lateral translation and keyed or dowelled to other intersecting members as required for lateral stability.

22.4.6

Not less than two No. 15 bars shall be provided around all window and door openings. Such bars shall extend at least 600 mm beyond the corners of the openings.

22.5 Pedestals

Pedestals subject to combined flexural and axial load shall be proportioned so the maximum compression stress under factored loads does not exceed $0.80\phi_c f'_c$ and the maximum tension stress does not exceed $0.4\lambda\phi_c\sqrt{f'_c}$. The minimum eccentricity shall be 0.1h.

22.6 Footings

22.6.1

The base area of the footing shall be determined from forces and moments transmitted by the footing to the soil and the soil pressure selected through the principles of soil mechanics.
Note: *See the National Building Code of Canada for information on Limit States Design of Foundations.*

22.6.2

The specified thickness of plain concrete footings shall be not less than 200 mm.

22.6.3

For footings cast against soil, the overall thickness, h, used in calculations shall be taken as 50 mm less than the specified thickness.

22.6.4 Critical Sections

22.6.4.1

The critical sections for moment and shear are specified in Clause 15.4.2.

22.6.4.2

Circular or regular polygonal concrete columns or pedestals may be treated as square members with the same area, for the location of critical sections for moment and shear.

22.6.5 Strength in Bending

The factored resistance in bending shall be based on a maximum stress in tension of $0.4\lambda\phi_c\sqrt{f'_c}$ and a maximum stress in compression of $0.8\phi_c f'_c$.

22.6.6 Shear Resistance

22.6.6.1 One-way Action

22.6.6.1.1

The maximum factored shear, V_f, shall be computed at a distance h from the face of the support, and sections located closer to the support may be designed for the same shear.

22.6.6.1.2

The factored shear resistance for rectangular sections shall be

$$V_r = \frac{2}{3}\left(0.2\lambda\phi_c\sqrt{f'_c}\,bh\right)$$ (22-3)

22.6.6.2 Two-Way Shear

22.6.6.2.1

The maximum factored shear, V_f, shall be computed at a critical section perpendicular to the plane of the footing and located so that its perimeter, b_o, is a minimum, but not closer than, h/2 to the perimeter of the concentrated load or reaction area.

N22.6.3

The reduced overall thickness for concrete cast against earth is to allow for unevenness of excavation and for some contamination of the concrete adjacent to the soil.

N22.6.6 Shear Resistance

Shear failure in plain concrete will be a diagonal tension failure occurring when the principal tensile stress near the centroidal axis reaches the tensile strength of the concrete.

Plain concrete members of usual proportions will be controlled by flexural tensile strength rather than shear strength.

For other than rectangular sections $V_r = 0.2 \lambda \phi_c \sqrt{f'_c} \left(\dfrac{Ib}{Q} \right)$ should be used in place of Eq. (22-3).

N22.6.6.2.1

The critical sections for shear in plain concrete footings are the same as those shown in Fig. N15.5.2(a) except that d is replaced by h.

22.6.6.2.2

The factored shear resistance shall be

$$V_r = \frac{2}{3}\left[\left(1 + \frac{2}{\beta_c}\right)\right] 0.2 \lambda \phi_c \sqrt{f'_c}\, b_o h \tag{22-4}$$

but

$$V_r \le \frac{2}{3}\left(0.4 \lambda \phi_c \sqrt{f'_c}\, b_o h\right) \tag{22-5}$$

22.7 Slabs on Ground

Plain concrete slabs shall be designed with due regard to loading and foundation conditions.

Note: *For information on the design of slabs on ground see "Design of Slabs on Grade", ACI 360R-92, American Concrete Institute.*

23. Tilt-Up Wall Panels

23.0 Notation

A_g = gross area of panel cross section
A_s = area of tension reinforcement
A_{seff} = effective area of tension reinforcement
b = width of compression face of panel within design width
b_b = bearing width for concentrated load
b_d = design width
b_s = width of support reaction
b_t = tributary width
c = distance from extreme compression fibre to neutral axis computed for the cracked transformed section
d = distance from extreme compression fibre to centroid of tension reinforcement
e = eccentricity of P_{rf} parallel to axis measured from the centroid of the section
E_c = modulus of elasticity of concrete (see Clause 8.6.2)
E_s = modulus of elasticity of reinforcement (see Clause 8.5.4)
f'_c = specified compressive strength of concrete
f_y = specified yield strength of reinforcement
h = overall thickness of panel
I_{cr} = moment of inertia of cracked transformed section expressed as the moment of inertia of the equivalent concrete section
I_e = effective moment of inertia for computation of deflection
K_b = panel bending stiffness
ℓ = effective panel height
M_a = maximum moment due to specified loads in panel at load stage at which deflection is computed, including P-Δ effects
M_b = maximum factored moment in panel at load stage at which deflection is computed, not including P-Δ effects
M_f = factored moment, including P-Δ effects

M_r = factored moment resistance, calculated using the assumptions in Clauses 10.1 and 10.3, and the resistance factors given in Clause 8.4

P_z = factored load at midheight of panel

P_{rf} = factored load from tributary roof or floor area

P_{wf} = factored weight of panel tributary to and above design section

w_f = factored uniformly distributed lateral load

Δ_o = initial panel out of straightness

Δ_s = panel midheight deflection under service lateral and vertical loads

δ_b = moment magnification factor to reflect the P-Δ effect

ϕ_c = resistance factor for concrete (see Clause 8.4.2)

ϕ_m = member resistance factor (see Clause 23.4.1.3)

ϕ_s = resistance factor for reinforcing bars (see Clause 8.4.3)

23.1 Scope

23.1.1
The provisions of Clause 23 shall apply to tilt-up wall panels, which are reinforced concrete panels, site-cast on a horizontal surface, and subsequently tilted to a vertical orientation where they form vertical and lateral load resisting building elements.
Note: *Explanatory material on tilt-up wall panels is given in Appendix C.*

23.1.2
The provisions of Clauses 1 through 15 and Clause 21 shall apply except as modified by the provisions in this Clause.

23.1.3
Tilt-up panels are slender vertical flexural slabs, resisting lateral wind or seismic loads and subject to very low axial stresses. Due to their high slenderness ratios, they shall be designed for second order P-Δ effects to ensure structural stability and satisfactory performance under specified loads.

23.2 Definitions
The following definitions apply in this Clause:

Design cross section — representative panel cross section at the maximum moment and deflection locations of the panel, for which the design forces and deflections are determined and from which the resistance and stiffness is calculated.

Design width — width of tilt-up panel to be reinforced to withstand the factored loads tributary to it.

Lifting stresses — stresses in a tilt-up panel during lifting.

Sandwich panel — panel consisting of two concrete layers or wythes separated by a layer of insulation which may or may not act in a composite manner.

Tributary width — width of panel attracting vertical and horizontal loads that the design width must support.

23.3 General

23.3.1 Effective Panel Height
The effective panel height, ℓ, shall be the centre-to-centre distance between lateral supports.

23.3.2 Minimum Panel Thickness
The minimum panel thickness for a prismatic load-bearing panel without stiffening elements shall be 140 mm.

23.3.3 Maximum Height to Thickness Ratios
The maximum effective panel height to thickness ratio shall be
(a) 50 for panels with a single mat of reinforcement at mid-depth; or
(b) 65 for panels with a mat of reinforcement near each face.

23.3.4 Minimum Reinforcement
Minimum panel reinforcement shall conform to Clauses 7.8, 10.5, 14.3.5, 14.3.6, 14.3.7, and 21.9.3.3.1 as applicable. The requirements of Clause 21.9.3.3.1 may be waived where structural analysis shows adequate strength, ductility, and stability.

23.3.5 Concrete Cover and Tolerances

23.3.5.1
If quality control procedures are followed so that the designer can be assured that the tilt-up contractor meets the requirements in CSA Standard A23.4 with respect to dimensional control, reinforcement placement, aggregate size, concrete quality, and curing, then the cover requirements of CSA Standard A23.4 may be used, except as required in Clause 23.3.5.2. Otherwise, the design shall comply with CSA Standard A23.1.

23.3.5.2
The cover and quality of concrete in tilt-up panels which must withstand the effects of aggressive or corrosive environments shall comply with CSA Standard A23.1.

23.3.5.3
Tilt-up panels requiring a fire resistance rating or forming part of a firewall shall meet thickness and cover requirements of the applicable Building Codes.

23.3.6 Thermal Effects
The design of tilt-up panels shall consider the effects of any thermal gradients that may occur through the panel.

23.3.7 Sandwich Panels
Sandwich wall panels, in addition to resisting applied loads, shall be designed to resist such effects as composite or noncomposite action between wythes, thermal effects between wythes where composite action is assumed, thermal bridging, lifting stresses imposed on one wythe

by the other, and vertical and torsional support of one wythe by the other.

23.3.8 Connections

23.3.8.1
The design of connections shall consider in- and out-of-plane forces and the additional effects of shrinkage, creep, temperature, and movement and the appropriate provisions of Clause 21.

23.3.8.2
The resistances of connections between the tilt-up panels and any adjoining elements shall be greater than the effects of factored loads.

23.3.9 Structural Integrity

23.3.9.1
Tension ties shall be provided in the transverse and longitudinal directions of the structure and around the perimeter of the structure to effectively tie the elements together.

23.3.9.2
Panels shall have connections top and bottom to resist a minimum factored force of 5 kN/m perpendicular to the panel.

23.4 Analysis and Design

23.4.1 Flexure and Axial Load Interaction and Slenderness Effects

23.4.1.1
All moment and deflection calculations in Clause 23.4 are based on simple support conditions top and bottom. For other support and fixity conditions, moments and deflections shall be calculated using established principles of structural mechanics.

23.4.1.2
In lieu of a more accurate analysis, the procedures given in Clauses 23.4.1.3 to 23.4.1.5 may be used when the factored vertical load stress at the cross section under consideration meets the following requirement:

$$\frac{P_{wf} + P_{tf}}{A_g} < 0.09 \phi_c f'_c \qquad (23\text{-}1)$$

23.4.1.3
The factored moment, M_f, shall be determined at the midheight of the panel and shall be equal to

$$M_f = M_b \delta_b \qquad (23\text{-}2)$$

where

$$M_b = \frac{w_f \ell^2}{8} + P_{tf} \frac{e}{2} + (P_{wf} + P_{tf}) \Delta_0 \qquad (23\text{-}3)$$

$$\delta_b = \frac{1}{1 - \dfrac{P_f}{\phi_m K_b}} \geq 1.0 \qquad (23\text{-}4)$$

$$P_f = P_{wf} + P_{tf} \qquad (23\text{-}5)$$

$$K_b = \frac{48 E_c I_{cr}}{5 \ell^2} \qquad (23\text{-}6)$$

$$I_{cr} = \frac{bc^3}{3} + \frac{E_s}{E_c} A_s (d - c)^2 \qquad (23\text{-}7)$$

and the member resistance factor, ϕ_m, is taken as 0.65.

23.4.1.4
The initial out of straightness, Δ_0, at midheight of the panel shall consider the effects of nonplanar and flexible casting beds, deformations caused by the tilting process, thermal gradients through the panel, and creep, and shall not be taken less than $\ell/400$.

23.4.1.5
The factored resisting moment, M_r, provided by the panel cross section shall be such that

$$M_r \geq M_f \qquad (23\text{-}8)$$

The resisting moment may be calculated using a modified area of reinforcement given by

$$A_{seff} = \frac{\phi_s A_s f_y + P_f}{\phi_s f_y} \qquad (23\text{-}9)$$

23.4.2 Deflection Limitations
Unless serviceability requirements indicate that a larger deflection is acceptable, the horizontal midheight deflection, Δ_s, under specified lateral and vertical loads shall not exceed $\ell/100$, but not greater than can be tolerated by attached structural or nonstructural elements. The horizontal midheight deflection may be computed by

$$\Delta_s = \frac{5 M_a \ell^2}{48 E_c I_e} \qquad (23\text{-}10)$$

where I_e is as defined in Clause 9.8.2.3.

23.5 Effects of Openings

23.5.1 Design Width

23.5.1.1
A design width on each side of an opening shall support the combined factored axial and lateral loads from its tributary width. This design width shall be used over the full height of the panel.

23.5.1.2
The design width shall be limited to
(a) 12 times the thickness of a solid panel; or
(b) 12 times the thickness of the structural wythe of a sandwich panel.

23.5.2
The tributary width for design shall be the design width plus one-half the width of adjacent openings (see Figure 23-1).

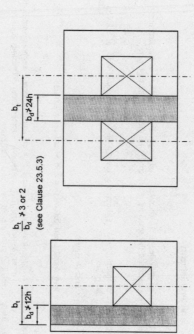

$$\frac{b_t}{b_d} \not> 3 \text{ or } 2$$

(see Clause 23.5.3)

Figure 23-1
Effect of Openings on Design Width, b_d
(See Clauses 23.5.2 and 23.5.3.)

23.5.3
Unless a more detailed analysis, accounting for the internal force effects, indicates otherwise, the ratio of tributary width to design width shall not exceed 3. For panels with a single layer of reinforcement and $\ell/h > 40$, the ratio shall not exceed 2.

23.6 Concentrated Loads or Reactions

23.6.1 Design Width
The design width, b_d, for a panel subjected to concentrated loads or concentrated reactions shall be determined from Figure 23-2.

23.6.2 Bearing
The allowable bearing stress at the contact surface between supported and supporting elements and between any intermediate bearing elements shall not exceed the bearing resistance for either surface, as given in Clause 10.8 or 11.5.4.

23.6.3
The design of connections to panels for concentrated loads or reactions shall consider lateral as well as vertical components in accordance with Clause 11.7.4.

23.6.4
For panels with concentrated vertical and lateral reactions at the bottom of the panel, the tributary width for vertical and lateral loading is as shown in Figure 23-2 and the total factored axial load and moment must be carried only by the design width. For panels with continuous lateral support at the top and bottom of the panel, the factored moment at the design cross section shall be assumed to be uniformly distributed across the full panel width.

23.6.5
Panels subjected to concentrated loads or reactions shall be designed in accordance with Clause 11.5.

23.7 Shear

23.7.1 In-Plane Shear

23.7.1.1
Where tilt-up panels are used as shear walls, analysis of the panels shall include the effects of in-plane stresses, local buckling, roof diaphragm connections, and panel stability. The connections between panels shall be designed to provide nominal ductility.

23.7.1.2
The design for factored shear forces in the plane of the panel shall be in accordance with the requirements of Clause 11.3 or 11.4.

23.7.2 Out-of-Plane Shear
The design for shear forces due to loads acting perpendicular to the face of the panel shall be in accordance with the requirements of Clause 11.3 or 11.4.

23.8 Lifting Stresses

23.8.1 General
The stresses imposed on a panel during lifting shall be limited to ensure that the performance of the erected panel is not impaired.

23.8.2 Elastic—Uncracked Analysis
Analysis of tilt-up panels during the lifting operation shall be based on elastic uncracked section properties using specified loads. Consideration shall be given to the effects of suction between the panel and the floor and impact loads from crane equipment.

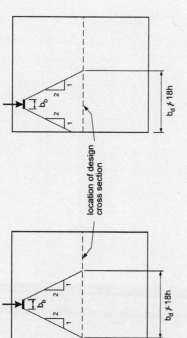

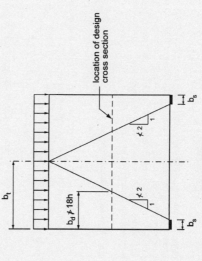

Figure 23-2
Effect of Concentrated Loads or Reactions on Design Width, b_d
(See Clauses 23.6.1 and 23.6.4.)

Appendix A
Excerpts from CSA Standard A23.1-94, Concrete Materials and Methods of Concrete Construction

Note: *This Appendix is not a mandatory part of this Standard.*

General

A number of Clauses from CSA Standard A23.1 that are especially important to design engineers are reprinted here. The Clauses are numbered as in CSA Standard A23.1 with a letter A prefixed. It is expected that CSA Standard A23.1 will be revised during the life of this Standard, resulting in minor changes or renumbering of the Clauses presented here. When this occurs, the new edition of CSA Standard A23.1 should be used. For this reason this Appendix is presented as a nonmandatory part of this Standard.

A12.   Fabrication and Placement of Reinforcement

A12.1 General

This Clause covers the fabrication and placement of reinforcement. The sizes and spacing of the reinforcement and its concrete cover shall be as shown on the drawings.

A12.2 Hooks and Bends

A12.2.1

Unless otherwise stated on the construction drawings, fabrication and detailing of hooks shall be as specified in Clause A12.2.2 through A12.2.5.

A12.2.2 Standard Hooks

The term "standard hook" as used herein shall mean

(a) a semicircular bend plus an extension of at least 4 bar diameters but not less than 60 mm at the free end of the bar;

(b) a 90° bend plus an extension of at least 12 bar diameters at the free end of the bar; or

(c) for stirrup and tie anchorage only, either a 90° or 135° bend plus an extension of at least 6 bar diameters, but not less than 60 mm at the free end of the bar.

Note: *Hooks for stirrups or ties must have a 135° bend, unless the concrete surrounding the hook can restrain the concrete from spalling. (See CSA Standard A23.3.)*

A12.2.3 Minimum Bend Diameter

The diameter of the bend measured on the inside of the bar for standard hooks, except stirrup and tie hooks, shall be not less than the values of Table A5.

Table A5
Bend Diameter for Standard Hooks

Bar size	Minimum bend diameter†, mm Steel grade		
	300 R	400 R or 500 R	400 W or 500 W
10	60	70	60
15	90	100	90
20		120	100
25		150	150
30		250	200
35		300	250
45		450*	400
55		600*	550

Special fabrication is required for bends exceeding 90° for bars of these sizes and grades.
†*Bend diameters shall not be reduced by more than 10% from those listed unless otherwise permitted by the Owner.*

A12.2.4 Stirrup and Tie Hooks

A12.2.4.1

The inside diameter of bends and 90° hooks for stirrups and ties shall be not less than 4 bar diameters.

A12.2.4.2

The inside diameter of 135° hooks shall be not less than 20 mm, 4 bar diameters, or the diameter of the bar enclosed by the hook, whichever is the greater.

A12.2.4.3

The inside diameter of bends in welded wire fabric for stirrups or ties shall be not less than 4 wire diameters. Bends with an inside diameter less than 8 wire diameters shall be not less than 4 wire diameters from the nearest welded intersection.

A12.2.5 Bending

A12.2.5.1

All bars shall be bent at temperatures between 10° and 100°C, unless otherwise permitted by the Owner.

A12.2.5.2

No bars partially embedded in concrete shall be field-bent except as shown on the drawings or as permitted by the Owner.

A12.2.5.3
The bending tolerances shall be sufficiently accurate to comply with the placing and protection tolerances stipulated in Clauses A12.8.

A12.3   Spirals

A12.3.1
The size and spacing of spirals shall be as shown on the construction drawings.

A12.3.5
Anchorage of spiral reinforcement shall be provided by 1-1/2 extra turns of spiral rod or wire at each end of the spiral unit.

A12.3.6
Splices in spirals shall have a minimum 50 rod diameter lap or be welded in accordance with CSA Standard W186.

A12.3.7
The reinforcing spiral shall extend from the floor level in any storey or from the top of the footing to the level of the lowest horizontal reinforcement in the slab, drop panel, or beam above.

A12.3.8
Where beams or brackets are not present on all sides of a column, ties shall extend above the termination of the spiral to the bottom of the slab or drop panel.

A12.3.9
In a column with a capital, the spiral shall extend to a plane at which the diameter or width of the capital is twice that of the column.

A12.4   Ties

A12.4.1
The size, spacing, and arrangement of ties shall be as shown on the construction drawings. When welded wire mesh of random length is used as tie reinforcement, the required splice length shall be indicated on the drawings.

A12.5   Spacing of Reinforcement

A12.5.1
The spacing of bars shall be as shown on the construction drawings.

A12.5.2
The clear distance between parallel bars or parallel bundles of bars shall be not less than 1.4 times the bar diameter, nor less than 1.4 times the nominal maximum size of the coarse aggregate, nor less than 30 mm. This clear distance shall apply to the distance between a contact lap splice and adjacent splices or bars.

A12.5.5
Where parallel reinforcement is placed in two or more layers, the bars in the upper layer shall be placed directly above those in the bottom layer.

A12.5.6
Spacing of post-tensioning ducts shall be as specified in Clause A25.6.3.3.

A12.6   Concrete Cover

A12.6.1   General

A12.6.1.1
Unless otherwise shown on the construction drawings, concrete cover shall be as required in Clauses A12.6.2, A12.6.3, and A12.6.4.

A12.6.1.2
Concrete cover shall be measured from the concrete surface to the nearest deformation (or surface, for smooth bars or wires) of the reinforcement. For textured architectural surfaces it shall be measured from the deepest point of the textured surface.

A12.6.2   Cover in a Noncorrosive Environment
The specified cover for reinforcement in prestressed and nonprestressed concrete shall be not less than as follows:

Exposure to earth or weather

	Exposed	Not exposed
(a) When cast against and permanently exposed to earth	75 mm	
(b) For		
(i) Beams, girders, columns and piles;		
principal reinforcement, No. 35 and smaller	50 mm	40 mm
ties, stirrups, and spirals	40 mm	30 mm
(ii) Slabs, walls, and joists, shells and folded plates:		
No. 20 and smaller	30 mm	20 mm
(c) For bars with a diameter d_b larger than listed above, the cover shall be at least	$1.5d_b$	$1.0d_b$
but need not be more than 60 mm		
(d) The ratio of the cover to the nominal maximum aggregate size shall be at least	1.5	1.0
(e) The cover for a bundle of bars shall be the same as that for a single bar with an equivalent area.		

A12.6.3 Cover in Corrosive Environments
The cover and protection for reinforcement in concrete utilized in a corrosive environment shall meet the requirements of Clause A15.1.7.

A12.6.4 Cover for Fire Resistance
Where a structural concrete member is required to have a fire-resistant rating, the minimum cover for reinforcement shall be specified by the Owner.

Note: *Detailed information can be found in the* National Building Code of Canada, *Subsection 3.1.5, Fire-Resistance Rating, and the Supplement to the* National Building Code of Canada, *Chapter 2, Fire-Performance Ratings.*

A12.7 Support of Reinforcement

A12.7.4 Rust Prevention

A12.7.4.3
Exposed reinforcing bars, inserts, and plates intended for bonding with future extensions shall be protected from corrosion.

A12.8 Tolerances for Placing Reinforcement
Unless otherwise specified by the Owner, reinforcement, prestressing steel, and post-tensioning ducts shall be placed within the following tolerances:

(a) Concrete cover .... ±12 mm
(but the concrete cover shall in no case be reduced more than one-third of the specified cover)

(b) Where the depth of a flexural member, the thickness of a wall, or the smallest dimension of a column is
  (i) 200 mm or less .... ±8 mm;
  (ii) larger than 200 mm but less than 600 mm .... ±12 mm;
  (iii) 600 mm or larger .... ±20 mm;

(c) Lateral spacing of bars .... ±30 mm;

(d) Longitudinal location of bends and ends of bars .... ±50 mm;

(e) As Item (d) at discontinuous ends of members .... ±20 mm

Note: *Where reinforcement is added to help provide a more rigid reinforcing mat or cage, as for instance in prefabricated reinforcing cages, such additional reinforcement is not subject to the tolerances of Clause A12.8 except for the minimum cover requirements.*

A12.10 Welding of Reinforcement

A12.10.1
Welding of reinforcement shall conform to the requirements of CSA Standard W186.

A12.10.2
Tack welding of reinforcing bars shall not be permitted unless performed in accordance with CSA Standard W186.

A13. Fabrication and Placement of Hardware and Other Embedded Items

A13.3 Tolerances for Placing Hardware

A13.3.1
Unless otherwise specified by the Owner, the location of anchor bolts and embedded items shall not vary from the dimensions shown on the erection drawings by more than the following (see also Figure A2):

(a) 3 mm centre-to-centre of any two bolts within an anchor bolt group, where an anchor bolt group is defined as the set of anchor bolts that receives a single fabricated steel or precast concrete member;

(b) 8 mm centre-to-centre of adjacent anchor bolt groups;

(c) A maximum accumulation of 8 mm per 30 m along the established column line of multiple anchor bolt groups, but not to exceed a total of 30 mm. The established column line is the actual field line most representative of the centres of the as-built anchor bolt groups along a line of columns;

(d) 8 mm from the centre of any anchor bolt group to the established column line through that group.

The tolerances of Items (b), (c), and (d) apply to offset dimensions, as shown on the construction drawings and measured perpendicular to the nearest column line.

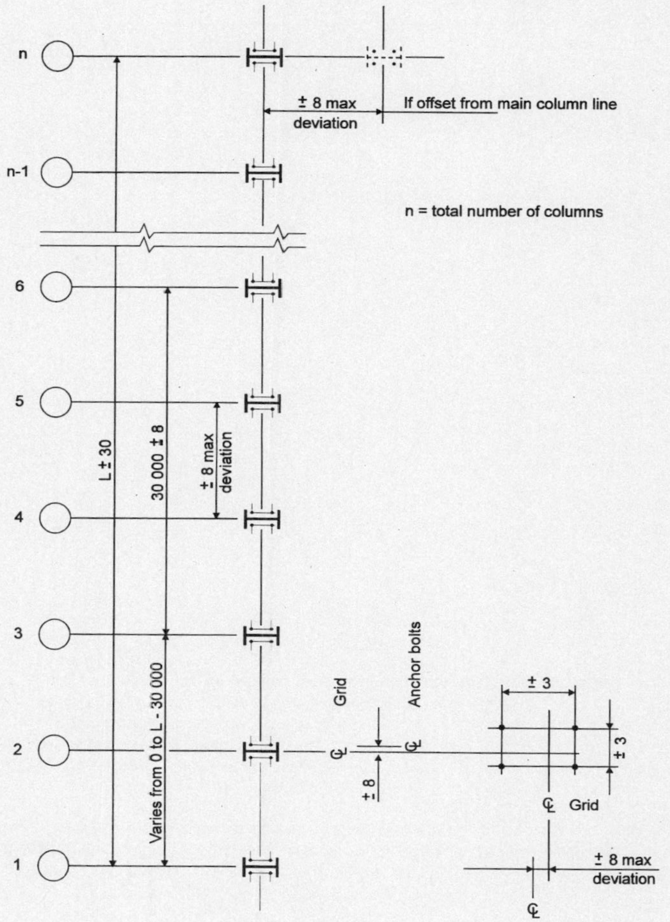

Figure A2
Tolerances on Anchor Bolt Placement

A13.3.2

Slope variations for hardware serving as bearing plates shall not exceed 1 mm in 40 mm, with a maximum of 3 mm for plates having side dimensions less than 300 mm and a maximum of 5 mm for plates having side dimensions of 300 mm or larger.

A13.3.3

Vertical alignment variations for anchor bolts shall not exceed 3 mm, or 1 mm in 40 mm, whichever is larger.

A13.4   Welding of Hardware

A13.4.2

Welding of reinforcing bars to hardware shall conform to the requirements of CSA Standard W186.

A13.4.3

Material and equipment for stud welding of bars and anchors shall be compatible and shall be used in accordance with the recommendations of the manufacturers of the material and equipment.

Note: *See the Supplement to American Welding Society, Standard D1.1.*

A15.   Durability Requirements

A15.1.7 Protection of Reinforcement for Concrete Exposed to Chlorides (Deicing Chemicals, Sea Water, or Other Chloride-Bearing Agents) — Class C-1, C-2, C-3, C-4 Exposure in Table 7

A15.1.7.1

The specified cover for reinforcing shall not be less than any of the following:

(a)   60 mm;

(b)   two times the nominal diameter of the reinforcement; and

(c)   two times the nominal maximum aggregate size.

Note: *As the exact positioning of reinforcement is difficult, it may be advisable to increase the specified cover to ensure adequate protection. In general there is a 90% probability that the actual cover will be within 20 mm of that specified.*

A15.1.7.2

Unprotected metal chairs and supports, hardware and embedded items, and miscellaneous items shall not extend to within 40 mm of the concrete surface. Form ties and bolts shall be cut back from the surface to a minimum depth of 25 mm. Patching shall be conducted in accordance with Clause A24.2.

A25. Post-Tensioning

A25.2 Unbonded Tendons

A25.2.4 Cover

A25.2.4.1
The concrete cover to the sheath shall be not less than 40 mm in noncorrosive environments and 50 mm in corrosive environments.

A25.2.4.2
The concrete cover to the anchorage shall be not less than 60 mm.

A25.6 Preparation for Post-tensioning

A25.6.2 Anchoring of Tendons

A25.6.2.1
The spacing between anchorages shall be sufficient to allow the operation of the stressing jacks to be unimpeded by adjacent stressed or unstressed tendons.

A25.6.2.2
The axis of the tendon shall be in line with the anchorage for a minimum distance of 0.4 m, or as approved by the Owner.

A25.6.3 Prestressing Tendons

A25.6.3.1 Cover
Cover requirements shall be as specified in Clause A12.6.2.

A25.6.3.2
Where it is necessary to curve tendons in the horizontal plane in order to bypass an opening, a maximum offset of one in five is required. A minimum clearance of 150 mm to the opening shall be maintained. The portion of tendon that passes by the opening shall be straight.

A25.6.3.3 Spacing

A25.6.3.3.1
The clear distance between parallel ducts in a layer shall be not less than the larger of the following:
(a) the diameter of the ducts;
(b) 1-1/3 times the nominal maximum size of the coarse aggregate; and
(c) 30 mm.

A25.6.3.3.2
To provide access for concrete placement and the insertion of vibrators, at least one-third of the spaces between ducts shall exceed 60 mm.

A25.6.3.3.3
Where parallel ducts are placed in two or more layers, the ducts in the upper layers shall be placed directly above those in the bottom layer, with the clear distance between layers not less than 30 mm, or 1-1/3 times the nominal maximum size of the aggregate, whichever is larger.

A25.6.3.4 Bundling
Monostrand tendons may be bundled, provided that
(a) concrete can be placed satisfactorily;
(b) steel, when tensioned, does not break into adjacent ducts; and
(c) ducts, if grouted, can be grouted individually without the flow of grout into adjacent ducts.

Appendix B
Rectangular Two-Way Slab Systems with Stiff Supports on Four Sides

Note: *This Appendix is not a mandatory part of this Standard.*

B0. Notation

b_w	=	width of beam web
$C_a$neg	=	moment coefficient for negative moment in short span
C_{ad}	=	moment coefficient for positive dead load moment in short span
C_{al}	=	moment coefficient for positive live load moment in short span
$C_b$neg	=	moment coefficient for negative moment in long span
C_{bd}	=	moment coefficient for positive dead load moment in long span
C_{bl}	=	moment coefficient for positive live load moment in long span
h_b	=	overall depth of supporting beam
h_s	=	overall depth of slab
ℓ_a	=	clear span of a two-way slab in short direction
ℓ_b	=	clear span of a two-way slab in long direction
ℓ_n	=	clear span of supporting beam
m	=	ratio of short to long span of a two-way slab = ℓ_a/ℓ_b
$M_a$neg	=	negative moment in short span
M_{ad}pos	=	positive dead load moment in short span
M_{al}pos	=	positive live load moment in short span
$M_b$neg	=	negative moment in long span
M_{bd}pos	=	positive dead load moment in long span
M_{bl}pos	=	positive live load moment in long span
w_f	=	factored load per unit area
w_{df}	=	factored dead load per unit area
w_{lf}	=	factored live load per unit area

B1. Scope and Definitions

B1.1

The provisions of this Appendix apply to rectangular two-way systems where the slab is reinforced in two directions and supported on four sides by walls or stiff beams. Subject to the specified limitations, they may be used to determine slab thicknesses and loads on supporting beams or walls and to determine the moments and shears in the slabs. All other requirements should be in accordance with the appropriate Clauses in the body of the Standard.

B1.2

A stiff supporting beam is defined as one in which $b_w h_b^3/\ell_n h_s^3$ is not less than 2.0

B2. Design Method

B2.1

The minimum slab thickness should be determined in accordance with Clause 13.3, but in no case should be less than

(a)   100 mm;
(b)   the perimeter of the slab divided by 140, in the case of slabs discontinuous on one or more edges; or
(c)   the perimeter of the slab divided by 160, in the case of fully continuous slabs.

B2.2

A two-way slab should be considered as consisting of strips in each direction as follows:

(a)   a middle strip, one-half of a panel in width, symmetrical about the panel centreline and extending through the panel in the direction in which moments are considered; and

(b)   a column strip, one-half of a panel in width, occupying the two quarter-panel areas outside the middle strip.

B2.3

Critical sections for moment should be assumed as follows:

(a)   for negative moment, along the edges of the panel at the faces of the supports; and
(b)   for positive moment, along the centrelines of the panels.

B2.4

Negative bending moments per unit width for the middle strips should be computed by the use of Equations (B-1) and (B-2) along with the coefficients given in Table B-1.

$$M_a\text{neg} = C_a\text{neg } w_f \ell_a^2 \qquad \text{(B-1)}$$

$$M_b\text{neg} = C_b\text{neg } w_f \ell_b^2 \qquad \text{(B-2)}$$

B2.5

Positive bending moments per unit width should be computed as the sum of Equations (B-3) and (B-4) for the middle strip in the short direction and Equations (B-5) and (B-6) for the middle strip in the long direction, using the coefficients given in Table B-2.

$$M_{al}\text{pos} = C_{al} \, w_{lf} \, \ell_a^2 \qquad \text{(B-3)}$$

$$M_{ad}\text{pos} = C_{ad} \, w_{df} \, \ell_a^2 \qquad \text{(B-4)}$$

$$M_{bl}\text{pos} = C_{bl} \, w_{lf} \, \ell_b^2 \qquad \text{(B-5)}$$

$$M_{bd}\text{pos} = C_{bd} \, w_{df} \, \ell_b^2 \qquad \text{(B-6)}$$

B2.6

The bending moments in the column strips should be two-thirds of the bending moments in the middle strip.

B2.7

Where the ratio, m, of short to long span is less than 0.5, the slab should be considered as a one-way slab in the short direction, but reinforcement for negative moments required for m equal to 0.5 should be provided in the long direction.

B2.8

At discontinuous edges of two-way slabs, a negative moment of three-quarters of the positive moment should be assumed.

B2.9

In all cases, special reinforcement should be provided at exterior corners in accordance with Clause 13.13.5.

B2.10

Where the negative moment on one side of a support is less than 80% of that on the other side, the difference should be distributed between the two slabs in proportion to their relative stiffnesses.

B2.11

The shear stresses in the slabs should be computed on the assumption that the load, w_f, is distributed to the supports in accordance with Clause B3.

B3. Loads on Slab Supports

B3.1

The loads on the supporting beams of a two-way rectangular panel may be assumed as the load within the tributary areas of the panel bounded by the intersection of 45° lines from the corners and the median line of the panel parallel to the long side.

B3.2

The bending moments in the supporting beams may be determined for design purposes by using an equivalent uniform load per unit length of beam for each panel supported, as follows:

(a) For the short span:

$$\frac{w_f \ell_a}{3}$$ (B-7)

(b) For the long span:

$$\frac{w_f \ell_b}{3} \times \frac{(3 - m^2)}{2}$$ (B-8)

**Table B-1
Coefficients for Negative Moments
(See Clause B2.4.)**

$M_a neg = C_a neg \; w_f \; \ell_a^2$
$M_b neg = C_b neg \; w_f \; \ell_b^2$

— means that supports are free to rotate.
═ means that supports are fixed against rotation.

$m = \ell_a/\ell_b$	Coefficient	Case 1	Case 2	Case 3	Case 4	Case 5	Case 6	Case 7	Case 8	Case 9
1.00	$C_a neg$	—	0.045	—	0.050	0.075	0.071	—	0.033	0.061
	$C_b neg$	—	0.045	0.076	0.050	—	—	0.071	0.061	0.033
0.95	$C_a neg$	—	0.050	—	0.055	0.079	0.075	—	0.038	0.065
	$C_b neg$	—	0.041	0.072	0.045	—	—	0.067	0.056	0.029
0.90	$C_a neg$	—	0.055	—	0.060	0.080	0.079	—	0.043	0.068
	$C_b neg$	—	0.036	0.070	0.040	—	—	0.062	0.052	0.025
0.85	$C_a neg$	—	0.060	—	0.066	0.082	0.083	—	0.049	0.072
	$C_b neg$	—	0.031	0.065	0.034	—	—	0.057	0.046	0.021
0.80	$C_a neg$	—	0.065	—	0.071	0.084	0.086	—	0.055	0.075
	$C_b neg$	—	0.026	0.061	0.029	—	—	0.051	0.041	0.017
0.75	$C_a neg$	—	0.069	—	0.076	0.085	0.088	—	0.061	0.078
	$C_b neg$	—	0.022	0.056	0.024	—	—	0.044	0.036	0.014
0.70	$C_a neg$	—	0.074	—	0.081	0.086	0.091	—	0.068	0.081
	$C_b neg$	—	0.017	0.050	0.019	—	—	0.038	0.029	0.011
0.65	$C_a neg$	—	0.077	—	0.085	0.087	0.093	—	0.074	0.083
	$C_b neg$	—	0.014	0.043	0.015	—	—	0.031	0.025	0.008
0.60	$C_a neg$	—	0.081	—	0.089	0.088	0.095	—	0.080	0.085
	$C_b neg$	—	0.010	0.035	0.011	—	—	0.024	0.018	0.006
0.55	$C_a neg$	—	0.084	—	0.092	0.089	0.096	—	0.085	0.086
	$C_b neg$	—	0.007	0.028	0.008	—	—	0.019	0.014	0.005
0.50	$C_a neg$	—	0.086	—	0.094	0.090	0.097	—	0.089	0.088
	$C_b neg$	—	0.006	0.022	0.006	—	—	0.014	0.010	0.003

Appendix C
Explanatory Comments to Clause 23, Tilt-Up Wall Panels

Notes:
(1) *This Appendix is not a mandatory part of this Standard.*
(2) *The Clauses are numbered as in Clause 23 with a letter C prefixed.*

Definition

The following definition applies in this Clause:

Strongback — external beam attached to a tilt-up panel in a manner to allow lifting stresses to be fully carried by the beam.

C23.1 Scope

The provisions of Clause 23 are based on experience, analysis, and testing of solid tilt-up panels in the 140 mm to 235 mm thickness range, spanning vertically up to 12 m and resisting factored wind or seismic loads up to 2.5 kPa and factored vertical stress up to 0.8 MPa. Clause 23 also has provisions for panel discontinuities and upper limits on out-of-plane loading and vertical stress.

C23.3 General

C23.3.2 Minimum Panel Thickness

Experience has shown this to be a reasonable minimum thickness for normal wind and gravity loads and is consistent with using common dimension lumber for edge forms. Integral pilasters are commonly used as stiffening elements.

C23.3.3 Maximum Height to Thickness Ratios

Given their high slenderness ratios, the cracked section and lateral stiffness properties of tilt-up panels vary significantly depending on whether the principal panel reinforcement is arranged in one or two mats. Typically, for a panel with one mat of reinforcement, the vertical reinforcement is positioned at mid-depth of the panel with the horizontal bars tied to the vertical bars on the side closer to the outside face of the panel. For a panel with two mats of reinforcement, the vertical bars in each mat are typically located as close to each face as cover requirements allow, with the horizontal reinforcement positioned inside the vertical bars and tied to them in an alternating arrangement. Experience has shown these limits to give reasonable lateral deflection performance. Actual lateral deflection calculations should be made for each situation and checked against allowable deflection criteria.

C23.3.6 Thermal Effects

Bowing of panels due to a thermal gradient within the panel can occur. Summer conditions with high temperatures on the exterior panel face coupled with cool interior temperatures, as in the case of air-conditioned offices, has resulted in permanent bowing of panels. A bow in the panel, besides being aesthetically objectionable, can significantly affect the structural performance of the panel. Distress in connections between panels, particularly at corners, can also occur.

Table B-2
Coefficients for Live and Dead Load Positive Moments
(See Clause B2.5.)

$$M_{aLpos} = C_{aL} w_f \ell_a^2 \qquad M_{aDpos} = C_{aD} w_{df} \ell_a^2$$
$$M_{bLpos} = C_{bL} w_f \ell_b^2 \qquad M_{bDpos} = C_{bD} w_{df} \ell_b^2$$

— means that supports are free to rotate.
═ means that supports are fixed against rotation.

$m = \ell_a/\ell_b$	Coefficient	Case 1	Case 2	Case 3	Case 4	Case 5	Case 6	Case 7	Case 8	Case 9
1.00	C_{aL}	0.036	0.027	0.027	0.032	0.032	0.035	0.032	0.028	0.030
	C_{aD}	0.036	0.018	0.018	0.027	0.027	0.033	0.027	0.020	0.023
	C_{bL}	0.036	0.027	0.032	0.032	0.027	0.032	0.035	0.030	0.028
	C_{bD}	0.036	0.018	0.027	0.027	0.018	0.027	0.033	0.023	0.020
0.95	C_{aL}	0.040	0.030	0.031	0.035	0.034	0.038	0.036	0.031	0.032
	C_{aD}	0.040	0.020	0.021	0.030	0.028	0.036	0.031	0.022	0.024
	C_{bL}	0.033	0.025	0.029	0.029	0.024	0.029	0.032	0.027	0.025
	C_{bD}	0.033	0.016	0.025	0.024	0.015	0.024	0.031	0.021	0.017
0.90	C_{aL}	0.045	0.034	0.035	0.039	0.037	0.042	0.040	0.035	0.036
	C_{aD}	0.045	0.022	0.025	0.033	0.029	0.039	0.035	0.025	0.026
	C_{bL}	0.029	0.022	0.027	0.026	0.021	0.025	0.029	0.024	0.022
	C_{bD}	0.029	0.014	0.024	0.022	0.013	0.021	0.028	0.019	0.015
0.85	C_{aL}	0.050	0.037	0.040	0.043	0.041	0.046	0.045	0.040	0.039
	C_{aD}	0.050	0.024	0.029	0.036	0.031	0.042	0.040	0.029	0.028
	C_{bL}	0.026	0.019	0.024	0.023	0.019	0.022	0.026	0.022	0.020
	C_{bD}	0.026	0.012	0.023	0.019	0.011	0.017	0.025	0.017	0.013
0.80	C_{aL}	0.055	0.041	0.045	0.048	0.044	0.051	0.051	0.044	0.042
	C_{aD}	0.055	0.026	0.034	0.039	0.032	0.045	0.045	0.032	0.029
	C_{bL}	0.023	0.017	0.022	0.020	0.016	0.019	0.023	0.019	0.017
	C_{bD}	0.023	0.011	0.020	0.016	0.009	0.014	0.022	0.015	0.010
0.75	C_{aL}	0.061	0.045	0.051	0.052	0.047	0.055	0.056	0.049	0.046
	C_{aD}	0.061	0.028	0.040	0.043	0.033	0.048	0.051	0.036	0.031
	C_{bL}	0.019	0.014	0.019	0.016	0.013	0.016	0.020	0.016	0.014
	C_{bD}	0.019	0.009	0.018	0.013	0.007	0.012	0.020	0.013	0.007
0.70	C_{aL}	0.068	0.049	0.057	0.057	0.051	0.060	0.063	0.054	0.050
	C_{aD}	0.068	0.030	0.046	0.046	0.035	0.051	0.058	0.040	0.033
	C_{bL}	0.016	0.012	0.016	0.014	0.011	0.013	0.017	0.014	0.012
	C_{bD}	0.016	0.007	0.016	0.011	0.005	0.009	0.017	0.011	0.006
0.65	C_{aL}	0.074	0.053	0.064	0.062	0.055	0.064	0.070	0.059	0.054
	C_{aD}	0.074	0.032	0.054	0.050	0.036	0.053	0.065	0.044	0.034
	C_{bL}	0.013	0.010	0.014	0.011	0.009	0.010	0.014	0.011	0.009
	C_{bD}	0.013	0.006	0.014	0.009	0.004	0.007	0.014	0.009	0.005
0.60	C_{aL}	0.081	0.058	0.072	0.067	0.059	0.068	0.077	0.065	0.059
	C_{aD}	0.081	0.034	0.062	0.053	0.037	0.056	0.073	0.048	0.036
	C_{bL}	0.010	0.007	0.011	0.009	0.007	0.008	0.011	0.009	0.007
	C_{bD}	0.010	0.004	0.011	0.007	0.003	0.006	0.012	0.007	0.004
0.55	C_{aL}	0.088	0.062	0.080	0.072	0.063	0.073	0.085	0.070	0.063
	C_{aD}	0.088	0.035	0.071	0.056	0.038	0.058	0.081	0.052	0.037
	C_{bL}	0.008	0.006	0.009	0.007	0.005	0.006	0.009	0.007	0.006
	C_{bD}	0.008	0.003	0.009	0.005	0.002	0.004	0.009	0.005	0.003
0.50	C_{aL}	0.095	0.066	0.088	0.077	0.067	0.078	0.092	0.076	0.067
	C_{aD}	0.095	0.037	0.080	0.059	0.039	0.061	0.089	0.056	0.038
	C_{bL}	0.006	0.004	0.007	0.005	0.004	0.005	0.007	0.005	0.004
	C_{bD}	0.006	0.002	0.007	0.004	0.001	0.003	0.007	0.004	0.002

C23.4   Analysis and Design

C23.4.1.2

Computer analysis has shown that for low axial stress, the bending stiffness is almost independent of curvature after flexural cracking has occurred. Furthermore, in the ultimate design state most of the panel will be cracked over the height, and the cracked section stiffness, $E_c I_{cr}$, is used as a reasonably accurate and conservative approximation of the actual stiffness for calculation of moment magnification, δ_b.

C23.4.1.4

Any or all of these effects may result in a panel having a bow in it. This provision for initial out of straightness reflects a reasonable allowance for these effects. Also, this provides the initial perturbation that most iterative analytical techniques require to predict stability effects for highly slender compression members.

C23.5   Effects of Openings

C23.5.3

This Clause is intended to limit the application of the procedures given in Clauses 23.4.1.1 to 23.4.1.5. For a large ratio of tributary width to design width, it may be necessary to add a thickening pilaster to the panel, use a thicker panel, or carry out a more detailed analysis. Caution is advised in situations where the ratios in Clause 23.5.3 are exceeded.

C23.6   Concentrated Loads or Reactions

C23.6.1

A series of equal concentrated loads may be considered a uniformly distributed load if the design widths overlap at the design cross section location.

C23.6.3

Horizontal reinforcement at the location of concentrated loads or reactions should be designed and detailed to resist tensile forces associated with restraint of panel shrinkage and restraint to thermal movements in addition to the effects of other loads.

C23.6.4

In determining the factored axial load and moment to be resisted by the design width, consideration must be given to the type of support conditions for the panel. If the supports at the base give rise to concentrated vertical reactions and if lateral support is provided at discrete locations, then both the factored axial load and moments must be resisted by the design width shown in Figure 23-2. If there are concentrated reactions for vertical loading, but continuous lateral support at the top and bottom of the panel, then the factored axial load is resisted by the design width shown in Figure 23-2; however, the factored moments can be assumed to be resisted by the full panel width.

C23.6.5

For panels subjected to concentrated loads, appropriately distributed reinforcement should be provided to carry tensile forces associated with the spreading of the load into the panel.

Panels with concentrated reactions may act as deep beams and therefore may require tension tie reinforcement at the bottom of the panel between supports. This tension tie reinforcement should be appropriately anchored into the support regions. The required tension tie reinforcement can be determined using the strut-and-tie design approach of Clause 11.5.

C23.7   Shear

C23.7.1.1

If panels are connected to adjacent panels for stability, they should be connected in groups with as few panels as required to satisfy overturning moments.

C23.8   Lifting Stresses

C23.8.1

The stresses imposed on a tilt-up panel during the lifting process often exceed those associated with the panel in its erected condition. To avoid unsightly cracking, serviceability problems, or overstressing conditions during the lifting process, the lifting configuration should be designed to maintain the panels in an uncracked condition.

C23.8.2   Elastic—Uncracked Analysis

An analysis can be made assuming a transformed section, thereby taking advantage of the reinforcement in the section. Where analysis shows that the panel as designed will crack during the lifting process, additional reinforcing steel or external strongbacks may be required.

The analysis of a tilt-up panel during lifting should accurately locate the panel centre of gravity including the effects of openings, recesses, projections, etc, so as to ensure that the panel lifts as predicted and hangs plumb.

As a panel is lifted, the flexural and shear stresses in the panel as well as shear and tension loads in the lift inserts continually change. It is therefore essential to analyze these stresses and loads incrementally to ensure an envelope is developed which correctly identifies the most severe combination of stresses and loads. The analysis of stresses in a tilt-up panel during the lifting process should consider the panel as it swings from the horizontal position to its final position.

Problems may occur if the centre of lifting is not kept an adequate distance above the panel centre of gravity. As these conditions can greatly complicate the lift operation and are potentially quite dangerous, a minimum slab reaction at the toe of the panel should be 10% of the panel weight at the onset of lift.

The minimum concrete flexural tensile strength at time of lifting should not be less than 3.0 MPa as determined by CSA Standards A23.2-3C and 8C. The allowable flexural tensile stresses in concrete during the lifting operation should not exceed 60% of the flexural tensile strength.

C23.8   Factor of Safety on Lift Inserts

Maximum shear and tensile loads placed on lift inserts shall be in accordance with the manufacturers' recommended safe working loads. Factors of safety on lift insert capacities shall also be in accordance with local Workers Compensation Board regulations.

Appendix D
Anchorage Systems

Note: *This Appendix is not a mandatory part of this Standard.*

D0. Notation

A = bearing area
d_a = nominal diameter of anchor
f'_c = specified compressive strength of concrete
$\sqrt{f'_c}$ = square root of specified compressive strength of concrete
f_y = minimum specified yield strength of anchor
f_{su} = minimum specified tensile strength of anchor steel
m = side cover distance of an anchor head or bar
n = number of embedments transferring load by bearing
P_r = factored pull-out resistance of concrete surrounding an anchorage loaded in tension
R_r = factored resistance of an expansion anchor
s = standard deviation of ultimate failure load in test
v_f = factored shear force
$\bar{x}$ = mean ultimate failure load in test
μ = coefficient of friction
λ = factor to allow for low density concrete (see Clause 8.6.5)
ϕ_c = resistance factor for concrete (see Clause 8.4.2)
ϕ_e = resistance factor for expansion anchors (see Clause D7.1(e))
ϕ_s = resistance factor for reinforcement (see Clause 8.4.3)
ϕ_a = resistance factor for structural steel (see Clause 8.4.3)

D1. Scope

D1.1
The provisions of Appendix D may be applied to the design of anchorage devices embedded in the concrete at the time of concrete placing or installed in concrete after the concrete has hardened, where the anchorage devices are essential to ensure the structural integrity of the building or parts of the building.
Note: *The provisions of this Appendix are not intended to apply to anchorage of appurtenances or mechanical equipment.*

D1.2
In addition to meeting the requirements of this Appendix, the effect of the forces applied to the embedment on the behaviour of the structure should be taken into account.

D2. Definitions
The following definitions apply in this Clause:

Adhesive anchor — rod, bar, or other device inserted in a predrilled hole in cured concrete and held in place by epoxy resin or other adhesive.

Anchor head — nut, washer, plate, stud, bolt head, or other steel component used to transmit anchor loads to the concrete by bearing.

Attachment — the structure external to the concrete that transmits loads to the embedment.

Axial spacing — distance between two centrelines of anchors.

Cast-in-place anchor — anchor device that is in its final location at the time of concrete placing.

Edge distance — distance between the anchor centreline and the edge of the load bearing base material.

Embedment — steel part of the anchorage device embedded in the concrete.

Embedment depth — distance from the bearing surface of the anchor to the surface of the load bearing base material.

Expansion anchor — standard manufactured item placed in a predrilled hole in cured concrete and that relies on lateral bearing or friction to transmit loads to the concrete.

Grouted anchor — anchorage system that has the anchor rod, bolt, or bar grouted or drypacked into a predrilled hole in cured concrete.

Shear lug — plate or bar attached to the embedded surface of an embedment that transmits shear forces acting on the embedment to the concrete.

D3. General Requirements

D3.1
Anchorage systems should be designed to transfer all load effects, as required by Clause 9, including effects of eccentricities and deformations.

D3.2
Where ductile behaviour is required, the anchorage system and its attachment should be designed such that yielding of a steel portion of the system will take place prior to failure of the concrete.

D3.3
Cast-in-place anchors should be designed in accordance with Clauses D3, D4, and D5.

D3.4
Grouted and adhesive anchors should be designed in accordance with Clauses D3, D4, D5, and D6.

D4. Design Requirements for Concrete Surrounding Anchorages

D4.1 Tension

D4.1.1

The factored pull-out resistance of concrete, P_r, for any anchorage should be based on a uniform factored tensile strength of $0.30\lambda\phi_c\sqrt{f'_c}$ acting on the effective stress area.

D4.1.2

The effective stress area is defined by the projected area of the stress pyramids radiating towards the concrete surface from the bearing edge of the anchors at an angle of inclination of 45°, as illustrated in Figures D1 and D2. The effective stress area should be limited by overlapping stress pyramids, by the intersection of pyramids with concrete surfaces, by the bearing area of the anchor heads, and by the overall thickness of the concrete.

Note: *The actual failure surface is a cone rather than a pyramid. The pyramidal surface has been used to simplify calculations.*

D4.2 Transfer of Tensile Load from Anchor to Concrete

D4.2.1

The load transfer from the anchor to concrete should be carried out by one of the following methods:

(a) an anchor head at the base of the portion of the embedment transmitting tensile force. To prevent failure due to lateral bursting forces at an anchor head, the minimum distance from the anchor head to any concrete surface, m, should be not less than given by

$$m = d_a \sqrt{\frac{f_{su}}{6\sqrt{f'_c}}} \qquad (D\text{-}1)$$

but not less than 50 mm;

(b) deformed reinforcing bars with bond length or hooks in accordance with Clause 12; or

(c) other means proven by testing.

Note: *In cases where embedments are loaded to less than their full capacity the value of d_a assumed in calculating m may be proportionately reduced, but m should not be less than 50 mm.*

D4.2.2

The bearing requirements of Clause 10.8 should apply to the maximum bearing stress at an anchor head or a shear lug, except as permitted by Clause D4.2.3.

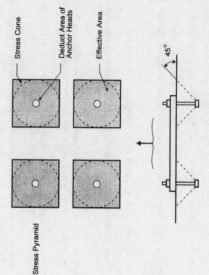

Plan

- Stress Cone
- Stress Pyramid
- Effective Area
- Deduct Area of Anchor Heads

Elevation — Stress Pyramids — 45°

(a) Stress Pyramids Intersect

- Stress Cone
- Deduct Area of Anchor Heads
- Effective Area

Stress Pyramid

45°

(b) Stress Pyramids Do Not Intersect

**Figure D1
Stress Pyramids for Tensile Loading**
(See Clause D4.1.2.)

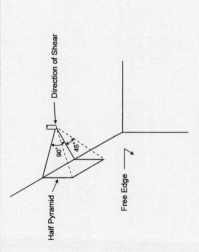

Figure D2
Pyramid for Shear Toward a Free Edge
(See Clauses D4.1.2 and D4.3.6.)

D4.2.3

The bearing requirements of Clause D4.2.2 may be waived for anchor heads if the component transmitting tensile force and the anchor head at the base of the component transmitting tensile force satisfies the following requirements:

(a) the minimum gross area of anchor head is at least 2.5 times the cross sectional area of the component transmitting tensile force;

(b) the thickness of the anchor head is at least equal to the greatest dimension from the outermost edge of the bearing surface of the head to the surface of the component transmitting tensile force;

(c) the bearing area of the anchor head is approximately evenly distributed around the perimeter of the component transmitting tensile force; and

(d) the yield strength of the component transmitting tensile force does not exceed 400 MPa.

Note: *A standard nut and washer will satisfy the requirements of Clause D4.2.3 if the yield strength of the component transmitting tensile force does not exceed 400 MPa.*

D4.3 Shear

D4.3.1

Transfer of shear from anchor to concrete may either be by lateral bearing of the embedment or shear lugs on the concrete, calculated in accordance with Clause D4.3.2, or by shear friction, calculated in accordance with Clause D4.3.5. When shears act toward a free edge, Clause D4.3.6 should be applied.

D4.3.2

When shear is transmitted by bearing of embedments or shear lugs on the concrete, the factored bearing resistance should be taken as $1.4\phi_c n A_1 f_c'$. For an anchor bolt, the area, A_1, should be assumed to have a width equal to the bolt diameter, d, and a depth of one-quarter of the embedment depth, but not more than 5d. For a shear lug, the area, A_1, should be taken as the projected area of the shear lug. For a headed stud welded to a plate at the level of the surface of the concrete, A_1 should be taken as the projected area of the stud.

D4.3.3

The depth of embedment of the anchor device should be adequate according to Clause D4.1.1 to develop a factored tensile resistance at least equal to the factored shear force being transferred, except that for anchors transferring load by shear friction, the factored tensile resistance should not be less than V_f/μ.

D4.3.4

Shear lugs should only be considered effective if they are approximately perpendicular to the shear force and are located in a concrete compression zone developed between the embedment and the concrete.

D4.3.5

Where shear force is transferred by shear friction, the factored resistance should be in accordance with Clause 11.6 with coefficients of friction of

(a) concrete or grout against as-rolled steel with a contact plane a full plate thickness below the concrete surface .... $\mu = 0.8\lambda$;

(b) concrete or grout against as-rolled steel with contact plane coincidental with the concrete surface .... $\mu = 0.6\lambda$;

(c) grouted or drypacked conditions with the contact plane between grout and as-rolled steel exterior to the concrete surface .... $\mu = 0.5$.

D4.3.6

When shear acts towards a free edge, the minimum distance from the anchorage to that edge should be such that the concrete between the anchorage and the edge does not fail in tension. The factored tensile resistance of concrete should be based on a uniform maximum tensile stress of $0.30\lambda\phi_c\sqrt{f_c'}$ acting on the effective stress area defined in Items (a), (b), and (c), as follows:

(a) for anchor bolts, studs, and rods the effective stress area should be the intersection of the free edge and a portion of a 90° pyramid with its apex at the surface of the concrete and the centre of the bolt, stud, or rod and with the axis of the pyramid parallel to the applied shear (see Figure D2);

(b) for shear lugs, the effective stress area should be defined by projected 45° planes from the edge of the shear lug to the free edge. The bearing area of the shear lug should be excluded from the effective stress area; and

(c) for cases where shear friction is employed, the effective stress area should be defined by projecting 45° planes from a line parallel to the free edge through the middle of the contact surface, and from the edges of the contact surface to the free edge (see Figure D3).

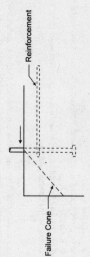

Figure D4
Reinforcement Across Potential Cracking Planes
(See Clause D4.4.)

D6. Grouted and Adhesive Anchors

D6.1
Materials for grout should be in accordance with CSA Standard A23.1. Grouts and adhesives should be formulated, mixed, and placed in accordance with approved procedures established by test.

D6.2
Randomly selected grouted and adhesive anchors should be tested to a minimum of 110% of the factored load effect to verify load transfer capabilities. Grouted and adhesive anchors installed in tensile zones of concrete members should be capable of sustaining design strength in cracked concrete. Tests should be carried out in accordance with Clause D8. The testing program should be established by the designer.

D6.3
The tests required by Clause D6.2 may be waived by the designer if acceptable tests and installation data are available to ensure that the grouted and adhesive anchors will function as designed or if the load transfer through the grout is by direct bearing or compression.

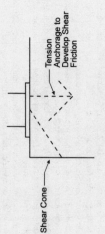

Figure D3
Effective Stress Area Where Shear Friction is Employed
(See Clause D4.3.6.)

D4.3.7
If the factored tensile resistance of concrete is not sufficient to resist the factored shear force, reinforcement should be provided satisfying Clause D4.4.

D4.4 Reinforcement
When the embedment depth or side cover is less than that required by Clauses D4.1, D4.2, and D4.3, reinforcement should be provided across the potential cracking planes. The reinforcement should be designed for the full force to be transferred by the anchor and should be detailed to develop the required forces on both sides of the potential cracks (see Figure D4).

D5. Design Requirements for Embedments
The factored resistance of embedments should be based on CSA Standard S16.1 for structural steel embedments or $\phi_s f_y$ for embedments made of reinforcement, but not greater than $0.8\phi_s f_{su}$ and in no case more than 600 MPa.

D7. Expansion Anchors

D7.1

The resistance of expansion anchors and their suitability for the type of loading should always be verified by test results supplied by the manufacturer of the anchor or by an approved testing agency. The following factors should be considered when assessing anchor resistance and performance:

(a) concrete strength;

(b) embedment depth—anchors should be installed to the embedment depth recommended by the anchor manufacturer;

(c) axial spacing—the manufacturer's recommended axial spacing should be used whenever possible. When using less than the recommended spacing, a reduction factor as published by the anchor manufacturer should be used in determining the capacity of the anchorage system;

(d) edge distance—the manufacturer's recommended edge distance should be used whenever possible and should take into account the direction of loading. When using less than the recommended edge distance, a reduction factor should be used in determining the capacity of the anchorage system. Where reduced edge distance is necessary on new concrete, reinforcing should be placed to satisfy Clause D4.4.1; and

(e) structural design—where the mean and standard deviation of the anchor strength are available from the manufacturer, the factored resistance, R_r, should be given by

$$R_r = \phi_e(\bar{x} - 2s) \qquad (D\text{-}2)$$

where
$\bar{x}$ = mean resistance in test
s = standard deviation of ultimate failure load in test
ϕ_e = resistance factor for expansion anchors taken as equal to 0.40

If the standard deviation of the anchor strength is not available, the factored resistance, R_r, should be given by

$$R_r = \frac{\phi_e \bar{x}}{1.33} \qquad (D\text{-}3)$$

D7.2

When using expansion anchors in tension zones of concrete members to resist vibratory or tensile loads, test data should be provided by the anchor manufacturer and/or tests should be conducted to verify the adequacy of the type and size of anchor under consideration for the application proposed.

D7.3

The installation of expansion anchors should, in all respects, conform to the installation practices recommended by the anchor manufacturer and to the installation practices used in anchor test verifications.

D8. Testing of Anchors

D8.1

Tests should be carried out by a testing agency or the anchor manufacturer in a manner acceptable to the designer and should be certified by a suitable qualified person. Test reports should describe the testing program, procedures, results, and conclusions.

D8.2

Tests should be representative of the anchorage system, including embedment, anchor spacing, edge distances, load application, concrete type and strength, grouts or adhesives used, and expected environmental conditions. A minimum of five tests should be carried out for each applicable combination of variables.

D8.3

Tests conducted in tension should be of the embedment length required to attain the full capacity of the anchor.

D8.4

When testing for the tensile strength of anchors, the testing device should not apply compression to the concrete surface surrounding the anchor being tested within a circle concentric with the anchor and with a diameter of 4 times the anchor embedment.

Note: For further information concerning anchorage to concrete refer to CSA Standard N287.3, Design Requirements for Concrete Containment Structures for CANDU Nuclear Power Plants; CPCI Metric Design Manual, Chapter 6; and "Guide to the Design of Anchor Bolts and Other Steel Embedments", Concrete International, July 1981.

INDEX

(**Note:** Clauses having Explanatory Notes are designated in **bold** type.)

NOTES

NOTES

NOTES

NOTES

PART II

Concrete Design Information
with
Design Examples
and
Design Aids

General

By J.G. MacGregor

M. Saatcioglu

S. Cumming

R. J. McGrath

Chapter 1
General

1.1 DESIGN METHOD

1.1.1 General

The objective of structural design and construction is to produce safe, serviceable, economic, durable and aesthetic structures. Each of these attributes will be examined more fully here or in other parts of this Handbook.

Safety — Structures must be able to withstand the loads acting on them during a reasonable lifetime. This is accomplished, first and foremost, by a careful selection of the structural system and a clear understanding of how that system will behave under load. This involves identifying and considering possible failure modes during construction and during the life of the structure. Once the structure is chosen, load factors and resistance factors are used in the proportioning of the members to minimize the risk arising from overloads and understrength elements. Care must be taken to avoid gross errors in the design process and in the construction process.

During its life the building should have adequate structural integrity to be able to adapt to unforeseen influences and localized damages without major spread of damage or collapse. This is discussed more fully in Section 1.6 of this Handbook. Similarly, building codes require that structures have specified minimum fire resistances so that they will retain their strength long enough for evacuation of occupants and for fire-fighting operations to be carried out. Design for fire is discussed in Section 1.4 of this Handbook.

Serviceability — In addition to having adequate strength building structures must behave in a satisfactory manner in service. They should not deflect excessively or vibrate excessively and those cracks which occur should not impair the function or the aesthetics of the structure.

Economy — Among other things, a project is judged by its first costs, its lifelong performance and the construction time. In many cases the structure forms a small part of the total cost of a project. Similarly, the cost of concrete and reinforcement form only a fraction of the cost of the structure. For these reasons, optimizing the structure itself may not lead to the most economical project. During the design process it is essential to consider construction costs and maintenance costs.

Durability — Durable structures survive exposure to the environment and corrosive agents and in doing so, maintenance costs are reduced. Inadequate durability has led to rusting reinforcement, spalling concrete and general deterioration of structures. Section 1.5 of this Handbook reviews the factors affecting durability.

Aesthetics — Buildings and bridges should have an attractive appearance and complement their surroundings. Concrete, as a material, allows a wide range of structural and architectural shapes and a wide range of surface treatments which can be used to develop pleasing buildings and bridges.

1.1.2 Load and Resistance Factors

The CSA Standard A23.3-94 "Design of Concrete Structures" has adopted the newly revised load factors and load combinations specified in the 1995 edition of the National Building Code of Canada. The resistance factors contained in CSA A23.3 Standard are applied to material strengths as noted in Section 1.1.4.

1.1.3 Effect of Factored Loads

Definitions and Magnitudes of Loads

The various loads to be considered in design are defined in Section 4.1 of the National Building Code

of Canada. They are:

D = dead loads, as provided for in Subsection 4.1.5.

Subsection 4.1.5. Dead Loads

4.1.5.1 Dead Loads

(1) The specified *dead load* for a structural member consists of

    (a) the weight of the member itself,
    (b) the weight of all materials of construction incorporated into the *building* to be supported permanently by the member, including permanent partitions,
    (c) the weight of *partitions*,
    (d) the weight of permanent equipment, and
    (e) forces due to prestressing.

(2) Except as provided in Sentence (5), in areas of a *building* where *partitions* other than permanent *partitions* are shown on the drawings, or where *partitions* might be added in the future, allowance shall be made for the weight of such *partitions*.

(3) The *partition* weight allowance shall be determined from the actual or anticipated weight of the *partitions* placed in any probable position, but shall be not less than 1 kN/m^2 over the area of floor being considered.

(4) *Partition* loads used in design shall be shown on the drawings as provided in Clause 2.4.4.3(1)(d).

(5) In cases where the *dead load* is counteractive, the load allowances as provided in Sentences (2) and (3) shall not be included in the design calculations.

Dead loads are computed from the specified dimensions and the densities of materials. Tables of the unit mass of construction materials are given in Section 1.7 of this Handbook.

Dead loads include an allowance for permanent and movable partitions as described in Clauses 4.1.5.1(2) through (5). Note that 4.1.5.1(5) implies that partition loads are applied in the pattern that gives the largest effect.

Note that although prestressing forces and the effects of prestressing are included in the NBC definition of Dead Loads, Clause 8.3.2.1 of CSA Standard A23.3 states they shall have a load factor of 1.0.

L = live loads due to intended use and occupancy (includes vertical loads due to cranes); snow, ice and rain; earth and hydrostatic pressure; horizontal components of static or inertia forces.

The live loads for use and occupancy specified by the NBC are given in Section 1.7 of this Handbook. These are selected as a high fractile of the loading distributions. Similarly, the specified loads due to snow, ice and rain represent a high fractile of the statistical distributions of these loads, typically one chance in 30 that the load will be exceeded in any given year. The National Building Code does not indicate whether the earth pressure should be a high fractile or a mean value. Hydrostatic pressure is normally computed as a mean value for fluids of known density.

W = live load due to wind,

E = loads due to earthquake,

T = loads due to contraction or expansion caused by temperature changes, shrinkage, moisture changes, cumulative effects of temperature, creep, shrinkage, and differential settlement.

This last category of loading (T) differs from the others in that it results from an imposed deformation. Since it is not caused by an external load, the resulting moments, forces and stresses must be self-equilibrating. Their magnitude is a function of the rigidity of the structure. If the structure becomes less rigid due to cracking, the stress due to T loads will generally decrease. On one hand, this helps the structural engineer since he may be able to count on cracking or creep to dissipate T stresses. On the other hand, however, the cracking which is required for this to occur may be unacceptable.

Load Factors and Load Combinations

The load factors and load combinations are given in A23.3 Clause 8.3. For load combinations not including earthquake the factored load combination shall be taken as:

$$\alpha_D D + \gamma\psi(\alpha_L L + \alpha_W W + \alpha_T T) \qquad (8\text{-}1)$$

For load combinations including earthquake the factored load combinations shall be taken as:

$$1.0D + \gamma(1.0E) \qquad (8\text{-}2)$$

and either:

(i) for storage and assembly occupancies:

$$1.0D + \gamma(1.0L + 1.0E); \text{ or} \qquad (8\text{-}3)$$

(ii) for all other occupancies:

$$1.0D + \gamma(0.5L + 1.0E). \qquad (8\text{-}4)$$

where α_D, α_L, α_W and α_T are the load factors on dead, live, wind and imposed deformation loadings. These factors have the values:

α_D = 1.25 except that if dead load resists overturning due to wind loads, uplift or stress reversal, α_D = 0.85.

α_L = 1.50

α_W = 1.50

α_T = 1.25

Prestressing forces and the effects of prestressing shall have a load factor of 1.0.

The term γ is an importance factor that is 1.0 except in rare cases where collapse is not likely to cause injury or other serious consequences.

The term ψ is a load combination factor which has the value 1.0 when only one of the loads, L, W or T is included in Eq. 8-1, 0.70 when two of these loads are included and 0.60 when all three of these loads are included in equation 8-1. Note that the load combination factor is no longer used with load combinations involving earthquake loads in the 1995 NBC.

For a building of normal importance ($\lambda = 1.0$) the resulting set of load combinations for loads not including earthquake is:

1.25D + 1.5L	(1.1)
1.25D + 1.5W	(1.2)
1.25D + 1.25T	(1.3)
1.25D + 1.05L + 1.05W	(1.4)

1.25D + 1.05L + 0.875T	(1.5)
1.25D + 1.05W + 0.875T	(1.6)
1.25D + 0.90L + 0.90W + 0.75T	(1.7)

The combination giving the most unfavourable effect shall be used.

In any of these the dead load factor α may have the value 1.25 or 0.85 if the dead load resists overturning, uplift, or stress reversal caused by the other loads. This is most apt to occur in combinations (1.2), (1.4) and (1.6) and in combination (1.1) if L includes earth pressure. It should be noted that it is not intended that $\alpha_D = 1.25$ and $\alpha_D = 0.85$ be used to form a checkerboard pattern of dead load on the structure.

Effect of Factored Loads

Clause 8.3.1 of CSA Standard A23.3-M94 uses the term "effect of factored loads" to refer to the moments, axial forces, shears, and torques calculated for the combinations of factored loads obtained from Eq. 8-1 through Eq. 8-4.

For problems which do not involve second-order effects (slenderness or PΔ effects in columns or frames), the analysis can either be based on factored loads, giving factored load effects directly, or on unfactored loads, giving unfactored load effects which must then be factored when they are combined. On the other hand, when second-order effects are significant, these effects are affected by the magnitude of the loads and hence the loads must be factored prior to carrying out the analysis.

The symbols M_f, V_f, P_f, T_f, etc. refer to moments, shears, axial forces and torques due to the factored loads. Thus, the subscript "f" signifies a load effect due to factored loads.

1.1.4 Factored Resistance

The 1994 edition of the CSA A23.3 Standard has retained the same method of expressing resistance factors as in the 1984 edition, where the resistance factor is applied to the material strength, $\phi_c f'_c$, or $\phi_s f_y$, rather than to the nominal resistance, ϕM_n, ϕV_n, etc.

Resistance factors account for a number of factors causing variability in strengths. These include:

(a) Variability in the strengths of concrete and reinforcement,

(b) Variability in dimensions,

(c) Approximations in the design equations,

(d) Mode of failure, brittle or ductile and the resulting warning of failure.

The resistance factor for steel, ϕ_s, accounts for variability of the strength of reinforcement and to a lesser extent the variability in d, etc. resulting from placement tolerances for reinforcement. Similarly, the variability of the strength of concrete and dimensions of concrete are reflected in the resistance factor for concrete, ϕ_c. The brittle nature of failures initiated by failure of the concrete and the higher variability of design equations for failure initiated by failure of the concrete (the shear V_c, for example) were accounted for by using a higher safety index when evaluating the value of ϕ_c than for ϕ_s.

Values of Resistance Factors

A23.3 Clauses 8.4.2 and 8.4.3 give the values of the resistance factors:

8.4.2 — The factored concrete strengths used in checking ultimate limit states shall be taken as $\phi_c f'_c$ and $\phi_c \sqrt{f'_c}$ where $\phi_c = 0.60$.

8.4.3 — The factored force in reinforcing bars, tendons, and structural shapes shall be taken as the product of the resistance factor, ϕ, and the respective steel force as specified in other Clauses of this Standard, where

$\phi_s = 0.85$ for reinforcing bars,
$\phi_p = 0.90$ for prestressing tendons,
$\phi_s = 0.90$ for structural steel.

Clause 16.1.3 of CSA Standard A23.3 now permits the use of $\phi_c = 0.65$ for precast elements manufactured and erected in accordance with the requirements of CSA Standard A23.4.

Use of Resistance Factors

The resistance factors ϕ_c, ϕ_s, ϕ_p and ϕ_a are included in the equations for calculating the factored resistances, M_r, V_r, P_r, T_r, etc.. The subscripts "r" in these notations refer to "factored resistance".

When concrete is used in compression its strength is taken as $\phi_c f'_c$. In defining the equivalent rectangular stress block, Clause 10.1.7 states that a concrete stress of $\alpha_1 \phi_c f'_c$ shall be used. When properties related to the concrete tensile strength are used in calculations, as in the calculation of V_c in Clause 11.3, the tensile strength is taken as a function of $\phi_c \sqrt{f'_c}$.

Clause 8.4.3 and 8.5.3.2 require that when determining the factored resistance of bars and tendons, the resistance factor, ϕ_s be applied to the bar *force*, $\phi_s A_s f_y$ or $\phi_s A_s E_s \epsilon_s$, regardless of whether the steel has yielded or not. The reason for this is that ϕ_s takes into account deviation in the location of the reinforcement and uncertainty in the prediction of resistance as well as variability in yield strength.

In addition to ϕ_s, ϕ_c and ϕ_p a member resistance factor ϕ_m is used in slender column calculations in Clause 10.15 and for certain brittle members in Clause 21.

Resistance factors ϕ_s, ϕ_c and ϕ_p are not included in equations giving empirical limits, such as Eq. 10.26 in Clause 10.18.2 or in the equation in Clause 12. In the latter case it was recognized that the equations in Clause 12 were empirical in nature and implicitly included a safety margin. The expression for the modulus of elasticity of concrete in Clause 8.6.2.2 does not include ϕ_c. When E_c is used in stability calculations in Clause 10.15 and 10.16 the variability of EI and P_c is taken into account using a member resistance factor ϕ_s.

1.2 STRUCTURAL CONCRETE

1.2.1 General

Performance of reinforced concrete structures is significantly influenced by the quality of concrete. Structural concrete is affected by the properties of constituent materials and the proportions in which they are mixed. Requirements for proportioning and producing quality concrete as well as acceptance tests for the constituent materials are specified in CSA Standards A23.1 and A23.4 for cast-in-place and precast concrete respectively.

Fig. 1.2 illustrates the range in proportions of materials used in producing concrete. The mass density of concrete is dependent on the aggregates, which constitute 60-80 percent of the total volume. Fine aggregates consisting of natural or manufactured sand, and coarse aggregates consisting of crushed stone, gravel or air-cooled iron blast-furnace slag are used to produce "Normal Density Concrete" with a mass density of about 2400 kg/m^3. Low density aggregates are used to produce "Structural Low Density Concrete" with a mass density not exceeding 1850 kg/m^3. Sometimes normal density fine aggregate is mixed with low density coarse aggregate to produce "Structural Semi Low Density Concrete" having a mass density between 1850 and 2150 kg/m^3. Occasionally high density aggregates are used to produce "High Density Concrete" for special applications.

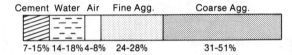

Cement Water Air   Fine Agg.   Coarse Agg.

7-15% 14-18% 4-8% 24-28%   31-51%

Fig. 1.2: Proportions of Constituent Materials by Absolute Volume — Air Entrained Concrete

In a properly mixed concrete, each particle of aggregate is coated with cement and water paste. Cement, in the presence of water, hydrates and hardens, binding the aggregate particles, to form a solid rocklike mass. The quality of cement paste largely depends on the water-cement ratio. Excess water in the paste reduces concrete quality in terms of strength, watertightness, abrasion resistance and durability.

Five types of Portland cement conforming to CSA Standard A5 are available for structural use. Type 10, Normal Portland Cement is used in general concrete construction when the special properties or the other types are not required. The cement types and their effects on concrete are summarized in Table 1.1.

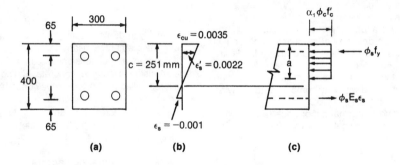

Fig. 1.1

1.2.2 Strength and Elastic Modulus

One of the most important properties of structural concrete is its compressive strength. Other properties of concrete, required in structural design, can approximately be expressed in terms of compressive strength f'_c. Therefore, the structural engineer is required to specify f'_c on the drawings or in related specifications. Unless otherwise specified, f'_c is based on the 28-day strength. Generally the concrete strengths used in structural applications vary between 20 MPa and 40 MPa. Higher strength concretes may be used for special applications and in prestressed concrete constructions. For design against seismic action, concrete strengths in excess of 55 MPa are not permitted by CSA Standard A23.3, Clause 21.2.3.1.

Low density concrete can be used for structural purposes only if the 28 day strength is in excess of 20 MPa. If the structural low density concrete is to be used for earthquake resistant design, the maximum concrete strength is limited to 30 MPa by Clause 21.2.3.2 of CSA Standard A23.3.

Concrete strength is usually determined by testing either 100 × 200 mm cylinders or 150 × 300 mm cylinders under axial compression. According to CSA A23.1, Clause 17.5.4.1, two cylinders are tested at 28 days, and the average of the two results is used as f'_c provided that neither of the cylinders shows a sign of defect. The specimens are prepared in accordance with CSA Test Method A23.2-3C and tested in accordance with CSA Test Method A23.2-9C.

Typical stress-strain relationships obtained from the standard cylinder tests are shown in Fig. 1.3. Tests indicate that the ultimate concrete strain recorded at failure varies from 0.003 to as high as 0.008. However, CSA Standard A23.3 limits the maximum usable compressive strain conservatively to 0.0035.

Modulus of elasticity is another important property of concrete that is often used in structural design to compute deformations. Generally the modulus of elasticity is a secant modulus based on the stress and strain at about 50% of f'_c. CSA Standard A23.3 provides an empirical equation for concrete modulus of elasticity based on the secant modulus. Accordingly,

$$E_c = \left(3300\sqrt{f'_c} + 6900\right)\left(\frac{\gamma_c}{2300}\right)^{1.5} \quad (1.8)$$

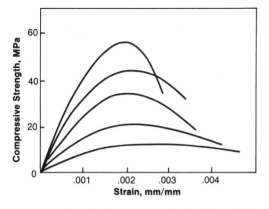

Fig. 1.3: Concrete Stress-Strain Relationships Obtained From Standard Cylinder Tests

where γ is the mass density of concrete in kg/m³ and f'_c is the compressive strength of concrete in MPa. The

above equation is provided for values of γ_c between 1500 and 2500 kg/m³. For normal density concrete E_c may be taken as $4500\sqrt{f'_c}$ where f'_c is in MPa.

1.2.3 Creep and Shrinkage

Creep of concrete is defined as the time dependent increase in strain under sustained loading. Other time dependent deformations are generally attributed to shrinkage and temperature changes in concrete.

Creep is usually expressed in terms of the creep coefficient C_t, defined as the ratio of creep strain ε_{cr} to initial immediate strain ε_i. Creep strain increases with time at a decreasing rate. This is illustrated in Fig. 1.4.

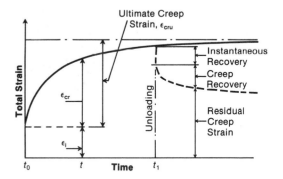

Fig. 1.4: Variation of Creep with Time

A commonly accepted procedure to determine the creep coefficient is to follow the ACI Committee 209 recommendation[*]. The following expression given by ACI Committee 209 is applicable to normal, semi-low and low density concretes.

$$C_t = \frac{t^{0.6}}{10 + t^{0.6}} C_u Q_{cr} \quad (1.9)$$

where t is time in days after loading, and C_u is the ultimate creep coefficient and varies between 1.30 and 4.15. In the absence of specific creep data for local aggregates and conditions, the average value suggested for C_u is 2.35.

The above equation was developed for sustained compressive stress not exceeding 50% of concrete strength. It consists of an expression for creep under standard conditions multiplied by the correction factor Q_{cr} to modify for non-standard conditions. The standard conditions and the correction factor Q_{cr} are specified in Table 1.2.

Shrinkage is the decrease in the volume of hardened concrete with time. Unlike creep, shrinkage is independent of externally applied loads. The decrease in volume is mainly attributed to the moisture loss caused by drying and hydration as well as the chemical changes that result in the carbonation of cement hydration products.

Shrinkage strains start taking place immediately after exposing concrete to a drying environment. Fig. 1.5 illustrates the variation of shrinkage with time. According to ACI Committee 209, the shrinkage strain ε_{sh} is determined using the expression given in Equation 1.10. This expression is applicable to normal, semi-low and low density concretes.

[*]"Prediction of Creep, Shrinkage, and Temperature Effects in Concrete Structures", Reported by ACI Committee 209, Report No. ACI 209R-82 (Reapproved 1986), American Concrete Institute, Special Publication SP-76, 1982, pp. 143-300.

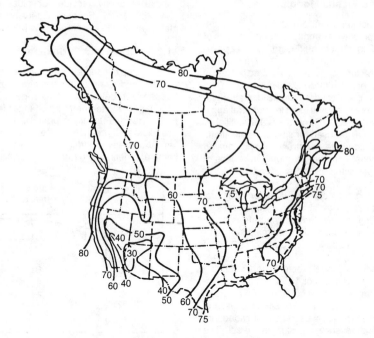

Fig. 1.6: Annual Average Ambient Relative Humidity (%)
(Reproduced from CPCI Metric Design Manual)

$$\varepsilon_{sh} = \frac{t}{C_s + t} \varepsilon_{shu} P_{sh} \qquad (1.10)$$

where t is time in days starting immediately after the initial wet curing. C_s is equal to 35 if concrete is moist cured for 7 days, and 55 if steam cured for 1-3 days. ε_{shu} is the ultimate shrinkage strain. In the absence of specific shrinkage data for local conditions, the average value of ε_{shu} suggested for use is 0.00078 mm/mm. P_{sh} is a correction factor for conditions that are other than the standard conditions specified in Table 1.2. The values of P_{sh} can be obtained from the same table.

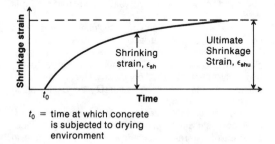

t_0 = time at which concrete
is subjected to drying
environment

Fig. 1.5: Variation of Shrinkage Strain with Time

Concrete creep and shrinkage are both sensitive to environmental factors such as relative humidity and temperature. Fig. 1.6 shows annual average relative humidity throughout North America. The effect of relative humidity on creep and shrinkage is empirically considered in Eqs. (1.9) and (1.10) through correction factors Q_{cr} and P_{sh}. The effect of temperature is usually considered to be less important than relative humidity. The expressions for creep and shrinkage given in this section are based on concrete temperature of $23 \pm 2°C$. It has been shown that structures exposed to high temperature for an extended

period of time experience higher creep strains. At 50°C, creep strain is approximately two to three times the creep strain at 19° to 24°C. Where temperature effects may be a significant design factor, it is recommended that an in-depth determination be made to establish more exact values of creep and shrinkage.

The creep coefficient and shrinkage strain given by Eqs. (1.9) and (1.10) are meant for unreinforced, unrestrained concrete. In reinforced concrete members, time-dependent deformations are restrained by the reinforcement. While the procedure described in this section provides acceptable results for lightly reinforced members, its application to most reinforced concrete members is questionable. A proper adjustment to these values is recommended to account for the effect of reinforcement. Empirical equations are available for this purpose.

Long term deformations due to creep and shrinkage can be several times the initial deformation. According to CSA Standard A23.3, the total deflection, including long term effects, can be as high as 3.0 times the immediate initial deflection, depending on the percentage of reinforcement and the time for which deflection is computed.

Shrinkage strain alone is in the order of 0.0002 to 0.0008 mm/mm. In reinforced concrete structures with commonly used percentages of reinforcement, the shrinkage strain is in the range of 0.0002 to 0.0003 mm/mm.

Example

A prestressed concrete beam with 8.0 m span and 400 mm by 600 mm rectangular cross-section is pretensioned using 15 Grade 1860 size 11 seven wire strands. The steel stress after transfer is 1300 MPa. If the beam is prestressed immediately after seven days of moist curing, determine the shortening in the beam 60 days after the moist curing, when it is erected for a structure in Calgary. Use the following concrete properties:

Concrete strength at 7 days	:	30 MPa
Air content	:	5%
Slump	:	100 mm

Fine aggregate	:	670 kg/m^3
Coarse aggregate	:	1000 kg/m^3
Type 10 cement	:	400 kg/m^3

Solution

i. Elastic concrete strain (ε_i):

$A_{ps} = (15)(74.2) = 1113 \text{ mm}^2$
$P_o = (1300)(1113) = 1447 \times 10^3 \text{ N}$
$P_o/A = 1447 \times 10^3/(400 \times 600) = 6.0 \text{ MPa}$
$E_c = 5000 \sqrt{30} = 27400 \text{ MPa}$
$\varepsilon_i = 6.0/27400 = 219 \times 10^{-6} \text{ mm/mm}$

ii. Creep and shrinkage modification factors, from Table 1.2:

Age at loading: 7 days, moist cured

$Q_a = 1.00$

Relative humidity: 70% for Calgary from Fig. 1.6

$Q_h = 0.80$
$P_h = 0.70$

Ratio of fine to total aggregate:
$$\frac{670}{670 + 1000} = 0.40 \text{ mm}$$

$Q_f = 0.98$
$P_h = 0.86$

Volume surface ratio: $\dfrac{(400)(600)}{2(400) + 2(600)} = 120 \text{ mm}$

$Q_f = 0.75$
$P_f = 0.69$

Slump: 100 mm

$Q_s = 1.08$
$P_s = 1.05$

Air %: 5

$Q_v = 1.00$
$P_v = 1.00$

Cement content: 400 kg/m^3

$P_c = 0.99$
$Q_{cr} = Q_a\,Q_h\,Q_f\,Q_r\,Q_s\,Q_v$
$\quad = (1.00)(0.80)(0.98)(0.75)(1.08)(1.00)$
$\quad = 0.635$
$P_{sh} = P_c\,P_h\,P_f\,P_r\,P_s\,P_v$
$\quad = (0.99)(0.70)(0.86)(0.69)(1.05)(1.00)$
$\quad = 0.432$

iii. Creep strain (ε_{cr})

$\varepsilon_{cr} = \varepsilon_i C_t$
$C_t = \dfrac{t^{0.6}}{10 + t^{0.6}} C_u Q_{cr}$ (from Eq. 1.9)
$C_u = 2.35$ (average value)
$C_t = \dfrac{(60)^{0.6}}{10 + (60)^{0.6}}(2.35)(0.635) = 0.80$
$\varepsilon_{cr} = (219 \times 10^{-6})(0.80) = 176 \times 10^{-6} \text{ mm/mm}$

iv. Shrinkage strain (ε_{sh}):

$\varepsilon_{sh} = \dfrac{t}{C_s + t}\,\varepsilon_{shu}\,P_{sh}$ (from Eq. 1.10)
$C_s = 35$ (moist cured for 7 days)

$\varepsilon_{shu} = 0.00078 \text{ mm/mm}$ (average value)
$\varepsilon_{sh} = \dfrac{60}{35 + 60}(0.00078)(0.432)$
$\quad = 213 \times 10^{-6} \text{ mm/mm}$

v. Total shortening due to creep and shrinkage

Total strain $= \varepsilon_{cr} + \varepsilon_{sh}$
$\quad = 176 \times 10^{-6} + 213 \times 10^{-6}$
Total shortening $= (389 \times 10^{-6})(8000) = 3.1 \text{ mm}$

1.2.4 Concrete Durability

Durability of concrete is affected by exposure conditions and the presence of chemical constituents and impurities that may react with cement. Severe weather, causing freeze-thaw cycles, may fracture the concrete. Air voids, if present in concrete, relieve the pressure caused by frozen water in concrete. Therefore, air-entrainment producing 5 to 8 percent air is strongly recommended for concretes subjected to severe exposure conditions. De-icing agents are known to accelerate freeze-thaw cycles. CSA Standard A23.1, Clause 15, provides specific requirements for durability.

Another harmful exposure condition is the soil or ground water that may have high sulphate content. The use of Type 20 or Type 50 cement, depending on the sulphate concentration, is recommended for protection against sulphate attack. Table 1.1 provides guidelines in selecting the cement type against sulphate action.

Certain chemical constituents and impurities that may be present in mixing water and aggregates are also potential sources of hazard to concrete. In some areas, the chemical composition of aggregate is such that it reacts with alkalies in cement, producing abnormal expansion and cracking. CSA Standard A23.1 should be consulted for the selection of mixing water and aggregates that are free of deleterious substances and organic impurities.

Structural engineers are also concerned with the durability of reinforced concrete and protection of reinforcement in concrete against corrosive environments. Calcium chloride, sometimes used as an accelerating admixture, is a potential corrosion hazard to prestressing tendons. Concrete cover requirements for different exposure conditions and the protection of reinforcement against corrosive environments are discussed in section 1.5.

1.3 REINFORCING AND PRESTRESSING STEEL

1.3.1 General

The design requirements for non-prestressed reinforcement and prestressing tendons are specified in CSA Standards A23.3 and A23.1. These requirements include a minimum specified yield strength, a minimum ultimate tensile strength, ductility, and a sufficient bendability for hooks.

Non-prestressed reinforcement consists of deformed bars, deformed wire reinforcement and welded wire fabric, fabricated using smooth or deformed wires. Plain reinforcing bars may be used for spirals, and if smaller than 10 mm in diameter, may also be used for stirrups and ties.

Prestressing steel consists of high strength smooth wire, seven-wire strands and high-strength alloy bars.

1.3.2 Strength and Elastic Modulus

Reinforcement is classified on the basis of its minimum specified strength for structural purposes. In the case of non-prestressed reinforcement, minimum specified yield strength, f_y in MPa defines the grade of steel. Hot-rolled deformed and plain billet-steel reinforcing bars conforming to CSA Standard G30.18 are produced in grades 400 and 500. Weldable low alloy steel bars conforming to CSA Standard G30.18 are also produced in grades 400 and 500.

Cold-drawn wires and welded wire fabric are produced with minimum specified yield strengths ranging between 450 and 515 MPa depending on the use, size and whether the wire is deformed or smooth. Mechanical properties of wires and welded wire fabric are discussed in section 1.3.4.

Typical stress-strain relationships for hot-rolled bars and cold-drawn wires are shown in Fig.1.7.

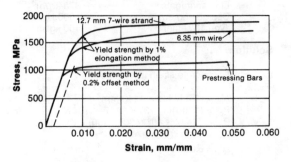

Fig. 1.8: Typical Stress-Strain Curves for Prestressing Tendons

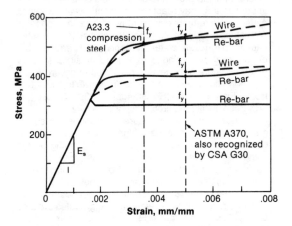

Fig. 1.7: Typical Stress-Strain Curves for Reinforcing Steel

CSA Standard A23.3 provides certain design limitations with respect to reinforcement strength. These limitations are summarized below.

i. The value of f_y to be used in design calculations is limited to 550 MPa except for prestressing steel. (See Clause 9.4.1.)

ii. If the compression reinforcement has a yield strength in excess of 400 MPa, the design calculations will be based on either the value of 400 MPa, or the stress corresponding to a strain of 0.0035. (See Clause 9.4.2.)

iii. In earthquake resistant design, when reinforcement conforming to CSA Standard G30.18 is used for members subjected to flexure and axial forces, the reinforcement strength is required to be closely controlled. Accordingly, the actual yield strength determined by mill tests is not permitted to exceed the specified minimum yield strength by more than 125 MPa for grade 400W reinforcement and 150 MPa for grade 500W reinforcement. Furthermore, the ultimate tensile strength of reinforcement is required to be at least 1.15 times the actual yield strength.

Steel grades for tendons depend on the minimum tensile strength, f_{pu} in MPa. Grades and properties of prestressing wires, strands and bars are listed in Tables 1.3 and 1.4.

High strength steels, used in prestressed concrete construction, do not have definite yield points. Typical stress-strain relationships are shown in Fig. 1.8. Yield strengths as specified by CSA Standard G279-M1982 are indicated in the same figure.

The elastic modulus of steel, E_s, is typically 200,000 MPa. For non-prestressed reinforcement, E_s is specified by CSA Standard A23.3 to be 200,000 MPa. For prestressing tendons, E_s is required to be determined by tests or supplied by the manufacturer.

1.3.3 Reinforcing Bar Properties

The standard reinforcing bar sizes and their properties are given in Table 1.5. Specifications for deformations on bars, bendability requirements and the related test procedures are given in CSA Standard G30.18 for hot-rolled steel bars and weldable low alloy steel reinforcement. Table 1.6 and 1.7 summarize the tensile and bond test requirements for reinforcing bars. Steel grades and stress-strain characteristics are discussed in Section 1.3.2.

1.3.4 Properties of Wire and Welded Wire Fabric

Specifications for smooth and deformed steel wire for concrete reinforcement are given in CSA Standards G30.3 and G30.14 respectively. At the present time the Metric wire sizes are soft converted from Imperial units. Therefore, wire sizes are expressed in terms of soft converted cross-sectional area in mm^2 prefixed with letters MW or MD for smooth and deformed wires respectively. Tensile and bend test requirements for smooth and deformed steel wire are summarized in Tables 1.8 and 1.9.

Wire reinforcement is generally used in the form of welded wire fabric, consisting of a series of longitudinal and transverse wires welded together to form a mesh. Fabrication requirements, mechanical properties and the test procedures for welded wire fabric are specified in CSA Standards G30.5 and G30.15 for smooth and deformed wires respectively. According to these Standards, welded wire fabric is produced on the basis of sizes and spacings specified by the purchaser. Welded wire fabric is designated with letters WWF followed by spacings and sizes of wires. Table 1.10 gives the sizes that are currently used in Canada.

1.3.5 Properties of Prestressing Steel

The standard tendon sizes and their properties are given in Tables 1.3 and 1.4. Specifications for prestressing wires, strands and bars are outlined in CSA Standard G279. Steel grades and stress-strain characteristics of prestressing tendons are discussed in Section 1.3.2.

1.4 REQUIREMENTS FOR FIRE RESISTANCE

1.4.1 INTRODUCTION

1.4.1.1 General

Note (1) to the Scope of CSA Standard A23.3 states:

"In addition to the requirements of this Standard it is necessary that the design of building structures of reinforced concrete be carried out in accordance with the provisions of applicable Building Codes governing fire resistance."

Thus, CSA Standard A23.3 does not cover any aspect of design to ensure that the fire resistance ratings which may be required by building codes are achieved.

In the design of structures, building code requirements for fire resistance are sometimes overlooked. Such omissions may require costly measures to rectify. For example, slab thickness designs which are adequate to satisfy CSA Standard A23.3 provisions may not be sufficient to provide the necessary fire resistance. Similarly, cover to reinforcement may need to be increased for fire design purposes.

The purpose of this section is to make the reader aware of the importance of first examining the fire resistance provisions of the governing building code before proceeding with the structural design.

The field of fire technology is highly involved and complex and it is not the intent here to deal with the chemical or physical characteristics of fire, nor with the behaviour of structures in real fire situations. Rather, the goal is to present some basic information as an aid to designers in establishing those fire protection features of construction which may impact their structural design work.

1.4.1.2 Definitions

- Fire resistance generally refers to the property of a material or assembly to withstand fire or give protection from it; as applied to elements of buildings, it is characterized by the ability to confine a fire or to continue to perform a given structural function, or both.

- Fire resistance rating is defined in NBC, 1995 as the time in hours or fraction thereof that a material or assembly of materials will withstand the passage of flame and transmission of heat when exposed to fire under specified conditions of test and performance criteria, or as determined by extension or interpretation of information derived therefrom as prescribed in this Code.

1.4.1.3 Test Criteria for Fire Resistance

The fire resistance rating of building components is determined in accordance with ULC Standard CAN4-S101-M, Standard Methods of Fire Endurance Tests of Building Construction and Materials. During these tests, a building assembly such as a portion of a floor, wall, roof or column is subjected to increasing temperatures that vary with time as shown in Fig. 1.9. Floor and roof specimens are exposed to the test fire from beneath, beams from the bottom and sides, walls from one side and columns from all sides.

The standard time-temperature curve approximates the conditions which would pertain during a fire within a moderate size compartment having a relatively

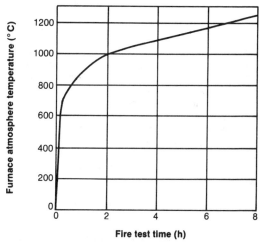

Fig. 1.9: Standard Time Temperature Curve

small amount of ventilation and a fire load of about 50 kg of combustibles per square metre, per hour of fire.

The end of the test is reached and the fire endurance of the specimen is established when any one of the following conditions first occurs.

For floor and roof assemblies and for bearing walls and partitions:

(1) The temperature of the unexposed surface rises an average of 140°C above its initial temperature or 180°C at any location. In addition, walls must sustain a hose stream test.

(2) Cotton waste placed on the unexposed side of a wall, floor or roof system is ignited through cracks or fissures developed in the specimen.

(3) The test assembly fails to sustain the full specified load required by CSA Standard A23.3. Additional criteria limiting the reinforcing steel temperature to 593°C also apply in the case of certain restrained and all unrestrained floors, roofs and beams tested restrained.

Though the complete requirements of ULC S101 and the conditions of acceptance are much too detailed for inclusion in this chapter, experience shows that the fire resistance of concrete floor/roof assemblies and walls is usually governed by heat transmission (item 1), and columns and beams by failure to sustain the applied loads (item 3), or beam reinforcement fails to meet the temperature rise criterion (item 3).

1.4.1.4 NBC Requirements

Most NBC requirements for fire resistance are set forth in Part 3 of the Code, Use and Occupancy. Part 9, Housing and Small Buildings, also contains similar requirements. For design of buildings under Part 9, the fire ratings prescribed in Table 9.10.3.A and 9.10.3.B for the assemblies listed, may be used.

The fire ratings which must be provided for major structural assemblies are set forth in NBC Subsection 3.2.2, Building Size and Construction Relative to Occupancy. In addition, such assemblies may be required to possess a fire resistance rating on the basis of the major occupancy separation requirements of Subsection 3.1.3, the spatial separation requirements of Subsection 3.2.3 or other fire separation requirements located throughout Sections 3.3, 3.4 and 3.5 of NBC. The rules which govern the determination of the fire resistance rating of a specific assembly are given in NBC Subsection 3.1.5, Fire Resistance Rating.

Subsection 3.1.5 requires that fire resistance ratings be determined on the basis of results of tests conducted in conformance with ULC S101. It also provides that assemblies may be assigned a rating according to Appendix "D" of the NBC. It should be noted that the ratings contained in Appendix "D" of the NBC apply strictly to assemblies and structural members of generic materials for which there exist nationally recognized standards. Appendix "D" does not apply to assemblies of materials or structural members whose fire performance depends on proprietary information or where specifications do not meet all Appendix "D" provisions.

In practice, the designer has three options. Two of these are clearly in keeping with Subsection 3.1.5, namely:

(a) Rate an assembly in accordance with Appendix "D" of the NBC.

(b) Use an existing ULC listing for the *specific* assembly for which the rating is required.

> **Note:** Relatively few reinforced concrete assemblies are included in ULC listings. While these should be used where applicable, the discussion included in this Section is aimed at the determination of fire resistance ratings, in accordance with Appendix "D", Fire Performance Ratings.

The third option is known as:

(c) "Rational Design"
Rational design, or analytical procedures for determining fire resistance, refers to an engineering method of calculating the duration that a structural element can be subjected to a standard fire exposure while performing its function, both structurally and as a barrier to heat. As the calculations used in this method are based on ULC S101 test criteria, they may be acceptable to an authority having jurisdiction under the Equivalent provisions of the General Requirements of NBC. It should be emphasized, however, that because no standard for rational design is currently referenced in NBC, specific *prior* approval must be obtained from the authority having jurisdiction for the use of rational design methods to establish fire ratings. Further detailed discussion of rational design techniques is beyond the scope of this brief Section and the reader is referred to References (1) and (2) for further information.

1.4.2 FACTORS WHICH INFLUENCE FIRE RESISTANCE RATINGS

1.4.2.1 General

In order to recognize all of the factors which influence the fire resistance rating which may be assigned to a building construction assembly, on the basis of Appendix "D", a thorough knowledge and understanding of that document is obviously necessary.

For the purposes of this brief Section, the following are the main factors applicable to reinforced concrete assemblies which influence their fire resistance rating.

1.4.2.2 Concrete Type

Concrete is considered to be one of the most highly fire resistive structural materials used in construction. Nonetheless, the properties of concrete and reinforcing steel change significantly in the high temperatures of fire. Strength and the modulus of elasticity are reduced, the coefficient of expansion increases, and creep and stress relaxations are considerably higher.

Two basic types of *normal weight concretes* are recognized in Appendix "D" of the NBC, namely:

- Type S concrete, in which the coarse aggregate is granite, quartzite, siliceous gravel or other dense materials containing at least 30% quartz, chert or flint; and

- Type N concrete, in which the coarse aggregate is limestone, calcareous gravel, traprock, sandstone, blast furnace slag or similar dense material containing not more than 30% quartz, chert or flint.

Appendix "D" of the NBC recognizes five different types of *low density concretes*. Structural Low Density concrete, as defined in CSA Standard A23.3, generally corresponds with:

- Type L40S concrete, in which the fine aggregate is sand and the coarse aggregate is low density material and the sand does not exceed 40% of the total volume of all of the aggregate.

The compressive strength of concrete during fire exposure mainly depends upon the aggregate it contains. Generally speaking, for structural concretes, the behaviour of Types N and L40S concrete is superior to that of Type S concrete. As these differences are recognized in the assignment of fire resistance ratings, the designer must clearly specify which aggregate type should be used in critical assemblies.

1.4.2.3 Member Dimensions

Other factors being equal, the fire resistance rating of an assembly is proportional to its thickness or overall cross section. In the case of slab-like members, such as floors, roofs or walls, sufficient thickness must be provided to achieve the desired rating without violation of the temperature limit on the unexposed surface of the assembly. It should be noted that, in the case of hollow core or voided cross sections and ribbed slabs, the "equivalent thickness" of the slab must be used. This is computed in accordance with the rules given in Appendix "D" of the NBC. For beams and columns, dimensionally larger cross sections take longer to heat up, as compared to smaller members. Larger cross sections thus suffer less average concrete strength loss than smaller ones for a given period of fire endurance.

1.4.2.4 Reinforcing Steel

As is the case with concrete, reinforcement loses strength at high temperatures. Hot rolled reinforcing steel used for deformed bars loses its strength less quickly than the cold drawn steel used for prestressing tendons. As the ability of a member to carry load depends largely upon the tensile strength of its reinforcement, its fire resistance rating depends upon the type of reinforcing steel it contains and the level of stress in the steel.

1.4.2.5 Cover To Reinforcement

The rate at which heat reaches the reinforcement of a member and hence the loss of strength of the steel, is inversely proportional to the concrete cover provided. Designers should bear in mind that the covers specified in CSA Standard A23.1 for various members and exposures may not be sufficient to meet the requirements of Appendix "D" of the NBC to provide the necessary fire resistance rating.

1.4.2.6 Restraint and Continuity

The provisions of Appendix "D" of the NBC generally only apply to the rating of simply supported assemblies. In that document it is stated that:

"It is known that both edge restraint of a floor or roof and end restraint of a beam can significantly extend the time before collapse in a standard test",

and also that:

"In a restrained condition the floor, roof or beams would probably have greater fire resistance (than that set forth in this Chapter), but the extent of this increase can be determined only by reference to behaviour in a standard test."

Thus, unless the designer has access to specific test data for restrained or continuous reinforced concrete slabs or beams, or is prepared to undertake rational design computations and have them approved as discussed previously, the benefits of restraint or continuity cannot be utilized. It must, however, be emphasized that in the case of a slab-like member whose fire resistance rating is governed by temperature rise on its unexposed surface and hence the thickness of the slab, no increase in rating can be obtained by rational design, even though the slab may be restrained or continuous.

1.4.4 GENERAL CONCRETE AND MASONRY PROVISIONS OF APPENDIX "D" of the NBC

1.4.2.7 Protected Construction

Appendix "D" of the NBC includes detailed provisions to enable the assessment of the contribution of plaster of gypsum wall board finish to the fire resistance of masonry or concrete. In addition, ULC data covering the use of sprayed fireproofing or special fire retardant mastics is also available. While consideration of protected construction is beyond the scope of this Section, information on the subject is readily available.

1.4.2.8 Column Eccentricities

The ratings for reinforced concrete columns provided in Appendix "D" of the NBC apply to concentrically loaded columns only. CSA Standard A23.3, Clause 10.15.3, limits computed end eccentricities to not less than (15 + 0.03h) mm for such columns. Data on the behaviour of eccentrically loaded columns at elevated temperatures is being developed, but is not currently reflected in Appendix "D".

1.4.3 DESIGN EXAMPLES

1.4.3.1 General

The following examples illustrate the determination of fire resistance ratings in accordance with Appendix "D" of the NBC 1995. Only those provisions of the code document needed to work the examples have been reproduced here. The numbering used for these is that of the original 1995 document.

Designers should refer to that edition of the NBC which is referenced in the provincial building code governing the building under design for complete information on the assignment of fire resistance ratings to assemblies under consideration.

D-1.3. Concrete

D-1.3.1 Aggregates in Concrete

Low density aggregate concretes generally exhibit better fire performance than natural stone aggregate concretes. A series of tests on concrete masonry walls, combined with mathematical analysis of the test results, has allowed further distinctions between certain low density aggregates to be made.

D-1.4. Types of Concrete

D-1.4.1 Description

1)   For purposes of this Appendix, concretes are described as Types S, N, L, L_1, L_2, L4OS, $L_1$2OS or $L_2$2OS as described in (2) to (8).

2)   Type S concrete is the type in which the coarse aggregate is granite, quartzite, siliceous gravel or other dense materials containing at least 30% quartz, chert or flint.

3)   Type N concrete is the type in which the coarse aggregate is cinders, broken brick, blast furnace slag, limestone, calcareous gravel, trap rock, sandstone or similar dense material containing not more than 30% of quartz, chert or flint.

4)   Type L concrete is the type in which all the aggregate is expanded slag, expanded clay, expanded shale or pumice.

5)   Type L_1 concrete is the type in which all the aggregate is expanded shale.

6) Type L_2 concrete is the type in which all the aggregate is expanded slag, expanded clay or pumice.

7) Type L4OS concrete is the type in which the fine portion of the aggregate is sand and low density aggregate in which the sand does not exceed 40% of the total volume of all aggregates in the concrete.

8) Type $L_1$2OS and Type $L_2$2OS concretes are the types in which the fine portion of the aggregate is sand and low density aggregate in which the sand does not exceed 20% of the total volume of all aggregates in the concrete.

D-1.4.2. Determination of Ratings

Where concretes are described as being of Type S, N, L, L_1 or L_2, the rating applies to the concrete containing the aggregate in the group that provides the least fire resistance. If the nature of an aggregate cannot be determined accurately enough to place it in one of the groups, the aggregates shall be considered as being in the group that requires a greater thickness of concrete for the required fire resistance.

D-1.4.3. Description of Aggregates

1) The descriptions of the aggregates in Type S and Type N concretes apply to the coarse aggregates only. Coarse aggregate for this purpose means that retained on a 5 mm sieve using the method of grading aggregates described in CAN/CSA-A23.1-M, *Concrete Materials and Methods of Concrete Construction.*

2) Increasing the proportions of sand as fine aggregate in low density concretes requires increased thicknesses of material to produce equivalent fire-resistance ratings. Low density aggregates for Type L and Types L-S concretes used in loadbearing components shall conform to ASTM C330, *Lightweight Aggregates for Structural Concrete.*

3) Non-loadbearing low density components of vermiculite and perlite concrete, in the absence of other test evidence, shall be rated on the basis of the values shown for Type L concrete.

D-1.6. Equivalent Thickness

D-1.6.1. Method of Calculating

1) The thickness of solid-unit masonry and concrete described in this Appendix shall be the thickness of solid material in the unit or component thickness. For units that contain cores or voids, the Tables refer to the equivalent thickness determined in conformance with (2) to (10).

2) Where a plaster finish is used, the equivalent thickness of a wall, floor, column or beam protection shall be equal to the sum of the equivalent thicknesses of the concrete or masonry units and the plaster finish measured at the point that will give the least value of equivalent thickness.

3) Except as provided in (5), the equivalent thickness of a hollow masonry unit shall be calculated as equal to the actual overall thickness of a unit in millimetres multiplied by a factor equal to the net volume of the unit and divided by its gross volume.

4) Net volume shall be determined using a volume displacement method that is not influenced by the porous nature of the units.

5) Gross volume of a masonry unit shall be equal to the actual length of the unit multiplied by the actual height of the unit multiplied by the actual thickness of the unit.

6) Where all the core spaces in a wall of hollow concrete masonry or hollow-core precast concrete units are filled with grout, mortar, or loose fill materials such as expanded slag, burned clay or shale (rotary kiln process), vermiculite or perlite, the equivalent thickness rating of the wall shall be considered to be the same as that of a wall of solid units, or a solid wall of the same concrete type and the same overall thickness.

7) The equivalent thickness of hollow-core concrete slabs and panels having a uniform thickness and cores of constant cross section throughout their length shall be obtained by dividing the net cross-sectional area of the slab or panel by its width.

8) The equivalent thickness of concrete panels with tapered cross sections shall be the cross section determined at a distance of 2 t or 150 mm, whichever is less, from the point of minimum thickness, where t is the minimum thickness.

9) Except as permitted in (10), the equivalent thickness of concrete panels with ribbed or undulating surfaces shall be

    a) ta for s less than or equal to 2 t,
    b) t + (4 t/s - 1)(ta-t) for s less than 4 t and greater than 2 t, and
    c) t for s greater than or equal to 4 t
        where
        t = minimum thickness of panel,
        ta = average thickness of panel (unit cross-sectional area divided by unit width), and
        s = centre to centre spacing of ribs or undulations.

10) Where the total thickness of a panel described in (9), exceeds 2 t, only that portion of the panel which is less than 2 t from the nonribbed surface shall be considered for the purpose of the calculations in (9).

1.4.5 MASONRY AND CONCRETE WALLS

1.4.5.1 Applicable Provisions of Appendix "D"

SECTION D.2 FIRE-RESISTANCE RATINGS

D-2.1 MASONRY AND CONCRETE WALLS

D-2.1.1. Minimum Equivalent Thickness for Fire-Resistance Rating

The minimum thicknesses of unit masonry and monolithic concrete walls are shown in Table D-2.1.1. Hollow masonry units and hollow-core concrete panels shall be rated on the basis of equivalent thickness as described in D-1.6.

Table D-2.1.1.
Forming Part of D-2.1.1.

Minimum Equivalent Thicknesses[1] of Unit Masonry and Monolithic Concrete Walls Loadbearing and Non-Loadbearing, mm							
Type of Wall	Fire-Resistance Rating						
	30 min	45 min	1 h	1.5 h	2h	3h	4h
Solid brick units (80% solid and over), actual overall thickness	63	76	90	108	128	152	178
Cored brick units and hollow tile units (less than 80% solid), equivalent thickness	50	60	726	86	102	122	142
Solid and hollow concrete masonry units, equivalent thickness							
Type S or N concrete[2]	44	59	73	95	113	142	167
Type L₁20S concrete	42	54	66	87	102	129	152
Type L₁ concrete	42	54	64	82	97	122	143
Type L₂20S concrete	42	54	64	81	94	116	134
Type L₂ concrete	42	54	63	79	91	111	127
Monolithic concrete and concrete panels, equivalent thicknesses							
Type S concrete	60	77	90	112	130	158	180
Type N concrete	59	74	87	108	124	150	171
Type L40S or Type L concrete	49	62	72	89	103	124	140

Notes to Table D-2.1.1:
1) See definition of equivalent thickness in D-1.6.
2) Hollow concrete masonry units made with Type S or N concrete shall have a minimum compressive strength of 15 MPa based on net area, as defined in CAN3-A165.1-94, "Concrete Masonry Units"

D-2.1.2. Applicability of Ratings

1) Ratings obtained as described in D-2.1.1. apply to either loadbearing or non-loadbearing walls, except for walls described in (2) to (6).

2) Ratings for walls with a thickness less than the minimum thickness prescribed for load-bearing walls in this Code apply to non-loadbearing walls only.

3) Masonry cavity walls (consisting of 2 wythes of masonry with an air space between) that are loaded to a maximum allowable compressive stress of 380 kPa have a fire resistance at least as great as that of a solid wall of a thickness equal to the sum of the equivalent thicknesses of the 2 wythes.

4) Masonry cavity walls that are loaded to a compressive stress exceeding 380 kPa are not considered to be within the scope of this Appendix.

5) A masonry wall consisting of 2 types of masonry units, either bonded together or in the form of a cavity wall, shall be considered to have a fire-resistance rating equal to that which would apply if the whole of the wall were of the material that gives the lesser rating.

6) A non-loadbearing cavity wall made up of 2 precast concrete panels with an air space or insulation in the cavity between them shall be considered to have a fire-resistance rating as great as that of a solid wall of a thickness equal to the sum of the thicknesses of the 2 panels.

D-2.1.3 Framed Beams and Joists

Beams and joists that are framed into a masonry or concrete fire separation shall not reduce the thickness of the fire separation to less than the equivalent thickness required for the fire separation.

D-2.1.4 Credit for Plaster Thickness

On monolithic walls and walls of unit masonry, the full plaster finish on one or both faces multiplied by the factor shown in Table D-1.7.1. shall be included in the wall thickness in Table D-2.1.1., under the conditions and using the methods described in D-1.7.

D-2.1.5 Walls Exposed to Fire on Both Sides

1) Except as permitted in (2), portions of loadbearing reinforced concrete walls, which do not form a complete fire separation and thus may be exposed to fire on both sides simultaneously, shall have minimum dimensions and minimum cover to steel reinforcement in conformance with D-2.8.2 to D-2.8.5.

2) A concrete wall exposed to fire from both sides as described in (1) has a fire-resistance rating of 2 h if the following conditions are met:

    a) its equivalent thickness is not less than 200 mm,
    b) its aspect ratio (width/thickness) is not less than 4.0,
    c) the minimum thickness of concrete cover over the steel reinforcement specified in (d) is not less than 50 mm,
    d) each face of the wall is reinforced with both vertical and horizontal steel reinforcement in conformance with either Clause 10 or Clause 14 of CAN3-A23.3-94, *Design of Concrete Structures*,
    e) the structural design of the wall is governed by the minimum eccentricity requirements of Clause 10.11.6.3. of CAN3-A23.3-94, *Design of Concrete Structures*, and
    f) the effective length of the wall, kl_u, is not more than 3.7 m
        where
        k = effective length factor obtained from CAN3-A23.3-94, *Design of Concrete Structures*,
        l_u = unsupported length of the wall in metres.

1.4.5.2 Determination of the Fire Resistance Rating of a Ribbed Panel Wall

Given:

The section of wall panel shown. Type L40S concrete.

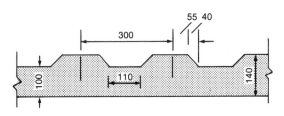

Problem:

Determine the fire resistance rating of the wall.

Solution:

Determine equivalent thickness per 1.6.6

$$t = 100 \text{ mm}$$

$$ta = \frac{(100 * 300) + (150 * 40)}{300} = 120 \text{ mm}$$

$$s = 300 \text{ mm}$$

As total thickness of panel does not exceed 2t, Sentence (2) does not apply. As s is less than 4t and greater than 2t, expression (b) of 1.6.6 applies and:

$$\text{Equivalent Thickness} = 100 + \left(\frac{400}{300} - 1\right)(120 - 100)$$

From Table 2.1A, 106.6 mm of L40S concrete qualifies for a 2 hour fire resistance rating.

1.4.6 REINFORCED AND PRESTRESSED FLOOR AND ROOF SLABS

1.4.6.1 Applicable Provisions of Appendix "D"

D-2.2. REINFORCED AND PRESTRESSED CONCRETE FLOOR AND ROOF SLABS

D-2.2.1 Assignment of Rating

1) Floors and roofs in a fire test are assigned a fire-resistance rating which relates to the time that an average temperature rise of 140°C or a maximum temperature rise of 180°C at any location is recorded on the unexposed side, or the time required for collapse to occur, whichever is the lesser. The thickness of concrete shown in Table D-2.2.1.A. shall be required to resist the transfer of heat during the fire resistance period shown.

Table D-2.2.1.A.
Forming Part of D-2.2.1.(1)

Minimum Thickness of Reinforced and Prestressed Concrete Floor or Roof Slabs, mm

Type of Concrete	Fire-Resistance Rating						
	30 min	45 min	1 h	1.5 h	2 h	3 h	4 h
Type S concrete	60	77	90	112	130	158	180
Type N concrete	59	74	87	108	124	150	171
Type L40S or Type L concrete	49	62	72	89	103	124	140

2) The concrete cover over the reinforcement and steel tendons shown in Table D-2.2.1.B. shall be required to maintain the integrity of the structure and prevent collapse during the same period.

Table D-2.2.1.B.
Forming Part of D-2.2.1.(2)

Minimum Concrete Cover over Reinforcement in Concrete Slabs, mm

Type of Concrete	Fire-Resistance Rating						
	30 min	45 min	1 h	1.5h	2 h	3 h	4 h
Type S, N, L40S or L concrete	20	20	20	20	25	32	39
Prestressed concrete slabs Type S, N, L40S or L concrete	20	25	25	32	39	50	64

D-2.2.2. Floors with Hollow Units

The fire resistance of floors containing hollow units may be determined on the basis of equivalent thickness as described in D-1.6.

D-2.2.3. Composite Slabs

1) For composite concrete floor and roof slabs consisting of one layer of Type S or N concrete and another layer of Type L40S or L concrete in which the minimum thickness of both the top and bottom layers is not less than 25 mm, the combined fire-resistance rating may be determined using the following expressions:

    a) when the base layer consists of Type S or N concrete,
$$R = 0.00018 \, t^2 - 0.00009 \, d \, t + (8.7/t)$$

    b) when the base layer consists of Type L40S or L concrete,
$$R = 0.0001 \, t^2 - 0.0002 \, d \, t - 0.0001 \, d^2 + (6.4/t)$$

where
    R = fire resistance of slab, h,
    t = total thickness of slab, mm, and
    d = thickness of base layer, mm.

2) If the base course described in (1) is covered by a top layer of material other than Type S, N, L40S or L concrete, the top course thickness may be converted to an equivalent concrete thickness by multiplying the actual thickness by the appropriate factor listed in Table D-2.2.3.A. This equivalent concrete thickness may be added to the thickness of the base course and the fire-resistance rating calculated using Table D-2.2.1.A.

Table D-2.2.3.A.
Forming Part of D-2.2.3.(2). Multiplying Factors for Equivalent Thickness

Multiplying Factors for Equivalent Thickness		
Top Course Material	Base Slab Normal Density Concrete (Type S or N)	Base Slab Low Density Concrete (Type L40S or L)
Gypsum wallboard	3	2.25
Cellular concrete (mass density 400 – 560 kg/m^3)	2	1.5
Vermiculite and perlite concrete (mass density 560 kg/m^3 or less)	1.75	1.5
Portland cement with sand aggregate	1	0.75
Terrazzo	1	0.75

3) The minimum concrete cover under the main reinforcement for composite floor and roof slabs with base slabs of less than 100 mm thick shall conform to Table D-2.2.3.B. For base slabs 100 mm or more thick, the minimum cover thickness requirements of Table D-2.2.1.B. shall apply.

Table D-2.2.3.B
Forming Part of D-2.2.3.(3)

Minimum Concrete Cover under Bottom Reinforcement in composite Concrete Slabs, mm							
Base Slab Concrete Type	Fire-Resistance Rating						
	30 min	45 min	1h	1.5h	2h	3h	4h
Reinforced Concrete Type S, N, L40S or L	15	15	20	25	30	40	55
Prestressed concrete Type S	20	25	30	40	50	65	75
Type N	20	20	25	35	45	60	70
Type L40S or L	20	20	25	30	40	50	60

4) Where the top layer of a 2-layer slab is less than 25 mm thick, the fire-resistance rating of the slab shall be calculated as though the entire slab were made up of the type of concrete with the lesser fire resistance.

D-2.2.4. Contribution of Plaster Finish

1) The contribution of plaster finish securely fastened to the underside of concrete may be taken into account in floor or roof slabs under the conditions and using the methods described in D-1.7.

2) Plaster finish on the underside of concrete floors or roofs may be used in lieu of concrete cover referred to in D-2.2.1.(2) under the conditions and using the methods described in D-1.7.

D-2.2.5 Concrete Cover

1) In prestressed concrete slab construction, the concrete cover over an individual tendon shall be the minimum thickness of concrete between the surface of the tendon and the fire-exposed surface of the slab, except that for ungrouted ducts the assumed cover thickness shall be the minimum thickness of concrete between the surface of the duct and the bottom of the slab. For slabs in which several tendons are used, the cover is assumed to be the average of those of individual tendons, except that the cover for any individual tendon shall be not less than half of the value given in Table D-2.2.1.B. nor less than 20 mm.

2) Except as provided in (3), in post-tensioned prestressed concrete slabs, the concrete cover to the tendon at the anchor shall be not less than 15 mm greater than the minimum cover required by (1). The minimum concrete cover to the anchorage bearing plate and to the end of the tendon, if it projects beyond the bearing plate, shall be 20 mm.

3) The requirements of (2) do not apply to those portions of slabs not likely to be exposed to fire, such as the ends and tops.

D-2.2.6. Minimum Dimensions for Cover

Minimum dimensions and cover to steel tendons of prestressed concrete beams shall conform to D-2.10.

1.4.6.2 Determination of the Fire Resistance Rating of a Hollow Core Slab

Given:

The section of prestressed concrete hollow core slab shown. Type N concrete slab, Type L40S topping. Cross sectional area of 1200 mm wide slab, from product literature = 134,000 mm^2. 12.7 mm diameter strand.

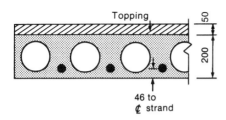

Topping

50

200

46 to
¢ strand

Problem:

Determine the fire resistance rating of the section, both without the topping and topped.

Solution:

(a) Untopped Section

Determine equivalent thickness of slab per 1.6.4

ET = 134,000/1200 = 112 mm

Rating for transfer of heat, per Table 2.2.A, Type N concrete is 1½ hours (+).

Rating for structural integrity, per Table 2. 2B

Concrete cover = 46 − 12.7 over 2 mm to strand

= 39.65 mm > 39 mm

∴ Rating for this cover is 2 hours.

However, as transfer of heat governs, rating is 1½ hours.

(b) Topped Section

As the base layer is Type N concrete and the topping Type L40S concrete, 2.2.3.(1)(a) governs, and

$$R = 0.0002t^2 - 0.0001\,d\,t + (10/t)$$

t = total equivalent thickness of slab = 112 + 50 = 162 mm

d = equivalent thickness of base slab = 112 mm

Thus R = $0.0002(162)^2 - 0.0001(112)(162) + \dfrac{10}{162}$

= 5.25 − 1.81 + .06
= 3.5 hours

However, by the provisions of 2.2.3(3), the minimum cover thickness of Table 2.2.B governs.

Thus, for 39 mm cover, a rating of 2 hours applies to the topped section.

D-2.8. REINFORCED CONCRETE COLUMNS

D-2.8.1 Minimum Dimensions

Minimum dimensions for reinforced concrete columns and minimum concrete cover for vertical steel reinforcement are obtained from D-2.8.2. to D-2.8.5., taking into account the type of concrete, the effective length of the column and the area of the vertical reinforcement.

D-2.8.2. Method

1)   The minimum dimension, t, in millimetres, of a rectangular reinforced concrete column shall be equal to

   (a) 75 f(R + 1) for all Types L and L40S concrete,
   (b) 80 f(R + 1) for Type S concrete when the design condition of the concrete column is defined in the second and fourth columns of Table D-2.8.2.,
   (c) 80 f(R + 0.75) for Type N concrete when the design condition of the concrete is defined in the second and fourth columns of Table D-2.8.2, and
   (d) 100 f(R + 1) for Types S and N concrete when the design condition of the concrete column is defined in the third column of Table D-2.8.2.

   where f = the value shown in Table D-2.8.2.,
          R = the required fire-resistance rating in hours,
          k = the effective length factor obtained from CAN3-A23.3-94, *Design of Concrete Structures*,
          h = the unsupported length of the column in metres, and
          ρ = the area of vertical reinforcement in the column as a percentage of the column area.

Table D-2.8.2[1]
Forming Part of D-2.8.2.

	Values of Factor "f"		
Overdesign Factor[2]	Where kh is not more than 3.7 m	Where kh is more than 3.7 m but not more than 7.3 m[3,4]	
		t is not more than 300 mm, ρ is not more than 3%	All other cases
1.00	1.0	1.2	1.0
1.25	0.9	1.1	0.9
1.50	0.83	1.0	0.83

Notes to Table D-2.8.2.:
1) For conditions that do not fall within the limits described in Table D-2.8.2., further information may be obtained from Reference (7) in D-6.1.
2) Overdesign factor is the ratio of the calculated load carrying capacity of the column to the column strength required to carry the specified loads determined in conformance with CAN3-A23.3-94, *Design of Concrete Structures*.
3) Where the factor "f" selected from the third column results in a "t" greater than 300 mm, the appropriate factor "f" selected from the fourth column shall be applicable.
4) Where "ρ" is equal to or less than 3% and the factor "f" selected from the fourth column results in a "t" less than 300 mm, the minimum thickness shall be 300 mm.

2)   The diameter of a round column shall be not less than 1.2 times the value "t" determined in (1) for a rectangular column.

D-2.8.3. Minimum Thickness of Concrete Cover

1)   Where the required fire-resistance rating of a concrete column is 3 h or less, the minimum thickness in millimetres of concrete cover over vertical steel reinforcement shall be equal to 25 times the number of hours of fire resistance required or 50 mm, whichever is less.

2) Where the required fire-resistance rating of a concrete column is greater than 3 h, the minimum thickness in millimetres of concrete cover over vertical steel reinforcement shall be equal to 50 plus 12.5 times the required number of hours of fire resistance in excess of 3 h.

3) Where the concrete cover over vertical steel required in (2) exceeds 62.5 mm, wire mesh reinforcement with 1.57 mm diameter wire and 100 mm openings shall be incorporated midway in the concrete cover to retain the concrete in position.

D-2.8.4. Minimum Requirements

The structural design standards may require minimum column dimensions or concrete cover over vertical steel reinforcement differing from those obtained in D-2.8.2(1) and (2). Where a difference occurs, the greater dimension shall govern.

D-2.8.5. Addition of Plaster

The addition of plaster finish to the concrete column may be taken into account in determining the cover over vertical steel reinforcement by applying the multiplying factors described in D-1.7. The addition of plaster shall not, however, justify any decrease in the minimum column sizes shown.

D-2.8.6. Built-In Columns

The fire-resistance rating of a reinforced concrete column that is built into a masonry or concrete wall so that not more than one face may be exposed to the possibility of fire at one time may be determined on the basis of cover to vertical reinforcing steel alone. In order to meet this condition, the wall shall conform to D-2.1. for the fire-resistance rating required.

1.4.7.2 Determination of the Fire Resistance of a Reinforced Concrete Column

Given:

300 × 300 mm column, Type S concrete
Column height = 3650 mm
Maximum specified load = 782 kN
Concrete strength f'_c = 35 MPa
Steel strength f_y = 400 MPa
Percentage steel, ρ = 4%
Effective length factor k = 1.0

Problem:

Determine the fire resistance rating of the column.

Solution:

Maximum specified load capacity of column, taking slenderness into account and an eccentricity of

$\dfrac{e}{t} = 0.1^*$ is 978 kN

*Note that eccentricity is within CSA Standard A23.3 limit for concentric loading.

Over design factor = $\dfrac{978}{782}$ = 1.25

∴ "f" factor from Table 2.8A = 0.9

Since   t   = 100 f (R + 1)

where   R   = effective fire resistance in hours,

then   R   = $\dfrac{t}{(100\ f)}$ − 1

since   t   = 300 mm and f = 0.9

R   = $\dfrac{300}{100 \times 0.9}$ − 1   = 2.33 hours

1.4.8 REINFORCED CONCRETE BEAMS

1.4.8.1 Applicable Provisions of Appendix "D"

D-2.9. REINFORCED CONCRETE BEAMS

D-2.9.1. Minimum Cover Thickness

The minimum thickness of cover over principal steel reinforcement in reinforced concrete beams is shown in Table D-2.9.1 for fire-resistance ratings from 30 min to 4h where the width of the beam or joist is at least 100 mm.

Table D-2.9.1.
Forming Part of D-2.9.1.

Minimum cover to Principal Steel Reinforcement in Reinforced Concrete Beams, mm

Type of Concrete	Fire-Resistance Rating						
	30 min	45 min	1h	1.5h	2h	3h	4h
Type S, N or L	20	20	20	25	25	39	50

D-2.9.2. Maximum Rating

No rating over 2 h may be assigned on the basis of Table D-2.9.1. to a beam or joist where the average width of the part that projects below the slab is less than 140 mm, and no rating over 3 h may be assigned where the average width of the part that projects below the slab is less than 165 mm.

D-2.9.3. Beam Integrated in Floor or Roof Slab

For the purposes of these ratings, a beam may be either independent of or integral with a floor or roof slab assembly.

D-2.9.4. Minimum Thickness

Where the upper extension or top flange of a joist or T-beam in a floor assembly contributes wholly or partly to the thickness of the slab above, the total thickness at any point shall be not less than the minimum thickness described in Table D-2.2.1.A. for the fire-resistance rating required.

D-2.9.5. Effect of Plaster

The addition of plaster finish to a reinforced concrete beam may be taken into account in determining the cover over principal reinforcing steel by applying the multiplying factors described in D-1.7.

1.4.8.2 Determination of the Fire Resistance of a Reinforced Concrete Beam

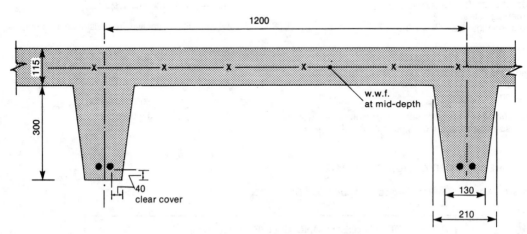

Given:

The section of reinforced concrete beam and slab shown:
  Type S concrete

Problem:

Determine the fire resistance of the section.

Solution:

(a) Determine the fire resistance of the beam section.

  For 40 mm cover, from Table 2.9.A, Type S concrete,

  Maximum rating = 3 hours
  Width of beam, average = 170 mm
  By 2.9.2; 170 mm > 165 mm
  ∴ Rating of 3 hours is justified for the beam

(b) Determine the fire resistance of the slab.

From Table 2.2.A, for 115 mm of Type S concrete

Rating to resist transfer of heat is 1½ hours.

From Table 2.2.B, for a clear cover of 55 mm, a structural rating in excess of 4 hours is achieved.

∴ heat transmission governs

Check to determine whether, by the provisions of 1.6.6, an increased equivalent thickness can be assumed.

$$t = 115 \text{ mm}$$
$$S = 1200 \text{ mm}$$
$$4t = 460 \text{ mm}$$

Because S exceeds 4t, no increased equivalent thickness can be assumed.

Thus, the total assembly qualifies for a 1½ hour rating.

1.4.9 PRESTRESSED CONCRETE BEAMS

1.4.9.1 Applicable Provisions of Appendix "D"

D-2.10. PRESTRESSED CONCRETE BEAMS

D-2.10.1 Minimum Cross-Sectional Area and Thickness of Cover

The minimum cross-sectional area and thickness of concrete cover over steel tendons in prestressed concrete beams for fire-resistance ratings from 30 min to 4 h are shown in Table D-2.10.1.

Table D-2.10.1.
Forming Part of D-2.10.1

Minimum Thickness of Concrete Cover over Steel Tendons in Prestressed Concrete Beams, mm[1]								
Type of Concrete	Area of Beam cm^2	Fire-Resistance Rating						
		30 min	45 min	1h	1.5h	2h	3h	4h
Type S or N	260 to 970	25	39	50	64	—	—	—
	over 970 to 1940	25	26	39	45	64	—	—
	Over 1940	25	26	39	39	50	77	102
Type L	Over 970	25	25	25	39	50	77	102

Note to Table D-2.10.1.:
[1] Where the thickness of concrete cover over the tendons exceeds 64 mm, a wire mesh reinforcement with 1.57 mm diameter wire and 100 mm by 100 mm openings shall be incorporated in the beams to retain the concrete in position around the tendons. The mesh reinforcement shall be located midway in the cover.

D-2.10.2. Minimum Cover Thickness

The cover for an individual tendon shall be the minimum thickness of concrete between the surface of the tendon and the fire-exposed surface of the beam, except that for ungrouted ducts the assumed cover thickness shall be the minimum thickness of concrete between the surface of the duct and the surface of the beam. For beams in which several tendons are used, the cover is assumed to be the average of the minimum cover of the individual tendons. The cover for any individual tendon shall be not less than half the value given in Table D-2.10.1. nor less than 25 mm.

D-2.10.3. Applicability of Ratings

The ratings in Table D-2.10.1. apply to a beam that is either independent of or integral with a floor or roof slab assembly. Minimum thickness of slab and minimum cover to steel tendons in prestressed concrete slabs are contained in D-2.2.

D-2.10.4. Effect of Plaster

The addition of plaster finish to a prestressed concrete beam may be taken into account in determining the cover over steel tendons by applying the multiplying factors described in D-1.7.

D-2.10.5 Minimum Cover

1) Except as provided in (2), in unbonded post-tensioned prestressed concrete beams, the concrete cover to the tendon at the anchor shall be not less than 15 mm greater than the minimum required away from the anchor. The concrete cover to the anchorage bearing plate and to the end of the tendon, if it projects beyond the bearing plate, shall be not less than 25 mm.

2) The requirements in (1) do not apply to those portions of beams not likely to be exposed to fire (such as the ends and the tops of flanges of beams immediately below slabs).

1.4.9.2 Determination of the Fire Resistance Rating of a Prestressed Concrete Beam

Given:

The section of prestressed concrete T-beam shown, Type S concrete, Eight, 12.7 mm diameter strand. Bottom cover to lowest strand, 40 mm.

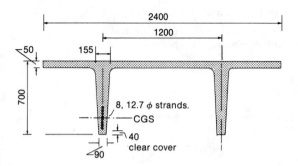

Problem:

Determine the structural fire resistance of the beam section.

Solution:

$$\text{Area of stem} = \frac{90 + 155}{2}(700 - 50) \text{ mm}^2$$

$$= 79625 \text{ mm}^2 = 796 \text{ cm}^2$$

Concrete cover to bottom strand of group = 40 mm

Distance from bottom of stem to CGS
$$= 40 + 4 \times 12.7 = 90.8 \text{ mm}$$

Width of stem at CGS $= 90 + [\frac{155 - 90}{650}] \times 90.8$
$$= 99.1 \text{ mm}$$

$\therefore$ Clear side cover at CGS $= \dfrac{99.1 - 12.7}{2} = 43.2$ mm

Minimum individual strand, bottom cover = 40 mm

Minimum individual strand, side cover

$$= 45 - \frac{12.7}{2} = 38.65 \text{ mm}$$

Fire resistance rating, based on side cover of centroid of strand group (from 2.10.2 and Table 2.10A)

$$= \tfrac{3}{4} \text{ hour } (39 \text{ mm} < 43.2 \text{ mm})$$

Check: Minimum cover to critical bottom tendon is greater than (39/2) = 19.5 mm and 25 mm

1.4.9.3 Single T Prestressed Concrete Beam, Tapered Flanges

Given:

The section of flange of prestressed concrete T-beam shown. Type N concrete beam and topping.

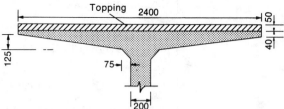

Problem:

Determine the fire resistance rating of the flange for heat transmission.

Solution:

The provisions of Subsection 1.6.5 apply.

Thickness at edge of flange = 50 + 40 = 90 mm = t

$$2t = 180 \text{ mm} > 150 \text{ mm}$$

$\therefore$ Determine thickness at 150 mm from edge

Slope is 125 mm in 1025 mm

At 150 mm, $t = 90 + \dfrac{125}{1025} \times 150$
$$= 90 + 18 = 108 \text{ mm}$$

From Table 2.2.A (see 1.4.6.1)

For Type N concrete, rating is 1½ hours.

1.4.10 REFERENCE PUBLICATIONS

(1)   Metric Design Manual - Precast and Prestressed Concrete; Canadian Prestressed Concrete Institute, 85 Albert Street, Ottawa, Ontario K1P 6A4

(2)   CRSI - Reinforced Concrete Fire Resistance; Concrete Reinforcing Steel Institute, 933 N. Plum Grove Road, Schaumburg, Illinois, 60195

1.5 SPECIAL REQUIREMENTS FOR CORROSIVE ENVIRONMENTS

1.5.1 Introduction

In common with other construction materials, unprotected or improperly designed concrete will suffer corrosion if exposed to an environment in which certain chemically aggressive agents are present.

The following provides information on means of minimizing or preventing loss of serviceability[*] and damage to concrete which may be exposed to commonly occurring corrosive environments.

1.5.2 De-Icer Salt Environment

CSA Standard A23.1 (Clause 15 and Table 8) requires that concrete subject to applications of de-icing chemicals be designated as Exposure Classes 'C-1 to C-4', which implies a low water:cementing materials ratio, a high content of entrained air and other mix design controls. CSA A23.1 Clause 15.1.7 provides requirements for concrete cover to reinforcement where the concrete is exposed to chlorides. It should be borne in mind that specified minimum covers are the minimum anywhere in the member. Reveals, architectural grooving and chamfers at joints, which may reduce the cover to less than acceptable minimum amounts, should not be ignored. Increased cover may also be required for fire resistance. For information on this subject, see Subsection 1.4 of this Handbook.

1.5.3 Sea Water Environment

CSA Standard A23.1, Clause 15 contains requirements for concrete in sea water environments. Deterioration problems due to the presence of salts in the air may occur in structures located within a kilometre of the ocean, particularly if covers to reinforcement are small or concrete properties inadequate.

Sea water contains significant amounts of sulphates and chlorides. Although sulphates in sea water are capable of attacking concrete, the presence of chlorides inhibits the expansive reaction that is characteristic of attack by sulphates in groundwaters or soils. Calcium sulphoaluminate, the reaction product of sulphate attack, is more soluble in a chloride solution and can be more readily leached out of the concrete, thus causing less destructive expansion. This is the major factor explaining observations from a number of sources that the performance of concretes in sea water with Portland cements having tricalcium aluminate (C_3A) contents as high as 10%, and sometimes greater, have shown satisfactory durability, providing the permeability of the concrete is low.

Maximum permissible water:cement ratios for the submerged portions of a structure should not exceed 0.45 by mass. For portions in the splash zone and above, maximum permissible water:cement ratios should not exceed 0.40 by mass. Water:cement ratios as high as 0.50 by mass may be used for submerged areas provided the C_3A content of the Portland cement does not exceed 8%.

Cements meeting the requirements of CSA Standard A5 and CSA Standard A362 and meeting the C_3A requirement noted above (that is, not more than 10%) are acceptable. In the case of blended cements, this limitation applies to the Portland cement clinker used in the blended cement.

Calcium chloride should not be used as an admixture in reinforced concrete to be exposed to sea water.

In addition to the proper selection of cement and adherence to the requirements, other requirements for quality concrete such as adequate air entrainment, low slump, low permeability, adequate consolidation, uniformity, adequate clear cover over reinforcement, and sufficient curing to develop the potential properties of the concrete are essential for securing economical and durable concrete exposed to sea water.

References:

- CSA Standard A23.1-94, Concrete Materials and Methods of Concrete Construction

- CSA Standard CAN3-A266.4-M78, Guidelines for the Use of Admixtures in Concrete

- ACI Publication SP-65, Performance of Concrete in Marine Environment

1.5.4 Sulphate Soils and Groundwater Exposure

CSA Standard A23.1, Clause 15.5 contains requirements for concrete which will be exposed to sulphate soils and groundwaters.

Sulphate attack on concrete can occur where soil and groundwater have a high sulphate content and where measures to prevent sulphate attack (such as those contained in CSA Standard A23.1) have not been taken. The attack is confined to concrete that is cool and moist, such as foundations and slabs on ground. It usually causes an expansion of the concrete because of the formation of solids as a result of chemical action. The amount of this expansion in some cases has been higher than 0.1% and the accompanying disruptive effect within the concrete can result in extensive cracking and deterioration.

References:

- CSA Standard A23.1-94, Concrete Materials and Methods of Concrete Construction

- ACI Publication SP-77, Sulphate Resistance of Concrete

1.5.5 Sewage and Waste Water Treatment Exposure

While sanitary engineering structures are considered to be "special structures" within the context of CSA Standard A23.3, the requirements of that Standard are generally valid for their structural design, provided that special consideration is given to control of cracking. ACI 350R-89, Concrete Sanitary Engineering Structures, contains detailed recommendations for loadings to be used, for the limitations of concrete and steel stresses at service loads and for the design of joints in such structures.

Specifications for concrete mix design and for construction should be drawn up to provide for dense, impermeable concrete which will be resistant to naturally occurring or commonly used chemicals and have a smooth, well formed surface finish. Recommendations towards obtaining these properties are also set forth in ACI 350R.

Generally speaking, additional protection against corrosion should not be necessary, provided the design and construction meet the requirements outlined above. Certain areas within water treatment plants or domestic sewage plants where chemically aggressive agents may be present, may require the use of protective coatings or linings. Industrial waste treatment plants will probably require the use of chemically resistant surface coatings, depending on the particular wastes being processed. Information on commonly occurring chemicals and advice on types of protective coatings is included in ACI 350R.

---

[*] For example, in parking structures, leakage of chloride-laden water onto parked cars constitutes an unserviceable condition.

Reference:

- ACI 350R-89, Environmental Engineering Concrete Structures

1.5.6 Chemical Attack of Concrete

Parts of some concrete structures, mainly for industrial uses, must be designed for exposure to chemicals, oils, food products and other solid, liquid or gaseous substances which may or may not cause corrosion of concrete.

To determine the effect that most such products or substances will have on exposed concrete surfaces, and for recommendations on protective coatings, the reader is referred to the following publications:

References:

- Effects of Substances on Concrete and Guide to Protective Treatment; Portland Cement Association (IS001.T)
- ACI 515.1R-79 (Revised 1985), A Guide to the Use of Waterproofing, Dampproofing, Protective and Decorative Barrier Systems for Concrete

1.6 STRUCTURAL INTEGRITY

1.6.1 Definition

A structure is said to have structural integrity if localized damage or failure of a structural member which may be initiated by an abnormal event does not lead to collapse of a disproportionately large part of the structure. Thus, the failure of one element should not lead to a "progressive collapse" or "incremental collapse" of the rest of the structure.

This definition is difficult to quantify. The extent of damage that is expected or acceptable is a function of the magnitude and extent of the overload causing the failure, the tributary area of the member which fails, the structural system and a host of other details. Thus, a multistorey concrete building with 16 to 20 main floor columns should have enough structural integrity to remain standing if one or two of the columns were destroyed in an explosion. However, a building having only two vertical supports would not have structural integrity unless its supports were designed to resist loads and forces of the magnitude created by the explosion.

1.6.2 Types of Incremental Collapse Observed in Reinforced Concrete Buildings

One of the most prominent cases of incremental collapse of a concrete structure occurred when a gas explosion blew two exterior walls out of a corner apartment on the 18th floor of a 22 storey precast building with walls and floors consisting of precast panels (Ronan Point, Canning Town, England). The loss of support of the floors above, caused this floor to collapse. The falling debris then caused all the floors and walls below to collapse progressively.

Progressive collapse failures are rare in continuously reinforced cast-in-place concrete structures. Formerly, a possible exception to this statement involved failure originating due to a punching shear failure at a column to slab connection in a flat plate. The portion of the slab supported by this connection could have then dropped, increasing the shear and moment at adjacent columns, causing them to fail. When this happened, the slab fell onto the slab below, causing it to fail as well. This progressed vertically down the building, causing each

lower slab to fail in turn. Such failures could have been initiated by premature form removal, formwork fires, inadequate slab thickness or insufficient slab column reinforcement. The 1994 edition of CSA Standard A23.3 addresses this situation by means of Clause 13.11.5.

Other examples of incremental collapse involve buildings which collapsed when a column or wall was removed by a vehicle collision, a chemical, gas or bomb explosion or similar event. Still others involve collapses which occurred when a floor member failed and, in doing so, displaced its support horizontally so that other floor members were pulled off their supports.

Precast structures or other structures with friction connections between walls and floors are particularly susceptible to such damage. References (1) and (2) review a number of buildings which have developed incremental collapses.

1.6.3 Basic Requirements of NBC and CSA Standard A23.3

Section 4.1.1.3(1) of the 1995 National Building Code of Canada includes structural integrity as a requirement for structural design:

4.1.1.3(1) — Buildings and their structural members including formwork and falsework shall be designed to have sufficient structural capacity and structural integrity to resist safely and effectively all loads and effects of loads and influences that may reasonably be expected, having regard to the expected service life of buildings, and shall in any case satisfy the requirements of this Section.

Further explanation is given in Appendix "D" of the National Building Code.

Clause 8.1.5 of CSA Standard A23.3 restates the NBCC requirement as follows:

8.1.5 — Consideration shall be given to the integrity of the overall structural system to minimize the likelihood of a progressive collapse.

This is followed by a note which states:

Note: Requirements contained in this Standard generally provide a satisfactory level of structural integrity for most concrete structures for buildings. Supplementary provisions for structural integrity may be required for two-way slabs (see Clause 13.11.5), precast concrete structures (see Clause 16.5), tilt-up structures (see Clause 23.3.9), mixed or unusual structural systems and structures exposed to severe loads such as vehicle impact or chemical explosion. For further guidance see Appendix "D" of the National Building Code.

Clause 16.5, entitled Structural Integrity, states:

In buildings where precast concrete elements constitute a portion of the structural system, all structural elements shall be effectively tied together.

A Note to this Clause gives a series of references providing guidance on design for structural integrity in precast buildings.

It should be noted that the governing NBC requirement calls for buildings to be capable of resisting loads and effects of loads and influences that may *reasonably be expected*. This clearly implies that only "accidental" abnormal events are to be considered. It must be recognized that well placed explosives or certain "acts of god" can bring down most structures. The Code does not require that buildings usually be designed to have structural integrity to resist collapse due to events like sabotage. Nonetheless, even such abnormal events might reasonably be expected under certain special circumstances and hence, in those specific cases, are worthy of consideration. For example, in countries where civil strife is the norm, sabotage of structures such as police stations is not unusual.

1.6.4 Design for Adequate Structural Integrity

As stated in the Note to Clause 8.1.5 of CSA Standard A23.3, most cast-in-place buildings designed in accordance with the Standard will possess a satisfactory level of structural integrity. This statement assumes that the layout of the structural systems and interaction between structural members will normally ensure a robust and stable design with sufficient redundancy. On this basis, no quantitative evaluation of structural integrity should be necessary insofar as the ordinary design conditions are concerned, which includes the effect of overloads during construction or those occurring in service which may cause localized failures. Thus, normally, only a general review of the structural system of such buildings will be needed to assess its likely failure modes. This review should ensure that no progressive collapse will result from any localized failures.

The Note to Clause 8.1.5 does, however, state that compliance with the requirement may need supplementary provisions to ensure structural integrity in the case of:

(a) precast concrete structures (as stated in Clause 16.3),

(b) for mixed or unusual structural systems and

(c) for structures exposed to severe overloads, such as those due to vehicle impact or chemical explosion.

This subsection will therefore review the basic concepts which may be employed in the design of those buildings whose unusual layout or structural system does not result in a robust and stable design and where sufficient redundancy is absent, or in the design of those other relatively uncommon structures which may reasonably be expected to suffer accidental overloads.

In suggesting these rules of good practice, it must be recognized that definitive guidance for all cases cannot be provided. Just as there are so many ways that a localized failure might be initiated – gas explosions, vehicular collision, flooding, foundation failure, corrosion, fire or just understrength materials – and there are so many different types of structural systems involving different types of potential failures in each of those systems, no one set of rules can be universally applicable.

Four different design strategies are discussed in the structural integrity literature (see for example Ref. (3)):

1. **Control of events causing abnormal loads.** An example would be placing energy absorbing devices adjacent to columns supporting the floor and walls of a building adjacent to a high speed roadway so that the energy from a vehicle colliding with the column is dissipated before it strikes the pier. Other examples would be control of building explosions by avoiding the use of natural gas stoves or heating or the relocation of a high-risk building from an area immediately downstream of a suspect dam. In many cases, however, this type of strategy is impractical and even when it is employed, the structure should be resistant to progressive collapse resulting from other causes.

2. **Design to resist abnormal loads.** An abnormal load is one that is not normally considered in the design of the particular type of structure under consideration such as gas explosion, vehicle impact, etc. If the abnormal load or event can be defined and if loss of a particular member in a structure due to that abnormal event would lead to a progressive collapse, then that member should be able to resist the particular abnormal event or load. In general, this is not a satisfactory design strategy. In some cases, however, such as when the structural integrity of a building depends on, say, less than four columns, it may be the only practical strategy to employ. (See Subsection 1.6.5.)

3. **Design for alternate load paths in the damaged structure.** In this design process, the designer imagines that a column, beam or other member has been removed from the structure and then checks whether the structure can bridge the gap without collapsing. Design is carried out at service load levels to ensure the structure can support the dead load, a third to a half of the live load, the wind load exceeded about once a month, plus any debris resulting from the failure. The structure is permitted to undergo a considerable amount of localized collapse and deformation, provided the damage does not spread progressively. For this to occur, the structure must have a good floor plan with proper layout of walls and columns and be well tied together horizontally and vertically. (See Subsection 1.6.6.)

4. **Design using specified loads and local resistance details.** In this design strategy the designer does not postulate any particular mode of failure. Instead, a minimum structural resistance is provided along with a minimum amount of reinforcement to tie various parts of the structure. In addition, consideration is given to providing strong points in the building to anchor the tie forces. (see Subsection 1.6.7.)

In summary, the first of these scenarios is generally outside the structural engineer's control. The second, third and fourth methods will be discussed further — not to provide hard and fast rules, but rather to form a basis for approaching the problems of progressive collapse.

1.6.5 Design to Resist Abnormal Loads

Adoption of this design strategy is generally less desirable and less economical than either design for alternate load paths or design for specified loads and local resistance details, but for some buildings it cannot be avoided. Where the integrity of the structure depends entirely on one or two structural elements, these elements cannot be assumed to be removed or relied upon to anchor tie forces. Thus if the removal of such an element by an abnormal event that may reasonably be expected would initiate progressive collapse, that element must be designed to remain functional when the abnormal event occurs. The problem with this strategy is that all reasonably foreseeable abnormal events have to be anticipated and their effect assessed.

Assessment of the magnitude of accidental loads is discussed in the reference publications, in particular those adopted in Great Britain, which primarily address gas explosion.

A recent Canadian proposal, which was not adopted for inclusion in the NBC, suggested that:

(a) Vertical load supporting columns and wall columns should be designed to withstand, over a one storey height, a uniformly distributed horizontal load of 44 kN/m and a vertical load consisting of the specified dead load, half the live load and 20% of the specified wind load, and

(b) Exterior bearing walls at corners should be designed for a horizontal load of 135 kN distributed over the storey height for the outer 1.5 m length of wall adjacent to a corner and the vertical load given in (a) above, and

(c) Indispensable structural elements other than columns or corner wall elements should be designed for a lateral force of 33 kN/m^2 and a vertical load as given in (a) above. The lateral force should be assumed to be acting perpendicular to the element over adjacent areas which are capable of transmitting the force to the element in question.

In conclusion, design to resist abnormal loads should normally only be considered as a last resort. In cases when this strategy is employed, the designer should have rationalized, for the building in question, the magnitude of the loads which may reasonably be anticipated. It should be emphasized that the loadings suggested above are only provided to suggest the order of magnitude which these loads and forces may assume.

1.6.6 Design for Alternate Load Paths

The basic method of designing for structural integrity is to design a structure in such a way that it can bridge over the gap left when a structural component is removed.

Two examples are shown in Fig. 1.10 and 1.11. In the first, a wall has failed due to an internal explosion, poor construction, vehicle impact (if on the main floor) or some similar cause. The remaining structure should be able to bridge over the gap. For this to occur, the walls above the lost wall must act as cantilevers to support the loads formerly supported by the missing wall. This requires horizontal tension resistance in the floors, effective vertical ties from floor to floor above the gap and effective ties to transfer the overturning moments generated in the rest of the building. This resistance may involve large deformations in the vicinity of the damaged area, but the extent of damage should be limited.

The floor in the storey below the damaged area should be able to support the weight of any debris which falls onto it. Since this could exceed the conventional capacity of the floor, the floor would be allowed to deflect 100 to 200, or even 300 millimetres under this load, until it carried the load by a catenary action, or carried load in the perpendicular direction, or both. For this to occur, tie forces must be developed in various directions as shown in Fig. 1.11.

It should be emphasized that these actions are accomplished with a load factor greater than 1.0 against total collapse under the loadings expected to occur before the building can be repaired or at least propped up. Typical load combinations to be considered would be

$$R_f \geq D + 0.5L + 0.2W$$
$$R_f \geq D - 0.3W$$

where R_f is the factored resistance and D, L and W are the specified dead, live and wind loads.

The following are a number of ways in which the necessary load resistance might be developed in a damaged structure:

1. **Good Floor Plan** —The use of a systematic floor plan with a proper layout or walls and columns is probably the most important single step in achieving structural integrity. Such things as number, location and continuity of lateral load resisting elements should be an arrangement of longitudinal spline walls to support and reduce the span of the cross-walls.

2. **Beam Action of Walls** — Walls can be used to span over an opening if sufficient tying steel is provided at the top and bottom of walls to allow them to act as beams with the slabs above and below possibly acting as flanges.

3. **Tensile Action of Floor Slabs** — When an interior support is removed, the floor span will increase. In this case, the sagging of the slab will stretch the reinforcement until the slab carries the load as a membrane. Such a structure can carry very large loads at large deflections provided the tensile forces are adequately anchored in the surrounding structure and provided that shear failures will not occur.

4. **Changing Direction of Span of Floor or Roof Slab** — The membrane action discussed in the preceding paragraph may occur in the original direction of the span or in some other direction if the shrinkage and temperature reinforcement can be counted on to act as membrane reinforcement.

5. **Strong Points** — In some designs certain elements may need to be strengthened to carry the abnormal loads in order to complete an alternate path. Sometimes a return or flange on a wall will allow it to be used as a strong point, especially when tension tie forces must be mobilized at right angles to the wall.

6. **Adequate Diaphragm Action** — Diaphragms should be reinforced with tension tie members around their perimeters and around notches and discontinuities to allow adequate load distribution.

7. **Lines of Weakness** — Occasionally it will be desirable to provide lines of weakness to limit the spread of damage. The effect of such weak areas on other load paths should be carefully examined.

When using this strategy, designers should consider the effect of removal, one at a time, of:

• One span of any floor or roof element,

• One column or hanger in any one storey, except that in a multi-column structure, the loss of resistance of a column need not be considered, providing all columns are designed to resist abnormal loads as discussed in 1.6.5, or

- One length of bearing wall panel for any storey equal to $1\frac{1}{2}$ times the storey height, unless the panels are prefabricated, when this length shall equal the panel length.

1.6.7 Design Using Specified Loads and Local Resistance Details

This design process is an attempt to provide alternate load paths without consideration of specific damage scenarios and specific load paths. This "deemed to satisfy" method is relatively well developed for precast panel buildings, much less so for cast-in-place buildings.

(a) Precast Buildings

Figure 1.12 shows the types of ties required to develop overall structural integrity in a precast structure. The longitudinal ties, often placed in the joints between floor planks, ensure that the floor can develop membrane or catenary action to span over broken wall panels or to support heavy debris loading. The transverse ties, generally placed in the horizontal joints between the walls above and below a floor, serve to tie a series of wall panels together and act as tension flanges if these walls have to cantilever or bridge over a missing support. The peripheral ties act as tension flanges for the diaphragm action of the floors and to provide anchorage of the longitudinal and transverse ties. They also help create an edge member in case a corner loses support. Vertical ties are provided to keep the walls above a damaged support from falling and to serve as a tension tieback to resist overturning moments. Specific recommendations concerning tie forces are contained in References (4), (5), and (6).

It is important the ties be ductile to enable them to survive the movements associated with local damage. The ties must be designed and detailed so that the connections can undergo deformations, resist impact from falling debris, and in some cases undergo load reversals.

(b) Cast-in-place Buildings

Cast-in-place concrete buildings have continuity and redundancy that produce an inherent structural integrity. CSA Standard A23.3 recognizes this and, with one exception, does not require any particular details for structural integrity in cast-in-place construction. The exception involves punching shear in column-slab joints in flat-plates. Clause 13.11.5 requires special reinforcement through the column at the bottom of the slab. This reinforcement is not intended to prevent shear failures from occurring. Once such a failure has occurred, however, the slab is prevented from dropping on the floor below.

1.6.8 References

(1) Allen, D.E. and Shriever, W.R., "Progressive Collapse, Abnormal Loads and Building Codes", *Structural Failures: Modes, Causes, Responsibilities*, American Society of Civil Engineers, 1973, pp 21-47.

(2) Taylor, D.A., "Progressive Collapse", Canadian Journal of Civil Engineering, Vol. 2, No. 4, Dec. 1975, pp 517-529.

(3) Breen, J.E., "Developing Structural Integrity in Bearing Wall Buildings", *Journal of the Prestressed Concrete Institute*, Vol. 25, No. 1, Jan.-Feb. 1980, pp 42-73; Closure, Vol. 25, No. 4, July-Aug. 1980, pp 146-152.

(4) PCI Committee on Precast Bearing Wall Buildings, "Consideration for the Design of Precast Bearing Wall Buildings to Withstand Abnormal Loads", *Journal of the Prestressed Concrete Institute*, Vol. 21, No. 2, March/April 1976, pp 18-51.

(5) Fintel, M., Schultz, D.M. and Iqbal, M., "Report 2, Philosophy of Structural Response to Normal and Abnormal Loads", *Design and Construction of Large-Panel Concrete Structures*, Portland Cement Association, Skokie, Illinois, PCA Publication EB092D, August 1976, 133 pp.

(6) Schultz, D.M., "Report 6, Design Methodology", *Design and Construction of Large-Panel Concrete Structures*, Portland Cement Association, Skokie, Illinois, PCA Publication EB096D, March 1979, 112 pp.

1.7 STRUCTURAL LOADS

Loads for use in structural design are specified in the National Building Code of Canada. Dead loads include the weight of structural and non-structural members including all construction materials that are supported permanently. Tables 1.11 and 1.12 contain dead loads due to commonly used construction materials. Live loads, based on intended use and occupancy, are tabulated in Table 1.13. For live loads due to snow, rain, wind, earthquake and other effects, users are referred to the National Building Code of Canada.

1.8 BEAM DIAGRAMS

Beam diagrams for single span beams with different support and loading conditions are provided in Table 1.14. The application of these diagrams can be extended to cases where more than one loading condition can be superimposed. Moments are positive if they cause compression in the top of the beam.

Bending moments and support reactions for continuous beams with equal spans are given in Tables 1.15, 1.16 and 1.17. These figures cover either uniformly distributed loads or concentrated loads at centres or at third points. Pattern loading, for design purposes, is also included.

Table 1.18 provides approximate design moments and the expressions specified in CSA Standard A23.3. The use of Table 1.18 is limited to beams with approximately equal spans, where the longer of the two adjacent spans is not greater than the shorter by more than 20 percent.

1.9 FRAME CONSTANTS

The majority of concrete construction consists of prismatic members between the supporting elements. However, one of the advantages of using concrete as a construction material is that it can be molded into any geometric shape. Sometimes the structural engineer makes use of this advantage and increases the cross section within a member where needed. This results in a change in stiffness and the distribution of moments. Furthermore, concrete members, monolithically cast with the adjoining members, have end regions that are integral parts of the adjoining members. These end regions are generally considered to have very high stiffness and affect the distribution of moments. Tables 1.19 through

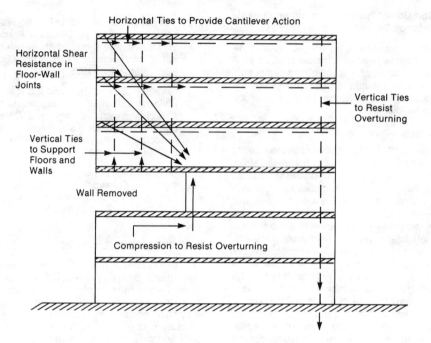

Horizontal Ties to Provide Cantilever Action

Horizontal Shear Resistance in Floor-Wall Joints

Vertical Ties to Resist Overturning

Vertical Ties to Support Floors and Walls

Wall Removed

Compression to Resist Overturning

Fig. 1.10   Development of Alternate Load Path

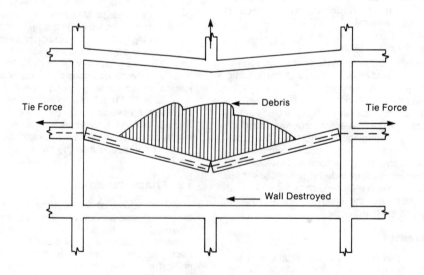

Tie Force

Debris

Tie Force

Wall Destroyed

Fig. 1.11   Catenary Action of Floor Slab

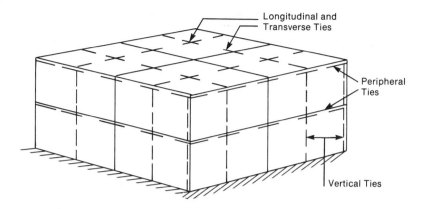

Fig. 1.12 Ties Required in a Precast Building

1.23 contain frame constants for non-prismatic members and members with one or two infinitely stiff end regions. The stiffness factors included in the tables are used to determine member stiffness K. (K = kEI/L).

1.10 SECTIONAL PROPERTIES

Geometric properties of various sections that may be required in a structural design process are given in Table 1.24. For sectional areas and moments of inertia and centroid of 'T' sections see Chapter 6.

Table 1.1: Cement Types and Their Effects on Concrete

CSA Cement Types		Type 10 Normal	Type 20 Moderate*	Type 30 High Early Strength	Type 40 Low Heat	Type 50 Sulphate Resistant
Heat of Hydration during the first 7 days (% of Type 10)**		100	80 to 85	Up to 150	40 to 60	60 to 75
Relative Compressive Strength (% of Type 10† at 28 days)	1 day	—	—	47	—	—
	3 days	47	38	83	32	40
	7 days	68	60	—	—	60
	28 days	100	100	—	94	100
	91 days	—	—	—	125	—
Type of cement to be used when % of SO₄ in soil	< 0.10	X	X	X	X	X
	0.10 - 0.20		X		X	X
	> 0.20					X
Type of cement to be used when SO₄ in ground water (mg/L)	< 150	X	X	X	X	X
	150-1000		X		X	X
	> 1000					X

*Moderate with respect to sulphate-resistance or heat of hydration.
**Temperature *rise* in normal portland cement concrete due to heat of hydration is *approximately* 20° C at 1 day and 30° C at 7 days.
†The values set forth in Table 1.1 reflect the minimum mortar cube strengths required by CSA Standard A5 and are not necessarily representative of concrete strengths. Factors such as variations in water-cement ratios, aggregate type and quantity, concrete admixtures used and curing will have a very significant effect on concrete strength at any age. These variables may also alter the strength relationship in the concrete between types of cement used.

Table 1.2: Creep and Shrinkage Modification Factors for Non-Standard Conditions

$$Q_{cr} = Q_a \, Q_h \, Q_f \, Q_r \, Q_s \, Q_v$$
$$P_{sh} = P_c \, P_h \, P_f \, P_r \, P_s \, P_v$$

Age at Loading days	Q_a	
	moist cured	steam cured
1	1.25	1.00
7	1.00	0.94
20	0.87	0.85
60	0.77	0.76

Relative Humidity %	Q_h	P_h
40	1.00	1.00
60	0.87	0.80
80	0.73	0.60
100	0.60	0.00

Ratio of Fine to Total Aggr.	Q_f	P_f
0.30	0.95	0.72
0.40	0.98	0.86
0.50	1.00	1.00
0.70	1.05	1.04

Volume Surface Ratio, mm	Q_r	P_r
38	1.00	1.00
75	0.82	0.84
150	0.70	0.59
250	0.67	0.37

Slump, mm	Q_s	P_s
50	0.95	0.97
70	1.00	1.00
125	1.15	1.09

Air %	Q_v	P_v
≤ 6	1.00	1.00
8	1.18	1.01
10	1.36	1.03

	Cement Content, kg/m³		
	225	300	410
P_c	0.89	0.93	1.00

Notes:
— Standard conditions produce modification factors of 1.0.
— Volume — surface ratio of a rectangular member having a × b cross-section is ab/(2a + 2b)
— Ratio of fine aggregate to total aggregate is expressed as the ratio of the weights
— For average ambient relative humidity see Fig. 1.6.

Table 1.3: Properties of Prestressing Wires and Seven-Wire Strands

Tendon Type	Grade f_{pu} MPa	Size Designation	Nominal Diameter mm	Nominal Area mm²	Nominal Mass kg/m
Prestressing Wire	1550	8	8.00	50.27	0.394
Prestressing Wire	1620	7	7.00	38.48	0.302
Prestressing Wire	1650	6	6.35	31.67	0.248
Prestressing Wire	1720	6	6.35	31.67	0.248
Prestressing Wire	1720	7	7.00	38.48	0.302
Prestressing Wire	1720	8	8.00	50.27	0.394
Prestressing Wire	1760	7	7.00	38.48	0.302
Seven Wire Strand	1720	6	6.35	23.2	0.182
Seven Wire Strand	1720	8	7.95	37.4	0.294
Seven Wire Strand	1720	9	9.53	51.6	0.405
Seven Wire Strand	1720	11	11.13	69.7	0.548
Seven Wire Strand	1720	13	12.70	92.9	0.730
Seven Wire Strand	1720	15	15.24	138.7	1.094
Seven Wire Strand	1760	16	15.47	148.4	1.173
Seven Wire Strand	1860	9	9.53	54.8	0.432
Seven Wire Strand	1860	11	11.13	74.2	0.582
Seven Wire Strand	1860	13	12.70	98.7	0.775
Seven Wire Strand	1860	15	15.24	140.0	1.109

Table 1.4: Properties of Plain and Deformed Prestressing Bars

Tendon Type	Grade f_{pu} MPa	Nominal Diameter mm	Nominal Area mm²	Nominal Mass kg/m
Plain Prestressing Bars	1030	19	284	2.23
Plain Prestressing Bars	1030	22	387	3.04
Plain Prestressing Bars	1030	25	503	3.97
Plain Prestressing Bars	1030	28	639	5.03
Plain Prestressing Bars	1030	32	794	6.21
Plain Prestressing Bars	1030	36	955	7.52
Plain Prestressing Bars	1100	19	284	2.23
Plain Prestressing Bars	1100	22	387	3.04
Plain Prestressing Bars	1100	25	503	3.97
Plain Prestressing Bars	1100	28	639	5.03
Plain Prestressing Bars	1100	32	794	6.21
Plain Prestressing Bars	1100	36	955	7.52
Deformed Prestressing Bars	1030	26	551	4.48
Deformed Prestressing Bars	1030	32	804	6.54
Deformed Prestressing Bars	1030	36	1018	8.28
Deformed Prestressing Bars	1080	15	177	1.46
Deformed Prestressing Bars	1080	20	314	2.56
Deformed Prestressing Bars	1100	26	551	4.48
Deformed Prestressing Bars	1100	32	804	6.54

Table 1.5: Properties of Deformed Reinforcing Bars

Bar Designation	Nominal Dimensions			Mass per Unit Length kg/m
	Diameter mm	Area mm²	Perimeter mm	
10	11.3	100	35.5	0.785
15	16.0	200	50.1	1.570
20	19.5	300	61.3	2.355
25	25.2	500	79.2	3.925
30	29.9	700	93.9	5.495
35	35.7	1000	112.2	7.850
45	43.7	1500	137.3	11.775
55	56.4	2500	177.2	19.625

Notes:
1. Bar numbers are based on the rounded off nominal diameter of the bars.
2. Nominal dimensions are equivalent to those of a plain round bar having the same mass per metre as the deformed bar.
3. Both Billet Steel Bars and Weldable Low Alloy Steel Bars are produced in the above standard sizes. However, all sizes may not be available; manufacturers should be consulted to verify availability.

Table 1.6: Tensile and Bend Test Requirements for Billet-Steel Bars Conforming to CSA G30.18-M92

	Grade 400	Grade 500
Tensile Strength, (Min) MPa	**1.25 × Actual Yield Strength**	**1.25 × Actual Yield Strength**
Yield Point Strength, Minimum MPA	400	500
Elongation in 200 mm Gauge Length Minimum Percent Bar Designation Number		
10,15,20	9	9
25	8	8
30,35,45,55	7	7
Diameter of Pin for Bend Tests[*] d = Nominal Diameter of Specimen Test Bends 180° Bar Designation Number		
10,15	4d	5d
20	5d	6d
25	6d	6d
30,35	8d	8d

[*] When specified by the purchaser, bar sizes No. 45 and 55 shall stand being bent through 90° around a pin of diameter equal to 10d.

Table 1.7: Tensile and Bend Test Requirements for Weldable Low Allow Steel Bars Conforming to CSA G30.18-M92

	400W	500W
Tensile strength, min MPa	400	500
Yield strength[*], min. MPa max. MPa	400 525	500 650
Elongation in 200 mm, minimum percent; Bar Designation Number 10,15,20 and 25	13	12
30,35,45,55	12	10
Diameter of Pin for Bend Tests; d = Nominal Diameter of Specimen Test Bends 180°, RBar Designation Number		
10,25	3d	3d
20,25	4d	4d
30,35	6d	6d
45,55	8d	8d

[*] Tensile strength shall be not less than 1.15 times the actual yield strength

Table 1.8: Tensile and Bend Test Requirements for Smooth Wires Conforming to CSA G30.3-M 1983

Size Number	Minimum Tensile Strength (MPa)	Minimum Yield Strength (MPa)
MW 7.7 and larger	515	450
Smaller than MW 7.7	485	385
	Bend test (180°)	
MW 45.2 and smaller	Bend around a pin the diameter of which is equal to the diameter of the specimen.	
Larger than MW 45.2	Bend around a pin the diameter of which is equal to twice the diameter of the specimen.	

Table 1.9: Tensile and Bend Test Requirements for Deformed Wires Conforming to CSA G30.14-M 1983

Use	Minimum Tensile Strength (MPa)	Minimum Yield Strength (MPa)
Wires *not* to be used for fabrication of welded fabric	585	515
Wires to be used for fabrication of welded fabric	550	485

Size Number	Bend test (90°)
MD 38.7 and smaller	Bend around a pin the diameter of which is equal to twice the nominal diameter of the specimen.
Larger than MD 38.7	Bend around a pin the diameter of which is equal to four times the nominal diameter of the specimen.

Table 1.10: Properties of Welded Wire Fabric

Designation*	Wire Diameter mm	Wire Cross-Sectional Area Long. mm²	Wire Cross-Sectional Area Transv. mm²	Mass per Unit Area kg/m²	Cross-Sectional Area Per Metre Width Long. mm²	Cross-Sectional Area Per Metre Width Transv. mm²
152 × 152 MW9.1 × MW9.1	3.40	9.1	9.1	1.04	59.8	59.8
152 × 152 MW11.1 × MW11.1	3.76	11.1	11.1	1.26	73.0	73.0
152 × 152 MW13.3 × MW13.3	4.12	13.3	13.3	1.50	87.5	87.5
152 × 152 MW18.7 × MW18.7	4.88	18.7	18.7	2.11	123.0	123.0
152 × 152 MW25.8 × MW25.8	5.74	25.8	25.8	2.91	170.0	170.0
152 × 152 MW34.9 × MW34.9	6.67	34.9	34.9	3.95	230.0	230.0
152 × 152 MW47.6 × MW47.6	7.79	47.6	47.6	5.38	313.0	313.0
102 × 102 MW9.1 × MW9.1	3.40	9.1	9.1	1.52	89.2	89.2
102 × 102 MW11.1 × MW11.1	3.76	11.1	11.1	1.83	109.0	109.0
102 × 102 MW13.3 × MW13.3	4.12	13.3	13.3	2.18	130.0	130.0
102 × 102 MW18.7 × MW18.7	4.88	18.7	18.7	3.07	183.0	183.0
102 × 102 MW25.8 × MW25.8	5.74	25.8	25.8	4.23	253.0	253.0
51 × 51 MW3.2 × MW3.2	2.03	3.2	3.2	1.03	62.8	62.8
51 × 51 MW5.6 × MW5.6	2.69	5.6	5.6	1.80	110.0	110.0
51 × 51 MW9.1 × MW9.1	3.40	9.1	9.1	2.94	178.0	178.0

*The first two numbers give the spacing in mm, and the second two give the size of wire.

Table 1.11:   Dead Loads for Floors, Ceilings, Roofs and Walls

	Load (kN/m²)
Floorings:	
Normal density concrete topping, per 10 mm of thickness	0.24
Semi-low density concrete (1900 kg/m³) topping, per 10 mm	0.19
Low density concrete (1500 kg/m³) topping, per 10 mm	0.15
22 mm hardwood floor on sleepers, clipped to concrete without fill	0.24
40 mm terrazzo floor finish directly on slab	0.95
40 mm terrazzo floor finish on 25 mm mortar bed	1.49
25 mm terrazzo floor finish on 50 mm concrete bed	1.79
20 mm ceramic or quarry tile on 12 mm mortar bed	0.80
20 mm ceramic or quarry tile on 25 mm mortar bed	1.06
8 mm linoleum or asphalt tile directly on concrete	0.06
8 mm linoleum or asphalt tile on 25 mm mortar bed	0.59
20 mm mastic floor	0.45
Hardwood flooring, 22 mm thick	0.19
Subflooring (softwood), 20 mm thick	0.13
Asphaltic concrete, 40 mm thick	0.90
Ceilings:	
12.7 mm gypsum board	0.10
15.9 mm gypsum board	0.12
19 mm gypsum board directly on concrete	0.24
20 mm plaster directly on concrete	0.26
20 mm plaster on metal lath furring	0.40
Suspended ceilings, add	0.10
Acoustical tile	0.05
Acoustical tile on wood furring strips	0.15
Mechanical duct allowance	0.19
Roofs:	
Five-ply felt and gravel (or slag)	0.31
Three-ply felt and gravel (or slag)	0.27
Five-ply felt composition roof, no gravel	0.20
Three-ply felt composition roof, no gravel	0.15
Asphalt strip shingles	0.15
Slate, 8 mm thick	0.57
Gypsum, per 10 mm of thickness	0.08
Insulating concrete, per 10 mm	0.06

(Continued)

	Load (kN/m²)		
	Unplastered	**One side Plastered**	**Both sides Plastered**
Walls (Brick, Concrete Block or Tile)			
100 mm brick wall	1.86	2.10	2.33
200 mm brick wall	3.77	4.00	4.24
300 mm brick wall	5.59	5.83	6.06
100 mm hollow normal density concrete block	1.37	1.61	1.84
150 mm hollow normal density concrete block	1.67	1.90	2.14
200 mm hollow normal density concrete block	2.11	2.34	2.58
250 mm hollow normal density concrete block	2.50	2.74	2.97
300 mm hollow normal density concrete block	2.94	3.18	3.38
100 mm hollow low density block or tile	1.08	1.31	1.55
150 mm hollow low density block or tile	1.28	1.51	1.75
200 mm hollow low density block or tile	1.62	1.85	2.09
250 mm hollow low density block or tile	1.91	2.15	2.38
300 mm hollow low density block or tile	2.26	2.49	2.73
100 mm brick 100 mm hollow normal density block backing	3.24	3.47	3.71
100 mm brick 200 mm hollow normal density block backing	3.97	4.21	4.44
100 mm brick 300 mm hollow normal density block backing	4.81	5.04	5.28
100 mm brick 100 mm hollow low density block backing	2.94	3.18	3.41
100 mm brick 200 mm hollow low density block backing	3.48	3.72	3.95
100 mm brick 300 mm hollow low density block backing	4.12	4.36	4.59

	Load (kN/m²)
Walls (Others):	
Windows, glass, frame and sash	0.38
100 mm stone	2.59
Steel or wood studs, lath, 20 mm plaster	0.86
Steel or wood studs, lath, 15.9 mm gypsum board each side	0.28
Steel or wood studs, 2 layers 12.7 mm gypsum board each side	0.44
Exterior stud walls with brick veneer	2.30

Table 1.12: Minimum Design Loads for Materials

Material	Load (kN/m³)	Material	Load (kN/m³)
Bituminous products:		Lead	111.6
Asphaltum	12.7	Lime	
Graphite	21.2	Hydrated, loose	5.0
Paraffin	8.8	Hydrated, compacted	7.1
Petroleum, crude	8.6	Masonry, ashlar:	
Petroleum, refined	7.9	Granite	25.9
Petroleum, benzine	7.2	Limestone, crystalline	25.9
Petroleum, gasoline	6.6	Limestone, oolitic	21.2
Pitch	10.8	Marble	27.2
Tar	11.8	Sandstone	22.6
Brass	82.7	Masonry, brick:	
Bronze	86.7	Hard (low absorption)	20.4
Cast-stone masonry (cement, stone, sand)	22.6	Medium (Medium absorption)	18.1
Cement, portland, loose	14.1	Soft (high absorption)	15.7
Ceramic tile	23.6	Masonry, rubble mortar:	
Charcoal	1.9	Granite	24.0
Cinder fill	9.0	Limestone, crystalline	23.1
Cinders, dry, in bulk	7.1	Limestone, oolitic	21.7
Coal		Marble	24.5
Anthracite, piled	8.2	Sandstone	21.5
Bituminous, piled	7.4	Mortar, hardened:	
Lignite, piled	7.4	Cement	20.4
Peat, dry, piled	3.6	Lime	17.3
Concrete, plain:		Particleboard	7.1
Cinder	17.0	Plywood	5.7
Expanded-slag aggregate	15.7	Riprap (not submerged):	
Haydite (burned-clay aggregate)	14.1	Limestone	13.0
Slag	20.7	Sandstone	14.1
Stone (including gravel)	22.6	Sand	
Vermiculite and perlite aggregate		Clean and dry	14.1
nonload-bearing	4.0-8.0	River, dry	16.7
Other light aggregate, load-bearing	11.0-16.5	Slag	
Concrete, reinforced:		Bank	11.0
Cinder	17.4	Bank screenings	17.0
Slag	21.7	Machine	15.1
Stone (including gravel)	23.6	Sand	8.2
Copper	87.4	Slate	27.0
Cork, compressed	2.3	Steel, cold-drawn	76.8
Earth (not submerged):		Stone, quarried, piled:	
Clay, dry	10.0	Basalt, granite, gneiss	15.1
Clay, damp	17.3	Limestone, marble, quartz	14.9
Clay and gravel, dry	15.7	Sandstone	12.9
Silt, moist, loose	12.3	Shale	14.5
Silt, moist, packed	15.1	Greenstone, hornblende	16.8
Silt, flowing	17.0	Terra cotta, architectural:	
Sand and gravel, dry, loose	15.7	Voids filled	18.9
Sand and gravel, dry, packed	17.3	Voids unfilled	11.3
Sand and gravel, wet	18.9	Tin	72.1
Earth (submerged):		Water	
Clay	12.6	Fresh	9.8
Soil	11.0	Sea	10.1
River mud	14.1	Wood, seasoned:	
Sand or gravel	9.4	Ash, commercial white	6.4
Sand or gravel, and clay	10.2	Cypress, southern	5.3
Gravel, dry	16.3	Fir, Douglas, coast region	5.3
Gypsum, loose	11.0	Hem fir	4.4
Gypsum wallboard	7.9	Oak, commercial reds and whites	7.4
Ice	9.0	Pine, southern yellow	5.8
Iron		Redwood	4.4
Cast	70.7	Spruce, red, white, and Sitka	4.6
Wrought	75.4	Western hemlock	5.0
		Zinc, rolled sheet	70.6

Table 1.13: Live Loads for Floors or Roofs Due to Use and Occupancy[1]

Uniformly Distributed Live Loads	
Use of Area of Floor or Roof	**Minimum Specified Load kN/m²**
Assembly areas with fixed seats that have backs over at least 80 per cent of the assembly area for the following uses: Churches, Classrooms (also without fixed seats), Courtrooms, Lecture halls, Theatres	2.4
Assembly areas other than those listed above, with or without fixed seats including: Arenas, Churches, Dance floors, Dining areas[2], foyers and entrance halls, Grandstands, reviewing stands and bleachers, Stages, Theatres, and other areas with similar uses	4.8
Attics accessible by a stairway in residential occupancies only	1.4
Attics having limited accessibility so that there is no storage of equipment or material	0.5
Balconies, exterior and interior[3]	4.8
Corridors, lobbies and aisles over 1200 mm wide (except upper floor corridors of residential areas of apartments, hotels and motels)[3]	4.8
Equipment areas and service rooms[4] including: Generator rooms, Mechanical equipment exclusive of elavators, Machine rooms, Pump rooms, Transformer vaults, Ventilating or air-conditioning equipment	3.6
Exits and fire excapes	4.8
Factories[4]	6.0
Garages for Passenger cars .... Unloaded buses and light trucks .... Loaded buses and trucks and all other trucking spaces	2.4 6.0 12.0
Kitchens (other than residential)	4.8
Libraries Stack rooms .... Reading and study rooms .... Mezzanines that could be used for the assembly of people as a viewing area[3]	7.2 2.9 4.8
Office areas in office buildings and other buildings (not including record storage and computer rooms) located in Basement and first floors .... Floors above first floor	4.8 2.4
Operating rooms and laboratories	3.6
Patients' bedrooms	1.9
Recreation areas that cannot be used for assembly purposes including: Billiard rooms, Bowling alleys, Pool rooms	3.6

Residential areas
Sleeping and living quarters of all buildings used for assembly occupancies[5], institutional and high hazard industrial occupancies ....
Sleeping and living quarters of all buildings exceeding 600 m² in building area or exceeding 3 storeys in building height used for residential occupancy, business and personal services occupancies, mercantile occupancy, medium and low hazard industrial occupancies ....
Buildings of 3 storeys or less in building height, having a building area not exceeding 600 m², used for residential occupancy, business and personal services occupancies, mercantile occupancy, medium and low hazard industrial occupancies
  i. Bedrooms ....
  ii. Other areas including stairs within dwelling units ....
	1.9
	
	1.9
	
	1.4
	1.9

Retail and wholesale areas	4.8
Roofs[6]	1.0
Sidewalks and driveways over areaways and basements	12.0
Storage areas[4]	4.8
Toilet areas	2.4
Underground slabs with earth cover[4]	—
Warehouse[4]	4.8

(Continued)

Table 1.13:   (Continued)

Concentrated Live Loads[7]	
Area of Floor or Roof	**Minimum Specified Concentrated Load, kN**
Roof surfaces	1.3
Floors of classrooms	4.5
Floors of offices, manufacturing buildings, hospital wards and stages	9.0
Floor and areas used by passenger cars	11
Floors and areas used by vehicles not exceeding 3600 kg gross weight	18
Floors and areas used by vehicles exceeding 3600 kg but not exceeding 9000 kg gross weight	36
Floors and areas used by vehicles exceeding 9000 kg gross weight	54
Driveways and sidewalks over areaways and basements	54

[1]Based on the National Building Code of Canada, 1985, Edition (NBC-85).

[2]The minimum specified load in Table 1.13 for dining areas may be reduced to 2.4 kN/m^2 for dining areas in buildings that have been converted for such purposes provided that the *floor area* does not exceed 100 m^2 and use of the dining area for other assembly purposes including dancing is precluded.

[3]Corridors, lobbies and aisles not over 1,200 mm in width, all upper floor corridors of residential areas of apartments, hotels and motels and interior balconies and mezzanines shall be designed to carry not less than the specified load required for the *occupancy* they serve provided they can not be used for the assembly of people as a viewing area.

[4]Exterior areas accessible to vehicular traffic shall be designed for their intended use, including the weight of fire fighting equipment, but not less than the *live loads* due to snow, ice and rain.

[5]For description of occupancies, see subsection 3.1.2 of NBC-85.

[6]For snow loads, see subsection 4.1.7 of NBC-85.

[7]Concentrated loads will be applied over an area of 750 mm by 750 mm.

Table 1.14: Beam Diagrams

Simple Beam — uniformly distributed load

$$R = V \quad = \frac{w\ell}{2}$$

$$V_x \quad = w\left(\frac{\ell}{2} - x\right)$$

$$M \text{ max. (at centre)} \quad = \frac{w\ell^2}{8}$$

$$M_x \quad = \frac{wx}{2}(\ell - x)$$

$$\Delta \text{max. (at centre)} \quad = \frac{5\,w\ell^4}{384\,EI}$$

$$\Delta_x \quad = \frac{wx}{24\,EI}(\ell^3 - 2\ell x^2 + x^3)$$

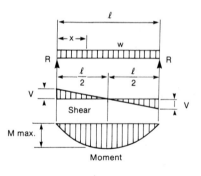

Simple Beam — load increasing uniformly to one end

$$R_1 = V_1 \quad = \frac{w\ell}{6}$$

$$R_2 = V_2 \quad = \frac{w\ell}{3}$$

$$V_x \quad = \frac{w\ell}{3} - \frac{wx^2}{2\ell}$$

$$M \text{ max. }\left(\text{at } x = \sqrt{\frac{\ell}{3}} = 0.5774\ell\right) \quad = \frac{w\ell^2}{9\sqrt{3}} = 0.06415\ell^2$$

$$M_x \quad = \frac{wx}{6\ell}(\ell^2 - x^2)$$

$$\Delta \text{max. }\left(\text{at } x = \ell\sqrt{1 - \sqrt{\frac{8}{15}}} = 0.5193\ell\right) \quad 0.00652\,\frac{w\ell^4}{EI}$$

$$\Delta_x \quad = \frac{wx}{360\,EI\ell}(3x^4 - 10\ell^2 x^2 + 7\ell^4)$$

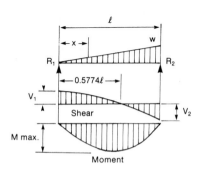

Simple Beam — load increasing uniformly to centre

$$R = V \quad = \frac{w\ell}{4}$$

$$V_x\left(\text{when } x < \frac{\ell}{2}\right) \quad = \frac{w}{4\ell}(\ell^2 - 4x^2)$$

$$M \text{ max. (at centre)} \quad = \frac{w\ell^2}{12}$$

$$M_x\left(\text{when } x < \frac{\ell}{2}\right) \quad = \frac{w\ell x}{2}\left(\frac{1}{2} - \frac{2x^2}{3\ell^2}\right)$$

$$\Delta \text{max. (at centre)} \quad = \frac{w\ell^4}{120\,EI}$$

$$\Delta_x \quad = \frac{wx}{960\,EI\ell}(5\ell^2 - 4x^2)^2$$

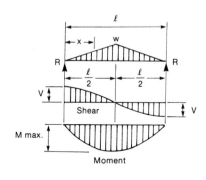

Note:
w: Distributed load per unit length. In the case of triangular distribution, w represents the maximum intensity of load per unit length.
P: Concentrated load.

Simple Beam — uniform load partially distributed

$R_1 = V_1$ (max. when $a < c$) .... $= \dfrac{wb}{2\ell}(2c + b)$

$R_2 = V_2$ (max. when $a > c$) .... $= \dfrac{wb}{2\ell}(2a + b)$

V_x (when $x > a$ and $< (a + b)$) .... $= R_1 - w(x - a)$

M max. $\left(\text{at } x = a + \dfrac{R_1}{w}\right)$ .... $= R_1\left(a + \dfrac{R_1}{2w}\right)$

M_x (when $x < a$) .... $= R_1 x$

M_x (when $x > a$ and $< (a + b)$) .... $= R_1 x - \dfrac{w}{2}(x - a)^2$

M_x (when $x > (a + b)$) .... $= R_2(\ell - x)$

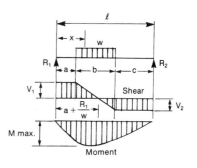

Beam fixed at both ends — symmetrical trapezoidal load

$R = V$ .... $= \dfrac{w\ell}{2}\left(1 - \dfrac{a}{\ell}\right)$

M_1 .... $= -\dfrac{w\ell^2}{12}\left(1 - 2\dfrac{a^2}{\ell^2} + \dfrac{a^3}{\ell^3}\right)$

M_2 .... $= \dfrac{w\ell^2}{24}\left(1 - 2\dfrac{a^3}{\ell^3}\right)$

M_x (when $x < a$) .... $= M_1 + R_1 x - \dfrac{wx^3}{6a}$

M_x (when $a < x < \ell - a$) .... $= M_1 + R_1 x - \dfrac{wa}{2}\left(x - \dfrac{2}{3}a\right)$
$\hspace{4cm} - \dfrac{w}{2}(x - a)^2$

Note: When $a = \ell/2$ loading is triangular

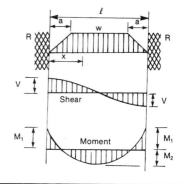

Simple Beam — concentrated load at any point

$R_1 = V_1$ (max. when $a < b$) .... $= \dfrac{Pb}{\ell}$

$R_2 = V_2$ (max. when $a > b$) .... $= \dfrac{Pa}{\ell}$

M max. (at point of load) .... $= \dfrac{Pab}{\ell}$

M_x (when $x < a$) .... $= \dfrac{Pbx}{\ell}$

Δmax. $\left(\text{at } x = \sqrt{\dfrac{a(a + 2b)}{3}} \text{ when } a > b\right)$ $= \dfrac{Pab(a + 2b)\sqrt{3a(a + 2b)}}{27\,EI\ell}$

Δa (at point of load) .... $= \dfrac{Pa^2 b^2}{3\,EI\ell}$

Δ_x (when $x < a$) .... $= \dfrac{Pbx}{6\,EI\ell}(\ell^2 - b^2 - x^2)$

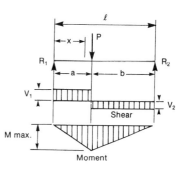

Note:
w: Distributed load per unit length. In the case of triangular distribution, w represents the maximum intensity of load per unit length.
P: Concentrated load.

Beam fixed at both ends — uniformly distributed loads

$R = V$ .... $= \dfrac{w\ell}{2}$

V_x .... $= w\left(\dfrac{\ell}{2} - x\right)$

M max. (at ends) .... $= -\dfrac{w\ell^2}{12}$

M_1 (at centre) .... $= \dfrac{w\ell^2}{24}$

M_x .... $= \dfrac{w}{12}(6\ell x - \ell^2 - 6x^2)$

Δmax. (at centre) .... $= \dfrac{w\ell^4}{384\,EI}$

Δ_x .... $= \dfrac{wx^2}{24\,EI}(\ell - x)^2$

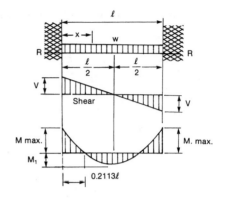

Beam fixed at both ends — concentrated load at any point

$R_1 = V_1$ (max. when a < b) .... $= \dfrac{Pb^2}{\ell^3}(3a + b)$

$R_2 = V_2$ (max. when a > b) .... $= \dfrac{Pa^2}{\ell^3}(a + 3b)$

M_1 (max. when a < b) .... $= -\dfrac{Pab^2}{\ell^2}$

M_2 (max. when a > b) .... $= -\dfrac{Pa^2b}{\ell^2}$

M_a (at point of load) .... $= \dfrac{2Pa^2b^2}{\ell^3}$

M_x (when x < a) .... $= R_1x - \dfrac{Pab^2}{\ell^2}$

Δmax. $\left(\text{when a > b at x} = \dfrac{2a\ell}{3a+b}\right)$ .... $= \dfrac{2Pa^3b^2}{3\,EI\,(3a+b)^2}$

Δ_a (at point of load) .... $= \dfrac{Pa^3b^3}{3\,EI\ell^3}$

Δ_x (when x < a) .... $= \dfrac{Pb^2x^2}{6\,EI\ell^3}(3a\ell - 3ax - bx)$

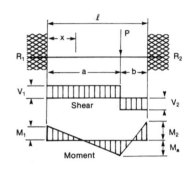

Beam fixed at both ends — uniform load partially distributed

M_1 .... $= \dfrac{w}{12\ell^2}\left[(\ell - a)^3(\ell + 3a) - c^3(4\ell - 3c)\right]$

M_2 .... $= \dfrac{w}{12\ell^2}\left[(\ell - c)^3(\ell + 3c) - a^3(4\ell - 3a)\right]$

$R_1 = V_1$ .... $= \dfrac{1}{\ell}\left[M_1 - M_2 + wc\left(c + \dfrac{b}{2}\right)\right]$

$R_2 = V_2$ .... $= \dfrac{1}{\ell}\left[M_2 - M_1 + wc\left(a + \dfrac{b}{2}\right)\right]$

M_x (when x < a) .... $= R_1x - M_1$

M_x (when a < x < (a + c)) .... $= R_1x - M_1 - \dfrac{w}{2}(x - a)^2$

M_x (when x > (a + c)) .... $= R_2(\ell - x) - M_2$

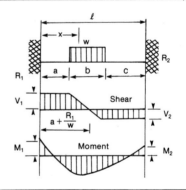

Note:
w: Distributed load per unit length. In the case of triangular distribution, w represents the maximum intensity of load per unit length.
P: Concentrated load.

Table 1.14:   (Continued)

Beam fixed at both ends — load increasing uniformly to one end

$R_1 = V_1$ .... $= \dfrac{3w\ell}{20}$

$R_2 = V_2$ .... $= \dfrac{7w\ell}{20}$

V_x .... $= \dfrac{3w\ell}{20} - \dfrac{wx^2}{2\ell}$

M_1 .... $= -\dfrac{w\ell^2}{30}$

M_2 .... $= -\dfrac{w\ell^2}{20}$

M_x .... $= \dfrac{3w\ell x}{20} - \dfrac{w\ell^2}{30} - \dfrac{wx^3}{6\ell}$

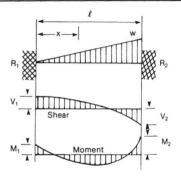

Beam fixed at one end, supported at other — uniformly distributed load

$R_1 = V_1$ .... $= \dfrac{3w\ell}{8}$

$R_2 = V_2$ max. .... $= \dfrac{5w\ell}{8}$

V_x .... $= R_1 - wx$

M max. .... $= -\dfrac{w\ell^2}{8}$

$M_1 \left(\text{at } x = \dfrac{3}{8}\ell \right)$ .... $= \dfrac{9}{128} w\ell^2$

M_x .... $= R_1 x - \dfrac{wx^2}{2}$

Δmax. $\left(\text{at } x = \dfrac{\ell}{16}(1 + \sqrt{33}) = 0.4215\ell \right)$. $= \dfrac{w\ell^4}{185\,EI}$

Δ_x .... $= \dfrac{wx}{48\,EI}(\ell^3 - 3\ell x^2 + 2x^3)$

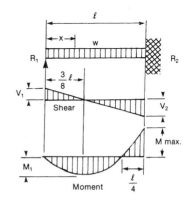

Beam fixed at one end, supported at other — concentrated load at any point

$R_1 = V_1$ .... $= \dfrac{Pb^2}{2\ell^3}(a + 2\ell)$

$R_2 = V_2$ .... $= \dfrac{Pa}{2\ell^3}(3\ell^2 - a^2)$

M_1 (at point of load) .... $= R_1 a$

M_2 (at fixed end) .... $= -\dfrac{Pab}{2\ell^2}(a + \ell)$

M_x (when $x < a$) .... $= R_1 x$

M_x (when $x > a$) .... $= R_1 x - P(x - a)$

Δmax. $\left(\text{when } a < 0.414\ell \text{ at } x = \ell\, \dfrac{\ell^2 + a^2}{3\ell^2 - a^2} \right) = \dfrac{Pa}{3\,EI}\, \dfrac{(\ell^2 - a^2)^3}{(3\ell^2 - a^2)^2}$

Δmax. $\left(\text{when } a > 0.414\ell \text{ at } x = \ell\, \sqrt{\dfrac{a}{2\ell + a}} \right) = \dfrac{Pab^2}{6\,EI}\, \sqrt{\dfrac{a}{2\ell + a}}$

Δa (at point of load) .... $= \dfrac{Pa^2 b^3}{12\,EI\ell^3}(3\ell + a)$

Δx (when $x < a$) .... $= \dfrac{Pb^2 x}{12\,EI\ell^3}(3a\ell^2 - 2\ell x^2 - ax^2)$

Δx (when $x > a$) .... $= \dfrac{Pa}{12\,EI\ell^3}(\ell - x)^2(3\ell^2 x - a^2 x - 2a^2\ell)$

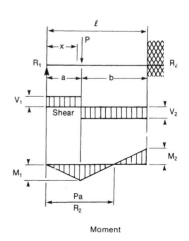

Note:
w: Distributed load per unit length. In the case of triangular distribution, w represents the maximum intensity of load per unit length.
P: Concentrated load.
Moments are positive if they cause compression in the top of the beam.

Table 1.14:   (Continued)

Cantilever Beam — uniformly distributed load

$R = V$ .... $= w\ell$

V_x .... $= wx$

M max. (at fixed end) .... $= -\dfrac{w\ell^2}{2}$

M_x .... $= \dfrac{wx^2}{2}$

Δmax. (at free end) .... $= \dfrac{w\ell^4}{8\,EI}$

Δ_x .... $= \dfrac{w}{24\,EI}\,(x^4 - 4\ell^3 x + 3\ell^4)$

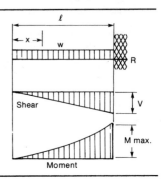

Cantilever Beam — load increasing uniformly to fixed end

$R = V$ .... $= \dfrac{w\ell}{2}$

V_x .... $= \dfrac{wx^2}{2\ell}$

M max. (at fixed end) .... $= -\dfrac{w\ell^2}{6}$

M_x .... $= \dfrac{wx^3}{6\ell}$

Δmax. (at free end) .... $= \dfrac{w\ell^4}{30\,EI}$

Δ_x .... $= \dfrac{w}{120\,EI\ell}\,(x^5 - 5\ell^4 x + 4\ell^5)$

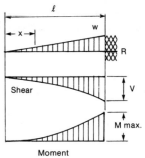

Cantilever Beam — concentrated load at any point

$R = V$ .... $= P$

M max. (at fixed end) .... $= -Pb$

M_x (when $x > a$) .... $= P\,(x - a)$

Δmax. (at free end) .... $= \dfrac{Pb^2}{6\,EI}\,(3\ell - b)$

Δa (at point of load) .... $= \dfrac{Pb^3}{3\,EI}$

Δ_x (when $x < a$) .... $= \dfrac{Pb^2}{6\,EI}\,(3\ell - 3x - b)$

Δ_x (when $x > a$) .... $= \dfrac{P\,(\ell - x)^2}{6\,EI}\,(3b - \ell + x)$

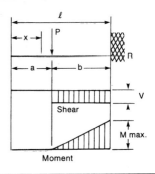

Note:
w: Distributed load per unit length. In the case of triangular distribution, w represents the maximum intensity of load per unit length.
P: Concentrated load.
Moments are positive if they cause compression in the top of the beam.

Beam overhanging one support — uniformly distributed load

$R_1 = V_1$ .... $= \dfrac{w}{2\ell}(\ell^2 - a^2)$

$R_2 = V_2 + V_3$ .... $= \dfrac{w}{2\ell}(\ell + a)^2$

V_2 .... $= wa$

V_3 .... $= \dfrac{w}{2\ell}(\ell^2 + a^2)$

V_x (between supports) .... $= R_1 - wx$

V_{x1} (for overhang) .... $= w(a - x_1)$

$M_1\left(\text{at } x = \dfrac{\ell}{2}\left[1 - \dfrac{a^2}{\ell^2}\right]\right)$ .... $= \dfrac{w}{8\ell^2}(\ell + a)^2(\ell - a)^2$

M_2 (at R_2) .... $= \dfrac{wa^2}{2}$

M_x (between supports) .... $= \dfrac{wx}{2\ell}(\ell^2 - a^2 - x\ell)$

M_{x1} (for overhang) .... $= \dfrac{w}{2}(a - x_1)^2$

Δ_x (between supports) .... $= \dfrac{wx}{24\,EI\ell}(\ell^4 - 2\ell^2x^2 + \ell x^3 - 2a^2\ell^2 + 2a^2x^2)$

Δ_{x1} (for overhang) .... $= \dfrac{wx_1}{24\,EI}(4a^2\ell - \ell^3 + 6a^2x_1 - 4ax_1{}^2 + x_1{}^3)$

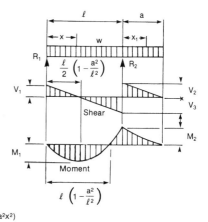

Beam overhanging one support — uniformly distributed load on overhang

$R_1 = V_1$ .... $= \dfrac{wa^2}{2\ell}$

$R_2 = V_1 + V_2$ .... $= \dfrac{wa}{2\ell}(2\ell + a)$

V_2 .... $= wa$

V_{x1} (for overhang) .... $= w(a - x_1)$

M max. (at R_2) .... $= \dfrac{wa^2}{2}$

M_x (between supports) .... $= \dfrac{wa^2x}{2\ell}$

M_{x1} (for overhang) .... $= \dfrac{w}{2}(a - x_1)^2$

Δmax. $\left(\text{between supports at } x = \dfrac{\ell}{\sqrt{3}}\right)$ ... $= \dfrac{wa^2\ell^2}{18\sqrt{3}\,EI} = 0.03208\,\dfrac{wa^2\ell^2}{EI}$

Δmax. (for overhang at $x_1 = a$) .... $= \dfrac{wa^3}{24\,EI}(4\ell + 3a)$

Δ_x (between supports) .... $= \dfrac{wa^2x}{12\,EI\ell}(\ell^2 - x^2)$

Δ_{x1} (for overhang) .... $= \dfrac{wx_1}{24\,EI}(4a^2\ell + 6a^2x_1 - 4ax_1{}^2 + x_1{}^3)$

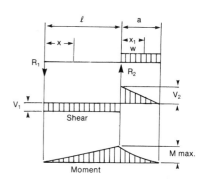

Note:
w: Distributed load per unit length. In the case of triangular distribution, w represents the maximum intensity of load per unit length.
P: Concentrated load.
Moments are positive if they cause compression in the top of the beam.

Table 1.14: Beam Diagrams

Beam overhanging one support — concentrated load at end of overhang

$R_1 = V_1$ .... $= \dfrac{Pa}{\ell}$

$R_2 = V_1 + V_2$ .... $= \dfrac{P}{\ell}(\ell + a)$

V_2 .... $= P$

M max. (at R_2) .... $= Pa$

M_x (between supports) .... $= \dfrac{Pax}{\ell}$

M_{x1} (for overhang) .... $= P(a - x_1)$

Δmax. $\left(\text{between supports at } x = \dfrac{\ell}{\sqrt{3}}\right)$ ... $= \dfrac{Pa\ell^2}{9\sqrt{3}\,EI} = 0.06415\dfrac{Pa\ell^2}{EI}$

Δmax. (for overhang at $x_1 = a$) .... $= \dfrac{Pa^2}{3\,EI}(\ell + a)$

Δ_x (between supports) .... $= \dfrac{Pax}{6\,EI\ell}(\ell^2 - x^2)$

Δ_{x1} (for overhang) .... $= \dfrac{Px_1}{6\,EI}(2a\ell + 3ax_1 - x_1^2)$

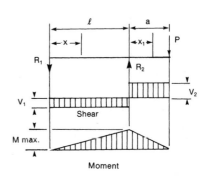

Note:
w: Distributed load per unit length. In the case of triangular distribution, w represents the maximum intensity of load per unit length.
P: Concentrated load.
Moments are positive if they cause compression in the top of the beam.

CPCA Concrete Design Handbook

Table 1.15: Moments and Reactions in Continuous Beams Uniformly Distributed Loads

Moment : Coefficient $\times w\ell^2$ w: Uniform load per unit length
Reaction: Coefficient $\times w\ell$ ℓ : Length of one span

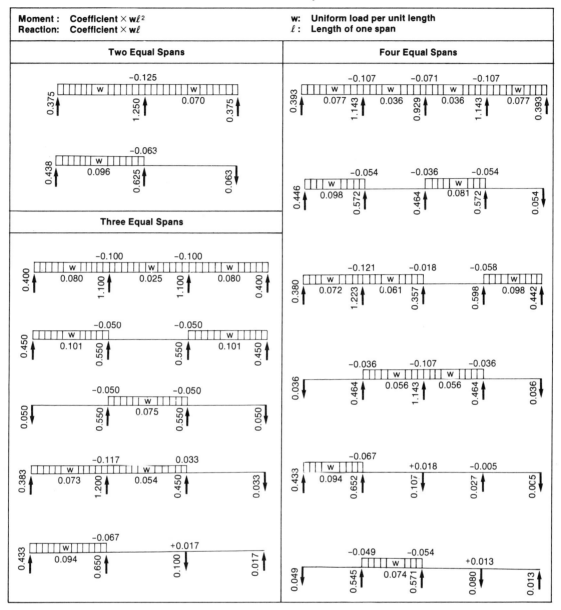

Table 1.16: Moments and Reactions in Continuous Beams Central Point Loads

Moment :	Coefficient × Pℓ	P:	Concentrated load
Reaction:	Coefficient × P	ℓ :	Length of one span

Two Equal Spans

P   P
−0.188
0.313 0.156 1.375 0.156 0.313

P
−0.094
0.406 0.203 0.688 0.094

Three Equal Spans

P   P   P
−0.150   −0.150
0.350 0.175 1.150 0.100 1.150 0.175 0.350

P   P
−0.075   −0.075
0.425 0.213 0.575 0.575 0.213 0.425

P
−0.075   −0.075
0.075 0.575 0.175 0.575 0.075

P   P
−0.175   −0.050
0.325 0.163 1.300 0.138 0.425 0.050

P
−0.100   +0.025
0.400 0.200 0.725 0.150 0.025

Four Equal Spans

P P P P
−0.161 −0.107 −0.161
0.339 0.170 1.214 0.116 0.893 0.116 1.214 0.170 0.339

P P
−0.080 −0.054 −0.080
0.420 0.210 0.607 0.446 0.183 0.607 0.080

P P
−0.181 −0.027 −0.087
0.319 0.160 1.335 0.146 0.286 0.647 0.207 0.413

P P
−0.054 −0.161 −0.054
0.054 0.446 0.143 1.214 0.143 0.446 0.054

P
−0.100 +0.027 −0.007
0.400 0.200 0.728 0.161 0.040 0.007

P
−0.074 −0.080 +0.020
0.074 0.567 0.173 0.607 0.121 0.020

Table 1.17: Moments and Reactions in Continuous Beams Point Loads at Third Points of Span

Moment : Coefficient × Pℓ   P: Total concentrated load on one span
Reaction: Coefficient × P   ℓ : Length of one span

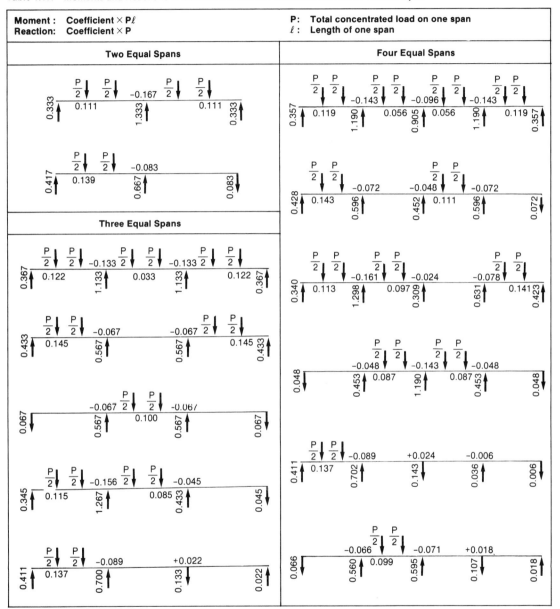

Table 1.18: Approximate Moments and Shears for Continuous Beams and One-Way Slabs

w: **Factored load per unit length**
ℓ_n: **Clear span length**
ℓ_a: **Average length of adjacent clear spans**

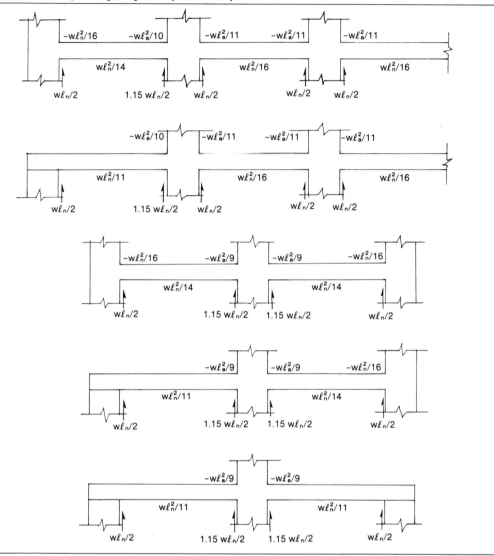

Notes:

1. This figure is applicable to prismatic members loaded with uniformly distributed load where the ratio of factored live load to factored dead load is not greater than 3.0, and the span lengths approximately equal, with the longer of the two adjacent spans not greater than the shorter by more than 20 per cent.

2. If the exterior support is a spandrel or girder, the negative moment at the interior face of exterior support is $w\ell_n^2/24$.

3. For slabs with spans not exceeding 3 m or beams with the ratio of the sum of the column stiffnesses to the beam stiffness exceeds eight at each end, the negative moment at all supports can be taken equal to $w\ell_n^2/12$.

Table 1.19: Beams with Prismatic Haunch at One End

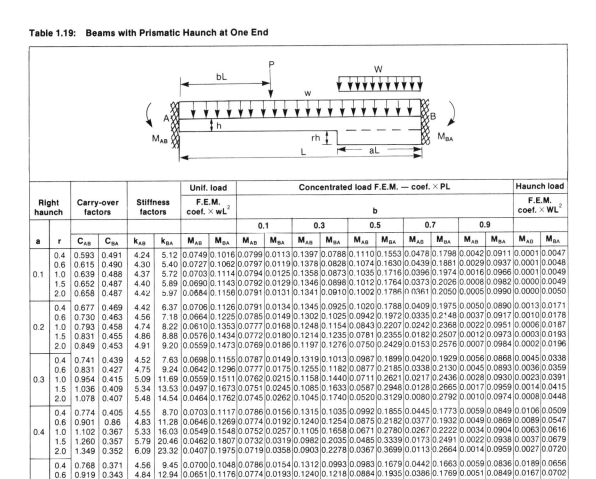

Right haunch		Carry-over factors		Stiffness factors		Unif. load F.E.M. coef. × wL²		Concentrated load F.E.M. — coef. × PL (b)										Haunch load F.E.M. coef. × WL²	
								0.1		0.3		0.5		0.7		0.9			
a	r	C_{AB}	C_{BA}	k_{AB}	k_{BA}	M_{AB}	M_{BA}	M_{AB}	M_{BA}	M_{AB}	M_{BA}	M_{AB}	M_{BA}	M_{AB}	M_{BA}	M_{AB}	M_{BA}	M_{AB}	M_{BA}
0.1	0.4	0.593	0.491	4.24	5.12	0.0749	0.1016	0.0799	0.0113	0.1397	0.0788	0.1110	0.1553	0.0478	0.1798	0.0042	0.0911	0.0001	0.0047
	0.6	0.615	0.490	4.30	5.40	0.0727	0.1062	0.0797	0.0119	0.1378	0.0828	0.1074	0.1630	0.0439	0.1881	0.0029	0.0937	0.0001	0.0048
	1.0	0.639	0.488	4.37	5.72	0.0703	0.1114	0.0794	0.0125	0.1358	0.0873	0.1035	0.1716	0.0396	0.1974	0.0016	0.0966	0.0001	0.0049
	1.5	0.652	0.487	4.40	5.89	0.0690	0.1143	0.0792	0.0129	0.1346	0.0898	0.1012	0.1764	0.0373	0.2026	0.0008	0.0982	0.0000	0.0049
	2.0	0.658	0.487	4.42	5.97	0.0684	0.1156	0.0791	0.0131	0.1341	0.0910	0.1002	0.1786	0.0361	0.2050	0.0005	0.0990	0.0000	0.0050
0.2	0.4	0.677	0.469	4.42	6.37	0.0706	0.1126	0.0791	0.0134	0.1345	0.0925	0.1020	0.1788	0.0409	0.1975	0.0050	0.0890	0.0013	0.0171
	0.6	0.730	0.463	4.56	7.18	0.0664	0.1225	0.0785	0.0149	0.1302	0.1025	0.0942	0.1972	0.0335	0.2148	0.0037	0.0917	0.0010	0.0178
	1.0	0.793	0.458	4.74	8.22	0.0610	0.1353	0.0777	0.0168	0.1248	0.1154	0.0843	0.2207	0.0242	0.2368	0.0022	0.0951	0.0006	0.0187
	1.5	0.831	0.455	4.86	8.88	0.0576	0.1434	0.0772	0.0180	0.1214	0.1235	0.0781	0.2355	0.0182	0.2507	0.0012	0.0973	0.0003	0.0193
	2.0	0.849	0.453	4.91	9.20	0.0559	0.1473	0.0769	0.0186	0.1197	0.1276	0.0750	0.2429	0.0153	0.2576	0.0007	0.0984	0.0002	0.0196
0.3	0.4	0.741	0.439	4.52	7.63	0.0698	0.1155	0.0787	0.0149	0.1319	0.1013	0.0987	0.1899	0.0420	0.1929	0.0056	0.0868	0.0045	0.0338
	0.6	0.831	0.427	4.75	9.24	0.0642	0.1296	0.0777	0.0175	0.1255	0.1182	0.0877	0.2185	0.0338	0.2130	0.0045	0.0893	0.0036	0.0359
	1.0	0.954	0.415	5.09	11.69	0.0559	0.1511	0.0762	0.0215	0.1158	0.1440	0.0711	0.2621	0.0217	0.2436	0.0028	0.0930	0.0023	0.0391
	1.5	1.036	0.409	5.34	13.53	0.0497	0.1673	0.0751	0.0245	0.1085	0.1633	0.0587	0.2948	0.0128	0.2665	0.0017	0.0959	0.0014	0.0415
	2.0	1.078	0.407	5.48	14.54	0.0464	0.1762	0.0745	0.0262	0.1045	0.1740	0.0520	0.3129	0.0080	0.2792	0.0010	0.0974	0.0008	0.0448
0.4	0.4	0.774	0.405	4.55	8.70	0.0703	0.1117	0.0786	0.0156	0.1315	0.1035	0.0992	0.1855	0.0445	0.1773	0.0059	0.0849	0.0106	0.0509
	0.6	0.901	0.86	4.83	11.28	0.0646	0.1269	0.0774	0.0192	0.1240	0.1254	0.0875	0.2182	0.0377	0.1932	0.0049	0.0869	0.0089	0.0547
	1.0	1.102	0.367	5.33	16.03	0.0549	0.1548	0.0752	0.0257	0.1105	0.1658	0.0671	0.2780	0.0267	0.2222	0.0034	0.0904	0.0063	0.0616
	1.5	1.260	0.357	5.79	20.46	0.0462	0.1807	0.0732	0.0319	0.0982	0.2035	0.0485	0.3339	0.0173	0.2491	0.0022	0.0938	0.0037	0.0679
	2.0	1.349	0.352	6.09	23.32	0.0407	0.1975	0.0719	0.0358	0.0903	0.2278	0.0367	0.3699	0.0113	0.2664	0.0014	0.0959	0.0027	0.0720
0.5	0.4	0.768	0.371	4.56	9.45	0.0700	0.1048	0.0786	0.0154	0.1312	0.0993	0.0983	0.1679	0.0442	0.1663	0.0059	0.0836	0.0189	0.0656
	0.6	0.919	0.343	4.84	12.94	0.0651	0.1176	0.0774	0.0193	0.1240	0.1218	0.0884	0.1935	0.0386	0.1769	0.0051	0.0849	0.0167	0.0702
	1.0	1.200	0.316	5.42	20.61	0.0561	0.1451	0.0749	0.0280	0.1096	0.1709	0.0706	0.2486	0.0299	0.1993	0.0038	0.0877	0.0131	0.0802
	1.5	1.470	0.301	6.10	29.74	0.0466	0.1777	0.0720	0.0384	0.0934	0.2290	0.0516	0.3137	0.0215	0.2255	0.0027	0.0909	0.0094	0.0918
	2.0	1.647	0.295	6.63	37.04	0.0393	0.2036	0.0698	0.0466	0.0807	0.2755	0.0370	0.3655	0.0153	0.2463	0.0019	0.0934	0.0067	0.1011
0.6	0.4	0.726	0.341	4.62	9.84	0.0675	0.0986	0.0782	0.0146	0.1280	0.0916	0.0923	0.1519	0.0419	0.1603	0.0056	0.0829	0.0283	0.0769
	0.6	0.872	0.305	4.88	13.97	0.0630	0.1072	0.0771	0.0183	0.1214	0.1096	0.0835	0.1664	0.0368	0.1666	0.0048	0.0837	0.0254	0.0813
	1.0	1.196	0.267	5.43	24.35	0.0560	0.1277	0.0748	0.0274	0.1092	0.1537	0.0705	0.1999	0.0299	0.1804	0.0038	0.0854	0.0212	0.0913
	1.5	1.588	0.247	6.18	39.79	0.0482	0.1572	0.0718	0.0408	0.0939	0.2183	0.0572	0.2478	0.0237	0.1997	0.0030	0.0878	0.0171	0.1055
	2.0	1.905	0.237	6.92	55.51	0.0412	0.1870	0.0688	0.0544	0.0792	0.2839	0.0455	0.2960	0.0186	0.2189	0.0023	0.0901	0.0136	0.1197
0.7	0.4	0.657	0.321	4.86	9.96	0.0631	0.0954	0.0770	0.0138	0.1175	0.0846	0.0844	0.1461	0.0392	0.1582	0.0053	0.0827	0.0372	0.0854
	0.6	0.770	0.275	5.14	14.39	0.0580	0.1006	0.0758	0.0167	0.1097	0.0955	0.0745	0.1543	0.0335	0.1621	0.0045	0.0832	0.0330	0.0890
	1.0	1.056	0.224	5.62	26.45	0.0516	0.1122	0.0738	0.0243	0.0992	0.1213	0.0626	0.1710	0.0269	0.1694	0.0035	0.0841	0.0280	0.0965
	1.5	1.491	0.196	6.24	47.48	0.0463	0.1304	0.0714	0.0371	0.0890	0.1633	0.0537	0.1959	0.0223	0.1796	0.0028	0.0854	0.0241	0.1076
	2.0	1.944	0.183	6.95	73.85	0.0417	0.1523	0.0687	0.0530	0.0793	0.2149	0.0468	0.2255	0.0191	0.1915	0.0024	0.0869	0.0210	0.1210
0.8	0.4	0.583	0.319	5.46	9.97	0.0585	0.0951	0.0741	0.0137	0.1040	0.0837	0.0793	0.1456	0.0380	0.1580	0.0053	0.0826	0.0452	0.0917
	0.6	0.645	0.263	5.89	14.44	0.0516	0.0990	0.0721	0.0160	0.0921	0.0907	0.0667	0.1520	0.0311	0.1614	0.0043	0.0831	0.0388	0.0951
	1.0	0.818	0.196	6.47	27.06	0.0435	0.1053	0.0696	0.0211	0.0781	0.1025	0.0521	0.1615	0.0232	0.1660	0.0031	0.0838	0.0314	0.1004
	1.5	1.128	0.155	6.98	50.85	0.0385	0.1130	0.0676	0.0296	0.0692	0.1175	0.0432	0.1715	0.0184	0.1705	0.0024	0.0844	0.0268	0.1064
	2.0	1.533	0.135	7.47	84.60	0.0355	0.1222	0.0658	0.0412	0.0638	0.1357	0.0384	0.1824	0.0159	0.1750	0.0020	0.0849	0.0242	0.1133
0.9	0.4	0.524	0.356	6.87	10.10	0.0604	0.0948	0.0674	0.0157	0.1031	0.0835	0.0844	0.1439	0.0418	0.1568	0.0059	0.0824	0.0550	0.0942
	0.6	0.542	0.295	7.95	14.58	0.0497	0.0991	0.0623	0.0184	0.0866	0.0913	0.0691	0.1510	0.0339	0.1605	0.0048	0.0830	0.0460	0.0985
	1.0	0.594	0.206	9.44	27.16	0.0372	0.1052	0.0553	0.0226	0.0642	0.1023	0.0484	0.1609	0.0231	0.1656	0.0032	0.0837	0.0337	0.1044
	1.5	0.695	0.142	10.48	51.25	0.0289	0.1098	0.0506	0.0266	0.0492	0.1105	0.0346	0.1680	0.0159	0.1692	0.0021	0.0842	0.0255	0.1089
	2.0	0.842	0.107	11.07	86.80	0.0245	0.1147	0.0481	0.0306	0.0414	0.1159	0.0274	0.1723	0.0121	0.1714	0.0016	0.0845	0.0213	0.1117

Table 1.20: Beams with Prismatic Haunch at Both Ends

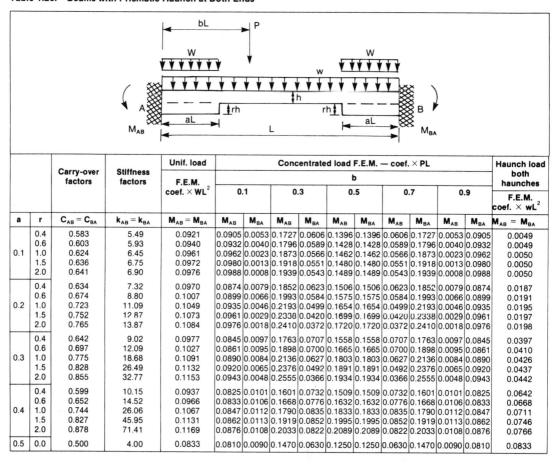

a	r	Carry-over factors $C_{AB} = C_{BA}$	Stiffness factors $k_{AB} = k_{BA}$	Unif. load F.E.M. coef. $\times WL^2$ $M_{AB} = M_{BA}$	b=0.1 M_{AB}	M_{BA}	b=0.3 M_{AB}	M_{BA}	b=0.5 M_{AB}	M_{BA}	b=0.7 M_{AB}	M_{BA}	b=0.9 M_{AB}	M_{BA}	Haunch load both haunches F.E.M. coef. $\times wL^2$ $M_{AB} = M_{BA}$
	0.4	0.583	5.49	0.0921	0.0905	0.0053	0.1727	0.0606	0.1396	0.1396	0.0606	0.1727	0.0053	0.0905	0.0049
	0.6	0.603	5.93	0.0940	0.0932	0.0040	0.1796	0.0589	0.1428	0.1428	0.0589	0.1796	0.0040	0.0932	0.0049
0.1	1.0	0.624	6.45	0.0961	0.0962	0.0023	0.1873	0.0566	0.1462	0.1462	0.0566	0.1873	0.0023	0.0962	0.0050
	1.5	0.636	6.75	0.0972	0.0980	0.0013	0.1918	0.0551	0.1480	0.1480	0.0551	0.1918	0.0013	0.0980	0.0050
	2.0	0.641	6.90	0.0976	0.0988	0.0008	0.1939	0.0543	0.1489	0.1489	0.0543	0.1939	0.0008	0.0988	0.0050
	0.4	0.634	7.32	0.0970	0.0874	0.0079	0.1852	0.0623	0.1506	0.1506	0.0623	0.1852	0.0079	0.0874	0.0187
	0.6	0.674	8.80	0.1007	0.0899	0.0066	0.1993	0.0584	0.1575	0.1575	0.0584	0.1993	0.0066	0.0899	0.0191
0.2	1.0	0.723	11.09	0.1049	0.0935	0.0046	0.2193	0.0499	0.1654	0.1654	0.0499	0.2193	0.0046	0.0935	0.0195
	1.5	0.752	12.87	0.1073	0.0961	0.0029	0.2338	0.0420	0.1699	0.1699	0.0420	0.2338	0.0029	0.0961	0.0197
	2.0	0.765	13.87	0.1084	0.0976	0.0018	0.2410	0.0372	0.1720	0.1720	0.0372	0.2410	0.0018	0.0976	0.0198
	0.4	0.642	9.02	0.0977	0.0845	0.0097	0.1763	0.0707	0.1558	0.1558	0.0707	0.1763	0.0097	0.0845	0.0397
	0.6	0.697	12.09	0.1027	0.0861	0.0095	0.1898	0.0700	0.1665	0.1665	0.0700	0.1898	0.0095	0.0861	0.0410
0.3	1.0	0.775	18.68	0.1091	0.0890	0.0084	0.2136	0.0627	0.1803	0.1803	0.0627	0.2136	0.0084	0.0890	0.0426
	1.5	0.828	26.49	0.1132	0.0920	0.0065	0.2376	0.0492	0.1891	0.1891	0.0492	0.2376	0.0065	0.0920	0.0437
	2.0	0.855	32.77	0.1153	0.0943	0.0048	0.2555	0.0366	0.1934	0.1934	0.0366	0.2555	0.0048	0.0943	0.0442
	0.4	0.599	10.15	0.0937	0.0825	0.0101	0.1601	0.0732	0.1509	0.1509	0.0732	0.1601	0.0101	0.0825	0.0642
	0.6	0.652	14.52	0.0966	0.0833	0.0106	0.1668	0.0776	0.1632	0.1632	0.0776	0.1668	0.0106	0.0833	0.0668
0.4	1.0	0.744	26.06	0.1067	0.0847	0.0112	0.1790	0.0835	0.1833	0.1833	0.0835	0.1790	0.0112	0.0847	0.0711
	1.5	0.827	45.95	0.1131	0.0862	0.0113	0.1919	0.0852	0.1995	0.1995	0.0852	0.1919	0.0113	0.0862	0.0746
	2.0	0.878	71.41	0.1169	0.0876	0.0108	0.2033	0.0822	0.2089	0.2089	0.0822	0.2033	0.0108	0.0876	0.0766
0.5	0.0	0.500	4.00	0.0833	0.0810	0.0090	0.1470	0.0630	0.1250	0.1250	0.0630	0.1470	0.0090	0.0810	0.0833

Table 1.21: Prismatic Member with Equal Infinitely Stiff End Regions

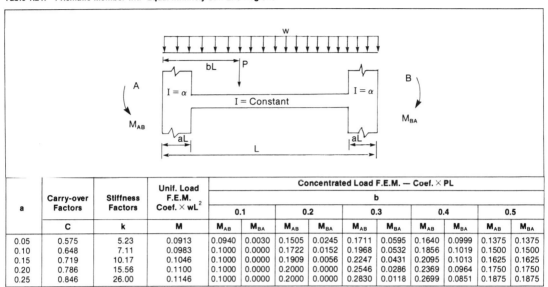

a	Carry-over Factors	Stiffness Factors	Unif. Load F.E.M. Coef. $\times$ wL^2	Concentrated Load F.E.M. — Coef. $\times$ PL									
				b									
				0.1		0.2		0.3		0.4		0.5	
	C	k	M	M_{AB}	M_{BA}	M_{AB}	M_{BA}	M_{AB}	M_{BA}	M_{AB}	M_{BA}	M_{AB}	M_{BA}
0.05	0.575	5.23	0.0913	0.0940	0.0030	0.1505	0.0245	0.1711	0.0595	0.1640	0.0999	0.1375	0.1375
0.10	0.648	7.11	0.0983	0.1000	0.0000	0.1722	0.0152	0.1968	0.0532	0.1856	0.1019	0.1500	0.1500
0.15	0.719	10.17	0.1046	0.1000	0.0000	0.1909	0.0056	0.2247	0.0431	0.2095	0.1013	0.1625	0.1625
0.20	0.786	15.56	0.1100	0.1000	0.0000	0.2000	0.0000	0.2546	0.0286	0.2369	0.0964	0.1750	0.1750
0.25	0.846	26.00	0.1146	0.1000	0.0000	0.2000	0.0000	0.2830	0.0118	0.2699	0.0851	0.1875	0.1875

Table 1.22: Prismatic Member with Infinitely Stiff Region at One End

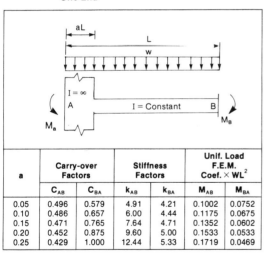

| a | Carry-over Factors | | Stiffness Factors | | Unif. Load F.E.M. Coef. $\times$ WL^2 | |
	C_{AB}	C_{BA}	k_{AB}	k_{BA}	M_{AB}	M_{BA}
0.05	0.496	0.579	4.91	4.21	0.1002	0.0752
0.10	0.486	0.657	6.00	4.44	0.1175	0.0675
0.15	0.471	0.765	7.64	4.71	0.1352	0.0602
0.20	0.452	0.875	9.60	5.00	0.1533	0.0533
0.25	0.429	1.000	12.44	5.33	0.1719	0.0469

Table 1.23: Prismatic Member with Unequal Infinitely Stiff End Regions

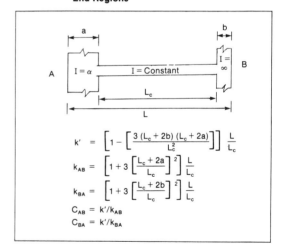

$$k' = \left[1 - \left[\frac{3\,(L_c + 2b)\,(L_c + 2a)}{L_c^2}\right]\right]\frac{L}{L_c}$$

$$k_{AB} = \left[1 + 3\left[\frac{L_c + 2a}{L_c}\right]^2\right]\frac{L}{L_c}$$

$$k_{BA} = \left[1 + 3\left[\frac{L_c + 2b}{L_c}\right]^2\right]\frac{L}{L_c}$$

$$C_{AB} = k'/k_{AB}$$

$$C_{BA} = k'/k_{BA}$$

Table 1.24: Sectional Properties

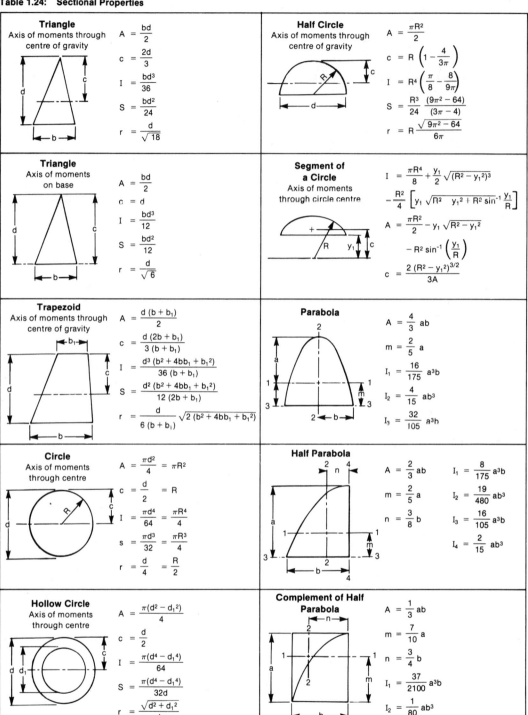

Triangle
Axis of moments through centre of gravity

$A = \dfrac{bd}{2}$

$c = \dfrac{2d}{3}$

$I = \dfrac{bd^3}{36}$

$S = \dfrac{bd^2}{24}$

$r = \dfrac{d}{\sqrt{18}}$

Half Circle
Axis of moments through centre of gravity

$A = \dfrac{\pi R^2}{2}$

$c = R\left(1 - \dfrac{4}{3\pi}\right)$

$I = R^4\left(\dfrac{\pi}{8} - \dfrac{8}{9\pi}\right)$

$S = \dfrac{R^3}{24}\dfrac{(9\pi^2 - 64)}{(3\pi - 4)}$

$r = R\dfrac{\sqrt{9\pi^2 - 64}}{6\pi}$

Triangle
Axis of moments on base

$A = \dfrac{bd}{2}$

$c = d$

$I = \dfrac{bd^3}{12}$

$S = \dfrac{bd^2}{12}$

$r = \dfrac{d}{\sqrt{6}}$

Segment of a Circle
Axis of moments through circle centre

$I = \dfrac{\pi R^4}{8} + \dfrac{y_1}{2}\sqrt{(R^2 - y_1^2)^3}$
$\qquad - \dfrac{R^2}{4}\left[y_1\sqrt{R^2 - y_1^2} + R^2 \sin^{-1}\dfrac{y_1}{R}\right]$

$A = \dfrac{\pi R^2}{2} - y_1\sqrt{R^2 - y_1^2}$
$\qquad - R^2 \sin^{-1}\left(\dfrac{y_1}{R}\right)$

$c = \dfrac{2\,(R^2 - y_1^2)^{3/2}}{3A}$

Trapezoid
Axis of moments through centre of gravity

$A = \dfrac{d\,(b + b_1)}{2}$

$c = \dfrac{d\,(2b + b_1)}{3\,(b + b_1)}$

$I = \dfrac{d^3\,(b^2 + 4bb_1 + b_1^2)}{36\,(b + b_1)}$

$S = \dfrac{d^2\,(b^2 + 4bb_1 + b_1^2)}{12\,(2b + b_1)}$

$r = \dfrac{d}{6\,(b + b_1)}\sqrt{2\,(b^2 + 4bb_1 + b_1^2)}$

Parabola

$A = \dfrac{4}{3}\,ab$

$m = \dfrac{2}{5}\,a$

$I_1 = \dfrac{16}{175}\,a^3b$

$I_2 = \dfrac{4}{15}\,ab^3$

$I_3 = \dfrac{32}{105}\,a^3b$

Circle
Axis of moments through centre

$A = \dfrac{\pi d^2}{4} = \pi R^2$

$c = \dfrac{d}{2} = R$

$I = \dfrac{\pi d^4}{64} = \dfrac{\pi R^4}{4}$

$s = \dfrac{\pi d^3}{32} = \dfrac{\pi R^3}{4}$

$r = \dfrac{d}{4} = \dfrac{R}{2}$

Half Parabola

$A = \dfrac{2}{3}\,ab$ $I_1 = \dfrac{8}{175}\,a^3b$

$m = \dfrac{2}{5}\,a$ $I_2 = \dfrac{19}{480}\,ab^3$

$n = \dfrac{3}{8}\,b$ $I_3 = \dfrac{16}{105}\,a^3b$

$\qquad\qquad\quad I_4 = \dfrac{2}{15}\,ab^3$

Hollow Circle
Axis of moments through centre

$A = \dfrac{\pi(d^2 - d_1^2)}{4}$

$c = \dfrac{d}{2}$

$I = \dfrac{\pi(d^4 - d_1^4)}{64}$

$S = \dfrac{\pi(d^4 - d_1^4)}{32d}$

$r = \dfrac{\sqrt{d^2 + d_1^2}}{4}$

Complement of Half Parabola

$A = \dfrac{1}{3}\,ab$

$m = \dfrac{7}{10}\,a$

$n = \dfrac{3}{4}\,b$

$I_1 = \dfrac{37}{2100}\,a^3b$

$I_2 = \dfrac{1}{80}\,ab^3$

Reproduced from the 'Metric Design Manual' with the permission of CPCI.

Square Axis of moments through centre	$A = d^2$ $c = \dfrac{d}{2}$ $I = \dfrac{d^4}{12}$ $S = \dfrac{d^3}{6}$ $r = \dfrac{d}{\sqrt{12}} = 0.288675\,d$	**Rectangle** Axis of moments on diagonal 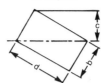	$A = bd$ $c = \dfrac{bd}{\sqrt{b^2 + d^2}}$ $I = \dfrac{b^3 d^3}{6\,(b^2 + d^2)}$ $S = \dfrac{b^2 d^2}{6\sqrt{b^2 + d^2}}$ $r = \dfrac{bd}{\sqrt{6\,(b^2 + d^2)}}$
Square Axis of moments on base	$A = d^2$ $c = d$ $I = \dfrac{d^4}{3}$ $S = \dfrac{d^3}{3}$ $r = \dfrac{d}{\sqrt{3}} = 0.577350\,d$	**Rectangle** Axis of moments any line through centre of gravity 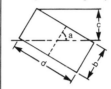	$A = bd$ $c = \dfrac{b \sin a + d \cos a}{2}$ $I = \dfrac{bd\,(b^2 \sin^2 a + d^2 \cos^2 a)}{12}$ $S = \dfrac{bd\,(b^2 \sin^2 a + d^2 \cos^2 a)}{6\,(b \sin a + d \cos a)}$ $r = \sqrt{\dfrac{b^2 \sin^2 a + d^2 \cos^2 a}{12}}$
Square Axis of moments on diagonal	$A = d^2$ $c = \dfrac{d}{\sqrt{2}} = 0.707107\,d$ $I = \dfrac{d^4}{12}$ $S = \dfrac{d^3}{6\sqrt{2}} = 0.117851\,d^3$ $r = \dfrac{d}{\sqrt{12}} = 0.288675\,d$	**Hollow Rectangle** Axis of moments through centre	$A = bd - b_1 d_1$ $c = \dfrac{d}{2}$ $I = \dfrac{bd^3 - b_1 d_1^3}{12}$ $S = \dfrac{bd^3 - b_1 d_1^3}{6d}$ $r = \sqrt{\dfrac{bd^3 - b_1 d_1^3}{12\,A}}$
Rectangle Axis of moments through centre	$A = bd$ $c = \dfrac{d}{2}$ $I = \dfrac{bd^3}{12}$ $S = \dfrac{bd^2}{6}$ $r = \dfrac{d}{\sqrt{12}} = 0.288675\,d$	**Equal Rectangles** Axis of moments through centre of gravity	$A = b\,(d - d_1)$ $c = \dfrac{d}{2}$ $I = \dfrac{b\,(d^3 - d_1^3)}{12}$ $S = \dfrac{b\,(d^3 - d_1^3)}{6d}$ $r = \sqrt{\dfrac{d^3 - d_1^3}{12\,(d - d_1)}}$
Rectangle Axis of moments on base	$A = bd$ $c = d$ $I = \dfrac{bd^3}{3}$ $S = \dfrac{bd^2}{3}$ $r = \dfrac{d}{\sqrt{3}} = 0.577350\,d$	**Unequal Rectangles** Axis of moments through centre of gravity	$A = bt + b_1 t_1$ $c = \dfrac{\frac{1}{2} bt^2 + b_1 t_1\,(d - \frac{1}{2} t_1)}{A}$ $I = \dfrac{bt^3}{12} + bty^2 + \dfrac{b_1 t_1^3}{12}$ $\quad + b_1 t_1 y_1^2$ $S = \dfrac{1}{c} \quad S_1 = \dfrac{1}{c_1}$ $r = \sqrt{\dfrac{1}{A}}$

Parabolic Fillet in Right Angle

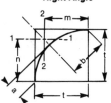

$$a = \frac{t}{2\sqrt{2}}$$

$$b = \frac{t}{\sqrt{2}}$$

$$A = \frac{1}{6}t^2$$

$$m = n = \frac{4}{5}t$$

$$I_1 = I_2 = \frac{11}{2100}t^4$$

*Half Ellipse

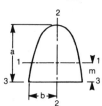

$$A = \frac{1}{2}\pi ab$$

$$m = \frac{4a}{3\pi}$$

$$I_1 = a^3b\left(\frac{\pi}{8} - \frac{8}{9\pi}\right)$$

$$I_2 = \frac{1}{8}\pi ab^3$$

$$I_3 = \frac{1}{8}\pi a^3b$$

*Quarter Ellipse

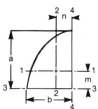

$$A = \frac{1}{4}\pi ab$$

$$m = \frac{4a}{3\pi}$$

$$n = \frac{4b}{3\pi}$$

$$I_1 = a^3b\left(\frac{\pi}{16} - \frac{4}{9\pi}\right)$$

$$I_2 = ab^3\left(\frac{\pi}{16} - \frac{4}{9\pi}\right)$$

$$I_3 = \frac{1}{16}\pi a^3b$$

$$I_4 = \frac{1}{16}\pi ab^3$$

*To obtain properties of half circles, quarter circle and circular complement, substitute a = b = R.

*Elliptic Complement

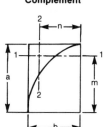

$$A = ab\left(1 - \frac{\pi}{4}\right)$$

$$m = \frac{a}{6\left(1 - \frac{\pi}{4}\right)}$$

$$n = \frac{b}{6\left(1 - \frac{\pi}{4}\right)}$$

$$I_1 = a^3b\left[\frac{1}{3} - \frac{\pi}{16} - \frac{1}{36\left(1 - \frac{\pi}{4}\right)}\right]$$

$$I_2 = ab^3\left[\frac{1}{3} - \frac{\pi}{16} - \frac{1}{36\left(1 - \frac{\pi}{4}\right)}\right]$$

Regular Polygon
Axis of moments through centre

$$n = \text{Number of sides}$$

$$\phi = \frac{180°}{n}$$

$$a = 2\sqrt{R^2 - R_1^2}$$

$$R = \frac{a}{2\sin\phi}$$

$$R_1 = \frac{a}{2\tan\phi}$$

$$A = \frac{1}{4}na^2\cot\phi = \frac{1}{2}nR^2\sin 2\phi = nR_1^2\tan\phi$$

$$I_1 = I_2 = \frac{A(6R^2 - a^2)}{24} = \frac{A(12R_1^2 + a^2)}{48}$$

$$r_1 = r_2 = \sqrt{\frac{6R^2 - a^2}{24}} = \sqrt{\frac{12R_1 + a^2}{48}}$$

Beams and Channels
Transverse force oblique through centre of gravity

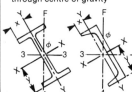

$$I_3 = I_x\sin^2\phi + I_y\cos^2\phi$$

$$I_4 = I_x\cos^2\phi + I_y\sin^2\phi$$

$$f_b = M\left[\frac{y}{I_x}\sin\phi + \frac{x}{I_y}\cos\phi\right]$$

where M is bending moment due to force F.

Angle
Axis of moments through centre of gravity

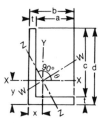

Z-Z is axis of minimum I

$$\tan 2\theta = \frac{2K}{I_y - I_x}$$

$$A = t(b + c) \quad x = \frac{b^2 + ct}{2(b + c)} \quad y = \frac{d^2 + at}{2(b + c)}$$

K = Product of Inertia about X-X & Y-Y

$$= \pm\frac{abcdt}{4(b + c)}$$

$$I_x = \frac{1}{3}\left[t(d - y)^3 + by^3 - a(y - t)^3\right]$$

$$I_y = \frac{1}{3}\left[t(b - x)^3 + dx^3 - c(x - t)^3\right]$$

$$I_z = I_x\sin^2\theta + I_y\cos^2\theta + K\sin 2\theta$$

$$I_w = I_x\cos^2\theta + I_y\sin^2\theta - K\sin 2\theta$$

K is negative when heel of angle, with respect to c.g., is in 1st or 3rd quadrant, positive when in 2nd or 4th quadrant.

Design for Flexure

By Murat Saatcioglu

Chapter 2
Design for Flexure

2.1 INTRODUCTION

The majority of structural members used in practice are subjected to flexural stresses caused by bending moments. Flexural stresses often occur in combination with other types of stresses caused by axial force, shear, and torsion. Typical examples of flexure dominant members include beams and slabs, although the concepts and design aids presented in this chapter also apply to other members that are subjected to flexure, including structural walls, retaining walls and footings.

Flexural design is performed in two stages. The first stage involves sectional design, including sections that are subjected to highest negative and positive bending moments. The second stage involves member design, including determination of bar lengths. Length of reinforcement and locations of cut-off points are affected by provisions specified for development length and splice length requirements, as discussed in Chapter 3.

Flexural design of a reinforced concrete section should conform to the Limit States Design provisions of CSA A23.3-94. Accordingly, the ultimate limit state expressed below should be satisfied to meet the required strength.

Moment Resistance ≥ Factored Moment

$$M_r \geq M_f$$

Factored moments are obtained by structural analysis under factored loads. Load factors and load combinations are discussed in Chapter 1.

2.2 MOMENT RESISTANCE (M_r)

Moment resistance M_r is obtained by computing the flexural strength of a section, with material resistance factors ϕ_c and ϕ_s applied to concrete cylinder strength f'_c and steel yield strength f_y respectively. The flexural strength is computed from internal forces that can be established by plane section analysis. Accordingly, plane sections of a reinforced concrete member before bending are assumed to remain plane after bending. Furthermore, perfect bond is assumed between the concrete and reinforcing steel. These assumptions lead to a linear distribution of strains across the section depth, with strains in steel and concrete proportional to their distances from the neutral axis. The corresponding stress distribution is obtained from material stress-strain relationships. This leads to a parabolic stress distribution for concrete in

compression. Concrete in tension is ignored without affecting the flexural resistance significantly. Internal forces in concrete and steel are then computed from the stress distribution, with due considerations given to the area of concrete and reinforcement. An iterative approach may have to be employed until the neutral axis location that satisfies force equilibrium is established. This procedure is referred to as strain compatibility analysis. The moment resistance is computed for a specific strain distribution that corresponds to a given load stage. Complete response of a section can be established if the analysis is carried out for different load stages and corresponding strain conditions. This is usually done in the form of a moment-curvature relationship (M – φ), as illustrated in Fig. 2.1.

While the plane section analysis is a powerful tool for establishing the characteristics of sectional response, only one point on the M – φ relationship, i.e. the maximum moment resistance, is of interest for design purposes. CSA A23.3-94 defines the strain condition corresponding to the maximum moment resistance in Clause 10.1.3. This condition is illustrated in Fig. 2.2. Accordingly, the maximum strain at the extreme compression fibre is assumed to be 0.0035 when the factored moment resistance is attained. CSA A23.3-94 also defines an equivalent rectangular stress block to represent the parabolic distribution of compression in concrete, simplifying the design process significantly. The rectangular stress block, with the parameters given in the standard, is applicable to the limiting strain condition, which is used to compute the maximum resistance of a section. The following expressions define the parameters of the rectangular stress distribution, which spreads over a depth of $a = \beta_1 c$ from the extreme compression fibre, with a constant intensity of $\alpha_1 \phi_c f'_c$.

$$\alpha_1 = 0.85 - 0.0015 f'_c \geq 0.67 \qquad (2.1)$$

$$\beta_1 = 0.97 - 0.0025 f'_c \geq 0.67 \qquad (2.2)$$

Reinforced concrete sections in flexure exhibit different modes of failure depending on the percentage of steel in the section. Sections with small percentage of steel develop yielding of reinforcement in tension, prior to crushing of concrete in compression. These sections are referred to as "under-reinforced" sections. Members designed to have under-reinforced sections deflect excessively prior to concrete crushing, exhibiting ductile

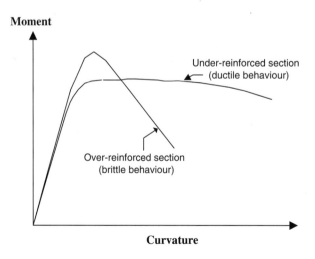

Fig. 2.1 Moment Curvature Relationship

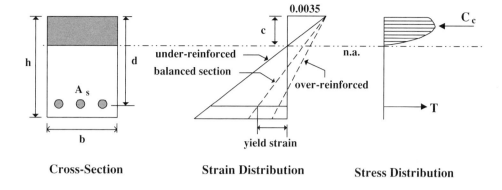

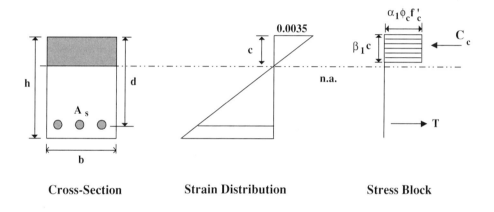

Fig. 2.2 Flexural Analysis of Reinforced Concrete Sections

behaviour with prior warning of an imminent failure. Sections with excessive tension steel may not develop yielding of reinforcement prior to concrete crushing. These members deflect very little until failure, and the failure is usually brittle, explosive and unexpected. These sections are referred to as "over-reinforced" sections.

The amount of tension steel that causes simultaneous crushing of concrete and yielding of tension steel is referred to as "balanced reinforcement," and the section is referred to as "balanced section." Fig. 2.2 shows the strain condition for each type of behaviour. Ductile behaviour of an under-reinforced section, and brittle behaviour of an over-reinforced section are illustrated in Fig. 2.1. It is preferable to design under-reinforced sections. Tension reinforcement, approximately equal to 50% of balanced reinforcement is usually believed to be economically optimum steel content, also producing ductile behaviour.

2.2.1 Limit of c/d for Yielding of Tension Reinforcement

Computation of factored moment resistance M_r may require strain compatibility analysis as described above.

If the section is under-reinforced, however, the tension steel yields prior to the attainment of the strain condition defined in A23.3 for computation of factored moment resistance. Hence, the internal tensile force in reinforcement becomes known, and the iterative procedure that is usually required for strain compatibility analysis is not needed. This simplifies the computation of M_r. The limiting strain condition for yielding of tension reinforcement is the same as the strain condition for balanced section. This limiting condition is expressed in Clause 10.5.2 of CSA A23.3-94 in terms of c/d ratio for balanced section. Accordingly, if the c/d ratio defined below is exceeded, the stress in tension reinforcement must be computed based on strain compatibility.

$$\left(\frac{c}{d}\right)_{max} = \frac{0.0035}{0.0035 + \varepsilon_y} = \frac{700}{700 + f_y} \quad (2.3)$$

2.2.2 Minimum Reinforcement

Reinforcement in concrete is not effective until after cracking. The flexural capacity of an uncracked concrete is essentially provided by concrete alone. Plain concrete members, on the other hand, fail rapidly as soon as the cracking moment M_{cr} is reached. Reinforced sections with very little reinforcement may behave similar to plain concrete sections, and may not be able to sustain M_{cr} upon cracking. Hence, a minimum amount of tension reinforcement may be necessary to provide adequate post-cracking strength as indicated in Eq. 2.4. This requirement may be waived when the factored moment of resistance M_r is at least one-third greater than the factored moment M_f.

$$M_r \geq 1.2 M_{cr} \tag{2.4}$$

where;

$$M_{cr} = 0.6 \lambda \sqrt{f_c'} \frac{I}{c_t} \tag{2.5}$$

"I" is the moment of inertia of the section based on gross cross-sectional dimensions, and c_t is the distance between the section centroid and extreme tension fibre. In lieu of the computation of cracking moment, the following expression may be used [Clause 10.5.1.2] to ensure that the section has the minimum required area of tension reinforcement.

$$A_{smin} = \frac{0.2\sqrt{f_c'}}{f_y} b_t h \tag{2.6}$$

where, b_t is the width of the tension zone in the section.

The minimum reinforcement for slabs is intended to provide some control of cracking due to shrinkage and temperature. It also provides minimum reinforcement to tie the cracked concrete together. A minimum area of $0.002 A_g$, in each direction, is found to be adequate for this purpose [Clause 7.8].

2.2.3 Rectangular Sections with Tension Reinforcement

Factored moment resistance M_r for rectangular sections with tension reinforcement is computed from the internal force couple illustrated in Fig. 2.2. The depth of rectangular concrete stress block can easily be determined from equilibrium of internal forces, especially for under-reinforced sections where the tension force in steel is readily available. This helps define the internal lever arm and the moment resistance.

$$C_c = T \tag{2.7}$$

$$\alpha_1 \phi_c f_c' \, ab = A_s \phi_s f_y \tag{2.8}$$

$$a = \frac{\phi_s A_s f_y}{\alpha_1 \phi_c f_c' \, b} \tag{2.9}$$

$$M_r = A_s \phi_s f_y \left(d - \frac{a}{2} \right) \tag{2.10}$$

Substituting "a" from Eq. 2.9, and expressing the area of steel in terms of reinforcement ratio $\rho = A_s / bd$;

$$M_r = bd^2 \left[1 - \frac{\phi_s \rho f_y}{2\alpha_1 f_c' \, \phi_c} \right] \rho \phi_s f_y \tag{2.11}$$

$$M_r = K_r bd^2 \times 10^{-6} \ kN \cdot m \tag{2.12}$$

where, M_r is expressed in $kN \cdot m$, and b and d are expressed in mm. The resistance factor K_r, given in Eq. 2.13, is dependent on material properties and related coefficients, and reinforcement ratio ρ.

$$K_r = \left[1 - \frac{\phi_s \rho f_y}{2\alpha_1 f_c' \, \phi_c} \right] \rho \phi_s f_y \ MPa \tag{2.13}$$

The required ρ can be computed for different material properties and values of K_r, and can be tabulated as a design aid. Table 2.1 was generated in this manner, and it can be used to compute the factored resistance of a rectangular section with tension reinforcement. It can also be used for design. In this case the factored resistance M_r should at least be equal to factored moment, M_f. Therefore, K_r is solved from Eq. 2.12 after substituting M_f in place of M_r. Table 2.1 can then be entered with K_r to read the required reinforcement ratio ρ.

2.2.4 Rectangular Sections with Compression Reinforcement

Flexural members are usually designed for tension reinforcement. Any requirement for an increase in capacity can be accommodated by an increase in tension reinforcement and/or section size. However, sometimes the cross-sectional dimensions may be limited by architectural and/or other functional requirements. The additional moment resistance required in such sections may be provided by placing extra reinforcement in compression and tension regions of the beam. The extra steel provided results in an internal force couple, increasing the flexural capacity. Fig. 2.3 illustrates the components of moment resistance provided in a rectangular section with compression reinforcement.

The compression reinforcement becomes effective in sections where they are needed. A lightly reinforced

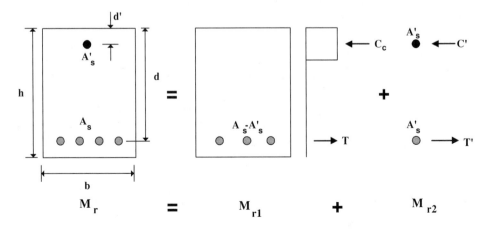

Fig. 2.3 Rectangular Sections with Compression Reinforcement

section requires little concrete in the compression zone to maintain equilibrium. The neutral axis of such a section approaches the extreme compression fibre. Hence, any reinforcement in the compression zone becomes ineffective. In most under-reinforced sections the extension of positive tension reinforcement into the negative compression zone usually does not contribute significantly to the negative moment resistance. Designers usually ignore the presence of bar extension into the compression zone or detailing reinforcement that may be present in the compression zone. A heavily reinforced section, on the other hand, requires a larger compression zone to maintain equilibrium, with neutral axis moving away from the extreme compression fibre. The reinforcement placed near the extreme compression fibre becomes fully effective when the section attains its capacity at 0.0035 fibre strain. When the required moment resistance can not be provided with heavy use of tension reinforcement, the designer may make use of the extension of tension reinforcement from nearby sections into the compression zone, provided that the development and lap length requirements of CSA A23.3-94 are met.

It is clear from the foregoing discussion that compression reinforcement is most effective when the neutral axis approaches the section centroid. The compression reinforcement placed in such a section usually yields when the section reaches its capacity (ε_c = 0.0035). If the compression reinforcement does not yield, it is usually very close to yielding. Hence, it is reasonable to assume, for design purposes, that the compression steel does yield at the limiting strain condition. This simplifies the design process considerably.

The moment resistance of a rectangular section with compression reinforcement can be obtained from the following expressions.

$$M_r = M_{r1} + M_{r2} \tag{2.14}$$

$$M_{r1} = K_r \, bd^2 \tag{2.15}$$

$$M_{r2} = A_s' \phi_S f_y (d - d') \tag{2.16}$$

$$M_{r2} = K_r' bd^2 \tag{2.17}$$

where;

$$K_r' = \rho' \phi_S f_y \left(1 - \frac{d'}{d}\right) \tag{2.18}$$

$$\rho' = \frac{A_s'}{bd} \tag{2.19}$$

Substituting Eqs. 2.15 and 2.17 into 2.14 yields;

$$M_r = (K_r + K_r') \, bd^2 \times 10^{-6} \tag{2.20}$$

where M_r is expressed in kN · m, K_r and K_r' are expressed in MPa, and b and d are expressed in mm. K_r is given in

Eq. 2.13, and is based on the reinforcement ratio $\rho = (A_s - A_s')/bd$. It can also be obtained from Table 2.1. The resistance factor K_r' can be obtained from Table 2.2 in terms of the compression reinforcement ratio ρ', and d'/d ratio.

2.2.5 T-Sections

Most concrete structures are built monolithically with slabs and beams cast together. Fig. 2.4 illustrates a typical reinforced concrete slab system where the floor slab and the supporting beams together provide flexural resistance to applied loading. The resulting structural system includes T-beams, each consisting of a rectangular beam section forming the web, and the slab near the web forming the flange. The slab width near the web, considered to be effective in contributing to load resistance, is referred to as the "effective flange width". The effective flange width, b_f, is defined in CSA A23.3-94 as illustrated in Table 2.4, and should be used in computing the sectional resistance.

Although the T-beam example given above is a direct consequence of monolithic construction, T shaped concrete cross-sections are sometimes produced intentionally because of their superior performance in positive bending. These sections provide increased area of compression concrete in the flange, with reduced dead load associated with reduced area of tension concrete in the web. Single T's and double T's are commonly used examples of beams in precast industry.

The flange width, in most T-sections is significantly wider than the web width. Therefore, the amount of tension reinforcement placed in the web can easily be equilibrated by part of the flange concrete compressed near the extreme compression fibre. This implies that the neutral axis falls within the flange. In fact, in most practical applications it is difficult to create a situation where the neutral axis falls below the flange, since this may require excessive tension force and associated reinforcement that could not be placed in the web without creating construction problems. Therefore, most T-sections behave as rectangular sections with flange width equal to the equivalent width of a rectangular section. T-sections in negative bending also behave as rectangular beams with web width equal to the equivalent width of a rectangular section, while the flange concrete is subjected to tension. However, sections with relatively narrow and thin flanges, subjected to positive bending, may require part of the web concrete below the flange to be compressed to equilibrate heavy tension steel that may be present in the web. In such cases the neutral axis lies within the web, forming concrete compression zone that has a T-shape. These sections are said to behave as T-sections.

The limiting condition for T-section behaviour occurs when the flange concrete is fully compressed. This condition can either be expressed in terms of the limiting area of tension reinforcement, or the limiting thickness of

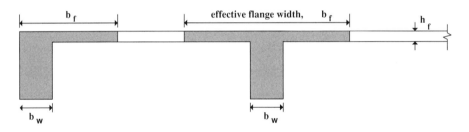

Fig. 2.4 T and L Beams

flange. The following inequalities define the conditions for T-section behaviour.

$$A_s \phi_s f_y > \alpha_1 \phi_c f'_c h_f b_f \qquad (2.21)$$

$$A_s > \frac{\alpha_1 \phi_c f'_c h_f b_f}{\phi_s f_y} \qquad (2.22)$$

$$h_f < \frac{A_s \phi_s f_y}{\alpha_1 \phi_c f'_c b_f} \qquad (2.23)$$

Fig. 2.5 illustrates the T-beam behaviour. The moment resistance of this section is provided by two internal force couples; one formed by the compression concrete in the overhangs and the corresponding tension steel (M_{rf}, A_{sf}), and the other by the compression in web concrete and the corresponding tension steel (M_{rw}, A_{sw}). Each moment component represents moment resistance of a rectangular section with tension reinforcement. Hence, the design aids prepared for rectangular sections can be used to find moment resistance of a section exhibiting T-beam behaviour. Consequently, Table 2.1 can be used with $\rho_f = A_{sf}/(b_f - b_w)d$ to determine M_{rf}, and with $\rho_w = A_{sw}/b_w d$ to find M_{rw}.

$$M_r = M_{rf} + M_{rw} \qquad (2.24)$$

$$M_{rf} = K_{rf}(b_f - b_w)d^2 \qquad (2.25)$$

with $\rho_f = \dfrac{A_{sf}}{(b_f - b_w)\, d}$

$$M_{rw} = K_{rw} b_w d^2 \qquad (2.26)$$

with $\rho_w = \dfrac{A_{sw}}{b_w d}$

where;

$$A_{sf} = \frac{\alpha_1 \phi_c f'_c (b_f - b_w) h_f}{\phi_s f_y} \qquad (2.27)$$

$$\rho_f = \frac{\alpha_1 \phi_c f'_c h_f}{\phi_s f_y d} \qquad (2.28)$$

$$A_{sw} = A_s - A_{sf} \qquad (2.29)$$

$$\rho_w = \frac{A_{sw}}{b_w d} \qquad (2.30)$$

Table 2.3 contains values of ρ_f for different material strengths and h_f/d ratios.

2.2.6 Joist Construction

Concrete floor joist is another example of a flexural member with a "T" cross-section. Regularly spaced joists, in either one or two directions, result in increased redundancy in the structural system, allowing redistribution of loads. Therefore, a monolithically cast joist system is considered to have adequate ductility against a potential shear failure, and may be exempt from the minimum shear reinforcement required in Clause 11.2.8.1, provided that the geometric limitations defined in Table 2.5, are satisfied [Clause 10.4.1].

2.3 PLACEMENT OF REINFORCEMENT

Flexural reinforcement is placed with due considerations given to the spacing of reinforcement and crack control. The crack control is achieved by using well distributed reinforcement. This may result in reduced spacing between the bars, which may create concrete placement problems. It is usually preferable to use sufficient number of small size bars, as opposed to fewer bars of larger size, while also respecting the spacing requirements. These requirements are discussed in the following sections.

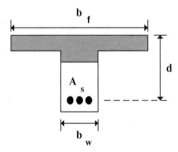

T-Section Behaviour

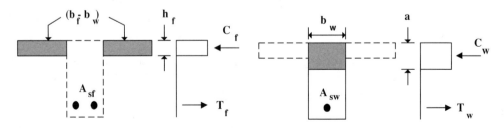

Contribution of Overhangs   **Web Contribution**

Fig. 2.5 T-Section Behaviour

2.3.1 Spacing of Longitudinal Reinforcement

Longitudinal reinforcement should be placed such that the spacing between the bars allow proper placement of concrete. The minimum spacing requirement for beam reinforcement is shown in Table 2.6. The maximum bar spacing in walls and one-way slabs, other than the joist construction illustrated in Table 2.5, is 3 times the member thickness or 500 mm, whichever is smaller [Clause 7.4.1.2]. The maximum spacing for minimum slab reinforcement is the smaller of either 5 times the slab thickness, or 500 mm [Clause 7.8.3].

2.3.2 Crack Control

Beams reinforced with few large size bars may experience wide cracking between the bars, even if the required area of tension reinforcement is provided and the sectional capacity is achieved. Crack widths in these members may exceed what is usually regarded as acceptable limits of cracking for various exposure conditions. The crack width limitation is specified in CSA A23.3-94 in terms of the quantity "z" given below:

$$z = f_s(d_c A)^{1/3} \qquad (2.31)$$

where; $z \leq 30000$ N/mm for interior exposure and 25000 N/mm for exterior exposure. The crack control is checked under service loads. Hence, the tensile stress in reinforcement, f_s, can be determined from the strain compatibility analysis presented earlier in Sec. 2.2. Because the strain condition is different than that at maximum factored resistance, the rectangular stress block defined in Sec. 2.2 can not be utilized. This may require the use of a parabolic stress distribution for concrete, and an iterative strain compatibility analysis to establish the stress in reinforcement. Alternatively, CSA A23.3-94 permits the use 60% of the yield strength f_y as an estimate of stress in steel under service loads. The other terms used in Eq. 2.31 are defined in Table 2.7.

2.3.3 Skin Reinforcement

In deep flexural members, the crack control provided by the above procedure may not be sufficient to control cracking near the mid-depth of the section, between the neutral axis and the tension concrete controlled by main flexural reinforcement. For members with a depth h > 750 mm, skin reinforcement with a total area of A_{sk} should be provided along the sides.

$$A_{sk} = \rho_{sk} A_{cs} \qquad (2.32)$$

where; $\rho_{sk} = 0.008$ for interior exposure and 0.010 for exterior exposure. The area of concrete, A_{cs}, to be controlled by skin reinforcement is defined in Table 2.8. The maximum spacing of skin reinforcement is limited to 200 mm, [Clause 10.6.2]. The contribution of skin reinforcement to flexural resistance may be included in design if the stress in steel is computed from a strain compatibility analysis.

2.3.4 Tension Reinforcement in T-Beam Flanges

The flexural resistance of T-shaped sections is discussed in Sec. 2.2.5. These sections behave as rectangular beams when subjected to negative bending. While the required reinforcement ratio may be computed using the web width "b_w", the placement of reinforcement should not be limited to the same width. Hence, CSA A23.3-94 calls for some distribution of tension reinforcement within the flange. Accordingly, part of the reinforcement is to be placed over a width of each overhang equal to 1/20 of the beam span, or the width defined in Table 2.9, which-

ever is smaller. The area of this reinforcement should not be less than 0.4% of the gross area of overhanging slab.

2.4 DESIGN EXAMPLES

Example 2.1 — Analysis of a Rectangular Beam with Tension Reinforcement

Compute moment resistance M_r for the rectangular section shown in the figure.

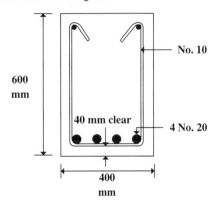

$f'_c = 30$ MPa; $f_y = 400$ MPa.

1. Calculate effective depth d:

    d = 600 − 40 − 11.3 − (19.5/2) = 539 mm

2. Calculate reinforcement ratio ρ :

    $\rho = A_s$ / bd = (4 × 300) / (400 × 539)
      = 0.0056 = 0.56%

3. Determine K_r corresponding to $\rho = 0.56\%$ from Table 2.1:

    $K_r = 1.78$ MPa

4. Calculate resisting moment M_r:

    $M_r = K_r bd^2 \times 10^{-6} = 1.78 \ (400) \ (539)^2 \times 10^{-6}$
      = 207 kN · m

Example 2.2 — Design of a Rectangular Beam with Tension Reinforcement

Design the rectangular beam shown in the figure for a factored moment of $M_f = 415$ kN · m. Use normal density concrete with $f'_c = 40$ MPa, $f_y = 400$ MPa, and maximum aggregate size of 25 mm. The beam is to be built in a non-corrosive environment, having interior exposure.

1. Estimate effective depth d, assuming No. 25 bars for flexural reinforcement and No. 10 stirrups for transverse reinforcement. Select a clear cover of 30 mm from Table 2.6 (for non-corrosive environment, interior exposure).

    d = 600 − 30 − 11.3 − (25.2/2) = 546 mm

2. Calculate resistance factor K_r : For design; $M_r \geq M_f = $ 415 kN · m

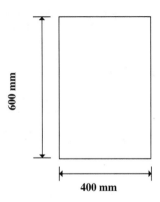

(a) Given Section

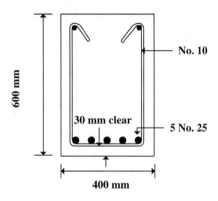

(b) Final Design

(Example 2.2)

$K_r = M_r \times 10^6 / bd^2 = 415 \times 10^6 / (400)(546)^2$
$= 3.48$ MPa

3. Determine reinforcement ratio ρ from Table 2.1 :
   $\rho = 1.14\%$

4. Determine required tension reinforcement :

   $A_s = \rho \, bd = 0.0114 \times 400 \times 546 = 2490$ mm^2
   No. of No. 25 bars required; $2490/500 = 4.98$
   Select 5 No. 25 bars

5. Check minimum steel requirement :
   $M_r \geq 1.2 \, M_{cr}$
   $M_r = 415$ kN $\cdot$ m for 5 No. 25 bars
   $M_{cr} = 0.6 \, \lambda \, \sqrt{f'_c} \, I/c_t$ (Eq. 2-5)
   $I = bh^3/12 = (400)(600)^3 / 12 = 7.2 \times 10^9$ mm^4
   $c_t = 600 / 2 = 300$ mm; $\lambda = 1.0$ (normal density concrete)
   $M_{cr} = 0.6 \, (1.0) \, \sqrt{40} \, (7.2 \times 10^9 \,) \, / \, (300) = 91 \times 10^6$ N.mm
   $M_r = 415$ kN $\cdot$ m $> 1.2 \, (91) = 109$ kN $\cdot$ m O.K.
   Note: Eq. 2-6 may be used in lieu of Eq. 2-5.
   $A_{smin} = 0.2 \, \sqrt{f'_c} \, b_t \, h \, / \, f_y$ (Eq. 2-6)
   $A_{smin} = 0.2 \, \sqrt{40} \, (400)(600)/(400) = 759$ mm^2
   $A_s = 5 \, (500) = 2500 > 759$ mm^2 O.K.

6. Check minimum bar spacing :
   $s = [400 - 2(30) - 2(11.3) - 5(25.2)] \, / \, 4 = 48$ mm

From Table 2.6; $s \geq 1.4 \, d_b = 1.4 \, (25.2) = 35$ mm O.K.
$s \geq 1.4 \, a_{max} = 1.4 \, (25) = 35$ mm O.K.
$s \geq 30$ mm O.K.

7. Check maximum bar spacing as governed by crack control :

   Compute quantity "z" from Eq. 2-31or Table 2.7:
   $z = f_s(d_c A)^{1/3}$
   Note: For calculation of A and d_c clear cover need not be taken greater than 50 mm.
   From Table 2.7; $y = h - d = 600 - 546 = 54$ mm; A = 2yb/5 = 2 (54) (400) / 5 = 8640 mm^2
   $f_s = 0.6 \, f_y = 0.6 \, (400) = 240$ MPa;
   $d_c = 600 - 546 = 54$ mm
   $z = 240 \, (54 \times 8640)^{1/3} = 18,614$ N/mm
   $z = 18,614$ N/mm $< 30,000$ N/mm (interior exposure) O.K.

8. Check if skin reinforcement is needed :
   $h \leq 750$ mm no skin reinforcement is needed.

9. Final design: Use 5 No. 25 bars as longitudinal tension reinforcement with No. 10 stirrups and 30 mm clear cover for the stirrup steel.

Example 2.3 — Analysis of a Rectangular Beam with Tension and Compression Reinforcement

Calculate the flexural resistance of the beam shown in the figure.

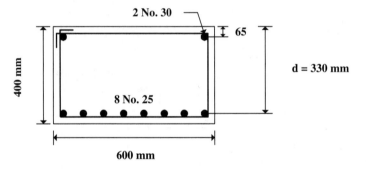

(Example 2.3)

$f'_c = 30$ MPa; $f_y = 400$ MPa.

1. Compute moment resistance provided by steel couple M'_r from Table 2.2 :

   Note : Total moment resistance = $M_r + M'_r$
   $\rho' = A'_s / bd = (2 \times 700) / (600 \times 330) = 0.0071$; $d'/d = 65 / 330 = 0.20$
   From Table 2.2; $M'_r = K'_r bd^2 \times 10^{-6}$ kN · m, and
   for $\rho' = 0.71$ %, $K'_r = 1.93$ MPa; $M'_r = 1.93 (600) (330)^2 \times 10^{-6} = 126$ kN · m

   Note: $M'_r = 126$ kN · m is found assuming that the compression steel is yielding.

2. Compute moment resistance provided by tension reinforcement ($A_s - A'_s$) from Table 2.1:

   $\rho = (A_s - A'_s) / bd = (8 \times 500 - 2 \times 700) / (600) (330) = 0.0131$
   From Table 2.1; $M_r = K_r bd^2 \times 10^{-6}$ kN · m, and
   for $\rho = 1.31$ %, $K_r = 3.78$ MPa; $M_r = 3.78 (600) (330)^2 \times 10^{-6} = 247$ kN · m

3. Total moment resistance of section:
   $M_r + M'_r = 247 + 126 = 373$ kN · m

Example 2.4 — Design of a Rectangular Beam with Tension and Compression Reinforcement

Design the rectangular beam section shown in the figure for a factored moment of $M_f = 675$ kN · m. The beam is to be built as part of a parking structure located in Ottawa, with a limited cross-sectional size due to functional requirements.

$f'_c = 30$ MPa; $f_y = 400$ MPa; maximum aggregate size = 25 mm.

1. Determine concrete cover for corrosive environment from Table 2.6 :

   Select 60 mm clear cover to stirrups.

2. Estimate effective depth d assuming No. 30 bars for longitudinal reinforcement and No. 10 stirrups.

   $d = 600 - 60 - 11.3 - (29.9/2) = 514$ mm

3. Determine required tension reinforcement from Table 2.1 :

   For design; $M_r \geq M_f = 675$ kN · m.
   For $M_r = 675$ kN · m; $K_r = M_r \times 10^6 / (bd^2) = 675 \times 10^6 / [(400)(514)^2] = 6.39$ MPa
   There is no ρ value given in Table 2.1 for $K_r = 6.39$ indicating that the section can not be designed unless compression reinforcement is used.

4. Determine required compression reinforcement from Table 2.2 :

   Provide maximum tension reinforcement given in Table 2.1.
   For $f'_c = 30$ MPa; select $\rho = 2.43$ %, and read corresponding $K_r = 5.9$ MPa
   Moment resistance provided by this reinforcement; $M_r = K_r bd^2 \times 10^{-6}$
   $M_r = 5.9 (400)(514)^2 \times 10^{-6} = 624$ kN · m
   Remaining moment resistance to be provided by compression reinforcement;
   $M'_r = M_f - M_r = 675 - 624 = 51$ kN · m
   $K'_r = M'_r \times 10^6 / bd^2 = 51 \times 10^6 / (400)(514)^2 = 0.48$ MPa
   Compute d' based on assumed bar size of No. 30;
   $d' = 60 + 11.3 + (29.9/2) = 86$ mm
   $d' / d = 86 / 514 = 0.17$; from Table 2.2; $\rho' = 0.17$ %
   $A'_s = \rho' bd = 0.0017(400)(514) = 350$ mm^2
   Use 2 No. 20 with $A'_s = 600$ mm^2 and d' = 86 mm.

5. Determine required tension reinforcement :

   $\rho + \rho' = 2.43 + 0.17 = 2.60$; $A_s = 0.0260 (400)(514) = 5346$ mm^2
   Use 8 No. 30 bars with $A_s = 5600$ mm^2.

   Note: 8 No. 30 bars can not be placed within b = 400 mm in a single row without violating the cover and/or minimum spacing limitations specified in Table 2.6. Therefore, use double layers of reinforcement and revise the design.

6. Revise d :

   Revise "d" based on No. 30 bars and 45 mm clear spacing between the two rows:

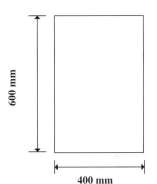

(a) Given Section

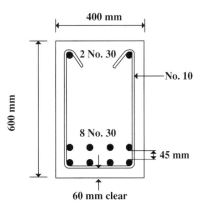

(b) Final Design

(Example 2.4)

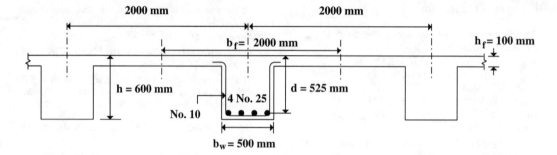

(Example 2.5)

$d = 600 - 60 - 11.3 - 29.9 - 45/2 = 476$ mm

Note: More reinforcement will be needed since "d" is reduced.

7. Determine required compression reinforcement from Table 2.2 :

Provide maximum tension reinforcement given in Table 2.1.

For $f'_c = 30$ MPa; select $\rho = 2.43$ %, and read corresponding $K_r = 5.9$ MPa

Moment resistance provided by this reinforcement;

$M_r = K_r bd^2 \times 10^{-6}$

$M_r = 5.9 (400)(476)^2 \times 10^{-6} = 535$ kN · m

Remaining moment resistance to be provided by compression reinforcement;

$M'_r = M_f - M_r = 675 - 535 = 140$ kN · m

$K'_r = M'_r \times 10^6 / bd^2 = 140 \times 10^6 / (400)(476)^2$
$= 1.54$ MPa

$d'/d = 86/476 = 0.18$; from Table 2.2 read $\rho' - 0.55\%$

$A'_s = \rho' \, bd = 0.0055(400)(476) = 1047$ mm^2

Use 2 No. 30 with $A'_s = 1400$ mm^2.

8. Determine required tension reinforcement from Table 2.1 :

$\rho + \rho' = 2.43 + 0.55 = 2.98$; $A_s = 0.0298 (400)(476)$
$= 5674$ mm^2

Use 8 No. 30 bars in two layers, with $A_s = 5600$ mm^2
(1.3% less than required).

9. Check spacing of tension reinforcement from Table 2.6 :

$s = [400 - 2(60) - 2(11.3) - 4(29.9)] / 3 = 46$ mm

46 mm $> 1.4 \, b_d = 1.4(29.9) = 42$ mm
$> 1.4 \, a_{max} = 1.4(25) = 35$ mm
> 30 mm

Note: This section is heavily reinforced in the tension region and hence is not likely to violate minimum steel and crack control requirements.

Final design is illustrated in the figure.

Example 2.5 — Analysis of a T-Section in Positive Bending Behaving as a Rectangular Section

Compute positive bending resistance of the T-beams shown in Fig. Ex. 2.5. The beams are continuous with a span length of 9.0 m.

$f'_c = 40$ MPa; $f_y = 400$ MPa.

1. Determine effective flange width b_{eff} from Table 2.4 :

Overhanging flange width

$b'_T \leq 12 \, h_f = 12 (100) = 1200$ mm
$\leq \ell / 10 = 9000 / 10 = 900$ mm
$\leq x$ or $y = 750$ mm

$b'_T = 750$ mm governs. $b_{eff} = 2 (750) + (500) = 2000$ mm

2. Determine if the section behaves as a T-section :

Condition for T-section behaviour : Use either Eq. 2-22 or Eq. 2-23.

For T-section behaviour Eq 2-22 gives; $A_s > (\alpha_1 \phi_c f'_c h_f b_f) / (\phi_s f_y)$

α_1 can be obtained from Table 2.1

$A_s = 4 (500) = 2000$ mm$^2 < [(0.79) (0.6) (40) (100) (2000)] / [(0.85) (400)] = 11153$ mm^2 Therefore, the section behaves as a rectangular section with $b = b_f$

Alternatively, for T-section behaviour Eq. 2-23 gives; $h_f < (A_s \phi_s f_y) / (\alpha_1 \phi_c f'_c b_f)$

$h_f = 100 > [(2000) (0.85) (400)] / [(0.79) (0.6) (40) (2000)] = 18$ mm

Hence, rectangular section behaviour.

3. Compute moment resistance M_r from Table 2.1 :

$\rho = A_s / bd = 2000 / (2000 \times 525) = 0.00190$

From Table 2.1 for $\rho = 0.190\%$ $K_r = 0.63$ MPa

$M_r = K_r bd^2 \times 10^{-6} = 0.63 (2000) (525)^2 \times 10^{-6} = 347$ kN · m

Example 2.6 — Analysis of an L-Section in Positive Bending Behaving as a T-Section

Compute factored moment resistance M_r of the L-section shown in the figure.

$f'_c = 30$ MPa; $f_y = 400$ MPa

1. Determine if the section behaves as a T-section :

Condition for T-section behaviour from Eq. 2-23;

$h_f < (A_s \phi_s f_y)/(\alpha_1 \phi_c f'_c b_f)$

$h_f = 100$ mm $< (6 \times 700 \times 0.85 \times 400) / (0.81 \times 0.6 \times 30 \times 800) = 122$ mm

Therefore, the section behaves as a T-section, and the moment resistance consists of two components; M_{rf} and M_{rw}.

2. Compute moment resistance provided by the overhanging flange, M_{rf} :

Determine ρ_f from Table 2.3: For $d/h_f = 360 / 100 = 3.6$ read $\rho_f = 1.21$ %

Determine K_{rf} from Table 2.1 using $\rho = \rho_f = 1.21$ %; $K_{rf} = 3.53$ MPa

$M_{rf} = K_{rf} (b_f - b_w) d^2 \times 10^{-6} = 183$ kN · m

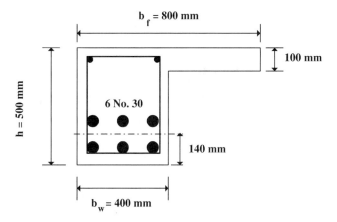

(Example 2.6)

3. Compute moment resistance provided by the web, M_{rw} :

$A_{sf} = \rho_f(b_f - b_w)d = 0.0121\ (800 - 400)\ (360) = 1742\ mm^2$

$A_{sw} = A_s - A_{sf} = 6 \times 700 - 1742 = 2458\ mm^2$

$\rho_w = A_{sw}/b_w d = 2458\ /\ (400 \times 360) = 0.0171 = 1.71\ \%$

Determine K_{rw} from Table 2.1 using $\rho = \rho_w = 1.71\ \%$; $K_{rw} = 4.64\ MPa$

$M_{rw} = K_{rw}b_w d^2 \times 10^{-6} = (4.64)\ (400)\ (360)^2 \times 10^{-6} = 241\ kN \cdot m$

4. Total moment resistance, M_r :

$M_r = M_{rf} + M_{rw} = 183 + 241 = 424\ kN \cdot m$

Example 2.7 — Design of a T-Section in Positive Bending

Design the T-section shown in the figure for a factored positive moment, $M_f = 1500\ kN \cdot m$. $f'_c = 30\ MPa$; $f_y = 400\ MPa$; clear cover to stirrups = 40 mm; interior exposure; maximum aggregate size $a_{max} = 25\ mm$.

1. Estimate effective depth d, assuming two layers of No. 30 bars with 45 mm spacing between the layers, and No. 10 stirrups.

$d = 1000 - 40 - 11.3 - 29.9 - 45/2 = 896\ mm$

2. Determine reinforcement ratio ρ from Table 2.1 assuming rectangular section behaviour :

$M_r \geq M_f$; $K_r = M_r \times 10^6\ /\ b\ d^2 = (1500 \times 10^6)\ /\ (1200)(896)^2 = 1.56\ MPa$

From Table 2.1 $\rho = 0.49\ \%$

3. Verify if the beam behaves as a rectangular section using Eq 2-22 :

$(\alpha_1 \phi_c f'_c\ h_f b_f)/(\phi_s f_y) = (0.81 \times 0.6 \times 30 \times 75 \times 1200)\ /\ (0.85 \times 400) = 3859\ mm^2$

$A_s = \rho b d = 0.0049\ (1200)\ (896)$
$\quad = 5268\ mm^2 > 3859\ mm^2$

therefore, the section behaves as a T-section, and hence must be designed as a T-section.

4. Compute the area of tension steel A_{sf} associated with moment resistance of the overhangs from Table 2.3:

for $d/h_f = 896\ /\ 75 = 11.9$; read $\rho_f = 0.36\ \%$

$A_{sf} = \rho_f(b_f - b_w)d = 0.0036(1200 - 400)(896)$
$\quad = 2580\ mm^2$

Moment resistance provided by $\rho_f = 0.0036$ from Table 2.1;

$K_{rf} = 1.17\ MPa$;
$M_{rf} = K_{rf}\ (b_f - b_w)d^2 \times 10^{-6}$
$\quad = 1.17(1200 - 400)(896)^2 \times 10^{-6}$
$\quad = 751\ kN \cdot m$

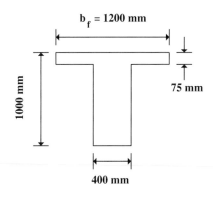

(a) Given Section

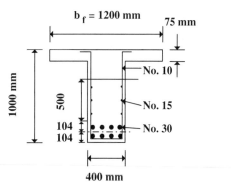

(b) Final Design

(Example 2.7)

5. Compute area of tension steel A_{sw} associated with web resistance from Table 2.1 :

   Moment resistance to be provided by web steel; M_{rw} = $M_f - M_{rf} = 1500 - 751 = 749$ kN · m

   $K_{rw} = M_{rw} \times 10^6 / b_w d^2 = (749 \times 10^6) / [(400)(896)^2]$ = 2.33 MPa

   From Table 2.1; $\rho_w = 0.76\% = 0.0076$; $A_{sw} = \rho_w b_w d$ = 0.0076 (400)(896) = 2724 mm^2

6. Total tension steel :

   $A_s = A_{sf} + A_{sw} = 2580 + 2724 = 5304$ mm^2

   Use 8 No. 30 bars in two rows, with $A_s = 8 \times 700 = 5600$ mm^2

7. Check minimum spacing of reinforcement using Table 2.6 :

   s = [400 − 2(40) − 2(11.3) − 4(29.9)] / 3 = 59 mm

   From Table 2.6;

   $s \geq 1.4\ d_b = 1.4\ (29.9) = 42$ mm O.K.

   $s \geq 1.4\ a_{max} = 1.4\ (25) = 35$ mm O.K.

   $s \geq 30$ mm O.K.

8. Check minimum reinforcement ratio :

   Use Eq. 2-6; $A_{smin} = 0.2\ \sqrt{f'_c}\ b_t\ h\ /\ f_y = 0.2\ \sqrt{30}\ (400)$ (1000) / (400) = 1095 mm^2

   $A_s = 5600 > 1095$ mm^2 O.K.

9. Check maximum bar spacing as governed by crack control :

   Compute quantity "z" from Eq. 2-31 or Table 2.7: $z = f_s(d_c A)^{1/3}$

   Note: For calculation of A and d_c clear cover need not be taken greater than 50 mm.

   From Table 2.7; $y = h - d = 1000 - 896 = 104$ mm; A = 2yb/8 = 2 (104) (400) / 8

   A = 10400 mm^2; $f_s = 0.6\ f_y = 0.6\ (400) = 240$ MPa; $d_c = 40 + 11.3 + 29.9/2 = 66$ mm

   $z = 240\ (66 \times 10400)^{1/3} = 21,171$ N/mm

   $z = 21,171$ N/mm < 30,000 N/mm (interior exposure) O.K.

10. Check if skin reinforcement is needed :

    h > 750 mm. Therefore, skin reinforcement as illustrated in Table 2.8 is needed.

    Area of skin reinforcement on each side, $A_{sk}/2$ = 0.008 $A_{cs}/2$ = 0.008 (2x)(h/2)

    Assuming No. 15 bars will be used, x = 40 + 11.3 + 16.0/2 = 59 mm

    $A_{sk}/2 = (0.008)(2)(59)(500) = 472$ mm

    Provide 3 No. 15 bars along each side face, uniformly placed within distance h/2 = 500 mm. Total $A_{sk} = 6\ (200) = 1200$ mm^2 (for two side faces).

    Note: The contribution of skin reinforcement to flexural resistance is ignored. Final design is illustrated in the figure.

Table 2.1 Reinforcement ratio ρ (%) for rectangular sections with tension reinforcement

$f_y = 400$ MPa

$$M_r = K_r b d^2 \times 10^{-6} \text{ kN} \cdot \text{m}; \quad K_r = \left[1 - \frac{\rho \phi_s f_y}{2\alpha_1 \phi_c f_c'}\right]\rho \phi_s f_y; \quad \rho = \frac{A_s}{bd}$$

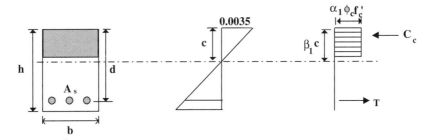

f_c' (MPa):	20	25	30	35	40	45	50	55	60
α_1 :	0.82	0.81	0.81	0.80	0.79	0.78	0.78	0.77	0.76
β_1 :	0.92	0.91	0.90	0.88	0.87	0.86	0.85	0.83	0.82
ρ_{bal} :	1.69	2.07	2.43	2.76	3.09	3.39	3.68	3.94	4.20

K_r					ρ (%)				
0.5	0.15	0.15	0.15	0.15	0.15	0.15	0.15	0.15	0.15
0.6	0.18	0.18	0.18	0.18	0.18	0.18	0.18	0.18	0.18
0.7	0.21	0.21	0.21	0.21	0.21	0.21	0.21	0.21	0.21
0.8	0.25	0.24	0.24	0.24	0.24	0.24	0.24	0.24	0.24
0.9	0.28	0.28	0.27	0.27	0.27	0.27	0.27	0.27	0.27
1.0	0.31	0.31	0.31	0.30	0.30	0.30	0.30	0.30	0.30
1.1	0.34	0.34	0.34	0.33	0.33	0.33	0.33	0.33	0.33
1.2	0.38	0.37	0.37	0.37	0.36	0.36	0.36	0.36	0.36
1.3	0.41	0.41	0.40	0.40	0.40	0.39	0.39	0.39	0.39
1.4	0.45	0.44	0.43	0.43	0.43	0.43	0.42	0.42	0.42
1.5	0.48	0.47	0.47	0.46	0.46	0.46	0.46	0.46	0.45
1.6	0.52	0.51	0.50	0.50	0.49	0.49	0.49	0.49	0.49
1.7	0.55	0.54	0.53	0.53	0.52	0.52	0.52	0.52	0.52
1.8	0.59	0.58	0.57	0.56	0.56	0.55	0.55	0.55	0.55
1.9	0.63	0.61	0.60	0.59	0.59	0.59	0.58	0.58	0.58
2.0	0.66	0.65	0.64	0.63	0.62	0.62	0.62	0.61	0.61
2.1	0.70	0.68	0.67	0.66	0.66	0.65	0.65	0.65	0.64
2.2	0.74	0.72	0.71	0.70	0.69	0.68	0.68	0.68	0.68
2.3	0.78	0.76	0.74	0.73	0.72	0.72	0.71	0.71	0.71
2.4	0.82	0.79	0.78	0.77	0.76	0.75	0.75	0.74	0.74
2.5	0.86	0.83	0.81	0.80	0.79	0.78	0.78	0.78	0.77
2.6	0.91	0.87	0.85	0.84	0.83	0.82	0.81	0.81	0.80
2.7	0.95	0.91	0.89	0.87	0.86	0.85	0.85	0.84	0.84
2.8	0.99	0.95	0.92	0.91	0.90	0.89	0.88	0.87	0.87
2.9	1.04	0.99	0.96	0.94	0.93	0.92	0.91	0.91	0.90
3.0	1.09	1.03	1.00	0.98	0.97	0.96	0.95	0.94	0.94
3.1	1.13	1.07	1.04	1.02	1.00	0.99	0.98	0.98	0.97
3.2	1.18	1.11	1.08	1.05	1.04	1.03	1.02	1.01	1.00
3.3	1.23	1.16	1.12	1.09	1.07	1.06	1.05	1.04	1.04
3.4	1.29	1.20	1.16	1.13	1.11	1.10	1.09	1.08	1.07
3.5	1.34	1.25	1.20	1.17	1.15	1.13	1.12	1.11	1.11
3.6	1.40	1.29	1.24	1.21	1.18	1.17	1.16	1.15	1.14
3.7	1.45	1.34	1.28	1.25	1.22	1.21	1.19	1.18	1.17
3.8	1.51	1.39	1.32	1.29	1.26	1.24	1.23	1.22	1.21
3.9	1.58	1.43	1.37	1.33	1.30	1.28	1.26	1.25	1.24

continued

Table 2.1 Cont'd

f_c' (MPa):	20	25	30	35	40	45	50	55	60
K_r					ρ (%)				
4.0	1.64	1.48	1.41	1.37	1.34	1.32	1.30	1.29	1.28
4.1		1.53	1.45	1.41	1.38	1.35	1.34	1.32	1.31
4.2		1.59	1.50	1.45	1.41	1.39	1.37	1.36	1.35
4.3		1.64	1.54	1.49	1.45	1.43	1.41	1.40	1.38
4.4		1.69	1.59	1.53	1.49	1.47	1.45	1.43	1.42
4.5		1.75	1.64	1.58	1.53	1.51	1.48	1.47	1.46
4.6		1.81	1.69	1.62	1.58	1.55	1.52	1.50	1.49
4.7		1.87	1.74	1.66	1.62	1.58	1.56	1.54	1.53
4.8		1.93	1.79	1.71	1.66	1.62	1.60	1.58	1.56
4.9		2.00	1.84	1.75	1.70	1.66	1.64	1.62	1.60
5.0		2.07	1.89	1.80	1.74	1.70	1.68	1.65	1.64
5.1			1.94	1.85	1.79	1.75	1.72	1.69	1.67
5.2			2.00	1.89	1.83	1.79	1.75	1.73	1.71
5.3			2.05	1.94	1.87	1.83	1.79	1.77	1.75
5.4			2.11	1.99	1.92	1.87	1.83	1.81	1.79
5.5			2.17	2.04	1.96	1.91	1.87	1.85	1.82
5.6			2.23	2.09	2.01	1.95	1.92	1.89	1.86
5.7			2.29	2.14	2.06	2.00	1.96	1.93	1.90
5.8			2.36	2.19	2.10	2.04	2.00	1.97	1.94
5.9			2.43	2.25	2.15	2.09	2.04	2.01	1.98
6.0				2.30	2.20	2.13	2.08	2.05	2.02
6.1				2.36	2.25	2.17	2.12	2.09	2.06
6.2				2.42	2.30	2.22	2.17	2.13	2.10
6.3				2.47	2.35	2.27	2.21	2.17	2.14
6.4				2.53	2.40	2.31	2.25	2.21	2.18
6.5				2.60	2.45	2.36	2.30	2.25	2.22
6.6				2.66	2.50	2.41	2.34	2.29	2.26
6.7				2.72	2.56	2.46	2.39	2.34	2.30
6.8					2.61	2.50	2.43	2.38	2.34
6.9					2.67	2.55	2.48	2.42	2.38
7.0					2.72	2.60	2.52	2.47	2.42
7.1					2.78	2.66	2.57	2.51	2.47
7.2					2.84	2.71	2.62	2.56	2.51
7.3					2.90	2.76	2.67	2.60	2.55
7.4					2.96	2.81	2.72	2.65	2.59
7.5					3.03	2.87	2.76	2.69	2.64
7.6						2.92	2.81	2.74	2.68
7.7						2.98	2.86	2.79	2.73
7.8						3.04	2.92	2.83	2.77
7.9						3.09	2.97	2.88	2.82
8.0						3.15	3.02	2.93	2.86
8.1						3.21	3.07	2.98	2.91
8.2						3.27	3.13	3.03	2.95
8.3						3.34	3.18	3.08	3.00
8.4							3.24	3.13	3.05
8.5							3.29	3.18	3.10
8.6							3.35	3.23	3.14
8.7							3.41	3.28	3.19
8.8							3.47	3.33	3.24
8.9							3.53	3.39	3.29
9.0							3.59	3.44	3.34
9.1							3.65	3.50	3.39
9.2								3.55	3.44
9.3								3.61	3.49
9.4								3.67	3.55

continued

Table 2.1 Cont'd

f'_c (MPa):	20	25	30	35	40	45	50	55	60
K_r					ρ (%)				
9.5								3.73	3.60
9.6								3.79	3.65
9.7								3.85	3.71
9.8								3.91	3.76
9.9									3.82
10.0									3.87
10.1									3.93
10.2									3.99
10.3									4.05
10.4									4.11
10.5									4.17

Table 2.2 Reinforcement ratio ρ' (%) for compression reinforcement

$f_y = 400$ MPa

$$M_r' = K_r'bd^2 \times 10^{-6} \text{ kN} \cdot \text{m}; \quad K_r' = \left[1 - \frac{d'}{d}\right]\rho'\phi_s f_y; \quad \rho' = \frac{A_s'}{bd}$$

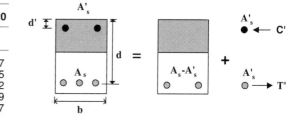

d'/d :	0.05	0.10	0.15	0.20
K_r'		ρ'		
0.20	0.06	0.07	0.07	0.07
0.40	0.12	0.13	0.14	0.15
0.60	0.19	0.20	0.21	0.22
0.80	0.25	0.26	0.28	0.29
1.00	0.31	0.33	0.35	0.37
1.20	0.37	0.39	0.42	0.44
1.40	0.43	0.46	0.48	0.51
1.60	0.50	0.52	0.55	0.59
1.80	0.56	0.59	0.62	0.66
2.00	0.62	0.65	0.69	0.74
2.20	0.68	0.72	0.76	0.81
2.40	0.74	0.78	0.83	0.88
2.60	0.80	0.85	0.90	0.96
2.80	0.87	0.92	0.97	1.03
3.00	0.93	0.98	1.04	1.10
3.20	0.99	1.05	1.11	1.18
3.40	1.05	1.11	1.18	1.25
3.60	1.11	1.18	1.25	1.32
3.80	1.18	1.24	1.31	1.40
4.00	1.24	1.31	1.38	1.47
4.20	1.30	1.37	1.45	1.54
4.40	1.36	1.44	1.52	1.62
4.60	1.42	1.50	1.59	1.69
4.80	1.49	1.57	1.66	1.76
5.00	1.55	1.63	1.73	1.84
5.20	1.61	1.70	1.80	1.91
5.40	1.67	1.76	1.87	1.99
5.60	1.73	1.83	1.94	2.06
5.80	1.80	1.90	2.01	2.13
6.00	1.86	1.96	2.08	2.21

Table 2.3 Reinforcement ratio, ρ_f (%), balancing concrete in overhang(s) in T or L beams

$$\rho_f = \frac{\alpha_1 \phi_c f'_c h_f}{\phi_s f_y d} \qquad\qquad f_y = 400 \text{ MPa}$$

$$M_{rf} = \rho_f (b_f - b_w)\, d\, \phi_s f_y \left(d - \frac{h_f}{2}\right); \quad \text{or} \quad M_{rf} = K_{rf}(b_f - b_w)d^2 \times 10^{-6}\ \text{kN} \cdot \text{m}$$

K_{rf} can be obtained from Table 2.1 using ρ_f

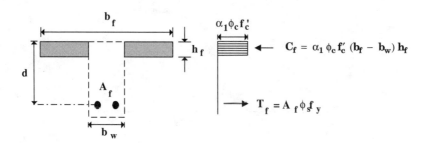

f'_c(MPa):	20	25	30	35	40	45	50	55	60
d/h_f					ρ_f (%)				
3.00	0.96	1.19	1.42	1.64	1.86	2.07	2.28	2.48	2.68
4.00	0.72	0.90	1.07	1.23	1.39	1.55	1.71	1.86	2.01
5.00	0.58	0.72	0.85	0.99	1.12	1.24	1.37	1.49	1.61
6.00	0.48	0.60	0.71	0.82	0.93	1.04	1.14	1.24	1.34
7.00	0.41	0.51	0.61	0.70	0.80	0.89	0.98	1.06	1.15
8.00	0.36	0.45	0.53	0.62	0.70	0.78	0.85	0.93	1.01
9.00	0.32	0.40	0.47	0.55	0.62	0.69	0.76	0.83	0.89
10.00	0.29	0.36	0.43	0.49	0.56	0.62	0.68	0.74	0.80
11.00	0.26	0.33	0.39	0.45	0.51	0.56	0.62	0.68	0.73
12.00	0.24	0.30	0.36	0.41	0.46	0.52	0.57	0.62	0.67
13.00	0.22	0.28	0.33	0.38	0.43	0.48	0.53	0.57	0.62
14.00	0.21	0.26	0.30	0.35	0.40	0.44	0.49	0.53	0.57
15.00	0.19	0.24	0.28	0.33	0.37	0.41	0.46	0.50	0.54

Table 2.4 Effective Flange Width in T and L-Sections

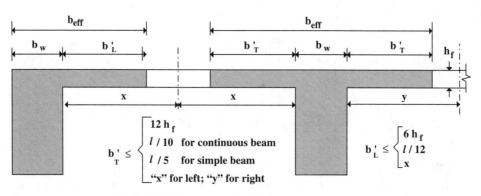

$$b'_T \le \begin{cases} 12\,h_f \\ l/10 \quad \text{for continuous beam} \\ l/5 \quad \text{for simple beam} \\ \text{``x'' for left; ``y'' for right} \end{cases}$$

$$b'_L \le \begin{cases} 6\,h_f \\ l/12 \\ x \end{cases}$$

where, l is the beam span length

Table 2.5 Concrete Joist Construction

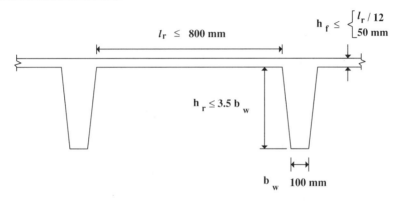

Table 2.6 Spacing and Cover Requirements for Beam Reinforcement

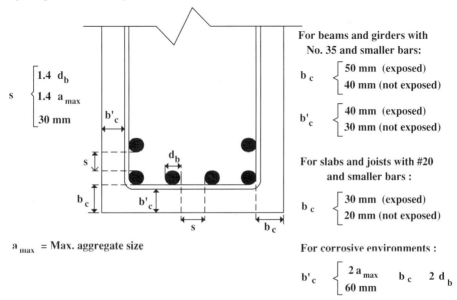

For beams and girders with No. 35 and smaller bars:

b_c $\begin{cases} 50 \text{ mm (exposed)} \\ 40 \text{ mm (not exposed)} \end{cases}$

b'_c $\begin{cases} 40 \text{ mm (exposed)} \\ 30 \text{ mm (not exposed)} \end{cases}$

For slabs and joists with #20 and smaller bars :

b_c $\begin{cases} 30 \text{ mm (exposed)} \\ 20 \text{ mm (not exposed)} \end{cases}$

For corrosive environments :

b'_c $\begin{cases} 2 a_{max} \\ 60 \text{ mm} \end{cases}$ b_c $2 d_b$

a_{max} = Max. aggregate size

Table 2.7 Crack Control Requirement

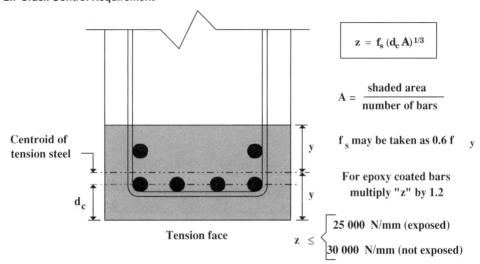

Centroid of tension steel

Tension face

$$z = f_s (d_c A)^{1/3}$$

$$A = \frac{\text{shaded area}}{\text{number of bars}}$$

f_s may be taken as $0.6 f_y$

For epoxy coated bars multiply "z" by 1.2

$z \leq \begin{cases} 25\ 000 \text{ N/mm (exposed)} \\ 30\ 000 \text{ N/mm (not exposed)} \end{cases}$

Table 2.8 Skin Reinforcement

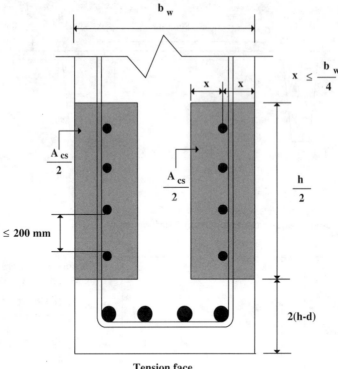

Tension face

$$\text{Area of skin reinforcement in each strip} \atop \text{when } h > 750 \text{ mm} = \begin{cases} 0.008 \, \dfrac{A_{cs}}{2} & \text{for interior exposure} \\ 0.010 \, \dfrac{A_{cs}}{2} & \text{for exterior exposure} \end{cases}$$

A_{cs}: Total shaded area

Table 2.9 Tension Reinforcement in Overhangs

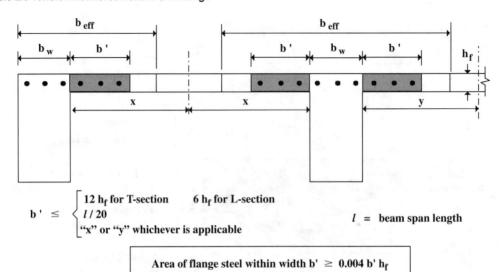

$$b' \leq \begin{cases} 12 \, h_f \text{ for T-section} \qquad 6 \, h_f \text{ for L-section} \\ l \, / \, 20 \\ \text{"x" or "y" whichever is applicable} \end{cases}$$

l = beam span length

$$\boxed{\text{Area of flange steel within width } b' \geq 0.004 \, b' \, h_f}$$

Development and Splices of Reinforcement

By T. Rezansoff

Chapter 3
Development and
Splices of
Reinforcement

3.1 INTRODUCTION

3.1.1 Design For Development

Development and splicing should not be the initial cause of a strength related failure, just as connections in steel construction, and joint details or shear and torsion resistance in concrete construction should not be the "weak link" when ensuring adequate strength and ductility. For instance, splices using mechanical connections or welds must provide at least 1.20 times the specified yield strength of the reinforcement and not less than 1.10 times the actual yield strength of the bar used in a compliance test, even for non-seismic design. This over-strength decreases the probability of a "bond" related failure, though no guarantee exists that good ductility will be available before failure occurs in a more "desirable" mode such as in flexure.

With small structurally efficient concrete covers and deformed reinforcement, failures in development or lap splices occur when the concrete confining the reinforcement splits away. This is due to the radial bursting component of the bearing force between the reinforcement deformations and the surrounding concrete in straight bar anchorages, and the additional lateral bursting forces imposed on the concrete with hooked anchorages or the cross wires that provide anchorage in welded wire fabric. In flexure, prying of the reinforcement on the confining concrete also occurs because of beam curvature, and at transverse crack locations. A "bond" splitting failure is prevented by providing sufficient confinement to the reinforcement along its anchorage to the concrete, using a combination of increased concrete confinement (development or splice length, concrete cover and bar spacing), and increased transverse reinforcing confinement provided by stirrups, ties and spirals that intercept bond splitting cracks. Features that improve confinement such as the restraint provided to bars from adjoining members framing into a common joint, or to the hook of a stirrup from a slab poured integrally with a beam, all require careful attention to detail to ensure realization of the expected strength. Since confinement provided by transverse reinforcement to tensile development and lap splicing of longitudinal reinforcement is now explicitly recognized, more attention needs to be paid to ensure that the hooks used in the transverse reinforcement will provide positive confinement to the longitudinal bars.

As in previous CSA A23.3 Standards, design for development uses empirical equations with full (unfactored) specified material strengths to ensure adequate "bond" resistance; unlike the factored material strengths used to determine factored resistances for flexure, shear, axial compression, etc.. The coefficients used in the equations are expected to provide the required factor of safety in the factored bond resistance without the use of material factors ϕ_c and ϕ_s. However, even though still based on regression analysis and correlations with test data, the design for development and lap splicing of deformed reinforcement anchorages in tension has undergone a major revision in CSA Standard A23.3-94, following extensive testing over the past 3 decades.

3.1.2 Major Code Changes

A brief outline of the major changes between the 1984 and 1994 editions of CSA Standard A23.3 in the area of development and splices of reinforcement are itemized as follows:

(i) Tension development and splicing of bars, wire and fabric

(a) Detailed approach

The revised [Equation (12-1)]* for development length in tension [Cl. 12.2.2] more accurately accounts for factors that produce beneficial confinement to a developing or lap spliced deformed bar, wire or welded wire fabric. The benefit of the magnitude of the concrete confinement, as measured by the covers and bar spacing provided, and of the amount of transverse reinforcement placed to intercept potential bond splitting cracks, is explicitly included and varies directly with the amount of total confinement present. In addition to the use of spirals as in past A23.3 Standards, stirrups are now also recognized for providing effective confinement to improve bond performance. A limit exists on the total confinement that may be considered to be effective, where bond failure changes from primarily splitting away of the confining concrete, to a pullout failure with crushing of the concrete in front of the reinforcement deformations in a heavily confined anchorage. With this latter bond failure mode, additional confinement is ineffective.

Rather than multiplying a calculated "basic" development length by modification factors to obtain a required development length as in past Standards, modification factors k_1 through k_4, defined in [Cl. 12.2.4], are now directly included in [Equation (12-1)]. In addition to the modification factors used in the past for bar location and concrete density, tests have shown that epoxy coating, used as corrosion protection for reinforcement, has a detrimental influence on bond development.

In tension reinforcement, reduction in bond resistance is particularly severe when smaller concrete covers and bar spacings are used. A new "coating" modification factor k_2, which depends on cover and spacing available along straight developing or lap spliced deformed bars and wires is required by [Cl. 12.2.4] to increase anchorage lengths when epoxy coating is present. Epoxy coated standard hooks in tension have a single penalty factor of 1.2 [Cl. 12.5.3(f)]. By contrast, new data has permitted the bar location factor for "top" placed horizontal reinforcement to be relaxed from 1.4 to 1.3. A new modification factor k_4 for bar size is needed to make [Equation (12-1)] applicable for all bar sizes.

As in the past, tension lap splice lengths are calculated by multiplying the development length by a splice "Class" factor which considers the excess bar area provided at the location of the splice, and the percentage of the bars that are spliced at the same location. However, tests have shown that the length requirements for development, and for transfer of a comparable stress along a lap splice are similar when the confinement provided along the anchorage is the same, resulting in a reduction of the number of "Classes" of splices that need to be considered [Cl. 12.15]. Class "C" splices are now eliminated, and maximum splice lengths need now only be 1.3 times the development length, alleviating some of the problems that previously existed in columns because of the extremely long lap lengths that were required. The elimination of the need for a Class C splice factor of 1.7 for tension lap splices

---

*References to the A23.3-94 Standard and Explanatory Notes are enclosed within square brackets [ ], while reference to Handbook material is not enclosed within brackets.

in [Cl. 12.15] is also reflected in [Cl. 12.13.5] for lap splices in stirrup legs, in [Cl. 12.17.3.2] for tension laps in columns and in [Cl. 12.18.1] for splices of welded deformed wire fabric in tension. The retention of the Class "B" factor of 1.3 is in keeping with past practice, where the lap lengths required were longer than development lengths, possibly because support precompression often improves confinement to developing bars, while similar precompression is not ordinarily available with lap splices.

The applicability of the empirical equations used for anchorage of reinforcement with high performance concretes has not been adequately investigated. The maximum concrete compressive strength that is permitted in defining bond resistance is therefore limited to $f'_c = 64$ MPa ($\sqrt{f'_c} = 8$ MPa in [Cl. 12.1.1]).

For development of welded deformed wire fabric in tension, the ℓ_d calculated for deformed bars and wires by [Cl. 12.2] is modified by factors which recognize the anchorage contribution provided by the cross wires [Cl. 12.7.2 & .3]. This is in contrast to providing new equations as in the past. For smooth welded wire fabric [Cl. 12.8], the equation for ℓ_d used in A23.3-M84 is retained in a modified form.

(b) Simple approach

As an alternate to the direct calculation and inclusion of the confinement available to an anchorage carrying tension, [Table 12-1] permits a simpler approach for obtaining ℓ_d when minimum designated concrete covers and minimum principal reinforcement spacings are provided. These minimum values are specified in [Cl. 12.2.3] in terms of the diameter d_b of the reinforcement being developed. The simple approach is similar to the methods used in past A23.3 Standards, but has been recalibrated on the basis of new experimental data. Two equation coefficients are provided in [Table 12-1], recognizing the degree of confinement available in an approximate fashion.

The simpler approach may be more convenient for routine design, since minimum spacings and some minimum covers on reinforcement specified in CSA Standard A23.1-94 [Appendix A of A23.3-94] are also specified in terms of the diameter d_b of the reinforcement being developed or spliced. Some of these requirements, such as the minimum spacing permitted between bars in a beam, are more restrictive than has been allowed in the past. However, if heavier confinement is available, the use of [Equation (12-1)] may be justified to reduce anchorage lengths. Using design aids, only a little extra design effort is needed for applying [Equation (12-1)] of the detailed approach. Non-compliance with [Cl. 12.2.3] for minimum concrete cover or bar spacing precludes the simple approach of [Table 12-1].

(ii) **Development and splicing of deformed bars in compression**

Requirements for development and splicing of compression reinforcement are essentially unchanged from A23.3-M84. However, in keeping with the benefit recognized when stirrups or ties are present to improve development of tension reinforcement, the provision of designated ties also permits the use of a reduction factor on the basic compression development length [Cl. 12.3.3(b)].

(iii) **Standard hooks**

Minimum bend diameters for standard hooks have been modified [Cl. A12.2.3 and Table A5], recognizing the better ductility available with weldable reinforcing bars. Minimum bends in stirrups and ties made with No. 20 and No. 25 bars are the same as with bends in other bars [Cls. 7.1.2 & 12.13.2(b)]. In stirrups and ties made with smaller bars and wire, requirements are now specified separately for 90° and 135° hooks [Cl. A12.2.4]. Dimensions for hook extensions remain unchanged. When confinement available at a hook of a stirrup or tie is not restrained, and the possibility that the leg of a 90° hook may unravel if the cover on the leg splits away, a 135° hook may be required [Cl. 7.1.2]. Ties in columns may still use a 90° hook if $f'_c \not> 50$ MPa. The spacing of ties in concrete with compressive strength exceeding 50 MPa is also tightened [Cl. 7.6.5.2] to 0.75 of the values specified in past Standards.

For cross ties [Cl. 7.1.3], at least one end must have a bend of at least 135°, while the other end can use a 90° hook to facilitate placing. Placement of such successive cross ties must alternate the position of the 90° hook between the two longitudinal bars that are being confined, to provide an average confinement to each longitudinal bar on the basis of alternating 135° hooks and the less positive 90° hooks.

(iv) **Anchorage of stirrups and ties**

Modifications have also been made to fine tune and clarify the requirements for anchorage of stirrups and ties [Cl. 12.13.2]. In general, legs of stirrups and ties may be developed in a shorter distance, recognizing the more positive anchorage that is ensured by stirrup and tie hooks satisfying [Cl. 7.1.2]. Stirrups and ties made of No. 15 and smaller diameter deformed bars and wire are now fully anchored by a standard stirrup or tie hook around longitudinal reinforcement, with no requirement for additional straight lead-In length prior to the hook. Stirrups and ties made with No. 20 and No. 25 bars still require a minimum lead-in distance of $0.33\ \ell_d$ measured from mid depth of the member, in addition to a hooked anchorage around a longitudinal bar.

(v) **Splices in columns**

Special splice requirements for columns in [Cl. 12.17] have been reworded to improve clarity and define the conditions when the longer Class B splices for tension must be used.

(vi) **Bar extensions**

A new provision [Cl. 11.3.8.2] ensures that sufficient tensile force can be developed in tensile reinforcement that extends into a simple support, an exterior support of a continuous span, or near the free end of a cantilever supporting a concentrated load, where termination of the member does not permit reinforcement to be extended into a "continuing" span. This provision serves a similar function as extending the cutoff locations of terminating bars along a span, a distance of d, 12 d_b, $\ell_n/16$, etc., beyond their theoretical cutoff points on the basis of flexural requirements alone, as required in previous Standards, as well as in A23.3-94, when the design for shear is made on the basis of the Simplified Method [Cl. 11.3]. Diagonal tension (flexural-shear) cracking may increase the magnitude of the tensile force in the longitudinal reinforcement above that predicted on the basis of bending alone, and the horizontal tensile component of the strut action force that is carried in the longitudinal bars must be capable of being developed through sufficient anchorage beyond the inside face of the bearing area.

3.2 DEVELOPMENT IN TENSION

3.2.1 General

Straight tensile reinforcement for flexure develops design forces through "bond" interaction between the reinforcement and the concrete. With deformed reinforcement, total confinement provided by concrete and transverse reinforcement up to an equivalent 2.5 bar diameters of concrete cover, is effective in preventing splitting bond failures. Confinement exceeding 2.5 bar diameters is considered ineffective as a pull-out failure may limit the force developed along the anchorage length.

3.2.2 Design Aids

Design aids, in the form of tables and figures, are gathered at the end of Chapter 3.

(a) Simple approach - [Table 12-1]

Tables 3.1 and 3.6 provide development lengths for standard deformed reinforcing bars and deformed wire made of Grade 400 steel when heavier confinement exists. The factors k_1, k_2 and k_4 for bar location, bar coating and bar size respectively are directly included, while for low and semi-low density concretes the development length must be multiplied by the appropriate factor k_3. For lighter confinement, but still satisfying [Cl. 12.2.3, "Other cases" in Table 12-1], lengths in Tables 3.1 and 3.6 are multiplied by 1.33. After applicable factors are applied, the development length must not be less than 300 mm, except when used to calculate tension lap splice lengths.

(b) Detailed approach - [Equation (12-1)]

Table 3.2 provides development lengths for deformed reinforcing bars made of Grade 400 steel based on a confinement index "C.I." which is the sum of the non-dimensionalized confinements provided by the concrete, d_{cs}/d_b, as obtained from Tables 3.3(a), (b) & (c), and by the transverse reinforcement K_{tr}/d_b, provided in Table 3.5. Design aids using the detailed approach are not provided for deformed wire.

(c) Welded wire fabric

Development lengths for the more common sizes of deformed and smooth welded wire fabric (WWF) are given in Tables 3.7 and 3.8 respectively. Fabric made from deformed wire sizes smaller than MD25 is not permitted by [Cl. 3.1.3(d)] because welding between crossed wires may not develop sufficient shear transfer with the smaller sizes.

3.2.3 Design Examples

Simple examples using deformed welded wire fabric are given in Examples 3.1 and 3.2. Examples which utilize the design aids in Chapter 3 follow Section 3.9 of the text, "Development of Cutoff and Continuing Reinforcement", and preceed the design aids.

3.3 STANDARD HOOKS IN TENSION

3.3.1 General

Following the approach first introduced in A23.3-M84, the development length of a standard hook is the total length of a hook plus the straight lead-in distance required up to the critical section to develop the full specified yield strength of the reinforcing bar. The basic hook development length ℓ_{hb}, before multiplying by applicable modification factors, is given by the equation in [Cl. 12.5.2] for Grade 400 reinforcement.

3.3.2 Design Aids

Basic hook development lengths ℓ_{hb}, for standard deformed bars are shown in Table 3.9 for $f_y = 400$ MPa. The dimensions of the hook itself to satisfy CSA Standard A23.1-94, as excerpted in CSA A23.3-94, Appendix A, are illustrated in Table 3.10.

Heavy confinement is necessary for hook development since large bursting and splitting forces are imposed by the hook into the concrete over a relatively short distance. For standard hooks at the ends of members, either the side cover, or the top (or bottom) cover over the hook must be used to enclose the hook as given by [Cl. 12.5.4]. Illustrations explaining the hook confinement required by [Cl. 12.5.4] are shown with Table 3.9. The use of excess reinforcement, larger covers, and larger covers coupled with enclosure within ties or stirrup-ties permit the use of modifiers which reduce the required hook development length. Factors that may be applied when good confinement is provided are shown in Fig. 3.1.

Modifying factors which increase the basic hook development length ℓ_{hb} apply for structural low density concrete, for epoxy coated reinforcement and for reinforcement grades with $f_y > 400$ MPa. The 1.3 factor used with straight "top" horizontal reinforcement is not used as a modifier for hook development lengths.

3.4 TENSION LAP SPLICES

3.4.1 General

As in past Standards, tension lap splices [Cl. 12.15] are calculated as the product of the development length in tension and the splice "Class Factor". However, the largest required lap is now a Class B splice with a factor of 1.3 when more than 50% of the bars are spliced at the same location and/or the reinforcing area provided at the splice location is less than twice the required area [Table 12-2].

3.4.2 Design Aids

Development lengths, which are multiplied by the Class Factor to give the lap length for deformed bars and wire in tension, are obtained in the same fashion as outlined in Sections 3.2.2 (a) & (b). The only difference is that for the "Detailed Approach" [Equation (12-1)], Tables 3.4 (a), (b) & (c), rather than Tables 3.3 (a), (b) & (c), are used to obtain the confinement index provided by the concrete, where the extra beam width needed by the contacting spliced bars along the lap is accounted for. As in A23.3-M84, the reduction in development length based on excess reinforcement [Cl. 12.2.5] is not used for lap splices, nor is the minimum development length of 300 mm specified in [Cl. 12.2.1]. However, after application of the Class Factor, the lap length must not be less than 300 mm [Cl. 12.15.1].

Tensile lap splice lengths for welded wire fabric are obtained by using development lengths from Tables 3.7

and 3.8, and [Cls. 12.18 & 12.19], as defined in [Figs. N12.18.1 and N12.19].

3.5 DEVELOPMENT OF SHEAR REINFORCEMENT

3.5.1 General

Ends of deformed bar and wire stirrup legs must be anchored around longitudinal reinforcement using 135° hooks [Cls. 12.13 & 7.1.2], unless a pair of stirrups, meeting the requirements of [Cl. 12.13.2] for lap splicing of straight legs (no hooks) is placed to form a single closed unit. A 90° hook is permitted if the concrete cover on the hook is restrained against spalling [Cl. 7.1.2]. In addition to the anchorage provided by the hook, bars and wire stirrups larger than No. 15 and MD200 respectively, require straight embedment defined by [Cl. 12.13.2 (b)] and illustrated in [Fig. N12.12].

With smooth wire fabric stirrups, hooked ends are not required on stirrups if the "cross" wires of the fabric, running in the longitudinal direction of the member, meet the spacing and location requirements of [Cls. 12.13.2 (c) & (d)], as illustrated in [Fig. N12.13]. The provision for single leg stirrups [Cl. 12.13.2 (c)] also applies for welded deformed wire fabric.

Between anchored ends, each bend in the continuous portion of a stirrup shall enclose a longitudinal bar [Cl. 12.13.3].

3.5.2 Design Aids

The effective depth d that is required to provide the necessary straight embedment, in addition to the hook anchorage at the ends of No. 20 and No. 25 stirrup legs [Cl. 12.13.2(b)] are given in Table 3.11. Illustrations showing the anchorages necessary for web reinforcement are given in [Figs. N12.13.2, N12.13.2(c) and N12.13.5].

3.6 DEVELOPMENT IN COMPRESSION

3.6.1 General

Development of deformed bars in compression is assisted by the end bearing of the bar on the concrete, and is not weakened by the existance of transverse flexural tensile cracking which leads to high localized bond stresses on either side of the crack in tensile development. Compression reinforcement must be confined inside of spirals or ties in compression members [Cls. 7.6.4 & 7.6.5]; and inside of stirrups or ties for beams and girders [Cl. 7.6.6].

These conditions reduce development lengths in compression compared to those required in tension. However, hooks cannot be used for compression development [Cl. 12.5.5]. Modifiers for excess reinforcement area, and for enclosure within a spiral or within ties can be used to reduce the required development length [Cl. 12.3.3]. The modified development length cannot be less than 200 mm [Cl.12.3.1].

3.6.2 Design Aids

Compression development lengths for standard deformed reinforcing bars are provided in Table 3.12.

3.7 COMPRESSION LAP SPLICES

3.7.1 General

Compression lap splicing of No. 45 and No. 55 bars is prohibited, unless these bars are lapped with No. 35 or smaller bars or dowels [Cls. 12.14.2.1, 12.16.2 & 15.8.2.5]. Modification factors for reducing the usual lap length apply for the improved confinement provided by special ties and spirals [Cls.12.17.3.4 & 5, and Fig. N12.17.3.4]. As with unspliced compression reinforcement, lap splices in compression in columns and beams must be enclosed within some transverse reinforcement [Cls. 7.6.4 - 6]. Compression lap splice lengths are summarized in Table 3.13.

3.7.2 Splices in Columns

Although the terms are used interchangeably, concentrically loaded columns are not practically possible in reinforced concrete design, and all columns are designed as beam-columns. The A23.3-94 Standard recognizes that some loading conditions, either external or temperature and shrinkage effects, may produce tension in column reinforcement, and requires the reinforcement in each face of a column to develop a minimum tensile resistance. Depending on the magnitude of the tensile resistance required, it may be possible to achieve sufficient tensile resistance at splice locations by staggering compression butt (end bearing) splices so that some reinforcement is continuous to develop tension. Alternately, compression lap splices may be sufficient to develop the required tensile resistance. Otherwise, tensile splicing is necessary. The tensile resistance requirements for column reinforcement are defined in [Cl. 12.17] and are illustrated in Fig. 3.2.

3.8 BUNDLED BARS

3.8.1 General

The use of bundled bars in columns and beams may be necessary to fit reinforcement into limited space. Bundled bar requirements are covered in [Cl. 7.4.2] for details, in [Cl. 12.4] for development, and in [Cl. 12.14.2.2] for lap splicing. Bars may be bundled in groups of 2, 3 or 4 bars, with no more than two bars in any one plane. For spacing and cover (including crack control) requirements, the unit of bundled bars is treated as a single bar with a diameter which provides the same area as all the bars in the bundle. However, for spacing considerations between contacting lap splices, the two bars along the lap are not considered to be a bundle.

3.8.2 Bundled Bars in Beams

Only No. 35 and smaller bars may be bundled in beams and girders. A typical flexural design utilizing bundled bars, where individual bars in the bundle are terminated with reducing moment, is illustrated in Fig. 3.3. [Cl. 7.4.2.3] requires the cutoff locations of individual bars to be staggered. [Cl. 12.4] requires a 20% increase in development length for an individual bar in a 3 bar bundle. Therefore, to achieve the design yield strength, bar $\dot{i}$ requires a tensile development length of 1.2 ℓ_d, where ℓ_d is the single bar development length from Table 3.1 or Table 3.2. Similarly, bar $\dot{a}$ requires a development length of 1.33 ℓ_d.

The two bars of each bundle which extend into the support in Fig. 3.3 require a development length based on the size of an equivalent bar with the same area as the two actual bars, if the recommendations of the ACI Committee 408, 1979 report referenced in [References, Ch. 12, Citation 12.1] are followed. The A23.3-94 Standard addresses only the development of an individual bar in a bundle [Cl. 12.4], and does not specify requirements for the simultaneous development of more than one bar in a bundle. A new provision in A23.3-94 [Cl. 11.3.8.2] requires that the terminating tensile reinforcement be capable of developing a minimum tensile resistance at the inside face of the support bearing area. See Section 3.1.2 (vi), "Bar extensions".

3.8.3 Splicing of Bundled Bars

For tension and compression lap splicing of individual bars in a bundle, [Cl. 12.14.2.2] requires the individual bar splices not to overlap. This requires the cutoff points of the individual bars to be staggered if the full strength is to be developed. The intent of [Cl. 12.14.2.2] is illustrated in Fig. 3.4(a) where the full strength splicing of a two bar bundle is achieved through the introduction of a separate "splice bar", to produce a 3 bar bundle along the total staggered splice length. In any splice length region (A to B, B to C or C to D), load transfer occurs only between two bars, thereby meeting the requirement that "individual bar splices do not overlap."

Bundled bar arrangements in columns, and the tensile resistances that can be developed with full strength compressive butt splices (end bearing or compression mechanical device), are summarized in Fig. 3.4(b). However, in many columns, the tensile resistance required is only a fraction of the compressive strength of the reinforcement [Cl. 12.17] as illustrated in Fig. 3.2. Full mechanical connection for tension, or welding can be used if a larger tensile resistance is necessary with unstaggered splices.

3.9 DEVELOPMENT OF CUTOFF AND CONTINUING REINFORCEMENT

3.9.1 General

It may be economical to reduce the total flexural reinforcing steel provided in slabs, beams and girders by using different lengths of bars for negative and /or positive moment requirements so that the flexural resistances (M_r) available at all sections more closely follow the factored moments (M_f) applied. For flat plates and slabs [Cl. 13.12.5 and Fig. 13-1] provide a guide for choosing bar lengths and cutoff locations. To ensure integrity against progressive collapse, a minimum area of bottom flexural reinforcement must be made effectively continuous through the column or support as specified in [Cl. 13.11.5].

For beams and girders, [Figs. N12.10.3(a), N12.10.3(b), N12.12 & N12.13.4] provide an overview of the embedment requirements to be satisfied for cutoff and continuing reinforcement to ensure development of the bar strengths required at the critical sections. As well, [Cl. 11.3.8.2] requires that terminating tensile reinforcement be capable of developing a minimum tensile resistance at the inside face of the support bearing area. [Fig. N12.10] also illustrates the embedment requirements necessary to limit "flexural bond" stresses in positive moment tension reinforcement at locations where moment is rapidly increasing (high shears), as required by [Cl. 11.11.3], when web reinforcement is designed by the "Simplified Method" [Cl. 11.3]. These requirements apply to points of zero moment, i.e.; the supports of simply supported beams and the points of inflection in continuous construction. The flexural bond provision, however, is waived in [Cl. 12.11.3] if the positive moment reinforcement terminates in a standard hook at a simple support, and the hooked anchorage or equivalent mechanical anchorage provides full development beyond the centreline of the simple support.

For web reinforcement designed by the "General Method" [Cl. 11.4], the rapid build-up of force in the flexural reinforcement is directly considered as illustrated in [Fig. N12.10.3(b)]. [Cl. 11.4.9.5] waives [Cl. 12.11.3], as well as [Cl. 12.10.5] for these designs.

3.9.2 Design Examples

Examples 3.4, 3.5 and 3.7 illustrate the design for cutoff and continuing reinforcement to ensure adequate development of the reinforcement when web reinforcement is designed by the "Simplified Method" [Cl. 11.3].

3.10 DESIGN EXAMPLES AND DESIGN AIDS

Design Examples 3.1 through 3.7 are presented consecutively on the following pages, and utilize many of the design aids (Tables 3.1 through 3.13 and Figs. 3.1 through 3.4), which appear at the end of Ch. 3.

Example 3.1:   Development of Deformed Welded Wire Fabric (WWF)

Find the development length for MD47.6 × MD47.6 WWF with a 152 × 152 grid and f_y = 400 MPa, to be used as temperature and shrinkage reinforcement in concrete with f'_c = 20 MPa (structural low density), where more than 300 mm of concrete is placed below the fabric. Wire diameter for MD47.6 is 7.79 mm from Table 3.7.

Solution and Comments;

From [Cl. 12.7.1, .2 and .3] and Tables 3.6 and 3.7, for deformed WWF;

ℓ_d fabric = ℓ_d wire × "wire fabric factor"

For ℓ_d wire from [Cl. 12.2.3] and [Table 12-1];

require clear cover = d_b, and clear spacing = $2d_b$ in slabs, to use 0.45 coefficient in Table [12-1].

Min. clear cover permitted = 20 mm	[Cl. A12.6.2]
20 mm > d_b = 7.79 mm	O.K.

Min. clear spcg = grid spcg - d_b = 152 - 7.79 = 144 mm
= 144 mm >> $2d_b$ O.K.

For "top" uncoated wire, and normal density concrete,
(k_1 = 1.3, k_2 = 1.0 and k_3 = 1.0)   [Cl. 12.2.4]
ℓ_d wire = 326 mm   Table 3.6

Modify for low density concrete (k_3 = 1.3)   [Cl. 12.2.4]
ℓ_d wire = 326 × 1.3 = 424 mm
Modify for the "wire fabric factor", assuming a cross wire lies within the development length to satisfy the figure in Table 3.7, and using Table 3.7,
∴ ℓ_d fabric = 424 × 0.4 = 170 mm ≮ 200 mm

Use 200 mm

If cross wires do not satisfy the figure in Table 3.7, "wire fabric factor" = 1.0 [Cl. 12.7.3]
∴ ℓ_d fabric = ℓ_d wire = 424 mm ≮ 300 mm

Use 424 mm

Example 3.2:   Lap Splicing of Deformed Welded Wire Fabric (WWF)

Calculate the lap splice length required for the deformed WWF in Example 3.1, assuming the cross wire locations satisfy [Cl. 12.18], as illustrated in [Fig. N12.17].

Solution and Comments;

ℓ_s = ℓ_d × 1.3 ≮ 200 mm   [Cl. 12.18]
= 170 × 1.3 = 221 mm ≮ 200 mm

Use 221 mm

Example 3.3:   Hooked Anchorages

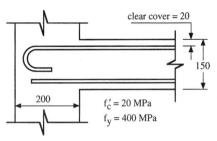

clear cover = 20

150

200

$f'_c = 20$ MPa
$f_y = 400$ MPa

Design negative moment reinforcement for the 150 mm slab and check anchorage into the 200 mm wall for:

A. M_f (neg.) = 25 kN.m per m of slab width using normal density concrete.

B. M_f (neg.) = 20 kN.m per m of slab width using structural low density concrete.

Solutions and Comments:

A. M_f (neg.) = 25 kN.m/m; normal density concrete
Assume No. 10 bars; d = 150 - 20 - 11.3/2 = 124 mm
$K_r = 25 \times 10^6/(1000 \times 124^2) = 1.63$ MPa
∴ ρ = 0.53%   Table 2.1

$A_s = \rho bd = 0.0053 \times 1000 \times 124 = 657$ mm^2/m
Number of No. 10 bars/m = 657/100 = 6.57 and
s = 1000/6.57 = 152 mm   Use s = 150 mm

Anchorage:
ℓ_{hb} (No. 10, f_y = 400 MPa, f'_c = 20 MPa) = 252 mm
[Cl. 12.5.2] and Table 3.9

Modifiers: Large cover modifier . . . . x 0.7
Excess area . . . . x 150/152
$\ell_{dh} = 252 \times 0.7 \times 150/152 = \underline{174 \text{ mm}}$

Check minimum hook length;   [Cl. 12.5.1]
$\ell_{dh} ≮ 8\, d_b = 8 \times 11.3 = 90$ mm   O.K.
≮ 150 mm   O.K.

Embedment available (Assuming 20 mm clear cover on a 180° standard hook)
Emb. = 200 − 20 = 180 mm > ℓ_{dh} = 174 mm O.K.

Note: With a 90° hook, require an end cover to the hook of ≮ 50 mm.   [Cl. 12.5.3(b)] and Fig. 3.1(a)
Max. embedment available = 200 − 50 = 150 mm

Emb. = 150 mm < ℓ_{dh} = 174 mm (no good unless excess reinforcement is provided)

Use No. 10 bars spaced at 150 mm, with a 180° hooked anchorage on the wall end and a 20 mm concrete cover on the hook.

B. M_f (neg.) = 20 kN.m/m; structural low density concrete

Using No. 10 bars and d = 124 mm for a 1 m width,
$K_r = 20 \times 10^6/(1000 \times 124^2) = 1.30$ MPa
∴ ρ = 0.41%   Table 2.1

$A_s = \rho bd = 0.0041 \times 1000 \times 124 = 508$ mm^2/m
Number of No. 10 bars/m = 508/100 = 5.08 and
s = 1000/5.08 = 197 mm   Try s = 195 mm

Anchorage; additional modifier on ℓ_{hb} for;
Structural low density concrete . . . . x 1.3
$\ell_{dh} = 252 \times 0.7 \times 1.3 = \underline{229 \text{ mm}} > 180$ mm No Good

(available embedment length of 180 mm is inadequate with a 180° standard hook)

∴ Provide additional reinforcement by reducing spacing to:
180/229 × 195 = 153 mm   Use 150 mm

Check minimum hook length;   [Cl. 12.5.1]
ℓ_{dh} = 180 mm ≮ 8 d_b = 8 × 11.3 = 90 mm   O.K.
≮ 150 mm   O.K.

Use No. 10 bars spaced at 150 mm, with a 180° hooked anchorage on the wall end and a 20 mm concrete cover on the hook.

Example 3.4:   Development of Flexural Reinforcement in a Cantilever Beam

A cantilever beam, illustrated in Fig. Ex. 3.4 with b × h = 400 mm × 500 mm and a length of 3500 mm, supports a total factored uniformly distributed load w_f = 36.5 kN/m. Material properties are f'_c = 25 MPa (structural low density concrete) and f_y = 400 MPa. Using a clear cover of 65 mm on the No. 10 vertical stirrups (assuming a large cover for a severe service environment) results in a design of 4 – No. 25 bars with a flexural resistance M_r = 232 kN.m for the maximum factored negative moment M_f = 224 kN.m. The No. 10 stirrups are spaced at 200 mm.

A.   Calculate the cutoff location for the two center No. 25 bars. With the 2 remaining No. 25 bars, M_r = 128 kN.m.

B.   Check development of all four No. 25 bars, using the cutoff location found in (A). Adjust the cutoff location as necessary.

C.   Check the adequacy of the stirrup spacing at the cutoff location using the simplified method of [Cl. 11.3].

D.   Check development of the stirrups.

Solutions and Comments:

From Fig. Ex. 3.4

A.   Minimum Cutoff Location for 2 – No. 25 Bars (Bars "B") From Face of Column:
Y = L − X + EXT; provided L − X ≥ ℓ_d for Bars "B"

$M_{r2} = w_f X^2/2$; X = $\sqrt{128 \times 2/36.5}$ = 2.648 m

EXT   = 12d_b ≮ d   [Cls. 12.10.3 and 11.3.8.1]
= 12 × 25.2 ≮ 411
= 302 mm ≮ 411 mm   Use 411 mm

Y = 3500 − 2648 + 411 = 1263 mm
(Provided the bars can be developed)
(NOTE: Part (B.) illustrates Bars "B" can't be developed with this cutoff.)

B.   Check Development and Cutoff Location

(a)   Short Bars "B" (cutoff before cantilever end)
Check use of [Table 12-1] for ℓ_d [Cl. 12.2.3]

Clear spacing between No. 25 bars;
(400 − 2(65 + 11.3) − 4 × 25.2)/3
= 48.9 mm = 1.94d_b > 1.4d_b
Clear cover to No. 25 bars
≈ 65 + 11.3 = 76.3 mm
≈ 3d_b > d_b

∴ Use [Table 12-1]

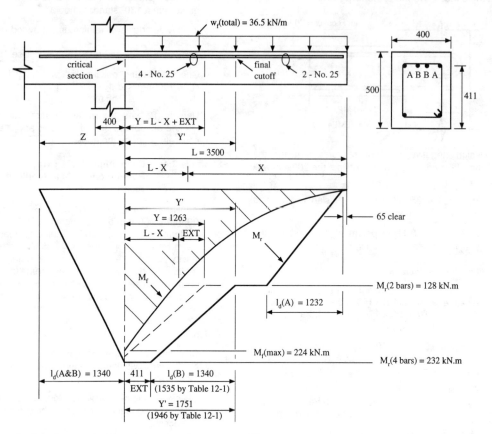

Fig. Ex 3.4   Development of Reinforcement in a Cantilever Beam

Check for minimum stirrups   [Cl. 11.2.8.4]

$A_v \geq A_v$ min. $= 0.06\sqrt{f'_c}\,\dfrac{b_w s}{f_y}$

$A_v = 2 \times 100 = 200$ mm^2

$\underline{200\text{ mm}^2} > 0.06\sqrt{25}\,\dfrac{400 \times 200}{400} = 60$ mm^2

$\qquad\qquad\qquad\qquad\qquad\qquad$ O.K.

$\therefore$ Use 0.45 coefficient in the equation for ℓ_d

$\qquad\qquad\qquad\qquad$ [Table 12-1]

Modification factors;   [Cl. 12.2.4]

Top bars (concrete below $\approx d = 402$ mm)
402 mm > 300 mm $k_1 = 1.3$

"Black" bars (no epoxy coating) $k_2 = 1.0$

From Table 3.1, for [Table 12-1], coeff. = 0.45,
$f'_c = 25$ MPa and No. 25 bars;
$\ell_d = 1181$ mm for normal density concrete

Modify for structural low density concrete
$\qquad\qquad\qquad\qquad\qquad\qquad k_3 = 1.3$

$\ell_d = 1181 \times 1.3 = \underline{1535\text{ mm}}$

Modifier for excess reinforcement (Bars "B")
$\qquad\qquad\qquad\qquad$ [Cl. 12.2.5]
(The use of this modifier is optional)

$\dfrac{A_s \text{ required}}{A_s \text{ provided}} = \dfrac{M_f \text{ max} - M_{r2}}{M_{r4} - M_{r2}} = \dfrac{224 - 128}{232 - 128}$

$\qquad\qquad\qquad = 0.923$

ℓ_d (Bars "B") $= 0.923 \times 1535 = 1417$ mm to develop M_f max. However, it is reasonable to provide anchorage for the full resistance of the reinforcement available, and ℓ_d (Bars "B") $= \ell_d = \underline{1535\text{ mm}}$ will be used to develop $M_r = 232$ kN.m.

Check available embedment length of short Bars "B" to the critical section at the column face

From Fig. Ex. 3.4
$L - X = 3500 - 2648 = 852$ mm
852 mm $< \ell_d = \underline{1535\text{ mm}}$ No Good

i.e., locating the cutoff of bars "B" at a distance $Y = L - X + EXT = 1263$ mm does not provide an M_r diagram which is shifted a minimum of a cutoff extension EXT from the M_f diagram as the support is approached.

$\therefore$ Extend cutoff to Y'

$Y' = \ell_d + EXT = 1535 + 411 = 1946$ mm past face of column to permit development of M_r at a distance EXT $= 411$ mm from the face of the column.

(b) Long Bars "A" (continuing to cantilever end)
As only 2 bars with a large clear spacing between them are being developed, an ℓ_d shorter than that required for the short cutoff Bars "B" may be used.

Clear cover = 65 mm on the No. 10 stirrups makes clear cover on the No. 25 bars ≈ 75 mm and Table 3.3(c) is applicable for the concrete confinement.

For b_w = 400 mm and n = 2, the concrete

confinement index = $\dfrac{d_{cs}}{d_b}$ = 2.5   Table 3.3(c)

Total confinement index = C.I. = $\dfrac{d_{cs}}{d_b} + \dfrac{K_{tr}}{d_b} \leq 2.5$

[Cl. 12.2.2]

∴ C.I. = 2.5, even if stirrup contribution to confinement is ignored.

From Table 3.2 for C.I. = 2.5, f'_c = 25 MPa and No. 25 bars;

ℓ_d (Bars "A") = 729$k_1 k_2 k_3$
ℓ_d = 729 × 1.3 × 1.0 × 1.3   = 1232 mm

(c) All Bars "A" and "B" left of the column
Assume loading on the beam to the left of the column is not critical for development, and the bars need only sufficient embedment to develop the bar strength at the right face of the column. All 4 bars are being developed simultaneously.

For illustration purposes, assume the stirrups in the beam to the left of the column are at the same 200 mm spacing as in the cantilever beam to obtain the transverse reinforcement

confinement index $\dfrac{K_{tr}}{d_b}$.

For b_w = 400 mm and n = 4,

$\dfrac{d_{cs}}{d_b}$ = 1.98   Table 3.3(c)

For s = 100 mm, n = 4 and No. 25 bars,

$\dfrac{K_{tr}}{d_b}$ = 0.75   Table 3.5

For s = 200 mm, $\dfrac{K_{tr}}{d_b} = \dfrac{0.75}{2}$ = 0.375

∴ C.I. = $\dfrac{d_{cs}}{d_b} + \dfrac{K_{tr}}{d_b}$ = 1.98 + 0.37 = 2.35

For C.I. = 2.30, f'_c = 25 MPa and No. 25 bars;

Table 3.2

ℓ_d (Bars "A") = 793$k_1 k_2 k_3$ = 793 × 1.3 × 1.0 × 1.3
= 1340 mm

(Interpolating for C.I. = 2.35 only reduces ℓ_d to 777 × 1.3 × 1.0 × 1.3 = 1313 mm − not warranted)

NOTE: The ℓ_d = 1340 mm calculated above could also be used as a more accurate value for the short Bars "B" in the cantilever beam to the right of the column, rather than the ℓ_d = 1535 mm obtained using the [Table 12-1] approximation for confinement. Then Y′ = ℓ_d + EXT = 1340 + 411 = 1751 mm.

Bar lengths
Bars "B" (short - cutoff)
Z + Y′ = 1340 + 1946 = 3286 mm [Table 12-1]
Z + Y′ = 1340 + 1751 = 3091 mm [Eqn. (12-1)]
and Tables 3.2, 3.3(c) and 3.5

Bars "A" (continuous)
Z + L − cover = 1340 + 3500 − 65 = 4775 mm

C. Check 200 mm Spacing of Vertical No. 10 Stirrups for Maximum Design Shear and at the Cutoff Location Using the Simple Design Approach [Cl. 11.2.11], [Cl. 11.3] and [Cl. 12.10.5]

Maximum design shear;
For s ≤ 600 mm or 0.7d, $v_f \leq 0.1\lambda\phi_c f'_c$
[Cl. 11.2.11(a)]
s = 200 mm ≤ 600 mm or 0.7d = 0.7 × 411 = 288 mm

Using d_v = d in [Cl. 11.4.5], and V_f max on basis of [Cl. 11.3.2];
$v_f = \dfrac{V_f \, max}{b_w d_v} = \dfrac{36.5 \times (3.5 - 0.411) \times 10^{-3}}{0.40 \times 0.411}$
= 0.686 MPa

v_f = 0.686 MPa <0.1 × 0.75 × 0.6 × 25 = 1.125 MPa
O.K.

Cutoff location;
V_f cutoff $\not>$ 2/3 ($V_c + V_s$)   [Cl. 12.10.5(a)]

Since stirrups satisfy [Cl. 11.2.8.4] for minimum stirrups - see Part B.;

$V_c = 0.2\lambda\phi_c \sqrt{f'_c} \, b_w d$ [Cl. 11.3.5.1]

V_c = 0.2 × 0.75 × 0.6 × $\sqrt{25}$ × 0.40 × 0.411
= 0.0740 MN = 74.0 kN

$V_s = \dfrac{\phi_s A_v f_y d}{s}$ [Cl. 11.3.7]

$V_s = \dfrac{0.85 \times 2 \times 100 \times 10^{-6} \times 400 \times 411}{200}$
= 0.1397 MN = 139.7 kN

Check [Cl. 12.10.5(a)] for the cutoff at Y′ = 1751 mm
V_f cutoff = 36.5(3.5 − 1.751) = 63.8 kN

V_f cutoff = 63.8 kN $\not>$ 2/3 (74.0 + 139.7) = 142.5 kN
O.K.

D. Check Development of Stirrups   [Cl.12.13]
No. 10 closed stirrups with 135° standard hooks anchored around longitudinal reinforcement satisfy [Cl.12.13.2(a)] with no further check required. O.K.

Example 3.5:   Development and Cutoffs in a Simply Supported Beam

A simply supported R/C beam in Fig. Ex. 3.5 rests on 800 mm wide masonry pilasters over a clear span of 10 m. Although anchored, the beam is not integral with the supports. The uniformly distributed loading on the beam is 22 kN/m dead (including self weight) and 25 kN/m live. Using f'_c = 30 MPa (normal density concrete with a maximum aggregate size = 28 mm) and f_y = 400 MPa, select the flexural reinforcement and make practical cutoffs. Assume interior exposure for crack control provisions, but a cover of 40 mm to the stirrups to provide a nominal fire resistance. Assume stirrups will be designed using the simplified method of [Cl. 11.3].

A. Design the Flexural Reinforcement:
$\ell = \ell_n + h \not> \ell_n + W$ [Cl. 8.7.1]
ℓ = 10000 + 750 $\not>$ 10000 + 800, use 10750 mm

$w_f = 1.25w_d + 1.5w_\ell$ [Cl. 9.2.3]
= 1.25 × 22 + 1.5 × 25 = 65.0 kN/m
$M_f = w_f \ell^2/8$ = 65.0 × 10.75^2/8 = 939 kN.m

(i) Assuming No. 10 stirrups and 5 No. 35 bars, [Cl. A12.5.2] and Table 2.1
d = 750 − 40 − 11.3 − 35.7/2 = 681 mm
$\rho\% = \dfrac{A_s \times 100}{b \times d} = \dfrac{5 \times 1000 \times 100}{500 \times 681}$ = 1.47%

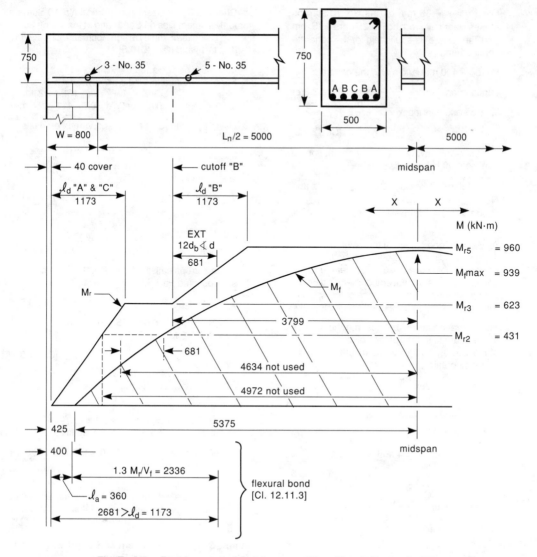

Fig. Ex 3.5: Development of Reinforcement in a Simply Supported Beam

$K_r = 4.14$ MPa, $M_r = K_r bd^2 \times 10^{-6}$
$M_r = 4.14 \times 500 \times 681^2 \times 10^{-6} = 960$ kN·m
5 – No. 35 bars provide $M_r = \overline{960 \text{ kN·m}} > M_f$ O.K.

Check bar spacing in one layer;   Table 3.3(b)
For clear cover = 40 + 11.3 = 51.3 mm ≈ 50 mm to
No. 35 bars, and $b_w = 500$ mm, a maximum of
5 No. 35 bars can be placed with clear spacing
≮ $1.4d_b$ and 30 mm   O.K.

Also, spacing ≮ $1.4d_b$ and 1.4(max. aggregate size)
                                                    [Cl. A12.5.2]
Since $d_b = 35.7$ mm > (max. aggregate size =
28 mm), aggregate size is O.K.

(ii)   Assuming No. 10 stirrups and 7 No. 30 bars,
       [Cl. A12.5.2] and Table 2.1
       $d = 750 - 40 - 11.3 - 29.9/2 = 684$ mm
       $\rho\% = \dfrac{A_s \times 100}{b \times d} = \dfrac{7 \times 700 \times 100}{500 \times 684} = 1.43\%$
       $K_r = 4.05$ MPa, $M_r = K_r bd^2 \times 10^{-6}$
       $M_r = 4.05 \times 500 \times 684^2 \times 10^{-6} = 947$ kN·m
       7 – No. 30 bars provide $M_r = \overline{947 \text{ kN·m}} > M_f$ O.K.

       Check bar spacing in one layer;   Table 3.3(b)
       For clear cover = 40 + 11.3 = 51.3 mm ≈ 50 mm to
       No. 30 bars, and $b_w = 500$ mm, a maximimum of
       only 6 No. 30 bars can be placed with clear spacing
       ≮ $1.4d_b$ and 30 mm.   No Good

       ∴ To avoid bundling or 2 layers, use 5 equally
       spaced No. 35 bars.

B.   Determination of Bar Cutoff Locations and Check-
     ing Development.   Fig. Ex. 3.5
     Assume Bars "B" are cutoff initially as M reduces,
     and possibly Bar "C" later, if practical.
     This satisfies the requirement of at least $1/3 \times A_s$
     into the supports.   [Cl. 12.11.1]

     With 2 bars cutoff (Bars "B"), $M_{r3} = 623$ kN·m
     With 3 bars cutoff (Bars "B" and "C"), $M_{r2} = 431$ kN·m

     For simplicity, use a single ℓ_d from [Table 12 -1]
     for all bars.   [Cl. 12.2.3]

     (Part A.(i) showed bar spacing and cover are O.K.,
     or, can show clear cover on No. 35 bars = $1.44d_b$ >
     d_b, and clear spacing between No. 35 bars =
     $1.53d_b > 1.4d_b$)

     ∴ Use [Table 12-1]

         Assume No. 10 stirrups are spaced at maxi-
         mum permitted for transverse shear;

         s ≯ 600 mm or 0.7d   [Cl.11.2.11(a)]
           ≯ 600 mm or $0.7 \times 681 = 476$ mm
                       use 400 mm practical spacing

         Check for minimum stirrups   [Cl. 11.2.8.4]
         $A_v \geq A_v$ min. $= 0.06\sqrt{f_c'}\,\dfrac{b_w s}{f_y}$
         A_v (2 legs of No. 10 bar) $= 2 \times 100 = 200$ mm^2
         $\underline{200 \text{ mm}^2} > 0.06\sqrt{30}\,\dfrac{500 \times 400}{400} = 164$ mm^2

     ∴ Use 0.45 coeff. in the equation for ℓ_d [Table 12-1]

     For uncoated bottom bars in normal density con-
     crete ($k_1 = k_2 = k_3 = 1$), $f_c' = 30$ MPa and No 35 bars,
     $\ell_d = 1173$ mm   Table 3.1

     Modifier for excess reinforcement   [Cl. 12.2.5]
     Use 1.0 to permit development of full $M_r = 960$ kN·m
                                            Fig. Ex. 3.5

$\ell_d = 1173$ mm

(i)   Cutoff location for 2 – "B" Bars
      Let EXT = minimum extension of reinforcement
      beyond cutoff required for flexure alone at distance X.

      EXT $= 12d_b \nless d$ [Cls. 12.10.3 and 11.3.8.1]
           $= 12 \times 35.7 \nless 681$
           $= 428$ mm ≮ 681 mm   Use 681 mm

      For X = $\ell/2 = 10750/2 = 5375$ mm, M = $M_f = 939$ kN·m
      Min. cutoff distance each way from midspan = X +
      EXT

      $X^2 = 5375^2/939 \times (939 - 623)$;
      $X = 3118$ mm;   X + EXT = 3799 mm
      $\ell_d = 1173$ mm < X + EXT = 3799 mm   O.K.

(ii) Cutoff location for 1 – "C" Bar
      $X^2 = 5375^2/939 \times (939 - 431)$;
      $X = 3953$ mm;   X + EXT = 4634 mm
      $\ell_d = 1173$ mm ≯ (4634 − 3799) = 835 mm No Good

      To satisy [Cl. 12.10.4], extend cutoff of Bar "C" to
      3799 + 1173 = 4972 mm either side of midspan.

      Since the half beam span is only 5375 mm, do not
      cutoff bar "C", but rather extend fully into the support
      along with Bars "A".

      Also, for crack control [Cl. 10.6.1], need a minimum
      of 3 No. 35 bars in $b_w = 500$ mm for interior exposure
      when clear cover to No. 10 stirrups is 40 mm.
      Calculations (not shown) give:
      z (3 bars) = 28030 N/mm < 30000 N/mm   OK.
      z (2 bars) = 32090 N/mm > 30000 N/mm   No Good
      ∴ Extend 3 bars, Bars "A" and "C" into the support.

C.   Check [Cl. 11.3.8.2] for Adequate Anchorage of the
     Three Bars at the Simple Support.
     This provision ensures a sufficient tensile resis-
     tance can be developed at the inside face of the
     pilaster to carry the horizontal component of the
     diagonal strut action necessary for developing
     shear resistance.

     T_r min. $= V_f - 0.5V_s$
     $V_f = 65.0 \times 5 = 325$ kN @ inside face of pilaster
     $V_s = \phi_s A_v f_{yt} d/s$ for stirrups @ inside face of pilaster
         $= 0.85 \times 2 \times 100 \times 400 \times 681/400 = 116$ kN
     T_r min. $= 325 - 116/2 = 267$ kN

     Available embedment of No. 35 bars to inside face
     of bearing area = $W_{pilaster} -$ cover = 800 − 40 =
     760 mm
     As $\ell_d >$ 760 mm, bar stress that is capable of being
     developed at inside face;
     $f_s = f_y \times 760/\ell_d = 400 \times 760/1173 = 259$ MPa
     ∴ $T_r = \phi_s f_s A_s$
         $= 0.85 \times 259 \times 3 \times 1000 \times 10^{-3}$ (3 No. 35 bars)
         $= \underline{660 \text{ kN}} > \underline{267 \text{ kN}}$ O.K.

D.   Check Flexural Bond Requirements at the Sup-
     ports:
     $1.3M_r/V_f + \ell_a > \ell_d$ [Cl. 12.11.3]

     $M_r = M_{r(3)} = 623$ kN.m, $\ell_d = 1173$ mm,
     $V_f = w_f \times \ell/2 = 65.0 \times 5.375 = 349$ kN
     Max $\ell_a = W/2$ 40 − 800/2 − 40 = 360 mm

     $1.3(623 \times 10^3)/349 + 360 = \underline{2681 \text{ mm}} > \underline{1390 \text{ mm}}$
                                                      O.K.

E. Summary

Bars "B": Cutoff at 3799 mm each side of midspan, $L_B = 2 \times 3799$ mm $\approx$ 7600 mm

Bars "A" and "C": Extend to within clear cover = 40 mm at each beam end, $L_A = L_C = 11520$ mm

NOTE: Checking adequacy of the nominal stirrup spacing provided on the basis of [Cl. 11.2.11(a)] is not included herein; however, an increased shear resistance is required at the cutoff locations of Bars "B" [Cl. 12.10.5], for stirrups designed using the simplified method of [Cl. 11.3].

See Ex. 3.4 for shear check at a cutoff location.

Example 3.6: Tensile Lap Splices

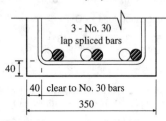

The beam section illustrated has b $\times$ h = 350 mm $\times$ 600 mm, is made of normal density concrete with f'_c = 25 MPa, and uses uncoated, grade 400 deformed reinforcement. The effective depth d is 545 mm. All 3 No. 30 bars are lap spliced in the same high stress region. No. 10 stirrups spaced at 200 mm confine the lap length. Compare the required lap length for the simple approach using [Table 12-1] with the detailed approach using [Cl. 12.2.2].

A. *Simple approach:* [Table 12-1] and Table 3.1

Check bar spacing and cover; [Cl. 12.2.3]

For clear cover = 40 mm to No. 30 bars, and b_w = 350 mm, a maximum of 3 No. 30 pairs of contact lap spliced bars can be placed with clear spacing $\not< 1.4\, d_b$ and 30 mm O.K. Table 3.4(a)
Clear cover = 40 mm $> d_b$ = 29.9 mm O.K.

Check for minimum stirrups; [Table 12-1]

$s \not> 600$ mm or 0.7 d [Cl.11.2.11(a)]
200 mm $\not> 600$ mm or $0.7 \times 545 = 382$ mm O.K.

$A_v \geq A_v$ min. $= 0.06\sqrt{f'_c}\dfrac{b_w s}{f_y}$ [Cl. 11.2.8.4]

A_v (2 legs of No. 10 bar) $= 2 \times 100 = 200$ mm^2

200 mm$^2 > 0.06\sqrt{25}\dfrac{350 \times 200}{400} = 52.5$ mm^2 O.K.

$\therefore$ Use 0.45 coefficient in the equation for ℓ_d [Table 12-1]
ℓ_d = 1075 mm for bottom, uncoated No. 30 bars in normal density concrete with f'_c = 25 MPa. Table 3.1

For Class B splices, $\ell_s = 1.3\, \ell_d$; [Cl. 12.15]
$\ell_s = 1.3 \times 1075 = \underline{1398 \text{ mm}}$

B. *Detailed approach:* [Cl. 12.2.2] and Table 3.2

Total confinement index $= \text{C.I.} = \dfrac{d_{cs}}{d_b} + \dfrac{K_{tr}}{d_b} \leq 2.5$

For 3 – No. 30 bars spliced over b_w = 350 mm, with 40 mm cover to the No. 30 bars; $d_{cs}/d_b = \underline{1.68}$ Table 3.4(a)

For 3 No. 30 bars being confined by No. 10 vertical stirrups (2 legs) @ s = 100 mm, $K_{tr}/d_b = 0.85$ Table 3.5
$\therefore$ For s = 200 mm, $K_{tr}/d_b = 0.85/2 = \underline{0.425}$

$\therefore$ Total confinement index = C.I. = 1.68 + 0.425 = 2.105
For C.I. = 2.1, f'_c = 25 MPa and No. 30 bars,

$\ell_d = 1027\, k_1 k_2 k_3$ Table 3.2

For bottom, uncoated bars in normal density concrete ($k_1 = k_2 = k_3 = 1.0$) $\ell_d = \underline{1027 \text{ mm}}$

$\therefore$ For a Class B splice, $\ell_s = 1.3 \times 1027 = \underline{1335 \text{ mm}}$ [Cl. 12.15]

C. *Comparison:*

The detailed approach results in a lap length which is 5% shorter in this design; there is little difference in computational effort by the two approaches when design aids are used.

Example 3.7: Cantilever Retaining Wall –Tension Splicing and Development of Reinforcement

A 3.5 m high uniform section cantilever retaining wall made of normal density concrete with f'_c = 25 MPa, requires No. 25 grade 400 vertical reinforcing spaced at 100 mm at the base to carry a hydrostatic lateral load in flexure. Clear cover on the vertical reinforcement is 75 mm to give an effective depth d = 162 mm. A third of the bars extend to the top of the wall and are spliced to dowels at the footing. The remaining 2/3 of the bars extend continuously into the footing. Half of these bars are cut off at one location while the remaining 1/3 of the total are cut off at a different location, as required for flexure. See Fig. Ex. 3.7.

Solutions and Comments:

Determine the cutoff locations, conservatively assuming that the moment resistance at sections with reduced bars is proportional to the number of bars present.

A. Bars "A": for 2/3 A_s, $M \approx (2/3)(wL^3/(6L)) = wX^3/(6L)$
$X = (2L^3/3)^{1/3} = [(2 \times 3.5^3)/3]^{1/3} = 3.058$ m

Let EXT = minimum extension of reinforcement beyond cutoff required for flexure alone at distance X.

EXT $= 12 d_b \not< d$ [Cls. 12.10.3 and 11.3.8.1]
$= 12 \times 25.2 \not< 162$
$= 302$ mm $\not< 162$ mm Use 302 mm

Development length of Bars "A";

Find concrete confinement d_{cs}: [Cl. 12.2.2, Eq. (12-1)]
As bond splitting is induced by development of Bars "A" and by lap splicing of Bars "C", use the spacing between these to define confinement.

Min. c. to c. spacing $= 100$ mm $- d_b = 100 - 25.2 = 74.8$ mm $\therefore d_{cs1} = 2/3(74.8) = 49.9$ mm $= 1.98\, d_b$

Min. cover to center of bars $= d_{cs2}$
$d_{cs2} = 75 + 25.2/2 = 87.6$ mm $= 3.48\, d_b$

$\therefore d_{cs} = 1.98\, d_b$, and in the absence of stirrups ($K_{tr} = 0$), the confinement index C.I. $= d_{cs}/d_b + K_{tr}/d_b = 1.98$.
For C.I = 2.0, $\ell_d = 912\, k_1 k_2 k_3$, Table 3.2
where $k_1 = 1.0$ for vertical bars, $k_2 = 1$ for uncoated bars and $k_3 = 1$ for normal density concrete.
[Cl. 12.2.4]
$\therefore \ell_{dA} = \underline{912 \text{ mm}}$

Cutoff of Bars "A" above footing is the larger of;

(i) $L - X + EXT = 3500 - 3058 + 302 = 744$ mm, or

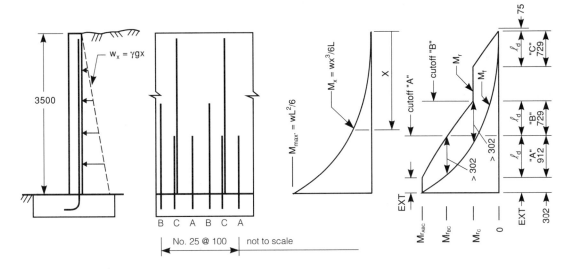

Fig. Ex 3.7   Cantilever Retaining Wall

(ii) ℓ_d + EXT, to ensure development, by keeping a separation of at least EXT between the M_r and M_f diagrams
ℓ_d + EXT = 912 + 302 = 1214 mm

B. Bars "B": for 1/3 A_s, X = $(1/3 \times 3.5^3)^{1/3}$ = 2.427 m
Development length of Bars "B";

Set up M_r diagram so only Bars "B" need to be developed at the same location, i.e., begin development starting at the cutoff location of bars "A", as shown in Fig. Ex. 3.7.

Spacing d_{cs} = 2/3(300) = 200 mm = 7.94 d_b > 2.5 d_b
Cover d_{cs} = 3.48 d_b > 2.5 d_b
∴ C.I. = 2.5 and ℓ_{dB} = 729 mm   Table 3.2

Cutoff of Bars "B" above footing is the larger of;

(i) L − X + EXT = 3500 − 2427 + 302 = 1375 mm, or

(ii) ℓ_{dB} + cutoff$_A$ = 729 + 1214 = 1943 mm

C. Bars "C":
Top end;
ℓ_d = 729 mm for large cover and spacing as for Bars "B".

Bottom end:
Splice length = projection of dowels above the footing.
Splice location has ℓ_d = 912 mm as for Bars "A".
For "Class B" splice, ℓ_s = 1.3 ℓ_d = 1.3 × 912 = 1186 mm;
Say extend lap to the cutoff location of Bars "A" @ 1214 mm above the footing.

Table 3.1 Development lengths^ (mm) based on [Table 12-1]* for heavier confined# deformed reinforcing bars~ with f_y = 400 MPa&, for normal density concrete@.

$$\ell_d = 0.45\ k_1\ k_2\ k_3\ k_4\ \frac{f_y}{\sqrt{f_c'}}\ d_b \not< 300\ \text{mm}^\$$$

Modification Factors Included [Clause 12.2.4]	f_c' (MPa)	No.10	No.15	No.20	No.25	No.30	No.35	No.45	No.55
k_1 = 1.0 – "bottom" bars	20	363	514	629	1016	1202	1436	1759	2271
	25	325	460	563	908	1075	1285	1573	2031
	30	297	420	514	829	981	1173	1436	1854
k_2 = 1.0 – "uncoated" bars	35	275	388	476	768	908	1086	1330	1717
	40	257	363	445	718	850	1016	1244	1606
k_3 = 1.0 – normal density concrete@	45	242	343	420	677	801	957	1173	1514
	50	230	325	398	642	760	908	1112	1436
	55	219	310	379	612	725	866	1061	1369
	60	210	297	363	586	694	829	1016	1311
	64	203	287	352	568	672	803	983	1269
k_1 = 1.0 – "bottom" bars	20	545	771	944	1523	1802	2154	2638	3406
	25	487	689	844	1362	1612	1927	2360	3047
	30	445	629	771	1244	1472	1759	2154	2781
k_2 = 1.5 – epoxy coated bars	35	412	583	714	1152	1362	1628	1994	2575
	40	385	545	667	1077	1274	1523	1866	2409
k_3 = 1.0 – normal density concrete@	45	363	514	629	1016	1202	1436	1759	2271
	50	345	487	597	963	1140	1362	1669	2154
	55	329	465	569	919	1087	1299	1591	2054
	60	315	445	545	879	1041	1244	1523	1967
	64	305	431	528	852	1008	1204	1475	1904
k_1 = 1.3 – "top" bars	20	472	668	818	1320	1562	1867	2287	2952
	25	422	597	732	1181	1397	1670	2045	2640
	30	386	545	668	1078	1275	1524	1867	2410
k_2 = 1.0 – "uncoated" bars	35	357	505	618	998	1181	1411	1729	2232
	40	334	472	578	934	1105	1320	1617	2087
k_3 = 1.0 – normal density concrete@	45	315	445	545	880	1041	1245	1524	1968
	50	299	422	517	835	988	1181	1446	1867
	55	285	403	493	796	942	1126	1379	1780
	60	273	386	472	762	902	1078	1320	1704
	64	264	373	457	738	873	1044	1278	1650
k_1 x k_2 = 1.7 (top location and epoxy coated bars)	20	618	874	1070	1726	2043	2442	2990	3860
	25	552	781	957	1544	1827	2184	2675	3453
	30	504	713	874	1410	1668	1993	2442	3152
	35	467	660	809	1305	1544	1846	2260	2918
k_3 = 1.0 – normal density concrete@	40	437	618	756	1221	1444	1726	2114	2730
	45	412	582	713	1151	1362	1628	1993	2574
	50	391	552	677	1092	1292	1544	1891	2442
	55	372	527	645	1041	1232	1472	1803	2328
	60	357	504	618	997	1179	1410	1726	2229
	64	345	488	598	965	1142	1365	1672	2158
Modification Factors Included [Clause 12.2.4]	f_c' (MPa)	No.10	No.15	No.20	No.25	No.30	No.35	No.45	No.55

* Clear cover and clear spacing of bars must be at least 1.0d_b and 1.4d_b, respectively. [Cl. 12.2.3]

\# For lighter confinement, "(Other cases)" in [Table 12-1], multiply the above table values by 1.33.

\# To qualify for heavier confinement, must have either: [Table 12-1]
    Member containing minimum stirrups or ties within ℓ_d, [Cl. 11.2.8.4 or Cl. 7.6.5]
    or
    Slabs, walls, shells or folded plates having clear spacing between bars being developed not less than 2d_b.

& For $f_y \neq$ 400 MPa, multiply development length by f_y/400.

@ Multiply table values by; k_3 = 1.3 for structural low density concrete
                     k_3 = 1.2 for structural semi-low density concrete

~ The appropriate bar size factor k_4 has been applied.

  For concrete strengths > 64 MPa, use development length for 64 MPa. [Cl. 12.1.1]

\$ After application of all modification factors, the development length must not be less than 300 mm.

Table 3.2 Development lengths (mm) for deformed reinforcing bars with f_y = 400 MPa[*], before factors k_1 to k_3 are applied[~], for the concrete strengths (f_c' in MPa) indicated, and for different total confinement indices (C.I.)[#].

Application	C.I.	f_c'	No.10	No.15	No.20	No.25	No.30	No.35	No.45	No.55
	1.5	20	486	688	842	1359	1608	1922	2354	3039
Ignoring, or in the absence of stirrups		25	435	615	753	1215	1438	1719	2105	2718
along the development length,		30	397	561	688	1110	1313	1569	1922	2481
the total confinement index indicated		35	368	520	637	1027	1215	1453	1779	2297
is available only for:		40	344	486	595	961	1137	1359	1664	2149
		45	324	458	561	906	1072	1281	1569	2026
Minimum clear cover = $1.0d_b$		50	307	435	533	859	1017	1215	1489	1922
Minimum clear spacing = $1.25d_b$ [@]		55	293	415	508	819	970	1159	1419	1832
		60	281	397	486	785	928	1110	1359	1754
[@] $1.4d_b$ is required by [Cl. A12.5.2]	1.5	64	272	384	471	760	899	1074	1316	1699
	1.6	20	456	645	789	1274	1507	1802	2207	2849
Ignoring, or in the absence of stirrups		25	408	577	706	1139	1348	1611	1974	2548
along the development length,		30	372	526	645	1040	1231	1471	1802	2326
the total confinement index indicated		35	345	487	597	963	1139	1362	1668	2153
is available only for:		40	322	456	558	901	1066	1274	1560	2014
		45	304	430	526	849	1005	1201	1471	1899
Minimum clear cover = $1.1d_b$		50	288	408	499	806	953	1139	1396	1802
Minimum clear spacing = $1.4d_b$		55	275	389	476	768	909	1086	1331	1718
		60	263	372	456	736	870	1040	1274	1645
	1.6	64	255	360	441	712	843	1007	1233	1592
	1.7	20	429	607	743	1199	1419	1696	2077	2681
Ignoring, or in the absence of stirrups		25	384	543	665	1072	1269	1517	1858	2398
along the development length,		30	350	495	607	979	1158	1385	1696	2189
the total confinement index indicated		35	324	459	562	906	1072	1282	1570	2027
is available only for:		40	303	429	525	848	1003	1199	1468	1896
		45	286	404	495	799	946	1130	1385	1787
Minimum clear cover = $1.2d_b$		50	271	384	470	758	897	1072	1313	1696
Minimum clear spacing = $1.55d_b$		55	259	366	448	723	856	1023	1252	1617
		60	248	350	429	692	819	979	1199	1548
	1.7	64	240	339	415	670	793	948	1161	1499
	1.8	20	405	573	702	1132	1340	1601	1961	2532
Ignoring, or in the absence of stirrups		25	362	512	628	1013	1198	1432	1754	2265
along the development length,		30	331	468	573	925	1094	1308	1601	2067
the total confinement index indicated		35	306	433	530	856	1013	1211	1483	1914
is available only for:		40	286	405	496	801	947	1132	1387	1790
		45	270	382	468	755	893	1068	1308	1688
Minimum clear cover = $1.3d_b$		50	256	362	444	716	847	1013	1240	1601
Minimum clear spacing = $1.7d_b$		55	244	346	423	683	808	966	1183	1527
		60	234	331	405	654	774	925	1132	1462
	1.8	64	226	320	392	633	749	895	1096	1416
	1.9	20	384	543	665	1073	1269	1517	1858	2399
Ignoring, or in the absence of stirrups		25	343	485	595	960	1135	1357	1662	2146
along the development length,		30	313	443	543	876	1036	1239	1517	1959
the total confinement index indicated		35	290	410	503	811	960	1147	1405	1813
is available only for:		40	271	384	470	759	898	1073	1314	1696
		45	256	362	443	715	846	1011	1239	1599
Minimum clear cover = $1.4d_b$		50	243	343	420	678	803	960	1175	1517
Minimum clear spacing = $1.85d_b$		55	231	327	401	647	765	915	1121	1447
		60	222	313	384	619	733	876	1073	1385
	1.9	64	215	303	372	600	710	848	1039	1341
Application	**C.I.**	f_c'	**No.10**	**No.15**	**No.20**	**No.25**	**No.30**	**No.35**	**No.45**	**No.55**

[*] For reinforcing yield strength $f_y \neq$ 400 MPa, multiply development length in table by $f_y/400$. [Cl. 12.2.2]

[#] Confinement Index (C.I.) = d_{cs}/d_b from Table 3.3 or $3.4 + K_{tr}/d_b$ from Table 3.5.

[~] Development lengths are for bottom bars, no epoxy coating, and normal density concrete ($k_1 = k_2 = k_3 = 1.0$).

After factors k_1 to k_3 are applied, development length must not be less than 300 mm.

For concrete strengths > 64 MPa, use length for 64 MPa. [Cl. 12.1.1]

Table 3.2 Development lengths (mm) for deformed reinforcing bars with f_y = 400 MPa[*], before factors k_1 to k_3
(cont'd) are applied[~], for the concrete strengths (f'_c in MPa) indicated, and for different total confinement indices (C.I.)[#].

Application	C.I.	f'_c	No.10	No.15	No.20	No.25	No.30	No.35	No.45	No.55
	2	20	365	516	632	1019	1206	1441	1765	2279
Ignoring, or in the absence of stirrups		25	326	461	565	912	1079	1289	1579	2038
along the development length,		30	298	421	516	832	985	1177	1441	1861
the total confinement index indicated		35	276	390	477	770	912	1090	1334	1723
is available only for:		40	258	365	447	721	853	1019	1248	1611
		45	243	344	421	679	804	961	1177	1519
Minimum clear cover = $1.5d_b$		50	231	326	399	645	763	912	1116	1441
Minimum clear spacing = $2.0d_b$		55	220	311	381	615	727	869	1064	1374
		60	211	298	365	588	696	832	1019	1316
	2	64	204	288	353	570	674	806	987	1274
	2.1	20	347	491	601	971	1148	1373	1681	2170
Ignoring, or in the absence of stirrups		25	311	439	538	868	1027	1228	1504	1941
along the development length,		30	284	401	491	793	938	1121	1373	1772
the total confinement index indicated		35	263	371	455	734	868	1038	1271	1641
is available only for:		40	246	347	425	686	812	971	1189	1535
		45	232	327	401	647	766	915	1121	1447
Minimum clear cover = $1.6d_b$		50	220	311	380	614	726	868	1063	1373
Minimum clear spacing = $2.15d_b$		55	209	296	363	585	693	828	1014	1309
		60	200	284	347	560	663	793	971	1253
	2.1	64	194	275	336	543	642	767	940	1213
	2.2	20	331	469	574	927	1096	1310	1605	2072
Ignoring, or in the absence of stirrups		25	296	419	514	829	981	1172	1435	1853
along the development length,		30	271	383	469	756	895	1070	1310	1692
the total confinement index indicated		35	251	354	434	700	829	990	1213	1566
is available only for:		40	234	331	406	655	775	927	1135	1465
		45	221	313	383	618	731	874	1070	1381
Minimum clear cover = $1.7d_b$		50	210	296	363	586	693	829	1015	1310
Minimum clear spacing = $2.3d_b$		55	200	283	346	559	661	790	968	1249
		60	191	271	331	535	633	756	927	1196
	2.2	64	185	262	321	518	613	732	897	1158
	2.3	20	317	448	549	886	1049	1253	1535	1982
Ignoring, or in the absence of stirrups		25	284	401	491	793	938	1121	1373	1772
along the development length,		30	259	366	448	724	856	1023	1253	1618
the total confinement index indicated		35	240	339	415	670	793	947	1160	1498
is available only for:		40	224	317	388	627	741	886	1085	1401
		45	211	299	366	591	699	836	1023	1321
Minimum clear cover = $1.8d_b$		50	201	284	347	560	663	793	971	1253
Minimum clear spacing = $2.45d_b$		55	191	270	331	534	632	756	926	1195
		60	183	259	317	512	605	724	886	1144
	2.3	64	177	251	307	495	586	701	858	1108
A total confinement index of ≥ 2.5	2.5	20	292	413	505	815	965	1153	1412	1823
gives the smallest development		25	261	369	452	729	863	1031	1263	1631
length permitted by A23.3, Eq. (12-1)		30	238	337	413	666	788	941	1153	1489
and is only applicable when heavy		35	221	312	382	616	729	872	1068	1378
confinement is available.		40	206	292	357	577	682	815	999	1289
		45	194	275	337	544	643	769	941	1215
Ignoring, or in the absence of stirrups:		50	184	261	320	516	610	729	893	1153
Minimum clear cover = $2.0d_b$		55	176	249	305	492	582	695	852	1099
Minimum clear spacing = $2.75d_b$		60	168	238	292	471	557	666	815	1053
	2.5	64	163	231	282	456	539	645	789	1019
Application	**C.I.**	**f'_c**	**No.10**	**No.15**	**No.20**	**No.25**	**No.30**	**No.35**	**No.45**	**No.55**

[*] For reinforcing yield strength $f_y \neq 400$ MPa,, multiply development length in table by $f_y/400$. [Cl. 12.2.2]

[#] Confinement Index (C.I.) = d_{cs}/d_b from Table 3.3 or $3.4 + K_{tr}/d_b$ from Table 3.5.

[~] Development lengths are for bottom bars, no epoxy coating, and normal density concrete ($k_1 = k_2 = k_3 = 1.0$).
   After factors k_1 to k_3 are applied, development length must not be less than 300 mm.
   For concrete strengths > 64 MPa, use length for 64 MPa. [Cl. 12.1.1]

Table 3.3(a) Concrete confinement index d_{cs}/d_b for n deformed bars with a clear cover of 40 mm (d_b for No. 45 and No. 55 bars), spaced uniformly across a stem width $b_w{}^\#$ (mm).

b_w	n	No.10	No.15	No.20	No.25	No.30	No.35
200	2	2.50	2.50	2.50	2.09	1.84	
	3	2.50	2.17	1.71			
250	2	2.50	2.50	2.50	2.09	1.84	1.62
	3	2.50	2.50	2.50	1.91		
	4	2.50	2.15	1.71			
300	3*	2.50	2.50	2.50	2.09	1.84	1.62
	4	2.50	2.50	2.28	1.72		
	5	2.50	2.13	1.71			
	6	2.47					
350	3*	2.50	2.50	2.50	2.09	1.84	1.62
	4	2.50	2.50	2.50	2.09	1.79	
	5	2.50	2.50	2.14	1.62		
	6	2.50	2.12	1.71			
	7	2.50					
400	4*	2.50	2.50	2.50	2.09	1.84	1.62
	5	2.50	2.50	2.50	1.95	1.62	
	6	2.50	2.50	2.05			
	7	2.50	2.12	1.71			
	8	2.50					
450	4*	2.50	2.50	2.50	2.09	1.84	1.62
	5	2.50	2.50	2.50	2.09	1.84	
	6	2.50	2.50	2.39	1.82		
	7	2.50	2.47	1.99			
	8	2.50	2.11	1.71			
	9	2.50					
500	5*	2.50	2.50	2.50	2.09	1.84	1.62
	6	2.50	2.50	2.50	2.09	1.74	
	7	2.50	2.50	2.28	1.74		
	8	2.50	2.41	1.95			
	9	2.50	2.11	1.71			
	10	2.50					
550	6*	2.50	2.50	2.50	2.09	1.84	1.62
	7	2.50	2.50	2.50	1.96	1.64	
	8	2.50	2.50	2.20	1.68		
	9	2.50	2.37	1.92			
	10	2.50	2.11	1.71			
	11	2.50					
600	6*	2.50	2.50	2.50	2.09	1.84	1.62
	7	2.50	2.50	2.50	2.09	1.82	
	8	2.50	2.50	2.44	1.87		
	9	2.50	2.50	2.13	1.63		
	10	2.50	2.34	1.90			
	11	2.50	2.11	1.71			
	12	2.50					
b_w	n	No.10	No.15	No.20	No.25	No.30	No.35

b_w	n	No.25	No.30	No.35	No.45	No.55
600	4*	2.09	1.84	1.62	1.50	1.50
	5	2.09	1.84	1.62	1.50	
	6	2.09	1.84	1.62		
	7	2.09	1.82			
	8	1.87				
	9	1.63				
650	4*	2.09	1.84	1.62	1.50	1.50
	5	2.09	1.84	1.62	1.50	
	6	2.09	1.84	1.62		
	7	2.09	1.84	1.62		
	8	2.06	1.72			
	9	1.80				
700	4*	2.09	1.84	1.62	1.50	1.50
	5	2.09	1.84	1.62	1.50	
	6	2.09	1.84	1.62	1.50	
	7	2.09	1.84	1.62		
	8	2.09	1.84			
	9	1.96	1.65			
	10	1.75				
750	5*	2.09	1.84	1.62	1.50	1.50
	6	2.09	1.84	1.62	1.50	
	7	2.09	1.84	1.62		
	8	2.09	1.84	1.62		
	9	2.09	1.79			
	10	1.89				
	11	1.70				
800	5*	2.09	1.84	1.62	1.50	1.50
	6	2.09	1.84	1.62	1.50	
	7	2.09	1.84	1.62	1.50	
	8	2.09	1.84	1.62		
	9	2.09	1.84			
	10	2.04	1.71			
	11	1.84				
	12	1.67				
900	6*	2.09	1.84	1.62	1.50	1.50
	7	2.09	1.84	1.62	1.50	
	8	2.09	1.84	1.62	1.50	
	9	2.09	1.84	1.62		
	10	2.09	1.84	1.62		
	11	2.09	1.76			
	12	1.91	1.60			
	13	1.75				
	14	1.62				
1000	7*	2.09	1.84	1.62	1.50	1.50
	8	2.09	1.84	1.62	1.50	
	9	2.09	1.84	1.62	1.50	
	10	2.09	1.84	1.62		
	11	2.09	1.84	1.62		
	12	2.09	1.81			
	13	1.97	1.66			
	14	1.82				
	15	1.69				
b_w	n	No.25	No.30	No.35	No.45	No.55

\# Values are provided only if a clear spacing of the larger of $1.4d_b$ and 30 mm is available between bars. [Cls. 12.2.3 and A12.5.2]

* The concrete confinement index value for a particular bar size applies for the n bars indicated and for fewer bars.

Table 3.3(b) Concrete confinement index d_{cs}/d_b for n deformed bars with a clear cover of 50 mm (60 mm for No. 45 and No. 55 bars), spaced uniformly across a stem width $b_w{}^\#$ (mm).

b_w	n	No.10	No.15	No.20	No.25	No.30	No.35
200	2	2.50	2.50	2.50	1.98		
	3	2.50					
250	2	2.50	2.50	2.50	2.48	2.17	1.90
	3	2.50	2.50	2.22	1.65		
	4	2.50					
300	2	2.50	2.50	2.50	2.48	2.17	1.90
	3	2.50	2.50	2.50	2.31	1.90	
	4	2.50	2.50	2.05			
	5	2.50	1.92				
350	3*	2.50	2.50	2.50	2.48	2.17	1.90
	4	2.50	2.50	2.50	1.98	1.64	
	5	2.50	2.44	1.97			
	6	2.50	1.96				
400	3*	2.50	2.50	2.50	2.48	2.17	1.90
	4	2.50	2.50	2.50	2.42	2.01	1.65
	5	2.50	2.50	2.39	1.81		
	6	2.50	2.37	1.91			
	7	2.50	1.98				
450	4*	2.50	2.50	2.50	2.48	2.17	1.90
	5	2.50	2.50	2.50	2.15	1.79	
	6	2.50	2.50	2.25	1.72		
	7	2.50	2.33	1.88			
	8	2.50	1.99				
	9	2.50					
500	4*	2.50	2.50	2.50	2.48	2.17	1.90
	5	2.50	2.50	2.50	2.48	2.07	1.70
	6	2.50	2.50	2.50	1.98	1.65	
	7	2.50	2.50	2.16	1.65		
	8	2.50	2.29	1.85			
	9	2.50	2.01				
	10	2.50					
550	5*	2.50	2.50	2.50	2.48	2.17	1.90
	6	2.50	2.50	2.50	2.24	1.88	
	7	2.50	2.50	2.45	1.87		
	8	2.50	2.50	2.10	1.60		
	9	2.50	2.27	1.84			
	10	2.50	2.01				
	11	2.50					
600	5*	2.50	2.50	2.50	2.48	2.17	1.90
	6	2.50	2.50	2.50	2.48	2.10	1.73
	7	2.50	2.50	2.50	2.09	1.75	
	8	2.50	2.50	2.34	1.79		
	9	2.50	2.50	2.05			
	10	2.50	2.25	1.82			
	11	2.50	2.02				
	12	2.50					
b_w	**n**	**No.10**	**No.15**	**No.20**	**No.25**	**No.30**	**No.35**

b_w	n	No.25	No.30	No.35	No.45	No.55
600	4*	2.48	2.17	1.90	1.87	1.56
	5	2.48	2.17	1.90	1.66	
	6	2.48	2.10	1.73		
	7	2.09	1.75			
	8	1.79				
650	4*	2.48	2.17	1.90	1.87	1.56
	5	2.48	2.17	1.90	1.85	
	6	2.48	2.17	1.90		
	7	2.31	1.94	1.60		
	8	1.98	1.66			
	9	1.73				
700	4*	2.48	2.17	1.90	1.87	1.56
	5	2.48	2.17	1.90	1.87	
	6	2.48	2.17	1.90	1.64	
	7	2.48	2.12	1.76		
	8	2.17	1.82			
	9	1.90				
	10	1.69				
750	5*	2.48	2.17	1.90	1.87	1.56
	6	2.48	2.17	1.90	1.79	
	7	2.48	2.17	1.90		
	8	2.36	1.98	1.64		
	9	2.06	1.73			
	10	1.83				
	11	1.65				
800	5*	2.48	2.17	1.90	1.87	1.56
	6	2.48	2.17	1.90	1.87	
	7	2.48	2.17	1.90	1.62	
	8	2.48	2.14	1.77		
	9	2.23	1.87			
	10	1.98	1.66			
	11	1.78				
	12	1.62				
900	6*	2.48	2.17	1.90	1.87	1.56
	7	2.48	2.17	1.90	1.87	
	8	2.48	2.17	1.90	1.60	
	9	2.48	2.15	1.78		
	10	2.27	1.91			
	11	2.05	1.72			
	12	1.86				
	13	1.71				
1000	7*	2.48	2.17	1.90	1.87	1.56
	8	2.48	2.17	1.90	1.82	
	9	2.48	2.17	1.90		
	10	2.48	2.16	1.79		
	11	2.31	1.94	1.61		
	12	2.10	1.77			
	13	1.93	1.62			
	14	1.78				
	15	1.65				
b_w	**n**	**No.25**	**No.30**	**No.35**	**No.45**	**No.55**

\# Values are provided only if a clear spacing of the larger of $1.4d_b$ and 30 mm is available between bars.   [Cls. 12.2.3 and A12.5.2]

* The concrete confinement index value for a particular bar size applies for the n bars indicated and for fewer bars.

Table 3.3(c) Concrete confinement index d_{cs}/d_b for n deformed bars with a clear cover of 75 mm, spaced uniformly across a stem width b_w# (mm).

b_w	n	No.10	No.15	No.20	No.25	No.30	No.35
250	2	2.50	2.50	2.50	1.98		
	3	2.50					
300	2	2.50	2.50	2.50	2.50	2.50	2.14
	3	2.50	2.50	2.22	1.65		
	4	2.50					
350	2	2.50	2.50	2.50	2.50	2.50	2.50
	3	2.50	2.50	2.50	2.31	1.90	
	4	2.50	2.50	2.05			
	5	2.50	1.92				
400	2	2.50	2.50	2.50	2.50	2.50	2.50
	3	2.50	2.50	2.50	2.50	2.46	2.00
	4	2.50	2.50	2.50	1.98	1.64	
	5	2.50	2.44	1.97			
	6	2.50	1.96				
450	2	2.50	2.50	2.50	2.50	2.50	2.50
	3	2.50	2.50	2.50	2.50	2.50	2.47
	4	2.50	2.50	2.50	2.42	2.01	1.65
	5	2.50	2.50	2.39	1.81		
	6	2.50	2.37	1.91			
	7	2.50	1.98				
500	3*	2.50	2.50	2.50	2.50	2.50	2.50
	4	2.50	2.50	2.50	2.50	2.38	1.96
	5	2.50	2.50	2.50	2.15	1.79	
	6	2.50	2.50	2.25	1.72		
	7	2.50	2.33	1.88			
	8	2.50	1.99				
	9	2.50					
550	3*	2.50	2.50	2.50	2.50	2.50	2.50
	4	2.50	2.50	2.50	2.50	2.50	2.27
	5	2.50	2.50	2.50	2.48	2.07	1.70
	6	2.50	2.50	2.50	1.98	1.65	
	7	2.50	2.50	2.16	1.65		
	8	2.50	2.29	1.85			
	9	2.50	2.01				
	10	2.50					
600	4*	2.50	2.50	2.50	2.50	2.50	2.50
	5	2.50	2.50	2.50	2.50	2.35	1.94
	6	2.50	2.50	2.50	2.24	1.88	
	7	2.50	2.50	2.45	1.87		
	8	2.50	2.50	2.10	1.60		
	9	2.50	2.27	1.84			
	10	2.50	2.01				
	11	2.50					
b_w	**n**	**No.10**	**No.15**	**No.20**	**No.25**	**No.30**	**No.35**

b_w	n	No.25	No.30	No.35	No.45	No.55
600	3*	2.50	2.50	2.50	2.22	1.83
	4	2.50	2.50	2.50	2.07	
	5	2.50	2.35	1.94		
	6	2.24	1.88			
	7	1.87				
	8	1.60				
650	3*	2.50	2.50	2.50	2.22	1.83
	4	2.50	2.50	2.50	2.22	1.75
	5	2.50	2.50	2.17	1.74	
	6	2.50	2.10	1.73		
	7	2.09	1.75			
	8	1.79				
700	4*	2.50	2.50	2.50	2.22	1.83
	5	2.50	2.50	2.40	1.93	
	6	2.50	2.32	1.92		
	7	2.31	1.94	1.60		
	8	1.98	1.66			
	9	1.73				
750	4*	2.50	2.50	2.50	2.22	1.83
	5	2.50	2.50	2.50	2.12	1.61
	6	2.50	2.50	2.11	1.70	
	7	2.50	2.12	1.76		
	8	2.17	1.82			
	9	1.90				
	10	1.69				
800	4*	2.50	2.50	2.50	2.22	1.83
	5	2.50	2.50	2.50	2.22	1.75
	6	2.50	2.50	2.30	1.85	
	7	2.50	2.31	1.91		
	8	2.36	1.98	1.64		
	9	2.06	1.73			
	10	1.83				
	11	1.65				
900	5*	2.50	2.50	2.50	2.22	1.83
	6	2.50	2.50	2.50	2.15	1.64
	7	2.50	2.50	2.22	1.80	
	8	2.50	2.30	1.91		
	9	2.39	2.01	1.67		
	10	2.13	1.79			
	11	1.91	1.61			
	12	1.74				
1000	6*	2.50	2.50	2.50	2.22	1.83
	7	2.50	2.50	2.50	2.05	
	8	2.50	2.50	2.17	1.76	
	9	2.50	2.29	1.90		
	10	2.42	2.03	1.69		
	11	2.18	1.83			
	12	1.98	1.66			
	13	1.82				
	14	1.68				
b_w	**n**	**No.25**	**No.30**	**No.35**	**No.45**	**No.55**

\# Values are provided only if a clear spacing of the larger of $1.4d_b$ and 30 mm is available between bars. [Cls. 12.2.3 and A12.5.2]

* The concrete confinement index value for a particular bar size applies for the n bars indicated and for fewer bars.

Table 3.4(a) Concrete confinement index d_{cs}/d_b for n pairs of contacting deformed lap spliced bars in tension with a clear cover of 40 mm, spaced uniformly across a stem width b_w# (mm).

b_w	n	No.10	No.15	No.20	No.25	No.30	No.35
200	2	2.50	2.50	2.09			
250	2	2.50	2.50	2.50	2.09	1.80	
	3	2.50	2.22				
300	2	2.50	2.50	2.50	2.09	1.84	1.62
	3	2.50	2.50	2.42			
	4	2.50	1.95				
350	2	2.50	2.50	2.50	2.09	1.84	1.62
	3	2.50	2.50	2.50	2.09	1.68	
	4	2.50	2.50	1.96			
	5	2.50					
400	3*	2.50	2.50	2.50	2.09	1.84	1.62
	4	2.50	2.50	2.50	1.71		
	5	2.50	2.34	1.73			
	6	2.50					
450	3*	2.50	2.50	2.50	2.09	1.84	1.62
	4	2.50	2.50	2.50	2.09	1.64	
	5	2.50	2.50	2.16			
	6	2.50	2.16				
	7	2.50					
500	3*	2.50	2.50	2.50	2.09	1.84	1.62
	4	2.50	2.50	2.50	2.09	1.84	
	5	2.50	2.50	2.50	1.77		
	6	2.50	2.50	1.93			
	7	2.50	2.04				
	8	2.50					
550	4*	2.50	2.50	2.50	2.09	1.84	1.62
	5	2.50	2.50	2.50	2.09	1.62	
	6	2.50	2.50	2.27			
	7	2.50	2.38	1.78			
	8	2.50	1.95				
	9	2.50					
600	4*	2.50	2.50	2.50	2.09	1.84	1.62
	5	2.50	2.50	2.50	2.09	1.84	
	6	2.50	2.50	2.50	1.81		
	7	2.50	2.50	2.07			
	8	2.50	2.25				
	9	2.50					
	10	2.50					
650	5*	2.50	2.50	2.50	2.09	1.84	1.62
	6	2.50	2.50	2.50	2.08	1.61	
	7	2.50	2.50	2.35	1.62		
	8	2.50	2.50	1.92			
	9	2.50	2.14				
	10	2.50					
	11	2.50					
b_w	**n**	**No.10**	**No.15**	**No.20**	**No.25**	**No.30**	**No.35**

b_w	n	No.15	No.20	No.25	No.30	No.35
700	5*	2.50	2.50	2.09	1.84	1.62
	6	2.50	2.50	2.09	1.84	
	7	2.50	2.50	1.84		
	8	2.50	2.16			
	9	2.40	1.81			
	10	2.06				
750	5*	2.50	2.50	2.09	1.84	1.62
	6	2.50	2.50	2.09	1.84	
	7	2.50	2.50	2.06	1.60	
	8	2.50	2.41	1.67		
	9	2.50	2.02			
	10	2.30	1.72			
	11	2.00				
800	6*	2.50	2.50	2.09	1.84	1.62
	7	2.50	2.50	2.09	1.79	
	8	2.50	2.50	1.86		
	9	2.50	2.24			
	10	2.50	1.91			
	11	2.21				
	12	1.95				
900	7*	2.50	2.50	2.09	1.84	1.62
	8	2.50	2.50	2.09	1.76	
	9	2.50	2.50	1.87		
	10	2.50	2.29			
	11	2.50	2.00			
	12	2.33	1.75			
	13	2.08				
1000	7*	2.50	2.50	2.09	1.84	1.62
	8	2.50	2.50	2.09	1.84	
	9	2.50	2.50	2.09	1.73	
	10	2.50	2.50	1.89		
	11	2.50	2.34	1.63		
	12	2.50	2.07			
	13	2.43	1.84			
	14	2.19				
	15	1.98				
1200	9*	2.50	2.50	2.09	1.84	1.62
	10	2.50	2.50	2.09	1.84	
	11	2.50	2.50	2.09	1.70	
	12	2.50	2.50	1.90		
	13	2.50	2.41	1.69		
	14	2.50	2.17			
	15	2.50	1.97			
	16	2.36	1.79			
	17	2.17				
	18	2.01				
b_w	**n**	**No.15**	**No.20**	**No.25**	**No.30**	**No.35**

\# Values are provided only if a clear spacing of the larger of $1.4d_b$ and 30 mm is available between bars.   [Cls. 12.2.3 and A12.5.2]

* The concrete confinement index value for a particular bar size applies for the n bars indicated and for fewer bars.

Table 3.4(b) Concrete confinement index d_{cs}/d_b for n pairs of contacting deformed lap spliced bars in tension with a clear cover of 50 mm, spaced uniformly across a stem width b_w[#] (mm).

b_w	n	No.10	No.15	No.20	No.25	No.30	No.35
200	2	2.50	2.18				
250	2	2.50	2.50	2.50	1.96		
	3	2.50					
300	2	2.50	2.50	2.50	2.48	2.17	1.74
	3	2.50	2.50	2.08			
	4	2.50					
350	2	2.50	2.50	2.50	2.48	2.17	1.90
	3	2.50	2.50	2.50	1.97		
	4	2.50	2.37	1.73			
	5	2.50					
400	2	2.50	2.50	2.50	2.48	2.17	1.90
	3	2.50	2.50	2.50	2.48	2.02	
	4	2.50	2.50	2.30			
	5	2.50	2.13				
	6	2.50					
450	3*	2.50	2.50	2.50	2.48	2.17	1.90
	4	2.50	2.50	2.50	1.97		
	5	2.50	2.50	1.98			
	6	2.50	1.99				
	7	2.50					
500	3*	2.50	2.50	2.50	2.48	2.17	1.90
	4	2.50	2.50	2.50	2.41	1.87	
	5	2.50	2.50	2.41	1.64		
	6	2.50	2.41	1.80			
	7	2.50					
	8	2.50					
550	3*	2.50	2.50	2.50	2.48	2.17	1.90
	4	2.50	2.50	2.50	2.48	2.17	1.69
	5	2.50	2.50	2.50	1.97		
	6	2.50	2.50	2.14			
	7	2.50	2.24				
	8	2.50					
	9	2.49					
600	4*	2.50	2.50	2.50	2.48	2.17	1.90
	5	2.50	2.50	2.50	2.30	1.79	
	6	2.50	2.50	2.48	1.71		
	7	2.50	2.50	1.95			
	8	2.50	2.13				
	9	2.50					
	10	2.47					
650	4*	2.50	2.50	2.50	2.48	2.17	1.90
	5	2.50	2.50	2.50	2.48	2.07	
	6	2.50	2.50	2.50	1.97		
	7	2.50	2.50	2.24			
	8	2.50	2.43	1.82			
	9	2.50	2.04				
	10	2.50					
	11	2.45					
b_w	n	No.10	No.15	No.20	No.25	No.30	No.35

b_w	n	No.15	No.20	No.25	No.30	No.35
700	4*	2.50	2.50	2.48	2.17	1.90
	5	2.50	2.50	2.48	2.17	1.80
	6	2.50	2.50	2.24	1.75	
	7	2.50	2.50	1.75		
	8	2.50	2.07			
	9	2.30	1.72			
	10	1.97				
750	5*	2.50	2.50	2.48	2.17	1.90
	6	2.50	2.50	2.48	1.97	
	7	2.50	2.50	1.97		
	8	2.50	2.31			
	9	2.50	1.94			
	10	2.20				
800	5*	2.50	2.50	2.48	2.17	1.90
	6	2.50	2.50	2.48	2.17	1.68
	7	2.50	2.50	2.19	1.72	
	8	2.50	2.50	1.79		
	9	2.50	2.15			
	10	2.43	1.84			
	11	2.12				
900	6*	2.50	2.50	2.48	2.17	1.90
	7	2.50	2.50	2.48	2.09	1.60
	8	2.50	2.50	2.16	1.69	
	9	2.50	2.50	1.81		
	10	2.50	2.22			
	11	2.50	1.93			
	12	2.25	1.69			
	13	2.01				
1000	7*	2.50	2.50	2.48	2.17	1.90
	8	2.50	2.50	2.48	2.01	
	9	2.50	2.50	2.14	1.68	
	10	2.50	2.50	1.83		
	11	2.50	2.27			
	12	2.50	2.00			
	13	2.36	1.78			
	14	2.12				
	15	1.92				
1200	8*	2.50	2.50	2.48	2.17	1.90
	9	2.50	2.50	2.48	2.17	1.74
	10	2.50	2.50	2.41	1.91	
	11	2.50	2.50	2.11	1.66	
	12	2.50	2.50	1.85		
	13	2.50	2.35	1.64		
	14	2.50	2.12			
	15	2.50	1.92			
	16	2.31	1.75			
	17	2.12				
	18	1.96				
b_w	n	No.15	No.20	No.25	No.30	No.35

[#] Values are provided only if a clear spacing of the larger of $1.4d_b$ and 30 mm is available between bars.   [Cls. 12.2.3 and A12.5.2]

* The concrete confinement index value for a particular bar size applies for the n bars indicated and for fewer bars.

Table 3.4(c)   Concrete confinement index d_{cs}/d_b for n pairs of contacting deformed lap spliced bars in tension with a clear cover of 75 mm, spaced uniformly across a stem width $b_w{}^\#$ (mm).

b_w	n	No.10	No.15	No.20	No.25	No.30	No.35
250	2	2.50	2.18				
300	2	2.50	2.50	2.50	1.96		
	3	2.50					
350	2	2.50	2.50	2.50	2.50	2.47	1.74
	3	2.50	2.50	2.08			
	4	2.50					
400	2	2.50	2.50	2.50	2.50	2.50	2.50
	3	2.50	2.50	2.50	1.97		
	4	2.50	2.37	1.73			
	5	2.50					
450	2	2.50	2.50	2.50	2.50	2.50	2.50
	3	2.50	2.50	2.50	2.50	2.02	
	4	2.50	2.50	2.30			
	5	2.50	2.13				
	6	2.50					
500	2	2.50	2.50	2.50	2.50	2.50	2.50
	3	2.50	2.50	2.50	2.50	2.50	1.94
	4	2.50	2.50	2.50	1.97		
	5	2.50	2.50	1.98			
	6	2.50	1.99				
	7	2.50					
550	2	2.50	2.50	2.50	2.50	2.50	2.50
	3	2.50	2.50	2.50	2.50	2.50	2.40
	4	2.50	2.50	2.50	2.41	1.87	
	5	2.50	2.50	2.41	1.64		
	6	2.50	2.41	1.80			
	7	2.50					
	8	2.50					
600	3*	2.50	2.50	2.50	2.50	2.50	2.50
	4	2.50	2.50	2.50	2.50	2.24	1.69
	5	2.50	2.50	2.50	1.97		
	6	2.50	2.50	2.14			
	7	2.50	2.24				
	8	2.50					
	9	2.49					
650	3*	2.50	2.50	2.50	2.50	2.50	2.50
	4	2.50	2.50	2.50	2.50	2.50	2.00
	5	2.50	2.50	2.50	2.30	1.79	
	6	2.50	2.50	2.48	1.71		
	7	2.50	2.50	1.95			
	8	2.50	2.13				
	9	2.50					
	10	2.47					

b_w	n	No.15	No.20	No.25	No.30	No.35
700	3*	2.50	2.50	2.50	2.50	2.50
	4	2.50	2.50	2.50	2.50	2.31
	5	2.50	2.50	2.50	2.07	
	6	2.50	2.50	1.97		
	7	2.50	2.24			
	8	2.43	1.82			
	9	2.04				
750	4*	2.50	2.50	2.50	2.50	2.50
	5	2.50	2.50	2.50	2.35	1.80
	6	2.50	2.50	2.24	1.75	
	7	2.50	2.50	1.75		
	8	2.50	2.07			
	9	2.30	1.72			
	10	1.97				
800	4*	2.50	2.50	2.50	2.50	2.50
	5	2.50	2.50	2.50	2.50	2.04
	6	2.50	2.50	2.50	1.97	
	7	2.50	2.50	1.97		
	8	2.50	2.31			
	9	2.50	1.94			
	10	2.20				
900	5*	2.50	2.50	2.50	2.50	2.50
	6	2.50	2.50	2.50	2.42	1.87
	7	2.50	2.50	2.41	1.90	
	8	2.50	2.50	1.97		
	9	2.50	2.36	1.64		
	10	2.50	2.03			
	11	2.33	1.76			
	12	2.06				
1000	5*	2.50	2.50	2.50	2.50	2.50
	6	2.50	2.50	2.50	2.50	2.24
	7	2.50	2.50	2.50	2.27	1.76
	8	2.50	2.50	2.35	1.85	
	9	2.50	2.50	1.97		
	10	2.50	2.41	1.68		
	11	2.50	2.10			
	12	2.44	1.85			
	13	2.18				
	14	1.96				
1200	6*	2.50	2.50	2.50	2.50	2.50
	7	2.50	2.50	2.50	2.50	2.38
	8	2.50	2.50	2.50	2.49	1.95
	9	2.50	2.50	2.50	2.10	1.62
	10	2.50	2.50	2.27	1.79	
	11	2.50	2.50	1.97		
	12	2.50	2.47	1.73		
	13	2.50	2.21			
	14	2.50	1.99			
	15	2.37	1.80			
	16	2.17				
	17	1.99				
b_w	n	No.15	No.20	No.25	No.30	No.35

\# Values are provided only if a clear spacing of the larger of $1.4d_b$ and 30 mm is available between bars.   [Cls. 12.2.3 and A12.5.2]

* The concrete confinement index value for a particular bar size applies for the n bars indicated and for fewer bars.

CPCA Concrete Design Handbook

Table 3.5 Transverse reinforcing confinement index[@] K_{tr}/d_b for No. 10[*] vertical stirrups with two legs and f_{yt} = 400[#] MPa, placed at a spacing s (mm), and providing confinement to n equally spaced main reinforcing bars or pairs of lap spliced bars, across the member width.

s	n	No.10	No.15	No.20	No.25	No.30	No.35	No.45	No.55	modifier for s	modifier for legs
75	2	4.50	3.18	2.60	2.01	1.70	1.42	1.16	0.90		
	3	3.00	2.12	1.73	1.34	1.13	0.95	0.77	0.60	For s = 150 mm,	For 3 legs at each
	4	2.25	1.59	1.30	1.01	0.85	0.71	0.58	0.45	divide values	stirrup location
	5	1.80	1.27	1.04	0.81	0.68	0.57	0.46	0.36	for s = 75 mm	and n $\geq$ 3, multiply
	6	1.50	1.06	0.87	0.67	0.57	0.47	0.39	0.30	by 2	values by 1.5
	7	1.29	0.91	0.74	0.58	0.49	0.41	0.33	0.26		
	8	1.13	0.80	0.65	0.50	0.43	0.36	0.29	0.23	For s = 300 mm,	For 4 legs at each
	9	1.00	0.71	0.58	0.45	0.38	0.32	0.26	0.20	divide values	stirrup location
	10	0.90	0.64	0.52	0.40	0.34	0.28	0.23	0.18	for s = 75 mm	and n $\geq$ 4, multiply
	11	0.82	0.58	0.47	0.37	0.31	0.26	0.21	0.16	by 4	values by 2
	12	0.75	0.53	0.43	0.34	0.28	0.24	0.19	0.15		
	13	0.69	0.49	0.40	0.31	0.26	0.22	0.18	0.14		For 5 legs at each
	14	0.64	0.45	0.37	0.29	0.24	0.20	0.17	0.13		stirrup location
	15	0.60	0.42	0.35	0.27	0.23	0.19	0.15	0.12		and n $\geq$ 5, multiply
	16	0.56	0.40	0.32	0.25	0.21	0.18	0.15	0.11		values by 2.5
100	2	3.38	2.39	1.95	1.51	1.28	1.07	0.87	0.68		
	3	2.25	1.59	1.30	1.01	0.85	0.71	0.58	0.45	For s = 200 mm,	For 6 legs at each
	4	1.69	1.19	0.97	0.75	0.64	0.53	0.44	0.34	divide values	stirrup location
	5	1.35	0.95	0.78	0.60	0.51	0.43	0.35	0.27	for s = 100 mm	and n $\geq$ 6, multiply
	6	1.13	0.80	0.65	0.50	0.43	0.36	0.29	0.23	by 2	values by 3
	7	0.96	0.68	0.56	0.43	0.36	0.31	0.25	0.19		
	8	0.84	0.60	0.49	0.38	0.32	0.27	0.22	0.17	For s = 400 mm,	
	9	0.75	0.53	0.43	0.34	0.28	0.24	0.19	0.15	divide values	
	10	0.68	0.48	0.39	0.30	0.26	0.21	0.17	0.14	for s = 100 mm	
	11	0.61	0.43	0.35	0.27	0.23	0.19	0.16	0.12	by 4	
	12	0.56	0.40	0.32	0.25	0.21	0.18	0.15	0.11		
	13	0.52	0.37	0.30	0.23	0.20	0.16	0.13	0.10		
	14	0.48	0.34	0.28	0.22	0.18	0.15	0.12	0.10		
	15	0.45	0.32	0.26	0.20	0.17	0.14	0.12	0.09		
	16	0.42	0.30	0.24	0.19	0.16	0.13	0.11	0.08		
125	2	2.70	1.91	1.56	1.21	1.02	0.85	0.70	0.54		
	3	1.80	1.27	1.04	0.81	0.68	0.57	0.46	0.36	For s = 250 mm,	
	4	1.35	0.95	0.78	0.60	0.51	0.43	0.35	0.27	divide values	as above
	5	1.08	0.76	0.62	0.48	0.41	0.34	0.28	0.22	for s = 125 mm	
	6	0.90	0.64	0.52	0.40	0.34	0.28	0.23	0.18	by 2	
	7	0.77	0.55	0.45	0.35	0.29	0.24	0.20	0.15		
	8	0.68	0.48	0.39	0.30	0.26	0.21	0.17	0.14	For s = 500 mm,	
	9	0.60	0.42	0.35	0.27	0.23	0.19	0.15	0.12	divide values	
	10	0.54	0.38	0.31	0.24	0.20	0.17	0.14	0.11	for s = 125 mm	
	11	0.49	0.35	0.28	0.22	0.19	0.16	0.13	0.10	by 4	
	12	0.45	0.32	0.26	0.20	0.17	0.14	0.12	0.09		
	13	0.42	0.29	0.24	0.19	0.16	0.13	0.11	0.08		
	14	0.39	0.27	0.22	0.17	0.15	0.12	0.10	0.08		
	15	0.36	0.25	0.21	0.16	0.14	0.11	0.09	0.07		
	16	0.34	0.24	0.19	0.15	0.13	0.11	0.09	0.07		
s	n	No.10	No.15	No.20	No.25	No.30	No.35	No.45	No.55	modifier for s	modifier for legs

[@] Transverse reinforcing confinement index = $\dfrac{K_{tr}}{d_b} = \dfrac{A_{tr}f_{yt}}{10.5\,n\,s\,d_b}$. [Cl. 12.2.2 and Equation (12-1)]

[*] For stirrups made of larger diameter deformed reinforcing bars, multiply transverse reinforcing confinement index values in the table by 2 for No. 15 stirrups, by 3 for No. 20 stirrups and by 5 for No. 25 stirrups.

[#] For $f_{yt} \neq 400$ MPa, multiply values in the table by $f_{yt}/400$.

Table 3.6 Development lengths^ (mm) based on [Table 12-1]* for heavier confined# deformed wire~ with f_y = 400 MPa&, for normal density concrete@.

$$\ell_d = 0.45\ k_1\ k_2\ k_3\ k_4\ \frac{f_y}{\sqrt{f'_c}}\ d_b \nless 300 \text{ mm}^\$$$

Modification Factors Included [Clause 12.2.4]	f'_c (MPa)	MD9.1	MD11.1	MD13.3	MD18.7	MD25.8	MD34.9	MD47.6
	20	110	121	133	157	185	215	251
k_1 = 1.0 – "bottom" bars	25	98	108	119	141	165	192	224
	30	89	99	108	128	151	175	205
k_2 = 1.0 – "uncoated" bars	35	83	92	100	119	140	162	189
	40	78	86	94	111	130	152	177
k_3 = 1.0 – normal density concrete@	45	73	81	88	105	123	143	167
	50	69	77	84	99	117	136	159
	55	66	73	80	95	111	129	151
	60	63	70	77	91	107	124	145
	64	61	68	74	88	103	120	140
	20	164	182	199	236	277	322	376
k_1 = 1.0 – "bottom" bars	25	147	162	178	211	248	288	336
	30	134	148	162	192	226	263	307
k_2 = 1.5 – epoxy coated bars	35	124	137	150	178	209	243	284
	40	116	128	141	167	196	228	266
k_3 = 1.0 – normal density concrete@	45	110	121	133	157	185	215	251
	50	104	115	126	149	175	204	238
	55	99	109	120	142	167	194	227
	60	95	105	115	136	160	186	217
	64	92	102	111	132	155	180	210
	20	142	157	172	204	240	279	326
k_1 = 1.3 – "top" bars	25	127	141	154	183	215	250	291
	30	116	128	141	167	196	228	266
k_2 = 1.0 – "uncoated" bars	35	108	119	130	154	181	211	246
	40	101	111	122	144	170	197	230
k_3 = 1.0 – normal density concrete@	45	95	105	115	136	160	186	217
	50	90	100	109	129	152	176	206
	55	86	95	104	123	145	168	197
	60	82	91	99	118	139	161	188
	64	80	88	96	114	134	156	182
	20	186	206	225	267	314	365	426
$k_1 \times k_2$ = 1.7 (top location and epoxy coated bars)	25	167	184	201	239	281	326	381
	30	152	168	184	218	256	298	348
	35	141	156	170	202	237	276	322
k_3 = 1.0 – normal density concrete@	40	132	146	159	189	222	258	301
	45	124	137	150	178	209	243	284
	50	118	130	142	169	198	231	270
	55	112	124	136	161	189	220	257
	60	108	119	130	154	181	211	246
	64	104	115	126	149	175	204	238
Modification Factors Included [Clause 12.2.4]	f'_c (MPa)	MD9.1	MD11.1	MD13.3	MD18.7	MD25.8	MD34.9	MD47.6

* Clear cover and clear spacing of bars must be at least $1.0d_b$ and $1.4d_b$, respectively. [Cl. 12.2.3]

\# For lighter confinement, "(Other cases)" in [Table 12-1], multiply the above table values by 1.33.

\# To qualify for heavier confinement, must have either: [Table 12-1]

    Member containing minimum stirrups or ties within ℓ_d, [Cl. 11.2.8.4 or Cl. 7.6.5]

    or

    Slabs, walls, shells or folded plates having clear spacing between bars being developed not less than $2d_b$.

& For $f_y \neq 400$ MPa, multiply development length by $f_y/400$.

@ Multiply table values by; k_3 = 1.3 for structural low density concrete

                       k_3 = 1.2 for structural semi-low density concrete

~ The appropriate bar size factor k_4 has been applied.

   For concrete strengths > 64 MPa, use development length for 64 MPa. [Cl. 12.1.1]

$ After application of all modification factors, the development length must not be less than 300 mm.

Table 3.7 Tension development lengths, ℓ_d, for welded deformed fabric with f_y = 400 MPa [Clause 12.7.1].

Designation	MD25.8[&]		MD34.9	MD47.6	MD37.4	MD51.6	MD100	MD200
Diam. (mm)	5.74		6.67	7.79	6.90	8.10	11.3	16.0
S_w	102	152	152	152	305	305	305	305

ℓ_d[*] = tension development length for deformed wire from Table 3.6, [Cl. 12.2.3] or [Cl. 12.2.2], multiplied by the wire fabric factor[#] [Cl. 12.7.2], but not less than 200 mm [Cl. 12.7.1][@]

ℓ_d[*] = tension development length for deformed bars (No. 10 bars for MD100 and No. 15 bars for MD200) from Table 3.1 or Table 3.2, multiplied by the wire fabric factor[#] [Cl. 12.7.2], but not less than 200 mm [Cl. 12.7.1][@]

[#] wire fabric factor = 0.4 for all MD fabric sizes listed.

[*] At least one cross wire must be within the development length, and this cross wire must be located not less than 50 mm from the critical section [Cl. 12.7.2]; otherwise the fabric factor = 1.0 [Cl. 12.7.3], the minimum length is 300 mm and the fabric is treated as deformed wire or bar rather than fabric.

[@] The minimum 200 mm development length is waived in the computation of lap splices [Cl. 12.18], and the development of web reinforcement [Cl. 12.13].

[&] Welded deformed wire fabric smaller than MD25.8 is not permitted by [Cl. 3.1.3(d)].

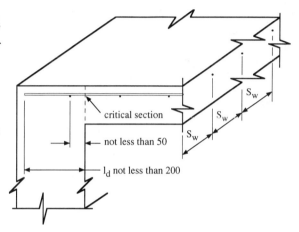

Table 3.8 Tension Development Lengths, ℓ_d, and Lap Splice Lengths, ℓ_s, for Welded Smooth Wire Fabric with f_y = 400 MPa for $f_c' \geq$ 20 MPa [Cls. 12.8 and 12.19].

As the standard welded smooth wire fabric sizes have small diameters, the minimum development lengths, ℓ_d, as given in [Cl. 12.8] (after all possible modifications), and the minimum splice lengths, ℓ_s, from [Cl. 12.19], control for the sizes tabulated below.

Designation Diameter (mm) Spacing (mm)	MW37.4 & MW51.6 6.90 & 8.10 305 × 305	MW9.1 to MW47.6 3.40 to 7.79 152 × 152	MW9.1 to MW25.8 3.4 to 5.74 102 × 102	MW9.1 3.4 51 × 51
ℓ_d[@] (mm)	355	200	150	150
ℓ_s[*] (mm)	355	200	150	150

[@] The development length, ℓ_d, for welded smooth wire fabric is measured *starting from the outer cross wire*. At least *two cross wires* must be within the development length with the closer cross wire not less than 50 mm from the critical section [Cl. 12.8].

[*] The lap length, ℓ_s, for welded smooth wire fabric is measured as the overlap distance between the outermost cross bars of each fabric sheet. The splice length depends on the ratio of A_s provided/(A_s required), and may be less than the values tabulated above when the ratio is greater than or equal to 2.0, as provided in [Cl. 12.19], and illustrated in [Fig. N12.19].

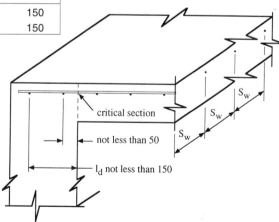

Table 3.9 Tension development lengths, ℓ_{dh}#, using standard hooks for deformed bars with fy = 400 MPa [Cl. 12.5.1].

ℓ_{dh}~ = ℓ_{hb}* × (factors from [Cl. 12.5.3]), but not less than 8d_b or 150 mm, whichever is greater.

* The values tabulated below give the basic hook development length ℓ_{hb} (mm), according to [Cl. 12.5.2].

f'$_c$ (MPa)	Nominal Deformed Reinforcing Bar Size							
	10	15	20	25	30	35	45	55
20	252	357	437	564	668	798	977	1262
25	226	319	391	505	597	714	874	1128
30	206	291	357	461	545	651	798	1030
35	191	270	330	426	505	603	739	954
40	178	252	309	399	472	564	691	892
45	168	238	291	376	445	532	651	841
50	160	226	276	357	422	505	618	798
55	152	215	264	340	403	481	589	761
60	146	206	252	326	385	461	564	728
≥ 64	141	199	244	315	373	446	546	705

The development length includes the out to out dimension of the hook and the straight length to the critical section.

~ The hooks must satisfy the dimensions for standard hooks shown in Table 3.10.

Special fabrication is required for bends greater than 90° for No. 45 and No. 55 bars for steel grades 400 R and 500 R [Table A5].

Cover Requirements

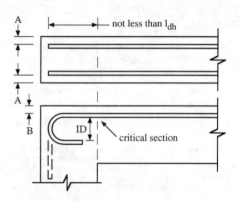

For all bar sizes, if both covers A and B are less than 60 mm (clear), then ties or stirrup ties defined by Fig. 3.1(b) *must* be provided, but the 0.8 modifer shall *not* apply [Cl. 12.5.4].

Factors Modifying Hook Development Length

[Cls. 12.5.3(a) to (f)]:
1. For bars with f$_y$ other than 400 MPa . . . . . × f$_y$/400
2. For large concrete cover on No.35 or smaller bars, (see Fig. 3.1(a)) . . . . × 0.7
3. For cover plus enclosure on No.35 or smaller bars (see Fig. 3.1(b)) . . . . × 0.8
4. For excess reinforcement . . . . × A$_s$ required/(A$_s$ provided)
5. For structural low density concrete . . . . × 1.3
6. For epoxy coated reinforcement . . . . × 1.2

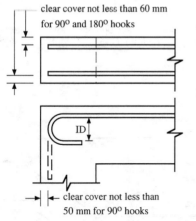

For No. 35 or smaller bars satisfying all shown covers, modification factor ... x 0.7

(a) Large concrete cover is provided [Cl. 12.5.3(b)]

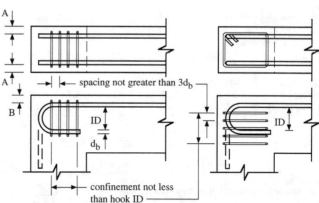

For No. 35 bars or smaller where either clear cover "A" or clear cover "B" is at least 60 mm, and at least 3 ties or stirrup-ties spaced not greater than 3d_b enclose the hook over a distance not less than ID of the hook ..... x 0.8

(b) Enclosure within ties or stirrup-ties is provided [Cl. 12.5.3(c)]

Notes:
  (i) If clear cover "A" and clear cover "B" are both less than 60 mm, provide this confinement, but *don't* use the "0.8" modifier [Cl. 12.5.4].
  (ii) For the relatively larger hook diameters needed with No. 30 and larger bars, at least 4 ties or stirrup-ties are required with No. 30 bars, and at least 5 are required with No. 35, No. 45 and No. 55 bars.
  (iii) The ties or stirrup-ties may be placed vertically or horizontally as illustrated.

Fig. 3.1 Modification Factors for Improved Confinement to Standard hooks.

Table 3.10 Detailing and estimating dimensions[#] (mm) for standard end hooks[~] for deformed reinforcing bars

Nominal Size	Steel Grade											
	300 R				400 R or 500 R				400 W or 500 W			
	180° Hook			90° Hook	180° Hook			90° Hook	180° Hook			90° Hook
	ID	J	G*	A or G	ID	J	G*	A or G	ID	J	G*	A or G
No.10	60	83	131	177	70	93	141	182	60	83	131	177
No.15	90	122	169	252	100	132	180	257	90	122	169	252
No.20					120	159	218	314	100	139	196	304
No.25					150	200	276	403	150	200	276	403
No.30					250	310	404	513	200	260	351	488
No.35					300	371	484	614	250	321	431	589
No.45					450	537	682	793	400	487	628	768
No.55					600	713	900	1033	550	663	847	1008

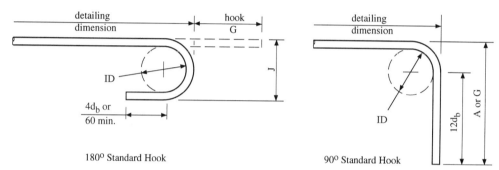

180° Standard Hook   90° Standard Hook

[#] The dimensions provided use the minimum bend diameters (ID) permitted in [Cl. A12.2.3 and Table A5]

[~] Standard hooks are defined in [Cl. A12.2.2].

* Add the additional hook dimension G to the detailing dimension to estimate the total bar length:
  For 180° hooks: $G = (4d_b \lessdot 60 \text{ mm}) + \pi(ID + d_b)/2 - ID/2 - d_b$
  For 90° hooks: $G \approx A = 12d_b + ID/2 + d_b$

[@] Special fabrication is required for bends exceeding 90° for No. 45 and No. 55 bars for steel grades 400 R or 500 R

Table 3.11 Minimum effective depth d* (mm) to provide anchorage for No. 20[@] and No. 25 deformed bar stirrups for shear, with hooks and bends placed around longitudinal reinforcement for vertical or bottom placed[$], uncoated[$] stirrups in normal density[$] concrete.

* $d = 2\{0.33\ell_d{}^{\#} + \text{clear cover}\}$ [Cl.12.13.2(b)]

[#] Development length ℓ_d is calculated from [Equation 12.2] using confinement provided by the cover specified in the table.

Clear cover to stirrup (mm)	30				40				65			
Nominal bar size	No.20		No.25		No.20		No.25		No.20		No.25	
f_{yt} (MPa)	400	500	400	500	400	500	400	500	400	500	400	500
Min. c. to c. spacing[~] (mm)	60	60	65	65	75	75	80	80	75	75	100	100
f'_c (MPa) 20	470	572	857	1056	413	497	725	886	463	547	668	803
25	426	518	772	951	378	453	657	801	428	503	611	732
30	394	478	710	873	352	420	607	738	402	470	569	679
35	370	447	662	813	332	395	568	690	382	445	537	638
40	350	422	623	764	316	375	536	650	366	425	511	606
45	333	401	591	724	302	358	510	618	352	408	489	578
50	319	384	564	690	291	344	488	590	341	394	470	555
55	307	369	540	660	281	331	469	566	331	381	454	536
60	297	356	520	635	273	321	452	546	323	371	441	518
64	289	346	505	617	266	313	441	531	316	363	431	506

[@] Smaller deformed bar and wire stirrups achieve sufficient anchorage using a standard stirrup hook [Cl. A12.2.4] around longitudinal reinforcement [Cl. 12.13.2(a) and Cl. 7.1.2].

[$] For a conservative estimate, multiply table value by;   [Cl. 12.2.4]
     $k_1 = 1.3$ for a "top" placed horizontal stirrup leg,
     $k_2 = 1.5$ for epoxy coated stirrups,
     $k_3 = 1.3$ for low density concrete,
     $k_3 = 1.2$ for semi low density concrete and
     $k_1 k_2 = 1.7$ for stirrups which are both "top" placed and epoxy coated.

[~] Smaller center to center spacing does not provide the necessary confinement assumed in calculating minimum d.
Web reinforcement shall be carried as close to the compression and tension surfaces of a member as cover requirements and proximity to other reinforcement will permit [Cl. 12.13.1].

Table 3.12 Compression development lengths, ℓ_d, for deformed reinforcing bars with f_y = 400 MPa [Cl. 12.3.1].

$\ell_d = \ell_{db}{}^* \times$ {factors from [Cl. 12.3.3]}, but not less than 200 mm.
* The values tabulated below give the basic development length, ℓ_{db} (mm), according to [Cl. 12.3.2].

f'_c (MPa)	Nominal Deformed Reinforcing Bar Size							
	No.10	No.15	No.20	No.25	No.30	No.35	No.45	No.55
20	242	343	420	542	641	766	938	1211
25	217	306	375	484	573	685	839	1083
≥ 30	199	281	344	444	525	628	769	993

Modification Factors [Cl. 12.3.3]:

1. The product of 2. and 3. below must not be less than 0.6
2. Reinforcement in excess of that required by analysis . . . . $\times$ A_s required/(A_s provided)
3. Enclosure within spiral reinforcement of not less than 6 mm diameter and a pitch not more than 100 mm pitch or within No. 10 ties in conformance with [Cl. 7.6.5] and spaced at not more than 100 mm on centre . . . . $\times$ 0.75

Table 3.13 Compression Lap Splice Lengths, ℓ_s (mm), for Deformed Reinforcing Bars with f_y = 400 MPa and Concrete f'_c > 20 MPa, Normal and Low Density [Cl. 12.3.1].

Confinement	Nominal Deformed Reinforcing Bar Size					
	10	15	20	25	30	35*
Usual	329	466	571	737	872	1042
Special Ties#	300	387	474	612	724	865
Spiral Columns~	300	349	428	553	654	781

* Larger bars (No. 45 and No. 55) may only be lapped with No. 35 or smaller bars in a compression splice. When bars of different sizes are lap spliced in compression, the splice length shall be the larger of; the development length of the larger bar from Table 3.12 or the splice length of the smaller bar from Table 3.13.   [Cls. 12.14.2.1, 12.16.2 and 15.8.2.5]

When ties are provided so that the effective tie area (A_{te}) along the splice in each direction (tie legs perpendicular to dimension h) satisfies A_{te} not less than 0.0015 hs, as illustrated in [Fig. N12.17.3.4 and Cl. N12.17.3.4] then:
$\ell_s = \ell_s$ (usual) $\times$ 0.83 but not less than 300 mm.   [Cl. N12.17.3.4]

~ When the lap splice is confined within the spiral of a spirally reinforced compression member:
$\ell_s = \ell_s$ (usual) $\times$ 0.75 but not less than 300 mm.   [Cl. 12.17.3.5]

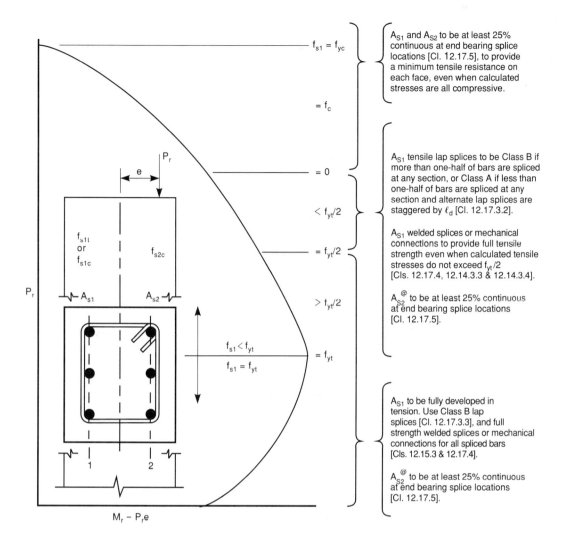

$M_r - P_r e$

@ Different loading conditions may produce moment reversal to switch the roles of A_{s1} and A_{s2}.

Typical notation:

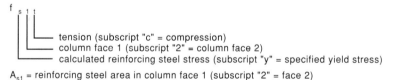

f_{s1t}

— tension (subscript "c" = compression)
— column face 1 (subscript "2" = column face 2)
— calculated reinforcing steel stress (subscript "y" = specified yield stress)

A_{s1} = reinforcing steel area in column face 1 (subscript "2" = face 2)

Fig. 3.2   Special Splice Requirements for Columns (Clause 12.17)

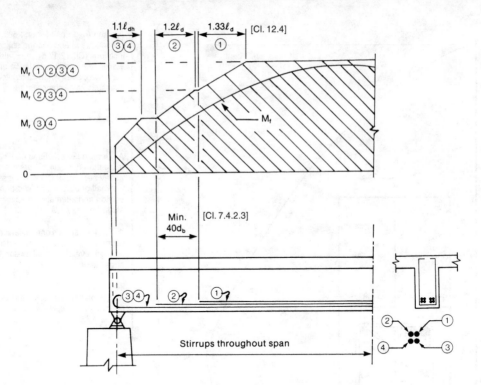

Fig. 3.3   Bundled Bars in Flexural Members

A two bar bundle is spliced in compression or tension to maintain the full strength of $2A_bf_y$, by providing staggered splices and a separate splice bar. With the splice bar, the arrangement becomes a 3 bar bundle, requiring a 20% increase in the individual bar splice length to $1.2\ell_s$ [Cl. 12.14.2.2]. Force transfer between spliced bars is assumed to occur linearly along the required splice length of $1.2\ell_s$.

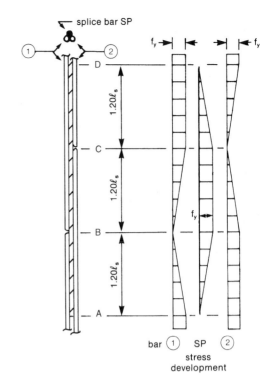

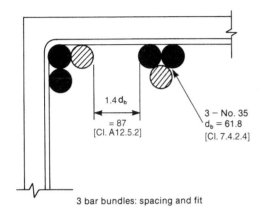

1.4 d_b

= 87
[Cl. A12.5.2]

3 – No. 35
$d_b = 61.8$
[Cl. 7.4.2.4]

3 bar bundles: spacing and fit

(a) Bundled bar splices for full strength in tension or compression.

			Splice Bar		
	bundle configuration	⊕⊕	⊕⊕	⊕⊕	⊕⊕
	continuing bars in bundle	4	3	3	2
A	length of splice bar	*	$2(1.33\ell_s)$	$2(1.33\ell_s)$	$2(1.20\ell_s)$
	tensile resistance (%)∼	0	33	33	50
B	length of splice bar	*	$4(1.33\ell_s)$	$4(1.33\ell_s)$	$3(1.20\ell_s)$
	tensile resistance (%)∼	75	100	100	100

A All bars butt spliced at same location (no tensile strength).
B Butt splice locations staggered.
* Splice bar not permitted — Makes a 5 bar bundle.
∼ % of area of continuing bars.

(b) Bundled bar lap splices for tensile resistance in columns.

Fig. 3.4 Bundled Bar Splices [Cl. 12.14.2.2]

Shear and Torsion

By Michael P. Collins

and Denis Mitchell

Chapter 4
Shear and Torsion

4.1 INTRODUCTION

Members subjected to shear and/or torsion may develop diagonal cracks. Unless these members contain appropriate amounts of properly detailed transverse and longitudinal reinforcement, these cracks can result in the premature and perhaps sudden failure of the members. Avoiding such failures is the objective of shear and torsion design.

CSA Standard A23.3-94 permits the use of two alternative design methods for shear and torsion – the simplified method and the general method. Detailed comments on the individual Code clauses of these two methods have been given in the "Explanatory Notes" section of this handbook. This Chapter will give an overview of the two methods, background information helpful in understanding the general method, together with detailed design examples illustrating the application of both methods.

4.2 SIMPLIFIED METHOD (CLAUSE 11.3)

The simplified method, which is suitable for the shear design of typical beams, is a much shortened version of the traditional ACI "$V_c + V_s$" approach (Ref. 4.1). In this method shear design is viewed as being primarily concerned with the design of transverse reinforcement ("shear reinforcement"). The amount of such reinforcement is chosen to ensure that the factored shear resistance, V_r, exceeds the applied factored shear, V_f.

The term, V_c, depends upon the tensile strength of the concrete and for typical sections is assumed equal to the diagonal cracking shear. The term, V_s, relies on the tensile strength of the transverse reinforcement and the compressive strength of the diagonally cracked concrete. The stirrups and the inclined compressive struts are assumed to act as members of a 45° truss and the term, V_s, is calculated based on this model.

For non-prestressed beams the factored shear resistance is given by

$$V_r = V_c + V_s$$
$$= 0.2\lambda\phi_c\sqrt{f'_c}\,b_w d + \phi_s \cdot \frac{A_v f_y}{s} \cdot d \quad (4-1)$$

However, irrespective of the amount of stirrups, V_r is not permitted to exceed $\lambda\phi_c\sqrt{f'_c}\,b_w d$

The stirrup design requirements of the simplified method are summarized in Fig. 4.1.

It can be seen from Fig. 4.1 that for many practical situations, where the nominal shear stress due to factored loads, v_f, is often less than 1 MPa, the amount of stirrups required will be governed by the minimum shear reinforcement requirement. Additionally, if No. 10 U-stirrups are being used, it will often be found that the 0.7d spacing requirement will govern the stirrup design. No. 10 U-stirrups at 0.7d spacing provide $V_s = 97$ kN for $f_y = 400$ MPa.

Example 4.1 illustrates the use of the simplified method for the shear design of a one-way slab without stirrups. The example emphasizes the consequences of the implementation of a "size effect factor" in this edition of the standard. See discussion under N11.3.5.

Example 4.3 demonstrates the use of the simplified method in designing the stirrups required in a heavily loaded continuous beam.

4.3 THE MODIFIED COMPRESSION FIELD THEORY

The general method of Clause 11.4 is based on a group of assumptions about the behaviour of cracked reinforced concrete that is known as the "modified compression field theory" (Refs. 4.2 and 4.3). In order that the methods given in Clause 11.4 can be more fully understood, a brief summary of this theory is given below.

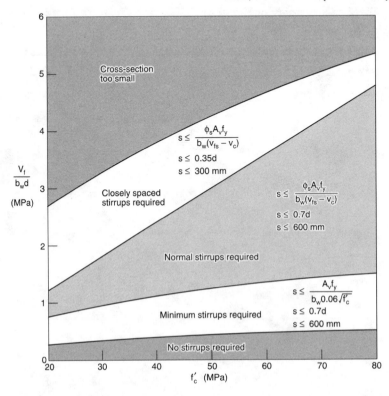

Fig. 4.1   Stirrup Design Requirements of Clause 11.3 for Non-Prestressed Beam with Normal Density Concrete

The cracked web of a reinforced concrete beam transmits shear stress in a relatively complex manner. As the load is increased, new cracks open and pre-existing cracks close. The cracks have rough surfaces capable of transmitting considerable shear stresses. The local stresses in both the concrete and the reinforcement vary from point to point, with high reinforcement stresses but low concrete tensile stresses occurring at crack locations.

The modified compression field theory (see Fig. 4.2) attempts to capture the essential features of the behaviour of cracked reinforced concrete without considering all of the details. The equilibrium conditions which relate the concrete stresses and the reinforcement stresses to the applied loads (see Fig. 4.2 a and b) are expressed in terms of average stresses. That is, stresses averaged over a length greater than the crack spacing. In a similar fashion, the compatibility conditions relating the strains in the cracked concrete to the strains in the reinforcement are expressed in terms of average strains, where the strains are measured over base lengths that are greater than the crack spacing (see Fig. 4.2c and d).

One of the key simplifying assumptions of the modified compression field theory is that "the direction that is subjected to the largest average compressive stress will coincide with the direction that is subjected to the largest average compressive strain" (Ref. 4.4). That is, the principal stress direction in the cracked concrete (θ_c in Fig. 4.2b) is assumed to coincide with the principal strain direction (θ in Fig. 4.2d).

It was found (Ref. 4.2) that the principal compressive stress in the cracked concrete, f_2, is a function, not only of the principal compressive strain, ε_2, but also of the coexisting principal tensile strain, ε_1 (see Fig. 4.2e). A suitable, simple relationship is

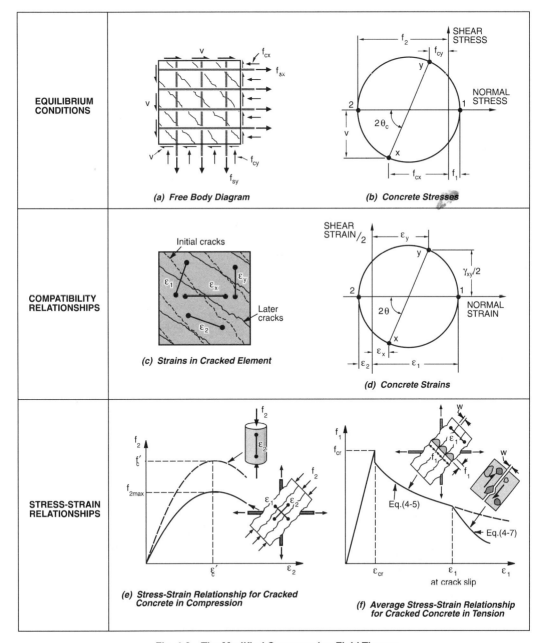

| EQUILIBRIUM CONDITIONS | (a) Free Body Diagram | (b) Concrete Stresses |

| COMPATIBILITY RELATIONSHIPS | (c) Strains in Cracked Element | (d) Concrete Strains |

| STRESS-STRAIN RELATIONSHIPS | (e) Stress-Strain Relationship for Cracked Concrete in Compression | (f) Average Stress-Strain Relationship for Cracked Concrete in Tension |

Fig. 4.2   The Modified Compression Field Theory

$$f_2 = f_{2max}\left[2\frac{\varepsilon_2}{\varepsilon_c'} - \left(\frac{\varepsilon_2}{\varepsilon_c'}\right)^2\right] \qquad (4\text{-}2)$$

where

$$f_{2max} = \frac{f_c'}{0.8 + 170\varepsilon_1} \leq f_c' \qquad (4\text{-}3)$$

Tests of reinforced concrete elements subjected to pure shear (Ref. 4.2) demonstrated that even after extensive cracking, tensile stresses still existed in the cracked concrete and these stresses significantly increased the ability of the cracked concrete to resist shear stresses. The average principal tensile stress in the concrete, f_1, was related to the principal tensile strain, ε_1, and to the crack width, w (see Fig. 4.2f). Prior to cracking (i.e., $\varepsilon_1 < \varepsilon_{cr}$)

$$f_1 = E_c \varepsilon_1 \qquad (4\text{-}4)$$

After cracking

$$f_1 = \frac{f_{cr}}{1 + \sqrt{500\varepsilon_1}} \qquad (4\text{-}5)$$

where

$$f_{cr} = 0.33\sqrt{f_c'} \qquad (4\text{-}6)$$

but

$$f_1 \leq \frac{0.18\sqrt{f_c'}\,\tan\theta}{0.3 + \dfrac{24w}{a + 16}} \qquad (4\text{-}7)$$

For large values of ε_1, the cracks will become wide and the magnitude of f_1 will be controlled by the yielding of the reinforcement at the crack and by the ability to transmit shear stresses across the crack, which is a function of the crack width, w, and the maximum aggregate size, a.

In checking the conditions at a crack, the actual complex crack pattern is idealized as a series of parallel cracks, all occurring at angle θ to the longitudinal reinforcement and spaced a distance, s_θ, apart. The crack width can then be estimated as

$$w = s_\theta \varepsilon_1 \qquad (4\text{-}8)$$

The spacing of the inclined cracks, s_θ, will depend upon the crack control characteristics of the longitudinal reinforcement (x direction), the crack control characteristics of the transverse reinforcement (y direction), and the inclination of the cracks. Based on element tests (Ref. 4.2), it is suggested that

$$s_\theta = \frac{1}{\dfrac{\sin\theta}{s_z} + \dfrac{\cos\theta}{s_y}} \qquad (4\text{-}9)$$

where s_z is the crack spacing that would result if the element was subjected to axial tension in the longitudinal direction, while s_y is the crack spacing that would result if the element was subjected to axial tension in the y direction.

The above assumptions about the stress-strain behaviour of cracked reinforced concrete can be used to predict the load-deformation response of reinforced concrete members loaded in shear. These assumptions have been incorporated into program RESPONSE, which is included in Ref. 4.3. As an example of the capabilities of such a program, Fig. 4.3 compares the predicted and observed load-deformation response of a large, high-strength concrete beam tested in shear. It can be seen that crack widths, longitudinal strains, and overall load-deformation response are all predicted with reasonable accuracy.

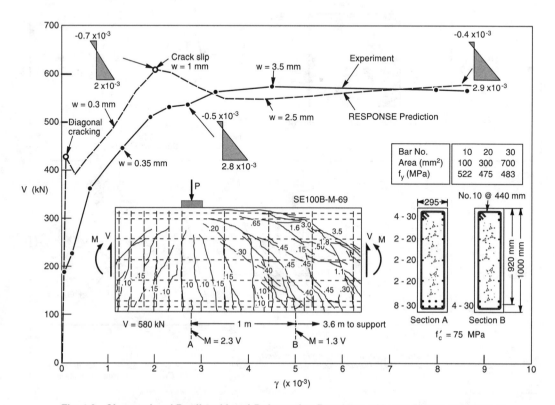

Fig. 4.3 Observed and Predicted Load-Deformation Response of Large Beam, at Section B

4.4 GENERAL METHOD (CLAUSE 11.4)

While the modified compression field theory is capable of predicting the complete load-deformation response of a reinforced concrete member loaded in shear, for design purposes, the prime requirement is to have an expression that can predict the shear strength of a section. In the general method of Clause 11.4, the modified compression field theory has been used to develop such expressions.

The factored shear strength of a non-prestressed concrete section, such as that shown in Fig. 4.4, can be expressed as

$$V_{rg} = V_{cg} + V_{sg}$$
$$V_{rg} = 1.3\phi_c \beta \sqrt{f_c'} b_w d_v + \phi_s \frac{A_v f_y}{s} \cdot d_v \cdot \cot\theta \quad (4\text{-}10)$$

Values of β and θ, determined from the modified compression field theory (Ref. 4.3), are given in Table 11-1 and Fig. 11-1 for members with web reinforcement, and in Table 11-2 and Fig. 11-2 for members without web reinforcement. The residual tensile stress factor, β, which indicates the ability of the cracked concrete to transmit tensile stresses, has been calculated from Eqs. (4-5) and (4-7). In using these equations the highest longitudinal strain, ε_x, occurring within the web is used to calculate the principal tensile strain, ε_1. As the straining increases, β decreases. For design calculations ε_x can be approximated as the strain in the "bottom chord" of an equivalent truss. Hence, for a non-prestressed member

$$\varepsilon_x = \frac{(M_f/d_v) + 0.5 N_f + 0.5 V_f \cot\theta}{E_s A_s} \quad (4\text{-}11)$$

where A_s is the area of longitudinal reinforcement on the flexural tension side of the member. The terms M_f and V_f are taken as positive, while N_f is positive for tension and negative for axial compression.

In determining the β values for members with web reinforcement (Fig. 11-1) it was assumed that sufficient stirrups would be present to limit the spacing of the diagonal cracks to about 300 mm. For members without stirrups the diagonal cracks will typically be more widely spaced, with the cracks becoming more widely spaced as θ approaches zero. The crack spacing when θ equals 90° is called s_z, and this spacing is primarily a function of the maximum distance between the longitudinal reinforcing bars. As s_z increases, β decreases and hence, the shear strength decreases.

In the general method, the shear strength of a section is strongly influenced by the longitudinal straining of the web of the member, ε_x. Increasing the magnitude of the moment or applying axial tension increases ε_x and hence, decreases both V_{cg} and V_{sg} (β decreases and θ increases). Applying axial compression or prestress, or increasing the area of longitudinal reinforcement decreases ε_x and hence, increases both V_{cg} and V_{sg}.

As was the case in the simplified method, it will often occur that the stirrup spacing is governed by the minimum reinforcement requirement of Clause 11.2.8.4 or the maximum spacing requirements of Clause 11.2.11, rather than the strength requirements of Clause 11.4.2. A normal density concrete section containing the minimum area of shear reinforcement can resist a factored shear force of

$$V_f = 1.3\phi_c \beta \sqrt{f_c'} b_w d_v + \phi_s \frac{A_v f_y}{s} d_v \cot\theta + \phi_p V_p$$
$$\therefore \quad v_f = \frac{V_f - \phi_p V_p}{b_w d_v} = 1.3\phi_c \beta \sqrt{f_c'} + \phi_s \frac{A_v f_y}{s b_w} \cot\theta$$
$$= 1.3 \times 0.6 \times \beta \sqrt{f_c'} + 0.85 \times 0.06 \sqrt{f_c'} \cot\theta$$
$$\frac{v_f}{\sqrt{f_c'}} = 0.78\beta + 0.051 \cot\theta \quad (4\text{-}12)$$

For a given value of ε_x, Eq. (4-12) can be evaluated using Table 11-1 to find the shear stress level, below which only minimum stirrups are required. These values are shown in Fig. 4.5. Thus, if ε_x, as determined from Eq. (11-22), is equal to zero, the factored shear stress, as determined from Eq. (11-21), can be as high as $0.416 \sqrt{f_c'}$ before more than minimum stirrups are required.

The use of the general method is illustrated in Examples 4.2, 4.4, 4.5, and 4.6.

4.5 DESIGN OF DISTURBED REGIONS NEAR DISCONTINUITIES

The manner in which the resisting compressive stresses flow in a beam determines the different regions that need to be considered in design. These different regions are illustrated in Fig. 4.6 and are described below.

(a) Regions of uniform compressive fields. In these regions the principal compressive stress trajectories can be approximated by a series of parallel lines at an angle of θ from the longitudinal axis of the beam, and the shear stress may be assumed to be uniformly distributed over the effective shear depth, d_v.

(b) Regions of fanning of compressive stresses. These disturbed regions are characterized by radiating compressive stresses near supports and in regions where the shear changes sign.

(c) Regions of compressive struts and tension ties. The flow of the forces in these disturbed regions can be visualized as struts of unidirectional compressive stresses together with tension ties provided by reinforcing bars.

The strut-and-tie model described in Clause 11.5 utilizes concepts from plasticity and truss models (Refs. 4.5, 4.6 and 4.7) developed in Europe, together with concepts

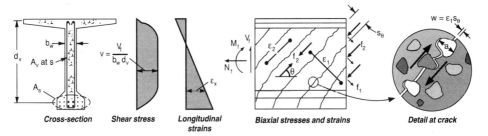

| Cross-section | Shear stress | Longitudinal strains | Biaxial stresses and strains | Detail at crack |

Fig. 4.4   Non-Prestressed Beam Subjected to Shear, Moment and Axial Load

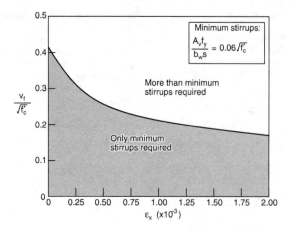

Fig. 4.5 **Factored Shear Stress That Can Be Resisted by Section with Minimum Stirrups**

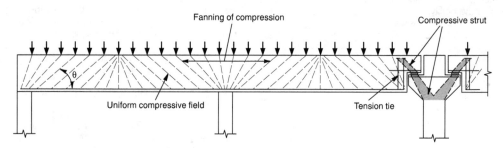

Fig. 4.6 **Regions of Uniform Compressive Fields and Disturbed Regions**

from the modified compression field theory (Ref. 4.3), to determine the crushing strength of the struts.

The geometry of the truss, which consists of concrete compressive struts and reinforcing tension ties, is determined by following the flow of the forces from the loading points to the support reactions. The intersection of compressive struts with the tension ties or the support reactions delineate the nodal regions of multi-directionally compressed concrete. Once the geometry of the truss is known the forces in the struts and ties can usually be determined by statics. The items to be checked in the design procedure with reference to the deep beam shown in Fig. 4.7 are listed below.

(i) Choose bearing areas at the loading points and the support reactions such that the nodal region stresses are not exceeded.

(ii) Determine the geometry of the truss by first locating the nodes of the truss at the points of intersection of the forces meeting at the nodal regions (see Fig. 4.7c). Solve for the forces in the members of the truss.

(iii) Choose the tension tie reinforcement such that the factored resistance equals or exceeds the tie force required.

(iv) Distribute the tension tie reinforcement such that the stress calculated by dividing the tie force by the effective area of concrete surrounding the tie reinforcement is less than the stress limit for the nodal region anchoring the tension tie. The effective area of concrete has the same centroid as the tension tie reinforcement (see Fig. 4.7b).

(v) Check that the tension tie can develop the required tensile force at the innermost edge of the nodal region. If the embedment length is not sufficient then hooks or mechanical anchorages should be provided in accordance with the requirements of Clause 12.

(vi) Check that the compressive stress, f_2, in the strut is less than the crushing limit, f_{cu}. The compressive stress, f_2, is determined by dividing the strut force by the width and the thickness of the strut. Since the compressive strut is crossed by a tension tie near the support nodal region (see Fig. 4.7a) then f_{cu} must be reduced to account for the presence of the principal tensile strain, ε_1. Figure N11.5.2.3 describes the variation of the crushing strength of the strut as a function of θ_s.

(vii) Provide uniformly distributed pairs of well anchored reinforcing bars in the vertical and horizontal directions to control diagonal cracking and to improve the ductility of the deep beam (Clause 11.5.5).

The application of the strut-and-tie model is demonstrated in the design of a deep beam subjected to uniform loading (Example 4.8), a deep beam subjected to concentrated loads (Example 4.9), a corbel (Example 4.10) and a beam with dapped ends (Example 4.11).

4.6 REFERENCES

4.1 ACI Committee 318, "Building Code Requirements for Reinforced Concrete (ACI 318-89)," American Concrete Institute, Detroit, 1989, 353 pp.

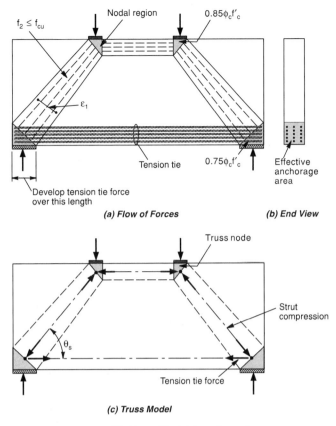

(a) Flow of Forces   (b) End View

(c) Truss Model

Fig. 4.7   Strut-and-Tie Truss Model for a Deep Beam

4.2   Vecchio, F.J., and Collins, M.P., "The Modified Compression Field Theory for Reinforced Concrete Elements Subjected to Shear," *ACI Journal*, Vol. 83, No. 2, Mar.-Apr. 1986, pp. 219-231.

4.3   Collins, M.P. and Mitchell, D., *Prestressed Concrete Structures*, Prentice Hall, Englewood Cliffs, 1991, 766 pp.

4.4   Collins, M.P., "Towards a Rational Theory for RC Members in Shear," *Journal of the Structural Division, ASCE*, Vol. 104, Apr. 1978, pp. 649-666.

4.5   Marti, P., "Basic Tools of Reinforced Concrete Beam Design," *ACI Journal*, Vol. 82, No. 1, Jan.-Feb. 1985, pp. 46-56.

4.6   Schlaich, J., Schäfer, K., and Jennewein, M., "Towards a Consistent Design of Reinforced Concrete Structures," *PCI Journal*, Vol. 32, No. 3, May-June 1987, pp. 74-150.

4.7   Nielsen, M.P., *Limit Analysis and Concrete Plasticity*, Prentice-Hall Inc., Englewood Cliffs, N.J., 1984, 420 pp.

EXAMPLE 4.1 DESIGN OF MEMBER WITHOUT STIRRUPS BY THE SIMPLIFIED METHOD OF CLAUSE 11.3

It is desired to construct a one-way slab without stirrups to span 16 m between two 400 mm thick bearing walls and carry a superimposed specified live load of 20 kN/m^2 due to soil overburden. Design the slab. Use f$_c'$ = 30 MPa and f$_y$ = 400 MPa.

1. *Estimate required slab thickness.*

   From Table 9-1 deflections need not be calculated if the slab thickness exceeds $\ell_n/20 = 15.6 \times 10^3/20 =$ 780 mm. Try a total thickness of 800 mm.

2. *Calculate the factored loads.*

   Taking a 1 m wide strip of slab and using a thickness of 800 gives

   $$w_f = 1.25D + 1.5L$$
   $$= 1.25 \times 0.8 \times 24 + 1.5 \times 20$$
   $$= 24 + 30 = 54 \text{ kN/m}$$

3. *Check shear strength near support.*

   Assuming a cover to the bottom bars of 40 mm and assuming that No. 30 bars are used for the principal reinforcement, the effective depth, d is

   $$d = 800 - 40 - 30/2 = 745 \text{ mm}$$

   Using the Simplified Method of Clause 11.3 for this member without stirrups having d > 300 mm, Equation (11-7) gives

   $$V_r = V_c = \frac{260}{1000 + d} \lambda \phi_c \sqrt{f_c'} \, b_w d$$

   $$= \frac{260}{1000 + 745} 1.0 \times 0.6 \sqrt{30} \times 1000 \times 745 \times 10^{-3}$$
   $$= 364.8 \text{ kN}$$

   For this slab with supports that introduce direct compression into the beam, the critical section for shear is located at a distance d from the inner edge of the bearing. At this location the factored shear, V$_f$ is

   $$V_f = (8 - 0.2 - 0.745) \, 54 = 381 \text{ kN}$$

   Since V$_r$ < V$_f$ it is necessary to increase the depth of the slab.

   Try h = 900 mm, resulting in d of 845 mm. The factored loading, w$_f$ becomes 57 kN/m and V$_f$ = (8 − 0.2 − 0.845) 57 = 396.4 kN. The factored resistance, V$_r$ = V$_c$ = 391.3 kN.

   Try h = 1000 mm, resulting in d of 945 mm. The factored loading, w$_f$ becomes 60 kN/m and V$_f$ = (8 − 0.2 − 0.945) 60 = 411.3 kN. The factored resistance, V$_r$ = V$_c$ = 415.1 kN.

   Note that as the depth was increased by 25%, the factored shear increased by 8% due to the increased self-weight, and the factored shear resistance increased only 14% because of the size effect factor in Equation (11-7).

   The shear force and bending moment diagrams for the chosen slab depth are shown in the figure below.

4. *Design longitudinal reinforcement at midspan.*

   The factored moment at midspan is

   $$M_f = w_f \ell^2/8 = (60 \times 16^2)/8 = 1920 \text{ kN} \cdot \text{m}$$

   In order to choose a trial area of reinforcement we will assume a flexural lever arm equal to 0.9d = 0.9 × 945 = 851 mm. Hence, the required area of reinforcement is about

   $$A_s = (1920 \times 1000)/(0.851 \times 0.85 \times 400)$$
   $$= 6636 \text{ mm}^2$$

   The minimum amount of flexural reinforcement required for this slab (Clause 7.8.1) is

   $$A_s = 0.002 \times 1000 \times 1000 = 2000 \text{ mm}^2/\text{m}$$

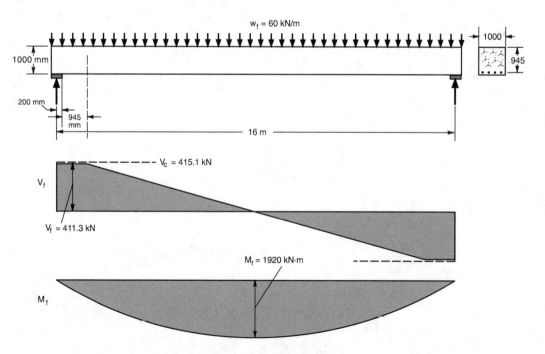

Try No. 30 at a spacing of 105 mm, giving A_s = 6667 mm². The stress block depth, a is

$$a = \frac{\phi_s A_s f_y}{\phi_c \alpha_1 f'_c b}$$

$$= \frac{0.85 \times 6667 \times 400}{0.6 \times 0.805 \times 30 \times 1000}$$

$$= 156 \text{ mm}$$

Hence, the factored moment resistance is

$$M_r = \phi_s A_s f_y (d - a/2)$$

$$= 0.85 \times 6667 \times 400 (945 - 156/2) \times 10^{-6}$$
$$= 1965 \text{ kN} \cdot \text{m}$$

Since $M_r > M_f$ the flexural capacity is sufficient.

Check the c/d limit (Clause 10.5.2). The c/d ratio must be less than or equal to $700/(700 + f_y) = 0.636$. The flexural stress block factor $\beta_1 = 0.97 - 0.0025 f'_c = 0.895$. For this slab $c = a/\beta_1 = 156/0.895 = 174$ mm and c/d = 174/945 = 0.184 <0.636.

Provide minimum reinforcement in the slab in the direction perpendicular to the span. Provide No. 20 bars at a spacing of 150 mm, giving $A_s = (1000/150)$ 300 = 2000 mm²/m.

5. *Check longitudinal reinforcement near support.*

For this slab without shear reinforcement, the longitudinal reinforcement must be capable of resisting a tensile force equal to V_f at the inside edge of the bearing. For the No. 30 bars with a clear spacing between the bars of 105 – 30 = 75 mm, Table 12-1 gives a development length of

$$\ell_d = 0.45 \, k_1 k_2 k_3 k_4 \frac{f_y}{\sqrt{f'_c}} d_b$$

$$= 0.45 \times 1 \times 1 \times 1 \times 1 \frac{400}{\sqrt{30}} 30$$

$$= 986 \text{ mm}$$

Assuming that the bars extend 360 mm into the support (see figure below) then the tensile capacity of

these bars will be $(360/986) \times 0.85 \times 400 \times 6667 \times 10^{-3}$ = 828 kN, which exceeds 411.3 kN. Hence only about one-half of the reinforcement need extend into the support to satisfy this requirement.

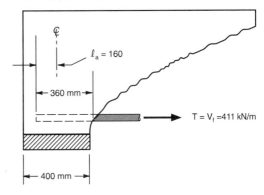

6. *Determine possible cut-off locations of longitudinal reinforcement.*

Consider the possibility of terminating every third bar. As shown in the figure below, the flexural capacity of the remaining two-thirds of the bars will be about $2/3 \times 1965 = 1310$ kN·m. The factored moment reaches this value at a location 4.62 m from midspan. Clause 11.3.8.1 requires that the flexural reinforcement be extended a distance d or 12 d_b past the location required for flexure alone. Hence, to meet this requirement, the cut-off location for the bars must be at least 5.56 m from midspan. However, Clause 12.10.5 requires that, for a member without stirrups, flexural reinforcement can only be terminated in a tension zone if the shear at the cut-off point is less than two-thirds of V_c. As shown in the figure below this means that the bars can not be cut-off at locations further than 4.61 m from midspan. Hence it is not possible to find a cut-off location without violating one of these requirements.

Therefore all of the No. 30 bars at 105 mm spacing will extend for the full length of the slab.

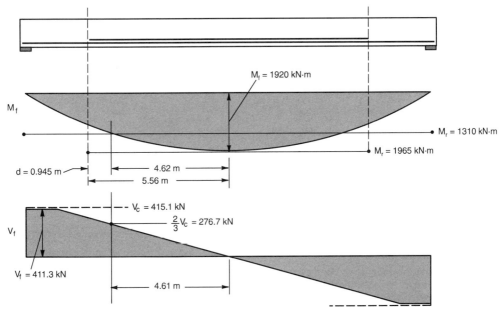

EXAMPLE 4.2 DESIGN OF MEMBER WITHOUT STIRRUPS BY THE GENERAL METHOD OF CLAUSE 11.4

Repeat Example 4.1 using the General Method to see if a thinner slab can be used.

1. *Estimate required slab thickness and factored loads.*

   Try a total thickness of 800 mm, that is, a minimum thickness conforming with Table 9-1.

   Taking a 1 m wide strip of slab and using a thickness of 800 mm gives

   $$w_f = 1.25D + 1.5L$$

   $$= 1.25 \times 0.8 \times 24 + 1.5 \times 20$$

   $$= 24 + 30 = 54 \text{ kN/m}$$

2. *Design longitudinal reinforcement at midspan.*

   The factored moment at midspan is

   $$M_f = w_f \ell^2/8 = (54 \times 16^2)/8 = 1728 \text{ kN} \cdot \text{m}$$

   In order to choose a trial area of reinforcement we will assume a flexural lever arm equal to 0.9d = 0.9 × 745 = 671 mm. Hence, the required area of reinforcement is about

   $$A_s = (1728 \times 1000)/(0.671 \times 0.85 \times 400)$$

   $$= 7574 \text{ mm}^2$$

   The minimum amount of flexural reinforcement required for this slab (Clause 7.8.1) is

   $$A_s = 0.002 \times 800 \times 1000 = 1600 \text{ mm}^2/\text{m}$$

   Try No. 30 at a spacing of 90 mm, giving $A_s = 7778 \text{ mm}^2$. The stress block depth, a is

   $$a = \frac{\phi_s A_s f_y}{\phi_c \alpha_1 f_c' b}$$

   $$= \frac{0.85 \times 7778 \times 400}{0.6 \times 0.805 \times 30 \times 1000}$$

   $$= 183 \text{ mm}$$

   Hence, the factored moment resistance is

   $$M_r = \phi_s A_s f_y (d - a/2)$$

   $$= 0.85 \times 7778 \times 400 (745 - 183/2) \times 10^{-6}$$

   $$= 1728 \text{ kN} \cdot \text{m}$$

   Since $M_r = M_f$ the flexural capacity is sufficient.

   Check the c/d limit (Clause 10.5.2). The c/d ratio must be less than or equal to 700/(700 + f_y) = 0.636. The flexural stress block factor β_1 = 0.97 − 0.0025 f_c' = 0.895. For this slab c = a/β_1 = 183/0.895 = 204 mm and c/d = 204/745 = 0.275 <0.636.

   Provide minimum reinforcement in the slab in the direction perpendicular to the span. Provide No. 25 bars at a spacing of 300 mm, giving A_s = (1000/300) 500 = 1667 mm²/m.

3. *Check the shear strength.*

   In the Simplified Method of shear design the predicted shear capacity is not affected by the magnitude of the moment or the amount of longitudinal reinforcement and hence V_c for nonprestressed members is pre-

dicted to remain constant along the length of the member. Because of this the critical section for shear will occur near the end of the beam where the factored shear force has its maximum value (see Example 4.1).

On the other hand, the shear strength determined by the General Method is influenced by the amount of longitudinal reinforcement and by the magnitude of the moment and hence, V_c varies along the length of a member.

For this simply supported, uniformly loaded slab we will first check the shear strength at a location a distance d_v from the face of the support. At this location

$$V_f = (8 - 0.2 - 0.671) \, 54 = 385.0 \text{ kN}$$

$$M_f = (0.671 + 0.2) \, 54 \times 8 - 54 (0.671 + 0.2)^2/2$$
$$= 356 \text{ kN} \cdot \text{m}$$

The effective shear depth, d_v will be taken as 0.9d = 0.9 × 745 = 671 mm. The indicator of longitudinal straining, ε_x is

$$\varepsilon_x = \frac{0.5V_f \cot\theta + M_f/d_v}{E_s A_s}$$

$$= \frac{0.5 \times 385.0 \times 10^3 \cot\theta + 356 \times 10^6/671}{200\,000 \times 7778}$$

$$= 0.12 \times 10^{-3} \cot\theta + 0.34 \times 10^{-3}$$

For this slab with only one layer of longitudinal reinforcement, the crack spacing parameter, s_z is

$$s_z = d_v = 671 \text{ mm}$$

From Fig. 11-2 for s_z = 671 mm and for ε_x about 0.5 × 10^{-3}, we read off θ = 46°. Hence,

$$\varepsilon_x = 0.12 \times 10^{-3} \cot 46° + 0.34 \times 10^{-3}$$

$$= 0.46 \times 10^{-3}$$

From Fig. 11-2, for s_z = 671 mm and ε_x = 0.46 × 10^{-3} we read off β = 0.19.

From Clause 11.4.3.1, the shear carried by the concrete is

$$V_{cg} = 1.3 \lambda \beta \phi_c \sqrt{f_c'} \, b_w d_v$$

$$= 1.3 \times 1 \times 0.19 \times 0.6 \sqrt{30} \times 1000 \times 671 \times 10^{-3}$$

$$= 545 \text{ kN}$$

As V_{cg} exceeds V_f the shear strength is adequate.

4. *Check tensile capacity of reinforcement at inside edge of bearing.*

   From Clause 11.4.9.4 the reinforcement must be capable of resisting a tensile force of

   $$V_f \cot\theta = 385 \cot 46° = 372 \text{ kN}.$$

   For the No. 30 bars with a clear spacing of 60 mm between bars the development length from Table 12-1

   $$\ell_d = 0.45 k_1 k_2 k_3 k_4 \frac{f_y}{\sqrt{f_c'}} d_b$$

   $$= 0.45 \times 1 \times 1 \times 1 \times 1 \frac{400}{\sqrt{30}} 30$$

   $$= 986 \text{ mm}$$

Hence, if all of the bars are continued into the support, the tensile capacity at the inner edge of the bearing would be $(360/986) \times 0.85 \times 400 \times 7778 \times 10^{-3} = 966$ kN. As 966 kN considerably exceeds the required force of 372 kN, consider reducing the number of bars going into the support.

5. *Choosing bar cut-offs.*

Consider the possibility of terminating every third bar. The flexural capacity of the remaining two-thirds of the bars is about $2/3 \times 1728 = 1152$ kN·m. The factored moment reaches this value at a location 4.62 m from midspan. Instead of calculating the additional tension required for shear, Clause 11.4.9.2 permits extending the reinforcement $d_v \cot\theta$ beyond the location needed by flexure alone. For $s_z = 671$ mm and ε_x greater than 0.5×10^{-3}, Fig. 11-2 indicates that θ will be greater than 45° and hence, it will be conservative to extend the bars $d_v = 671$ mm. As shown in the figure below, the bars are terminated 5.3 m from midspan (i.e., the shorter bars are 10.6 m long).

6. *Check influence of bar cut-offs on shear capacity.*

(a) Section d_v from face of support.

We will redo the calculations of the shear capacity for a section d_v from the face of the support to determine the influence of the reduced area of reinforcement, $A_s = 2/3 \times 7778 = 5185$ mm^2. The indicator of longitudinal straining, ε_x is

$$\varepsilon_x = \frac{0.5 \times 385.0 \times 10^3 \cot\theta + 356 \times 10^6/671}{200\,000 \times 5185}$$

$$= 0.18 \times 10^{-3} \cot\theta + 0.51 \times 10^{-3}$$

From Fig. 11-2 for $s_z = 671$ mm and for ε_x about 0.68×10^{-3}, we read off $\theta = 46°$. Hence,

$$\varepsilon_x = 0.18 \times 10^{-3} \cot46° + 0.51 \times 10^{-3}$$

$$= 0.68 \times 10^{-3}$$

From Fig. 11-2, for $s_z = 671$ mm and $\varepsilon_x = 0.68 \times 10^{-3}$ we read off $\beta = 0.17$.

From Clause 11.4.3.1, the shear carried by the concrete is

$$V_{cg} = 1.3 \times 1 \times 0.17 \times 0.6\sqrt{30} \times 1000 \times 671 \times 10^{-3}$$

$$= 487 \text{ kN}$$

As V_{cg} exceeds $V_f = 385$ kN the shear strength at this location is adequate.

(b) Section at bar cut-off location

The section at the ends of the cut-off bars may be more critical in shear than the section near the support. At this location 5.3 m from midspan

$$V_f = 286 \text{ kN and}$$

$$M_f = 970 \text{ kN·m}$$

$$\varepsilon_x = \frac{0.5 \times 286 \times 10^3 \cot\theta + 970 \times 10^6/671}{200\,000 \times 5185}$$

$$= 0.14 \times 10^{-3} \cot\theta + 1.39 \times 10^{-3}$$

From Fig. 11-2, for $\varepsilon_x = 1.49 \times 10^{-3}$ and $\theta = 55°$, $\beta = 0.115$.

From Clause 11.4.3.1, the shear carried by the concrete is

$$V_{cg} = 1.3 \times 1 \times 0.115 \times 0.6\sqrt{30} \times 1000 \times 671 \times 10^{-3}$$

$$= 330 \text{ kN}$$

As V_{cg} exceeds $V_f = 286$ kN the shear strength at this location is adequate.

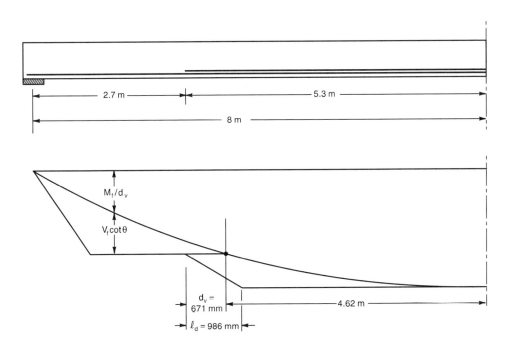

The figure shown below illustrates the influence on the shear capacity of cutting off one-third of the steel. Note that cutting off one-third of the longitudinal reinforcement has resulted in an 18% drop in the shear capacity at the ends of the cut-off bars.

7. *Summary of design.*

Note that the use of the General Method has resulted in a thinner slab having about the same total volume of reinforcement, as summarized in the table below. It is assumed that the width of the slab is 50 m.

	Simplified Method (Clause 11.3)	General Method (Clause 11.4)
Volume of concrete, m³	820	656
Weight of steel, kg		
– principal steel	42.8	49.8
– temperature steel (including splices)	10.8	10.3
Total steel	53.6	60.1

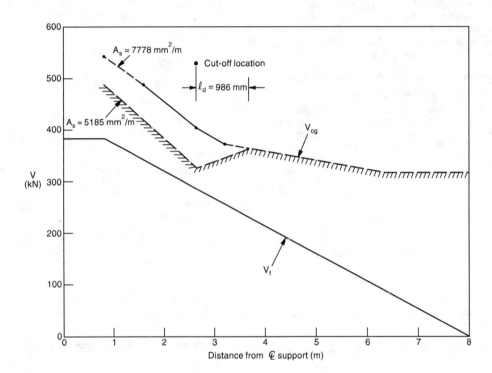

EXAMPLE 4.3 STIRRUP DESIGN FOR A HEAVILY LOADED CONTINUOUS BEAM USING THE SIMPLIFIED METHOD OF CLAUSE 11.3

The factored shear force envelope for a continuous interior beam is shown below. Determine the stirrups required for this beam using the Simplified Method of Clause 11.3.

1. *Check that the section size is adequate.*

The factored shear, V_f at a distance of d from the support face (Clause 11.3.2), is

$$= 750 \times (5.25 - 0.755)/5.25 = 642 \text{ kN}$$

For this beam containing stirrups (Clause 11.3.5.1)

$$V_c = 0.2\lambda\phi_c\sqrt{f'_c}\,b_w d$$

$$= 0.2 \times 1 \times 0.6\sqrt{25} \times 450 \times 755 \times 10^{-3}$$

$$= 204 \text{ kN}$$

The maximum factored resistance permitted by Clause 11.3.4 is

$$V_r \not> V_c + 0.8\lambda\phi_c\sqrt{f'_c}\,b_w d$$

$$= 204 + 0.8 \times 1 \times 0.6\sqrt{25} \times 450 \times 755 \times 10^{-3}$$

$$= 1019 \text{ kN}$$

Since $V_f < 1019$ kN, the section size is adequate.

2. *Design of stirrups near support.*

The shear, V_s to be carried by the stirrups, from Clause 11.3.4, is

$$V_s = V_f - V_c = 642 - 204 = 438 \text{ kN}$$

Assuming No. 10 U stirrups gives $A_v = 200 \text{ mm}^2$. Hence, from Clause 11.3.7, the required stirrup spacing is

$$s = \frac{\phi_s A_v f_y d}{V_s}$$

$$= \frac{0.85 \times 200 \times 400 \times 755}{438 \times 10^3}$$

$$= 117 \text{ mm}$$

From Clause 11.2.11, determine the shear stress level

$$\frac{V_f}{b_w d} = \frac{642 \times 10^3}{450 \times 755} = 1.89 \text{ MPa}$$

Since this shear stress exceeds $0.1\lambda\phi_c f'_c = 0.1 \times 1 \times 0.6 \times 25 = 1.50$ MPa, the spacing must not exceed 300 mm or $0.35d = 0.35 \times 755 = 264$ mm.

In order to satisfy the minimum shear reinforcement requirements of Clause 11.2.8.4

$$s \leq \frac{A_v f_y}{0.06\sqrt{f'_c}\,b_w}$$

$$= \frac{200 \times 400}{0.06\sqrt{25} \times 450}$$

$$= 593 \text{ mm}$$

Therefore, use a practical stirrup spacing of 100 mm near the supports.

3. *Design stirrups in other regions of beam.*

Near the midspan of the beam a minimum area of shear reinforcement is required in regions where $V_f > 0.5V_c$. Additionally, if $V_f > 0.5V_c$ (i.e., $V_f > 0.5 \times 0.6 \times 450 \times 755 = 102$ kN) the stirrup spacing must not exceed 600 mm or $0.7d = 0.7 \times 755 = 529$ mm. Hence, in the regions of lower shear near midspan, the maximum stirrup spacing is 500 mm.

The stirrup spacings can be determined by directly comparing V_r with V_f along the length of the beam. In determining V_r near locations where the stirrup spacing changes, the average amount of stirrups within a length of d can be used. With this procedure the stirrup arrangement shown below is chosen.

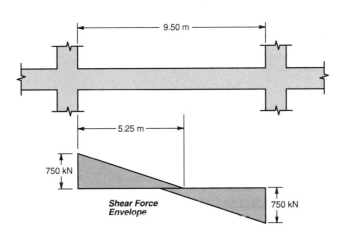

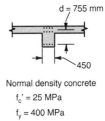

d = 755 mm

450

Normal density concrete
$f_c' = 25$ MPa
$f_y = 400$ MPa

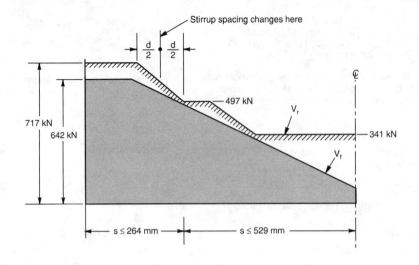

Stirrup spacing changes here

497 kN

717 kN
642 kN

V_r

341 kN

V_f

s ≤ 264 mm   s ≤ 529 mm

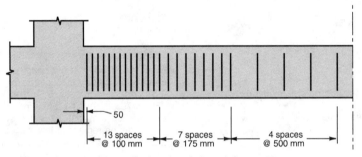

50

13 spaces @ 100 mm   7 spaces @ 175 mm   4 spaces @ 500 mm

Total number of stirrups in beam = 52

EXAMPLE 4.4   DESIGN FOR SHEAR AND MOMENT USING THE GENERAL METHOD OF CLAUSE 11.4

The beam shown below is subjected to a specified live load of 35.0 kN/m and a dead load of 30 kN/m (including the weight of the beam). Design the required transverse and longitudinal reinforcement for shear and moment by the General Method (Clause 11.4).

1. *Determine Shear and Moment Envelopes.*

   For calculations of shear and moments assume that the reinforced masonry wall supports result in a uniform bearing stress across each support.

Consider factored dead load with factored live load on cantilever span and main span   9.2.3

$$w_f = 1.25w_D + 1.50w_L$$
$$= 1.25 \times 30 + 1.5 \times 35$$
$$= 90 \text{ kN/m}$$

Also consider factored dead load on both spans, with factored live load placed either on cantilever span or on main span.   9.2.3

The factored shear and factored moment envelopes are illustrated below.

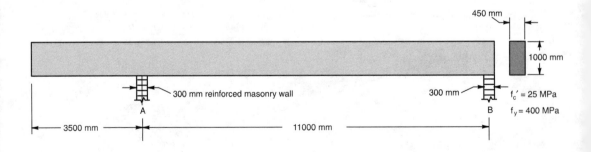

450 mm

1000 mm

300 mm reinforced masonry wall

300 mm

$f_c' = 25$ MPa
$f_y = 400$ MPa

A

B

3500 mm   11000 mm

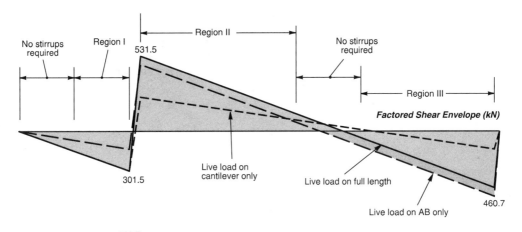

Factored Shear Envelope (kN)

Region I · Region II · No stirrups required · Region III

531.5 · No stirrups required · 301.5 · Live load on cantilever only · Live load on full length · Live load on AB only · 460.7

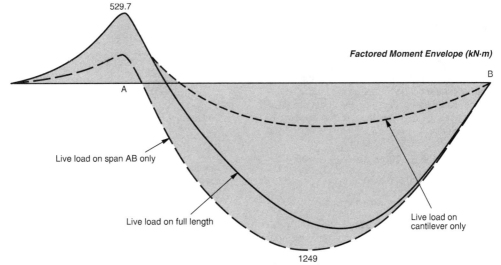

Factored Moment Envelope (kN·m)

529.7 · A · B · Live load on span AB only · Live load on full length · Live load on cantilever only · 1249

2. *Determine flexural reinforcement required at locations of maximum moments.*

The following reinforcement is required.

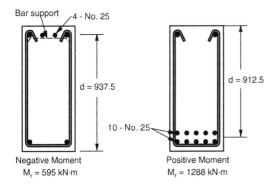

Bar support

4 - No. 25

d = 937.5

10 - No. 25

d = 912.5

Negative Moment
$M_r = 595$ kN·m

Positive Moment
$M_r = 1288$ kN·m

3. *Determine regions that require stirrups.*

Stirrups are not required for regions where V_f is less than $0.5V_c$. That is, | 11.2.8.1 |

$$V_f \le 0.5V_c$$

which, for this purpose, can be taken as | 11.2.8.2 |

$$V_f \le 0.1\lambda\phi_c\sqrt{f'_c}\,b_w d$$
$$= 0.1 \times 1.0 \times 0.6\sqrt{25} \times 450 \times 913 \times 10^{-3}$$

$$= 123.3\,\text{kN}$$

The regions over which no stirrups are required are shown on the shear envelope. Hence, there are three regions of the member that require stirrups: region I in the cantilever, region II to right of support A, and region III to the left of support B.

4. *Design of stirrups.*

Although the stirrups can be designed section-by-section, the stirrups are usually placed in bands, in which the spacing is uniform. It is therefore only necessary to design the stirrups for a relatively small number of sections.

(a) Section d_v from face of support in region II

Take | 11.0 |

$$d_v = 0.9d$$

$$= 0.9 \times 938 = 844\,\text{mm}$$

At a distance of 844 mm from the support face

$$V_f = 531.5 - 0.844 \times 90$$

$$= 455.5\,\text{kN}$$

Hence, the factored shear stress, v_f is

$$v_f = \frac{V_f}{b_w d_v}$$

$$= \frac{455.5 \times 1000}{450 \times 844}$$

$$= 1.20 \, \text{MPa}$$

The factored shear stress ratio is

$$\frac{v_f}{\lambda \phi_c f_c'} = \frac{1.20}{1.0 \times 0.6 \times 25} = 0.080$$

In order to determine θ and β from Table 11-1 or Fig. 11-1, it is necessary to estimate the longitudinal strain, ε_x, where $\boxed{11.4.6}$

$$\varepsilon_x = \frac{0.5 V_f \cot\theta + M_f/d_v}{E_s A_s}$$

While it is easier and more conservative to simply combine the V_f and M_f values from the shear and moment envelopes, it is more accurate to use the shear and corresponding moment for consistent loading cases. For the section under consideration, the highest shear occurs when the live load is on the full length of the beam. For this case, the moment at a distance of d_v from the face of the support is 54 kN·m. Hence,

$$\varepsilon_x = \frac{0.5 \times 455.5 \times 10^3 \cot\theta + \dfrac{54 \times 10^6}{844}}{200\,000 \times 2000}$$

$$= 0.569 \times 10^{-3} \cot\theta + 0.16 \times 10^{-3}$$

Because ε_x and θ are interrelated, the use of Table 11-1 or Fig. 11-1 requires a small amount of trial and error. In this process it is important to recognize that overestimating ε_x and the shear stress ratio gives conservative values of θ and β.

For example, in using Table 11-1 for this case, we will choose to use the row for $v_f/(\lambda \phi_c f_c') \le 0.1$. If we guess that the appropriate cell of the table is that corresponding to $\varepsilon_x \le 0.00075$ then θ would be 34°. With this value of θ the calculated value of ε_x is

$$\varepsilon_x = 0.569 \times 10^{-3} \cot 34° + 0.16 \times 10^{-3}$$

$$= 1.004 \times 10^{-3}$$

Since this calculated value of ε_x exceeds 0.00075, we must choose another cell from the table. Trying the values for $\varepsilon_x \le 0.0010$ gives $\theta = 36°$ and hence,

$$\varepsilon_x = 0.569 \times 10^{-3} \cot 36° + 0.16 \times 10^{-3}$$

$$= 0.943 \times 10^{-3}$$

As the calculated value is less than 0.0010, we can use $\theta = 36°$ and $\beta = 0.174$.

Hence, the factored shear resistance attributed to the concrete is $\boxed{11.4.3.1}$

$$V_{cg} = 1.3 \lambda \phi_c \beta \sqrt{f_c'} \, b_w d_v$$

$$= 1.3 \times 1.0 \times 0.6 \times 0.174 \sqrt{25} \times 450 \times 844 \times 10^{-3}$$

$$= 257.7 \, \text{kN}$$

Hence, the minimum value for the factored shear resistance provided by the stirrups is $\boxed{11.4.3}$

$$V_{sg} = V_f - V_{cg}$$

$$= 455.5 - 257.7$$

$$= 197.8 \, \text{kN}$$

Assuming No. 10 U-stirrups are used, the stirrup spacing required is $\boxed{11.4.3.2}$

$$s \le \frac{\phi_s A_v f_y d_v \cot\theta}{V_{sg}}$$

$$\le \frac{0.85 \times 200 \times 400 \times 844 \cot 36°}{197.8 \times 10^3}$$

$$\le 399 \, \text{mm}$$

In addition to this strength requirement, the stirrup spacing must also satisfy the minimum shear reinforcement requirement and the maximum stirrup spacing requirement. Hence, for minimum shear reinforcement $\boxed{11.2.8.4}$

$$s \le \frac{A_v f_y}{0.06 \sqrt{f_c'} \, b_w}$$

$$\le \frac{200 \times 400}{0.06 \sqrt{25} \times 450}$$

$$\le 593 \, \text{mm}$$

For maximum spacing

$$\frac{V_f}{b_w d} = \frac{455.5 \times 10^3}{450 \times 938}$$

$$= 1.08 \, \text{MPa} < 0.1 \lambda \phi_c f_c' = 1.50 \, \text{MPa}$$

Hence,

$$s \le 600 \, \text{mm}$$

$$\le 0.7d = 0.7 \times 938 = 657 \, \text{mm}$$

Based on the 3 requirements above, choose No. 10 U-stirrups at a spacing of 400 mm.

(b) Calculations for other sections along the beam

The calculations for other sections are tabulated below.

Section	V_f (kN)	M_f (kN·m)	A_s, mm² (d_v, mm)	$\dfrac{v_f}{\phi_c\,f'_c}$	$(\varepsilon_x \times 10^3)$ θ β	V_{cg} (kN)	V_{sg} required (kN)	s (mm)	V_{sg} provided (kN)
d_v from support in cantilever	225.5	283	2000 (844)	0.040	(0.282cotθ + 0.838) 41° 0.162	240	–	550*	120
d_v from support A in span	455.5	54	2000 (844)	0.080	(0.569cotθ + 0.16) 36° 0.174	258	198	400	197
2 m from support A in span	322**	671.3	5000 (821)	0.058	(0.161cotθ + 0.818) 40° 0.158	225	96.8	550*	121
2 m from support A in span	352***	413	5000 (821)	0.064	(0.176cotθ + 0.503) 36° 0.179	258	94	550*	140
d_v from support B	387	418	5000 (821)	0.070	(0.194cotθ + 0.509) 36° 0.179	258	129	550*	140

* controlled by maximum spacing
** live load on AB only
*** live load on total length

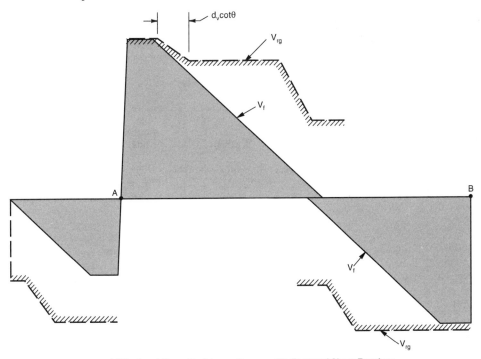

(a) Factored Shear Resistance Compared to Factored Shear Envelope

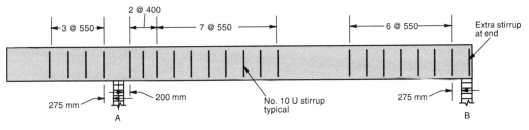

(b) Stirrups Provided

5. *Design of longitudinal reinforcement.*

The longitudinal reinforcement must be proportioned to resist the tensile forces induced by the combined effects of moment and shear. Hence, the required force in the longitudinal steel at all sections, N_s, is

11.4.9.1

$$N_s \geq \frac{M_f}{d_v} + (V_f - 0.5 V_{sg}) \cot \theta$$

In determining the force that can be developed in the steel, we must account for the development length of the reinforcement. For the No. 25 bottom bars, in regions containing minimum stirrups,

$$\ell_d = 0.45 \, k_1 k_2 k_3 k_4 \frac{f_y}{\sqrt{f_c'}} d_b$$

$$= 0.45 \times 1 \times 1 \times 1 \times 1 \times \frac{400}{\sqrt{25}} \times 25$$

$$= 900 \text{ mm}$$

For the No. 25 top bars, in regions containing minimum stirrups,

$$\ell_d = 0.45 \times 1.3 \times 1 \times 1 \times 1 \times \frac{400}{\sqrt{25}} \times 25$$

$$= 1170 \text{ mm}$$

For the No. 25 top bars in regions without stirrups,

$$\ell_d = 0.6 \times 1.3 \times 1 \times 1 \times 1 \times \frac{400}{\sqrt{25}} \times 25$$

$$= 1560 \text{ mm}$$

It is assumed that the tensile capacity of a bar varies linearly from zero at the free ends, to a value of $\phi_s A_b f_y$ at a distance of ℓ_d from the free end. Hence, for an embedment length of ℓ_e

$$N_s = \phi_s A_s \frac{\ell_e}{\ell_d} f_y \leq \phi_s A_s f_y$$

The calculations required to compare N_s required, with N_s provided, are summarized in the table below.

The development length of the No. 25 bottom bars, in this beam containing stirrups, can be determined from Table 12-1 as

$$\ell_d = 0.45 \, k_1 k_2 k_3 k_4 \frac{f_y}{\sqrt{f_c'}} d_b$$

$$= 0.45 \times 1 \times 1 \times 1 \times 1 \times \frac{400}{\sqrt{30}} \times 25$$

$$= 822 \text{ mm}$$

The No. 25 top bars have more than 300 mm of fresh concrete cast below the bars and hence, the bar location factor, k_1 is 1.3. Therefore, for the No.25 top bars, $\ell_d = 1.3 \times 822 = 1068$ mm.

The figure shown below compares the factored tensile resistance of the longitudinal reinforcement with the tension force required to resist the combined moment and shears along the length of the beam. In determining the factored tensile resistance of the reinforcement, it was assumed that the stress in the reinforcement varied linearly over the development length.

Section	M_f (kN·m)	d_v (mm)	V_f (kN)	V_{sg} (kN)	θ	N_s required (kN)	A_s, mm^2 (ℓ_e, mm)	N_s provided (kN)
inner edge of bearing support B	0	821	460.7	140	36°	538	5000 (260)	578
d_v from support in cantilever	283	844	225.5	120	41°	526	2000	680
d_v from support A in span	54	844	455.5	197	36°	555	2000	680
2 m from support A in span	671**	821	322	121	40°	1129	5000	1700
2 m from support A in span	413***	821	352	140	36°	891	5000	1700
d_v from support B	418	821	387	140	36°	945	5000	1700
d_v from support A in span (bottom steel)	229	821	429	120	36°	786	2500	850

**   live load on AB only
***   live load on total length

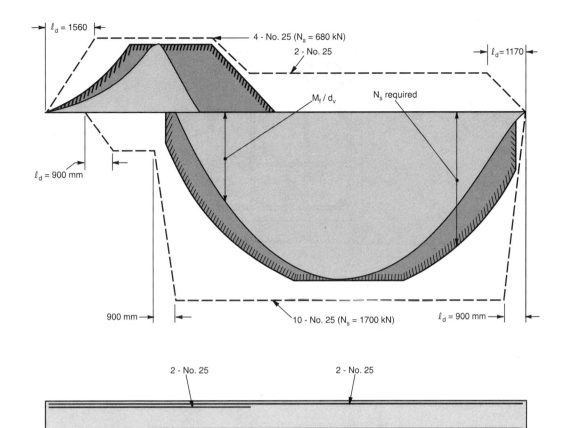

$\ell_d = 1560$

4 - No. 25 ($N_s = 680$ kN)

2 - No. 25

M_f / d_v

N_s required

$\ell_d = 1170$

$\ell_d = 900$ mm

900 mm

10 - No. 25 ($N_s = 1700$ kN)

$\ell_d = 900$ mm

2 - No. 25

2 - No. 25

2 - No. 25

8 - No. 25

EXAMPLE 4.5 DESIGN OF COLUMN FOR SHEAR

The ties in the ground storey columns of a high-rise building have been dimensioned to satisfy the column detailing requirements of Clause 7.6.5. Under wind loading, the leeward exterior columns are subjected to compression and the windward exterior columns are subjected to tension. The two loading cases and the details of these columns are shown below.

Check if the tie reinforcement is adequate for shear and if necessary, adjust the tie spacing.

1. *Determine factored loads at critical section.*

For columns with a regular array of longitudinal steel it is convenient to take A_s as the area of the bars in one-half of the column cross section. Hence, assuming that A_s consists of 6 – No. 35 bars, their centroid is located at a distance of x from the tension face, where x is

$$x = \frac{70 \times 4000 + 223 \times 2000}{6000} = 121 \text{ mm}$$

Therefore, d = 600 – 121 = 479 mm, and the effective shear depth $d_v = 0.9d = 0.9 \times 479 = 431$ mm.

At the critical section, d_v from the ends of the column, the factored loads are

(a) Case I $V_f = 522$ kN

$N_f = -2000$ kN

$M_f = 900 - 522 \times 0.431 = 675$ kN·m

(b) Case II $V_f = 420$ kN

$N_f = +300$ kN

$M_f = 725 - 420 \times 0.431 = 544$ kN·m

2. *Determine required tie spacing for Case I.*

The factored shear stress ratio is

$$\frac{v_f}{\lambda \phi_c f'_c} = \frac{V_f}{\lambda \phi_c f'_c b_w d_v}$$

$$= \frac{522 \times 10^3}{1 \times 0.6 \times 35 \times 600 \times 431} = 0.096$$

For this member, subjected to an axial force of 2000 kN, the indicator of longitudinal strain, ε_x, from Clause 11.4.6 is

$$\varepsilon_x = \frac{0.5(N_f + V_f \cot\theta) + M_f/d_v}{E_s A_s}$$

$$= \frac{0.5(-2000 + 522 \cot\theta) \times 10^3 + 675 \times 10^6/431}{200\,000 \times 6000}$$

$$= 0.218 \times 10^{-3} \cot\theta + 0.472 \times 10^{-3}$$

From Fig. 11-1, try $\theta = 34°$, corresponding to $\varepsilon_x = 0.80 \times 10^{-3}$. Substituting $\theta = 34°$ into the above expression gives $\varepsilon_x = 0.79 \times 10^{-3}$. Use $\beta = 0.19$.

Hence, from Clause 11.4.3.1

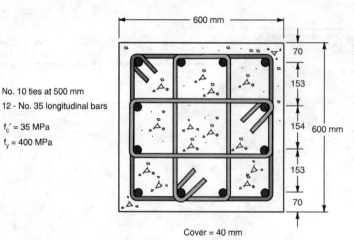

No. 10 ties at 500 mm

12 - No. 35 longitudinal bars

$f_c' = 35$ MPa

$f_y = 400$ MPa

Cover = 40 mm

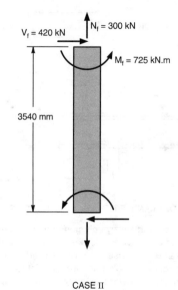

CASE I   CASE II

$V_{cg} = 1.3\lambda\phi_c\beta\sqrt{f_c'}\,b_w d_v$

$\quad = 1.3 \times 1 \times 0.6 \times 0.19\sqrt{35} \times 600 \times 431 \times 10^{-3}$

$\quad = 227$ kN

The shear to be carried by the ties, $V_{sg} = 522 - 227 = 295$ kN. From Clause 11.4.3.2, the required spacing is

$$s \leq \frac{\phi_s A_v f_y d_v \cot\theta}{V_{sg}}$$

$$= \frac{0.85 \times 4 \times 100 \times 400 \times 431\cot34°}{295 \times 10^3}$$

$$= 295 \text{ mm}$$

3. *Determine required tie spacing for Case II.*

The factored shear stress ratio is

$$\frac{v_f}{\lambda\phi_c f_c'} = \frac{420 \times 10^3}{1 \times 0.6 \times 35 \times 600 \times 431} = 0.077$$

For this column, subjected to an axial force of +300 kN, the longitudinal strain, ε_x is

$$\varepsilon_x = \frac{0.5(+300 + 420\cot\theta) \times 10^3 + 544 \times 10^6/431}{200\,000 \times 6000}$$

$$= 0.175 \times 10^{-3}\cot\theta + 1.18 \times 10^{-3}$$

From Table 11-1, try $\theta = 38.5°$, corresponding to $\varepsilon_x = 1.4 \times 10^{-3}$. Substituting $\theta = 38.5°$ into the above expression gives $\varepsilon_x = 1.40 \times 10^{-3}$. Use $\beta = 0.16$.

Hence, from Clause 11.4.3.1

$$V_{cg} = 1.3 \times 1 \times 0.6 \times 0.16\sqrt{35} \times 600 \times 431 \times 10^{-3}$$

$$= 191 \text{ kN}$$

The shear to be carried by the ties is $420 - 191 = 229$ kN. From Clause 11.4.3.2 the required spacing is

$$s \leq \frac{0.85 \times 4 \times 100 \times 400 \times 431\cot38.5°}{229 \times 10^3}$$

$$= 322 \text{ mm}$$

4. *Check maximum spacing requirements.*

The maximum factored shear stress occurs for Case I where

$$\frac{V_f}{b_w d} = \frac{522 \times 10^3}{600 \times 431} = 2.02 \, \text{MPa}$$

Since this shear stress ratio exceeds $0.1\lambda\phi_c f'_c = 0.1 \times 1 \times 0.6 \times 35 = 2.10 \, \text{MPa}$ the maximum tie spacing from Clause 11.2.11 is 600 mm or $0.7d = 0.7 \times 479 = 335$ mm.

The minimum amount of shear reinforcement from Clause 11.2.8.4 requires a spacing

$$s \le \frac{A_v f_y}{0.06\sqrt{f'_c} b_w}$$

$$= \frac{4 \times 100 \times 400}{0.06\sqrt{35} \times 600}$$

$$= 751 \, \text{mm}$$

5. *Final choice of tie spacing.*

The tie spacing is governed by the shear strength requirements of Case I. Hence, use a tie spacing of 290 mm.

EXAMPLE 4.6   DESIGN OF SPANDREL BEAM SUPPORTING BALCONY SLAB

The balcony slab shown below is subjected to a specified live load of 3 kN /m². Design the longitudinal and transverse reinforcement required in the spandrel beam. Assume the beam is fully fixed against rotation at the column faces.

1. *Determine loads acting on spandrel beam.*

Take a 1 m length of slab and beam.

$$w_f = 1.25D + 1.50L = 1.25(6.72 + 1.35 + 3.60)$$
$$+ 1.50 \times 5.70$$

$$= \underline{23.14 \, \text{kN/m}}$$

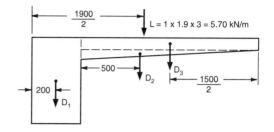

$$D_1 = 0.4 \times 0.7 \times 24 = 6.72 \, \text{kN/m}$$

$$D_2 = 0.5 \times 1.5 \times 0.075 \times 24 = 1.35 \, \text{kN/m}$$

$$D_3 = 1.5 \times 0.10 \times 24 = 3.60 \, \text{kN/m}$$

$$m_f = 1.25[1.35(0.20 + 0.50) + 3.60(0.20 + 0.75)]$$
$$+ 1.50 \times 5.70(0.95 - 0.20)$$

$$= 11.87 \, \text{kN·m/m}$$

2. *Determine M_f, T_f, V_f along spandrel.*

3. *Check if torsion significant.*

From Clause 11.2.9.1

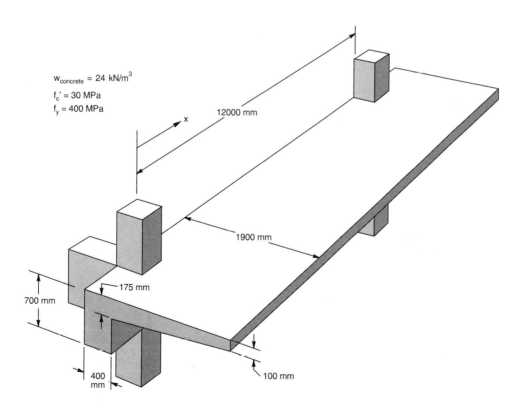

$$w_{concrete} = 24 \, \text{kN/m}^3$$
$$f'_c = 30 \, \text{MPa}$$
$$f_y = 400 \, \text{MPa}$$

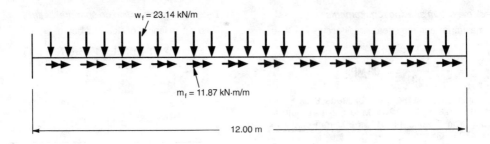

$w_f = 23.14$ kN/m

$m_f = 11.87$ kN·m/m

12.00 m

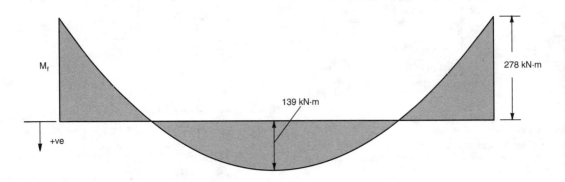

M_f

278 kN·m

139 kN·m

+ve

T_f

71 kN·m

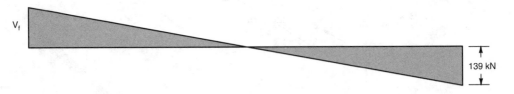

V_f

139 kN

$T_{cr} = (A_c^2/p_c)\, 0.4\lambda\phi_c\sqrt{f_c'}$

$= \dfrac{(400 \times 700)^2}{2 \times (400 + 700)}\, 0.4 \times 1.0 \times 0.60\sqrt{30} \times 10^{-6}$

$= \underline{46.8 \text{ kN·m}}$

$A_{oh} = 310 \times 610 = 189 \times 10^3 \text{ mm}^2$

$p_h = 2(310 + 610) = 1840 \text{ mm}$

As $T_f > 0.25T_{cr}$, torsion must be considered.

4. *Determine section parameters* b_w, d_v, A_{oh}, p_h.

Assume cover = 40 mm

$b_w = 400$ mm

Assuming No. 25 bars gives

$d = 700 - 40 - 10 - \dfrac{25}{2} = 637.5$ mm

$d_v = 0.9d = 0.9 \times 637.5 = 574$ mm

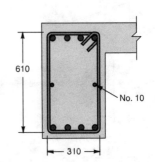

No. 10

610

310

5. *Design of closed stirrups near support.*

At a critical section d_v from the face of the support

$$V_f = 139 - 23.14 \times 0.574 = 125.7\,kN$$

$$T_f = 71 - 11.87 \times 0.574 = 64.2\,kN \cdot m$$

$$M_f = -278 + \left(\frac{139 + 125.7}{2}\right) 0.574 = -202\,kN \cdot m$$

The shear stress given by Equation (11-27) is

$$
\begin{aligned}
v_f &= \sqrt{\left(\frac{V_f}{b_w d_v}\right)^2 + \left(\frac{T_f\,p_h}{A_{oh}^2}\right)^2} \\
&= \sqrt{\left(\frac{125.7 \times 10^3}{400 \times 574}\right)^2 + \left(\frac{64.2 \times 10^6 \times 1840}{(189 \times 10^3)^2}\right)^2} \\
&= \sqrt{(0.547)^2 + (3.307)^2} \\
&= 3.352\,MPa
\end{aligned}
$$

Hence, the factored shear stress ratio is

$$\frac{v_f}{\lambda \phi_c f_c'} = \frac{3.352}{1 \times 0.6 \times 30} = 0.186$$

Since the longitudinal reinforcement has not yet been chosen, take $\varepsilon_x = 0.002$ as permitted by Clause 11.4.10.3. From Fig. 11-1, with $\varepsilon_x = 2 \times 10^{-3}$ and the shear stress ratio of 0.186 we get $\theta = 35.5°$ and $\beta = 0.09$.

The shear carried by the concrete is

$$
\begin{aligned}
V_{cg} &= 1.3\lambda \phi_c \beta \sqrt{f_c'}\, b_w d_v \\
&= 1.3 \times 1 \times 0.6 \times 0.09\sqrt{30} \times 400 \times 574 \times 10^{-3} \\
&= 88.3\,kN
\end{aligned}
$$

The shear required to be carried by the stirrups, $V_{sg} = 125.7 - 88.3 = 37.4\,kN$.

Hence, from Clause 11.4.3.2, the amount of stirrups required for shear is

$$
\begin{aligned}
\frac{A_v}{s} &= \frac{V_{sg}}{\phi_c f_y d_v \cot\theta} \\
&= \frac{37.4 \times 10^3}{0.85 \times 400 \times 574 \times \cot 35.5°} \\
&= 0.137\,mm^2/mm
\end{aligned}
$$

The amount of closed stirrups required for torsion, from Clause 11.4.10.3, is

$$\frac{A_t}{s} = \frac{T_{rg}}{2A_o \phi_s f_y \cot\theta}$$

where A_o is taken as $0.85A_{oh}$.

Hence,

$$
\begin{aligned}
\frac{A_t}{s} &= \frac{64.2 \times 10^6}{2 \times 0.85 \times 189 \times 10^3 \times 0.85 \times 400 \times \cot 35.5°} \\
&= 0.419\,mm^2/mm
\end{aligned}
$$

According to Clause 11.4.10.1 the transverse reinforcement required shall be equal to the sum of that required for shear and the co-existing torsion. Recognizing that A_v is the area of two legs, while A_t is the

area of one leg, the required spacing of the No. 10 closed stirrups can be found from

$$
\begin{aligned}
\frac{A_t}{s} + 0.5\frac{A_v}{s} &= 0.419 + 0.5 \times 0.137 \\
&= 0.488\,mm^2/mm
\end{aligned}
$$

Hence,

$$s \le \frac{100}{0.488} = 205\,mm$$

Clause 11.2.11 specifies maximum spacing limits based on the magnitude of the factored shear stress on the concrete. If the shear stress exceeds $0.1\lambda \phi_c f_c' = 0.1 \times 1 \times 0.6 \times 30 = 1.80\,MPa$ the tie spacing must not exceed 300 mm or $0.35d = 0.35 \times 637 = 223\,mm$. The total factored shear stress from both shear and torsion, in accordance with Equation (11-27) is 3.352 MPa. Hence, the spacing at this location cannot exceed 223 mm.

The maximum spacing required to satisfy the minimum transverse reinforcement of Clause 11.2.8.4 is

$$
\begin{aligned}
s &\le \frac{A_v f_y}{0.06\sqrt{f_c'}\, b_w} \\
&= \frac{200 \times 400}{0.06\sqrt{30} \times 400} \\
&= 609\,mm
\end{aligned}
$$

Therefore, at this location, use a stirrup spacing of 200 mm.

6. *Design of closed stirrups at location 3.5 m from support.*

It is evident from Step 5 that the spacing of the stirrups will be controlled by the spacing limit of 0.35d until the factored shear stress drops below the 1.80 MPa limit. As V_f and T_f vary linearly along the span, the shear stress, v_f will also vary linearly along the span. Therefore, this stress will drop below 1.80 MPa at a location about 3.1 m from the support. We will do the calculations at a section 3.5 m from the support. At this location

$$V_f = 58.0\,kN$$

$$T_f = 29.5\,kN \cdot m$$

$$M_f = +66.8\,kN \cdot m$$

$$v_f = \sqrt{(0.252)^2 + (1.518)^2} = 1.538\,MPa$$

$$\frac{v_f}{\lambda \phi_c f_c'} = 0.086$$

Using $\varepsilon_x = 2 \times 10^{-3}$, for this factored shear stress ratio, $\theta = 40.5°$ and $\beta = 0.13$.

$$
\begin{aligned}
V_{cg} &= 1.3 \times 1 \times 0.6 \times 0.13\sqrt{30} \times 400 \times 574 \times 10^{-3} \\
&= 127.5\,kN
\end{aligned}
$$

Since $V_{cg} > V_f$ at this location, no stirrups are required to resist the shear.

The amount of closed stirrups required for torsion is

$$
\begin{aligned}
\frac{A_t}{s} &= \frac{29.5 \times 10^6}{2 \times 0.85 \times 189 \times 10^3 \times 0.85 \times 400 \times \cot 40.5°} \\
&= 0.231\,mm^2/mm
\end{aligned}
$$

Hence, the spacing of No. 10 closed stirrups is $100/0.231 = 433$ mm.

Since v_f is less than 1.80 MPa at this section, the spacing must not exceed 600 mm or $0.7d = 0.7 \times 637 = 446$ mm.

Therefore, use a spacing of 400 mm.

7. *Determine locations where stirrups are no longer required.*

According to Clause 11.2.9.1, closed stirrups for torsion are no longer required when (see Step 3)

$$T_f \le 0.25 T_{cr}$$

$$= 0.25 \times 46.8 = 11.7 \, kN \cdot m$$

The torsion becomes less than this value at a location 5 m from the support.

According to Clause 11.2.8, stirrups are no longer required to resist shear when

$$V_f \le 0.1 \lambda \phi_c \sqrt{f_c'} \, b_w d$$

$$= 0.1 \times 1 \times 0.6 \sqrt{30} \times 400 \times 637 \times 10^{-3}$$

$$= 83.7 \, kN$$

The shear becomes less than this value at a location 2.4 m from the support.

Therefore, closed stirrups are not required in the central 2 m of the span.

8. *Design of longitudinal reinforcement at support face.*

Torsion will increase the need for longitudinal reinforcement, even at sections of maximum moment. Torsion is resisted by diagonal compressive stresses that spiral around all faces of the section, which increases the demand for tensile capacity in the longitudinal reinforcement. In addition, the support reactions resisting torsion do not introduce direct compression into the flexural compression face of the member. Therefore, according to Clause 11.4.9.3, it is necessary to design for additional longitudinal forces due to torsion, even at the support faces.

At the support face:

$$V_f = 139 \, kN$$

$$T_f = 71 \, kN \cdot m$$

$$M_f = 278 \, kN \cdot m$$

From Clause 11.4.10.4, the required factored resistance of the longitudinal reinforcement, at the top of the beam, is

$$\phi_s A_s f_y \ge \frac{M_f}{d_v} + \cot\theta \sqrt{(V_f - 0.5 V_{sg})^2 + \left(\frac{0.45 p_h T_f}{2 A_o}\right)^2}$$

$$= \left[\frac{278 \times 10^6}{574} + \cot 35.5 \sqrt{(139 \times 10^3 - 0.5 \times 37.4 \times 10^3)^2 + \left(\frac{0.45 \times 1840 \times 71 \times 10^6}{2 \times 0.85 \times 189 \times 10^3}\right)^2}\right] \times 10^{-3}$$

$$= 484 + 307$$

$$= 791 \, kN$$

Therefore, the area of top reinforcement is

$$A_s \ge \frac{791 \times 10^3}{0.85 \times 400} = 2326 \, mm^2$$

Hence, use 5 – No. 25 bars.

At the bottom face of the beam, at the support, the compression from the flexure dominates and hence, we need only satisfy the requirements of Clause 12.11.1 that one-fourth of the bottom steel extend into the support.

In order to check if the beam is over-reinforced, we will calculate the depth of compression, c, required to balance the total tensile force required, $T = 791$ kN. In calculating the stress block depth, a, the stress block factor $\alpha_1 = 0.85 - 0.0015 f_c' = 0.805$. Hence,

$$a = \frac{T}{\alpha_1 \phi_c' f_c' b}$$

$$= \frac{791 \times 10^3}{0.805 \times 0.6 \times 30 \times 400}$$

$$= 137 \, mm$$

The stress block factor $\beta_1 = 0.97 - 0.0025 f_c' = 0.895$ and therefore, the depth of compression, $c = a/\beta_1 = 137/0.895 = 153$ mm. The ratio $c/d = 153/637 = 0.240$, which is less than the limit $700/(700 + f_y) = 0.636$. Therefore, the beam is not over-reinforced.

9. *Check required longitudinal reinforcement at point of contraflexure.*

The point of contraflexure is located 2.54 m from the support. At this location

$$V_f = 80.2 \, kN$$

$$T_f = 41.0 \, kN \cdot m$$

Hence,

$$\frac{v_f}{\lambda \phi_c f_c'} = 0.186 \times \frac{41.0}{64.2} = 0.119$$

This gives $\theta = 38°$ from Fig. 11-1.

From Clause 11.4.10.4 the required tension force is

$$\left[\frac{0}{574} + \cot 38° \times \right.$$

$$\left. \sqrt{(80.2 \times 10^3 - 0)^2 + \left(\frac{0.45 \times 1840 \times 41 \times 10^6}{2 \times 0.85 \times 189 \times 10^3}\right)^2}\right] \times 10$$

$$= 169.8 \, kN$$

This tensile force is required on the top and bottom face. The area of longitudinal steel required at this location is

$$A_s \geq \frac{169.8 \times 10^3}{0.85 \times 400} = 499 \text{ mm}^2$$

Hence, provide 2 – No. 25 bars as minimum required bars, top and bottom, to support the stirrups.

Note that Clause 11.2.7 requires that the diameter of the longitudinal bars in the corners of the closed hoops required for torsion not be less than $s/16$ = 200/16 = 12.5 mm. Note that when the spacing of the closed stirrups increases to 400 mm a No. 25 corner bar is required.

These bars will also satisfy the requirements of Clause 12.12.2 that at least one-third of the total tension reinforcement must extend beyond the point of inflection.

10. *Determine required longitudinal reinforcement at midspan.*

At midspan, the factored moment is 139 kN·m. We will estimate the required reinforcement assuming a lever arm of 0.9d = 574 mm. Hence, the required force is 139/0.574 = 242 kN and the required A_s = 242 × 10^3/(0.85 × 400) = 712 mm^2. Therefore, use 2 – No. 25 bars.

A check of the flexural capacity is carried out below

$$a = \frac{\phi_s A_s f_y}{\alpha_1 \phi_c f'_c b} = \frac{0.85 \times 1000 \times 400}{0.805 \times 0.6 \times 30 \times 400} = 59 \text{ mm}$$

$$M_r = \phi_s A_s f_y (d - a/2) = 0.85 \times 1000 \times 400 (637 - 59/2) \times 10^{-6}$$

$$= 207 \text{ kN·m} > M_f$$

$$c/d = \frac{(59/0.895)}{637} = 0.104 < 0.636$$

11. *Bar cut-off locations.*

The figure shown below shows the variations of required tensile force in the longitudinal reinforcement, as well as the factored resistance of the reinforcement provided. For this beam, with closed stirrups, the tensile development length for the bottom bars (from Table 12-1) is

$$\ell_d = 0.45 k_1 k_2 k_3 k_4 \frac{f_y}{\sqrt{f'_c}} d_b$$

$$= 0.45 \times 1 \times 1 \times 1 \times 1 \times \frac{400}{\sqrt{30}} \times 25 = 822 \text{ mm}$$

For the top bars $\ell_d = 1.3 \times 822 = 1068$ mm.

The bar cut-offs are illustrated in the figure on page 4-26. In determining the factored tensile resistance of the steel, it has been assumed that the bar force varies linearly over the development length.

EXAMPLE 4.7 TORSIONAL DESIGN OF SPANDREL BEAM IN TWO-WAY SLAB

The design of a two-way slab has resulted in a calculated factored moment at the edge of the slab of 17.57 kN·m/m. This moment causes torsions in the spandrel beam as shown in the figure below. In addition, the spandrel beam has a factored moment, M_f, at the face of the column, of 135.3 kN·m, while the factored shear, d from the face of the column, is 83.5 kN.

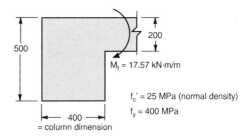

M_f = 17.57 kN·m/m

f'_c = 25 MPa (normal density)
f_y = 400 MPa

400 = column dimension

1. *Determine torsions in spandrels having spans of 7500 mm.*

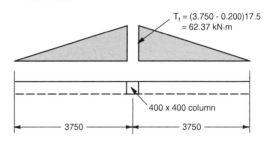

T_f = (3.750 - 0.200)17.5 = 62.37 kN·m

400 x 400 column

3750   3750

2. *Determine if torsion is significant.*

The cracking torque, T_{cr}, from Clause 11.2.9.1 is

$$T_{cr} = (A_c^2/p_c) 0.4 \lambda \phi_c \sqrt{f'_c}$$

$$= \frac{(400 \times 500)^2}{2(400 + 500)} \times 0.4 \times 1.0 \times 0.6 \sqrt{25} \times 10^{-6}$$

$$= 26.67 \text{ kN·m}$$

Since T_f exceeds 0.25T_{cr}, torsion must be considered.

3. *Adjust torsion diagram to account for redistribution.*

When a reinforced concrete beam cracks in torsion, there is a considerable loss of torsional stiffness. In statically indeterminate structures, where the magnitude of the torsion is a function of the torsional stiffness, considerable redistribution occurs after torsional cracking. Because of this, Clause 11.2.9.2 permits the maximum torsion at the face of the support to be reduced to 0.67T_{cr} provided that appropriate adjustments are made to the moments in adjoining members. The resulting torsions are illustrated in the figure below.

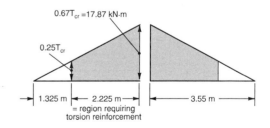

0.67T_{cr} =17.87 kN·m

0.25T_{cr}

1.325 m   2.225 m   3.55 m
= region requiring torsion reinforcement

4. *Check if section size is adequate.*

Determine required cross-sectional properties.

Assuming No. 10 closed stirrups, No. 20 longitudinal bars, and a clear cover of 30 mm for interior exposure gives

$$d = 500 - 30 - 10 - \frac{20}{2} = 450 \text{ mm}$$

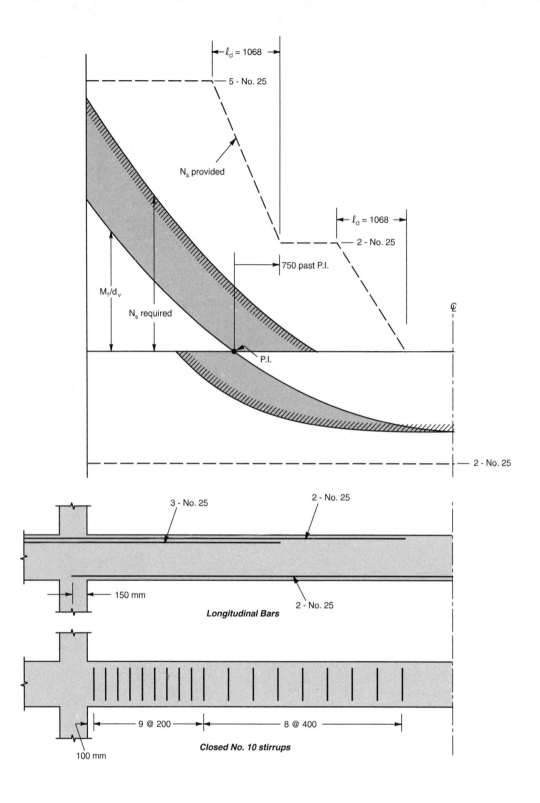

$\ell_d = 1068$

5 - No. 25

N_s provided

$\ell_d = 1068$

2 - No. 25

750 past P.I.

M_f/d_v

N_s required

P.I.

₵

2 - No. 25

3 - No. 25

2 - No. 25

150 mm

2 - No. 25

Longitudinal Bars

9 @ 200

8 @ 400

Closed No. 10 stirrups

100 mm

$$A_{oh} = \left(500 - 30 - \frac{10}{2}\right)\left(400 - 30 - \frac{10}{2}\right)$$

$$= 169\,725 \text{ mm}^2$$

$$p_h = 2(465 + 365) = 1660 \text{ mm}$$

V_f at a distance d from the face of the support is 83.5 kN.

T_f at d from the support face is

$$T_f = \frac{(3.55 - 0.45)}{3.55} \times 17.87 = 15.6 \text{ kN·m}$$

The factored shear stress on the cross section is

$$\frac{V_f}{b_w d} + \frac{T_f p_h}{A_{oh}^2}$$

$$= \frac{83.5 \times 10^3}{400 \times 450} + \frac{15.6 \times 10^6 \times 1660}{(169\,725)^2}$$

$$= 0.464 + 0.899$$

$$= 1.363 \text{ MPa}$$

Since this factored shear stress is less than $0.25\,\phi_c\,f_c' = 0.25 \times 0.6 \times 25 = 3.75$ MPa, the section size is adequate, according to Clause 11.3.9.8.

5. *Design of transverse reinforcement for shear and torsion.*

At the section d from the face of the support, the required amount of closed stirrups for torsion can be calculated from Clause 11.3.9.4 as

$$\frac{A_t}{s} = \frac{T_f}{2\,A_o\,\phi_s\,f_y}$$

$$= \frac{15.6 \times 10^6}{2 \times 0.85 \times 169\,725 \times 0.85 \times 400}$$

$$= 0.159 \text{ mm}^2/\text{mm}$$

From Clause 11.3.5.1, the shear carried by the concrete, V_c, is

$$V_c = 0.2\lambda\,\phi_c\,\sqrt{f_c'}\,b_w d$$

$$= 0.2 \times 1 \times 0.6\sqrt{25} \times 400 \times 450 \times 10^{-3}$$

$$= 108 \text{ kN}$$

As V_f is less than V_c, no shear reinforcement is required to satisfy the strength requirement.

Hence, the total amount of closed stirrups required to provide the shear and torsional strengths is

$$\frac{A_t}{s} + 0.5\frac{A_v}{s} = 0.159 + 0 = 0.159 \text{ mm}^2/\text{mm}$$

The required spacing of No. 10 closed stirrups is $100/0.159 = 629$ mm.

Clause 11.2.8.4 requires that a minimum amount of transverse reinforcement be provided. The required spacing of No. 10 closed stirrups is

$$s \le \frac{A_v\,f_y}{0.06\sqrt{f_c'}\,b_w}$$

$$= \frac{2 \times 100 \times 400}{0.06\sqrt{25} \times 400} = 667 \text{ mm}$$

Hence, this requirement will not govern.

The factored shear stress for torsion and shear is 1.363 MPa. Clause 11.2.11 requires a stirrup spacing not exceeding 600 mm or $0.7d = 0.7 \times 450 = 315$ mm, provided that the factored shear stress is less than $0.1\lambda\,\phi_c\,f_c' = 0.1 \times 1 \times 0.6 \times 25 = 1.50$ MPa.

Therefore, provide No. 10 closed stirrups at a spacing of 300 mm.

According to Clause 11.2.9.1, no stirrups are required when the factored torque is less than $0.25T_{cr}$. This occurs at a distance of 2.225 m from the face of the column (see figure).

6. *Design of longitudinal reinforcement.*

The factored moment at the face of the column is 135.3 kN·m. Assuming a lever arm of $0.9d = 0.9 \times 450 = 405$ mm, gives a required area of flexural reinforcement of

$$A_s \ge \frac{135.3 \times 10^6}{405 \times 0.85 \times 400}$$

$$= 983 \text{ mm}^2$$

From Clause 11.3.9.5, the total area of longitudinal reinforcement to resist torsion is

$$A_\ell = \frac{A_t}{s}\,p_h$$

$$= 0.159 \times 1660$$

$$= 264 \text{ mm}^2$$

This required area of longitudinal reinforcement is to be distributed symmetrically around the cross section.

The area of top bars required at the column face is

$$A_s = 983 + \frac{264}{2} = 1115 \text{ mm}^2$$

Hence, use 4 – No. 20 bars. It is noted that, according to Clause 11.2.7, the corner bars must have a minimum diameter of $s/16 = 300/16 = 19$ mm.

The area of bottom bars required in the flexural compression zone at the face of the column (Clause 11.3.9.6) is

$$A_s = \frac{A_\ell}{2} - \frac{M_f}{0.9d\,f_y}$$

$$= \frac{264}{2} - \frac{135.3 \times 10^6}{0.9 \times 450 \times 400}$$

$$= 132 - 835 = -703 \text{ mm}^2$$

Hence, provide 2 – No. 20 corner bars in the bottom of the beam to satisfy the requirements of Clause 11.2.7.

Note: The design of the spandrel beam assumed redistribution of moments after torsional cracking. This gives reduced torsions in the spandrel beam and therefore, the moments in the slab design strips perpendicular to the spandrel must be adjusted accordingly. That is, the end moments should be reduced and the positive moment increased.

EXAMPLE 4.8   DESIGN OF A DEEP BEAM
SUBJECTED TO UNIFORM LOAD

Design the reinforcement for the laterally supported transfer girder shown below.

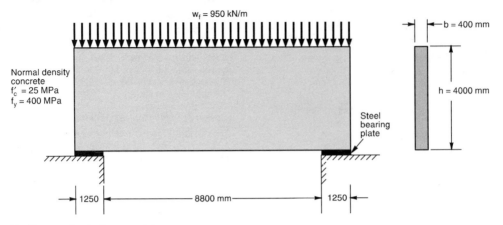

$w_f = 950$ kN/m

Normal density concrete
$f'_c = 25$ MPa
$f_y = 400$ MPa

Steel bearing plate

$b = 400$ mm

$h = 4000$ mm

1250   8800 mm   1250

1. *Idealize member by truss model.*

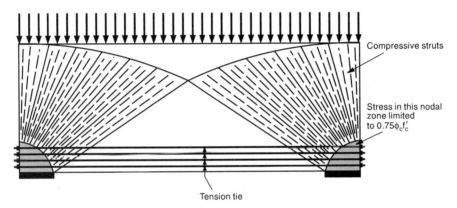

Compressive struts

Stress in this nodal zone limited to $0.75\phi_c f'_c$

Tension tie

2. *Check bearing stress.*

Support reaction = $950 \times (4.4 + 1.25) = 5368$ kN

Bearing stress = $5368 \times 10^3/(400 \times 1250) = 10.74$ MPa

Allowable bearing stress on nodal zone = $0.75 \times 0.60 \times 25 = 11.25$ MPa

As 10.74 MPa $<$11.25 MPa, bearing area is adequate.

3. *Calculate required tension in tie of truss.*

Consider free-body diagram shown below.

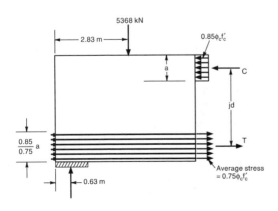

5368 kN

2.83 m

$0.85\phi_c f'_c$

a

C

jd

T

$\frac{0.85}{0.75}$ a

Average stress = $0.75\phi_c f'_c$

0.63 m

To limit stresses in the nodal zone the tension tie reinforcement must be distributed over a depth sufficient to produce an average stress of $0.75\phi_c f'_c$. 　11.5.4.1(b)

If the depth of the compression zone at mid-span is a, then since C = T, the depth over which the tie reinforcement is distributed is

$$\frac{0.85}{0.75}a = 1.13a$$

∴ The lever arm jd $= h - \frac{a}{2} - 1.13\frac{a}{2} = h - 1.065a$

Equating the external moment with the internal moment, we have

$$5368 \times 10^3 \times (2.83 - 0.63) \times 10^3 = c \cdot jd$$

$$= 0.85 \times 0.60 \times 25 \times a \times 400 \times (4000 - 1.065a)$$

$$\therefore a = 716 \text{ mm}$$

Hence,

$$C = T = 0.85 \times 0.60 \times 25 \times 400 \times 716 \times 10^{-3}$$

$$= \underline{3652 \text{ kN}}$$

4. *Choose reinforcement for tension tie.*

Required area

$\phi_s A_s f_y = T = 3652 \text{ kN}$

$\therefore A_s = 3652 \times 10^3 / (0.85 \times 400)$

$\qquad = \underline{10\ 740\ \text{mm}^2}$

To satisfy 11.5.4.2(b) this reinforcement must be distributed over a depth of $1.13 \times 716 = \underline{809\ \text{mm}}$.

The tension tie reinforcement must be anchored within the nodal zone. Hence, development length must be less than 1200 mm. Thus, bar size must be No. 30 or smaller. 12.2.3

Provide 22 – No. 25 bars distributed as shown.

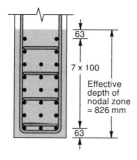

63

7 x 100

Effective depth of nodal zone = 826 mm

63

5. *Calculate minimum shear reinforcement for crack control and ductility.*

Using 2-leg No. 10 stirrups, $A_v = 2 \times 100 = 200 \text{ mm}^2$.

Required spacing of transverse reinforcement is 11.5.5

$$s \le \frac{200}{0.002 \times 400} = \underline{250\ \text{mm}}$$

$$< 300 \text{ mm}$$

Provide No. 10 U-stirrups at 250 mm.

To satisfy the minimum longitudinal requirements, provide pairs of No. 10 longitudinal bars at 250 mm centres. 11.5.5

6. *Summarize design.*

To provide some restraint against possible vertical splitting at the ends of the beam, No. 10 horizontal U-bars have been added as shown.

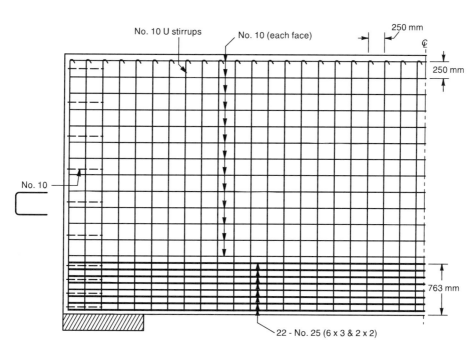

No. 10 U stirrups   No. 10 (each face)   250 mm

250 mm

No. 10

763 mm

22 - No. 25 (6 x 3 & 2 x 2)

EXAMPLE 4.9   DESIGN OF A DEEP BEAM SUBJECTED TO CONCENTRATED LOADS

Design the reinforcement for the laterally supported transfer girder shown on page 4-30. Use $f'_c = 25$ MPa and $f_y = 400$ MPa.

1. *Check bearing stresses at supports and loading points.*

Support reaction = 4000 kN

Bearing stress = $4000 \times 1000 / (400 \times 1250) = 8.00$ MPa

Allowable bearing stress = $0.75 \times 0.60 \times 25 = 11.25$ MPa   11.5.4.1(b)

(tension tie present)

Bearing stress < Allowable   O.K.

Bearing stress at loading point

$= 4000 \times 1000 / (400 \times 800)$

$= 12.50$ MPa

Allowable bearing stress = $0.85 \times 0.6 \times 25 = 12.75$ MPa   11.5.4.1(a)

Bearing stress < Allowable   O.K.

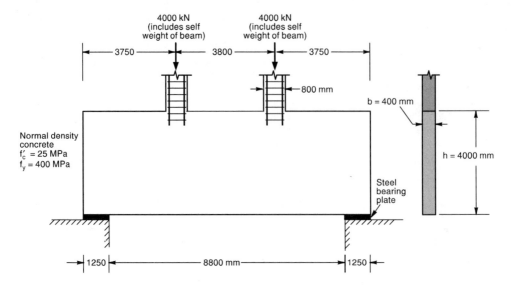

4000 kN (includes self weight of beam) 4000 kN (includes self weight of beam)

Normal density concrete
$f'_c = 25$ MPa
$f_y = 400$ MPa

800 mm

b = 400 mm

Steel bearing plate

h = 4000 mm

1250   8800 mm   1250

2. *Calculate required tension in tie of truss.*

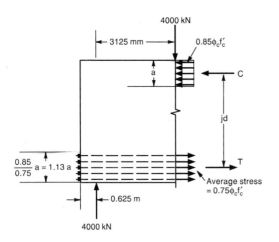

Due to the presence of the tension tie, the nodal zone stress at support   11.5.4.1(b)

$$= 0.75\phi_c f'_c$$

Since C = T, the depth over which the tie force is distributed is

$$\frac{0.85}{0.75}a = 1.13a$$

The lever arm, $jd = h - \frac{a}{2} - 1.13\frac{a}{2} = h - 1.065a$

Equating the external moment with the internal moment, we have

$$4000 \times 10^3 \times 3125 = 0.85 \times 0.60 \times 25 \times 400 \times a(4000 - 1.065a)$$

$$\therefore a = 771 \text{ mm}$$

Therefore,

$$C = T = 0.85 \times 0.60 \times 25 \times 400 \times 771 \times 10^{-3}$$

$$= 3932 \text{ kN}$$

3. *Choose reinforcement for tension tie.*

$$A_s = \frac{3932 \times 1000}{0.85 \times 400} = 11\ 565 \text{ mm}^2$$

Provide 24 – No. 25 bars, $A_s = 24 \times 500 = 12000$ mm²
Minimum nodal zone depth $= 1.13 \times 771 = \underline{871 \text{ mm}}$
11.5.4.2

If the 24 bars are placed in 8 layers of 3 bars, as shown in the figure, the effective nodal zone depth will be 896 mm.

As the tension tie depth is somewhat greater than assumed, the lever arm will be somewhat reduced.

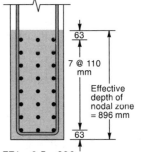

63

7 @ 110 mm

Effective depth of nodal zone = 896 mm

63

Effective depth of nodal zone = 896 mm

$$jd = 4000 - 0.5 \times 771 - 0.5 \times 896$$
$$= 3167 \text{ mm}$$

Required tension tie force

$$= \frac{4000 \times 3125}{3167} = 3947 \text{ kN}$$

Stress in tension tie

$$= \frac{3947 \times 1000}{24 \times 500} = 329 \text{ MPa}$$

$$\le \phi_s f_y = 0.85 \times 400 = 340 \text{ MPa} \qquad \text{O.K.}$$

Note that as the development length for No. 25 bars is 900 mm, the tensile tie can be transferred to the nodal zone within the 1250 mm bearing length.   11.5.3.2

4. *Sketch idealized truss model.*

The idealized truss model is shown in the figure on page 4-31.

5. *Check for compressive strut crushing.*

Force in strut is $\dfrac{4000}{\sin 45.4°} = 5618$ kN

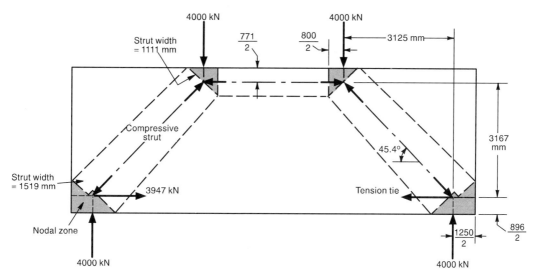

At the top of the strut the stress in the strut is

$$f_2 = \frac{5618 \times 1000}{400 \times 1111} = 12.64\,\text{MPa}$$

Since no tension ties cross the strut in this region (i.e., ε_1 is about zero) the permissible compressive stress near the top of the strut is $\boxed{11.5.2}$

$$\phi_c\,f_{cu} = \phi_c\,0.85\,f'_c = 12.75\,\text{MPa}$$

Since $f_2 < \phi_c\,f_{cu}$ stresses   O.K.

At the bottom of the strut the stress in the strut is

$$f_2 = \frac{5618 \times 1000}{400 \times 1519} = 9.25\,\text{MPa}$$

The compressive strut in this region is crossed by a tension tie and therefore the limiting stress, f_{cu} is reduced.

Since the tension tie reinforcing bars are being developed in this region, assume an average strain, ε_s, in the tension tie at the centre of the strut to be equal to $\frac{1}{2} \times$ yield strain $= 0.001$.

The principal tensile strain, $\boxed{11.5.2.3}$

$$\varepsilon_1 = \varepsilon_s + (\varepsilon_s + 0.002)\cot^2\theta_s$$

$$= 0.001 + (0.001 + 0.002)\cot^2 45.4°$$

$$= 0.00392$$

The limiting stress in the strut, $\boxed{11.5.2}$

$$\phi_c\,f_{cu} = \phi_c\,f'_c / (0.8 + 170\varepsilon_1)$$

$$= 0.6 \times 25 / (0.8 + 170 \times 0.00392)$$

$$= 10.23\,\text{MPa}$$

Since $f_2 < \phi_c\,f_{cu}$ strut stresses are acceptable.

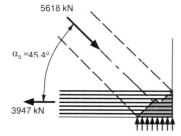

6. *Calculate minimum shear reinforcement required for crack control and ductility.*

   Using No. 10 U-stirrups, $A_v = 2 \times 100 = 200\,\text{mm}^2$

   Required spacing of transverse reinforcement $\boxed{11.5.5}$

   $$\leq \frac{200}{0.002 \times 400} = 250\,\text{mm}$$

   $$< 300\,\text{mm}$$

   Provide No. 10 U-stirrups at 250 mm spacing.

   To satisfy the longitudinal steel requirement provide pairs of No. 10 longitudinal bars. $\boxed{11.5.5}$

7. *Summarize design.*

   To provide some restraint against vertical splitting at the ends of the beam, No. 10 horizontal U-bars have been added as shown on page 4-32.

EXAMPLE 4.10 DESIGN OF CORBEL FOR EXTERIOR COLUMN

As shown in the figure, a corbel projecting from a 350 mm $\times$ 350 mm column supports a precast girder. The corbel is subjected to a vertical specified dead load of 80 kN and a vertical specified live load of 100 kN. Calculations indicate that due to restraint of beam creep and shrinkage deformations, a horizontal force of 35 kN will develop.

Design the corbel assuming $f'_c = 35\,\text{MPa}$ (normal density) and $f_y = 300\,\text{MPa}$ (weldable).

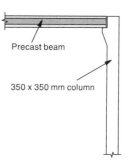

1. *Determine factored loads.*

   Vertical factored load: $\boxed{8.3}$

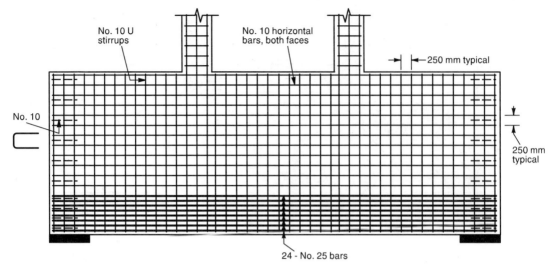

No. 10 U stirrups

No. 10 horizontal bars, both faces

250 mm typical

No. 10

250 mm typical

24 - No. 25 bars

$V_f = \alpha_D D + \alpha_L L$

$= 1.25 \times 80 + 1.5 \times 100 = 250\,kN$

Horizontal factored load: | 8.3 |

$N_f = \alpha_T T = 1.25 \times 35 = 44\ kN$

$N_f > 0.2 V_f = 50\ kN$ | 11.7.4 |

Therefore, use $N_f = 50$ kN.

2. *Determining bearing plate dimensions.*

Assume that bearing plate extends across a width of $350 - (2 \times 40) = 270$ mm

Minimum width of bearing plate | 11.5.4.1(b) |

$= \dfrac{V_f}{0.75\phi_c\,f'_c\,b} = \dfrac{250 \times 1000}{0.75 \times 0.6 \times 35 \times 270} = 59\ mm$

Therefore, use a $270 \times 75 \times 25$ mm bearing plate.

3. *Choose corbel dimensions.*

Choose an overall corbel depth at column face of 500 mm. If reinforcement turns out to be excessive, this dimension may have to be increased.

Choose the depth at the free end of the corbel to ensure that the depth at the outside of the bearing area is at least 0.5×500 mm = 250 mm. | 11.7.3 |
The external dimensions chosen for the corbel are summarized in the figure below.

4. *Determine geometry of strut-and-tie model.*

To allow for load eccentricities and erection tolerances, consider the vertical load to be placed 25 mm towards edge of corbel from centre of bearing plate. | 16.4.4.3 |
The assumed compressive strut, tension tie and nodal zone model for the corbel is shown on page 4-33. To clarify the geometry of the assumed truss, a separate line drawing of the truss is also given.

Nodes A and B are located at the intersections of the centrelines of the tension ties. Node C is located at the intersection of the centreline of the upper tension tie and the line of action of the resultant applied load. Node D is located at the intersection of the centreline of the lower tension tie and the centreline of the

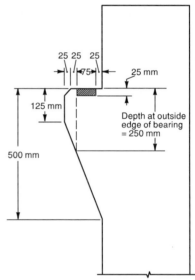

25 25 25

75

25 mm

125 mm

Depth at outside edge of bearing = 250 mm

500 mm

vertical compressive strut below the corbel. The location of this strut centreline is found by calculating the strut width "a".

The compressive force in the strut, N_c, can be found by taking moments about Node A.

$$250 \times 372 + 50 \times 467 = N_c \times (290 - a/2)$$

As the stress on the nodal zone at D is to be limited to $0.75\,\phi_c\,f'_c = 15.75$ MPa, we have | 11.5.4.1(b) |

$$a = \dfrac{N_c}{15.75 \times 350}$$

Solving these two equations gives

$$N_c = 470\ kN$$

and

$$a = 85\ mm$$

This fixes the geometry of the truss and means that member CD has a horizontal projection of $82 + 85/2 = 125$ mm, while member BD has a horizontal projection of 248 mm.

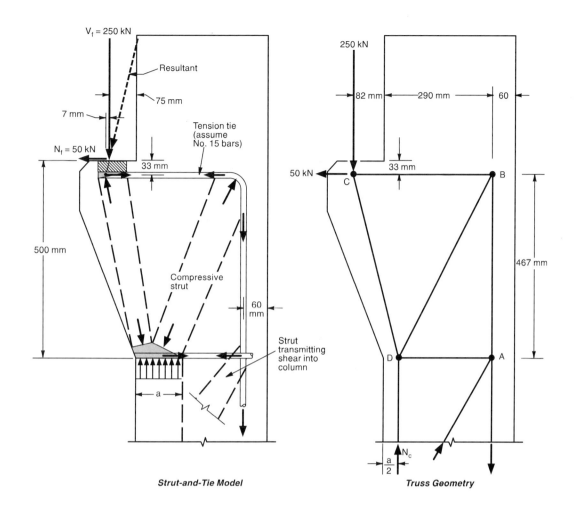

Strut-and-Tie Model

Truss Geometry

5. *Determine forces in truss by statics.*

Member	CD	CB	BD	BA	DA
Force (kN)	−259	+117	−249	+220	+50

Positive indicates tension, negative compression.

6. *Design of tension ties.*

The area of reinforcement required for tension tie CB is

$$= \frac{117 \times 1000}{0.85 \times 300} = 459 \ mm^2$$

Hence, use 3 – No. 15 bars.

Although tie BA has a larger tension, it must be appreciated that the longitudinal reinforcement in the column will have been designed to resist this longitudinal tensile force. Hence, continue the 3 – No. 15 bars for a sufficient distance down the column to fully develop these bars.

The area of reinforcement required for tension tie DA is

$$= \frac{50 \times 1000}{0.85 \times 300} = 196 \ mm^2$$

Hence, use one additional No. 10 column tie at location DA.

7. *Design of nodal zones.*

The width "a" of nodal zone D was chosen in Step 4 to satisfy the stress limits on this nodal zone.

The longitudinal column bars and the column ties will assist in anchoring the tension ties in nodal zones D, A and B.

To anchor tension tie CB in nodal zone C, weld the 3 – No. 15 bars to the bearing plate and also weld a No. 15 cross bar to these bars as shown in the figure below.

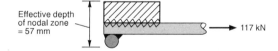

Effective depth of nodal zone = 57 mm

117 kN

To satisfy the nodal zone stress limits, the tension tie reinforcement must engage an effective depth of concrete at least equal to 11.5.4.2(b)

$$= \frac{117 \times 1000}{0.75 \times 0.60 \times 35 \times 270} = 28 \ mm$$

∴ O.K.

8. *Checking compressive struts.*

As the compressive struts are not crossed by tension ties, f_{cu} for these struts will be 0.85 f_c'. Since this stress exceeds the stress checked for in the nodal zone, the strut stresses will not be critical. 11.5.2

9. *Check minimum reinforcement requirements.*

The area, A_{st}, of the primary tensile tie reinforcement must satisfy $\boxed{11.7.6}$

$$A_{st} \geq 0.04\frac{f'_c}{f_y}bd$$

$$= 0.04\frac{35}{300} \times 350 \times 467$$

$$= 763 \text{ mm}^2$$

Hence, increase tension tie to 4 – No. 15 bars. Having to increase the tension tie reinforcement to satisfy the minimum reinforcement requirement indicates that the 500 mm depth of the corbel could have been reduced.

Provide additional closed stirrups of area $A_{st}/2 =$ 400 mm^2 over a depth of $\frac{2}{3} \times 467 = 311$ mm. $\boxed{11.7.5}$ Use 2 – No. 10 closed stirrups.

10. *Summarize design.*

The final details of the corbel are shown on the figure below.

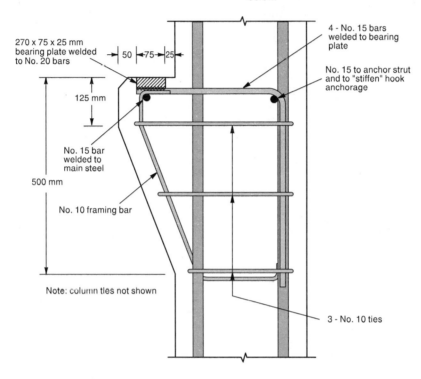

270 x 75 x 25 mm bearing plate welded to No. 20 bars

50 ←75→ 25

125 mm

No. 15 bar welded to main steel

500 mm

No. 10 framing bar

Note: column ties not shown

4 - No. 15 bars welded to bearing plate

No. 15 to anchor strut and to "stiffen" hook anchorage

3 - No. 10 ties

EXAMPLE 4.11 DESIGN OF BEAM WITH DAPPED ENDS

The beam shown on page 4-35 is subjected to a factored uniform load of 127 kN/m over a span of 6.3 m. Design the reinforcement for this beam.

1. *Design flexural reinforcement at midspan.*

Factored moment at midspan is

$$M_f = 127 \times 6.3^2/8 = 630 \text{ kN·m}$$

If the tension reinforcement consists of 5 – No. 30 bars as shown below, the factored moment resistance, including a tension of 80 kN, can be calculated as:

$$\alpha = \frac{0.85 \times 5 \times 700 \times 400 - (80 \times 10^3)}{0.79 \times 0.6 \times 40 \times 400}$$

$$= 146.4 \text{ mm}$$

$$M_r = 0.79 \times 0.6 \times 40 \times 400 \times 146.4 \times (350 - \frac{146.4}{2})$$

$$+ 0.85 \times 5 \times 700 \times 400 \times (350 - 60)] \times 10^{-6}$$

$$= 652.4 \text{ kN·m}$$

As $M_r > M_f$ flexural reinforcement   O.K.

2. *Identify design regions of beam.*

The design regions of the beam and some important components of the load carrying path are identified in the figure on page 4-35.

3. *Determine bearing area at support.*

Assuming that a 320 mm long steel angle across the width of the beam is to be used at the support, the required bearing length $\boxed{11.5.4}$

$$= \frac{V_f}{0.75\phi_c f'_c b}$$

$$= \frac{400 \times 1000}{0.75 \times 0.60 \times 40 \times 320} = 69 \text{ mm}$$

Provide a 100 × 100 × 16 mm thick angle.

4. *Determine geometry of strut and tie model.*

A strut-and-tie model of one-half the beam is shown below. This truss was designed to reasonably approximate the flow of forces in the beam. This included providing a tension hanger BC near the face of the dap, anchoring the horizontal tie AD by two

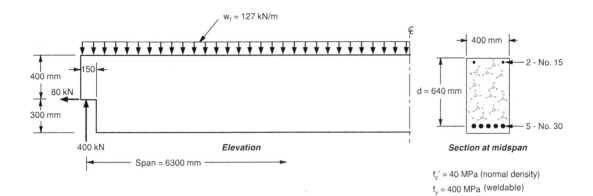

$w_f = 127$ kN/m

400 mm

150

80 kN

300 mm

400 kN

Span = 6300 mm

Elevation

400 mm

d = 640 mm

2 - No. 15

5 - No. 30

Section at midspan

$f_c' = 40$ MPa (normal density)
$f_y = 400$ MPa (weldable)

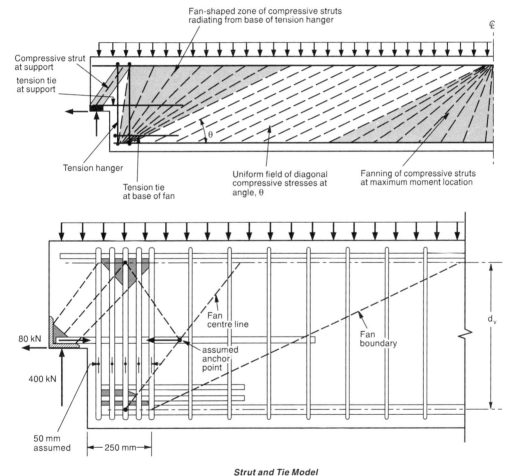

Fan-shaped zone of compressive struts
radiating from base of tension hanger

Compressive strut
at support

tension tie
at support

Tension hanger

Tension tie
at base of fan

Uniform field of diagonal
compressive stresses at
angle, θ

Fanning of compressive struts
at maximum moment location

θ

80 kN

400 kN

50 mm
assumed

250 mm

Fan
centre line

assumed
anchor
point

Fan
boundary

d_v

Strut and Tie Model

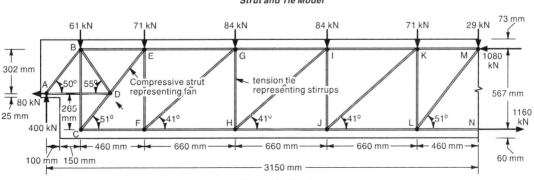

61 kN   71 kN   84 kN   84 kN   71 kN   29 kN   73 mm

302 mm

B   E   G   I   K   M   1080
kN

A   50° 55°   Compressive strut   tension tie
                      representing fan   representing stirrups

80 kN   D   567 mm
25 mm   205
        mm

400 kN   C   51°   F   41°   H   41°   J   41°   L   51°   N   1160
                                                                 kN

100 mm 150 mm   460 mm   660 mm   660 mm   660 mm   460 mm   60 mm

3150 mm

Truss Idealization

diagonal compressive struts, and modelling the fanning action at midspan and near the supports.

The specific geometry for this strut-and-tie model was chosen in the following manner. The bottom chord of the truss was located along the centreline of the bottom longitudinal reinforcement. The top chord was located at the level of the centroid of the compressive force due to flexure, at midspan. Nodes B and C, which define the centreline of the hanger, were located just far enough from the face of the dap to distribute the tension steel in the hanger over a region large enough to establish a nodal zone capable of resisting the applied strut and tie forces. Near the supports and at midspan, narrower frames were used to model the steep angle of the fanning compressive stresses in these regions. The remainder of the beam was divided into approximately square truss panels.

5. *Determine forces in truss by statics.*

   Positive indicates tension, negative compression.

Member	Force (kN)
AB	−519
DB	−331
AD	+411
CB	+609
CD	−784
DE	−436
BE	−139
CF	+494

Member	Force (kN)
EF	+268
EG	−414
FG	−411
FH	+806
GH	+184
GI	−726
HI	−282
HJ	+1020

Member	Force (kN)
IJ	+100
IK	−940
JK	−153
JL	+1136
KL	+29
KM	−1056
LM	−37
LN	+1160

6. *Design of tension ties.*

   The following areas of reinforcement are required for the tension ties.

   Tie AD:

   $$A_s = \frac{411\,000}{0.85 \times 400} = 1209\,\text{mm}^2$$

   Use 5 − No. 20 bars.

   Hanger CB:

   $$A_s = \frac{609\,000}{0.85 \times 400} = 1791\,\text{mm}^2$$

   Use 5 − No. 15 closed stirrups.

   Tie CF:

   $$A_s = \frac{494\,000}{0.85 \times 400} = 1453\,\text{mm}^2$$

   Area of 5 − No. 30 bars sufficient but anchorage will need to be checked.

   The forces in tension ties EF, GH, IJ, and KL determine the amount of shear reinforcement required in these regions (bands).

   Stirrup Band EF: Tie force = 268 kN

   Capacity of a No. 10 closed stirrup is 68 kN.

   $\therefore$ 268/68 = 3.94 stirrups are required over a width of 660 mm

   $$s < \frac{660}{3.94} = 167\,\text{mm}$$

   Check minimum shear reinforcement requirements: | 11.2.8.4 |

   $$s < \frac{A_v\,f_y}{0.06\sqrt{f_c'}\,b_w} = \frac{200 \times 400}{0.06\sqrt{40} \times 400} = 527\,\text{mm}$$

   Check minimum spacing requirements: | 11.2.11 |

   $$\frac{V_f}{b_w d} = \frac{309\,880}{400 \times 640} = 1.21\,\text{MPa} < 0.1\,\phi_c\,f_c'$$

   $$= 2.4\,\text{MPa}$$

   $\therefore$ s < 0.7d = 448 mm

   Check crack control requirement: | 11.5.5 |

   $$s < 300\,\text{mm}$$

   Strength requirement governs: $\therefore$ use s = 150 mm.

   Stirrup band GH: tie force = 184 kN

   184/68 = 2.71 No. 10 closed stirrups are required over 660 mm length

   s_{max} = 244 mm governs: $\therefore$ use s = 240 mm

   Stirrup band IJ: tie force = 100 kN

   100/68 = 1.47 No. 10 closed stirrups are required over 660 mm length

   s < 449 mm. Crack control requirement governs: $\therefore$ use s = 300 mm

   Stirrup band KL: tie force = 29 kN

   Crack control requirement governs: $\therefore$ use s = 300 mm

7. *Design of nodal zones.*

   Nodal Zone A — The 100 mm horizontal leg length of the angle was chosen to satisfy the nodal stress limit in Step 3.

   The required depth of the nodal zone | 11.5.4 |

   $$= \frac{(411 - 80)1000}{0.75 \times 0.60 \times 40 \times 320} = 57\,\text{mm}$$

   $\therefore$ 100 mm provided is adequate.

   Nodal Zone B — Because of a concern about spalling of the concrete cover, neglect the concrete outside of the anchoring tension tie reinforcement.

   The required width of the nodal zone | 11.5.4 |

$$= \frac{609 \times 1000}{0.75 \times 0.60 \times 40 \times 320} = 106 \text{ mm}$$

A spacing of 50 mm between the 5 – No. 15 closed stirrups will provide a nodal zone width of $4 \times 50 + 16 = 216$ mm, which is conservative.

Nodal Zone C — This nodal zone anchors two tension ties. Hence, required width | 11.5.4 |

$$= \frac{609 \times 1000}{0.65 \times 0.60 \times 40 \times 320} = 122 \text{ mm}$$

Thus, 216 mm still O.K.

Required depth of nodal zone | 11.5.4 |

$$= \frac{494 \times 1000}{0.65 \times 0.60 \times 40 \times 320} = 99 \text{ mm}$$

To provide this nodal zone depth, provide 2 – No. 15 horizontal U-bars with 50 mm spacings above the layer of No. 30 bars.

Also check the anchorage of tension tie CF in Nodal Zone C.

As the No. 30 bars emerge from Nodal Zone C, they can resist a tensile force of approximately

$$= \frac{216}{\ell_d} \times \phi_s A_s f_y = \frac{216}{854} \times 0.85 \times 3500 \times 400 \times 10^{-3}$$

$$= 301 \text{ kN}$$

The 2 – No. 15 U-bars will be capable of resisting a tension of

$$0.85 \times 2 \times 2 \times 200 \times 400 \times 10^{-3} = 272 \text{ kN}$$

Hence, total tensile capacity at face of nodal zone

$$= 301 + 272 = 573 \text{ kN}$$

As 573 kN > 494 kN, anchorage   O.K.

Extend the No. 15 bars at least ℓ_d (= 426 mm) beyond the nodal zone and far enough for the 5 – No. 30 bars to be capable of carrying the 494 kN tie force on their own (i.e., 354 mm from the end of the No. 30 bars).

Although the addition of the No. 15 U-bars will raise the location of node C somewhat, this secondary effect will be neglected.

8. *Checking compressive struts.*

As the compressive strut CD-DE represents a fan-shaped region of radiating struts and as the nodal zone stresses at the base of the fan have been checked, further checks are not required.

Check compressive stress in struts which meet at Node B. See drawing above.

If the nodal zone is to be in equilibrium under a "hydrostatic" stress condition, the length of the faces of the nodal zone must be proportional to the loads applied to these faces and the faces must be perpendicular to the loads. Hence, the lengths of the compressive strut bearing surfaces at Nodal Zone B are

$$\ell_{AB} = \frac{519}{670} \times 216 = 167 \text{ mm}$$

$$\ell_{DB} = \frac{331}{670} \times 216 = 107 \text{ mm}$$

$$\ell_{EB} = \frac{139}{670} \times 216 = 45 \text{ mm}$$

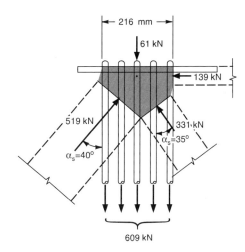

Thus, the stress in all struts at Nodal Zone B (neglecting concrete cover) equals

$$f_2 = \frac{331 \times 1000}{107 \times 320} = 9.67 \text{ MPa}$$

As the line of action of strut DB is closest to that of tie CB, strut DB will have the lowest diagonal crushing strength.

The average tensile strain in tension tie CB can be estimated as

$$\varepsilon_s = \frac{609\,000}{10 \times 200 \times 0.85 \times 200 \times 10^3} = 1.79 \times 10^{-3}$$

(The average strain will actually be somewhat smaller than this due to tension stiffening effects).

The strain ε_1 perpendicular to the strut is | 11.5.2.3 |

$$\varepsilon_1 = \varepsilon_s + (\varepsilon_s + 0.002) \cot^2 \theta_s$$

$$- 1.79 \times 10^{-3} + (1.79 + 2.0) \times 10^{-3} \cot^2 35°$$

$$= 9.52 \times 10^{-3}$$

Diagonal crushing strength is

$$\phi_c f_{cu} = \phi_c f_c' /(0.8 + 170\varepsilon_1)$$

$$= 0.6 \times 40 /(0.8 + 170 \times 9.52 \times 10^{-3})$$

$$= \underline{9.92 \text{ MPa}}$$

As $f_2 < \phi_c f_{cu}$, compressive stress in strut   O.K.

The other struts meeting at Node B will have the same compressive stress but smaller values of ε_1. Hence they will not be critical.

9. *Other detailing considerations.*

To improve crack control and ductility, provide a minimum amount of horizontal reinforcement parallel to the primary tensile tie reinforcement in the region above the support. If the dapped end is treated as a bracket, the required area of such additional reinforcement would be | 11.7.5 |

$$0.5 \times A_s = 0.5 \times 5 \times 300 - 750 \text{ mm}^2$$

Use 2 – No. 15 horizontal U-bars distributed over two-thirds of the effective depth. Extend these bars at least ℓ_d beyond face of dap.

To improve the support conditions for the highly stressed compressive struts AB and DB, use two additional No. 15 top longitudinal bars in the region of Node B.

10. *Summarize design.*

The final details of the dap ended beam are shown in the figure below.

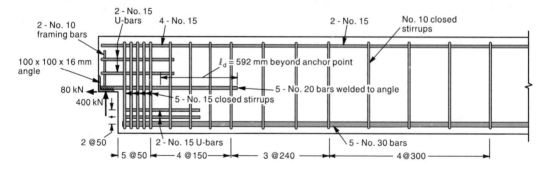

5

Slabs

By Sidney H. Simmonds

Chapter 5
Slabs

5.1 INTRODUCTION

Reinforced concrete slabs are a common building system because they can be built economically with essentially any plan geometry and supported by randomly located beams, columns and walls. Slabs must have sufficient strength to carry loads safely but must not deflect or crack excessively. It is these two serviceability factors that provide the criteria on which the success of a slab design is ultimately judged and their importance cannot be overly emphasized.

In theory, because they are highly statically indeterminate structures, the analysis of reinforced concrete slabs is complex. Fortunately, for most slabs, a satisfactory design can be obtained by uncoupling the strength and serviceability requirements leading to relatively simple design procedures. Since slab sections are usually lightly reinforced, they can maintain an essentially constant moment capacity after yielding of the reinforcement for large changes in curvature thereby permitting considerable redistribution of moments within the slab. This leads to simpler moment fields and patterns of reinforcement. Deflection requirements are met by selecting appropriate slab thickness.

The structural behaviour of reinforced concrete slab structures depends primarily on how they are supported. Slabs supported so that they tend to deform into a cylindrical surface carry load essentially in one direction only and are referred to as one-way slabs. Such slabs may be designed as beam strips in the direction of curvature. Slabs supported on regularly spaced columns, or walls, forming approximately square panels deform to carry load in two orthogonal directions. Such slabs are referred to as regular two-way slabs (see Clause 13.1) and may be designed for uniformly distributed gravity loads using the simplification of perpendicular design strips. Slabs supported on randomly spaced columns and/or with randomly placed beams, walls or openings are referred to as irregular slabs. With irregular slabs, the loads in different regions will be carried by combinations of either one-way or two-way action and considerable judgment is needed by the designer to ensure both strength and serviceability requirements are met.

The design of any slab system may be divided into the following steps.

Step 1 — Select slab thickness
Step 2 — Obtain design moments
Step 3 — Choose flexural reinforcement
Step 4 — Check shear capacity
Step 5 — Design beams and/or other elements (if any).

The above steps are not independent and indeed may not be completed in the order listed. For example, it is usual to make at least a preliminary evaluation of shear capacity when selecting slab thickness. Nevertheless, these steps correspond to the grouping of the design calculations and are used as the major divisions in the remainder of this chapter and in the design examples.

There are a number of calculations in the design of slab systems that are tedious when performed manually even with the use of electronic calculators. Design aids in the form of charts or tables are provided to facilitate many of these calculations.

Design examples are presented to assist in interpreting the provisions of specific clauses of the Standard and to illustrate the use of the design aids. As a result, each example is an incomplete design in that only portions of the slab system are considered and computations described in other chapters of this Handbook are usually omitted.

5.2 SELECTING SLAB THICKNESS

5.2.1 General

Selection of the slab thickness requires consideration of both serviceability and strength. In some instances, fire resistance requirements may govern both the cover and slab thickness.

Economy suggests that the slab be as thin as practical with few stiffening elements to permit ease of forming. On the other hand, the slab must have sufficient thickness to provide required shear capacity and flexural rigidity to ensure that deflections and cracking are kept within acceptable limits. In certain cases it is economical to use a thinner slab and provide either beams between the supports or add column capitals and/or drop panels.

Generally, the initial trial slab thickness is selected for serviceability by one of two methods. The first is to select a convenient thickness and then compute the expected deflections using the provisions of Clause 13.3.6. Examples of such deflection computations are given in Chapter 6 of this Handbook. These deflections are then compared to the maximum permissible values given in Clause 9 of the Standard. The second is to select a thickness that is equal to or greater than the minimum thickness specified in Clause 13.3. This method does not require computing the deflections and is the method used in this Chapter. When using this method, selecting a slab thickness approaching the minimum thickness should be done with caution. The minimum specified thicknesses are, as the name implies, minimums and for two-way slabs are valid only for slabs on regularly spaced supports with usual dimensions and loading and require good workmanship and shoring practice. For many designs the optimum thickness will be greater than the specified minimum thickness.

The trial thickness must also be evaluated for shear strength. At this stage of the design, especially for slabs without beams, only a preliminary check for shear capacity can be made since the moments to be transferred by eccentricity of shear are yet to be determined.

The increment of thickness used is a matter of designer judgment and local practice. Another consideration is the availability of "high chairs" for the top layers of reinforcement. In the examples of this Chapter an increment of 10 mm is used.

5.2.2 One-way slabs

The minimum thickness that may be used for one-way slabs not supporting or attached to partitions or other construction likely to be damaged by large deflections, without the need to compute deflections, is given in Table 9-1 of the Standard as a fraction of the clear span, ℓ_n, for different support conditions. If the slab is supporting construction likely to be damaged by large deflections, calculations are required to show that expected deflections, including time effects, will be satisfactory for the specific application.

For one-way slabs in buildings, it would be unusual for shear capacity to govern. Nonetheless, it must be checked.

5.2.3 Two-way slabs without beams

In the Standard, the phrase "slabs without beams" includes flat plate construction, slabs with drop panels and/or column capitals and slabs with beams only along discontinuous edges. For a slab to be considered a slab with beams there must be beams between all supports. See Fig. 5.1.

Provisions for the minimum thickness of flat plates or slabs with column capitals only, without the requirement of showing by calculation that the deflections are satisfactory, are given in Clause 13.3.3. For panels with all edges continuous or panels with a beam along all discontinuous edges having a stiffness ratio, α, at least equal to 0.8 (see Section 5.2.5), the specified minimum thickness is 1/30 of the longer clear span for reinforcement with $f_y = 400$ MPa.

For slabs with drop panels, the minimum slab thickness provisions for which deflection calculations are not required have been changed. In previous editions of the Standard, minimum dimensions for the drop panel were given for which a decrease in slab thickness of 10% was permitted. If the designer were to use a larger or thicker drop panel, there was no provision to decrease the thickness further. In Clause 13.3.4 of the current Standard there are no minimum dimensions for drop panels and an expression is given for the minimum slab thickness as a function of the drop panel dimensions chosen.

For two-way slabs without beams, the other critical design condition is the shear capacity of the slab at the supports. This is especially true for slabs supported on columns without capitals or drops and at exterior columns where there are significant shear stresses due to the transfer of the unbalanced moment between slab and column. Thus, although the slab thickness is generally selected for deflection considerations, it is prudent to make a preliminary shear capacity check before proceeding to the next design step. For the trial thickness, the total loading on the slab is known and the corresponding value of the factored shear force at each column, V_f, can be determined. At this stage, the unbalanced moments are unknown and their effects can only be estimated. One procedure for doing this is to multiply the factored shear force by the following factors before comparing the factored shear stress to the maximum shear stress resistance (see Example 5.4).

    interior column   1.2
    edge column   1.6
    corner column   2.0

Example 5.3 illustrates a situation where a slab thickness satisfactory for deflection considerations is inadequate for strength. Options available to the designer are, listed in order of economy, add column capitals, add drop panels, increase column dimensions, increase slab thickness or increase concrete strength. In Example 5.3 drop panels were added to the interior columns. The decision in this Example to use an edge beam of sufficient size to stiffen the discontinuous edge and to support the exterior wall meant that a preliminary shear check at the edge column was not required for selecting slab thickness.

A discussion of the calculations for a final shear strength evaluation are given in Section 5.6 and illustrated in Example 5.4.

5.2.4 Two-way slabs with beams between all supports

The deflection of slab panels with beams on all sides depends not only on the panel aspect ratio but also on the relative stiffness of the beams in the two directions. If beams in one direction are significantly stiffer than in the other, even for columns located on an essentially square grid, the slab will tend to act as a one-way slab spanning between the stiffer beams. To develop an expression for minimum slab thickness so that deflection calculations that demonstrate satisfactory performance are not required means imposing some geometric limitations to the slab system for which the expression is applicable. For

regular slab systems as defined in Clause 13.1, such an expression is given by Eqn (13-3) in Clause 13.3.5.

Eqn (13-3) is a simplification of similar expressions contained in previous editions. Since the minimum thickness is given as a function of the longer clear span, ℓ_n, the panel aspect ratio is considered by the term β. Obviously, the slab deflections will decrease as the stiffness of the beams along the panel boundaries increases. This is accounted for by the parameter α_m which is the average of the beam stiffness ratios (beam stiffness ratio is discussed in detail in Section 5.2.5) of the beams along the four panel edges. So that the slab thickness does not become too thin, the maximum effective value of α_m is limited to 2.0.

As the average effective beam stiffness approaches zero, the required minimum thickness given by Eqn (13-3) approaches the value for slabs without beams, Eqn (13-1) as expected.

For panels with a discontinuous edge, the edge beam must have a beam stiffness ratio, α, at least equal to 0.8 or the panel thickness must be increased by 10%.

5.2.5 Beam stiffness ratio, α

The beam stiffness ratio, α, is defined in Clause 13.0 as "ratio of moment of inertia of beam section to moment of inertia of a width of slab bounded laterally by centrelines of adjacent panels (if any) on each side of the beam". Since the slab acts as a compression flange over the central portion of the beam, some decision as to the effective cross section of the beam is required. Clause 13.1 recommends that the beam cross section includes that portion of the slab on each side of the beam extending a distance equal to the projection of the beam above or below the slab, whichever is greatest, but not greater than 4 times the slab thickness.

The calculation of α requires the prior selection of the slab thickness and beam dimensions. Furthermore, the calculation of α is tedious in that it involves computing the location of the centroidal axis of the T-beam section and the moment of inertia about that axis for the beam cross section. Initial trial dimensions are selected on the basis of construction practice and designer experience. Once selected, values of α can be obtained quickly for edge and interior beams using Tables 5.1 and 5.2, respectively, and the trial thickness evaluated. In these Tables, the break in the curves at a/h = 5 reflects the width of slab flange considered when governed by the 4 h limit. The break at a/h = 2 reflects the change in scale used when producing the charts. The use of these Tables is illustrated in Example 5.2.

5.3 SLAB MOMENTS

5.3.1 General

One-way slabs are analyzed and reinforced for moments as wide beams. For convenience it is usual to consider a strip of unit width spanning perpendicular to the supports and to analyze this strip for moments and shears as a continuous beam. When the loading and geometry satisfy the requirements of Clause 9.3.3, design moments and shears may be obtained directly from the coefficients given therein. This procedure is used in Example 5.1. Otherwise an elastic analysis is required.

For two-way slabs, the design procedures for flexure have been expanded considerably over provisions in previous editions. There is still the general provision (Clause 13.6.1) that states "A slab may be designed by any procedure satisfying conditions of equilibrium and compatibility with the supports provided it is shown that the factored resistance at every section is at least equal to the effects of the factored loads, and that all serviceability conditions, including specified limits on deflections, are met".

Guidance to assist designers in making assumptions that will result in solutions that will simulate reinforced concrete slab behaviour when applying techniques based on elastic plate theory (finite element and finite difference) and theorems of plasticity (yield line and strip method) are included for the first time . The requirements for elastic frame analogies to determine design moments and shears for gravity loading have been generalized and provisions for the lateral distribution of moments implicit in these analogies has been moved to the section on slab reinforcement. The former 'Direct Design Method' which in previous editions was intended as a complete design procedure has been simplified and reduced to a specialized simple elastic frame analogy. In this Chapter, discussion and examples of analysis for two-way slab systems will be limited to elastic frame analogies and the simplified 'Direct Design Method' as these are the most frequently used procedures in design offices.

5.3.2 Elastic frame analogies

The concept behind the use of elastic frame analogies is that satisfactory values for design moments and shears can be obtained by considering the slab and adjacent columns to consist of design strips located along the support lines and bounded by the centre lines of the adjacent panels. These design strips are then analyzed as elastic planar frames. For gravity loading, the frame analysis may be simplified to consider only one level of slab at a time by assuming that the far ends of supports are fixed against rotation.

The success in applying this method is in the appropriate apportioning of stiffness to the members of the frame so that the elastic analysis of the two dimensional frame will approximate that of the non-linear three-dimensional slab-beam-column system. The design moments so obtained at the critical sections of the frame must then be distributed laterally across the design strip in a manner that will approximate the behaviour of the three-dimensional slab-beam-column system.

In a typical planar frame analysis it is assumed that at a beam-column connection all members meeting at a joint undergo the same rotation. For slabs supported only by columns the slab will be restrained only locally by the column. For gravity loading, this reduced restraint is accounted for by reducing the effective column stiffness as discussed later in this Section.

Clause 13.6.3 indicates that a frame analogy may be used for lateral loads acting on unbraced systems when effects of cracking and reinforcement are taken into account in assigning member stiffness. The Standard contains no guidance for selecting these properties but, by analogy, would require reducing the effective stiffness of the beam members.

Throughout the years there have been different recommendations for assigning member properties to account for the size of the joints and the effects of rotational restraint under gravity loading. The provisions in the previous edition were developed at the time when the only practical method for analyzing an elastic frame was by the 'moment distribution' procedure. Thus recommendations for assigning member stiffness to determine stiffness and carry-over-factors were made with that procedure in mind. One way of reducing the effective column stiffness is to introduce the concept of an attached torsional member (see Fig. 5.3) in which the effective column stiffness is determined from the sum of

the flexibilities of the attached torsional member and the column. This was the basis of the Equivalent Frame Method contained in the previous edition. The essence of this method is retained in the current Standard under the term 'non-prismatic modelling' of member stiffness. With this procedure the frame is modelled using member centrelines which requires that the moments obtained at the beam member ends must be reduced to obtain the design moments at the critical sections at the face of supports. To use this method for electronic computation requires writing a special program that incorporates use of attached torsional members. The program ADOSS™ Analysis and Design of Slab Systems, Canadian Portland Cement Association, Ottawa is a complete slab design program that incorporates this procedure.

Today all design offices have a computer program for the elastic analysis of frames that is based on the direct stiffness method in which the stiffness matrix is formed by the direct combination of the stiffness matrices of prismatic elements. So that these programs can be used for the analysis of slab systems, the Standard now contains coefficients for reducing the effective stiffness of 'prismatic' column members. If the frame is modelled using only centreline dimensions, then centreline moments at the ends of the beam members must be reduced to obtain design moments at the critical sections as required with 'non-prismatic' modelling. However, with little effort, the designer may introduce joints at the critical sections to obtain design moments directly.

Once the effective geometry of the frame has been selected using either prismatic or non-prismatic members, it is analyzed elastically for a number of defined patterned loadings to obtain the maximum effects at all critical sections in the slab and supporting members (see Fig. 5.4). When the live load is uniformly distributed and does not exceed three-quarters of the specified dead load, slab moments can be obtained assuming full factored design load on the entire slab system. This implies that pattern loadings are not required to compute unbalanced moments transferred at interior supports for this case.

The question invariably asked is "are there any limitations that need to be imposed on the slab geometry to ensure that the elastic frame concept is applicable?". Obviously the definition of the design strips assumes that support lines and adjacent panels are readily identifiable. This is the case for slab systems supported on columns along lines to create essentially rectangular panels. Recommendations for assigning stiffness values to the members of the frame and the provisions for the lateral distribution of the design moments at the critical sections were all derived assuming rectangular panels. These are the reasons for limiting the method to regular two-way slab systems as defined in the Standard in Clause 13.1. It may be argued that elastic frames can be defined for slabs not meeting the limitations for regular two-way slab systems and analyses of such frames performed to obtain moments at the critical sections. However, it must be realized that the lateral distribution of these moments across the design strip may differ significantly from the distribution given for regular two-way slab systems.

5.3.3 Direct Design Method

In the current Standard, the Direct Design Method has been reduced from a complete design method to a simplified elastic frame method in that provisions apply only to obtaining design moments at the critical sections. The same design strip is used as for the elastic frame analogy except that the columns are not included. Column dimensions are considered by using clear spans. The essence of the method is to distribute the total factored moment in each span of the frame to the critical sections using a set of coefficients. To ensure that the coefficients are applicable, additional restraints on the slab geometry are imposed. The unbalanced moments in interior columns and walls are determined from an expression involving partial loading on adjacent spans.

For slabs meeting the geometric requirements for use of the Direct Design Method, the curtailment of reinforcement may be obtained from Fig. 3-1 of the Standard.

5.4 SLAB REINFORCEMENT

5.4.1 General

For all slabs, sufficient flexural reinforcement is required at each section to resist the factored moments at that section. The minimum area of reinforcement required in each direction is $0.002 A_g$, however, for exposure conditions where crack control is essential, this minimum area of reinforcement must be increased (Clause 7.8.2).

Positive moment reinforcement perpendicular to a discontinuous edge shall extend to the edge of the slab. Negative reinforcement perpendicular to a discontinuous edge shall be bent, hooked or otherwise anchored to develop the calculated tension in the bar.

Other requirements pertain specifically to either one-way or two-way slabs and are discussed separately.

5.4.2 One-way slabs

For solid one-way slabs flexural reinforcement must be spaced not further than 3 times the slab thickness or 500 mm and cut-off points and development lengths are computed as for beams. In addition, to limit width of flexural cracking, spacing of the principal flexural reinforcement at critical sections shall be such that the crack control parameter, z, (Clause 10.6.1) does not exceed 30 000 N/mm for interior exposure and 25 000 N/mm for exterior exposure.

Where the slab is considered as a T-beam flange and the principal reinforcement in the slab is parallel to that beam, Clause 10.5.3.2 requires flexural reinforcement perpendicular to this beam in the top of the slab. In this clause the phrase "clear distance between the webs of the T-beams" refers to the supporting beams so that, for a one-way slab, this corresponds to the clear span of the one-way slab.

5.4.3 Two-way slabs

New provisions for bar spacing permit greater designer judgment in the placing of slab reinforcement. Furthermore, for regular slabs without beams, the lateral placing of reinforcement to resist the design moments at critical sections other than the exterior negative section are given as ranges. Thus, for the first time, the Standard recognizes explicitly the use of uniform bottom mats and isolated top mats at the columns for many slab designs.

Based on the advantages of having negative reinforcement in the vicinity of a column support for slabs without beams, new provisions are included that require a minimum amount of reinforcement that must be placed within a band extending a distance of $1.5\ h_s$ from the sides of the column.

Unless beams containing shear reinforcement are provided in all spans framing into the column, integrity reinforcement is required to prevent progressive collapse. The new requirements have been made more general and are given in terms of the total area of anchored bottom reinforcement on all faces of the periphery of the column.

5.5 SHEAR AND SHEAR-MOMENT TRANSFER

For slabs, one speaks of "beam" shear where the slab is considered to fail in shear as in a wide beam and "perimeter" or "two-way" shear where failure is considered to be a punching of the support through the slab (see Fig. 5.5).

One-way slabs are designed for beam shear only. Two-way slabs are also checked for beam shear although this type is generally not critical. For slabs with beams between all supports, the slab is treated as unit strips spanning to the beams. For slabs without beams, the slab is considered as a wide beam extending across the entire width. The exception is for a corner column where the critical section is along a straight line of minimum length located not further than d/2 from the corner column (Clause 13.4.6.2).

Perimeter shear capacity in two-way slabs is evaluated by comparing a factored shear stress computed at a critical section to a factored shear stress resistance. The critical section is located so that the perimeter is a minimum but need not approach closer than d/2 to the face of the support. Examples of critical sections are given in the Notes accompanying Clause 13.4.3.1. The factored shear resistance is a function of the concrete compressive strength and the shape and size of the support (Clause 13.4.4).

The factored shear stress is computed from Eqn (13-8) and includes terms for unbalanced factored moments transferred to the support about the principal axes of the critical section. Expressions for evaluating b_o, γ_v, e and J in this equation for different column locations are given in Fig. 5.6 where it is seen that these terms are functions of c_1, c_2 and d only. This permits rewriting Eqn (13-8) in the form

$$v_f = kV_f + k_1 M_1 + k_2 M_2$$

where values of the coefficients k, k_1 and k_2 can be obtained from design charts given in Tables 5.3 to 5.9.

Some judgment is required when assigning values for V_f, M_1 and M_2 in the above equation. Clause 13.4.5.5 indicates that the values used should be from a "consistent loading". For an interior column, the maximum factored shear force, V_f, occurs with all adjacent panels loaded whereas the maximum values of the unbalanced moments occur with selected partial loadings. Thus maximum values for all three terms cannot occur simultaneously and the consistent loading that would result in the sum of all three terms being a maximum is not easily determined. For an interior column, it is suggested that a satisfactory value of v_f can be obtained by adding the full V_f term to one of the unbalanced moment terms to obtain the larger sum. For an edge column, the maximum value of v_f will occur when both adjacent panels are loaded. Thus, for equal spans, the unbalanced moment about an axis perpendicular to the edge may be neglected. For corner columns, the maximum value of all three terms occurs simultaneously when the corner panel is loaded. Example 5.4 contains computations for all three column locations using design aids and the above concepts.

5.6 TWO-WAY SLABS WITH STIFF SUPPORTS ON FOUR SIDES

A not uncommon construction is for slab panels to be supported on all sides by walls or beams of sufficient stiffness that under load their curvature is much smaller than that required for the adjacent slab to develop significant moment resistance. Thus, for determining slab moments and shears, the panel boundaries may be considered as non-deflecting. Obviously, design procedures based on strips located along support lines are not applicable. One possible approach is to treat each panel separately with moments determined from tabulated coefficients obtained from classical plate theory. For continuous slab systems, any difference in negative moments in adjacent panels at their common support can be distributed. This is the basis for the method given in Appendix B of the Standard and is illustrated in Example 5.5.

Obviously some criteria is required in the case of slabs with beams on all sides to determine whether the beam may be considered stiff. Appendix B defines a beam as stiff when the ratio $b_w h_b{}^3/\ell_n h_s{}^3$ is not less than 2.0. Hence the determination as to whether the beam is stiff requires prior knowledge of the slab thickness, h_s. It should be noted that this ratio is considerably different from the definition of α_m used previously and a direct comparison of numerical values is not valid. Notwithstanding this, a trial slab thickness can be obtained using Eqn (13-3) in Clause 13.3.5 of the Standard with $\alpha_m = 2.0$. This trial thickness must not be less than the perimeter of the panel divided by 160 in the case of fully continuous slabs or the perimeter of the panel divided by 140 in the case of slabs discontinuous on one or more edges.

The procedure described in Appendix B also uses the terms "middle" and "column" strips but the definitions are different from those used for reinforcement distribution in slabs analyzed using frame analogies. When the panel boundaries are prevented from deflecting, the larger moments are in the central portions of the panel or "middle" strips. Coefficients for determining design moments in these strips are given. The two portions of the slab outside this central half are referred to as "column" strips even though there may only be wall supports. Moments in these strips are determined from the "middle" strip moments. When slabs are designed using Appendix B, all other requirements of the Standard such as area of minimum reinforcement, etc. apply.

Example 5.1 — One-way Slab

The geometry of a typical floor slab supported on beams and columns shown below is such that one-way behaviour dominates. Note that column lines A and C lie along the outer edge of beams resulting in differing clear spans. Fire protection requires a clear cover of 25 mm. For all beams, b = 300 mm.

Given: $f'_c = 25$ MPa (normal weight), $f_y = 400$ MPa

superimposed dead load = 1.3 kN/m^2

superimposed live load = 2.4 kN/m^2

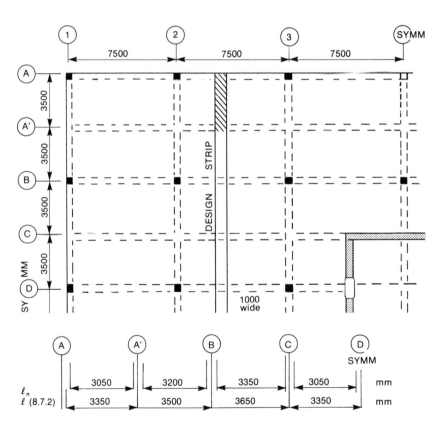

CPCA Concrete Design Handbook

Step 1 — Slab Thickness (9.8.2.1)

Deflection requirements (Table 9-1)
Exterior span AA' $h_{min} = \ell_n/24 = 3050/24 = 127$ mm
Interior span $\quad h_{min} = \ell_n/28 = 3350/28 = 120$ mm

Use h_s = 130 mm

Factored Loading

Self wt $(130/1000 \times 2.4 \times 9.81)1.25 = 3.83$ kN/m²
Superimposed dead $\quad (1.3)1.25 = 1.63$
Live load $\qquad (2.4)1.50 = \underline{3.60}$
$\qquad\qquad\qquad\qquad w_f = 9.06$ kN/m²

Step 2 — Design Moments

For design strip 1 metre wide, $w_f = 9.06$ N/mm
Limitations for use of Clause 9.3.3 are satisfied;
∴ use coefficients in Clause 9.3.3.

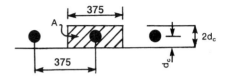

$d_c = 30$ mm
$A = 375 \times 2 \times 30 = 22\,500$ mm²/m
$f_s = 0.6 \times 400 = 240$ MPa
$z = f_s\sqrt[3]{d_c A} = 240 \times \sqrt[3]{30 \times 22500}$
$\quad = 21\,053$ N/mm $< 30\,000$ N/mm

**Use No. 10 @ 375 mm for bottom reinforcement
in each direction
Use No. 10 @ 375 mm for top neg. moment
reinf. across beam lines A and D
Use No. 10 @ 350 mm for top neg. moment
reinf. across beam lines A', B and C**

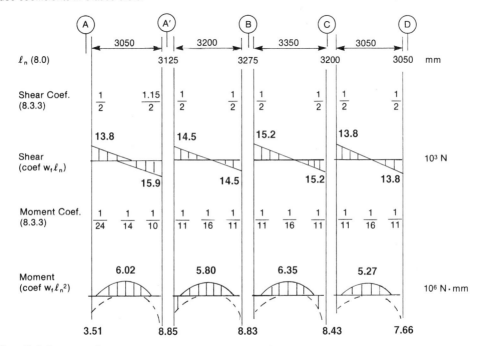

Step 3 — Reinforcement

Primary Reinforcement

effective depth = 130 − 25 − 10/2 = 100 mm
assume $d − a/2 = 0.9d$; $A_s = M_u/(\phi_s f_y 0.9d)$

Col. line	(A)	(A')	(B)	(C)	(D)	
$A_{s\ pos}$		197	190	208	172		mm²/m width
$A_{s\ neg}$	114	289	288	275	250	mm²/m width

s_{max} (7.4.1.2) = 3h = 3 × 130 = 390 < 500 mm

Minimum Reinforcement (7.8.1)

$A_{s\ min} = 0.002A_g = 0.002 \times 1000 \times 130$
$\qquad\qquad\qquad = 260$ mm²/m width
s_{max} (7.8.3) – 5h but not greater than 500 mm

From Table 5.10, try No. 10 @ 375 mm

Crack Control (10.6.1)

Transverse Reinforcement (10.5.3.2)

$A_{s\ min} = \dfrac{0.2\sqrt{f'_c}}{f_y}\, b_t\, h = \dfrac{0.2 \times \sqrt{25}}{400} \times 1000 \times 130$
$\qquad\qquad = 325$ mm²/m width

length of bars – 2(0.3 × 3650) + 300 = 2490 mm

Use No. 10 bars @ 300 mm across tops of girders.
These bars should be staggered so that they do not all
terminate in a line. Alternatively, one may detail minimum

reinforcement in this region to be at top and add bars to obtain required area.

Step 4 — Shear Capacity (11.2.8.1and 11.3)

from shear force diagram in Step 2,

$V_{f\,max} = 15.9 \times 10^3$ N

$V_r = V_c = 0.2\lambda\phi_c\sqrt{f_c'}\,b_w\,d$

$= 0.2 \times 0.6\sqrt{25} \times 1000 \times 100$

$= 60 \times 10^3$ N $> V_{f\,max}$ OK

Step 5 — Design Supporting Beams

Beams and girders designed for vertical reactions from slab, self weight of stem and all loads applied directly to member. Edge beams also designed for torsion corresponding to negative moments assumed in slab design.

Example 5.2 — Slab with Beams Between all Supports

The floor system shown, material properties and loading are the same as for Example 5.1 except that the only beams provided are between columns. For interior beams, b = 300 mm, h=550 mm; for exterior beams, b = 400 mm, h = 550 mm and for all columns $c_1 = c_2 =$ 400 mm, $h_c = 3800$ mm.

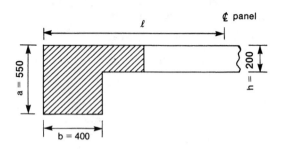

$a/h = 550/200 = 2.75$
$b/h = 400/200 = 2.00$
From Table 5.1, f = 1.34

For beam along column line 1

$\ell = (7500 - 400/2)/2 + 200 = 3850$ mm

$\alpha_1 = (b/\ell)(a/h)^3 f = (400/3850)(2.75)^3 1.34 = 2.90$

For beam along column line A

$\ell = (7000 - 400/2)/2 + 200 = 3600$ mm

$\alpha_A = (400/3600)(2.75)^3 1.34 = 3.10$

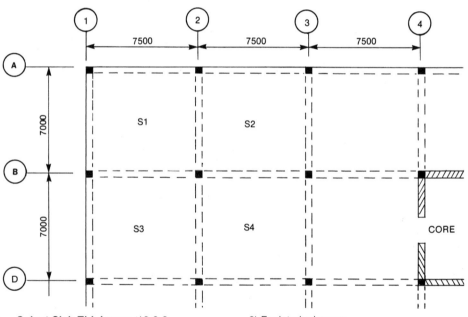

Step 1 — Select Slab Thickness (13.3.2)

Deflection requirements (13.3.5)

Consider interior panel S4

$\ell_{n\,max} = 7500 - 2(300/2) = 7200$ mm

$\beta = 7200/6700 = 1.07$

for absolute minimum thickness assume $\alpha_m = 2.0$

$h_{min} = \dfrac{7200(0.6 + 400/1000)}{30 + 4 \times 1.07 \times 2.0} = 187$ mm

Try $h_s = 200$ mm

Compute α for beams

1) For edge beams

2) For interior beams

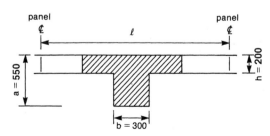

$a/h = 550/200 = 2.75$
$b/h = 300/200 - 1.50$
From Table 5.2, f = 1.67

For column line 2

$\ell = 7400$; $\alpha_2 = (300/7400)(2.75)^3 1.67 = 1.41$

For column line 3

$\ell = 7500$; $\alpha_3 = (300/7500)(2.75)^3 1.67 = 1.39$

For column line B

$\ell = 6900$; $\alpha_B = (300/6900)(2.75)^3 1.67 = 1.51$

For column line D

$\ell = 7000$; $\alpha_D = (300/7000)(2.75)^3 1.67 = 1.49$

Consider corner panel S1

$\ell_{n_\ell} = 7500 - 400 - 300/2 = 6950$ mm

$\ell_{n_s} = 7000 - 400 - 300/2 = 6450$ mm

$\beta = 6950/6450 = 1.08$

$\alpha_m = (2.90+3.10+1.41+1.51)/4$
$= 2.23 > 2.0$

$\therefore$ use $\alpha_m = 2.0$

$h_{min} = \dfrac{6950(0.6 + 400/1000)}{30 + 4 \times 1.08 \times 2.0} = 180$ mm

Consider edge panel S2

$\ell_{n_\ell} = 7500 - 300 = 7200$ mm

$\ell_{n_s} = 7000 - 400 - 300/2 = 6450$ mm

$\beta = 7200/6450 = 1.12$

$\alpha_m = (3.10+1.41+1.51+1.39)/4 = 1.85$

$h_{min} = \dfrac{7200(0.6 + 400)/1000}{30 + 4 \times 1.07 \times 1.45} = 188$ mm

Consider interior panel S4

$\ell_{n_\ell} = 7500 - 300 = 7200$ mm

$\ell_{n_s} = 7000 - 300 = 6700$ mm

$\beta = 7200/6700 = 1.07$

$\alpha_m = (1.41+1.39+1.51+1.49)/4 = 1.45$

$h_{min} = \dfrac{7200(0.6 + \dfrac{400}{1000})}{30 + 4 \times 1.07 \times 1.45} = 199$ mm

Use h_s = 200 mm

Factored loading

self wt (slab only)

$(200/1000 \times 2.4 \times 9.81)1.25 = 5.89$ kN/m^2

Dead	$(1.3)1.25$	$= 1.63$
Live	$(2.4)1.5$	$= \underline{3.60}$
		$w_f = 11.12$ kN/m^2

Step 2 — Design Moments

Consider design strip along column line 2

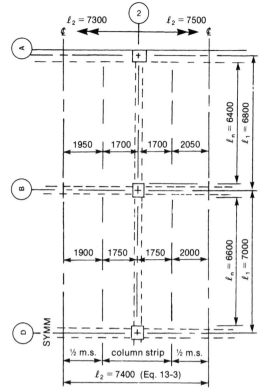

Solution 1 — Direct Design Method

All limitations on geometry and loading for use of DDM (13.10.1) are satisfied.

	A		B		D	
ℓ_n		6400		6600		mm
M_o (13.10.2.2)		421		448		$\times 10^6$ N·mm
%M_o (13.10.3)	0.16	0.59	0.70	0.65	0.35	0.65
$M_{DES\ slab}$	-67	248	-295	-291	157	-291	$\times 10^6$ N·mm
$M_{DES\ beam}$*	-2	8	-9	-9	5	-9	$\times 10^6$ N·mm
M_{DES}**	-69	256	-304	-300	162	-300	$\times 10^6$ N·mm

* From self weight of beam stem of 2.5 N/mm
** Values of M_{DES} may be modified by 15% provided the value of M_o is maintained in each span (13.10.3.3).

Solution 2 — Elastic frame analogies

Note — The 1984 edition of the CPCA Handbook contained Tables for determining stiffness factors, fixed end moments and carry-over-factors and a manual solution using these Tables was presented. Since such manual solutions are not practical in a design office, they are not repeated in this edition. However many design offices have computer programs that can be used for the analysis of slab systems based on elastic frame analogies. Examples of such programs are ADOSS™ which uses the attached torsional member concept and PCA-FRAME™ which permits using both prismatic and non-prismatic members. These programs are available from local offices of the Canadian Portland Cement Association. Solutions obtained from these programs for M_{DES} are presented to permit comparison of the methods. Values of M_{DES} include weight of beam stem.

a) non-prismatic members (attached torsional members) using ADOSS™

	A		B		D	
M_{DES}*	-72	239	-347	-328	175	-277	$\times 10^6$ N·mm

* Negative design moments may be increased or decreased up to 20% provided the total static moment in the panel is maintained (9.2.4).

b) prismatic members using PCA-FRAME™

	A		B		D	
M_{DES}*	-81	239	-329	-313	164	-283	$\times 10^6$ N·mm

* Negative design moments may be increased or decreased up to 20% provided the total static moment in the panel is maintained (9.2.4).

Step 3 — Select Slab Reinforcement (13.13)

Portion of slab moment in span AB resisted by beam (13.13.2.1)

$= \alpha_1/[1+(\ell_1/\ell_2)^2] = 1.41/[1+(7400/6800)^2] = 0.65$

∴ slab reinforced for moments corresponding to $(1-0.65)M_{DES\ slab} = 0.35\ M_{DES\ slab}$.
This reinforcement may be distributed uniformly across slab.

Portion of slab moment in span BD resisted by beam $= 1.41/[1+(7400/7000)^2] = 0.67$
∴ slab reinforced for moments corresponding to $(1-0.65)M_{DES\ slab} = 0.35\ M_{DES\ slab}$.

This reinforcement may be distributed uniformly across slab.

Step 4 — Check Shear Capacity

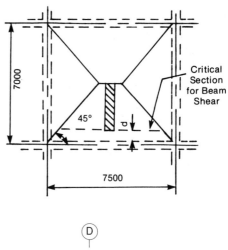

Consider tributary areas to beams for panel S4 (13.5.1)

Consider shaded strip having width = 1000 mm.

$d_v = 200 - 25 - 10 = 165$ mm.

$V_f = (11.12 \times 10^{-3})(7000/2 - 150 - 165)1000$
$= 35.4 \times 10^3$ N

$V_r = (0.2)0.6\sqrt{25}(1000)(165) = 99 \times 10^3$ N $> V_f$ OK

Step 5 — Design of Beams

Beam flexural reinforcement provided to resist moments corresponding to that portion of $M_{DES\ slab}$ not carried by slab plus $M_{DES\ beam}$ plus any loads applied directly to beam. Shear reinforcement provided to resist all loads carried by beam.

Example 5.3 — Two-way Slab Without Beams

The slab in Example 5.3 has the same geometry, materials and loading as that in Example 5.2 except that beams are provided only along the discontinuous edges to provide stiffness and to support the exterior walls.

Step 1 — Select Slab Thickness

a) Deflection Requirements (13.3.3)

ℓ_n max = 7500 − 400 = 7100 mm

$h_{s\,min} = \ell_n(0.6 + f_y/1000)/30$
= 7100(0.6 + 400/1000)/30 = 237 mm
Try h_s = 240 mm

b) Preliminary Shear Capacity Check (13.4.3)

Trial factored loading

self wt (slab only)
= (240/1000 × 2.4 × 9.81)1.25 = 7.06 kN/m²
Dead   = (1.3)1.25   = 1.63
Live   = (2.4)1.5   = 3.60
                 w_f = 12.29 kN/m²

Check interior column D3; edge columns not critical in shear as edge beams are provided. From Example 5.2, stiffness of edge beams are such that multiplier in Clauses 13.3.3 does not apply.

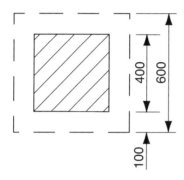

d_v = 240 − 25 − 15 = 200 mm
v_f = 12.29(7.5 × 7 − (0.6)²)10³/(4 × 600 × 200)
= 1.33 MPa
v_r = 0.4 × 0.6 $\sqrt{25}$ = 1.2 MPa

Since v_r not greater than 1.2v_f; trial thickness not satisfactory in shear.

Use drop panels

a) Deflection Requirements (13.3.4)

try h_s = 200 mm, h_d = 290 mm and drop extending approximately $\ell_n/6$ into each span so that plan dimensions of drop are 2500 mm × 2340 mm

ℓ_n = 7000 − 400 = 6600 mm;

x_d = 1170 − 400/2 = 970 mm

$h_{s\,min}$ (Eqn 13-2)
= 6600/(30[1 + (2 × 970/6600) (90/200)])
= 194 mm < 200 mm OK

b) Preliminary Shear Capacity Check (13.4.3)

Trial factored loading

self wt (slab only)
= (200/1000 × 2.4 × 9.81)1.25 = 5.89 kN/m²
Dead   = (1.3)1.25   = 1.63
Live   = (2.4)1.5   = 3.60
                  w_f = 11.12 kN/m²

drop below slab
= (90/1000 × 2.4 × 9.81)1.25 = 2.65 kN/m²

Capacity around column B3 (13.4.3.1)

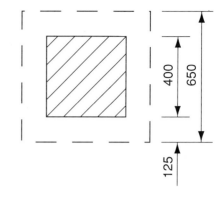

d_v = 290 − 25 − 15 = 250 mm
V_f = 11.12(7.5 × 7 − (0.6)²) + 2.65(2.5 × 2.34 − (0.6)²)
= 594 kN
v_f = V_f/b_od = 594 × 10³/(4 × 650 × 250) = 0.91 MPa
v_r = 0.4 × 0.6$\sqrt{25}$ = 1.2 MPa > 1.2v_f OK

Capacity around drop (13.4.3.2 and 13.4.4)

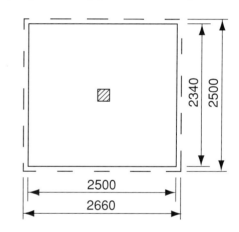

d_v = 200 − 25 − 15 = 160 mm
b_o = 2(2660 + 2500) = 10320 mm; α_s = 4
v_f = 11.12(7.5 × 7 − 2.66 × 2.5)10³/[(10320)160]
= 0.31 MPa
v_r = [(4(160)/10320) + 0.2]0.6$\sqrt{25}$
= 0.79 MPa > 0.52 MPa OK

Use h_s = 200 mm; h_d = 290 mm and 2500 mm × 2340 mm drop

Step 2 — Design Moments

Consider design strip along column line 2

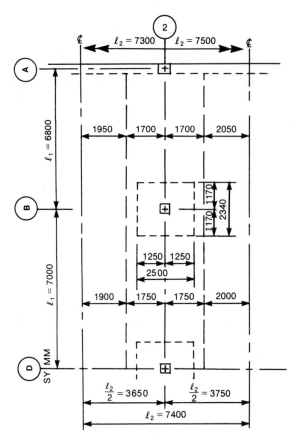

Column strip widths (13.1)

Span AB $c_{\text{col strip}} = 2(\ell_1/4) = 2(6800/4) = 3400$ mm

Span BD $c_{\text{col strip}} = 2(\ell_1/4) = 2(7000/4) = 3500$ mm

Middle strip widths are remainder of design strip (13.1).

Modification of factored load due to weight of drop panel.

It is conservative to average mass of drop panel over slab surface.

$w_f = 11.12 + 2.65(2.5 \times 2.34)/(7.4 \times 6.9)$
$\quad = 11.42$ kN/m^2

Solution 1 — Direct Design Method (13.10)

	A			B			D	
ℓ_n		6400			6600			mm
M_o (13.10.2.2)		433			460			$\times 10^6$ N·mm
%M_o (13.10.3)	0.26	0.52	0.70	0.65	0.35	0.65		
M_{DES}*		−113	225	−303	−299	161	−299	$\times 10^6$ N·mm

* Values of M_{DES} may be modified by 15% provided the value of M_o in each span is maintained (13.10.3.3).

Solution 2 — Elastic frame analogies (13.9)

a) non-prismatic members (attached torsional members) using ADOSS™

	A			B			D	
M_{DES}*		−129	182	−373	−354	139	−301	$\times 10^6$ N·mm

* Negative design moments may be increased or decreased up to 20% provided the total static moment in each span is maintained (9.2.4).

b) prismatic members using PCA-FRAME™

M_{DES}* -65 233 -337 -323 163 -274 $\times 10^6$ N · mm

* Negative design moments may be increased or decreased up to 20% provided the total static moment in the panel is maintained (9.2.4).

Step 3 — Select Slab Reinforcement (13.12)

Assume No. 15 bars; Place E-W reinf. in outer layers
N-S reinf. in inner layers

Positive moment (bottom) reinforcement

Minimum reinforcement (7.8.1)

$A_{s\,min}$ (for design strip)
= $0.002 \times 200 \times 7400 = 2960$ mm^2

Minimum reinforcement for structural integrity (13.11.5)

self wt (slab only)
= $0.2 \times 2.4 \times 9.81$ = 4.71 kN/m^2
Dead   = 1.30
Live   = 2.40
total specified load   = 8.41 kN/m^2
self wt. drop
= $0.09 \times 2.4 \times 9.81$ = 2.10 kN/m^2

$V_{se} = 8.41(7.5 \times 7 - (0.6)^2) + 2.1(2.5 \times 2.34 - (0.6)^2)$
= 450 kN

but not less than $2[4.71(7.5 \times 7 - (0.6)^2) + 2.1$
$(2.5 \times 2.34 - (0.6)^2)] = 514$ kN

$\Sigma A_{sb} = 2V_{se}/f_y = 2(514 \times 10^3)/400 = 2571$ mm^2
placed equally through all four faces,
$A_{sb/face} = 643$ mm^2/face

Span AB; $M_{DES} = 225 \times 10^6$ N · mm
$d = 200 - 25 - 15 - 8 = 152$ mm
$A_s = 225 \times 10^6/(0.85 \times 400 \times 0.9 \times 152)$
= 4840 mm^2 > $A_{s\,min} = 2960$ mm^2

Use 24 No. 15 bars; place 4 bars through column and 10 on each side

Check spacing; s_{max} (13.11.3) = $3h_s = 3(200) = 600$
or 500 mm
$s = (3750 - 200)/10 = 355$ mm < s_{max} OK

Note — to ease congestion through column, integrity reinforcement may consist of 1 No. 20 and 2 No. 15 bars instead of 4 No. 15 bars.

Reinforcement at exterior support

Determine distribution of negative moment along exterior beam (11.2.9.2)

$T_{cr} = (A_c^2/p_c)\, 0.4\phi_c\, \sqrt{f'_c} = [(550 \times 400)^2/(2(550+400))]$
$0.4 \times 0.6 \times \sqrt{25} = 30.57 \times 10^6$ N · mm
$0.67\, T_{cr} = 0.67 \times 30.57 \times 10^6 = 20.48 \times 10^6$ N · mm

Set torque at face of column to $0.67\, T_{cr}$.

Portion of exterior moment at column
= $113 - 2(20.48) = 72.0$ kN · m

$A_s = 72 \times 10^6/(0.85 \times 400 \times 0.9 \times 152) = 1548$ mm^2;
try 8 No. 15 bars placed in width $3h_s + c_2 = 3(200) + 400 = 1000$ mm (13.13.4.2)

Check capacity of concrete

$M_r = 0.85 \times 400 \times 1600 \left(152 - \dfrac{0.85 \times 400 \times 1600}{1.7 \times 0.6 \times 25 \times 1000}\right)$

= 71.1 kN · m OK

Use 8 No. 15 bars across 1000 mm centered on column and No. 15's @ 500 mm spacing across remainder of section.

Reinforcement at interior support

Column strip; assume 75% of M_{DES} apportioned to column strip (13.12.2)

$M_f = 0.75 \times 303 \times 10^6 = 227 \times 10^6$ N · mm
maximum $h_{d\,eff}$ (13.11.6) = $200 + (1170 - 200)/4$
= 442 mm > 290 mm
$d_{eff} = 290 - 25 - 15 - 8 = 242$ mm
$A_s = 227 \times 10^6/(0.85 \times 400 \times 0.9 \times 242) = 3065$ mm^2
try 16 No. 15 bars; $A_s = 3200$ mm^2
Check concrete capacity; width of drop = 2500 mm

$M_r = 0.85 \times 400 \times 3200 \left(242 - \dfrac{0.85 \times 400 \times 3200}{1.7 \times 0.6 \times 25 \times 1000}\right)$

= 217×10^6 N · mm OK

Middle strip; (13.12.3.1)
$M_f = 0.25 \times 303 \times 10^6 = 76 \times 10^6$ N · mm
$d = 200 - 25 - 15 - 8 = 152$ mm
$A_s = 76 \times 10^6/(0.85 \times 400 \times 0.9 \times 152) = 1630$ mm^2
try 8 No. 15 bars; $A_s = 1600$ mm^2

Note — If cracking is important this reinforcing should be increased (13.12.4)

Check requirement of Clause 13.12.2.1
Band width = $3h_s + c_2 = 3(200) + 400 = 1000$ mm wide
$A_{sb} = 1/3$(total reinf.) = $1/3(3200 + 1600)$
= 1600 mm^2 or 8 No. 15 bars
$s = 1000/8 = 125$ mm < $s_{max} = 250$ mm (13.11.3) OK

Use No. 15 bars: 8 placed in central 1000 mm of column strip, 8 in remainder of column strip and 4 in each half middle strip.

Step 4 — Check Shear Capacity (13.4.5.5 and 13.10.4)

Explanation for these calculations given in Example 5.4, Step 4

Interior column B2
$V_f = 594 \times 10^3$ N (from Step 1)
$M_{f\,unbal}$ about column line B = M_1
$M_1 = 0.07[(7.52 + 0.5 \times 3.6)(7.4)(7.0)^2$
$\qquad - (7.52)(7.4)(6.8)^2]10^6 = 56.4 \times 10^6$ N · mm
$M_{f\,unbal}$ about column line 2 = M_2
$M_2 = 0.07[(7.52 + 0.5 \times 3.6)(6.9)(7.5)^2$
$\qquad - (7.52)(6.9)(7.0)^2]10^6 = 75.2 \times 10^6$ N · mm

From Table 5.3;

$d = 250$, $2(c_1 + c_2) = 1600$; $k = 1.55 \times 10^{-6}/mm^2$

From Table 5.4;

$c_1 = c_2 = 400$, $c_1 - c_2 = 0$; $k_1 = k_2 = 2.7 \times 10^{-9}/mm^3$

Service Loading

Live	$= 1.9 \text{ kN/m}^2$
Partitions (fixed)	$= 1.2 \text{ kN/m}^2$
Exterior precast panels	$= 2.4 \text{ kN/m}$

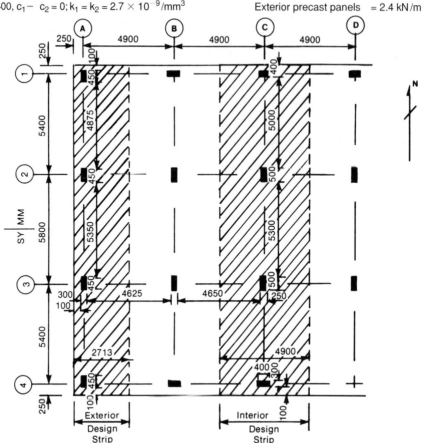

$v_f = (1.55 \times 10^{-6})(594 \times 10^3) + (2.7 \times 10^{-9})$
$\qquad (75.2 \times 10^6) = 1.12 \text{ MPa}$

$v_r = 1.2 \text{ MPa} > v_f = 1.12 \text{ MPa}$ OK

Step 5 — Design Beams

Edge beams designed for flexure for loads from slab plus loads applied directly to beam. To be consistent with slab design, edge beams must also be designed for torsion varying from zero at panel centrelines to $0.67 \, T_{cr}$ at face of column (11.2.9.2).

Example 5.4 — Two-way Slab Without Beams (Flat Plate)

Note — The purpose of this example is to supplement Example 5.3 by illustrating computations for reinforcement placement and shear-moment transfer at exterior columns when no edge beam is provided. Hence only selected portions of the design related to these computations are presented.

Consider the portion of an apartment building floor shown. The slab projects 100 mm beyond the exterior column face to support wall panels and assist with shear transfer.

Given: $f'_c = 25 \text{ MPa}$ (normal weight) $f_y = 400 \text{ MPa}$

Step 1 — Select Slab Thickness

a) Deflection requirements (13.3.3)

$\ell_{n\,max}$ (exterior panel) $= 5800 - (500+450)/2 = 5325 \text{ mm}$

$h_{s\,min} = 1.1 \times 5325(0.6+400/1000)/30 = 195 \text{ mm}$

Try $h_s = 200 \text{ mm}$

Effective depths with No. 15 bars, 25 mm clear cover outer layers in N-S direction

$d_v = 200 - 25 - 15 = 160 \text{ mm}$, $d_v/2 = 80 \text{ mm}$

Trial factored loading

self wt	$= (.2 \times 2.4 \times 9.81)1.25$	$= 5.89 \text{ kN/m}^2$
partitions	$= (1.2)1.25$	$= \underline{1.50}$
		$w_{Df} = 7.39 \text{ kN/m}^2$
live load reduction factor = 0.9 (NBC 1995)		
w_{Lf}	$= (0.9 \times 1.9)1.5$	$= \underline{2.57} \text{ kN/m}^2$
		$w_f = 9.96 \text{ kN/m}^2$

b) Shear capacity requirements (13.4)

Note — Since unbalanced moments to be transferred between slab and column are not known at this stage of design, the preliminary shear check is based on V_f alone. For this reason the ratio v_r/v_f for preliminary design should exceed the following:

i)   interior columns   1.2
ii) edge columns   1.6
iii) corner columns   2.0

Interior column C2

Factored shear stress resistance (13.4.4)

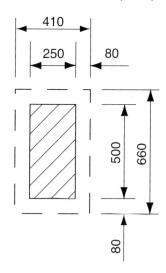

$b_o = 2(410 + 660) = 2140$ mm

$\beta_c = 500/250 = 2;\ (1 + 2/\beta_c)\ 0.2 = 0.4$

$\alpha_s = 4;\ (\alpha_s \times d/b_o) + 0.2 = ((4 \times 160/2140) + 0.2)$
$= 0.5$

$v_r = 0.4 \times 0.6 \times \sqrt{25} = 1.2$ MPa

$V_f = 9.96[(4.9 \times 5.6) - (0.41 \times 0.64)]10^3$
$= 271 \times 10^3$ N

$v_f = V_f/(b_o d) = 271 \times 10^3/(2140 \times 160) = 0.79$ MPa

$v_r/v_f = 1.2/0.79 = 1.51 > 1.2;$ proceed

Exterior column C1

$v_r = 0.4 \times 0.6 \times \sqrt{25} = 1.2$ MPa

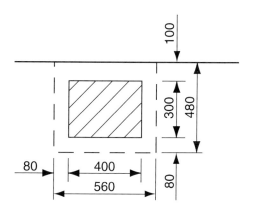

$V_f = V_{slab} + V_{wall} = 9.96[(4.9 \times 2.95) - (0.56 \times 0.48)]$
$+ (2.4)(1.25)(4.9 - .56) = 154$ kN $= 154 \times 10^3$ N

$v_f = 154 \times 10^3/[2(560 + 480) \times 160)] = 0.46$ MPa

$v_r/v_f = 1.2/0.46 = 2.61 > 1.6;$ proceed

Corner column A1

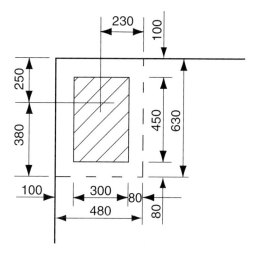

$v_r = 0.4 \times 0.6 \times \sqrt{25} = 1.2$ MPa

$V_f = V_{slab} + V_{wall} = 9.96[(2.70 \times 2.99) - (0.48 \times 0.63)]$
$+ (2.4)(1.25)(4.9/2 - 0.23 + 5.4/2 - 0.38) = 91.0$ kN

$v_f = 91.0 \times 10^3/[(480 + 630) \times 160)] = 0.51$ MPa

$v_r/v_f = 1.2/0.51 = 2.35 > 2;$ proceed

Use $h_s = 200$ mm

Step 2 — Design Moments

Since the limitations of (13.10.1) are satisfied, use Direct Design Method

Note — Only unbalanced moments for checking shear capacity are computed.

Interior column C2

For interior columns with approximately equal spans, the maximum unbalanced moments result from Eqn. (13-17).

$M_{f\ unbal}$ about column line 2 = M_1

$M_1 = 0.07[(7.39 + 0.5 \times 2.57)(4.9)(5.3)^2$
$- (7.39)(4.9)(5.0)^2]10^6 = 20.2 \times 10^6$ N·mm

$M_{f\ unbal}$ about column line C = M_2

$M_2 = 0.07[(7.39 + 0.5 \times 2.57)(5.6)(4.65)^2$
$- (7.39)(5.6)(4.65)^2]10^6 = 10.9 \times 10^6$ N·mm

Exterior column C1

$M_{f\ unbal}$ about column line C may be assumed zero since spans are equal

$M_{f\ unbal}$ about column line 1 = M_{DES} at exterior support

$M_{DES} = 0.26\ M_o = 0.26[9.96(4.9)(5.0)^2/8]10^6$
$= 39.65 \times 10^6$ N·mm

Corner column A1

$M_{f\ unbal}$ about column lines are strip M_{DES} including moment due to wall panels

$M_{f\ unbal}$ about column line 1 = M_1

$M_1 = 0.26[9.96(2.71)(4.875)^2/8 + (2.4 \times 1.25)$
$(4.875)^2/8]10^6 = 23.16 \times 10^6$ N·mm

$M_{f\ unbal}$ about column line A = M_2

$M_2 = 0.26[9.96(2.95)(4.55)^2/8 + (2.4 \times 1.25)$
$(4.55)^2/8]10^6 = 21.79 \times 10^6$ N·mm

Step 3 — Slab reinforcement

Column C1 (along column line C only)

Outer layers in the N-S direction (longer spans) with No. 10 bars; d = 200 − 25 − 5 = 170 mm

Positive moment (bottom) reinforcement, Span 1-2

Minimum reinforcement (7.8.1)

$A_{s\,min}$ (for design strip) = 0.002 × 200 × 4900
= 1960 mm^2

Minimum reinforcement for structural integrity (13.11.5)

self wt. slab = 0.2 × 2.4 × 9.81	= 4.71 kN/m^2
partitions	= 1.20
Live	= 1.90
total specified load	= 7.81 kN/m^2

V_{se} = 7.81[(4.9 × 2.9)−(0.56 × 0.48)] + (2.4)(4.9 − .56)
= 119 kN

but not less than 2(4.71)[(4.9 × 2.9)−(0.56 × 0.48)]
= 131 kN

ΣA_{sb} = 2V_{se}/f_y = 2(131 × 10^3)/400 = 655 mm^2
Require 7 No. 10 bars; 2 on each side face and 3 on front face

Design moment, Span 1-2

M_{DES} = 0.52 M_o = 0.52[9.96(4.9)(5.0)^2/8]10^6
= 79.3 × 10^6 N · mm

A_s = (79.3 × 10^6)/(0.85 × 400 × 0.9 × 170)
= 1525 mm^2 < $A_{s\,min}$ = 1960 mm^2

Use 21 No. 10 bars; 3 through column and 9 on each side.

Anchorage requirements for the 3 bars through column are given in Clause 13.11.5.3

Negative moment (top) reinforcement at exterior support

M_{DES} = 0.26 M_o = 39.65 × 10^6 N · mm
A_s = (39.65 × 10^6)/(0.85 × 400 × 0.9 × 170) = 765 mm^2

try 8 No. 10 bars
For slabs without edge beams (13.12.2.2), all reinforcement to be placed in band of width (3 h_s + c_2)

width of band = 3(200) + 400 = 1000 mm

spacing in band = 1000/7 ≅ 143 mm < 1.5 h_s (13.11.3)

Use 8 No. 10 bars in band 1000 mm wide centred on column.

Note that these bars must be fully anchored to develop yield strength. While not required for strength, it would be usual to place additional top bars at not greater than 500 mm spacing along the remainder of the edge to improve serviceability.

Step 4 — Check shear capacity

Interior column C2

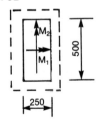

It is conservative to compute v_f as the larger of
a) $kV_f + k_1M_1$
b) $kV_f + k_2M_2$
V_f = 271 × 10^3 N; M_1 = 20.2 × 10^6 N · mm
M_2 = 10.9 × 10^6 N · mm

From Table 5.3;
d =160, 2(c_1 + c_2) = 1500; k = 2.9 × 10^{-6}/mm^2

From Table 5.4;
c_1 = 500, c_2 = 250, c_1 − c_2 = 250; k_1 = 6.9 × 10^{-9}/mm^3

From Table 5.4;
c_1 = 250, c_2 = 500, c_2 − c_1 = 250; k_2 = 6.5 × 10^{-9}/mm^3
v_f = (2.9 × 10^{-6})(271 × 10^3) + (6.9 × 10^{-9})(20.2 × 10^6)
= 0.93 MPa; or
v_f = (2.9 × 10^{-6})(271 × 10^3) + (6.5 × 10^{-9})(10.9 × 10^6)
= 0.86 MPa
v_r = 1.2 MPa > v_f = 0.93 MPa OK

Edge column C1

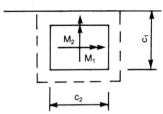

V_f = 154 × 10^3 N; M_1 = 39.65 × 10^6 N · mm

See sketch for definition of c_1 and c_2 when using Tables 5.5 to 5.9.

From Table 5.5;
c_1 = c_2 = 400, 2c_1 + c_2 = 1200; k = 4.1 × 10^{-6}/mm^2
From Table 5.6;
c_2 = 400, c_1 − c_2 = 0; k_1 = 8.7 × 10^{-9}/mm^3
v_f = (4.1 × 10^{-6})(154 × 10^3) + (8.7 × 10^{-9})(39.65 × 10^6)
= 0.98 MPa
v_r = 1.2 MPa > v_f = 0.98 MPa OK

Corner column A1

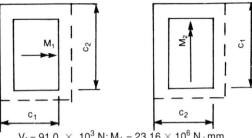

V_f = 91.0 × 10^3 N; M_1 = 23.16 × 10^6 N · mm
M_2 = 21.79 × 10^6 N · mm

From Table 5.8;
d =160, (c_1 + c_2) = 950; k = 5.6 × 10^{-6}/mm^2
From Table 5.9;
c_1 = 550, c_2 = 400, c_1 − c_2 = 150; k_1 = 9.8 × 10^{-9}/mm^3
From Table 5.9;
c_1 = 400, c_2 = 550, c_2 − c_1 = 150; k_2 = 8.5 × 10^{-9}/mm^3
v_f = (5.6 × 10^{-6})(91.0 × 10^3) + (9.8 × 10^{-9})(23.16 × 10^6)
= 0.74 MPa; or

$v_f = (5.6 \times 10^{-6})(91.0 \times 10^3) + (8.5 \times 10^{-9})$
$\qquad (21.79 \times 10^6) = 0.69$ MPa
$v_r = 1.2$ MPa $> v_f = 0.74$ MPa OK

Check one-way shear (13.4.6.2)

assume critical section at 45° (generally conservative assumption)

length of critical section $= 2(400\sqrt{2}+80) + 150\sqrt{2}$
$\qquad = 1503$ mm

$v_f = (91.0 \times 10^3)/(1503 \times 160) = 0.378$ MPa
$v_r = 0.2(0.6)\sqrt{25} = 0.6$ MPa $> v_f = 0.378$ MPa OK

Example 5.5 Two-way Slab with Stiff Supports

Consider a roof slab over "self storage" units. All panels are supported by concrete block walls on three edges and by a stiff beam across the edge with access door. To obtain a 2 hr. fire rating, use a clear cover of 25 mm on all reinforcement.

Given: $f'_c = 25$ MPa (normal weight), $f_y = 400$ MPa

ground snow – 2.0 kN/m²

roofing – 3 ply felt and gravel – 27.0 kg/m²

insulation, sprinkler, mech. – 1.0 kN/m²

additional storage on roof – 5.0 kN/m²

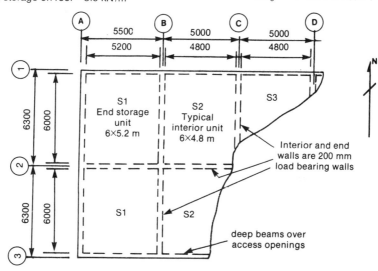

Step 1 — Slab Thickness

Deflection requirements (13.3.5 and Appendix B)

Corner panel S1 governs,

(13.3.5) $\beta = 6000/5200 = 1.15$, assume $\alpha_m = 2.0$,

$h_{s\,min} = 6000(0.6 + 400/1000)/(30 + 4(2.0)1.15)$
$\qquad = 153$ mm

(B2.1 (b)) $h_{s\,min} = $ perimeter/140 $= 2(6000 + 5200)/140$
$\qquad = 160$ mm

Try $h_s = 160$ mm

Loading:

self wt. (0.16 $\times$ 2.4 $\times$ 9.81)		= 3.77 kN/m²
roofing (27 $\times$ 9.81/1000)		= 0.27
mechanical		= 1.00
$w_{Df} = 1.25 \times$	5.04	= 6.30 kN/m²
additional live load		= 5.00 kN/m²
snow (not exposed) 0.8(2.0)		= 1.60
$w_{Lf} = 1.50 \times$	6.60	= 9.90 kN/m²

Step 2 — Design Moments

Middle strip moments

Panel S1; $\ell_a/\ell_b = 5200/6000 \approx 0.85$; Case 4

Negative moment at continuous edges (B2.4)
$M_{a\,neg} = 0.066(6.3+9.9)(5.2)^2 = 28.91$ kN·m/m
$M_{b\,neg} = 0.034(6.3+9.9)(6.0)^2 = 19.83$ kN·m/m

Positive moments (B2.5)

$M_{al\,pos} = 0.043(9.9)(5.2)^2$	= 11.51	
$M_{ad\,pos} = 0.036(6.3)(5.2)^2$	= 6.13	
$M_{a\,pos}$	= 17.64 kN·m/m	
$M_{bl\,pos} = 0.023(9.9)(6.0)^2$	= 8.20	
$M_{bd\,pos} = 0.019(6.3)(6.0)^2$	= 4.3	
$M_{b\,pos}$	= 12.51 kN·m/m	

Negative moment at discontinuous edge (B2.8)
$M_{a\,neg} = 3/4(17.64) = 13.23$ kN·m/m
$M_{b\,neg} = 3/4(12.51) = 9.38$ kN·m/m

Panel S2; $\ell_a/\ell_b = 4800/6000 = 0.8$; Case 9

Negative moment at continuous edges (B2.4)
$M_{a\,neg} = 0.075(6.3+9.9)(4.8)^2 = 27.99$ kN·m/m

$M_{b\,neg} = 0.017(6.3+9.9)(6.0)^2 = 9.91$ kN·m/m

Positive moments (B2.4)

$M_{al\,pos} = 0.042(9.9)(4.8)^2$	= 9.58	
$M_{ad\,pos} = 0.029(6.3)(4.8)^2$	= 4.21	
$M_{a\,pos}$	= 13.79 kN·m/m	
$M_{bl\,pos} = 0.017(9.9)(6.0)^2$	= 6.06	
$M_{bd\,pos} = 0.010(6.3)(6.0)^2$	= 2.27	
$M_{b\,pos}$	= 8.33 kN·m/m	

Negative moment at discontinuous edge (B2.8)
$M_{b\,neg} = 3/4(8.33) = 6.25$ kN·m/m

Unbalanced negative moment (B2.10)

Consider unbalanced moment $M_{a\,neg}$ between panels S1 and S2

$(M_{a\,neg})_{S2}/(M_{a\,neg})_{S1} = 27.99/28.91 = 0.97 < 0.8$

∴ not necessary to distribute difference by (B2.10)

Although not required, distribute difference in ratio of stiffnesses

$$(M_{a\,neg})_{S1} = 28.91 - [(1/5.2)/(1/5.2+1/4.8)] \times (28.91 - 27.99)$$

$$= 28.47 \text{ kN} \cdot \text{m/m} = (M_{a\,neg})_{S2}$$

Summary of Design Moments; Panel S1

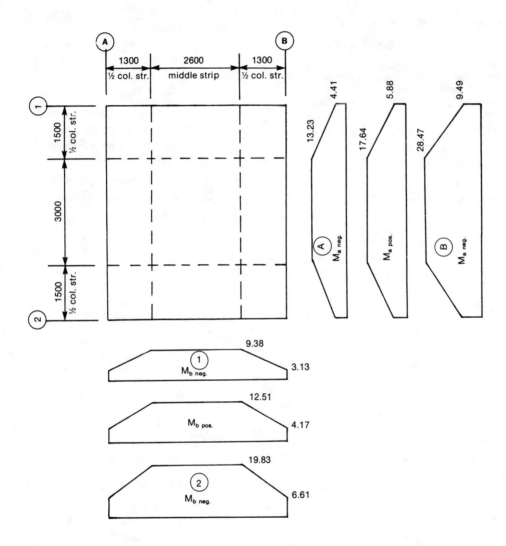

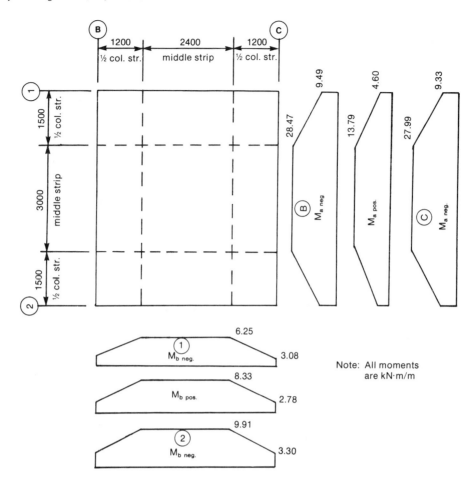

Note: All moments are kN·m/m

Step 3 — Slab Reinforcement

$d_{EW} = 160 - 25 - 10/2 = 130$ mm

$d_{NS} = 160 - 25 - 10 - 10/2 = 120$ mm

Minimum reinforcement (7.8.1)

$A_{s\ min\ EW} = 0.002A_g = 0.002(160)6000 = 1920$ mm^2

$A_{s\ min\ NS}$ (Panel S1) $= 0.002A_g = 0.002(160)5200$
$= 1664$ mm^2

$A_{s\ min\ NS}$ (Panel S2) $= 0.002A_g = 0.002(160)4800$
$= 1536$ mm^2

Minimum reinforcement satisfied with No. 10 @ 300 mm

$s_{max} = 5\ h_s$ or 500 mm > 300 mm OK (7.8.3)

Moment reinforcement

$s_{max} = 3\ h_s$ or 500 mm; 500 mm governs (13.11.3)

assume j = 0.94

Moment resistance with minimum reinforcement

EW; $M_r = \phi_s f_y A_s(d - a/2) = 14.2$ kN · m/m

NS; $M_r = \phi_s f_y A_s(d - a/2) = 13.1$ kN · m/m

Use No. 10 @ 300 mm at all sections where moment is less than that provided by minimum reinforcement.

Panel S1

$M^2_{b\ neg}$; $A_s = \dfrac{19.83 \times 10^6}{0.85(400).94(120)} = 517$ mm^2/m

middle strip $A_s = 2.6(517) = 1344$ mm^2

Use 14 - No. 10 bars

½ column strip $A_s = 1.3(2/3 \times 517) = 448$ mm^2

Use 5 - No. 10 bars in each ½ column strip

$M_{a\ pos}$; $A_s = \dfrac{17.64 \times 10^6}{0.85(400).94(130)} = 425$ mm^2/m

middle strip $A_s = 3.0(425) = 1275$ mm^2

Use 13 - No. 10 bars

½ column strip $A_s = 1.5(2/3 \times 425) = 425$ mm^2

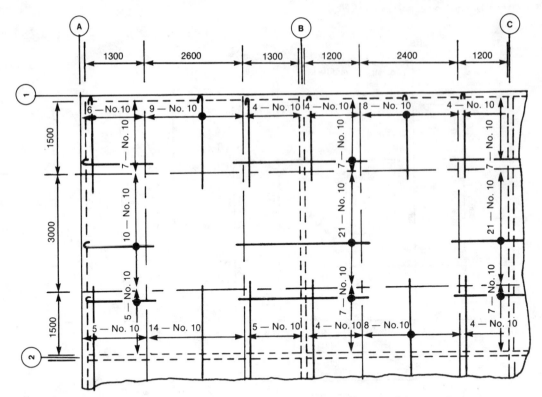

Use 5 - No. 10 bars in each ½ column strip

$$M_{a\,neg}^{B}; A_s = \frac{28.47 \times 10^6}{0.85(400).94(130)} = 685 \text{ mm}^2/\text{m}$$

middle strip $A_s = 3.0(685) = 2055 \text{ mm}^2$

Use 21 - No. 10 bars

½ column strip $A_s = 1.5(2/3 \times 685) = 685 \text{ mm}^2$

Use 7 - No. 10 bars in each ½ column strip

Corner reinforcement (13.13.5)

$A_{s\,req'd} = A_s$ for $M_{a\,pos} = 425 \text{ mm}^2/\text{m}$

width $= \ell/5 = 6000/5 = 1200 \text{ mm}$

$A_s = 1.2(425) = 510 \text{ mm}^2$

Add 2 - No. 10 both directions top and bottom in exterior corner

Panel S2

$$M_{a\,neg}^{C}; A_s = \frac{27.99 \times 10^6}{0.85(400).94(130)} = 674 \text{ mm}^2/\text{m}$$

middle strip $A_s = 3.0(674) = 2021 \text{ mm}^2$

Use 21 - No. 10 bars

½ column strip $A_s = 1.5(2/3 \times 674)$
$= 674 \text{ mm}^2$

Use 7 - No. 10 bars in each ½ column strip

Summary of top reinforcement

Summary of bottom reinforcement

Bottom mat – No. 10 @ 300 mm both directions
add 1 - No. 10 EW in middle strip panel S1 only
3 - No. 10 both directions between mat bars
at discontinuous corner. Min. length = 1200 mm

Step 4 — Check Shear Capacity (B2.11)

$V_{f\,max} = (5200/2 - 125)(6.3 + 9.9) = 40.1 \times 10^3 \text{ N}$
$V_r = 0.2(0.6)\sqrt{25}(1000)(125) = 75 \times 10^3 \text{ N} > V_{f\,max}$
Satisfactory in shear

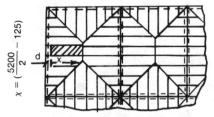

Step 5 — Design of Supports (B3)

Beams over openings on column lines 1 and 3 designed to resist equivalent load $w_f \ell_a/3$. Walls support load from shaded areas shown above.

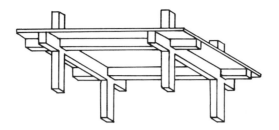

(a) 2-way slab with beams

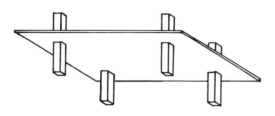

(b) 2-way slab without beams
(flat plate)

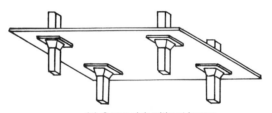

(c) 2-way slab without beams
(drop panels and column capitals)

Fig. 5.1   Types of 2-way Slabs

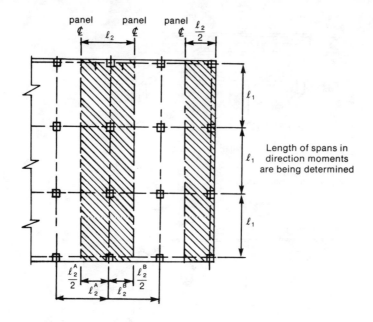

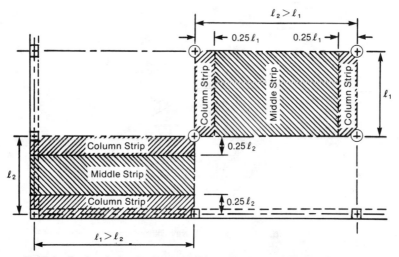

Fig. 5.2   Design Strips for Use with Direct Design and Elastic Frame Analogies

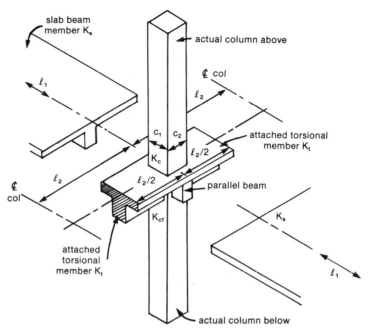

Fig. 5.3 Equivalent Column and Attached Torsional Members

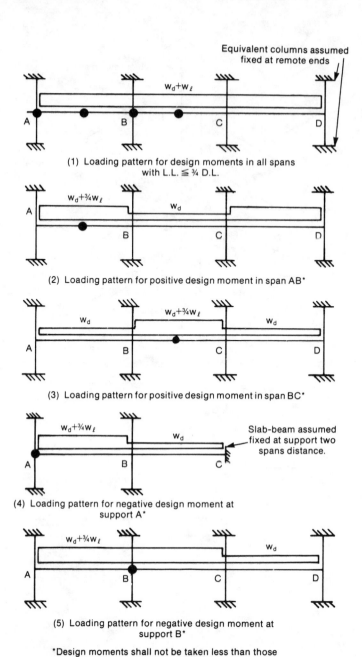

(1) Loading pattern for design moments in all spans with L.L. $\leq$ ¾ D.L.

(2) Loading pattern for positive design moment in span AB*

(3) Loading pattern for positive design moment in span BC*

(4) Loading pattern for negative design moment at support A*

(5) Loading pattern for negative design moment at support B*

*Design moments shall not be taken less than those occurring for loading pattern (1).

Fig. 5.4   Partial Frame and Loading Patterns for Elastic Frame Analogies

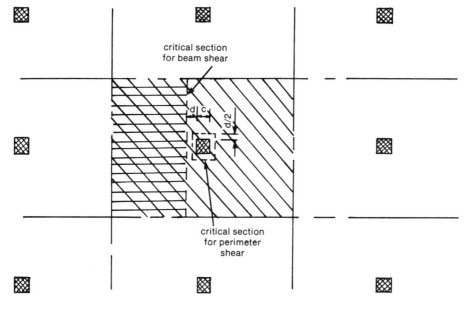

critical section
for beam shear

critical section
for perimeter
shear

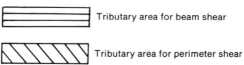

Tributary area for beam shear

Tributary area for perimeter shear

Fig. 5.5   Critical Sections for Shear in Slabs

INTERIOR COLUMN

$A = 2d(c_1 + c_2 + 2d)$

$e = (c_1 + d)/2$

$J = (c_1 + d)d^3/6 + (c_1 + d)^3 d/6$
$\quad + d(c_2 + d)(c_1 + d)^2/2$

$\gamma_v = 1 - \dfrac{1}{1 + \dfrac{2}{3}\sqrt{\dfrac{c_1 + d}{c_2 + d}}}$

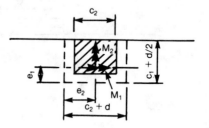

EDGE COLUMN

$A = d(2c_1 + c_2 + 2d)$

$e_1 = (c_1 + d/2)^2/(2c_1 + c_2 + 2d)$

$e_2 = (c_2 + d)/2$

$J_1 = [(c_1 + d/2)d^3 + (c_1 + d/2)^3 d]/6$
$\quad + (c_2 + d)d[e_1]^2 + 2(c_1 + d/2)d[(c_1 + d/2)/2 - e_1]^2$

$J_2 = [(c_2 + d)d^3 + (c_2 + d)^3 d]/12 + 2(c_1 + d/2)d[e_2]^2$

$\gamma_{v1} = 1 - \dfrac{1}{1 + \dfrac{2}{3}\sqrt{\dfrac{c_1 + d/2}{c_2 + d}}}$

$\gamma_{v2} = 1 - \dfrac{1}{1 + \dfrac{2}{3}\sqrt{\dfrac{c_2 + d}{c_1 + d/2}}}$

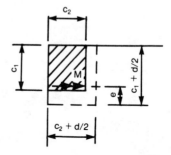

CORNER COLUMN

$A = d(c_1 + c_2 + d)$

$e = (c_1 + d/2)^2/[2(c_1 + c_2 + d)]$

$J = [(c_1 + d/2)d^3 + (c_1 + d/2)^3 d]/12$
$\quad + (c_2 + d/2)de^2 + (c_1 + d/2)d[(c_1 + d/2)/2 - e]^2$

$\gamma_v = 1 - \dfrac{1}{1 + \dfrac{2}{3}\sqrt{\dfrac{c_1 + d/2}{c_2 + d/2}}}$

Fig. 5.6 Geometric Expressions for Shear-Moment Transfer

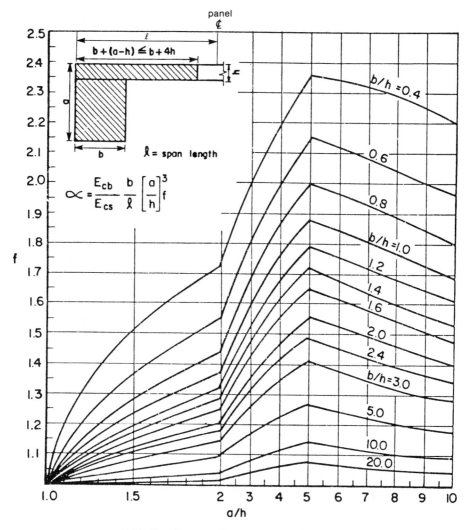

Table 5.1   Beam to Slab Ratio $\propto$ (Edge Beams)

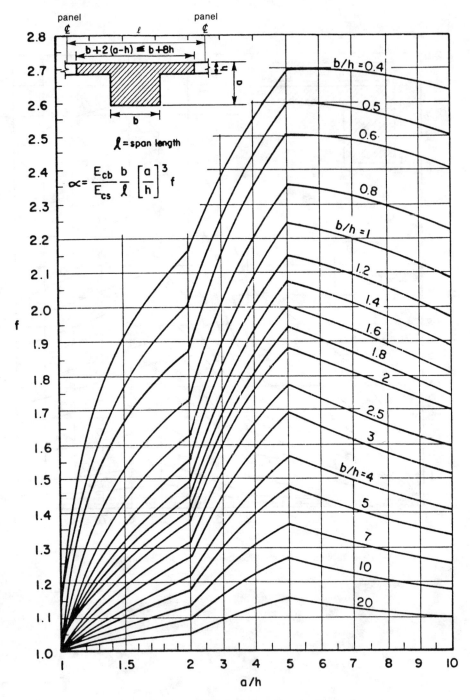

Table 5.2   Beam to Slab Ratio ∝ (Interior Beams)

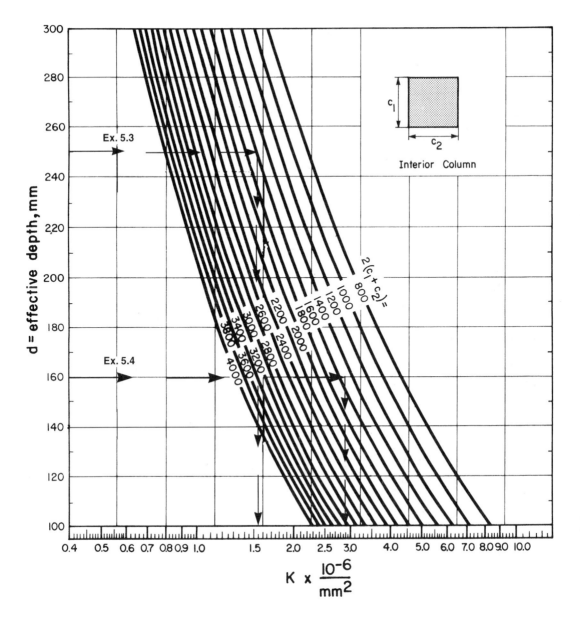

Table 5.3   Factor k, Shear-Moment Transfer, Interior Column

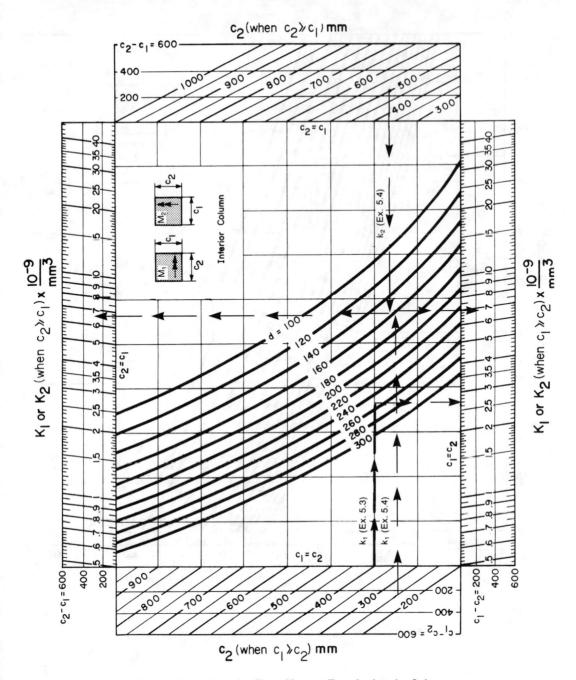

Table 5.4   Factor k_1 or k_2, Shear-Moment Transfer, Interior Column

CPCA Concrete Design Handbook

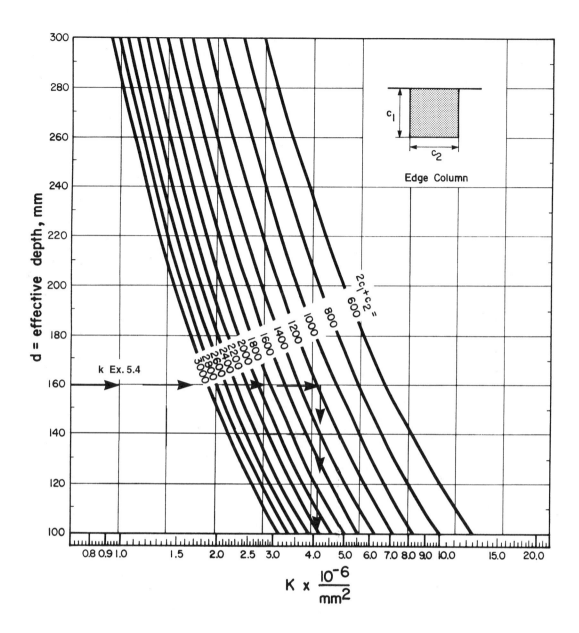

Table 5.5   Factor k, Shear-Moment Transfer, Edge Column

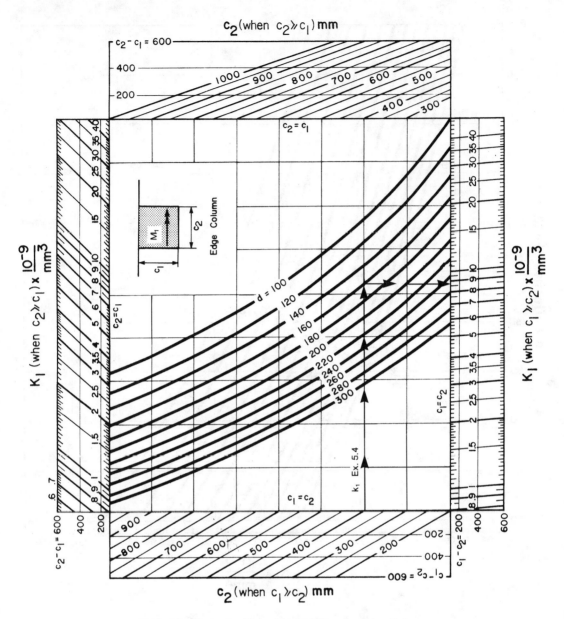

Table 5.6   Factor k_1, Shear-Moment Transfer, Edge Column

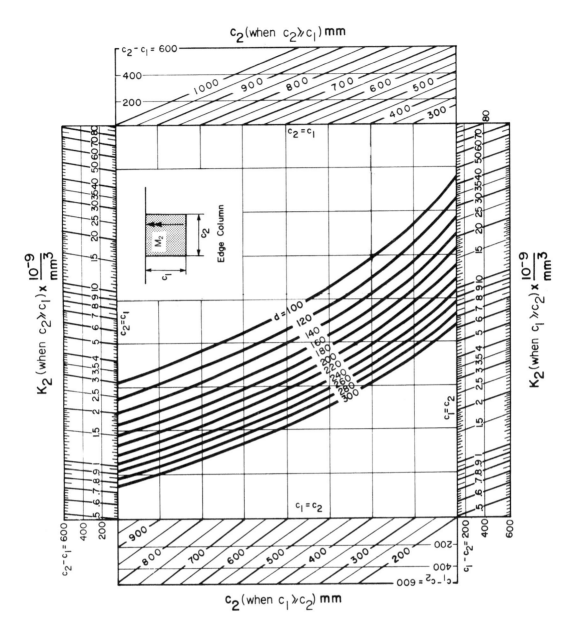

Table 5.7   Factor k_2, Shear-Moment Transfer, Edge Column

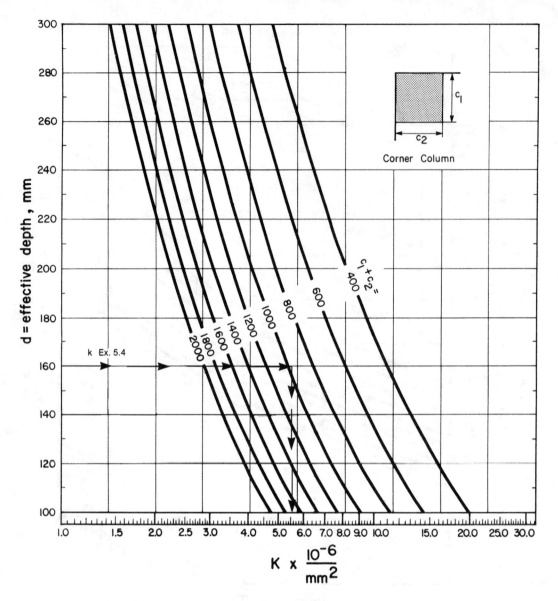

Table 5.8   Factor k, Shear-Moment Transfer, Corner Column

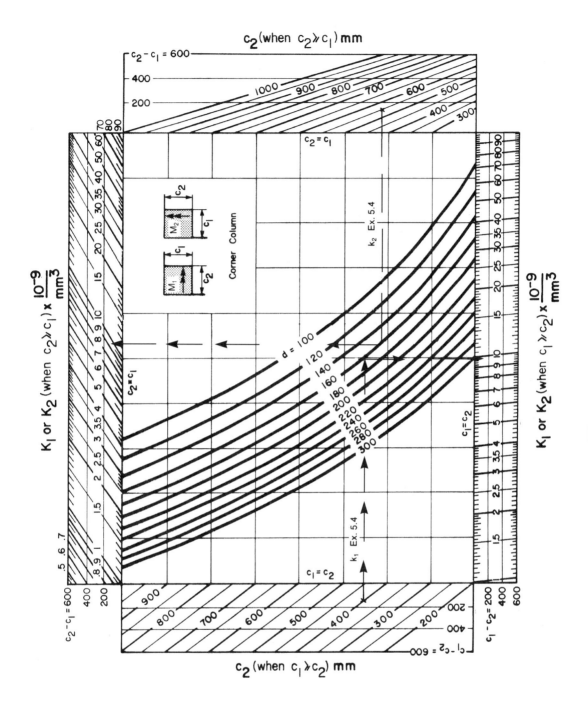

Table 5.9   Factor k_1 or k_2, Shear-Moment Transfer, Corner Column

Table 5.10 Area of Reinforcing Steel (A_s mm^2) Per One Metre Strip

Bar Spacing mm	Bar Size (No.)					
	10	15	20	25	30	35
50	2000	4000	6000	10000	14000	20000
80	1250	2500	3750	6250	8750	12500
100	1000	2000	3000	5000	7000	10000
120	833	1667	2500	4167	5833	8333
150	667	1333	2000	3333	4667	6667
180	556	1111	1667	2778	3889	5556
200	500	1000	1500	2500	3500	5000
220	455	909	1364	2273	3182	4545
240	417	833	1250	2083	2917	4167
250	400	800	1200	2000	2800	4000
260	385	769	1154	1923	2692	3846
280	357	714	1071	1786	2500	3571
300	333	667	1000	1667	2333	3333
320	313	625	938	1563	2188	3125
340	294	588	882	1471	2059	2941
360	278	556	833	1389	1944	2778
380	263	526	789	1316	1842	2632
400	250	500	750	1250	1750	2500
420	238	476	714	1190	1667	2381
440	227	455	682	1136	1591	2273
460	217	435	652	1087	1522	2174

6

Deflections

By A. Scanlon, N. J. Gardner

Chapter 6
Deflections

6.1 INTRODUCTION

CSA Standard A23.3 Clause 9.8 requires that structures and structural members be designed to ensure that deflections are within acceptable limits for their intended use. Serviceability requirements for deflection are to be checked at specified load levels including effects of sustained load.

Deflections of concrete members depend on a large number of factors including the degree of cracking at specified load levels, cracking due to construction loads, creep and shrinkage characteristics of the concrete, modulus of elasticity, and support conditions. Because of the high degree of variability of factors affecting deformations, relatively simple procedures, as given in CSA Standard A23.3 may be used in deflection computations, however, undue reliance should not be placed on computed results.

Two approaches are available for control of deflections in one-way and two-way non-prestressed construction. In the first approach, deflection requirements are considered to be satisfied, under certain circumstances, by providing a member thickness equal to or exceeding a specified fraction of the span length. In the second approach, deflections must be calculated and compared with specified maximum permissible values. Situations not covered by the specified maximum permissible values must be considered on an individual basis.

6.2 DEFLECTION CONTROL BY SPAN TO DEPTH RATIOS

6.2.1 One-way Construction (Non-prestressed)

For one-way construction *not* supporting or attached to partitions or other construction likely to be damaged by large deflections, deflections need not be computed if the member thickness equals or exceeds the value given in Table 6.1 (Table 9.1 of CSA Standard A23.3). If the member supports, or is attached to non-structural elements likely to be damaged by large deflections, the table of minimum thicknesses does not apply and deflections must be computed or otherwise shown to satisfy maximum permissible values.

6.2.2 Two-way Construction (Non-prestressed)

For two-way construction, if the slab thickness equals or exceeds the minimum thickness value given in Clauses 13.3.3 to 13.3.5, deflections need not be computed. These minimum thickness values apply whether or not the slab is supporting partitions or other construction likely to be damaged by large deflections.

Minimum thickness equations for two-way construction, based on CSA Standard A23.3, are given in Table 6.2.

Excessive deflections of two-way slabs present a serious serviceability problem not easily remedied, particularly after installation of non-structural elements and mechanical services. It is preferable, therefore, to err on the side of thicker rather than thinner slabs.

6.3 DEFLECTION LIMITS

Computed deflections must not exceed the limits given in Table 6.3 (Table 9.2 of CSA Standard A23.3) expressed as fractions of the clear span length, ℓ_n.

Deflections to be considered are,

a) immediate deflection due to specified live load, L

b) deflection occurring after attachment of non-structural elements (due to sustained load + live load).

Two conditions are considered in Table 6.3, namely, members either attached or not attached to non-structural elements. Requirements are more stringent for members attached to non-structural elements likely to be damaged by large deflections.

Other deflection criteria may have to be considered by the designer. For example, where excessive deflection may result in either aesthetic or functional problems, such as objectionable visual sagging, ponding of water, vibration, or improper operation of sliding doors, total deflection should be considered. Guidance on deflection limits for a range of design situations is given in Ref. 1.

6.4 DEFLECTION COMPUTATIONS

6.4.1 Computation of Immediate Deflections for Beams and One-way Slabs (Non-prestressed)

For uniformly loaded members, immediate deflections can be computed using the expression:

$$\Delta = K \left(\frac{5}{48} \right) \frac{M\ell^2}{E_c I_e} \qquad (6.1)$$

where M = support moment for cantilever, midspan moment for simple and continuous beams

ℓ = span length

E_c = modulus of elasticity of concrete

$(3300 \sqrt{f'_c} + 6900)(\gamma_c/2300)^{1.5}$

$(1500 \le \gamma_c \le 2500 \text{ kg/m}^3)$

= $4500 \sqrt{f'_c}$ for normal weight concrete

I_e = effective moment of inertia

K = coefficient as follows

	K
Cantilevers (fixed end)*	2.400
Simple spans	1.0
Fixed-Hinged Beams	
—Midspan deflection	0.800
—Max deflection (when using	
max. moment)	0.738
Fixed-Fixed Beams	0.600
Continuous Spans	$1.20 - 0.20 M_o/M_m$

where $M_o = w\ell^2/8$ and M_m is the net midspan moment.

*In the case of cantilevers, the deflection due to the rotation at the support must also be included.

For loading other than uniformly distributed, the formulae given in Chapter 1 of this Handbook can be used.

The effective moment of inertia, I_e, is given by

$$I_e = \left(\frac{M_{cr}}{M_a} \right)^3 I_g + [1 - \left(\frac{M_{cr}}{M_a} \right)^3] I_{cr} \qquad (6.2)$$

where $M_{cr} = \dfrac{f_r I_g}{y_t}$ $\qquad (6.3)$

f_r = $0.6 \lambda \sqrt{f'_c}$ $\qquad (6.4)$

λ = 1.00 for normal density concrete

λ = 0.85 for structural semi-low density concrete

M_a = moment at load level under consideration

The quantities I_g, I_{cr}, and y_t can be calculated for rectangular and T-sections using the equations and charts given in Tables 6-4 to 6-9. Use of the Design Aids is illustrated in the Design Examples. I_e should be evaluated based on moment at the support for cantilevers, and midspan moment for simply supported beams. For continuous beams average values of I_e based on support moments and midspan moments should be used. CSA A23.3 states that I_e may be taken as a weighted average as given by the following expressions:

One end continuous:

$$I_e \text{ (avg)} = 0.85 \, I_e \text{ (pos)} + 0.15 \, I_e \text{ (neg)} \quad (6.5)$$

Both ends continuous:

$$I_e \text{ (avg)} = 0.70 \, I_e \text{ (pos)} + \quad (6.6)$$

$$0.30 \frac{[I_e \text{(neg)}_{\text{left}} + I_e \text{(neg)}_{\text{right}}]}{2}$$

For column supported end spans where partial fixity is provided by the exterior column the following expression is suggested:

$$I_e \text{ (avg)} = 0.75 \, I_e \text{ (pos)} + 0.25 \, I_e \text{ (neg)} \quad (6.7)$$

I_e should normally be calculated based on the load level under consideration. For example, dead load deflection should be calculated with I_e based on the dead load moment. Deflection under combined dead plus live load should be calculated with I_e based on total load moment. Live load deflection would then be taken as the difference between total load deflection and dead load deflection. The use of I_e based on total load moments to compute all terms would tend to overestimate the dead load deflections and underestimate the live load deflections.

When construction procedures are likely to result in high loads at early age, such as in multi-story floor construction, I_e for all cases should be based on the construction load level as discussed in Section 6.4.3.

6.4.2 Computation of Long-Time Deflection for Beams and One-Way Slabs (Non-prestressed)

Having calculated the immediate deflection Δ_i corresponding to the sustained load level, the additional long-time deflection, Δ_t, due to creep and shrinkage may be calculated using Eq. 6.8.

$$\Delta_t = \frac{S}{1 + 50\rho'} \Delta_i \quad (6.8)$$

where S = 2.0 (5 years or more)

  = 1.4 (12 months)

  = 1.0 (3 months)

The variation of S with time is shown graphically in Fig. 6.1. The use of a single multiplier for both creep and shrinkage effects is sufficiently accurate for most situations. However, since creep is stress-dependent while shrinkage is not, it may be desirable in some cases to consider the two effects separately. For example, in lightly loaded slabs reinforced on one face only, it may be necessary to consider the effect of shrinkage warping separately from the creep deflection due to sustained load. To calculate the long-time deflection components

due to creep and shrinkage separately, the following equations may be used.

$$\Delta_t = \Delta_{cp} + \Delta_{sh} \quad (6.9)$$

The creep deflection is given by

$$\Delta_{cp} = k_r \, C_t \, \Delta_t \quad (6.10)$$

where $k_r = \dfrac{0.85}{1 + 50 \, \rho'}$

The ultimate value of C, may be taken as 1.6 for average conditions. For intermediate times,

$$C_t = \frac{1.6}{2.0} \, S \quad (6.11)$$

The shrinkage deflection is given by:

$$\Delta_{sh} = K_{sh} \, \phi_{sh} \, \ell^2 \quad (6.12)$$

$$\phi_{sh} = \frac{A_{sh} \, \varepsilon_{sh}}{h} \quad (6.13)$$

For this purpose, the ultimate value of ε_{sh} may be taken as 400×10^{-6} for average conditions. For intermediate times

$$\varepsilon_{sh} = \frac{S}{2.0} \, 400 \times 10^{-6} \quad (6.14)$$

The term A_{sh} is obtained from Table 6.10. The steel percentages used in determining A_{sh} refer to the support section of cantilevers and the midspan section of simple and continuous spans. For T-beams, use $p = 100 \, (\rho + \rho_w) / 2$ in determining A_{sh}, where $\rho_w = A_s / (b_w d)$. The following values of K_{sh} can be used in Eq. 6.11.

	K_{sh}
Cantilevers	0.500
Simple beams	0.125
Beams continuous at one end only	0.090
Beams continuous at both ends	0.065

Design Example 6.1

Required: Calculate midspan deflections for exterior span of Tee Beam shown. Compare calculated deflections with CSA Standard A23.3 Maximum Permissible Values.

1.   Loads

Dead Load
Slab:	= 16.5 kN /m
Wall:	= 8.6
Beam:	= 2.4
Superimposed:	= 4.6

Total Dead Load w_D = 32.1 kN /m

Live Load
Total Live Load w_L = 8.4 kN/m
(Assume 20% sustained)   = 1.7 kN/m)

Total Load
$w_D + w_L = 40.5$ kN/m

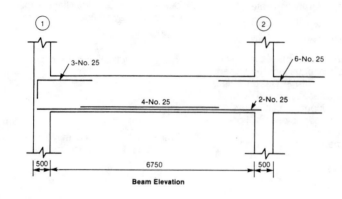

Beam Elevation

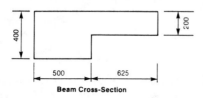

Beam Cross-Section

2. Bending Moments

	Exterior Support	Midspan	Interior Support	
Clear span (ℓ_n)	6750	6750	6875	mm
Moment Coeff. (C_m)	1/16	1/14	1/10	
$M_D = C_m w_D \ell_n^2$	91.4	104.5	151.7	$\times 10^6$ N·mm
$M_{D+L} = C_m (w_D + w_L) \ell_n^2$	115.3	131.8	191.4	$\times 10^6$ N·mm

3. Modulus of rupture, modulus of elasticity, modular ratio

$f_r = 0.6 \sqrt{25} = 3$ MPa
$E_c = 4500 \sqrt{25} = 22{,}500$ MPa
$n = E_s/E_c = 200{,}000/22{,}500 = 8.89$

4. Gross Moment of Inertia, I_g

a) Using chart: Table 6.7
  $b/b_w = 1125/500 = 2.25$, $h_f/h = 200/400 = 0.5$
  Read $I_g/bh^3 = 0.054$

b) Alternatively, using equations from Table 6.6

$$A_r = 200/400 \left[\frac{1125}{500} - 1 \right] = 0.625$$

$$C_T = \frac{4(0.625)\left(1 - \frac{200}{400}\right)^2 + \left(1 + 0.625\,\frac{200}{400}\right)^2}{12\,\frac{1125}{500}(1 + 0.625)}$$

$$= 0.0535$$

$$I_g = (0.0535)(1125)(400)^3 = \underline{3852 \times 10^6 \text{ mm}^4}$$

5. Cracking Moment, M_{cr}

(i) Positive Moment Region: tension on bottom face

a) Using Chart Table 6.8

$b/b_w = 1125/500 = 2.25$: $h_f/h = 200/400$
$= 0.5$

Read $y_{tb}/h = 0.6$ i.e. $y_{tb} = (0.6)(400)$
$= \underline{240 \text{ mm}}$

$$M_{cr} = \frac{(3)(3852 \times 10^6)}{240} = \underline{48.2 \times 10^6 \text{ N·mm}}$$

b) Alternatively, using Equation: Table 6.8

$$\frac{y_{tb}}{h} = \frac{\left(\frac{1125}{500}\right)\left(\frac{200}{400}\right)\left(1 - \frac{1}{2}\left(\frac{200}{400}\right)\right)^2 + \frac{1}{2}\left(1 - \frac{200}{400}\right)^2}{\left(\frac{1125}{500}\right)\left(\frac{200}{400}\right) + \left(1 - \frac{200}{400}\right)}$$

$$= 0.60$$

i.e. $y_{tb} = (0.60)(400) = \underline{240 \text{ mm}}$

(ii) Negative Moment Region, Interior Support: tension top face

$y_{tt} = h - y_{tb} = 400 - 240 = 160$ mm

$$M_{cr} = \frac{(3)(3852 \times 10^6)}{160} = 72.2 \times 10^6 \text{ N·mm}$$

6. Cracked Transformed Moment of Inertia, I_{cr}

(i) Positive Moment Region

Assume N.A. in flange: treat as rectangular section.

$b = 1125$ mm
$b_w = 500$ mm
$A_s = 2000$ mm^2
$d = 335$ mm

a) Using Chart: Table 6.5

$$\rho' = 0: \rho n = \frac{A_s}{bd} \cdot n = \frac{2000}{(1125)(336)} \cdot 8.89$$

$$= 0.047$$

Read $I_{cr}/bd^3 = 0.031$

i.e. $I_{cr} = (0.031)(1125)(335)^3 = \underline{1323 \times 10^6 \text{ mm}^4}$

b) Alternatively using equations from Table 6.4

$$B = \frac{1125}{8.89(2000)} = 0.0633$$

$$kd = \frac{\sqrt{2(336)(0.0633) + 1} - 1}{0.0633}$$

$kd = 88.4 \text{ mm} < 200$

∴ N.A. in flange

$$I_{cr} = \frac{1125(88.4)^3}{3} + 8.89(2000)(336 - 88.4)^2$$
$$= \underline{1349 \times 10^6 \text{ mm}^4}$$

(ii) Negative Moment Region – Interior Support

Treat as rectangular section

b = 500 mm
A_s = 3000 mm²
A_s' = 1000 mm²
Note: Since the bottom bars are not developed as compression bars, their contribution could be neglected as a conservative assumption. We will include them here to illustrate the calculation procedure for compression steel.
d = 336 mm
d' = 64 mm

a) Using Chart: Table 6.5

$$\rho'n'(1 - d'/d) = \frac{1000(7.89)}{(500)(336)}(1 - \frac{64}{336})$$
$$= 0.0380$$

$$\rho n + \rho'n' = \frac{(3000)(8.89)}{(500)(336)} + \frac{(1000)(7.89)}{(500)(336)}$$
$$= 0.2057$$

Read $I_{cr}/bd^3 = 0.086$

d'/d = 64/336 = 0.19

Read $I_{cr}/bd^3 = 0.006$

Net value of $I_{cr}/bd^3 = 0.086 - 0.006 = 0.080$

i.e. $I_{cr} = (0.080)(500)(336)^3 = \underline{1517 \times 10^6 \text{ mm}^4}$

b) Alternatively using Equations from Table 6.4

$$B = \frac{500}{(8.89)(3000)} \qquad r = \frac{(7.89)(1000)}{(8.89)(3000)}$$
$$= 0.0187 \qquad = 0.296$$

$$kd =$$

$$\frac{\left[\sqrt{2(336)(0.0187)(1 + \frac{(0.296)(64)}{336}) + (1 + 0.296)^2} - (1 + 0.296)\right]}{0.0187}$$

$$= 137 \text{ mm}$$

$$I_{cr} = \frac{500(137)^3}{3} + 8.89(3000)(336 - 137)^2$$

$$+ 7.89(1000)(137 - 64)^2$$
$$= \underline{1527 \times 10^6 \text{ mm}^4}$$

7. Effective Moment of Inertia, I_e

(i) Positive Moment Region

a) Dead Load Level $(I_e)_D$

$$(I_e)_D = \left[(\frac{48.2}{104.5})^3 (3852) + (1 - (\frac{48.2}{104.5})^3)\right.$$
$$\left.(1349)\right](\times 10^6 \text{ mm}^4)$$

$$= 378 + 1217 = \underline{1595 \times 10^6 \text{ mm}^4}$$

b) Dead + Live Load Level $(I_e)_{D+L}$

$$(I_e)_{D+L} = \left[(\frac{48.2}{131.8})^3 (3852) + (1 - (\frac{48.2}{131.8})^3)\right.$$

$$\left.(1349)\right](\times 10^6 \text{ mm}^4)$$

$$= 188 + 1283 = \underline{1471 \times 10^6 \text{ mm}^4}$$

(ii) Negative Moment Region, Interior Support

a) Dead Load Level $(I_e)_D$

$$(I_e)_D = \left[(\frac{72.2}{151.7})^3 (3852) + (1 - (\frac{72.2}{151.7})^3)\right.$$
$$\left.(1527)\right] \times 10^6 \text{ mm}^4$$

$$= 415 + 1362 = \underline{1777 \times 10^6 \text{ mm}^4}$$

b) Dead + Live Load Level

$$(I_e)_{D+L} = \left[\left(\frac{72.2}{191.4}\right)^3 (3852) + \left(1 - \left(\frac{72.2}{191.4}\right)^3\right)\right.\times$$

$$\left.(1527)\right] \times 10^6 \text{ mm}^4$$

$$= 207 + 1445 = \underline{1652 \times 10^6 \text{ mm}^4}$$

(iii) Average I_e (Eq. 6.7)

a) Dead Load Level

$$(I_e) = [0.75(1595) + 0.25(1777)] \times$$
$$10^6 \text{ mm}^4$$
$$= \underline{1641 \times 10^6 \text{ mm}^4}$$

b) Dead + Live Load Level

$$(I_e)_{D+L} = [0.75(1471) + 0.25(1652)] \times$$
$$10^6 \text{ mm}^4 = \underline{1516 \times 10^6 \text{ mm}^4}$$

8. Immediate Deflection

$$\Delta = K(\frac{5}{48})\frac{M\ell^2}{E_c I_e}$$

a) Dead Load

$$K = (1.20 - 0.2 M_o/M_m) = (1.20 - 0.2$$
$$(183/104.5)) = 0.85$$

$$\Delta_D = (0.85)\,(\frac{5}{48})\,\frac{104.5 \times 6.75^2}{22,500 \times 1641} \times 10^6$$

$$= 11.4 \text{ mm}$$

b) Dead + Live Load

$$\Delta_{D+L} = 0.85\,(\frac{5}{48})\,\frac{131.8 \times 6.75^2}{22,500 \times 1516} \times 10^6$$

$$= 15.6 \text{ mm}$$

c) Live Load

$$\Delta_L = 15.6 - 11.4 = \underline{4.2 \text{ mm}}$$

d) Permissible Deflection (Table 6.3)

(i) $\ell/180 = 6750/180 = 37.5$ mm > 4.2 mm OK

(ii) $\ell/360 = 6750/360 = 18.8$ mm > 4.2 mm OK

9. Long-Time Deflection

$1 + 50\rho' = 1$ for positive moment

$$= 1 + 50\,\frac{(1000)}{(500)(336)}$$

$$= 1.30 \text{ for negative moment}$$

Average $= 0.75\,(1.0) + 0.25\,(1.30) = 1.08$

Assume nonstructural elements installed after 1 month.

Sustained Load Deflection at one month, $S = 0.5$

$$\Delta_{1 \text{ mo.}} = (1 + \frac{0.5}{1.08})\,11.4 + (1 + \frac{0.5}{1.08})\,(0.2)\,(4.2)$$

$$= 16.7 + 1.2 = \underline{17.9 \text{ mm}}$$

Sustained Load Deflection at 5 years, $S = 2.0$

$$\Delta_{1 \text{ yrs.}} = (1 + \frac{2.0}{1.08})\,11.4 + (1 + \frac{2.0}{1.08})\,(0.2)\,(4.2)$$

$$= 32.5 + 2.4 = 34.9 \text{ mm}$$

Incremental Deflection = 34.9 − 17.9 =   17.0 mm
Add Live Load Deflection = (0.8)(4.2) =   <u>3.4 mm</u>
  20.4 mm

Permissible Deflection (Table 6.3)

$\ell/240 = 6750/240 = 28.1$ mm > 20.4 mm   OK
$\ell/480 = 6750/480 = 14.0$ mm < 20.4 mm NOT OK

6.4.3 Computation of Immediate Deflection for Non-Prestressed Two-way Construction

An approximate procedure using the equations developed in Section 6.4.1 for one-way construction can be used to calculate deflections for two-way slab system designed by the Direct Design Method or Equivalent Frame Method of Clause 13 of CSA Standard A23.3. The basis for the procedure is illustrated in Fig. 6.2 where parts (a) and (b) of the figure were drawn assuming the edges parallel to ℓ_y and ℓ_x, respectively, do not deflect. The deflection, Δ_{mp}, at midpanel of a two-way slab can be considered as the sum of the column strip deflection Δ_c, and the deflection of the perpendicular middle strip deflection, Δ_m.

$$\Delta_{mp} = \Delta_{cx} + \Delta_{my} = \Delta_{cy} + \Delta_{mx} \qquad (6.15)$$

Both the column strip and middle strip can be treated as continuous beams for which the end moments and midspan moments are M_1, M_2, and M_m. These moments will have been calculated at factored load levels for proportioning flexural reinforcement. To calculate deflections the factored moments must be scaled down to the appropriate specified load level. Column and middle strip deflections can then be calculated using Eq. 6.1. However, in determining the coefficient K, the total static moment M_o should be calculated on the basis of the end moments and midspan moment, rather than the uniformly distributed applied load, w.

i.e.

$$M_o = \frac{1}{2}\,(M_1 + M_2) + M_m \qquad (6.16)$$

where M_1, M_2 = end moments
   M_m = midspan moment.

For irregular panel layouts and non-uniform loading conditions, computer based procedures such as the finite element method should be considered for calculating deflections.

As suggested in Ref. 2, effects of cracking may be included by applying the effective moment of inertia concept to element stiffness values in orthogonal reinforcement directions. Using a linear elastic plate bending program, bending moments in orthogonal reinforcement directions can be calculated ignoring effects of cracking. A second analysis can then be made with reduced stiffness values reflecting the ratio of cracking moment to applied moment in each element. This procedure can be automated as described in Ref. 3. It should be emphasized that a finite element or other type of analysis that does not include the effect of reduced stiffness due to cracking is likely to underestimate deflections by a significant amount.

Effective Moment of Inertia

I_e can be calculated for column and middle strips using the expressions given in Section 6.4.1 for beams. However, since slabs are generally lightly reinforced, with design moments in many cases less than the theoretical cracking moment, M_{cr}, the effects on deflection of cracking due to construction loads and shrinkage restraint must be considered (2, 3, 4, 5). Normal shoring and re-shoring procedures may induce construction loads in excess of twice the slab dead load at early age. Thus, the loads during construction may exceed the specified design loads leading to a greater degree of cracking than would be expected based on design loads alone. For multi-story construction it is suggested that I_e for all load cases be based on moments due to construction loads. A construction load of 2.0 to 2.2 times the slab dead load is suggested. Detailed procedures for calculating construction loads when the construction procedure is known are provided in Refs. 22, 23, and 24. To account for the effect of shrinkage restraint cracking, a reduced effective modulus of rupture of one-half the value given in CSA Standard A23.3 is used.

6.4.4 Computation of Long-Time Deflection for Two-Way Construction

The same procedures as outlined in Section 6.4.2 for one way systems can be used, by applying the long-time multipliers to immediate column and middle strip deflections.

6.4.5 Deflection Limits for Two-Way Construction

Deflection limits referred to in Section 6.3 apply to two-way as well as one-way construction. In two-way construction, three components of deflection should be considered, namely, column strip, middle strip, and mid-panel deflection. Span lengths to be used are the column

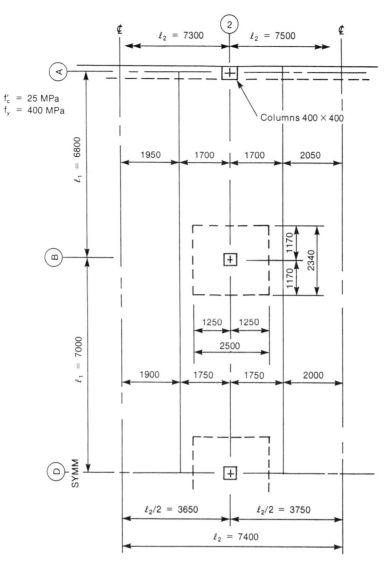

strip span for column strip deflection, middle strip span for middle strip deflection, and length of span measured diagonally between columns for mid-panel deflection.

Design Example 6.2

Required: Deflection calculations for two-way slab systems with drop panels. Calculations based on specified loads and $f_r = 0.3 \sqrt{f'_c}$ MPa.

Slab Thickness, $h_s = 170$ mm
Drop Panel Thickness, $h_d = 290$ mm

Minimum thickness, h_s (min):

$$h_s(\text{min}) = \frac{\ell_n(0.6 + fy/1000)}{30 \left[1 + \left(\dfrac{2x_d}{\ell_n}\right)\left(\dfrac{h_d - h_s}{h_s}\right)\right]} \quad \begin{array}{l} h_d = 290 \\ \\ h_s = 170 \end{array}$$

$\ell_n = 7000 - 400 = 6600$ mm

$x_d = 1170 - 200 = 970$ mm

$$h_s(\text{min}) = \frac{6600\,(0.6 + 0.4)}{30 \left[1 + \dfrac{2(970)}{6600} \cdot \left(\dfrac{290-170}{170}\right)\right]}$$

$$= \frac{220}{(1 + 0.207)} = 182 \text{ mm} > 170 \text{ mm}$$

∴ Deflection calculations required

Concrete compressive strength: $f'_c = 25$ MPa
Steel yield strength: $f_y = 400$ MPa

Deflection Limits:

a) Deflection due to live load: $\ell/360$
b) Deflection after attachment of non-structural elements: $\ell/480$

1. Slab design moments and reinforcement

    Design slab flexural reinf. using d = 170 mm and $h_d = 290$ mm

    Loads
w_{slab} = (170/1000)(2.4)(9.81)		= 4.0 kN/m²
w_{drop} = (120/1000)(2.4)(9.81)		= 0.4 kN/m²
(6.25/51.06)		
w_{SDL}		= 1.3 kN/m²
w_D		= 5.7 kN/m²
w_L		= 2.4 kN/m²
w_{D+L}		= 8.1 kN/m²

Total Static Moment, M_o (Span 1)

Specified Loads

$$M_o = \frac{(8.1)(7400)(6.4)^2}{8} \times 10^3 = 307 \times 10^6 \text{ N·mm}$$

Factored Loads

$$w_f = (1.25)(5.7) + (1.5)(2.4) = 10.7 \text{ kN/m}^2$$

$$M_o = \frac{(10.7)(7400)(6.4)^2}{8} \, 10^3 = 407 \times 10^6 \text{ N · mm}$$

Distribute M_o to Positive and Negative Moment, Column and Middle Strips by Direct Design Method

	(A)			(B)
M_o		407		$\times 10^6$ N·mm
	(M_1)	(M_m)	(M_2)	
M_{DES}	122	203	284	$\times 10^6$ N·mm
M_{COL}	115	122	213	$\times 10^6$ N·mm
M_{MID}	7	81	71	$\times 10^6$ N·mm
A_s (Col)	15–No. 15	16–No. 15	15–No. 15	
	(3000)	(3200)	(3000)	mm^2
A_s (Mid)	10–No. 15	11–No. 15	10–No. 15	
	(2000)	(2200)	(2000)	mm^2

2. Gross Moment of Inertia, I_g

    a) Column Strip (b = 3450)
        Midspan: $I_g = 1/12 \,(3450)(170)^3$
        $= 1412 \times 10^6$ mm^4
        Interior Support: $I_g = (0.071)(3450)(290)^3$
        (Table 6.7) $= 5970 \times 10^6$ mm^4

    b) Middle Strip (b = 3950)
        Midspan: $I_g = 1/12 \,(3950)(170)^3$
        $= 1617 \times 10^6$ mm^4
        Interior Support: I_g $= 1617 \times 10^6$ mm^4

3. Cracking Moment: $M_{cr} = \dfrac{f_r I_g}{y_t}$ $f_r = 0.3\sqrt{25}$
    $= 1.5$ MPa

    Column Strip

    Midspan: $M_{cr} = \dfrac{(1.5)(1412) \times 10^6}{(85)}$
    $= 25 \times 10^6$ N · mm

    Interior Support:

    $$M_{cr} = \frac{(1.5)(5970) \times 10^6}{(133)} = 67 \times 10^5 \text{ N·mm}$$

    Middle Strip

    Midspan: $M_{cr} = \dfrac{(1.5)(1617) \times 10^6}{85}$
    $= 28 \times 10^6$ N · mm

    Interior Support: $M_{cr} = 28 \times 10^6$ N·mm

4. Moments at Specified Load Level (Unfactored)

    a) Dead Load: $w_D/w_f = 5.7/10.7 = 0.53$
        $M_o = 214 \times 10^6$ N·mm

    b) Dead + Live Load: $w_{D+l}/w_f = 8.1/10.7 = 0.76$
        $M_o = 307 \times 10^6$ N·mm

Scale factored design moment to specified load level

		A		B
		M_1	M_m	M_2
a)	Dead Load			
	M_{COL}	61	65	113×10^6 N·mm
	M_{MID}	4	43	38×10^6 N·mm
b)	Dead + Live Load			
	M_{COL}	87	93	162×10^6 N·mm
	M_{MID}	5	62	54×10^6 N·mm

5. Moment of Inertia of Cracked Transformed Section, I_{cr}

    a) Column Strip

        Midspan: $A_s = 3200$ mm^2, b = 3450, d = 128 mm

        $$\rho_n = \frac{(3200)(8)}{(3450)(128)} = 0.058$$

        From Table 6.5 Read $I_{cr}/bd^3 = 0.035$

        $I_{cr} = (0.035)(3450)(128)^3 = \underline{253 \times 10^5 \text{ mm}^4}$

        Interior Support: $A_s = 3000$, b = 2500, d = 248

        $$\rho n = \frac{(3000)(8)}{(2500)(248)} = 0.039$$

        From Table 6.5 Read $I_{cr}/bd^3 = 0.026$

        $I_{cr} = (0.026)(2500)(248)^3 = \underline{990 \times 10^6 \text{ mm}^4}$

    b) Middle Strip: calculated as for column strip

        Midspan: $I_{cr} = \underline{182 \times 10^6 \text{ mm}^4}$

        Interior Support: $I_{cr} = \underline{166 \times 10^6 \text{ mm}^4}$

6. Effective Moment of Inertia

    Dead Load

        Column Strip

        Midspan:

        $I_e = [(25/65)^3 \, 1412 + [1 - (25/65)^3] \, 253]$
        $\times 10^6$ mm^4
        $= 80 + 238 = \underline{318 \times 10^6 \text{ mm}^4}$

        Interior Support:

        $I_e = [(57/113)^3 \, 5970 + [1 - (57/113)^3]$
        $990] \times 10^6$ mm^4
        $= 764 + 863 = 1627 \times 10^6$ mm^4

        Average $I_e = 0.75 \,(318) + 0.25 \,(1627)$
        $= 645 \times 10^6$ mm^4

Middle Strip

   Midspan:

$$I_e = [(28/43)^3 \, 1617 + [1 - (28/43)^3] \, 182] \\ \times 10^6 \text{ mm}^4 \\ = 446 + 132 = 578 \times 10^6 \text{ mm}^4$$

   Interior Support:

$$I_e = [(28/38)^3 \, 1617 + [1 - (28/38)^3] \, 166] \\ \times 10^6 \text{ mm}^4 \\ = 647 + 100 = 747 \times 10^6 \text{ mm}^4$$

Average $I_e = 0.75 \, (578) + 0.25 \, (747)$
$$= 620 \times 10^6 \text{ mm}^4$$

Similarly for other cases:

Dead + Live Load

   Column Strip

      Average $I_e = 554 \times 10^6 \text{ mm}^4$

   Middle Strip

      Average $I_e = 327 \times 10^6 \text{ mm}^4$

7.   Column Strip Deflections

  a) Dead Load Deflection

$$M_o = 1/2 \, (M_1 + M_2) + M_m = 1/2 \, (61 + 113) + 65 \\ = 152 \times 10^6 \text{ N·mm}$$
$$K = 1.20 - 0.20 \, (152/65) = 0.73$$
$$M_m = 65 \times 10^6 \text{ N·mm}$$
$$E_c = 22,500 \text{ MPa}$$
$$I_e = 645 \times 10^6 \text{ mm}^4$$

$$\Delta_D = (0.73)(\frac{5}{48}) \frac{(65 \times 10^6)(6.4)^2 \, (\times 10^6)}{(22,500)(645 \times 10^6)} \\ = 14 \text{ mm}$$

  b) Dead + Live Load Deflection

$$M_o = 1/2 \, (87 + 162) + 93 = 217 \times 10^6 \text{ N·mm}$$
$$K = 1.20 - 0.20 \, (217/93) = 0.73$$
$$M_m = 93 \times 10^6 \text{ N·mm}$$
$$I_e = 554 \times 10^6 \text{ mm}^4$$

$$\Delta_{D+L} = (0.73)(\frac{5}{48}) \frac{(93 \times 10^6)(6.4)^2 \, (\times 10^6)}{(22,500)(554 \times 10^6)} \\ = 23 \text{ mm}$$

  c) Live Load Deflection

$$\Delta_L = 23 - 14 = 9 \text{ mm}$$

  d) Permissible Live Load Deflection

$$\ell/360 = 6400/360 = 17.8 > 9 \text{ mm} \qquad \text{OK}$$

  e) Long Time Deflection

$$\rho' = 0$$

Assume non-structural elements installed after 1 month, and 20% live load sustained.

Sustained Load Deflection at 1 month: S = 0.5

$$\Delta_{1mo} = (1 + 0.5)(14) + (1 + 0.5)(0.2)(9) \\ = 21 + 2.7 = 23.7 \text{ mm}$$

Sustained Load Deflection at $\geq$ 5 years: S = 2.0

$$\Delta_{5yr} = (1 + 2)(14) + (1 + 2)(0.2)(9) \\ = 42 + 5.4 = 47.4 \text{ mm}$$

Incremental Deflection = 47.4 − 23.7 = 23.7
Add Live Load Deflection = (0.8)(9) =   7.2

                            30.9 mm

  f) Permissible Long-Time Deflection

$$\ell/480 = 6400/480 = 13.3 \text{ mm} < 30.9 \text{ mm} \\ \text{NOT OK}$$

8.   Middle Strip Deflections

  a) Dead Load Deflection

$$K = 0.80 \text{ (Assume fixed-hinged condition)}$$
$$M_m = 43 \times 10^6 \text{ N·mm}$$
$$I_e = 620 \times 10^6 \text{ mm}^4$$

$$\Delta_D = (0.80) \frac{5}{48} \frac{(43 \times 10^6)(6.4)^2 \times 10^6}{(22,500)(620 \times 10^6)} \\ = 10.5 \text{ mm}$$

  b) Dead ı Live Load Deflection

$$M_m = 62 \times 10^6 \text{ N·mm}$$
$$I_e = 327 \times 10^6 \text{ mm}^4$$

$$\Delta_{D+L} = (0.80) \, (\frac{5}{48}) \frac{(62 \times 10^6)(6.4)^2 \times 10^6}{(22,500)(327 \times 10^6)} \\ = 28.8 \text{ mm}$$

  c) Live Load Deflection

$$\Delta_L = 28.8 - 10.5 = 18.3 \text{ mm}$$

  d) Permissible Live Load Deflection

$$\ell/360 = 17.8 < 18.3 \text{ mm} \qquad \text{NOT OK}$$

  e) Long Time Deflection

$$\Delta_{1mo} = (1 + 0.5)(10.5) + (1 + 0.5)(0.2)(18.3) \\ = 21.3 \text{ mm}$$

$$\Delta_{5yr} = (1 + 2)(10.5) + (1 + 2)(0.2)(18.3) \\ = 42.5 \text{ mm}$$

Incremental Deflection = 42.5 − 21.3 = 21.2 mm
Add Live Load Deflection = (0.8)(18.3) = 14.6 mm

                            35.8 mm

  f) Permissible Long-Time Deflection

$$\ell/480 = 13.3 < 35.8 \text{ mm} \qquad \text{NOT OK}$$

9.   Mid Panel Deflections

Midpanel deflection is obtained by superimposing orthogonal column and middle strip deflections

$$\Delta_{mp} = \Delta_c + \Delta_m$$

In this example, deflections were calculated for parallel column and middle strip deflections. However, these calculated deflections will be used, assuming orthogonal strips, to illustrate the calculation of mid-panel deflections.

  a) Span length $= \sqrt{6.4^2 + 6.4^2} = \sqrt{81.92} = 9.0 \text{ m}$
     (Measured diagonally between columns)

  b) Dead Load Deflection

$$\Delta_{mp} = 14 + 10.5 = 24.5 \text{ mm}$$

c) Dead + Live Load Deflection

$\Delta_{mp} = 23 + 28.8 = 51.8$ mm

d) Live Load Deflection

$\Delta_{mp} = 51.8 - 24.5 = 27.3$ mm

e) Permissible Live Load Deflection

$\ell/360 = 9000/360 = 25$ mm < 27.3 mm

NOT OK

f) Long Time Deflection

$\Delta_{mp} = 28.9 + 35.8 = 64.7$ mm

g) Permissible Long Time Deflection

$\ell/480 = 9000/480 = 18.8$ mm < 64.7 mm

NOT OK

Design Example 6.3

Required: Repeat example 6.2 using construction loads and $f_r = 0.3 \sqrt{f_c'}$ MPa.

1. See design example 6.2 for calculation of I_g, I_{cr}, and deflection limits

2. Loads

$w_{slab} = 4.0$ kN/m^2
$w_{drop} = \underline{0.4}$ kN/m^2
$\qquad\quad 4.4$ kN/m^2

Allowance for Construction Loads $\times \quad \underline{2.2}$
$\qquad\qquad\qquad\qquad\qquad\qquad\quad 9.7$ kN/m^2

(ie. max load on slab during construction is 2.2 × (slab dead load))

3. Moments

Factored D + L from example 6.2 = 10.7 kN/m^2.
Scale factored moments from Design Example 6.2 by 9.7/10.7 = 0.907

	A		B
	M_1	M_m	M_2
M_{col}	104	111	193×10^6 N·mm
M_{cr}		25	67×10^6 N·mm
I_g		1412	2970×10^6 mm^4
I_{cr}		253	990×10^6 mm^4
I_e			
(See step 4 below)		< 499 >	$\times 10^6$ mm^4
M_{Mid}	6	73	64×10^6 N·mm^4
M_{cr}		28	28×10^6 N·mm
I_g		1617	1617×10^6 mm^4
I_{cr}		182	166×10^6 mm^4
I_e			
(See step 4 below)		< 268 >	$\times 10^6$ mm^4

4. Effective Moment of Inertia (See Example 6.2, step 6 for calculation procedure)

Column Strip

Average $I_e = 499 \times 10^6$ mm^4

Middle Strip

Average $I_e = 268 \times 10^6$ mm^4

5. Column Strip Deflection (due to construction load)

$M_o = 1/2 (104 + 193) + 111 = 260 \times 10^6$ N·mm
$K = 0.73$
$M_m = 111 \times 10^6$ N·mm
$E_c = 22,500$ MPa
$I_e = 499 \times 10^6$ mm^4

$\Delta_{const} = (0.73) \left(\dfrac{5}{48}\right) \dfrac{(111 \times 10^6)(6.4)^2(\times 10^6)}{(22500)(499 \times 10^6)}$

$\qquad = 30.8$ mm

$\Delta_D = 30.8 (5.7/9.7) = 18.1$ mm
$\Delta_L = 30.8 (2.4/9.7) = 7.6$ mm
$\ell/360 = 6400/360 = 17.8 > 7.6$ mm $\qquad$ OK

Long-time Deflection

$\Delta_{1mo} = (1 + 0.5)(18.1) + (1 + 0.5)(0.2)(7.6)$
$\qquad = 29.4$ mm

$\Delta_{5yr} = (1 + 2)(18.1) + (1 + 2)(0.2)(7.6)$
$\qquad = 58.9$ mm

Incremental Deflection = $58.9 - 29.4 = \quad 29.5$
Add Live Load Deflection = $(0.8)(7.6) = \quad \underline{6.1}$
$\qquad\qquad\qquad\qquad\qquad\qquad\quad 35.6$ mm

$\ell/480 = 6400/480 = 13.3 < 35.6$ mm $\qquad$ NOT OK

6. Middle Strip Deflection

$M_o = 1/2 (6 + 64) + 73 = 108 \times 10^6$ N·mm
$K = 0.80$
$M_m = 73 \times 10^6$ N·mm
$E_c = 22,500$ MPa
$I_e = 268 \times 10^6$ mm^4

$\Delta_{cont} = (0.80) \dfrac{5}{48} \dfrac{(73 \times 10^6)(6.4)^2(\times 10^6)}{(22,500)(268 \times 10^6)}$

$\qquad = 41.3$ mm

$\Delta_D = 41.3 (5.7/9.7) = 24.3$ mm
$\Delta_L = 41.3 (2.4/9.7) = 10.2$ mm

$\ell/360 = 6400/360 = 17.8 > 10.2$ mm $\qquad$ OK

Long Term Deflection

$\Delta_{1mo} = (1 + 0.5)(24.3) + (1 + 0.5)(0.2)(10.2)$
$\qquad = 39.6$ mm

$\Delta_{5yr} = (1 + 2)(24.3) + (1 + 2)(0.2)(10.2)$
$\qquad = 79.0$ mm

Incremental Deflection = $79.0 - 39.6 = \quad 39.4$
Add Live Load Deflection = $\qquad\qquad\quad \underline{10.2}$
$\qquad\qquad\qquad\qquad\qquad\qquad\quad 49.6$ mm

$\ell/480 = 6400/480 = 13.3 < 49.6$ mm $\qquad$ NOT OK

7. Mid-Panel Deflections

$\Delta_L = 7.6 + 10.2 = 17.8 < 25.0$ mm $\qquad$ OK
$\Delta_{LT} = 35.6 + 49.6 = 85.2 > 18.8$ mm $\qquad$ NOT OK

8. Discussion

Calculated deflections and deflection limits for the two-way slab examples 6.2 and 6.3 are summarized in Table A. The sensitivity of calculated deflections to effects of construction loads is evident from the significant differences between calculated deflections occurring after attachment of non-structural elements for the two cases considered. For these examples the slab did not meet minimum thickness requirements and for all three cases, specified deflection limits were exceeded.

*6.5 NON-PRESTRESSED COMPOSITE MEMBERS

6.5.1 Minimum Thickness

In the case of shored composite members, the minimum thicknesses in Table 6.1 (CSA Standard A23.3 Table 9.1) apply as for monolithic T-beams. In the case of unshored construction, if the thickness of a non-prestressed precast member meets the requirements of Table 6.1, deflections need not be computed, according to Clause 9.8.5.1. Clause 9.8.5.2 also states that, if the thickness of an unshored non-prestressed composite member meets the requirements of Table 6.1, deflections occurring after the member becomes composite, need not be calculated. However, the long-time deflection of the precast members should be investigated for the magnitude and duration of load prior to the beginning of effective composite action. It should be noted that these comments refer only to the conditions in Table 6.1.

6.5.2 Computation of Deflection

The ultimate (in time) deflection of unshored and shored composite members is computed by Eqs. (6-17) to (6-20).** Subscripts 1 and 2 are used to refer to the slab (or effect of the slab under dead load) and precast beam, respectively.

These procedures are illustrated for a composite beam in which both unshored and shored construction is assumed. Examples 6.4 and 6.5 demonstrate the beneficial effect of shoring on deflections.

Unshored Composite Members

$$
\overbrace{(1)}^{} \quad \overbrace{\quad(2)\quad}^{} \quad \overbrace{\quad\quad(3)\quad\quad}^{} \quad \overbrace{\quad(4)\quad}^{}
$$

$$
\Delta_u = (\Delta_i)_2 + 0.70\, k_r\, (\Delta_i)_2 + 0.90\, k_r\, (\Delta_i)_2 \frac{I_2}{I_c} + 0.20\, \Delta_{sh}
$$

$$
\overbrace{(5)}^{} \quad \overbrace{(6)}^{} \quad \overbrace{\quad(7)\quad}^{} \quad \overbrace{(8)}^{}
$$

$$
+ 0.80\, \Delta_{sh} \frac{I_2}{I_c} + (\Delta_i)_1 + 1.40\, k_r\, (\Delta_i)_1 \frac{I_2}{I_c} + \Delta_{DS}
$$

$$
\overbrace{(9)}^{} \quad \overbrace{(10)}^{}
$$

$$
+ (\Delta_i)_L + (\Delta_{cp})_L \tag{6-17}
$$

When $k_r = 0.85$ (no compression steel in precast beam) and Δ_{DS} is assumed to be equal to $0.50\,(\Delta_i)_1$, Eq. (6-17) reduces to Eq. (6-18).

$$
\overbrace{\quad\quad(1 + 2 + 3)\quad\quad}^{} \quad \overbrace{\quad(4 + 5)\quad}^{}
$$

$$
\Delta_u = (1.60 + 0.77\, \frac{I_2}{I_c})\,(\Delta_i)_2 + (0.20 + 0.80\, \frac{I_2}{I_c})\, \Delta_{sh}
$$

$$
\overbrace{\quad(6 + 7 + 8)\quad}^{} \quad \overbrace{(9)}^{} \quad \overbrace{(10)}^{}
$$

$$
+ (1.50 + 1.19\, \frac{I_2}{I_c})\,(\Delta_i)_1 + (\Delta_i)_L + (\Delta_{cp})_L \tag{6-18}
$$

---

* Note: Section 6.5 was originally prepared by Professor Dan E. Branson for a previous edition of the CPCA Metric Design Handbook
** Derived in detail in References 6 and 7.

Term (1) is the initial dead load deflection of the precast beam using Eq. (6.1).

In Eq. (6.1) $M = M_2 =$ midspan moment due to precast beam dead load. For computing $(I_e)_2$ in Eq. (6.2), M_a refers to the precast beam dead load and M_{cr}, I_g, I_{cr}, to the precast beam.

Term (2) is the dead load creep deflection of the precast beam up to the time of slab casting ($C_t = 0.70$ part of 1.60).

From Eq. (6-10), $k_r = 0.85/(1 + 50\,\rho')$, where ρ' refers to the compressive steel in the precast beam at midspan.

Term (3) is the creep deflection of the composite beam following slab casting due to the precast beam dead load ($C_t = 0.90$ part of 1.60).

The ratio, I_2/I_c, modifies the initial stress (strain) and accounts for the effect of the composite section in restraining additional creep curvature (strain) after the composite section becomes effective. As a simple approximation, use $I_2/I_c = ((I_2/I_c)_g + (I_2/I_c)_{cr})/2$.

Term (4) is the deflection due to shrinkage warping of the precast beam up to the time of slab casting (20% of total shrinkage), using Eqs. (6-12) and (6-13).

Term (5) is the shrinkage deflection of the composite beam following slab casting due to the shrinkage of the precast beam concrete (80% of total shrinkage), but not including the effect of differential shrinkage and creep which is given by Term (8).

Term (6) is the initial deflection of the precast beam under slab dead load. For incremental deflections, $(\Delta_i)_1 = ((\Delta_i)_1 + (\Delta_i)_2) - (\Delta_i)_2$, where $((\Delta_i)_1 + (\Delta_i)_2) =$ Eq. (6-1), with $M = M_1 + M_2$ $(\Delta_i)_2$ is from Term (1), and $M_1 =$ midspan moment due to the slab dead load. For computing $(I_e)_{1+2}$ in Eq. (6-2), M_a refers to the precast beam plus slab dead load and M_{cr}, I_g, I_{cr}, to the precast beam. When partitions, roofing, etc., are placed at the same time as the slab, or soon thereafter, their dead load is also included in M_1 and M_a.

Term (7) is the creep deflection of the composite beam due to slab dead load.

$C_t = 1.40$ (instead of 1.60) is used because of the later loading age.

Term (8) is the deflection due to differential shrinkage and creep.***

As an approximation, use $\Delta_{DS} = 0.50\,(\Delta_i)_1$, where $(\Delta_i)_1$ is based on the slab dead load deflection only in Term (6).

Term (9) is the initial live load (plus other loads applied to the composite beam and not included in Term (6) deflection of the composite beam using Eq. (6-1) with $M = M_L$ and $I_e = (I_c)_{cr}$.

This is a simple approximation used instead of the usual incremental deflection calculation with I_e, since the incremental loads are resisted by different sections (members).

Term (10) is the partial live load creep deflection for any sustained live load (and other loads) applied to the composite beam, using Eq. (6-10) in which ρ' refers to any slab compression steel that may be taken into account.

***Details can be found in References 6 and 7.

Shored Composite Beams

(assuming the composite beam supports all dead and live load).

$$\underbrace{\Delta_u = (\Delta_i)_{1+2}}_{(1)} + \underbrace{1.80\, k_r\, (\Delta_i)_{1+2}}_{(2)} + \underbrace{\Delta_{sh}\frac{I_2}{I_c}}_{(3)}$$

$$+ \underbrace{\Delta_{DS}}_{(4)} + \underbrace{(\Delta_i)_L}_{(5)} + \underbrace{(\Delta_{cp})_L}_{(6)} \qquad (6\text{-}19)$$

When $k_r = 0.85$ (neglecting any effect of slab compression steel) and Δ_{DS} is assumed to be equal to $(\Delta_i)_{1+2}$, Eq. (6-19) reduces to Eq. (6-20).

$$\Delta_u = \underbrace{3.53\,(\Delta_i)_{1+2}}_{(1+2+4)} + \underbrace{\Delta_{sh}\frac{I_2}{I_c}}_{(3)} + \underbrace{(\Delta_i)_L}_{(5)} + \underbrace{(\Delta_{cp})_L}_{(6)}$$

Term (1) is the initial deflection of the composite beam due to slab plus precast beam dead load (plus partitions, roofing, etc.) using Eq. (6-1), with $M = M_1 + M_2 =$ midspan moment due to span plus precast beam (etc.) dead load.

For computing $(I_e)_{1+2}$ in Eq. (6-2), M_a refers to the moment, $M_1 + M_2$, and M_{cr}, I_g, I_{cr}, to the composite section.

Term (2) is the creep deflection of the composite beam due to the dead load in Term (1).

$C_t = 1.80$ (instead of 1.60) because of a typical loading age for the slab concrete when the shores are removed.

From Eq. (6-10), $k_r = 0.85/(1 + 50\,\rho')$, where ρ' refers to any slab compression steel that may be taken into account.

Term (3) is the shrinkage deflection of the composite beam after the shores are removed due to the shrinkage of the precast beam concrete, but not including the effect of differential shrinkage and creep which is given by Term (4).

Eqs. (6-12) and (6-13) may be used with $\Delta_{sh} = 300 \times 10^{-6}$ mm/mm. The ratio, I_2/I_c, is explained in Term (3) of Eq. (6-17).

Term (4) is the deflection due to differential shrinkage and creep.*

As an approximation, use $\Delta_{DS} = (\Delta_i)_{1+2}$, where $(\Delta_i)_{1+2}$ is based on the slab plus precast beam dead load deflection only in Term (1).

Term (5) is the initial live load deflection of the composite beam using Eq. (6-1).

The calculation for the incremental live load deflection follows the same procedure as that for a monolithic beam.

Term (6) is the partial live load creep deflection for any sustained live load.

This is the same as Term (10) of Eq. (6-17).

The calculation of deflection for the shored composite beam is essentially the same as for a monolithic beam, except for the deflection due to shrinkage warping of the precast beam which is resisted by the composite section, and the deflection due to differential shrinkage and creep

of the composite beam. These effects are represented by Terms (3) and (4) in Eq. (6-19).

6.5.3 Permissible Deflection

The maximum permissible computed deflections are given in Table 6.3.

Example 6.4   Unshored Non-Prestressed Composite Beam, Normal Density Concrete

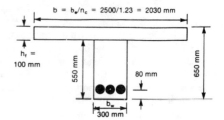

Given: Slab: $(E_c)_1 = 22,600$ MPa
Precast Beam: $(E_c)_2 = 27,700$
$(f_r)_2 = 3.29$ MPa

$f_y = 350$ MPa
Simple span = 10 m
Beam spacing = 2.5 m
Live load = 3.5 kN/m^2
$A_s = 3 - $ No. 30 = 2100 mm^2
$b_e = 0.4\,(10,000) = 4000$ mm
or spacing = 2500 mm Use
or 24 (100) + 300 = 2700 mm

Required: Deflection analysis

1. Loads and moments:

$w_1 = (2400$ kg/m$^3)$ (1.04 for steel) $\times$ (0.00981 kN/m^3 per kg/m$^3)\times$ (0.100 $\times$ 2.500) = 6.12 kN/m
$w_2 = (2400)$ (1.04) (0.00981) (0.300 $\times$ 0.550)
      = 4.04 kN/m
$w_L = (3.5$ kN/m$^2)$ (2.500 m) = 8.75 kN/m
$M_1 = w_1\ell^2/8 = (6.12)\,(10)^2/8 = 76.5$ kN·m
$M_2 = w_2\ell^2/8 = (4.04)\,(10)^2/8 = 50.5$ kN·m
$M_L = w_L\ell^2/8 = (8.75)\,(10)^2/8 = 109.4$ kN·m

2. Minimum thickness:

Min. $h = \ell/17.4 = 10,000/17.4 = 575$ mm, which is met by the composite beam, but not by the precast beam. Hence, for members not supporting or attached to partitions or other construction likely to be damaged by deflections (condition in Table 6.3), only the long-time deflection of the precast beam before composite action is effective need be investigated. However, deflections will be calculated and compared with all allowable values in CSA Standard A23.3, Table 6.3.

3. Modulus of rupture, modulus of elasticity, modular ratios:

$(E_c)_1 = 22,600$ MPa
$(f_r)_2 = 3.29$ MPa
$(E_c)_2 = 27,700$ MPa
$n_c = (E_c)_2/(E_c)_1 = 27,700/22,600 = 1.23$
$E_s = 200,000$ MPa, $n = E_s/(E_c)_2 = 200/27.7 = 7.2$

---

*Details can be found in References 6 and 7.

4. Gross and cracked section moments of inertia:

Precast Section

I_g = b h³/12 = (300)(550)³/12 = 4159 × 10⁶ mm⁴
I_{cr} = 1851 × 10⁶ mm⁴ (Table 6.4)
Check by Table 6.5, OK

Composite Section

y_t = 454 mm (Table 6.6), I_g = 13,940 × 10⁶ mm⁴
(Table 6.6). Check by Table 6.9, OK
I_{cr} = 3972 × 10⁶ mm⁴ (Table 6.4 since a < h_f).
Check by Table 6.5, OK
$I_2/I_c = [(I_2/I_c)_g + (I_2/I_c)_{cr}]/2$ (Term 3 of Eq. (6-16)
= [(4159/13,940) + (1851/3972)]/2 = 0.382

5. Effective moments of inertia:

In Term (1), Eq. (6-17) − Precast section,

M_{cr} = $f_r I_g/y_t$ = (3.29)(4159 × 10⁶)(10)⁻⁶ ÷ 275
= 49.8 kN·m
M_{cr}/M_2 = 49.8/50.5 = 0.986, (0.986)³ = 0.959
$(I_e)_2$ = $(M_{cr}/M_2)^3 I_g + [1 − (M_{cr}/M_2)^3] I_{cr}$
= (0.959)(4159 × 10⁶) + [1 − 0.959] ×
(1851 × 10⁶)
= 4060 × 10⁶ mm⁴

In Term (6), Eq. (6-17) − Precast section,

$M_{cr}/(M_1 + M_2)$ = 49.8/(76.5 + 50.5) = 0.392, (0.392)³
= 0.060
$(I_e)_{1+2}$ = (0.060)(4159 × 10⁶) + [1 − 0.060] (1851 × 10⁶) = 1990 × 10⁶ mm⁴

6. Deflections:

Solution by Eq. (6-17)

Term (1), $(\Delta_i)_2 = \dfrac{K(5/48) M_2 \ell^2}{(E_c)_2 (I_c)_2}$

$= \dfrac{(1)(5/48)(50.5)(10)^2(10)^{12}}{(27,700)(4060 \times 10^6)}$

= 4.68 mm

Term (2), k_r = 0.85 (no precast beam compression steel)
$0.70 k_r (\Delta_i)_2$ = (0.70)(0.85)(4.68)
= 2.8 mm

Term (3), $0.90 k_r (\Delta_i)_2 \dfrac{I_2}{I_c}$ = (0.90)(0.85)(4.68)(0.382)

= 1.4 mm

Term (4), K_{sh} = 0.125, ρ' = 0
ρ = 100 (2100)/((300)(470)) = 1.49%
From Table 6.10, A_{sh} = 0.80
ϕ_{sh} = $A_{sh}\varepsilon_{sh}/h$ = (0.80)(400 × 10⁻⁶)/550
= 0.58 × 10⁻⁶
Δ_{sh} = $K_{sh}\phi_{sh}\ell^2$ = (0.125)(0.58 × 10⁻⁶)(10,000)²
= 7.25 mm
$0.20\Delta_{sh}$ = (0.20)(7.25) = 1.5 mm

Term (5), $0.80 \Delta_{sh} \dfrac{I_2}{I_c}$ = (0.80)(7.25)(0.382)

= 2.2 mm

Term (6), $(\Delta_i)_1 = \dfrac{K(5/48)(M_1 + M_2)\ell^2}{(E_c)_2(I_e)_{1+2}} - (\Delta_i)_2$

$= \dfrac{(1)(5/48)(76.5 + 50.5)(10)^2(10)^{12}}{(27,700)(1990 \times 10^6)} - 4.68$

= 19.32 mm

Term (7), $1.40 k_r (\Delta_i)_1 \dfrac{I_2}{I_c}$ = (1.40)(0.85)(19.32)(0.382)

= 8.8 mm

Term (8), Δ_{DS} = 0.50 $(\Delta_i)_1$ = (0.50)(19.32)
= 9.7 mm (rough estimate)

Term (9), $(\Delta_i)_: = \dfrac{K(5/48)M_L\ell^2}{(E_c)_2(I_c)_{cr}}$

$= \dfrac{(1)(5/48)(109.4)(10)^2(10)^{12}}{(27,700)(3972 \times 10^6)}$

= 10.4 mm

$\qquad$(1)$\quad$(2)$\quad$(3)$\quad$(4)$\quad$(5)$\quad$(6)$\quad$(7)$\quad$(8)$\quad$(9)
Δ_u = 4.7 + 2.8 + 1.4 + 1.5 + 2.2 + 19.3 + 8.8 + 9.7 + 10.4

= 60.8 mm (Solution by Eq. (6-17))

Checking solution by Eq. (6-18)

Δ_u = $(1.60 + 0.77 \dfrac{I_2}{I_c}) (\Delta_i)_2 + (0.20 + 0.80 \dfrac{I_2}{I_c}) \Delta_{sh}$

$\quad + (1.50 + 1.19 \dfrac{I_2}{I_c}) (\Delta_i) + (\Delta_i)_L$

= (1.60 + 0.77 × 0.382) (4.68)
+ (0.20 + 0.80 × 0.382) (7.25)
+ (1.50 + 1.19 × 0.382) (19.32) + 10.4
= 60.7 mm $\qquad$ OK

Assuming non-structural elements are installed after the composite slab has hardened, $\Delta_t + \Delta_L$ = Terms (3) + (5) + (7) + (8) + (9) = 1.4 + 2.2 + 8.8 + 9.7 + 10.4 = 32.5 mm should be a reasonable estimate.

Comparison with allowable deflections in CSA Standard A23.3: Flat roofs not supporting or attached to non-structural elements likely to be damaged by large deflections − $(\Delta_i)_L \le \ell/180$ = 10,000/180 = 56 mm versus 10 mm. $\qquad$ OK

Floors not supporting or attached to non-structural elements likely to be damaged by large deflections − $\Delta_t + (\Delta_i)_L \le \ell/360$ = 10,000/360 = 28 mm versus 10 mm. OK

Roof or floor construction supporting or attached to non-structural elements likely to be damaged by large deflections $\Delta_t + (\Delta_i)_L \le \ell/480$ = 10,000/480 = 21 mm versus 33 mm. $\qquad$ NOT OK

Roof or floor construction supporting or attached to non-structural elements not likely to be damaged by large deflections − $\Delta_t + (\Delta_i)_L \le \ell/240$ = 10,000/240 = 42 mm versus 33 mm. $\qquad$ OK

Example 6.5$\quad$Shored Non-Prestressed Composite Beam, Normal Density Concrete

Given: $\quad$ Same as Example 6.4, except using shored construction.

Required· $\quad$ Deflection analysis

1. Effective moments of inertia:
In Term (1), Eq. (6-19) − Composite section,

M_{cr} = $f_r I_g/y_t$ = (3.29)(13,940 × 10⁶)(10)⁻⁶/454

$= 101.0$ kN·m

$M_{cr}/(M_1 + M_2) = 101.0/(76.5 + 50.5) = 0.795,$
$(0.795)^3$

$\qquad = 0.502$

$(I_e)_{1+2} = (M_{cr}/M_{1+2})^3 I_g + [1 - (M_{cr}/M_{1+2})^3] I_{cr}$
$\qquad = (0.502)(13,490 \times 10^6) +$
$\qquad \quad [1 - 0.502] (3972 \times 10^6)$
$\qquad = 8980 \times 10^6$ mm^4

In Term (5), Eq. (6-19) − Composite section.

$M_{cr}/(M_1 + M_2 + M_L) = 101.0/(76.5 + 50.5 + 109.4)$
$\qquad = 0.427, (0.427)^3 = 0.078$

$(I_e)_{D+L} = (0.078)(13,940 \times 10^6) +$
$\qquad \quad [1 - 0.078] (3972 \times 10^6)$
$\qquad = 4750 \times 10^6$ mm^4

2. Deflections:

Solution by Eq. (6-19)

Term (1), $(\Delta_i)_{1+2} = \dfrac{K (5/48)(M_1 + M_2) \ell^2}{(E_c)_2 (I_e)_{1+2}}$

$\qquad = \dfrac{(1)(5/48)(76.5 + 50.5)(10)^2(10)^{12}}{(27,700)(8980 \times 10^6)}$

$\qquad = 5.32$ mm

Term (2), $k_r = 0.85$ (neglecting effect of any slab compression steel)
$1.80 k_r (\Delta_i)_{1+2} = (1.80)(0.85)(5.32) = 8.1$ mm

Term (3), using $\varepsilon_{sh} = 300 \times 10^{-6}$ mm/mm instead of 400×10^{-6}

From Ex. 6.5, $\Delta_{sh} = (7.25)(300/400) = 5.44$ mm

$\Delta_{sh} \dfrac{I_2}{I_c} = (5.44)(0.382) = 2.1$ mm

Term (4), $\Delta_{DS} = (\Delta_i)_{1+2} = 5.3$ mm (rough estimate)

Term (5), $(\Delta_i)_L = \dfrac{K (5/48)(M_{D+L}) \ell^2}{(E_c)_2 (I_e)_{D+L}} - (\Delta_i)_{1+2}$

$\qquad = \dfrac{(1)(5/48)(76.5 + 50.5 + 109.4)(10)^2(10)^{12}}{(27,700)(4750 \times 10^6)} - 53$

$\qquad = 13.4$ mm

$\qquad$ (1) $\quad$ (2) $\quad$ (3) $\quad$ (4) $\quad$ (5)
$\Delta_u = 5.3 + 8.1 + 2.1 + 5.3 + 13.4 = 34.2$ mm

(Solution by Eq. (6-19) versus 60.8 mm in Ex. 6.4 Step 6 for the unshored case.

Checking solution by Eq. (6-20)

$\Delta_u = 3.53 (\Delta_i)_{1+2} + \Delta_{sh} \dfrac{I_2}{I_c} + (\Delta_i)_L$

$\qquad = (3.53) (5.32) + 2.1 + 13.4 = 34.3$ mm $\qquad$ OK

Assuming non-structural elements are installed after the shores are removed, $\Delta_t + (\Delta)_L$ will be taken as $\Delta_u - (\Delta_i)_{1+2} = 34.2 - 5.3 = 28.9$ mm versus 32.5 mm in Ex. 6.5 for the unshored case. In both the unshored (Ex. 6.4) and shored (Ex. 6.5) cases, three of the four deflection criteria in CSA Standard A23.3, Table 5, are met, but not the most stringent limitation of $\Delta_t + (\Delta)_L \leq \ell/480 = 10,000/480 = 21$ mm versus 29 mm in Ex. 6.5 and 33 mm in Ex. 6.4.

6.6 CONCLUDING REMARKS

For additional information on deflections of concrete members the reader is referred to the references listed in Section 6.7.

6.7 REFERENCES

1. Subcommittee 1, ACI Committee 435, "Allowable Deflections," ACI Journal, Proceedings V. 65, No. 6, June 1968, pp. 433-444. Also ACI Manual of Concrete Practice, Part 2.

2. Scanlon, A. and Murray, D. W., "Practical Calculation of Two-Way Slab Deflections," Concrete International, November 1983, pp. 43-50.

3. Graham, C. J., and Scanlon, A., "Deflection of Reinforced Concrete Slabs under Construction Loading," Structural Engineering Report No. 117, The University of Alberta, August, 1984, 201 pp.

4. Sbarounis, J. A., "Multi-story Flat Plate Buildings: Effect of Construction Loads on Long-Term Deflections," Concrete International, Vol. 6, No. 4, April 1984, pp. 62-70.

5. Jokinsen, E. P. and Scanlon, A., "Field-Measured Two-Way Slab Deflections," Proceedings of Annual Conference, Canadian Society for Civil Engineering, Saskatoon, Saskatchewan, May, 1985.

6. Branson, D. E. Deformation of Concrete Structures, McGraw-Hill Advanced Book Program, 1977, pp. 1-546.

7. Branson, D. E., Chapter 4 − "Reinforced Concrete Composite Flexural Members," Handbook of Composite Construction Engineering, Editor, G. M. Sabnis, Van Nostrand Reinhold Co., 1978.

8. ACI Committee 435, "Deflections of Reinforced Concrete Flexural Members," ACI Journal, Proceedings V. 63, No. 6, June 1966, pp. 637-674. Also ACI Manual of Concrete Practice, Part 2.

9. American Concrete Institute, "Designing for Effects of Creep, Shrinkage, and Temperature in Concrete Structures," ACI Publication SP 27, 1970, pp. 1-430.

10. Subcommittee 2, ACI Committee 435, "Variability of Deflections of Simply Supported Reinforced Concrete Beams," ACI Journal, Proceedings, V. 69, No. 1, Jan. 1972, pp. 29-35, Discussion in ACI Journal, Proceedings, V 69, No. 7, July 1972, pp. 449-451, Also ACI Manual of Concrete Practice, Part 2.

11. Subcommittee 5, ACI Committee 435, "State-of-the-Art Report: Deflection of Two-Way Reinforced Concrete Floor Systems," ACI Publication SP-43, 1974, pp. 55-81.

12. Subcommittee 7, ACI Committee 435, "Deflections of Continuous Concrete Beams," ACI Journal, Proceedings V. 70, No. 12, Dec. 1973, pp. 781-787. Also ACI Manual of Concrete Practice, Part 2.

13. American Concrete Institute, "Deflections of Concrete Structures," ACI Publication SP 43, 1974, pp. 1-637.

14. Building Code Subcommittee, ACI Committee 435, "Proposed ACI Code and Commentary Provision on Deflections," Nov. 1975, April 1977, pp. 1-25.

15. Branson, D. E., "Instantaneous and Time-Dependent Deflections of Simple and Continuous Reinforced Concrete Beams," HPR Report No. 7,

Part 1, Alabama Highway Department, Bureau of Public Roads, Aug. 1963., p. 1-78.

16. Lutz, L. A. "Graphical Evaluation of the Effective Moment of Inertia for Deflection," ACI Journal, Proceedings, V. 70, No. 3 March 1973, pp. 207-213.

17. Fling, R. S., Chapter 2 — "Deflections," Handbook of Concrete Engineering, M. Fintel, Editor, Van Nostrand Reinhold Co., 1974, pp. 44-54.

18. Branson, D. E., "Compression Steel Effect on Long-Time Deflections," ACI Journal, Proceedings V. 68, No. 8, August 1971, pp. 555-559.

19. Nilson, A. H., and Walters, D. B., "Deflection of Two-Way Floor Systems by the Equivalent Frame Method," ACI Journal, Proceedings, V. 72, No. 5, May 1975, pp. 210-218.

20. Kripanarayanan, K. M., and Branson, D. E., "Short-Time Deflections of Flat Plates, Flat Slabs, and Two-Way Slabs," ACI Journal, Proceedings V. 73, NO. 12, Dec. 1976, pp. 686-690.

21. Neville, A. M., Dilger, W. H. and Brooks, J. J., "Creep of Plain and Structural Concrete," Construction Press, London, New York, 1983, 351 pp.

22. Grundy, R., and Kabaila, A., "Construction Loads on Slabs with Shored Formwork in Multistory Buildings," ACI Journal, Proceedings V. 60, NO. 12, Dec. 1963, pp. 1729-1738.

23. Agarwal, R. K., and Gardner, N. J., "Form and Shore Requirements for Multistory Flat Slab Type Buildings," ACI Journal Proceedings V. 71, No. 11, Nov. 1974, pp. 559-569.

24. Gardner, N. J., "Design and Construction Interdependence," Concrete International, Nov. 1990, pp. 32-38.

Table A Summary of Calculated Deflections for Two-Way Slab Examples

Design Example	Location of Deflection	Live Load Deflection		Deflection After Attachment of Non-Structural Elements	
		Calculated (mm)	Permissible (mm)	Calculated (mm)	Permissible (mm)
(6.2) Specified Loads $f_r = 0.3\sqrt{f_c'}$	Column Strip	9.0	17.8	28.9	13.3
	Middle Strip	18.3	17.8	35.8	13.3
	Mid-Panel	27.3	25.0	64.7	18.5
(6.3) Construction Loads $f_r = 0.3\sqrt{f_c'}$ MPa	Column Strip	7.6	17.8	35.6	13.3
	Middle Strip	10.2	17.8	49.6	13.3
	Mid-Panel	17.8	25.0	85.2	18.8

*Table 6.1. Thickness Below Which Deflections Must be Computed for Non Prestressed Beams or One-Way Slabs Not Supporting or Attached to Partitions or Other Construction Likely to be Damaged by Large Deflections

Solid one-way slabs	Minimum thickness, h			
	Simply supported	One end continuous	Both ends continuous	Cantilever
	$\ell_n/20$	$\ell_n/24$	$\ell_n/28$	ℓ_n10
Beams or ribbed one-way slabs	$\ell_n/16$	$\ell_n/18.5$	$\ell_n/21$	$\ell_n/8$

Values given shall be used directly for members with normal density concrete ($\gamma_c > 2150$ kg/m^3) and Grade 400 reinforcement. For other conditions, the values shall be modified as follows:

(a) For structural low density concrete and structural semi-low density concrete, the values shall be multiplied by $(1.65 - 0.0003\,\gamma_c)$, but not less than 1.00, where γ_c is the density in kg/m^3.

(b) For f_y other than 400 MPa, the values shall be multiplied by $(0.4 + f_y/670)$.

*This table also appears in CSA Standard A23.3 as Table 9.1.

Table 6.2 CSA Standard A23.3 Minimum Thickness for Two-Way Construction Expressed as a Fraction of the Longer Span Length, ℓ_n

a) Flat Plates and Slabs with Column Capitals

$$h_s \geq \frac{\ell_n(0.6 + f_y/1000)}{30} \tag{Eq. 13-1}$$

b) Slabs with Drop Panels

$$h_s \geq \frac{\ell_n(0.6 + f_y/1000)}{30\left[1 + \left(\dfrac{2x_d}{\ell_n}\right)\left(\dfrac{h_d - h_s}{h_s}\right)\right]} \tag{Eq. 13-2}$$

c) Slabs with Beams Between Supports

$$h_s \geq \frac{\ell_n(0.6 + f_y/1000)}{30 + 4\,\beta\alpha_m} \tag{Eq. 13-3}$$

Notes: 1) Ratio of long to short span (β) not exceeding 2.

2) Stiffness ratio, α, for beam at discontinuous edge must not be less than 0.8, or increase minimum thickness by at least 10%. A beam with $h \geq 2\,h_{slab}$ and $b_wh \geq 4(h_{slab})^2$ will always give $\alpha = 0.8$ or greater.

Table 6.3* Maximum Permissible Computed Deflections

Type of Member	Deflections to be Considered	Deflection Limitation
Flat roofs not supporting or attached to non-structural elements likely to be damaged by large deflections	Immediate deflection due to the specified live load, L	$\dfrac{\ell}{180}$ **
Floors not supporting or attached to non-structural elements likely to be damaged by large deflections	Immediate deflection due to the specified live load, L	$\dfrac{\ell}{360}$
Roof or floor construction supporting or attached to non-structural elements likely to be damaged by large deflections	That part of the total deflection which occurs after attachment of the non-structural elements, the sum of the long-time deflection due to all sustained loads and the immediate deflection due to any additional live load+	$\dfrac{\ell_n}{480}$ ++
Roof or floor construction supporting or attached to non-structural elements not likely to be damaged by large deflections		$\dfrac{\ell}{240}$ &

* This table is identical to Table 9.2 of CSA Standard A23.3
** This limit is not intended to safeguard against ponding, ponding should be checked by suitable calculations of deflection including long-time effects of all sustained loads, camber construction tolerances, and reliability of provisions for drainage.
+ Long-time deflections shall be determined in accordance with Clause 9.8.2.5 or 9.8.4.4 of CSA Standard A23.3 but may be reduced by the amount of deflection calculated to occur before attachment of non-structural elements.
++ This limit may be exceeded if adequate measures are taken to prevent damage to supported or attached elements.
& But not greater than the tolerance provided for the non-structural elements. This limit may be exceeded if camber is provided so that the total deflection minus the camber does not exceed the limitation.

Table 6.4 Section Properties for Rectangular Cross-Section

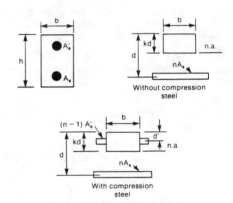

Moment of Inertia of Gross Section, I_g

$$I_g = \frac{1}{12} b h^3$$

Cracking Moment, M_{cr}

$$M_{cr} = \frac{f_r I_g}{y_t} \qquad y_t = \frac{h}{2}$$

Moment of Inertia of Cracked Transformed Section, I_{cr}

$$B = \frac{b}{n A_s} \qquad r = \frac{(n-1)A'_s}{n A_s}$$

a) Without compression steel

$$kd = \frac{(\sqrt{2dB + 1} - 1)}{B}$$

$$I_{cr} = \frac{1}{3}b(kd)^3 + nA_s (1 - k)^2$$

b) With Compression Steel

$$kd = \frac{[\sqrt{2dB (1+\frac{rd'}{d}) + (1 + r)^2} - (1 + r)]}{B}$$

$$I_{cr} = \frac{1}{3} b(kd)^3 + nA_s d^2 (1-k)^2 + (n-1)A'_s(kd-d')^2$$

(Note: See Table 6.5 for graphical evaluation of I_{cr})

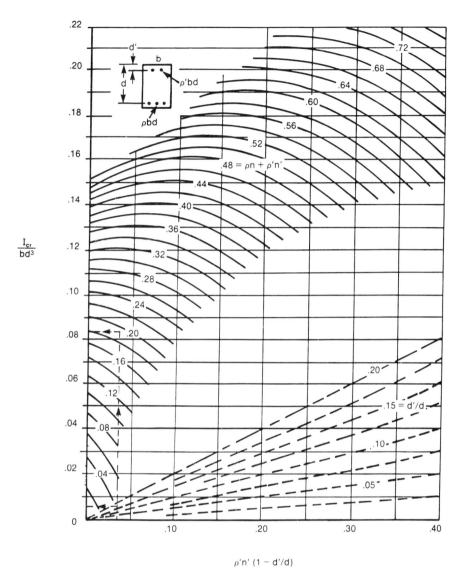

$$\frac{I_{cr}}{bd^3}$$

$$\rho'n' \, (1 - d'/d)$$

Table 6.5   Cracked Section Moment of Inertia, I_{cr} for Rectangular Section [16]

Table 6.6 Section Properties for Tee Cross-Section

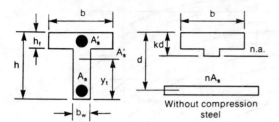

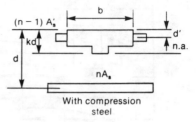

| Without compression steel | With compression steel |

Moment of Inertia of Gross Section, I_g

$$A_r = \frac{h_f}{h} \left(\frac{b}{b_w} - 1\right) : I_g = C_T \, b \, h^3$$

$$C_T = \frac{[4A_r (1 - \frac{h_f}{h})^2 + (1 + A_r \frac{h_f}{h})^2]}{12 \frac{b}{b_w} (1 + A_r)}$$

(Note: See Table 6.7 for graphical evaluation of I_g)

Cracking Moment, M_{cr}

a) Tension at bottom face

$$\frac{y_{tb}}{h} = \frac{[\frac{b}{b_w} \frac{h_f}{h} (1 - \frac{1}{2} \frac{h_f}{h}) + \frac{1}{2} (1 - \frac{h_f}{h})^2]}{[\frac{b}{b_w} \frac{h_f}{h} + (1 - \frac{h_f}{h})]}$$

$$M_{cr} = \frac{f_r I_g}{y_{tb}}$$

(Note: See Table 6.8 for graphical evaluation of y_{tb})

b) Tension at top face

$$y_{tt} = h - y_{tb} \quad M_{cr} = \frac{f_r I_g}{y_{tt}}$$

Moment of Inertia of Cracked Transformed Section, I_{cr}

a) Tension at bottom face

$$C = \frac{b_w}{nA_s} \qquad f = \frac{h_f (b - b_w)}{nA_s}$$

$$kd = \frac{[\sqrt{C (2d + h_f) + (1 + f)^2} - (1 + f)]}{C}$$

$$I_{cr} = \frac{(b - b_w) h_f^3}{12} + \frac{b_w (kd)^3}{3} + (b - b_w) \, h_f \, (kd - \frac{h_f}{2})^2$$

$$+ nA_s \, d^2 \, (1 - k)^2$$

(Note: See Table 6.9 for graphical evaluation of I_{cr})

b) Tension at top face: same as rectangular section with width $b = b_w$

Table 6.7   Gross Moment of Inertia, I_g[16]

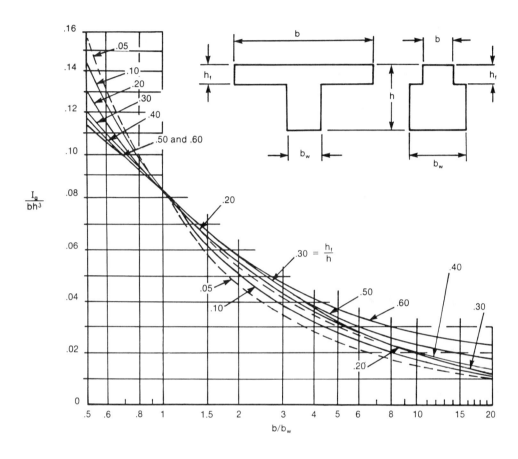

Table 6.8   Distance from centroid to bottom fibre

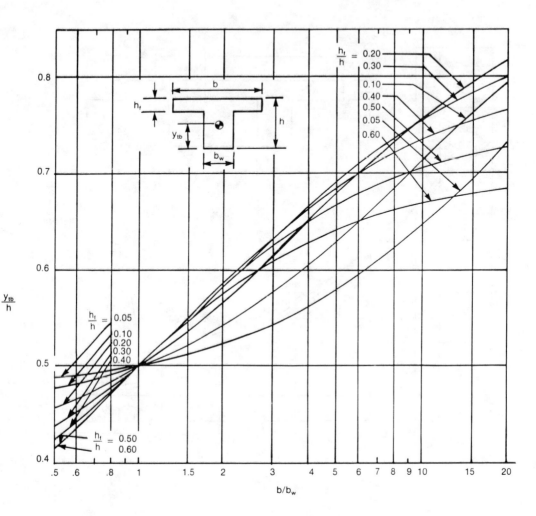

Table 6.9   Cracked Section Moment of Inertia, I_{cr} for T-Section[16]

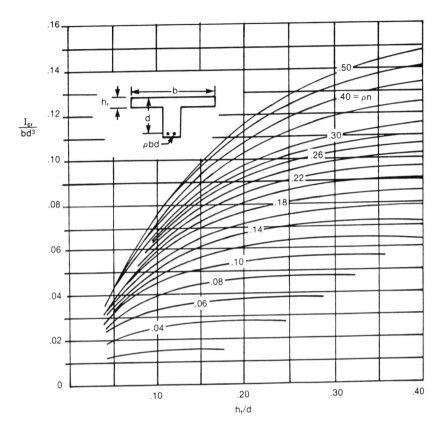

Table 6.10 Values of A_{sh} for Calculating Shrinkage Curvature in Eq. (6.12)*

p' / p	0.00	0.25	0.50	0.75	1.00	1.25	1.50	1.75	2.00	2.25	2.50	2.75	3.00
0.25	0.44	0.00	–	–	–	–	–	–	–	–	–	–	–
0.50	0.56	0.31	0.00	–	–	–	–	–	–	–	–	–	–
0.85	0.64	0.45	0.25	0.00	–	–	–	–	–	–	–	–	–
1.00	0.70	0.55	0.39	0.22	0.00	–	–	–	–	–	–	–	–
1.25	0.75	0.63	0.49	0,35	0.20	0.00	–	–	–	–	–	–	–
1.50	0.80	0.69	0.57	0.45	0.32	0.18	0.00	–	–	–	–	–	–
1.75	0.84	0.74	0.64	0.57	0.42	0.30	0.17	0.00	–	–	–	–	–
2.00	0.88	0.79	0.69	0.64	0.50	0.39	0.28	0.16	0.00	–	–	–	–
2.25	0.92	0.83	0.74	0.69	0.56	0.47	0.37	0.26	0.15	0.00	–	–	–
2.50	0.95	0.87	0.79	0.74	0.62	0.53	0.44	0.35	0.25	0.14	0.00	–	–
2.75	0.98	0.91	0.83	0.79	0.67	0.59	0.51	0.42	0.33	0.24	0.13	0.00	–
3.00	1.00	0.94	0.87	0.83	0.72	0.64	0.57	0.49	0.40	0.32	0.23	0.13	0.00
3.25	1.00	0.97	0.90	0,87	0.76	0.69	0.62	0.54	0.47	0.39	0.31	0.22	0.12
3.50	1.00	1.00	0.94	0.90	0.80	0.74	0.67	0.60	0.52	0.45	0.37	0.29	0.32
3.75	1.00	1.00	1.00	0.94	0.84	0.78	0.71	0.64	0.58	0.52	0.44	0.36	0.28
4.00	1.00	1.00	1.00	1.00	0.88	0.81	0.75	0.69	0.62	0.56	0.49	0.42	0.35

*p = 100 As /(bd), p' = 100 A$'_s$ /(bd). When p' > p, interchange p' and p to obtain corresponding solution in opposite direction.

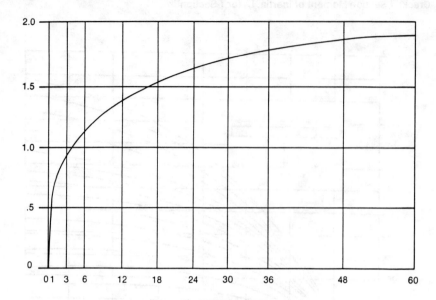

Fig. 6.1　Variation of S with Load Duration

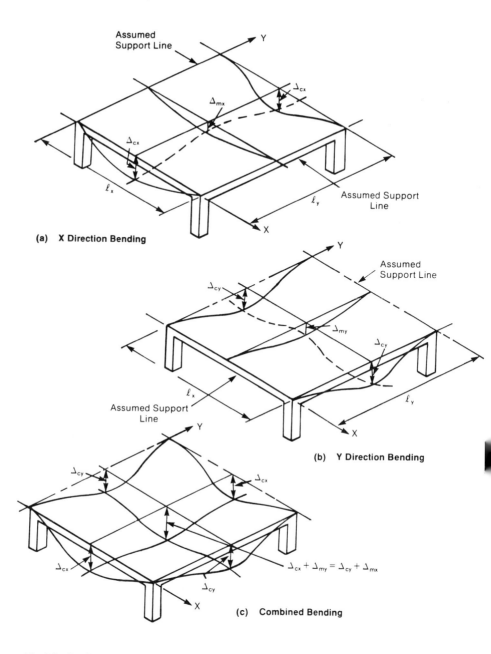

(a)   X Direction Bending

(b)   Y Direction Bending

(c)   Combined Bending

Fig 6.2   Basis of Equivalent Frame Method for Deflection Analysis

7

Short Columns

By Robert Loov

Chapter 7
Short Columns

7.1 GENERAL REMARKS

Columns must be proportioned with a capacity to resist bending moment as well as axial load. The capacity of column cross sections is described using interaction diagrams (Tables 7.4 through 7.7).

Clause 10.15.2 of CSA Standard A23.3* defines a limiting slenderness ratio $k\ell_u/r$ below which slenderness effects will be insignificant for non-sway frames. (see Table 8.1). The design of slender columns is covered in chapter 8 of this handbook.

7.2 MAXIMUM AXIAL RESISTANCE UNDER SMALL MOMENTS

Column cross sections can resist more axial load when moments are small. Clause 10.10.4 of CSA Standard A23.3 sets a maximum axial load resistance based on the assumption that some moment is inevitable. Values of the maximum axial loads, P_{rmax}, for tied columns are shown in Tables 7.1.1 to 7.1.5 for common sizes of cross sections, concrete strengths of 25, 30, 35, 40 and 45 MPa and steel strengths of 400 MPa and 500 MPa. The material resistance factors $\phi_c = 0.60$ and $\phi_s = 0.85$ are incorporated into the graphs. Precast concrete columns for which $\phi_c = 0.65$ will have slightly higher capacities.

These graphs can be used as an estimating design aid as each displays the possible square column sizes and column areas appropriate for a specific axial load. They can also be used for rectangular and circular tied columns by choosing comparable areas. The diameter of a circular column is 1.128 times the size of a square column of the same area.

The capacity, P_{rmax}, of spiral columns will be $6\frac{1}{4}\%$ larger than the tied columns shown because the upper limit is based on $0.85\,P_{ro}$ rather than $0.80\,P_{ro}$ (see Clauses 10.10.4). This difference exists only for small eccentricities. The remaining portions of the interaction curves are the same (See Tables 7.7.1 to 7.7.16).

When ρ_t exceeds 4%, welded splices, mechanical connections, or end-bearing splices have to be staggered to satisfy Clause 12.17.2 of CSA Standard A23.3. Columns with lapped splices can seldom have much more than 4% steel while, even with end-bearing splices, ρ_t will seldom exceed 6%.

Steeper lines correspond to ρ_t ratios between $\frac{1}{2}$ and 1%. Columns with these low steel ratios may be useful in upper storeys to reduce the number of size changes in a column stack. The sharp change in capacity is based on the application of Clause 10.10.5.

7.3 VALUES OF GAMMA FOR COLUMNS

Table 7.2 provides values of γ for common sizes of columns, with 40 mm and 50 mm cover to No. 10 ties or spirals. The value γ is the ratio of the centre to centre distance between the outermost reinforcing bars (measured perpendicular to the axis of bending) to the overall depth of the column, h. For other covers $\gamma = \gamma_{40} + 2(40-c)/h$.

7.4 MINIMUM COLUMN SIZES AND COVERS FOR FIRE AND DURABILITY

Table 7.3 summarizes the requirements for minimum column size and cover for different fire ratings, column lengths, steel ratios, concrete type and overdesign factors. The overdesign factor is P_r/P_f. Concrete types and the requirements for fire resistance are discussed in Section 1 of this handbook.

Cover requirements for corrosion protection are also shown in this table. Cover requirements for durability are specified in Clauses 12.6.2 and 15.1.7.1 of CSA Standard A23.1-94 "Concrete Materials and Methods of Concrete Construction".

Section 1 of this handbook provides information on construction intended for a deicer salt environment. Bearing walls and columns which support slabs and ramps may be splashed with deicers and are hence subject to corrosion. Such supporting elements should be constructed using at least the same quality of concrete and cover recommended for slabs and ramps. The use of a sealer should be considered to protect the first metre or so of exposed walls and columns above the level of trafficked surfaces.

7.5 INTERACTION DIAGRAMS

The strength of column cross sections can be determined using interaction diagrams which display the factored axial resistance as the ordinate and the factored moment resistance as abscissa. To make the graphs applicable to all column sizes, P_r has been divided by A_g and M_r has been divided by $A_g h$. Four graphs with different values of γ are included for each concrete strength, column shape and reinforcing pattern. The interaction diagrams are plotted for 3 reinforcement patterns for rectangular cross sections and for circular sections with circular ties, helical ties or spirals.

Tied rectangular column cross sections include those with equal amounts of reinforcement in each of the four faces (Tables 7.4.1 to 7.4.20); equal amounts of reinforcement in the two faces parallel to the axis of bending (Tables 7.5.1 to 7.5.20); and columns with equal amounts of reinforcement in the two side faces perpendicular to the axis of bending (Tables 7.6.1 to 7.6.20). Tables 7.5.1 to 7.5.20 should be used for columns with 4 bars since all 4 bars are located the same distance from the axis of the column.

To simplify the use of the charts for circular columns, they have been plotted using P_r/h^2 and M_r/h^3. The capacities of circular tied and spiral columns differ only at very small eccentricities when Clause 10.10.4 governs. The charts in Tables 7.7.1 to 7.7.16 can be used for both cases. A shaded line shows the additional capacity of spiral columns.

The material resistance factors $\phi_c = 0.60$ and $\phi_s = 0.85$ have been included so the charts give P_r/A_g, and $M_r/(A_g h)$ without modification. Adjustments are needed for precast columns for which $\phi_c = 0.65$.

Three radial lines in each diagram give values of the tensile steel stress in the steel layer closest to the tensile face of the column. These are used to determine the type of column splices required. See Clauses 12.14, 12.15, 12.16 and 12.17 of CSA Standard A23.3

Some description of the calculation of these interaction curves may be of interest. Calculations have been based on a limiting strain of 0.0035 in the extreme compression fibre. The interaction curves have been based on an equivalent rectangular concrete stress block of depth $\beta_1 c$ with a uniform stress $\phi_c \alpha_1 f'_c$. The effect of the concrete displaced by the area of steel in regions of compressed concrete has been taken into account by deducting ϕ_c times the concrete stress from the stress in the compressed reinforcement. For this purpose the concrete stress was assumed to be εE_c at low compressive strains and $\alpha_1 f'_c$ at high strains.

In situations with a small moment which would have $c > h$, the graphs have been approximated by a straight line from P_{ro} to the P_r and M_r corresponding to $c = h$.

---

*CSA Standard A23.3-94 "Design of Concrete Structures." From here on referred to as CSA Standard A23.3.

The interaction curves in Table 7.5.1 to 7.5.20 were developed for equal reinforcement on the two end faces. All of the other charts have been based on 5 layers of steel. The curves for circular columns have been based on 8 bars located with 2 bars directly on the axis of bending as shown in the sketches on Tables 7.7.1 to 7.7.16 and the remaining bars uniformly spaced around the column. These curves are reasonably conservative for any number of longitudinal bars ranging down to the minimum of 6 allowed for spirals and even the 4 allowed for circular ties.

Gamma, γ, is the ratio of the distance between the centres of the outermost reinforcing bars and the overall column depth, h. Gamma does not affect the column capacity P_{rmax} with low moment. It has maximum effect at balanced conditions ($f_s/f_y = 1.0$) and with higher values of ρ_t. It is conservative to use an interaction chart with γ smaller than the expected value. Only when the expected value of γ approaches that of the next higher graph and $f_s/f_y > 0$ is it worthwhile to interpolate between graphs with different γ.

7.5.1 Column Stiffness

As an aid in determining slenderness effects, the values of EI are given on each strength interaction graph. If the effective stiffness of cross sections were determined without the influence of reinforcement,

$$EI_{19} = 0.25E_c I_g \text{ (Eq. 10-19 of CSA Standard A23.3)}$$

The modulus of elasticity has been based on Eq. 8-6 of the A23.3 Standard with a concrete density of 2400 kg/m^3.

$$E_c = (3300\sqrt{f'_c} + 6900)\left(\frac{\gamma_c}{2300}\right)^{1.5}$$

For rectangular columns $I_g = bh^3/12$. The value of EI_{19} is given with each set of interaction graphs as a constant times bh^3.

For circular columns $I_g = \pi h^4/64$ so EI_{19} is shown as a constant times h^4.

Equation 10-18

The alternate equation for EI reflects the influence of longitudinal reinforcement

$$EI_{18} = (0.2 E_c I_g + E_s I_{st})/(1+\beta_d)$$

(Eq. 10-18 of CSA Standard A23.3)

The values of I_{st} can be determined for each pattern of reinforcing.

Reinforcing on End Faces Only

For rectangular columns with the reinforcing on the two end faces all of the reinforcing is centred a distance $\frac{1}{2}\gamma h$ from the column centreline

$$\therefore I_{st} = A_{st}\gamma^2 h^2/4 = \rho_t\gamma^2 bh^3/4$$

$$EI_{18} = [0.2 E_c I_g + E_s\rho_t\gamma^2 bh^3/4]/(1 + \beta_d)$$

$$EI_{18} = \left[\frac{E_c}{60} + \frac{E_s \rho_t \gamma^2}{4}\right] bh^3/(1 + \beta_d) = k\, bh^3/(1 + \beta_d)$$

where $k = E_c/60 + E_s\rho_t\gamma^2/4$

The value of k has been shown for each value of ρ_t on each interaction chart.

Reinforcing on Side Faces

With reinforcing on the side faces, the value of I_{st} reduces as the number of bars is increased:

$$\text{For 3 bars } I_{st} = \frac{2}{3}\frac{A_{st}\gamma^2 h^2}{4} = \rho_t\gamma^2 bh^3/6$$

$$\text{For 5 bars } I_{st} = \frac{2}{5}\frac{A_{st}\gamma^2 h^2}{4} + \frac{2}{5}\frac{A_{st}\gamma^2 h^2}{16} = \rho_t\gamma^2 bh^3/8$$

for 7 bars $I_{st} = \rho_t\gamma^2 bh^3/9$

for ∞ bars $I_{st} = \rho_t\gamma^2 bh^3/12$

The chosen value of I_{st} of $\rho_t\gamma^2 bh^3/8$ has been based on a practical maximum of 5 bars/face; thus

$$k = E_c/60 + E_s\rho_t\gamma^2/8$$

Equal Reinforcement on all 4 Faces

When there are an equal number of bars on each face the number of bars/face does affect I_{st}, but the change is not as pronounced as it is for side face reinforcement. A conservative value of

$$I_{st} = \frac{1}{2}\left(\rho_t\gamma^2 bh^3/4 + \rho_t\gamma^2 bh^3/12\right) \text{ has been chosen}$$

$$\therefore I_{st} = \rho_t\gamma^2 bh^3/6 \text{ and } k = E_c/60 + E_s\rho_t\gamma^2/6$$

Circular Columns

For circular columns I_g is $\pi h^4/64$ and I_{st} varies depending upon both the number and orientation of the bars relative to the axis of bending. For 4, 8 or an infinite number of bars $I_{st} = A_s\gamma^2 h^2/8$. Using this value for I_{st}:

$$EI_{18} = kh^4/(1 + \beta_d)$$

where $k = \dfrac{\pi}{4}(E_c/80 + E_s\rho_t\gamma^2/8)$

7.5.2 Steel or Concrete Strengths which differ from charted values

The interaction curves have been based on 400 MPa reinforcement. For locations in the interaction diagrams where the steel strains in the compression or tension reinforcement are higher than ε_y, the interaction curves can be used for other steel strengths by using a modified ρ_t adjusted by multiplication by 400/f_y. This adjustment is appropriate for the region near P_{rmax} and is also applicable for low values of P_r/A_g up to approximately 3/4 of the value at $f_s/f_y = 1.0$. In other regions of the interaction diagram there will be little benefit from the increased steel strength.

Interaction curves have been produced for concrete strengths of 25, 30, 35, 40 and 45 MPa. The curves for $f'_c = 25$ MPa can be used for lower concrete strengths by modifying P_r/A_g, $M_r/(A_g h)$ and ρ_t as follows:

Enter curves with adjusted P_r/A_g and $M_r/(A_g h)$.

$$\left(\frac{P_r}{A_g}\right)_{25} \approx \left(\frac{P_r}{A_g}\right)_{f'_c}\left(\frac{25}{f'_c}\right)$$

$$\left(\frac{M_r}{A_g h}\right)_{25} \approx \left(\frac{M_r}{A_g h}\right)_{f'_c}\left(\frac{25}{f'_c}\right)$$

The required ρ_t determined from the interaction curves must be adjusted by the ratio $f'_c/25$. The variation of α_1 and β_1 as f'_c is reduced does not have a significant effect and the prediction is conservative.

Using adjustments similar to those indicated above, the curves for 45 MPa may be used to estimate the strength of columns with higher concrete strengths. In this case the reduction in α_1 should be included.

$$\left(\frac{P_r}{A_g}\right)_{45} \approx \left(\frac{P_r}{A_g}\right)_{f'_c} \left(\frac{45}{f'_c}\right) \left(\frac{\alpha_{1(45)}}{\alpha_{1(f'_c)}}\right)$$

$$\left(\frac{M_r}{A_g h}\right)_{45} \approx \left(\frac{M_r}{A_g h}\right)_{f'_c} \left(\frac{45}{f'_c}\right) \left(\frac{\alpha_{1(45)}}{\alpha_{1(f'_c)}}\right)$$

The required ρ_t found from the 45 MPa interaction curves must then be adjusted to $\rho_{t(f'_c)} = \rho_{t(45)}(f'_c/45)$.

7.5.3 Biaxial Bending

All rectangular cross sections subjected to biaxial bending and axial compression must be checked to ensure adequate strength under this combination of loads. A common way of estimating the column strength under biaxial bending is the reciprocal load method suggested by Bresler*:

$$\frac{1}{P_r/A_g} = \frac{1}{P_{rx}/A_g} + \frac{1}{P_{ry}/A_g} - \frac{1}{P_{ro}/A_g}$$

where P_{rx} = factored axial load resistance if the load were applied at the eccentricity e_x with $e_y = 0$.

P_{ry} = factored axial load resistance if the load were applied at the eccentricity e_y with $e_x = 0$.

P_{ro} = factored axial load resistance if e_x and e_y were 0.

(P_{ro} may be obtained as 1.25 times the P_{rmax} shown as a horizontal line on the interaction curves.)

Design for biaxial bending can be started by using a bending moment augmented by about 10 percent. The resultant moment can be considered to act about the principal axis nearest the resultant axial load, and the cross section dimensions and reinforcement can be selected. The selected section may then be checked using Bresler's equation.

Circular columns can be designed directly by computing $M_f = (M_{fx}2 + M_{fy}2)^{1/2}$.

7.6 NUMBER OF BARS REQUIRED TO OBTAIN DESIRED STEEL RATIOS

Construction costs can be minimized if column forms are reused as often as possible without readjustment during the construction of successive storeys. The ground floor columns of multi-storey frames should normally therefore be proportioned for high steel ratios. The reinforcement ratio can usually be increased to approximately 4 percent before the splices create clearance problems. After a high steel ratio has been used at the ground floor columns, the reduction of axial load at each higher floor permits the use of successively lower steel ratios without changes in the column forms.

Tables 7-8 to 7-10 are provided to assist in the choice of column reinforcement. All the bar combinations shown may be spliced with welded splices, mechanical connections or bearing type splices. If $\rho_t > 4\%$, splice locations must be staggered by at least 750 mm. | 12.17.2 |

The bar combinations above the solid zigzag line may be spliced using either tangential splices or radial splices.

When a reinforcing ratio, ρ_t, less than 0.01 is used as permitted by Clause 10.10.4, the column resistance shall be based on the resistance reduced by the ratio $\rho_t/0.01$.

Blank values correspond to ρ_t less than $1/2\%$ or greater than 8% or to combinations of bars which would violate the minimum or maximum bar spacing requirements or would result in γ less than about 0.5.

7.6.1 Reinforcement For Rectangular Columns

Tables 7.8 and 7.9 give the reinforcing ratios $\rho_t = A_{st}/bh$ for a wide range of b and h values for rectangular columns with various bar sizes and placement patterns.

7.6.2 Reinforcement for Circular Columns

Table 7.10 gives reinforcing ratios when various numbers of reinforcing bars are used in circular columns.

Table 7.11 indicates the maximum pitch, s, for No. 10 or No. 15 spirals with 25, 30, 35, 40, 45, or 50 MPa concrete. The table includes spirals made with 400 MPa and with 500 MPa reinforcement. Clause 12.5.2 of CSA Standard A23.1 limits the nominal maximum aggregate size to $(s - d_b)/1.4$. Spirals have not been shown which require clear spacings less than 25 mm.

7.7 COMPRESSION DEVELOPMENT AND LAP LENGTHS

Table 7.12 is a tabulation of compression development lengths for deformed bars with $f_y = 400$ MPa.

Table 7.13 is a tabulation of lap lengths for 400 MPa reinforcement in normal density concrete.

7.8 NOTATION

A_g = gross area of concrete cross section

A_{st} = total area of longitudinal reinforcing bars

b = width of compression face of member

c = distance from extreme compression fibre to neutral axis

c = cover to surface of reinforcement

d_b = nominal diameter of bar

EI = flexural stiffness of compression member

E_c = modulus of elasticity of concrete

E_s = modulus of elasticity of reinforcement

f'_c = specified compressive strength of concrete

f_s = calculated stress in reinforcement under factored load

f_y = specified yield strength of reinforcement

h = overall thickness of member

I_g = moment of inertia of gross concrete section about centroidal axis, neglecting reinforcement

I_{st} = moment of inertia of reinforcement about centroidal axis of member cross section

k = effective length factor for compression members

k = factor equal to $(0.2 E_c I_g + E_s I_{st})/bh^3$

ℓ_d = development length

ℓ_u = unsupported length of compression member

M_f = factored moment

M_r = factored moment resistance

---

*Bresler, Boris, "Design Criteria for Reinforced Columns under Axial Load and Biaxial Bending," ACI Journal, Proceedings V. 57, No. 11, Nov. 1960, pp. 481–490.

P_f	=	factored axial load
P_r	=	factored axial load resistance
P_{rmax}	=	maximum factored axial load resistance
P_{ro}	=	factored axial load resistance if e_x and e_y were zero
P_{rx}	=	factored axial load resistance if the load were applied at eccentricity e_x with $e_y = 0$
P_{ry}	=	factored axial load resistance if the load were applied at eccentricity e_y with $e_x = 0$
r	=	radius of gyration of cross section of a compression member
R	=	required fire-resistance rating in hours
s	=	pitch or distance between turns of a spiral
α_1	=	ratio of average stress in rectangular stress block to the specified concrete strength
β_1	=	ratio of depth of rectangular compression block to depth to the neutral axis
β_d	=	factor defined in Clause 10.0 of CSA Standard A23.3 to account for the effects of sustained loads
γ	=	ratio of the centre to centre distance between the outermost reinforcing bars to the overall depth
γ_c	=	density of concrete
ε	=	strain in concrete
ρ_t	=	ratio of Ast/A_g
ϕ_c	=	resistance factor for concrete
ϕ_s	=	resistance factor for steel

Estimate of Column Loads for Examples

Assume 350×350 mm edge columns spaced at 7.5 m with a 200 mm two-way flat slab spanning 6.8 m to the interior columns. Assume a 350 mm wide edge beam projecting 300 mm below the slab. Allow for a wall load averaging 2.35 kN/m². Assume a floor to floor height of 3.6 m. Assume a roof dead load of $(0.2\text{ m})(24\text{ kN/m}^3)$ plus 2.2 kPa for roofing, insulation and an allowance for mechanical equipment. Assume the dead load for the floor is (0.2 m) (24 kN/m^3) plus 1.2 kPa for flooring and partitions.

Tributary area: $(6.8/2 + 0.175)(7.5) = 27$ m²

Dead Load (typical floor)

Factored floor load	= 1.25(6.0)(27)	= 203
Edge Beam + column	= 1.25(28)	= 35
Wall (2.35 kN/m²)	= 1.25(2.35)(3.6)(7.5)	= 79
		317 kN

Dead Load (Roof)

Roofing + slab	= 1.25(7.0)(27)	= 236
Edge Beam + column	= 1.25(28)	= 35
include ≈ ½ of wall?		= 40
		311 kN

Live Load Roof

Snow	1.5(0.8)(3)(27)	= 97 kN

Floor Load

Office loading	1.5(2.4)(27)	= 97 kN

Reduce live floor load by the tributary area reduction factor $= 0.3 + (9.8/B)^{1/2}$ where B is the tributary area supported by the member (m²).

Lateral support is provided by shear walls so the columns can be designed as non-sway frames.

Level Supported	Factored Snow + Dead	Cumulative Snow + Dead	Factored Live	Cumulative Live	Cumulative Area	Area Factor	Reduced Live	P_f=Dead + Reduced Live
Roof	kN	kN	kN	kN	m²		kN	MN
	311 + 97	408						0.41
8	317	725	97	97	27	0.902	88	0.81
7	317	1042	97	194	54	0.726	141	1.18
6	317	1359	97	291	81	0.648	189	1.55
5	317	1676	97	388	108	0.601	233	1.91
4	317	1993	97	485	135	0.569	276	2.27
3	317	2310	97	582	162	0.546	318	2.63
2	317	2627	97	679	189	0.528	358	2.99

Example 7.1   Tied Column Design

Assume a 3 h fire rating with Type S concrete. From Table 7.3 it can be seen that columns with their smaller dimension equal to at least 320 mm do not need to be overdesigned. They may also have $k\ell_u$ as large as 7.3 m and have any reinforcement ratio. A minimum cover of 50 mm to the main steel is required for a 3 h fire rating (Table 7.3).

Assume columns exposed to earth or weather. Minimum of 40 mm cover required to ties and 50 mm to main steel No. 35 and smaller (Table 7.3). 40 mm cover to No. 10 ties will satisfy all these requirements. Assume $f'_c = 40$ MPa, $f_y = 400$ MPa. Assume all steel lap spliced. | 10.9.2 |

Bar size ≤ No. 35. | 12.14.2.1 |
Storey height 3600 mm.
Slab thickness 200 mm.
$\ell_u = 3600 - 200 = 3400$ mm. | 10.14.3.1 |

Assume condition elastic + at both the top and bottom of the column (Fig. N10.15.2 of Handbook).
$k \approx 0.9$
$k\ell_u \approx 0.9(3400) = 3060$ mm
$r = 0.3h = 0.3(350) = 105$ mm | 10.14.2 |
$k\ell_u/r = 3060/105 = 29.1$

Column Supporting 2nd Floor

$P_f = 2.99$ MN, $M_f = 0.100$ MN · m
From Table 7.1.4 a 350×350 mm column with $\rho_t > 3.7\%$ will be adequate if the effects of moment are negligible. Try 350×350 mm column, $A_g = 0.1225$ m²

Equation 10-15 indicates the limiting $k\ell_u/r$ which can be used in non-sway frames without considering slenderness. The column being designed may be considered fixed at the far ends under the given loads. | 9.3.2 |

The column moment at the far end will thus have the opposite sign to the column moment at the floor where the moment is applied. M_1/M_2 will be approximately -0.5. The maximum value of $k\ell_u/r$ which can be designed as a short column is therefore:

$$\frac{k\ell_u}{r} \leq \frac{25 - 10(-0.5)}{\sqrt{2.99/(40\,(0.1225))}} = 38.4$$

Slenderness may therefore be neglected.
From Tables 7.8 and 7.9 it seems that 8-No. 30 bars giving $\rho_t = 4.57$ will be needed to get $\rho_t > 3.7\%$.
From Table 7.2 $\gamma = 0.62$ for No. 30 bars.
$P_f/A_g = 2.99/0.1225 = 24.4$ MPa
$M_f/(A_gh) = 0.100/(0.35^3) = 2.33$ MPa
From Table 7.4.13, $\rho_t \geq 4\%$
8-No. 30 bars O.K.
From Table 7.4.13 $f_s/f_y < 0.0$ ∴ compression splice
From Table 7.13 a splice length of 880 mm $\boxed{12.16.1}$
is required. $\rho_t > 4\%$ therefore stagger splices at least 880 mm to avoid having more than 8% reinforcement at any section. $\boxed{10.9.2}$

Column supporting 3rd floor

$P_f = 2.63$ MN, $M_f = 0.100$ MN $\cdot$ m
Try 350×350 mm column with $\rho_t > 2.5\%$ (Table 7.1.4)
Consider reinforcement concentrated on interior and exterior faces, 6 - No. 30 bars, $\rho_t = 3.43\%$ (Table 7.9)
$P_f/A_g = 2.63/0.1225 = 21.5$ MPa
$M_f/A_gh = 2.33$ MPa
For $\gamma = 0.60$, required $\rho_t \approx 2.9\%$ (Table 7.5.14)
Use 6-No. 30 bars, $\rho_t = 3.43\%$

Capacity of Column With Minimum Reinforcing

Determine the minimum and maximum axial loads P_r for a 350×350 mm column with $M_f = 0.10$ MN $\cdot$ m and $\rho_t = 1\%$.
Use 4-No. 20 bars $\rho_t = 0.98\%$ (Table 7.9)
For $\gamma = 0.60$, $M_r/(A_gh) = 2.33$ MPA and $\rho_t = 1\%$,
3.2 MPa $\leq P_r/A_g \leq 15.5$ MPa (from Table 7.5.14)
$3.2(0.1225) = 0.39$ MN $\leq P_r \leq 15.5(0.1225) = 1.90$ MN
A 350×350 mm column with 4-No. 20 bars is appropriate for supporting floor 5 through 8. The column supporting the roof is borderline so will require further checking. It may require additional reinforcement if the moment is higher at that level.

Example 7.1(a)   Tied Column with Uncharted Material Strengths

Assume $f'_c = 50$ MPa, $f_y = 500$ MPa
$P_f = 2.99$ MN, $M_f = 0.100$ MN $\cdot$ m
Try 350×350 mm column with $\gamma = 0.6$
Use Table 7.5.18 for $f'_c = 45$ MPa, $f_y = 400$ MPa
Adjust values

$$\left(\frac{P_r}{A_g}\right)_{45} = \frac{2.99}{0.35^2}\left(\frac{45}{50}\right)\left(\frac{0.7825}{0.775}\right) = 22.2\,\text{MPa}$$

$$\left(\frac{M_r}{A_gh}\right)_{45} = \frac{0.100}{0.35^3}\left(\frac{45}{50}\right)\left(\frac{0.7825}{0.775}\right) = 2.12\,\text{MPa}$$

$\rho_{t(45,400)} \approx 2.2\%$ (Table 7.5.18)

Adjust $\rho_{t(50,500)} \approx 2.2\left(\frac{400}{500}\right)\left(\frac{50}{45}\right) = 1.96\%$

Use 4-No.30, $\rho_t = 2.29\%$ (Table 7.9)
$\gamma = 0.62$ (Table 7.2)

Example 7.2(a)   Circular Tied Column

Assume: $P_f = 4.8$ MN
$\qquad\qquad M_f = 0.12$ MN $\cdot$ m
Assume: $f'_c = 40$ MPa, $f_y = 400$ MPa, $\rho_t \approx 4.0\%$
From Table 7.1.4, A_g required ≈ 0.18 m^2

$$h \approx \left[(4/\pi)\,0.18\right]^{1/2} = 0.48\,\text{m}$$

Try $h = 500$ mm
$P_f/h^2 = 4.8/0.5^2 = 19.2$ MPa
$M_f/h^3 = 0.12/0.5^3 = 0.96$ MPa
$\rho_t \approx 3.6\%$ (Table 7.7.10)
Use 7-No. 35, $\rho_t = 3.57\%$ (Table 7.10)
No. 10 ties
$s < 16(35) = 560$ mm
$s \leq 48(10) = 480$ mm $\leftarrow$ governs $\qquad$ $\boxed{7.6.5.2}$
$s \leq 500$ mm
Use No. 10 helical ties @ 480 mm pitch.
Note: this is a tied column. The helical ties don't meet the steel volume requirements of Clause 10.9.4., or the spacing requirements of Clause 7.6.4.

Example 7.2(b)   Circular Spiral Column

Assume $\quad P_f = 4.8$ MN
$\qquad\qquad M_f = 0.12$ MN $\cdot$ m
Use 500 mm column
$P_f/h^2 = 19.2$ MPa
$M_f/(h^3) = 0.96$ MPa
Use $\rho_t \geq 3.1\%$ (Shaded lines in Table 7.7.10)
Use 9-No. 30, $\rho_t = 3.21\%$ (Table 7.10)
Use No. 10 spiral. $\qquad\qquad\qquad\qquad$ $\boxed{7.6.4}$
Pitch = 50 mm (Table 7.11) $\qquad\qquad\qquad$ $\boxed{10.9.4}$

Example 7.3   Biaxial Bending

Assume the following loads:
$P_f = 1.75$ MN
$M_{fy} = 0.10$ MN $\cdot$ m
$M_{fx} = 0.06$ MN $\cdot$ m
Consider a 350×350 mm column with corner reinforcing only (4 bars) (Table 7.9)
$P_f/A_g = 1.75/0.1225 = 14.3$ MPa
$M_{fy}/(A_gh) = 0.10/0.35^3 = 2.33$ MPa
$M_{fx}/(A_gh) = 0.06/0.35^3 = 1.40$ MPa
Try 4-No. 25 bars, $\rho_t = 1.63\%$ (Table 7.9)
$\gamma = 0.63$ (Table 7.2)

$$\frac{P_{rmax}}{A_g} \approx 19.1\,\text{MPa (Table 7.5.14)}$$

$$P_{ro}/A_g = \frac{19.1}{0.8} \approx 23.9\,\text{MPa (Clause 10.10.4(b))}$$

P_{rx}/A_g and P_{ry}/A_g are obtained from Table 7.5.14. Extend the lines from the origin through the points 1.4, 14.3 and 2.33, 14.3 until they cross the line for $\rho_t = 1.63\%$. These intersection points are P_{rx}/A_g and P_{ry}/A_g.

Table 7.5.14 Interaction Diagrams for Rectangular Columns with Bars in the Two End Faces Only.

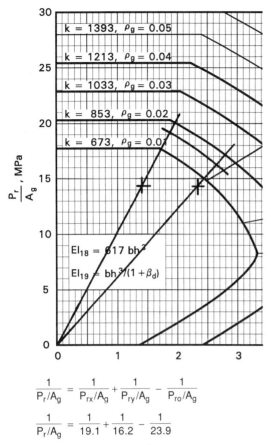

$$\frac{1}{P_r/A_g} = \frac{1}{P_{rx}/A_g} + \frac{1}{P_{ry}/A_g} - \frac{1}{P_{ro}/A_g}$$

$$\frac{1}{P_r/A_g} = \frac{1}{19.1} + \frac{1}{16.2} - \frac{1}{23.9}$$

$P_r/A_g = 14.1$, $P_r = 14.1(0.35^2) = 1.73$ MN.
The capacity is slightly greater because actual $\gamma = 0.63$, therefore the design is satisfactory.

Table 7.1.1   Axial Load Limit P_{rmax} for Tied Columns, $f'_c = 25$ MPa

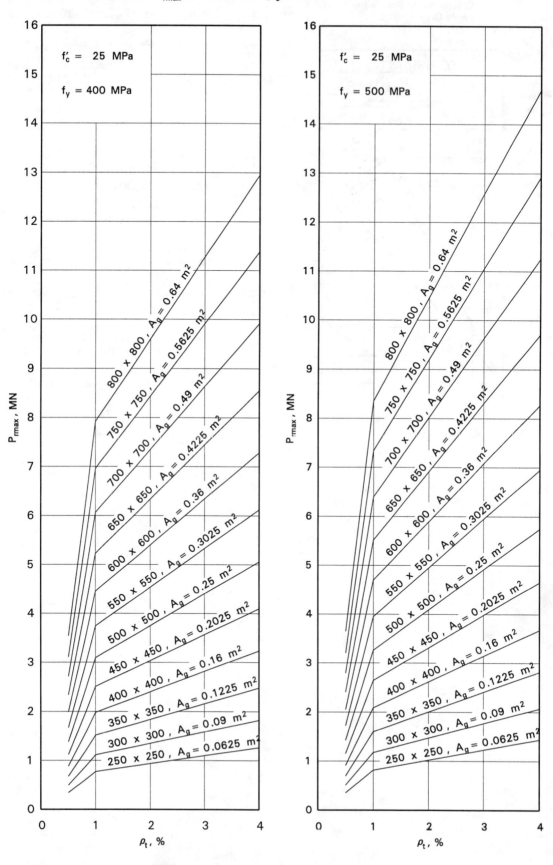

CPCA Concrete Design Handbook

Table 7.1.2   Axial Load Limit P_{rmax} for Tied Columns, f'_c = 30 MPa

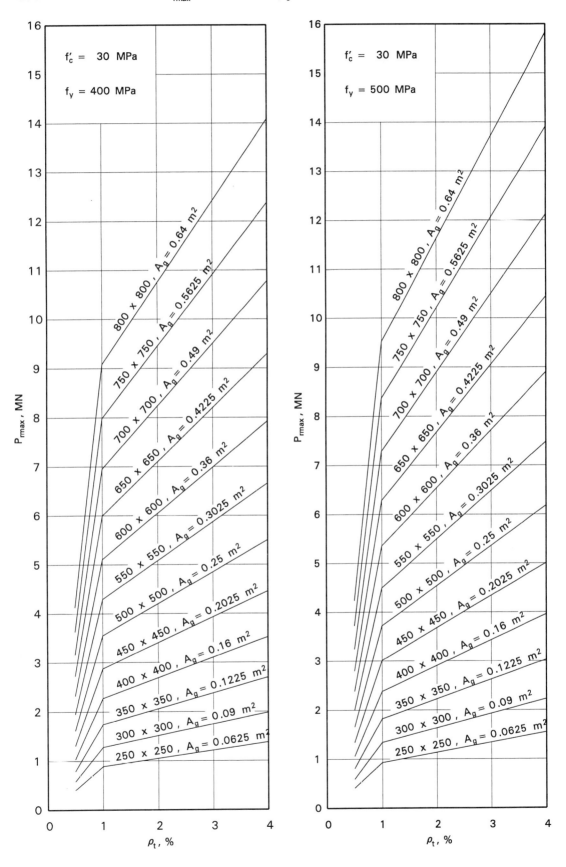

Table 7.1.3   Axial Load Limit P_{rmax} for Tied Columns, $f'_c = 35$ MPa

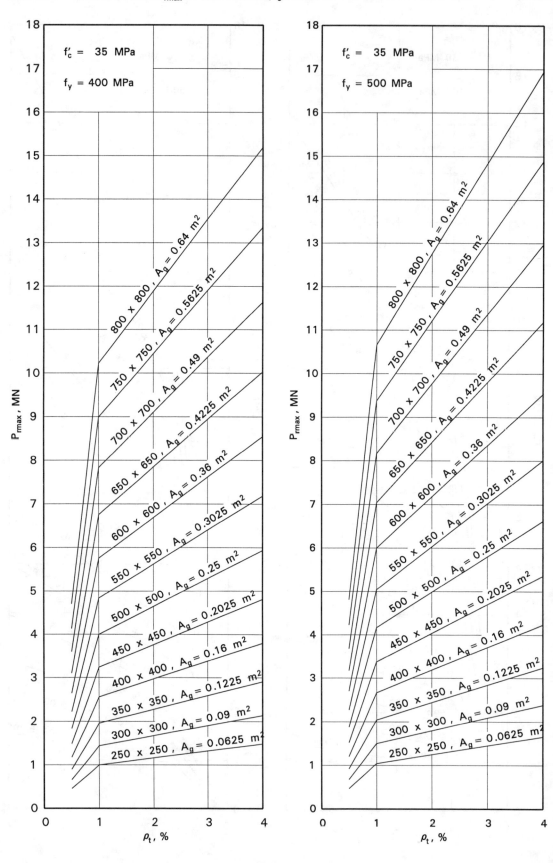

Table 7.1.4   Axial Load Limit P_{rmax} for Tied Columns, f'_c = 40 MPa

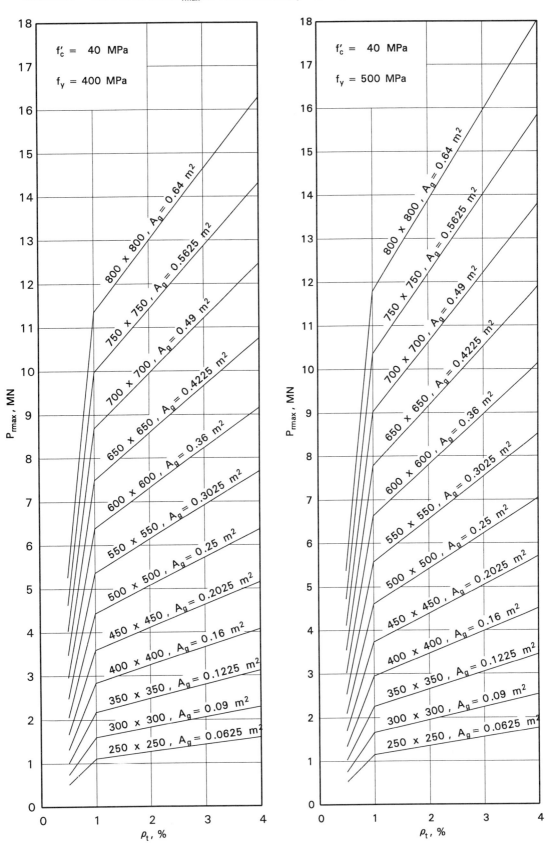

Table 7.1.5　　Axial Load Limit P_{rmax} for Tied Columns, $f'_c = 45$ MPa

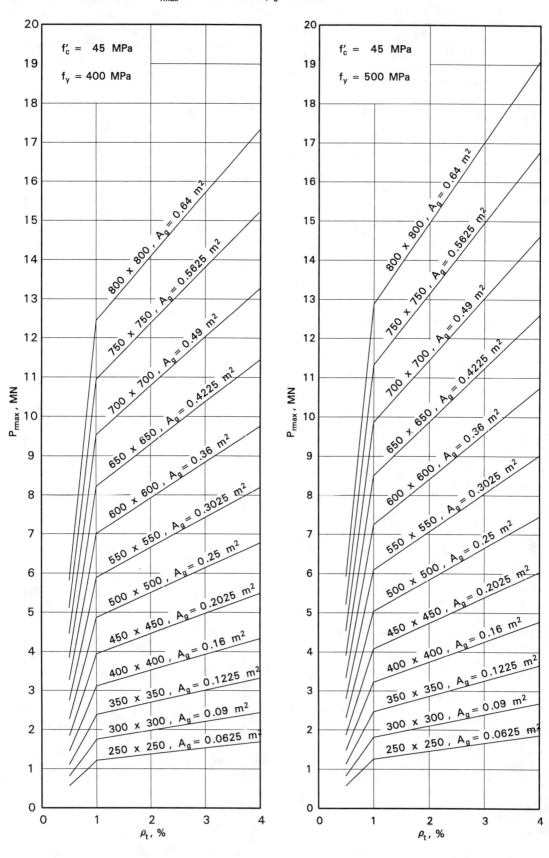

Table 7.2 Values of gamma, γ, for Columns

h	Longitudinal Bar Size						
mm	15	20	25	30	35	45	55
	40 mm cover to No. 10 ties						
250	0.53	0.51	0.49	0.47			
300	0.60	0.59	0.57	0.56	0.54	0.51	
350	0.66	0.65	0.63	0.62	0.60	0.58	
400	0.70	0.69	0.68	0.67	0.65	0.63	
450	0.74	0.73	0.72	0.71	0.69	0.67	
500	0.76	0.76	0.74	0.73	0.72	0.71	
550	0.78	0.78	0.77	0.76	0.75	0.73	
600	0.80	0.80	0.79	0.78	0.77	0.76	
650	0.82	0.81	0.80	0.80	0.79	0.77	
700	0.83	0.83	0.82	0.81	0.80	0.79	
750	0.84	0.84	0.83	0.82	0.82	0.80	
800	0.85	0.85	0.84	0.83	0.83	0.82	
850	0.86	0.86	0.85	0.84	0.84	0.83	
900	0.87	0.86	0.86	0.85	0.85	0.84	
950	0.88	0.87	0.87	0.86	0.85	0.85	
1000	0.88	0.88	0.87	0.87	0.86	0.85	
1100	0.89	0.89	0.88	0.88	0.87	0.87	
1200	0.90	0.90	0.89	0.89	0.88	0.88	
1300	0.91	0.91	0.90	0.90	0.89	0.89	
1400	0.92	0.91	0.91	0.91	0.90	0.90	
1500	0.92	0.92	0.91	0.91	0.91	0.90	
1600	0.93	0.92	0.92	0.92	0.91	0.91	
	50 mm cover to No. 10 ties						
300	0.54	0.53	0.51	0.49			
350	0.60	0.59	0.58	0.56	0.55	0.52	0.49
400	0.65	0.64	0.63	0.62	0.60	0.58	0.55
450	0.69	0.68	0.67	0.66	0.65	0.63	0.60
500	0.72	0.72	0.70	0.69	0.68	0.67	0.64
550	0.75	0.74	0.73	0.72	0.71	0.70	0.67
600	0.77	0.76	0.75	0.75	0.74	0.72	0.70
650	0.79	0.78	0.77	0.77	0.76	0.74	0.72
700	0.80	0.80	0.79	0.78	0.77	0.76	0.74
750	0.82	0.81	0.80	0.80	0.79	0.78	0.76
800	0.83	0.82	0.82	0.81	0.80	0.79	0.78
850	0.84	0.83	0.83	0.82	0.81	0.80	0.79
900	0.85	0.84	0.84	0.83	0.82	0.82	0.80
950	0.85	0.85	0.84	0.84	0.83	0.82	0.81
1000	0.86	0.86	0.85	0.85	0.84	0.83	0.82
1100	0.87	0.87	0.87	0.86	0.86	0.85	0.84
1200	0.88	0.88	0.88	0.87	0.87	0.86	0.85
1300	0.89	0.89	0.89	0.88	0.88	0.87	0.86
1400	0.90	0.90	0.89	0.89	0.89	0.88	0.87
1500	0.91	0.91	0.90	0.90	0.89	0.89	0.88
1600	0.91	0.91	0.91	0.90	0.90	0.90	0.89

Table 7.3 Minimum Column Dimensions and Cover Requirements for Rectangular or Circular* Columns with $k\ell_u \leq 7.3$ m

Condition	Concrete Type	Over-design Factor	Fire Rating, R Hours		
			1	2	3
$3.7 < k\ell_u \leq 7.3$ and $\rho_t \leq 3\%$	L or L40S	1.00	180	270	300
		1.25	165	248	300
		1.50	150	225	300
	S	1.00	240	300	320
		1.25	220	300	300
		1.50	200	300	300
	N	1.00	240	300	300
		1.25	220	300	300
		1.50	200	300	300
All Other Conditions	L or L40S	1.00	150	225	300
		1.25	135	203	270
		1.50	125	187	249
	S	1.00	160	240	320
		1.25	144	216	288
		1.50	133	199	266
	N	1.00	140	220	300
		1.25	126	198	270
		1.50	116	183	249
Cover to Principal Reinforcement for fire protection			25	50	50

Cover to Principal Reinforcement for Corrosion Protection

Not exposed to earth or weather, No. 35 bars & smaller		40
Not exposed to earth or weather, No. 45 bars		45
Exposed to earth or weather, No. 35 bars and smaller		50
Not exposed to earth or weather, No. 55 bars		55
Exposed to earth or weather, No. 45 and No. 55 bars		60
Exposed to chlorides#	No. 35	70
	No. 45	90
	No. 55	110

Cover to Ties and Spirals for Corrosion Protection

Not exposed to earth or weather	30
Exposed to earth or weather	40
Exposed to chlorides#	60
Cast against & permanently exposed to earth, all sizes	75

*Circular columns must have a diameter at least 1.2 times the size shown in the table.

The column sizes and cover requirements for fire are in accordance with Appendix D of the supplement to the NATIONAL BUILDING CODE OF CANADA, 1995.

#For parking structures, bridges, and offshore structures see CSA Standards S413, S6, and S474.

Table 7.4.1   Interaction Diagrams for Rectangular Columns with an Equal Number of Bars on all Four Faces.

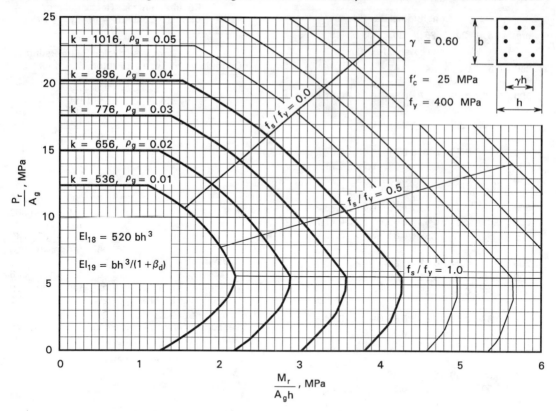

Table 7.4.2   Interaction Diagrams for Rectangular Columns with an Equal Number of Bars on all Four Faces.

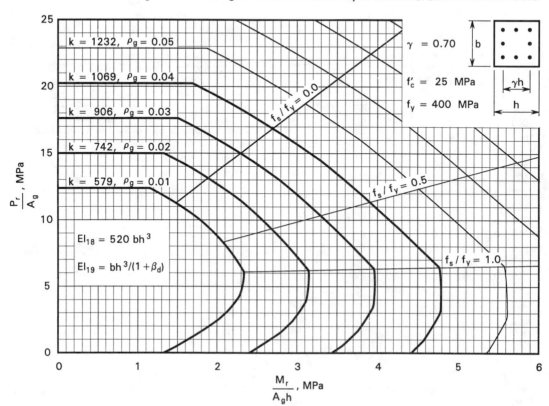

Table 7.4.3   Interaction Diagrams for Rectangular Columns with an Equal Number of Bars on all Four Faces.

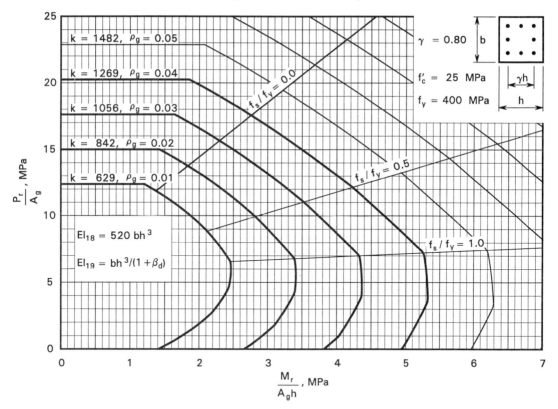

Table 7.4.4   Interaction Diagrams for Rectangular Columns with an Equal Number of Bars on all Four Faces.

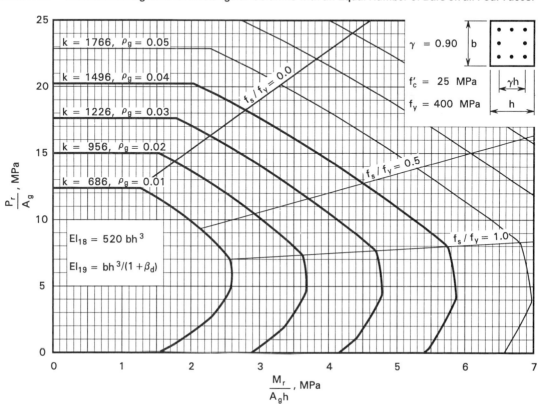

Table 7.4.5   Interaction Diagrams for Rectangular Columns with an Equal Number of Bars on all Four Faces.

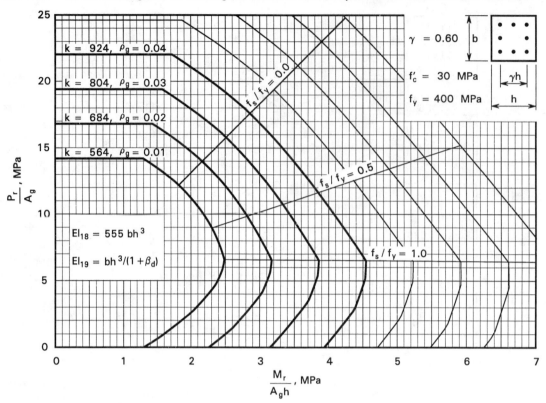

Table 7.4.5   Interaction Diagrams for Rectangular Columns with an Equal Number of Bars on all Four Faces.

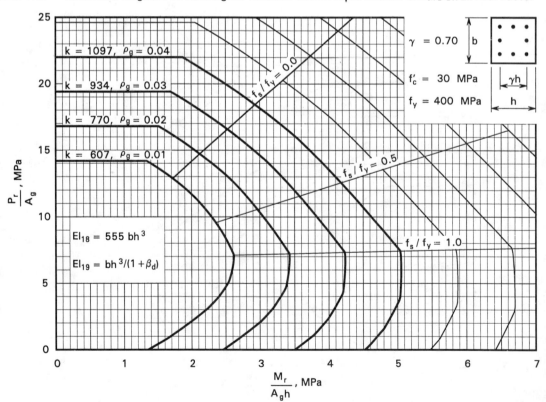

CPCA Concrete Design Handbook

Table 7.4.7   Interaction Diagrams for Rectangular Columns with an Equal Number of Bars on all Four Faces.

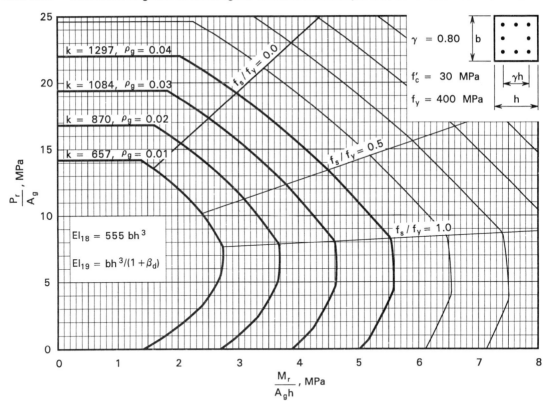

Table 7.4.8   Interaction Diagrams for Rectangular Columns with an Equal Number of Bars on all Four Faces.

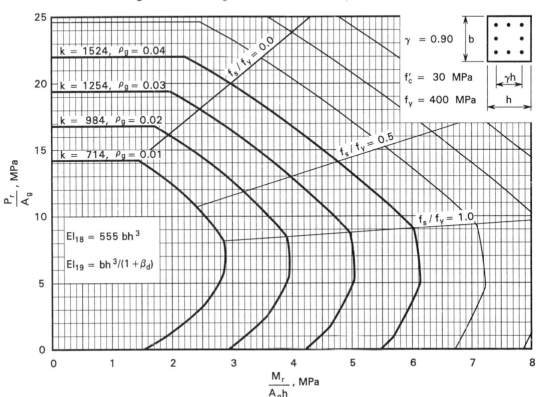

Table 7.4.9   Interaction Diagrams for Rectangular Columns with an Equal Number of Bars on all Four Faces.

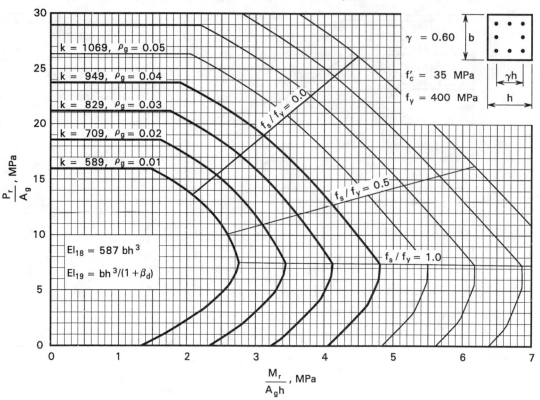

$$\frac{M_r}{A_g h}, MPa$$

Table 7.4.10   Interaction Diagrams for Rectangular Columns with an Equal Number of Bars on all Four Faces.

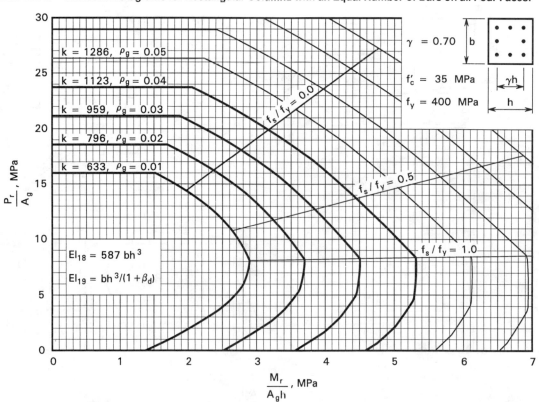

$$\frac{M_r}{A_g h}, MPa$$

Table 7.4.11 Interaction Diagrams for Rectangular Columns with an Equal Number of Bars on all Four Faces.

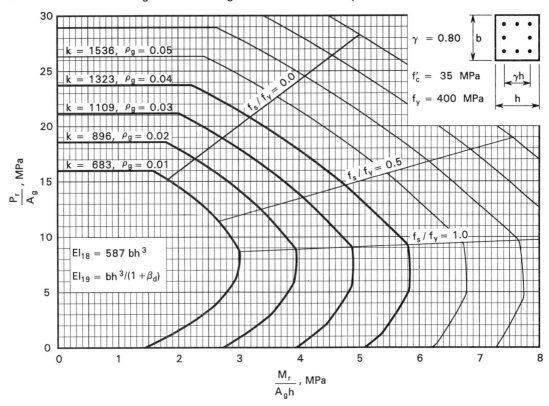

Table 7.4.12 Interaction Diagrams for Rectangular Columns with an Equal Number of Bars on all Four Faces.

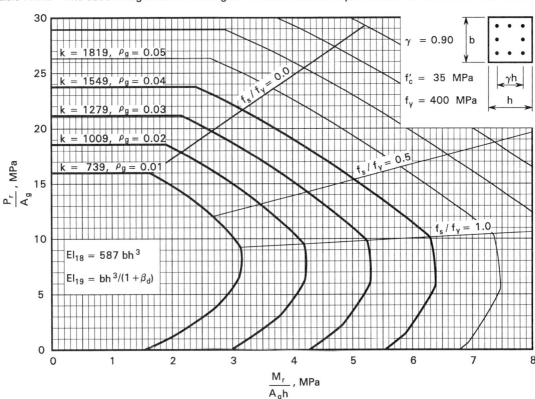

Table 7.4.13   Interaction Diagrams for Rectangular Columns with an Equal Number of Bars on all Four Faces.

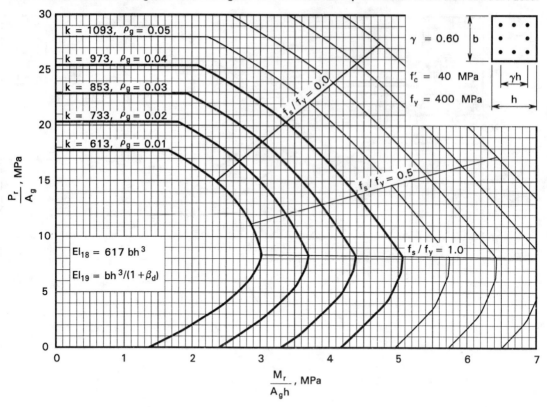

Table 7.4.14   Interaction Diagrams for Rectangular Columns with an Equal Number of Bars on all Four Faces.

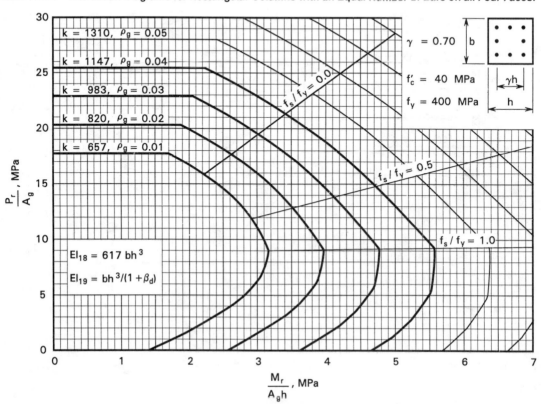

Table 7.4.15   Interaction Diagrams for Rectangular Columns with an Equal Number of Bars on all Four Faces.

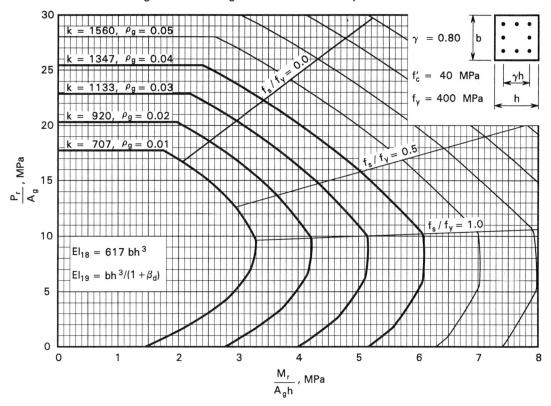

Table 7.4.16   Interaction Diagrams for Rectangular Columns with an Equal Number of Bars on all Four Faces.

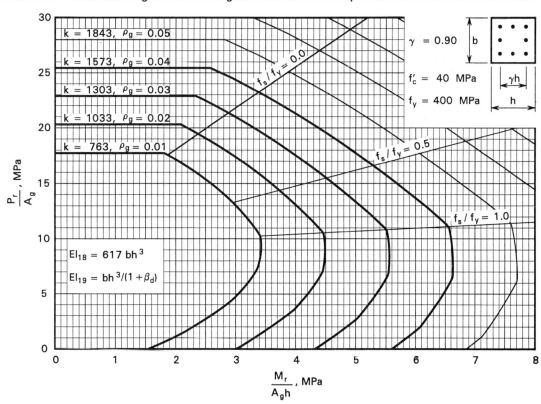

Table 7.4.17   Interaction Diagrams for Rectangular Columns with an Equal Number of Bars on all Four Faces.

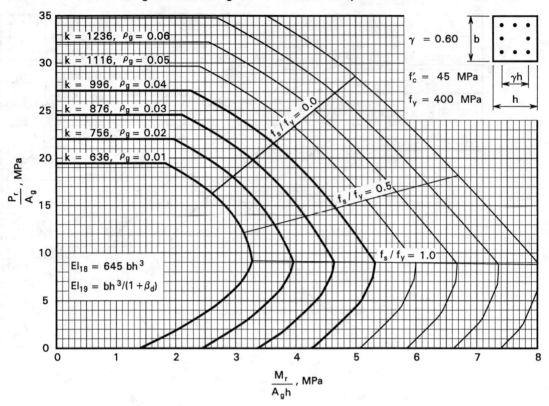

Table 7.4.18   Interaction Diagrams for Rectangular Columns with an Equal Number of Bars on all Four Faces.

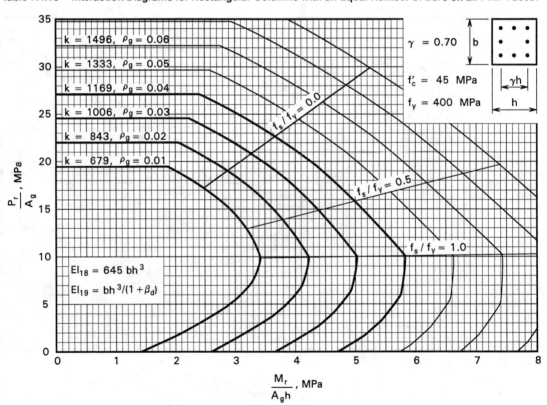

Table 7.4.19   Interaction Diagrams for Rectangular Columns with an Equal Number of Bars on all Four Faces.

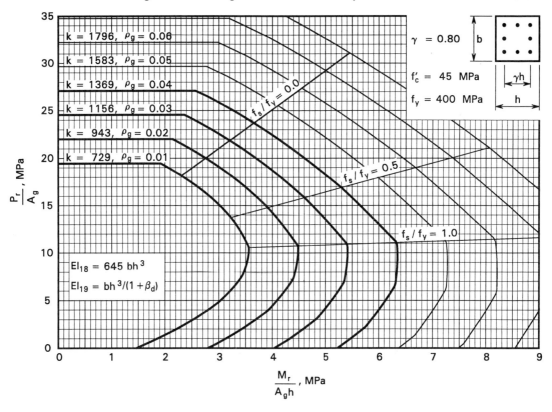

Table 7.4.20   Interaction Diagrams for Rectangular Columns with an Equal Number of Bars on all Four Faces.

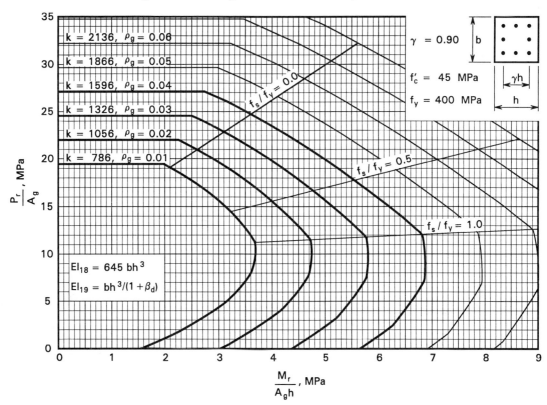

Table 7.5.1   Interaction Diagrams for Rectangular Columns with Bars in the Two End Faces Only.

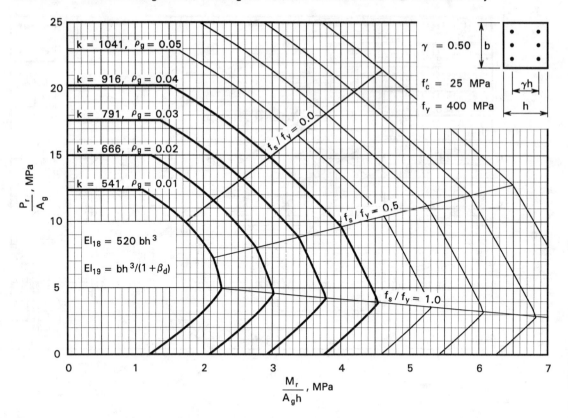

Table 7.5.2   Interaction Diagrams for Rectangular Columns with Bars in the Two End Faces Only.

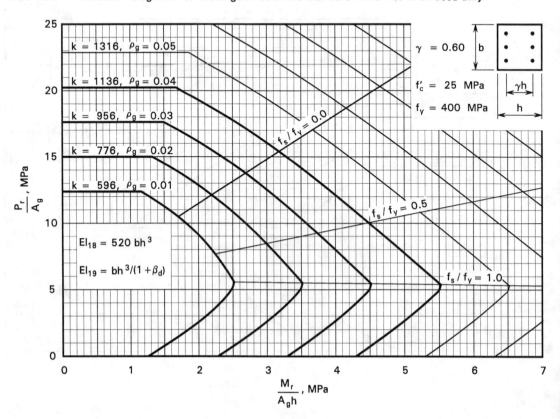

Table 7.5.3   Interaction Diagrams for Rectangular Columns with Bars in the Two End Faces Only.

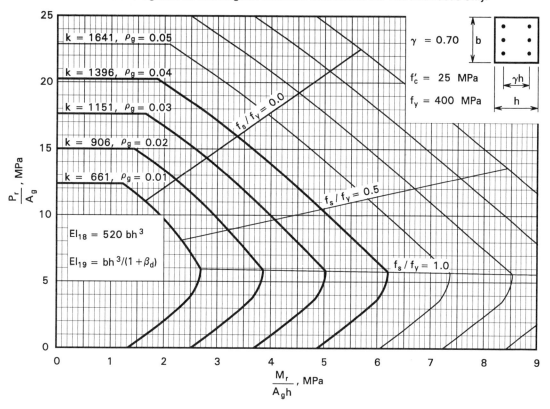

Table 7.5.4   Interaction Diagrams for Rectangular Columns with Bars in the Two End Faces Only.

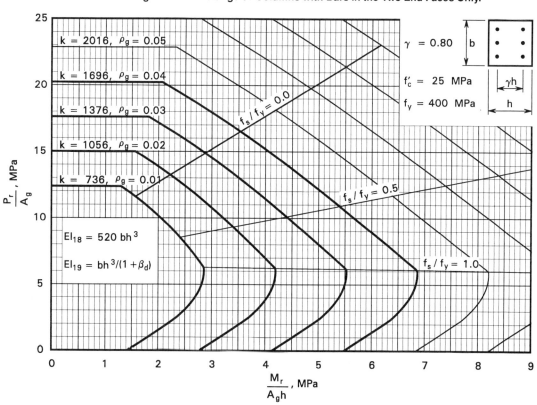

Table 7.5.5   Interaction Diagrams for Rectangular Columns with Bars in the Two End Faces Only.

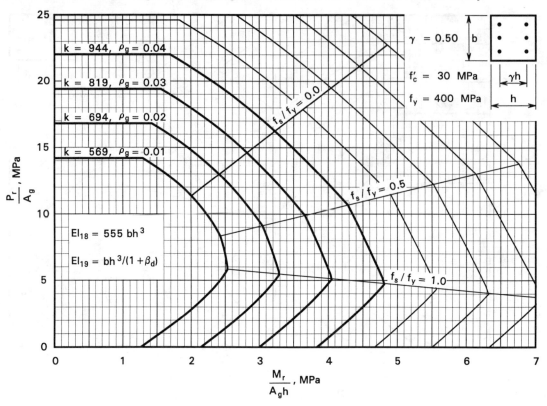

Table 7.5.6   Interaction Diagrams for Rectangular Columns with Bars in the Two End Faces Only.

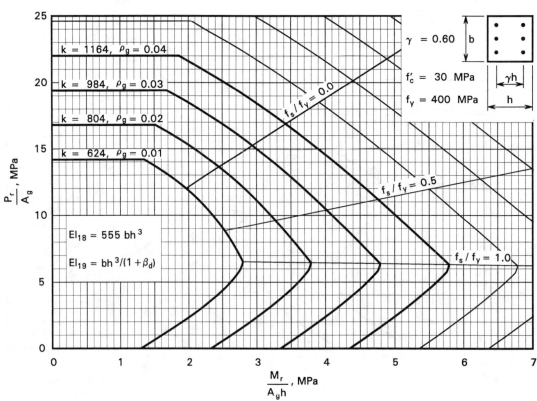

Table 7.5.7   Interaction Diagrams for Rectangular Columns with Bars in the Two End Faces Only.

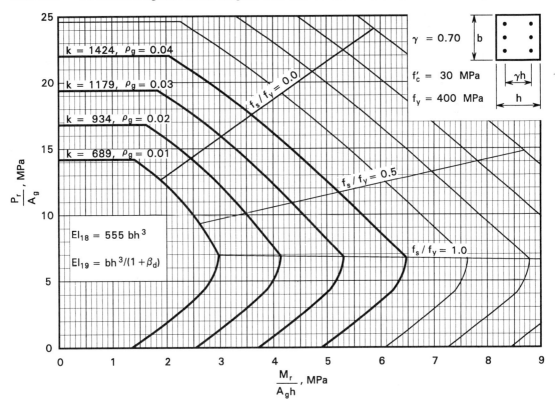

Table 7.5.8   Interaction Diagrams for Rectangular Columns with Bars in the Two End Faces Only.

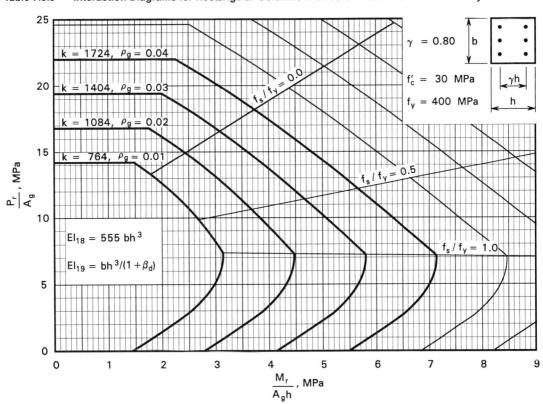

Table 7.5.9   Interaction Diagrams for Rectangular Columns with Bars in the Two End Faces Only.

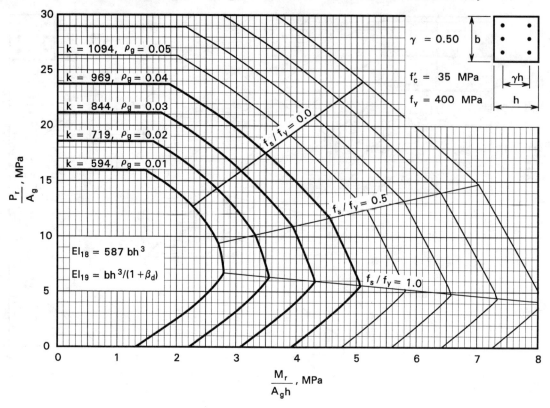

Table 7.5.10   Interaction Diagrams for Rectangular Columns with Bars in the Two End Faces Only.

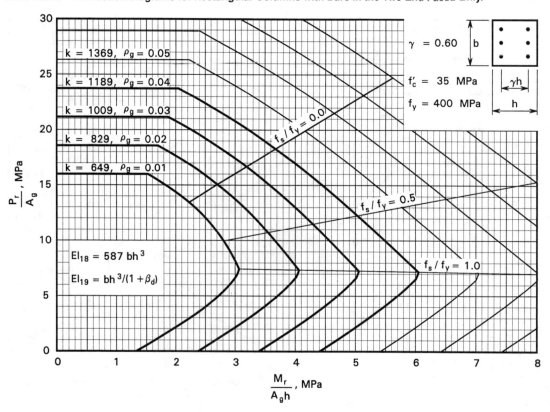

Table 7.5.11   Interaction Diagrams for Rectangular Columns with Bars in the Two End Faces Only.

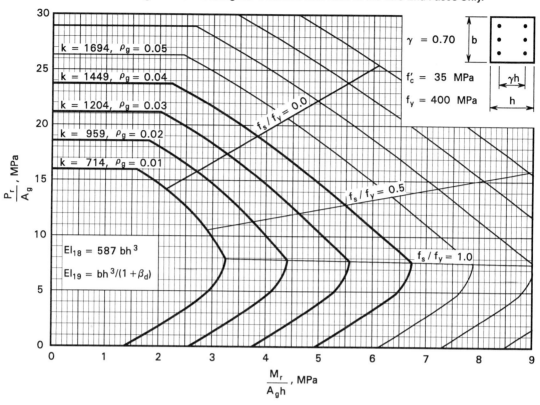

Table 7.5.12   Interaction Diagrams for Rectangular Columns with Bars in the Two End Faces Only.

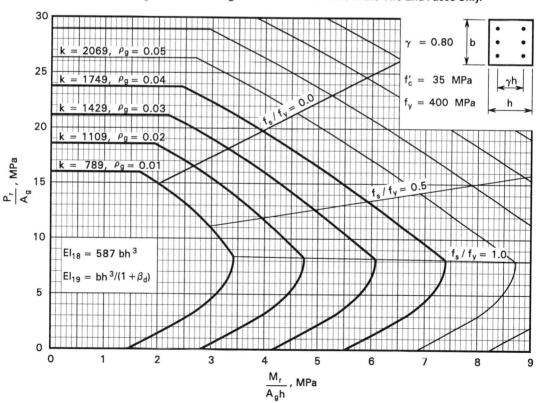

Table 7.5.13   Interaction Diagrams for Rectangular Columns with Bars in the Two End Faces Only.

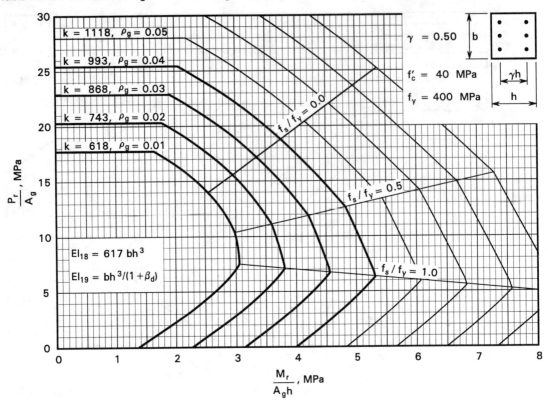

Table 7.5.14   Interaction Diagrams for Rectangular Columns with Bars in the Two End Faces Only.

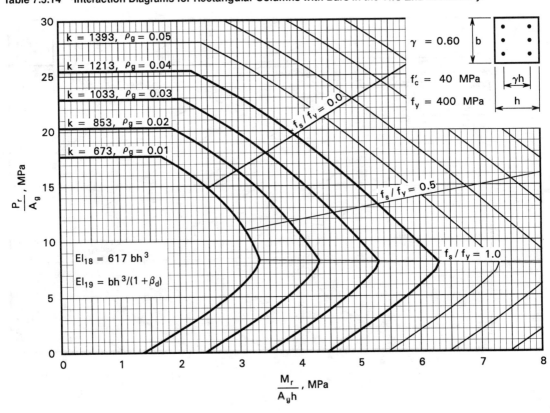

Table 7.5.15 Interaction Diagrams for Rectangular Columns with Bars in the Two End Faces Only.

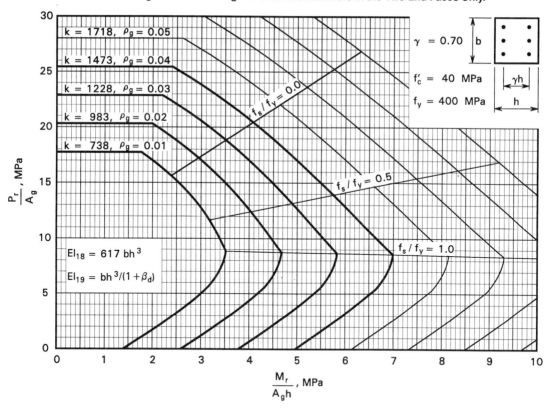

Table 7.5.16 Interaction Diagrams for Rectangular Columns with Bars in the Two End Faces Only.

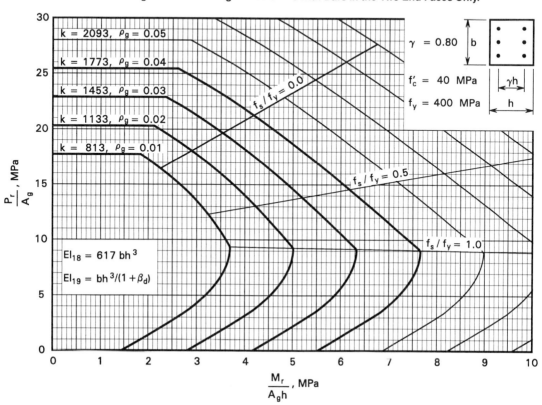

Table 7.5.17   Interaction Diagrams for Rectangular Columns with Bars in the Two End Faces Only.

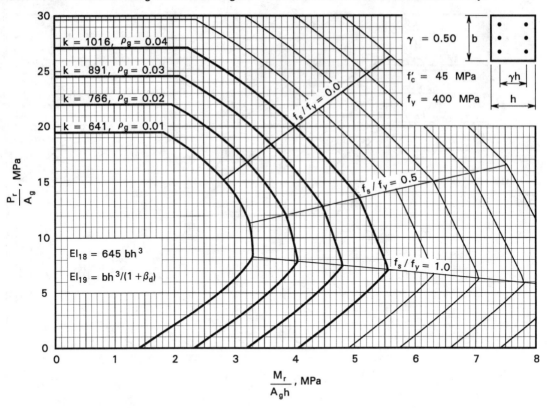

Table 7.5.18   Interaction Diagrams for Rectangular Columns with Bars in the Two End Faces Only.

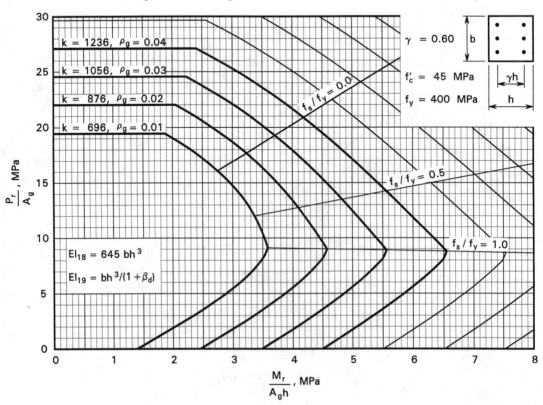

Table 7.5.19   Interaction Diagrams for Rectangular Columns with Bars in the Two End Faces Only.

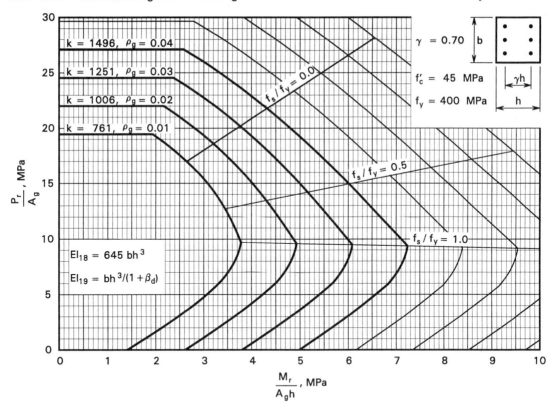

Table 7.5.20   Interaction Diagrams for Rectangular Columns with Bars in the Two End Faces Only.

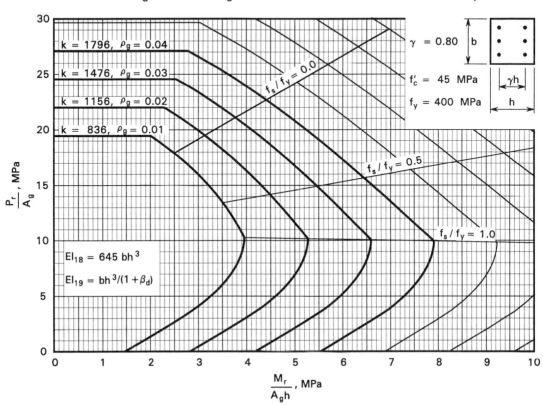

Table 7.6.1   Interaction Diagrams for Rectangular Columns with Bars in the Two Side Faces Only.

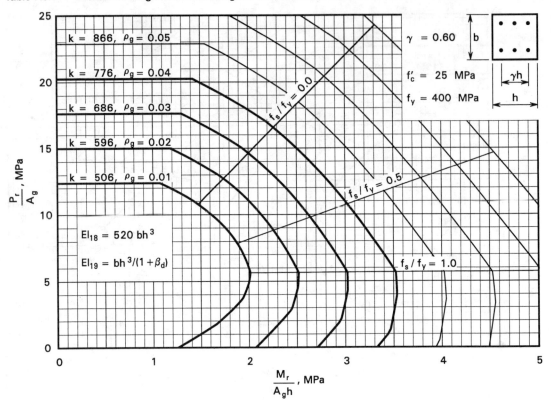

Table 7.6.2   Interaction Diagrams for Rectangular Columns with Bars in the Two Side Faces Only.

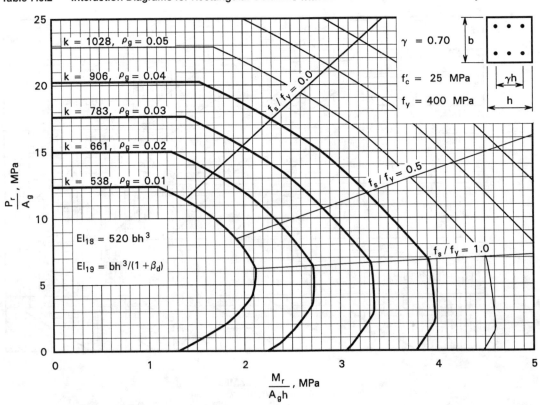

CPCA Concrete Design Handbook

Table 7.6.3 Interaction Diagrams for Rectangular Columns with Bars in the Two Side Faces Only.

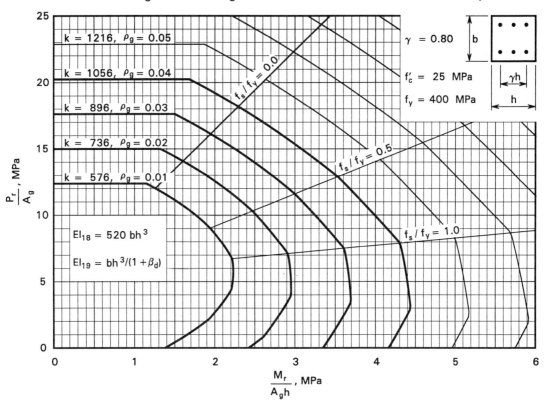

Table 7.6.4 Interaction Diagrams for Rectangular Columns with Bars in the Two Side Faces Only.

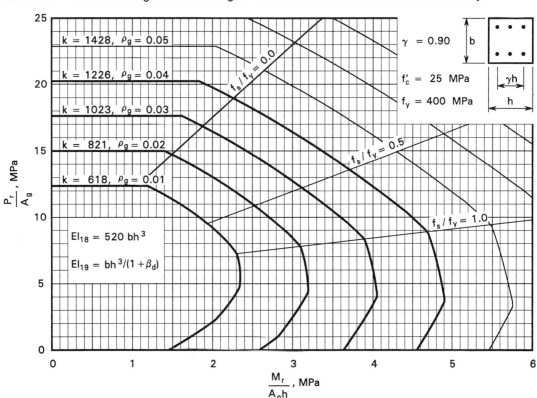

Table 7.6.5   Interaction Diagrams for Rectangular Columns with Bars in the Two Side Faces Only.

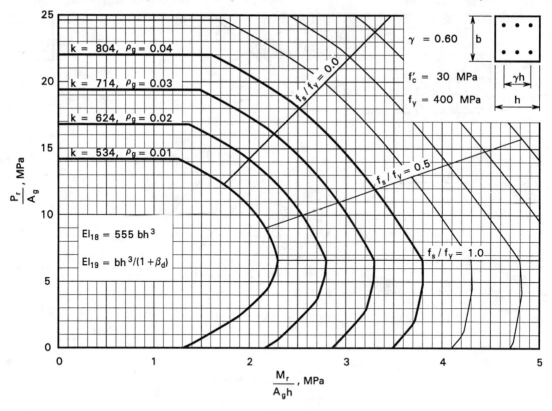

Table 7.6.6   Interaction Diagrams for Rectangular Columns with Bars in the Two Side Faces Only.

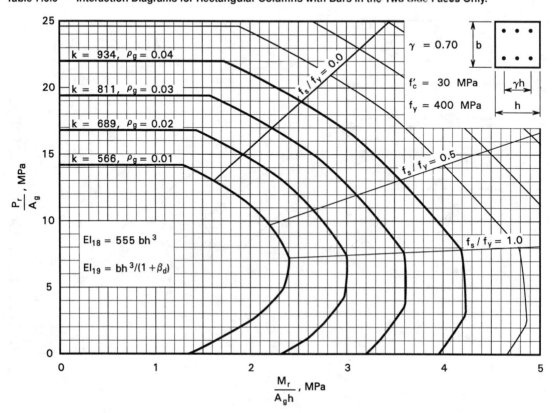

Table 7.6.7   Interaction Diagrams for Rectangular Columns with Bars in the Two Side Faces Only.

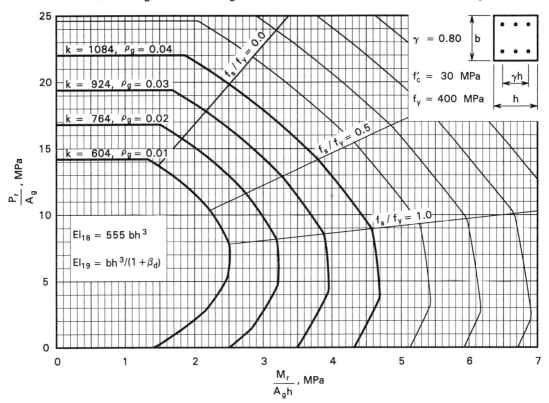

Table 7.6.8   Interaction Diagrams for Rectangular Columns with Bars in the Two Side Faces Only.

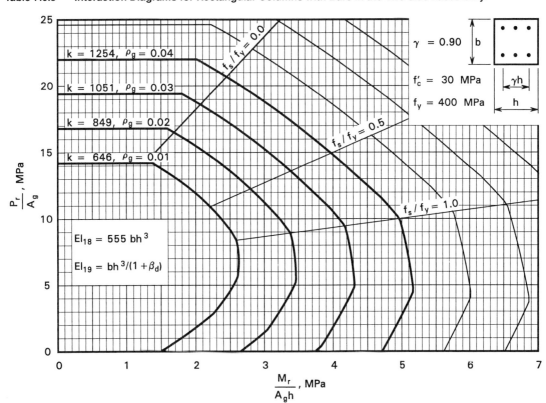

Table 7.6.9   Interaction Diagrams for Rectangular Columns with Bars in the Two Side Faces Only.

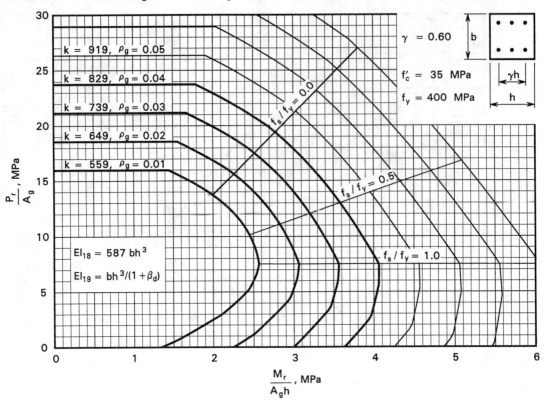

Table 7.6.10   Interaction Diagrams for Rectangular Columns with Bars in the Two Side Faces Only.

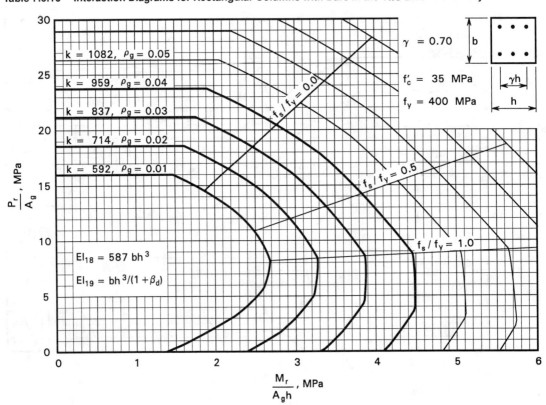

Table 7.6.11   Interaction Diagrams for Rectangular Columns with Bars in the Two Side Faces Only.

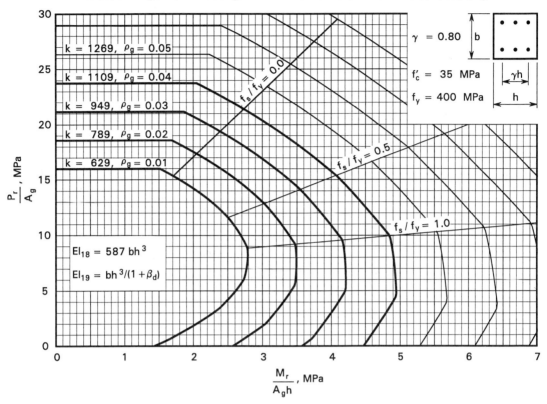

Table 7.6.12   Interaction Diagrams for Rectangular Columns with Bars in the Two Side Faces Only.

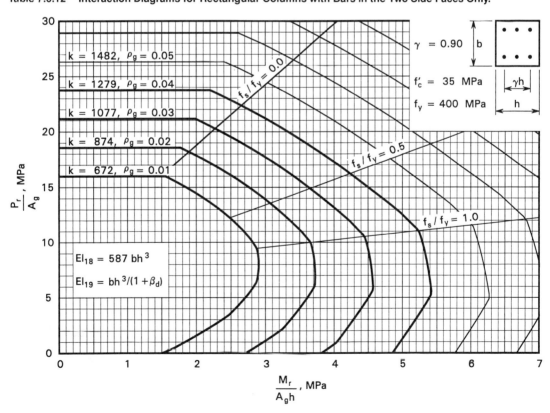

Table 7.6.13   Interaction Diagrams for Rectangular Columns with Bars in the Two Side Faces Only.

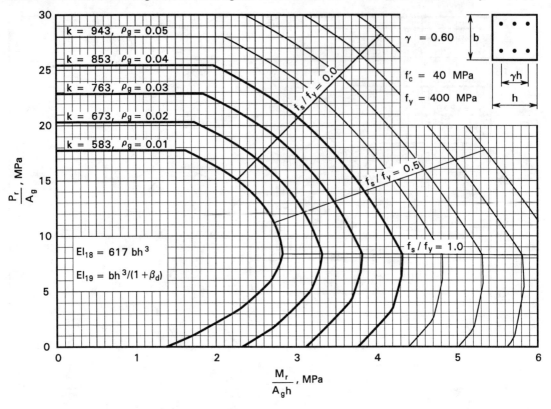

Table 7.6.14   Interaction Diagrams for Rectangular Columns with Bars in the Two Side Faces Only.

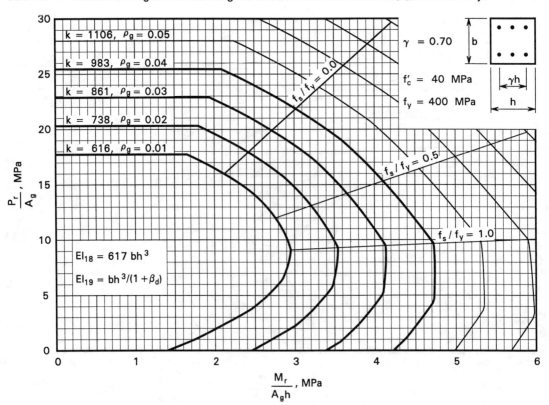

Table 7.6.15 Interaction Diagrams for Rectangular Columns with Bars in the Two Side Faces Only.

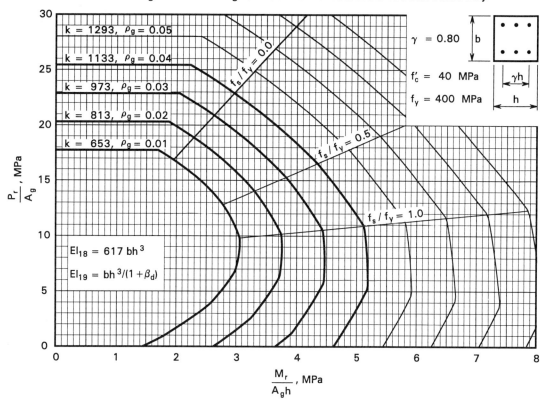

Table 7.6.16 Interaction Diagrams for Rectangular Columns with Bars in the Two Side Faces Only.

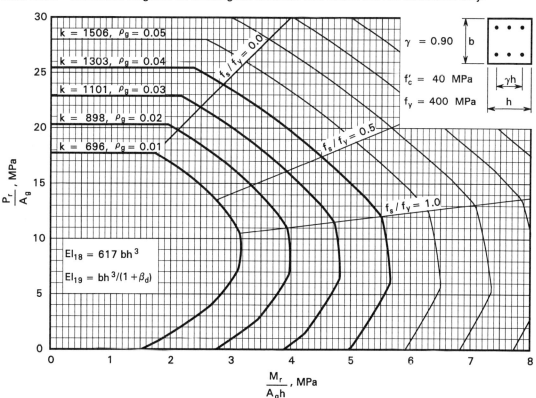

Table 7.6.17   Interaction Diagrams for Rectangular Columns with Bars in the Two Side Faces Only.

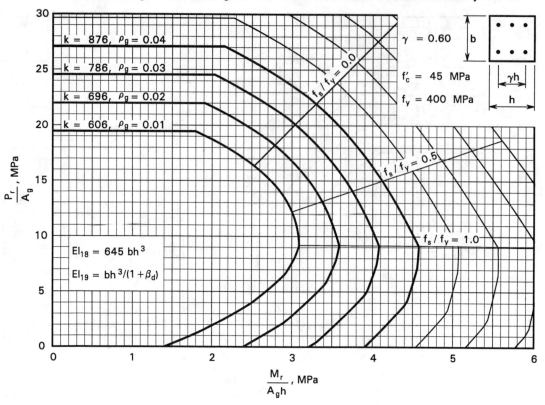

Table 7.6.18   Interaction Diagrams for Rectangular Columns with Bars in the Two Side Faces Only.

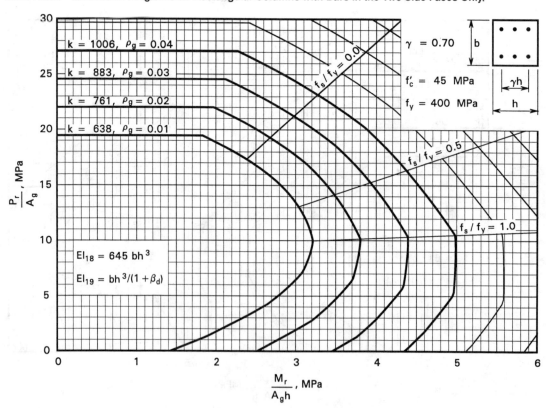

Table 7.6.19   Interaction Diagrams for Rectangular Columns with Bars in the Two Side Faces Only.

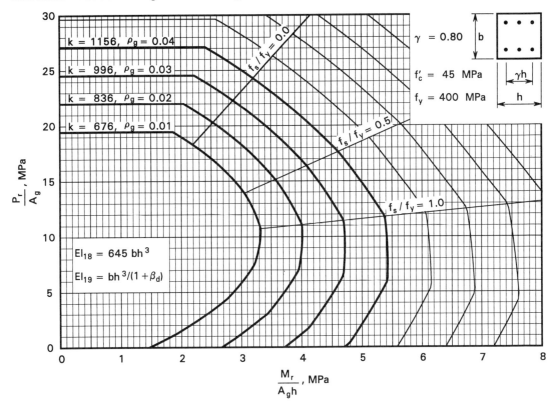

Table 7.6.20   Interaction Diagrams for Rectangular Columns with Bars in the Two Side Faces Only.

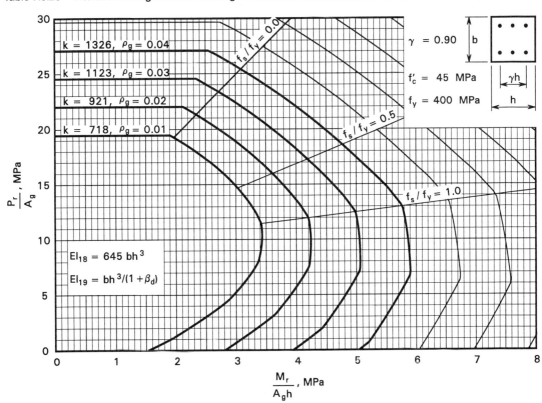

Table 7.7.1 Interaction Diagrams for Circular Tied or Spiral Columns.

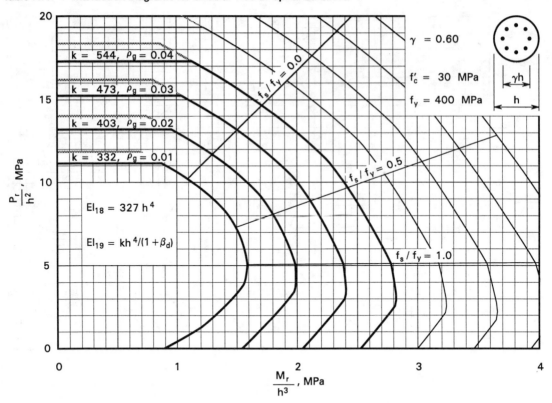

Table 7.7.2 Interaction Diagrams for Circular Tied or Spiral Columns.

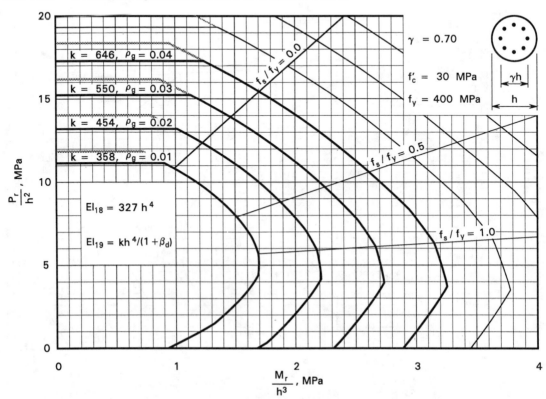

Table 7.7.3   Interaction Diagrams for Circular Tied or Spiral Columns.

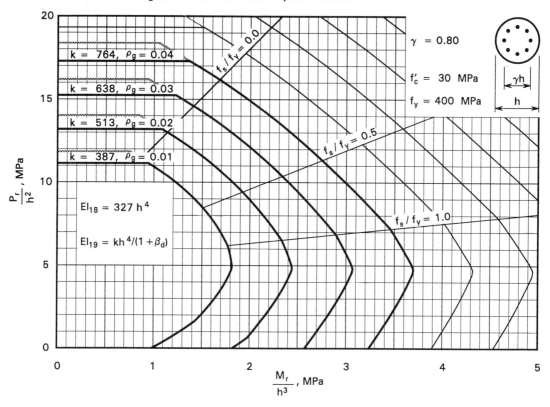

Table 7.7.4   Interaction Diagrams for Circular Tied or Spiral Columns.

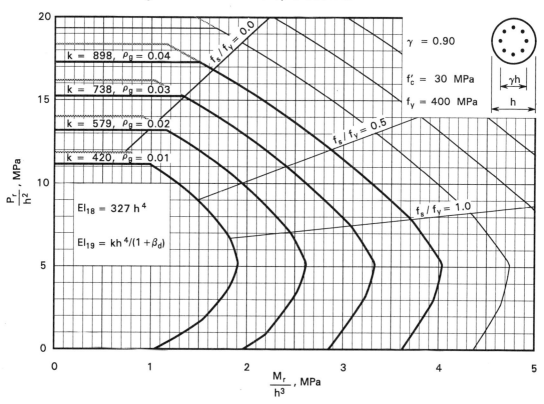

Table 7.7.5   Interaction Diagrams for Circular Tied or Spiral Columns.

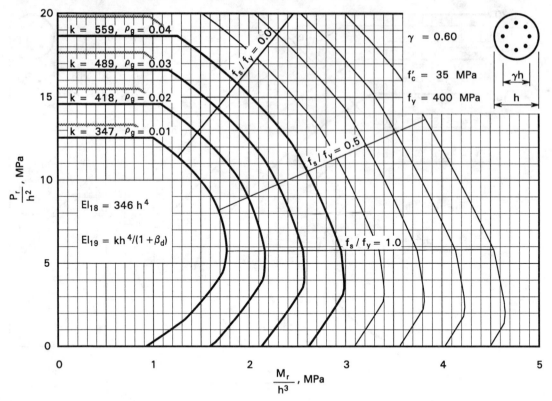

Table 7.7.6   Interaction Diagrams for Circular Tied or Spiral Columns.

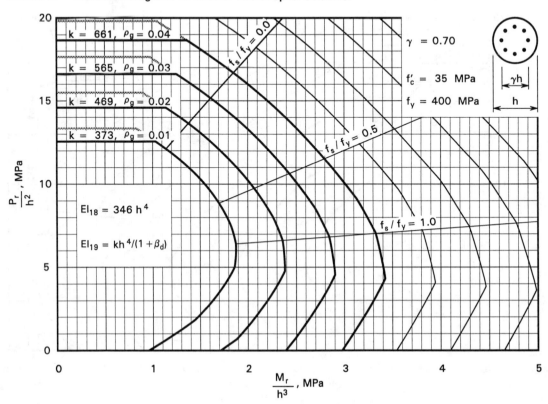

Table 7.7.7   Interaction Diagrams for Circular Tied or Spiral Columns.

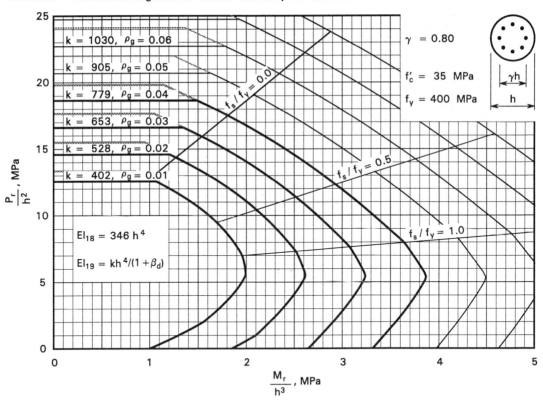

Table 7.7.8   Interaction Diagrams for Circular Tied or Spiral Columns.

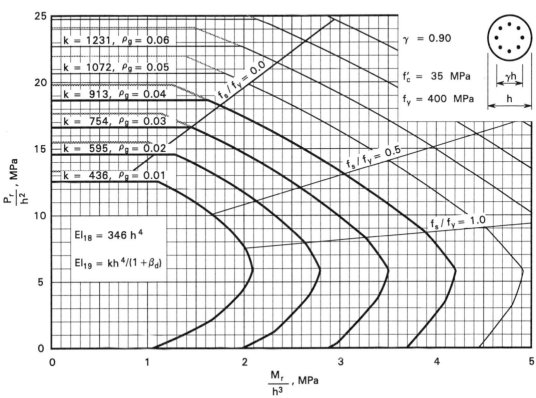

Table 7.7.9   Interaction Diagrams for Circular Tied or Spiral Columns.

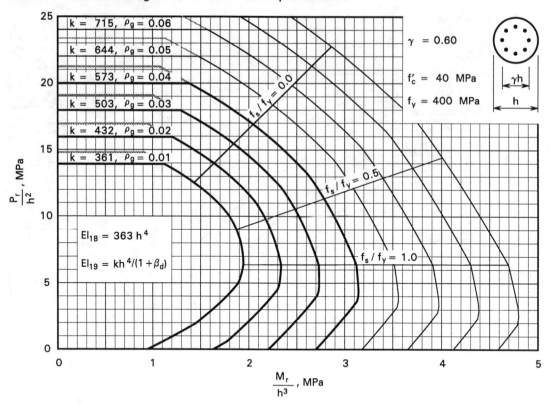

Table 7.7.10   Interaction Diagrams for Circular Tied or Spiral Columns.

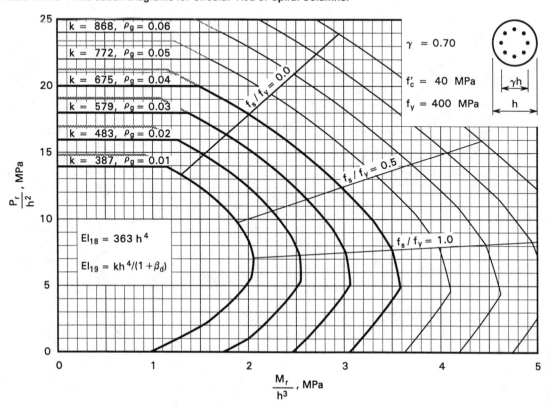

Table 7.7.11   Interaction Diagrams for Circular Tied or Spiral Columns.

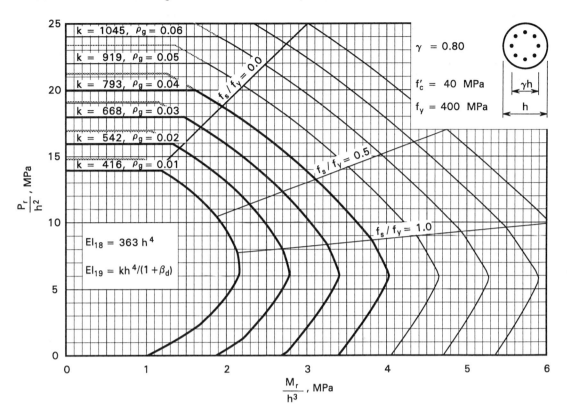

Table 7.7.12   Interaction Diagrams for Circular Tied or Spiral Columns.

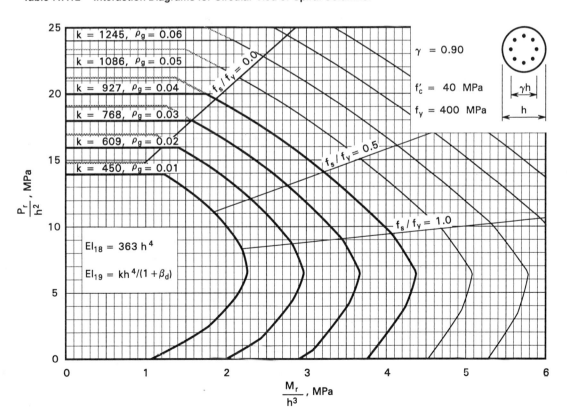

Table 7.7.13   Interaction Diagrams for Circular Tied or Spiral Columns.

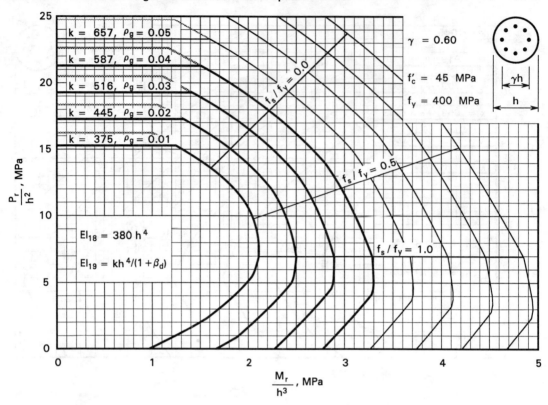

Table 7.7.14   Interaction Diagrams for Circular Tied or Spiral Columns.

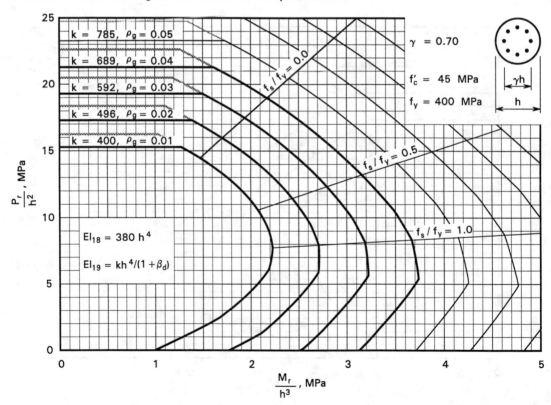

Table 7.7.15   Interaction Diagrams for Circular Tied or Spiral Columns.

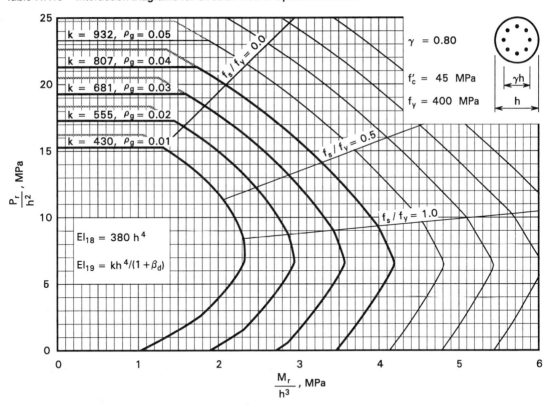

Table 7.7.16   Interaction Diagrams for Circular Tied or Spiral Columns.

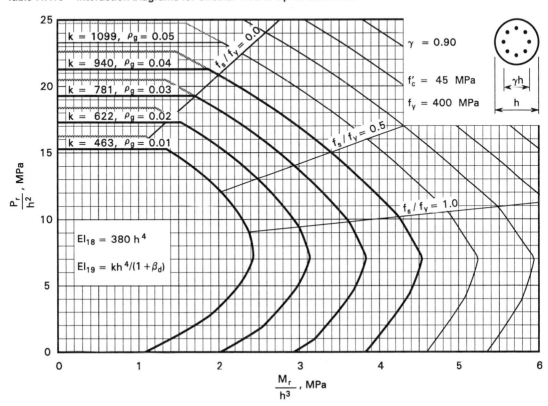

Table 7.8 Reinforcement Ratios for Rectangular Columns Reinforced on Four Faces, 40 mm Cover to No. 10 Ties

b or h = 300

Bars Total → Size ↓	8	12	16	20	8	12	16	20	8	12	16	20	8	12	16	20	8	12	16	20
b or h →	300				350				400				450				500			
15	1.78	2.67			1.52	2.29			1.33	2.00			1.19	1.78			1.07	1.60		
20	2.67	4.00			2.29	3.43			2.00	3.00			1.78	2.67			1.60	2.40		
25	4.44				3.81				3.33				2.96				2.67			
30	6.22				5.33				4.67				4.15				3.73			

b or h = 350

Size	8	12	16	20	8	12	16	20	8	12	16	20	8	12	16	20	8	12	16	20
b or h →	350				400				450				500				550			
15	1.31	1.96	2.61		1.14	1.71	2.29		1.02	1.52	2.03		0.91	1.37	1.83		0.83	1.25	1.66	
20	1.96	2.94	3.92		1.71	2.57	3.43		1.52	2.29	3.05		1.37	2.06	2.74		1.25	1.87	2.49	
25	3.27	4.90			2.86	4.29			2.54	3.81			2.29	3.43			2.08	3.12		
30	4.57				4.00				3.56				3.20				2.91			
35	6.53				5.71				5.08				4.57				4.16			

b or h = 400

Size	8	12	16	20	8	12	16	20	8	12	16	20	8	12	16	20	8	12	16	20
b or h →	400				450				500				550				600			
15	1.00	1.50	2.00	2.50	0.89	1.33	1.78	2.22	0.80	1.20	1.60	2.00	0.73	1.09	1.45	1.82	0.67	1.00	1.33	1.67
20	1.50	2.25	3.00	3.75	1.33	2.00	2.67	3.33	1.20	1.80	2.40	3.00	1.09	1.64	2.18	2.73	1.00	1.50	2.00	2.50
25	2.50	3.75	5.00		2.22	3.33	4.44		2.00	3.00	4.00		1.82	2.73	3.64		1.67	2.50	3.33	
30	3.50	5.25			3.11	4.67			2.80	4.20			2.55	3.82			2.33	3.50		
35	5.00				4.44				4.00				3.64				3.33			

b or h = 450

Size	8	12	16	20	8	12	16	20	8	12	16	20	8	12	16	20	8	12	16	20
b or h →	450				500				550				600				650			
15	0.79	1.19	1.58	1.98	0.71	1.07	1.42	1.78	0.65	0.97	1.29	1.62	0.59	0.89	1.19	1.48	0.55	0.82	1.09	1.37
20	1.19	1.78	2.37	2.96	1.07	1.60	2.13	2.67	0.97	1.45	1.94	2.42	0.89	1.33	1.78	2.22	0.82	1.23	1.64	2.05
25	1.98	2.96	3.95	4.94	1.78	2.67	3.56	4.44	1.62	2.42	3.23	4.04	1.48	2.22	2.96	3.70	1.37	2.05	2.74	3.42
30	2.77	4.15	5.53		2.49	3.73	4.98		2.26	3.39	4.53		2.07	3.11	4.15		1.91	2.87	3.83	
35	3.95	5.93			3.56	5.33			3.23	4.85			2.96	4.44			2.74	4.10		

b or h = 500

Size	8	12	16	20	8	12	16	20	8	12	16	20	8	12	16	20	8	12	16	20
b or h →	500				550				600				650				700			
20	0.96	1.44	1.92	2.40	0.87	1.31	1.75	2.18	0.80	1.20	1.60	2.00	0.74	1.11	1.48	1.85	0.69	1.03	1.37	1.71
25	1.60	2.40	3.20	4.00	1.45	2.18	2.91	3.64	1.33	2.00	2.67	3.33	1.23	1.85	2.46	3.08	1.14	1.71	2.29	2.86
30	2.24	3.36	4.48	5.60	2.04	3.05	4.07	5.09	1.87	2.80	3.73	4.67	1.72	2.58	3.45	4.31	1.60	2.40	3.20	4.00
35	3.20	4.80	6.40		2.91	4.36	5.82		2.67	4.00	5.33		2.46	3.69	4.92		2.29	3.43	4.57	

b or h = 550

Size	8	12	16	20	8	12	16	20	8	12	16	20	8	12	16	20	8	12	16	20
b or h →	550				600				650				700				750			
20	0.79	1.19	1.59	1.98	0.73	1.09	1.45	1.82	0.67	1.01	1.34	1.68	0.62	0.94	1.25	1.56	0.58	0.87	1.16	1.45
25	1.32	1.98	2.64	3.31	1.21	1.82	2.42	3.03	1.12	1.68	2.24	2.80	1.04	1.56	2.08	2.60	0.97	1.45	1.94	2.42
30	1.85	2.78	3.70	4.63	1.70	2.55	3.39	4.24	1.57	2.35	3.13	3.92	1.45	2.18	2.91	3.64	1.36	2.04	2.72	3.39
35	2.64	3.97	5.29		2.42	3.64	4.85		2.24	3.36	4.48		2.08	3.12	4.16		1.94	2.91	3.88	

b or h = 600

Size	8	12	16	20	8	12	16	20	8	12	16	20	8	12	16	20	8	12	16	20
b or h →	600				650				700				750				800			
20	0.67	1.00	1.33	1.67	0.62	0.92	1.23	1.54	0.57	0.86	1.14	1.43	0.53	0.80	1.07	1.33	0.50	0.75	1.00	1.25
25	1.11	1.67	2.22	2.78	1.03	1.54	2.05	2.56	0.95	1.43	1.90	2.38	0.89	1.33	1.78	2.22	0.83	1.25	1.67	2.08
30	1.56	2.33	3.11	3.89	1.44	2.15	2.87	3.59	1.33	2.00	2.67	3.33	1.24	1.87	2.49	3.11	1.17	1.75	2.33	2.92
35	2.22	3.33	4.44	5.56	2.05	3.08	4.10	5.13	1.90	2.86	3.81	4.76	1.78	2.67	3.56	4.44	1.67	2.50	3.33	4.17

b or h = 650

Size	8	12	16	20	8	12	16	20	8	12	16	20	8	12	16	20	8	12	16	20
b or h →	650				700				750				800				850			
20	0.57	0.85	1.14	1.42	0.53	0.79	1.05	1.32		0.74	0.98	1.23		0.69	0.92	1.15		0.65	0.87	1.09
25	0.95	1.42	1.89	2.37	0.88	1.32	1.76	2.20	0.82	1.23	1.64	2.05	0.77	1.15	1.54	1.92	0.72	1.09	1.45	1.81
30	1.33	1.99	2.65	3.31	1.23	1.85	2.46	3.08	1.15	1.72	2.30	2.87	1.08	1.62	2.15	2.69	1.01	1.52	2.03	2.53
35	1.89	2.84	3.79	4.73	1.76	2.64	3.52	4.40	1.64	2.46	3.28	4.10	1.54	2.31	3.08	3.85	1.45	2.17	2.90	3.62

All bar combinations shown may be spliced with bearing splices. Values above the line may be spliced with tangential or radial splices. If a reinforcement ratio greater than 4% is used, the splice location must be staggered by at least 750 mm.

If reinforcement ratios less than 1% are used, the factored resistance must be reduced as specified in Clause 10.10.5.

Table 7.9   Reinforcement Ratios for Rectangular Columns Reinforced on Two Faces, 40 mm Cover to No. 10 Ties

Bars	Total	4	6	8	10	12	4	6	8	10	12	4	6	8	10	12	4	6	8	10	12
	Size	h = 250					300					350					400				
b = 250	15	1.28	1.92				1.07	1.60				0.91	1.37				0.80	1.20			
	20	1.92	2.88				1.60	2.40				1.37	2.06				1.20	1.80			
300	15	1.07	1.60	2.13			0.89	1.33	1.78			0.76	1.14	1.52			0.67	1.00	1.33		
	20	1.60	2.40	3.20			1.33	2.00	2.67			1.14	1.71	2.29			1.00	1.50	2.00		
	25	2.67	4.00				2.22	3.33				1.90	2.86				1.67	2.50			
	30						3.11	4.67				2.67	4.00				2.33	3.50			
350	15	0.91	1.37	1.83	2.29	2.74	0.76	1.14	1.52	1.90	2.29	0.65	0.98	1.31	1.63	1.96	0.57	0.86	1.14	1.43	1.71
	20	1.37	2.06	2.74	3.43		1.14	1.71	2.29	2.86		0.98	1.47	1.96	2.45		0.86	1.29	1.71	2.14	
	25	2.29	3.43	4.57			1.90	2.86	3.81			1.63	2.45	3.27			1.43	2.14	2.86		
	30						2.67	4.00	5.33			2.29	3.43	4.57			2.00	3.00	4.00		
	35						3.81	5.71				3.27	4.90				2.86	4.29			
400	15	0.80	1.20	1.60	2.00	2.40	0.67	1.00	1.33	1.67	2.00	0.57	0.86	1.14	1.43	1.71	0.50	0.75	1.00	1.25	1.50
	20	1.20	1.80	2.40	3.00	3.60	1.00	1.50	2.00	2.50	3.00	0.86	1.29	1.71	2.14	2.57	0.75	1.13	1.50	1.88	2.25
	25	2.00	3.00	4.00	5.00		1.67	2.50	3.33	4.17		1.43	2.14	2.86	3.57		1.25	1.88	2.50	3.13	
	30						2.33	3.50	4.67			2.00	3.00	4.00			1.75	2.63	3.50		
	35						3.33	5.00	6.67			2.86	4.29	5.71			2.50	3.75	5.00		
450	15	0.71	1.07	1.42	1.78	2.13	0.59	0.89	1.19	1.48	1.78	0.51	0.76	1.02	1.27	1.52		0.67	0.89	1.11	1.33
	20	1.07	1.60	2.13	2.67	3.20	0.89	1.33	1.78	2.22	2.67	0.76	1.14	1.52	1.90	2.29	0.67	1.00	1.33	1.67	2.00
	25	1.78	2.67	3.56	4.44	5.33	1.48	2.22	2.96	3.70	4.44	1.27	1.90	2.54	3.17	3.81	1.11	1.67	2.22	2.78	3.33
	30						2.07	3.11	4.15	5.19		1.78	2.67	3.56	4.44		1.56	2.33	3.11	3.89	
	35						2.96	4.44	5.93			2.54	3.81	5.08			2.22	3.33	4.44		
500	15	0.64	0.96	1.28	1.60	1.92	0.53	0.80	1.07	1.33	1.60		0.69	0.91	1.14	1.37		0.60	0.80	1.00	1.20
	20	0.96	1.44	1.92	2.40	2.88	0.80	1.20	1.60	2.00	2.40	0.69	1.03	1.37	1.71	2.06	0.60	0.90	1.20	1.50	1.80
	25	1.60	2.40	3.20	4.00	4.80	1.33	2.00	2.67	3.33	4.00	1.14	1.71	2.29	2.86	3.43	1.00	1.50	2.00	2.50	3.00
	30						1.87	2.80	3.73	4.67	5.60	1.60	2.40	3.20	4.00	4.80	1.40	2.10	2.80	3.50	4.20
	35						2.67	4.00	5.33	6.67		2.29	3.43	4.57	5.71		2.00	3.00	4.00	5.00	
550	15	0.58	0.87	1.16	1.45	1.75		0.73	0.97	1.21	1.45		0.62	0.83	1.04	1.25		0.55	0.73	0.91	1.09
	20	0.87	1.31	1.75	2.18	2.62	0.73	1.09	1.45	1.82	2.18	0.62	0.94	1.25	1.56	1.87	0.55	0.82	1.09	1.36	1.64
	25	1.45	2.18	2.91	3.64	4.36	1.21	1.82	2.42	3.03	3.64	1.04	1.56	2.08	2.60	3.12	0.91	1.36	1.82	2.27	2.73
	30						1.70	2.55	3.39	4.24	5.09	1.45	2.18	2.91	3.64	4.36	1.27	1.91	2.55	3.18	3.82
	35						2.42	3.64	4.85	6.06		2.08	3.12	4.16	5.19		1.82	2.73	3.64	4.55	
600	20	0.80	1.20	1.60	2.00	2.40	0.67	1.00	1.33	1.67	2.00	0.57	0.86	1.14	1.43	1.71	0.50	0.75	1.00	1.25	1.50
	25	1.33	2.00	2.67	3.33	4.00	1.11	1.67	2.22	2.78	3.33	0.95	1.43	1.90	2.38	2.86	0.83	1.25	1.67	2.08	2.50
	30						1.56	2.33	3.11	3.89	4.67	1.33	2.00	2.67	3.33	4.00	1.17	1.75	2.33	2.92	3.50
	35						2.22	3.33	4.44	5.56	6.67	1.90	2.86	3.81	4.76	5.71	1.67	2.50	3.33	4.17	5.00
650	20		1.11	1.48	1.85	2.22		0.92	1.23	1.54	1.85		0.79	1.05	1.32	1.58		0.69	0.92	1.15	1.38
	25	1.23	1.85	2.46	3.08	3.69	1.03	1.54	2.05	2.56	3.08	0.88	1.32	1.76	2.20	2.64	0.77	1.15	1.54	1.92	2.31
	30						1.44	2.15	2.87	3.59	4.31	1.23	1.85	2.46	3.08	3.69	1.08	1.62	2.15	2.69	3.23
	35						2.05	3.08	4.10	5.13	6.15	1.76	2.64	3.52	4.40	5.27	1.54	2.31	3.08	3.85	4.62
700	20		1.03	1.37	1.71	2.06		0.86	1.14	1.43	1.71		0.73	0.98	1.22	1.47		0.64	0.86	1.07	1.29
	25		1.71	2.29	2.86	3.43		1.43	1.90	2.38	2.86		1.22	1.63	2.04	2.45		1.07	1.43	1.79	2.14
	30							2.00	2.67	3.33	4.00		1.71	2.29	2.86	3.43		1.50	2.00	2.50	3.00
	35							2.86	3.81	4.76	5.71		2.45	3.27	4.08	4.90		2.14	2.86	3.57	4.29

All bar combinations shown may be spliced with bearing splices. Values above the line may be spliced with tangential or radial splices. If a reinforcement ratio greater than 4% is used, the splice location must be staggered by at least 750 mm.

If reinforcement ratios less than 1% are used, the factored resistance must be reduced as specified in Clause 10.10.5.

Table 7.10 Reinforcement Ratios for Circular Columns, 40 mm Cover to No. 10 Ties or Spirals

Bars	Total Size	6	7	8	9	10	11	12	13	14	15	16	17	18	19	20	21	22	23
Column diameter 300	15	1.70	1.98	2.26	2.55	2.83	3.11	3.40											
	20	2.55	2.97	3.40	3.82	4.24	4.67												
	25	4.24	4.95	5.66															
	30	5.94	6.93																
350	15	1.25	1.46	1.66	1.87	2.08	2.29	2.49	2.70	2.91	3.12								
	20	1.87	2.18	2.49	2.81	3.12	3.43	3.74	4.05	4.37									
	25	3.12	3.64	4.16	4.68	5.20	5.72												
	30	4.37	5.09	5.82	6.55														
	35	6.24	7.28																
400	15	0.95	1.11	1.27	1.43	1.59	1.75	1.91	2.07	2.23	2.39	2.55	2.71	2.86	3.02				
	20	1.43	1.67	1.91	2.15	2.39	2.63	2.86	3.10	3.34	3.58	3.82	4.06						
	25	2.39	2.79	3.18	3.58	3.98	4.38	4.77	5.17	5.57									
	30	3.34	3.90	4.46	5.01	5.57	6.13												
	35	4.77	5.57	6.37	7.16														
450	15	0.75	0.88	1.01	1.13	1.26	1.38	1.51	1.63	1.76	1.89	2.01	2.14	2.26	2.39	2.52	2.64	2.77	
	20	1.13	1.32	1.51	1.70	1.89	2.07	2.26	2.45	2.64	2.83	3.02	3.21	3.40	3.58	3.77			
	25	1.89	2.20	2.52	2.83	3.14	3.46	3.77	4.09	4.40	4.72	5.03							
	30	2.64	3.08	3.52	3.96	4.40	4.84	5.28	5.72										
	35	3.77	4.40	5.03	5.66	6.29	6.92												
500	20	0.92	1.07	1.22	1.38	1.53	1.68	1.83	1.99	2.14	2.29	2.44	2.60	2.75	2.90	3.06	3.21	3.36	3.51
	25	1.53	1.78	2.04	2.29	2.55	2.80	3.06	3.31	3.57	3.82	4.07	4.33	4.58	4.84				
	30	2.14	2.50	2.85	3.21	3.57	3.92	4.28	4.63	4.99	5.35								
	35	3.06	3.57	4.07	4.58	5.09	5.60	6.11	6.62										
550	20	0.76	0.88	1.01	1.14	1.26	1.39	1.52	1.64	1.77	1.89	2.02	2.15	2.27	2.40	2.53	2.65	2.78	2.90
	25	1.26	1.47	1.68	1.89	2.10	2.31	2.53	2.74	2.95	3.16	3.37	3.58	3.79	4.00	4.21	4.42		
	30	1.77	2.06	2.36	2.65	2.95	3.24	3.54	3.83	4.12	4.42	4.71	5.01	5.30					
	35	2.53	2.95	3.37	3.79	4.21	4.63	5.05	5.47	5.89									
600	20	0.64	0.74	0.85	0.95	1.06	1.17	1.27	1.38	1.49	1.59	1.70	1.80	1.91	2.02	2.12	2.23	2.33	2.44
	25	1.06	1.24	1.41	1.59	1.77	1.95	2.12	2.30	2.48	2.65	2.83	3.01	3.18	3.36	3.54	3.71	3.89	4.07
	30	1.49	1.73	1.98	2.23	2.48	2.72	2.97	3.22	3.47	3.71	3.96	4.21	4.46	4.70	4.95			
	35	2.12	2.48	2.83	3.18	3.54	3.89	4.24	4.60	4.95	5.31	5.66							
650	20	0.54	0.63	0.72	0.81	0.90	0.99	1.08	1.18	1.27	1.36	1.45	1.54	1.63	1.72	1.81	1.90	1.99	2.08
	25	0.90	1.05	1.21	1.36	1.51	1.66	1.81	1.96	2.11	2.26	2.41	2.56	2.71	2.86	3.01	3.16	3.31	3.47
	30	1.27	1.48	1.69	1.90	2.11	2.32	2.53	2.74	2.95	3.16	3.38	3.59	3.80	4.01	4.22	4.43	4.64	
	35	1.81	2.11	2.41	2.71	3.01	3.31	3.62	3.92	4.22	4.52	4.82	5.12	5.42					
700	20		0.55	0.62	0.70	0.78	0.86	0.94	1.01	1.09	1.17	1.25	1.33	1.40	1.48	1.56	1.64	1.71	1.79
	25	0.78	0.91	1.04	1.17	1.30	1.43	1.56	1.69	1.82	1.95	2.08	2.21	2.34	2.47	2.60	2.73	2.86	2.99
	30	1.09	1.27	1.46	1.64	1.82	2.00	2.18	2.36	2.55	2.73	2.91	3.09	3.27	3.46	3.64	3.82	4.00	4.18
	35	1.56	1.82	2.08	2.34	2.60	2.86	3.12	3.38	3.64	3.90	4.16	4.42	4.68	4.94	5.20			
750	20			0.54	0.61	0.68	0.75	0.81	0.88	0.95	1.02	1.09	1.15	1.22	1.29	1.36	1.43	1.49	1.56
	25	0.68	0.79	0.91	1.02	1.13	1.24	1.36	1.47	1.58	1.70	1.81	1.92	2.04	2.15	2.26	2.38	2.49	2.60
	30	0.95	1.11	1.27	1.43	1.58	1.74	1.90	2.06	2.22	2.38	2.54	2.69	2.85	3.01	3.17	3.33	3.49	3.64
	35	1.36	1.58	1.81	2.04	2.26	2.49	2.72	2.94	3.17	3.40	3.62	3.85	4.07	4.30	4.53	4.75	4.98	5.21

All bar combinations shown may be spliced with bearing splices. Values above the line may be spliced with tangential or radial splices. If a reinforcing ratio greater than 4% is used the splice location must be staggered by at least 750 mm. If reinforcing ratios less than 1% are used the factored resistance must be reduced as specified in Clause 10.10.5.

Table 7.11 Maximum Allowable Spiral Pitch for Circular Spiral Columns, 40 mm cover to the Spiral

	Column Diameter	Concrete Strength, MPa					
		25	30	35	40	45	50
No. 10 Spiral $f_y=400$ MPa	300 mm	35	35	35	35	35	35
	350	45	45	45	45	40	35
	400	55	55	55	50	40	40
	450	60	60	55	50	45	40
	500	70	65	55	50	45	40
	550	80	65	55	50	45	40
	600	80	65	60	50	45	40
	650-950	80	70	60	50	45	40
	1000-1200	85	70	60	55	45	40
	1250-1350	85	70	60	55	45	45
	1400-2450	85	70	60	55	50	45
No. 15 Spiral $f_y=400$ MPa	350 mm	45	45	45	45	45	45
	400	55	55	55	55	55	55
	450	60	60	60	60	60	60
	500	70	70	70	70	70	70
	550	80	80	80	80	80	80
	600	85	85	85	85	85	80
	650-800	90	90	90	90	90	80
	850-3600	90	90	90	90	90	85
No. 10 Spiral $f_y=500$ MPa	300 mm	35	35	35	35	35	35
	350	45	45	45	45	45	45
	400	55	55	55	55	55	50
	450	60	60	60	60	55	50
	500	70	70	70	60	55	50
	550	80	80	70	60	55	50
	600	85	85	70	65	55	50
	650-750	85	85	75	65	55	50
	800-950	85	85	75	65	60	50
	1000-1850	85	85	75	65	60	55
	1900-2200	85	85	75	70	60	55
No. 15 Spiral $f_y=500$ MPa	350 mm	45	45	45	45	45	45
	400	55	55	55	55	55	55
	450	60	60	60	60	60	60
	500	70	70	70	70	70	70
	550	80	80	80	80	80	80
	600	85	85	85	85	85	85
	650 +	90	90	90	90	90	90

Table 7.12 Compression Development Lengths, ℓ_d, for Deformed Bars with $f_y = 400$ MPa*

f'_c MPa	Bar Size						
	No. 15	No. 20	No. 25	No. 30	No. 35	No. 45	No. 55
20	320	430	540	640	750	970	1180
25	290	380	480	580	670	860	1060
$f'_c \geq 30$	260	350	440	530	620	790	970

* For f_y of 500 MPa multiply lengths by 1.25
See Clause 12.4 for additional lengths for bundled bars
See Clause 12.3.3 for reduced lengths with additional transverse reinforcement

Table 7.13 Lap lengths for Uncoated[†] Reinforcement[‡] with $f_y = 400$ MPa in Normal Density Concrete[†]

Category	f'_c MPa	Bar size				
		No. 15	No. 20	No. 25	No. 30	No. 35
Compression only*		440	580	730	880	1020
Class A Tension Splice[#] $0 < (f_s/f_y)_{max} < 0.5$ With no more than 50% spliced within required lap length	20	480	640	1010	1210	1410
	25	430	580	900	1080	1260
	30	390	530	820	990	1150
	35	370	490	760	910	1060
	40	340	460	710	850	1000
	45	320	430	670	800	940
	50	310	410	640	760	890
Class B Tension Splice[#] for All other Situations	20	630	840	1310	1570	1830
	25	560	750	1170	1400	1640
	30	510	680	1070	1280	1500
	35	470	630	990	1190	1380
	40	440	590	920	1110	1290
	45	420	560	870	1050	1220
	50	400	530	830	990	1160

* For f_y of 500 MPa multiply compression lap by 1.46
# For f_y of 500 MPa multiply tension lap length by 1.25
† See Clause 12.2.4 for increased lengths for epoxy-coated reinforcement and for concrete with lower densities
‡ See Clause 12.14.2.2 for increased lap lengths for bundled bars
See Clause 12.17.3 for reduced lap lengths with additional transverse reinforcement

Slender Columns

By Murat Saatcioglu

Chapter 8
Slender Columns

8.1 INTRODUCTION

The majority of reinforced concrete columns are subjected to primary stresses caused by flexure, axial force, and shear. Secondary stresses associated with deformations are usually very small in most columns used in practice. These columns are referred to as "short columns." Short columns are designed using the interaction diagrams presented in Chapter 7. The capacity of a short column is the same as the capacity of its section under primary stresses, irrespective of its length.

Long columns, columns with small cross-sectional dimensions, and columns with little end restraints may develop secondary stresses associated with column deformations, especially if they are not braced laterally. These columns are referred to as "slender columns". Fig. 8.1 illustrates secondary moments generated in a slender column by P-Δ effect. Consequently, slender columns resist lower axial loads than short columns with the same cross-section. This is illustrated in Fig. 8.1. Failure of a slender column is initiated either by the material failure of a section, or instability of the column as a member, depending on the level of slenderness. The latter is known as column buckling.

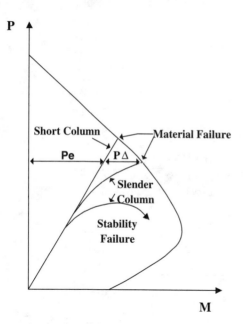

Fig. 8.1   Failure Modes in Short and Slender Columns

It is clear from the foregoing discussion that slender columns are subjected to higher bending moments than those computed by a first-order structural analysis that engineers conduct routinely for design purposes. This increase in moment due to secondary effects should be accounted for in design if the interaction diagrams given in Chapter 7 are to be used for design purposes.

8.2   SLENDERNESS RATIO

The degree of slenderness in a column is expressed in terms of "slenderness ratio" as defined below:

Slenderness Ratio : $k\ell_u/r$

where, ℓ_u is unsupported column length; k is effective length factor reflecting end restraint and lateral bracing conditions of a column; and r is radius of gyration reflecting the size and shape of a column cross-section.

8.2.1   Unsupported Length, ℓ_u

The unsupported length ℓ_u of a column is measured as the clear distance between the underside of the beam, slab, or column capital above, and the top of the beam or slab below. The unsupported length of a column may be different in two orthogonal directions depending on the supporting elements in respective directions. Table 8.1 provides examples of different support conditions and corresponding unsupported lengths (ℓ_u).

8.2.2   Effective Length Factor, k

The effective length factor k reflects end restraint (support) and lateral bracing conditions of a column relative to a pin-ended and laterally braced "reference column." The reference column, shown in Fig. 8.2(a), follows a half sine wave when it buckles, and is assigned a k factor of 1.0. Therefore, the effective length $k\ell_u$ for this column is equal to the unsupported column length ℓ_u. A column with fully restrained end conditions develops the deflected shape illustrated in Fig. 8.2(b). The portion of the column between the points of contraflexure follows a half sign wave, the same deflected shape as that of the reference column. This segment is equal to 50% of the unsupported column length ℓ_u. Therefore, the effective length factor k for this case is equal to 0.5. Effective length factors for columns with idealized supports can be determined from Fig. 8.2. It may be of interest to note that k varies between 0.5 and 1.0 for laterally braced columns, and 1.0 and ∞ for unbraced columns. A discussion of lateral bracing is provided in Sec. 8.3 to establish whether a given column can be considered to be as part of a sway or non-sway frame.

Most columns have end restraints that are neither perfectly hinged nor fully fixed. The degree of end restraint depends on the stiffness of adjoining beams relative to that of the columns. Jackson and Moreland alignment charts, given in Tables 8.2 and 8.3 can be used to determine the effective length factor k for different values of relative stiffnesses at column ends. The stiffness ratios ψ_A and ψ_B used in Tables 8.2 and 8.3 should reflect concrete cracking, and the effects of sustained loading. Beams and slabs are flexure dominant members and may crack significantly more than columns which are compression members. The reduced stiffness values recommended by CSA A23.3-94 are given in Table 8.4, and should be used in determining k. Alternatively, Table 8.5 may be used to establish conservative values of k for braced columns.

8.2.3   Radius of Gyration, r

The radius of gyration reflects the effect of cross-sectional size and shape on slenderness. For the same cross-sectional area, a section with higher moment of inertia produces a more stable column with a lower slenderness ratio. The radius of gyration r is defined below.

$$r = \sqrt{\frac{I}{A}} \qquad (8.1)$$

It is permissible to use the approximations of r = 0.3h for square and rectangular sections, and r = 0.25d for circular sections.

8.3   LATERAL BRACING AND DESIGNATION OF FRAMES AS NON-SWAY

A frame is considered to be "non-sway" if it is sufficiently braced by lateral bracing elements like structural walls. Otherwise, it may be designated as a "sway" frame.

Frames that provide resistance to lateral loads by columns only are considered to be sway frames. Structural walls that appear in the form of elevator shafts, stairwells, partial building enclosures or simply used as interior stiffening elements provide substantial drift control and lateral bracing. In most cases, even a few structural walls

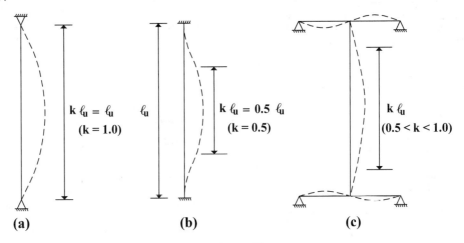

(a)   **(b)**   **(c)**

Columns in Non-Sway Frames

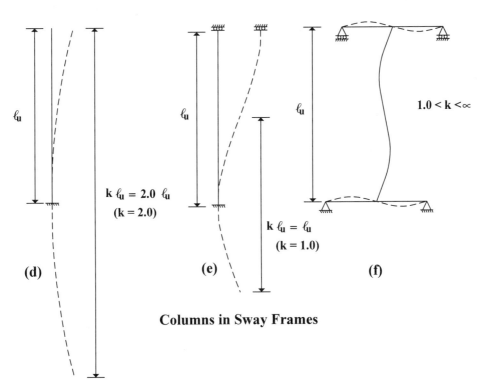

(d)   **(e)**   **(f)**

Columns in Sway Frames

Fig. 8.2 Effective Length Factor (k) for Columns in Non-Sway and Sway Frames

may be sufficient to brace a multi-storey multi-bay building. The designer can usually decide whether the frame is non-sway or sway by inspecting the floor plan. Frames with lateral bracing elements, where the total lateral stiffness of the bracing elements exceeds six times the summation of the stiffnesses of all the columns, may be classified as non-sway. A more accurate approach is specified in CSA A23.3-94 [Clause 10.14.4] based on the stability index "Q" defined in Eq. 8.2. Accordingly, if $Q \leq 0.05$, the frame may be designated as non-sway, and the columns of the frame as braced.

$$Q = \frac{\sum P_f \Delta_0}{V_f \ell_c} \qquad (8.2)$$

where $\sum P_f$ is the total factored axial load acting on all the columns in a storey, V_f is the total factored storey shear, Δ_0 is the lateral storey drift (deflection of the top of the storey relative to the bottom of that storey) due to V_f. The storey drift Δ_0 should be computed using the modified EI values given in Table 8.4 with β_d defined as the ratio of the maximum factored sustained shear within a storey to the maximum factored shear in that storey. If Q exceeds approximately 0.2, the structure may have to be stiffened laterally to provide overall structural stability.

8.4 DESIGN OF SLENDER COLUMNS

Design of a slender column should be based on a second-order analysis which incorporates member cur-vature and lateral drift effects, as well as material non-linearity and sustained load effects. An alternative approach is specified in CSA A23.3-94 for columns with slenderness ratios not exceeding 100. This approach is commonly referred to as the "Moment Magnification Method," and is based on magnifying the end moments to account for secondary stresses. The application of this procedure is outlined in the following sections.

8.4.1 Slender Columns in Non-Sway Frames

Slenderness effects may be ignored for columns in non-sway frames if the following inequality is satisfied:

$$\frac{k\ell_u}{r} \leq \frac{25 - 10(M_1/M_2)}{\sqrt{P_f/(f'_c A_g)}} \qquad (8.3)$$

where M_1/M_2 is the ratio of smaller to larger end moments, with a negative value when the column is bent in double curvature, and a positive value when it is bent in single curvature. Fig. 8.3 illustrates columns in double and single curvatures. Columns are more stable, and the secondary effects are smaller, in double curvature than in single curvature. This is reflected in Eq. 8.3 through the sign of M_1/M_2 ratio. For negative values of this ratio the limit of slenderness, specified in Eq. 8.3 increases, allowing a wider range of columns to be treated as short columns. The M_1/M_2 ratio is not to be taken less than -0.5 when used in Eq. 8.3.

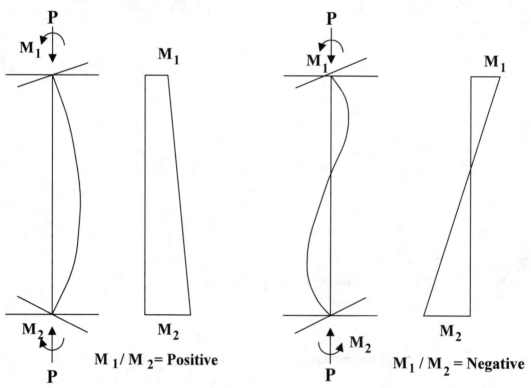

Single Curvature   **Double Curvature**

Fig. 8.3 Columns in Single and Double Curvature

Slender columns in non-sway frames are designed for factored axial force P_f and amplified moment M_c. The amplified moment is obtained by magnifying the larger of the two end moments (M_2) to account for member curvature and resulting secondary moments between the supports, while the supports are braced against sidesway. If M_c computed for the curvature effect between the ends is smaller than the larger end moment M_2, the design is carried out for M_2.

$$M_c = \frac{C_m M_2}{1 - \dfrac{P_f}{\phi_m P_c}} \tag{8.4}$$

where, $\phi_m = 0.75$, and the critical column load, P_c (Euler buckling load) is;

$$P_c = \frac{\pi^2 EI}{(k\ell_u)^2} \tag{8.5}$$

EI in Eq. 8.5 is computed either with due considerations given to the presence of reinforcement in the section as specified in Eq. 8.6, or approximately using Eq. 8.7.

$$EI = \frac{0.2E_c I_g + E_s I_{st}}{1 + \beta_d} \tag{8.6}$$

where β_d is the ratio of the maximum factored axial dead load to the total factored axial load. The moment of inertia of reinforcement about cross-sectional centroid (I_{st}) can be computed using Table 8.6.

$$EI = 0.25E_c I_g \tag{8.7}$$

Coefficient C_m is equal to 1.0 for members with transverse loads between the supports. For the more common case of columns without transverse loads between the supports;

$$C_m = 0.6 + 0.4\frac{M_1}{M_2} \geq 0.4 \tag{8.8}$$

Furthermore, the product $C_m M_2$ should not be less than the moment associated with minimum eccentricity.

$$C_m M_2 \geq P_f (15 + 0.03h) \tag{8.9}$$

where h is the cross-sectional dimension in mm in the direction of eccentricity. Once the amplified moment M_c is obtained, the designer can use the appropriate interaction diagram from Chapter 7 to determine the required percentage of longitudinal reinforcement.

8.4.2 Slender Columns in Sway Frames

Columns in sway frames are designed for the factored axial load P_f and the combination of factored gravity load moments and magnified sway moments. This is specified below, and illustrated in Table 8.7.

$$M_1 = M_{1ns} + \delta_s M_{1s} \tag{8.10}$$

$$M_2 = M_{2ns} + \delta_s M_{2s} \tag{8.11}$$

where, M_{1ns} and M_{2ns} are end moments due to factored gravity loads; and M_{1s} and M_{2s} are sway moments normally caused by factored lateral loads. All of these moments can be obtained from a first-order elastic frame analysis. Magnified sway moments $\delta_s M_{1s}$ and $\delta_s M_{2s}$ are obtained either from a second order frame analysis, with member stiffnesses as specified in Table 8.4, or by magnifying the end moments by sway magnification factor δ_s.

$$\delta_s = \frac{1}{1 - \dfrac{\Sigma P_f}{\phi_m \Sigma P_c}} \tag{8.12}$$

In a sway frame, all the columns of a given storey participate in sway mechanism and the stability of columns. Therefore, Eq. 8.12 includes ΣP_f and ΣP_c which give the summations of factored axial loads and critical loads for all the columns in the storey, respectively. The critical column load P_c can be computed using Eqs. 8.5 through 8.7 with the effective length factor k computed for unbraced columns (for sway frames), and β_d as the ratio of the maximum factored sustained shear within the storey to the maximum total factored shear in the storey. Eq. 8.12 provides an average δ_s for all the columns in a storey. Therefore, it yields acceptable results if all the columns in a storey undergo the same storey drift. When significant torsion is anticipated under lateral loading, a second order analysis is recommended for finding the amplified sway moment, $\delta_s M_s$.

An alternative to Eq. 8.12 is given below for cases where Q has been computed from Eq. 8.2 to be less than or equal to 1/3.

$$\delta_s = \frac{1}{1 - Q} \tag{8.13}$$

The sidesway magnification discussed above is intended to amplify the end moments associated with lateral drift. Although the amplified end moment is commonly the critical moment for most sway columns, additional magnification may become necessary due to the curvature of the column between the ends. This occurs if the slenderness ratio is high. The magnification of moment due to the curvature of column between the ends is similar to that discussed for braced columns in non-sway frames. This additional magnification is required for columns that satisfy the following condition:

$$\frac{\ell_u}{r} > \frac{35}{\sqrt{P_f/(f'_c A_g)}} \tag{8.14}$$

The larger of the end moments computed by Eqs. 8.10 and 8.11, for the load combination used in computing P_f, is then magnified using Eqs 8.4 through 8.8. As in the case of braced columns, the effective length factor k used in Eq. 8.5 is computed as if the column were a braced column, from Table 8.2, and β_d used in Eq. 8.6 is taken as the ratio of the factored axial dead load to the total factored axial load.

Sometimes columns of a sway frame may buckle under gravity loads alone, without the effects of lateral loading. In this case the gravity load combination of (1.25D + 1.5L) may govern the stability of columns. The reduction of EI under sustained gravity loads may be another factor contributing to the vulnerability of sway columns to gravity loads. Therefore, an additional provision is provided in CSA A23.3-94 as Clause 10.16.5 to safeguard against column buckling in sway frames under gravity loads alone. Accordingly, the strength and stability of the structure is reconsidered depending on the method of amplification used for sway moments. If a second order analysis has been conducted to find $\delta_s M_{2s}$, two additional analyses are necessary using the reduced stiffness values given in Table 8.4 with β_d taken as the ratio of the factored sustained axial dead load to the total factored axial load. First, a second-order analysis is conducted using (1.25D + 1.5L) as gravity load and 0.5% of this load as lateral load. Second, a first-order analysis is conducted under the same loading condition. The ratio of lateral drift obtained by the second-order analysis to that obtained by the first-order analysis should then be limited to 2.5.

If the sway moment has been amplified through the sway magnification factor, then δ_s computed by using $(1.25D + 1.5 L)$ is required to be positive and less than or equal to 2.5 to ensure the stability of the column.

8.5 DESIGN EXAMPLES

Example 8.1 — Design of an interior column braced against sidesway

Consider a 10-storey office building, laterally braced against sidesway by an elevator shaft (Q is computed to be much less than 0.05). The building has an atrium opening at the second floor level with a two-storey high column in the middle of the opening to be designed. Design the column for the design forces given below, obtained from a first-order analysis. The framing beams are 400 mm wide and 500 mm deep with 7.0 m (centre-to-centre) spans. The beam depth includes a slab thickness of 150 mm. The storey height is 4.3 m, and 40 MPa concrete is used in all the beams and columns. $f_y = 400$ MPa. (See figure for Example 8.1)

Unfactored Loads:	Dead Load	Live Load
Axial load (kN) :	1776	1320
Top moment (kN·m):	−112	−66
Bottom moment (kN·m):	−12	−7

Note: Moments are positive if counterclockwise at column ends. The column is bent in double curvature.

1. Determine factored design forces:

   $P_f = 1.25 P_D + 1.50 P_L = 1.25(1776) + 1.50(1320) =$ 4200 kN
   $M_2 = 1.25 M_D + 1.50 M_L = 1.25(112) + 1.50(66) =$ 239 kN·m
   $M_1 = 1.25 M_D + 1.5 M_L = 1.25(12) + 1.50(7) =$ 26 kN·m
   Note: M_1 is the lower, and M_2 is the higher end moment.

2. Estimate the column size:

   For $P_f = 4200$ kN, select 500×500 mm from Table 7.1.4 which, with $\rho_t > 0.015$, may be sufficient to resist the applied moment .

3. Calculate slenderness ratio $k\ell_u/r$:

   The unsupported column length (Table 8.1);
   $\ell_u = 8600 - 250 - 250 = 8100$ mm
   The radius of gyration for a square column;
   $r = 0.3 h = 0.3 (500) = 150$ mm
   Compute the effective length factor "k" from Table 8.2.

   First find stiffness ratios at the ends.
   Beam moment of inertia (T-section) :
   $I_g = 7.7 \times 10^9 mm^4$
   Column moment of inertia :
   $I_g = bh^3/12 = (500)(500)^3 /12 = 5.2 \times 10^9$ mm^4
   Find reduced EI values as per Table 8.4;
   $(EI)_{beam} = (10361)(7.7 \times 10^9) = 8.0 \times 10^{13}$ N·mm^2
   $(EI)_{col} = (20721)(5.2 \times 10^9) = 1.1 \times 10^{14}$ N·mm^2
   $(EI/\ell)_{beam} = (8.0 \times 10^{13}) / (7000) = 1.1 \times 10^{10}$ N·mm
   for both left and right beams
   $(EI/\ell_c)_{col} = (1.1 \times 10^{14}) / (8600) = 1.3 \times 10^{10}$ N·mm
   for the atrium column to be designed

$(EI/\ell_c)_{col} = (1.1 \times 10^{14}) / (4300) = 2.6 \times 10^{10}$ N·mm
for columns above and below
$\psi = (\Sigma EI/\ell_c)_{col} / (\Sigma EI/\ell)_{beam} = [(EI/\ell_c)_{col, above} + (EI/\ell_c)_{col, below}] / [(EI/\ell)_{beam, left} + (EI/\ell)_{beam, right}]$
$\psi_A = (2.6 \times 10^{10} + 1.3 \times 10^{10}) / (1.1 \times 10^{10} + 1.1 \times 10^{10}) = 1.8$
for $\psi_B = \psi_A = 1.8$; select k = 0.84 from Table 8.2
(Note that Table 8.5 gives a conservative value of k = 0.90)
$k\ell_u/r = 0.84 (8100) / 150 = 45.4$

4. Check if slenderness can be neglected :

   From Eq. 8.3;
   if $k\ell_u / r \le [25 - 10(M_1/M_2)] / \sqrt{P_f/(f'_c A_g)}$ then slenderness can be neglected.
   Note: M_1/M_2 can not be less than −0.5. In this problem $M_1/M_2 = -26/239 = -0.11$
   $k\ell_u/r = 45.4 > [25 - 10 (-0.11)] / \sqrt{4200 \times 10^3 /(40 \times 500 \times 500)} = 40.3$
   Therefore, consider slenderness.

5. Compute critical load, P_c from Eq. 8.5 and associated EI from Eq. 8.6 or 8.7 :

   EI from Eq. 8.6 for assumed reinforcement ratio of $\rho_t = 0.025$, equally distributed on all faces with $\gamma = 0.75$;
   $E_c = 29602$ MPa (from Table 8.4); $E_s = 200,000$ MPa;
   $I_g = 5.2 \times 10^9$ mm^4
   $I_{st} = 0.18 \rho_t b h^3 \gamma^2$ (from Table 8.6);
   $I_{st} = 0.18 (0.025)(500)(500)^3 (0.75)^2 = 1.6 \times 10^8$ mm^4
   $\beta_d = 2220 / 4200 = 0.53$ EI $= (0.2E_cI_g + E_sI_{st}) / (1 + \beta_d)$
   EI $= [(0.2 \times 29602 \times 5.2 \times 10^9) + (200000 \times 1.6 \times 10^8)] / (1 + 0.53) = 4.1 \times 10^{13}$ N·mm^2

   Alternatively, EI from Eq 8.7;
   EI $= 0.25 E_cI_g = 0.25 \times 29602 \times 5.2 \times 10^9$
   $= 3.8 \times 10^{13}$ N·mm^2
   From Eq. 8.5; $P_c = \pi^2$ EI $/ (k \ell_u)^2$
   $= \pi^2 \times 4.1 \times 10^{13} / (0.84 \times 8100)^2 = 8741 \times 10^3$ N

6. Compute C_m from Eq. 8.8 :

   $C_m = 0.6 + 0.4 M_1/M_2 \ge 0.4$
   $C_m = 0.6 + 0.4 (-0.11) = 0.56$

7. Compute magnified moment M_c from Eq. 8.4 :

   $M_c = C_m M_2 / [1 - P_f / (\phi_m P_c)]$
   $= 0.56 (239) / [1 - 4200 / (0.75 \times 8741)]$
   $M_c = 1.56 \times 239 = 373$ kN.m (magnified moment)
   Check against minimum design moment as per Eq. 8.9;
   $M_c \ge P_f (15 + 0.03h)$
   $= 4200 \times 10^3 (15 + 0.03 \times 500) = 126 \times 10^6$ N.mm; O.K.

8. Select reinforcement ratio and design the column section:

   Select the appropriate interaction diagram from Chapter 7. For $f'_c = 40$ MPa; $f_y = 400$ MPa, $\gamma = 0.75$ (assumed in step 5), and equal reinforcement on all four sides, select Tables 7.4.14 and 7.4.15, and interpolate between the two:

   $P_f /A_g = 4200 \times 10^3 / (500)^2 = 16.8$ MPa
   $M_c / A_gh = 373 \times 10^6 / [(500)^2(500)] = 2.98$ MPa

   From Table 7.4.14 for $\gamma = 0.7$; $\rho_t = 0.022$
   From Table 7.4.15 for $\gamma = 0.8$; $\rho_t = 0.020$

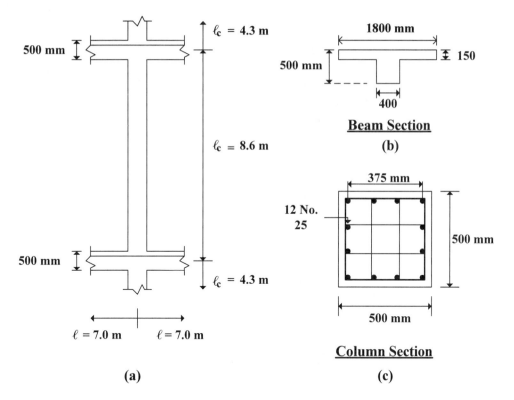

Beam Section

(b)

Column Section

(c)

(a)

Example 8.1

Interpolating for $\gamma = 0.75$; $\rho_t = 0.021$
$A_{st} = \rho_t A_g = 0.021 (500)^2 = 5250 \text{ mm}^2$ try # 25 bars
$(A_{st} = 500 \text{ mm}^2)$; 5250 / 500 = 10.5
Use 12 No. 25 longitudinal reinforcement, equally distributed on all sides.
Note: For further details of cross-sectional design refer to Chapter 7.

Example 8.2 — Design of an exterior column in a sway frame

A typical floor plan and a section through a four-storey apartment building is shown in the figure. Design column 3-A at the ground level for combined gravity and east-west wind loading.

$f'_c = 40 \text{ MPa}$; $f_y = 400 \text{ MPa}$.

1. Consider the applicable load combinations:

   The structure is not braced against sidesway. There-fore, the column will be designed considering the loads that cause sidesway. Note that sidesway in this structure is caused by wind loading. No signifi-cant sidesway is anticipated due to the gravity loads since the structure is symmetric. The load combina-tions that include wind loading;

   Load Combination I: U = 1.25D + 0.70 (1.5L + 1.5W)
   Load Combination II: U = 1.25D + 1.5W

   Load combination for gravity loading;

   Load Combination III: U = 1.25D + 1.5L

   Note: The column may be critical under gravity loading only, even if it is part of a sway frame (CSA A23.3-94, Clause 10.16.5).

Conduct a frame analysis to determine first-order design forces. Use the stiffness values given in Table 8.4 for the analysis.

Try the preliminary column section given in the figure.

2. Determine the effective length factor k for all col-umns at the ground level:

   Note: All columns have the same geometry.
   $I_{beam} = 2.3 \times 10^{10} \text{ mm}^4$ (for T-section)
   $I_{col} = (500)(500)^3/12 = 5.2 \times 10^9 \text{ mm}^4$

   Find reduced EI values from Table 8.4 for 40 MPa concrete;
   $(E_c I)_{beam} = 10361 \, I_{beam} = 10361 (2.3 \times 10^{10})$
   $= 2.4 \times 10^{14} \text{ N} \cdot \text{mm}^2$
   $(E_c I)_{col} = 20721 \, I_{col} = 20721 (5.2 \times 10^9)$
   $= 1.1 \times 10^{14} \text{ N} \cdot \text{mm}^2$
   $(EI/\ell)_{beam} = 2.4 \times 10^{14} / 5000 = 4.8 \times 10^{10} \text{ N} \cdot \text{mm}$
   $(EI/\ell_c)_{col, above} = 1.1 \times 10^{14} / 3500 = 3.1 \times 10^{10}$ N·mm
   $(EI/\ell_c)_{col, below} = 1.1 \times 10^{14} / 5500 = 2.0 \times 10^{10}$ N·mm
   $\psi = (\Sigma EI/\ell_c)_{col} / (\Sigma EI/\ell)_{beam} = [(EI/\ell_c)_{col, above} + (EI/\ell_c)_{col, below}] / [(EI/\ell)_{beam, left} + (EI/\ell)_{beam, right}]$

   i) For exterior columns (columns on lines A and D):

   $\psi_A = (3.1 \times 10^{10} + 2.0 \times 10^{10}) / 4.8 \times 10^{10} = 1.06$
   $\psi_B = \psi_A = 1.06$; from Table 8.3 k = 1.35 (for unbraced frame)
   k = 0.78 from Table 8.2 for a braced column. This value is computed for further magnification of moments, if necessary, for column 3-A as per CSA A23.3-94, Clause 10.16.4.

   ii) For interior columns (columns on lines B and C):

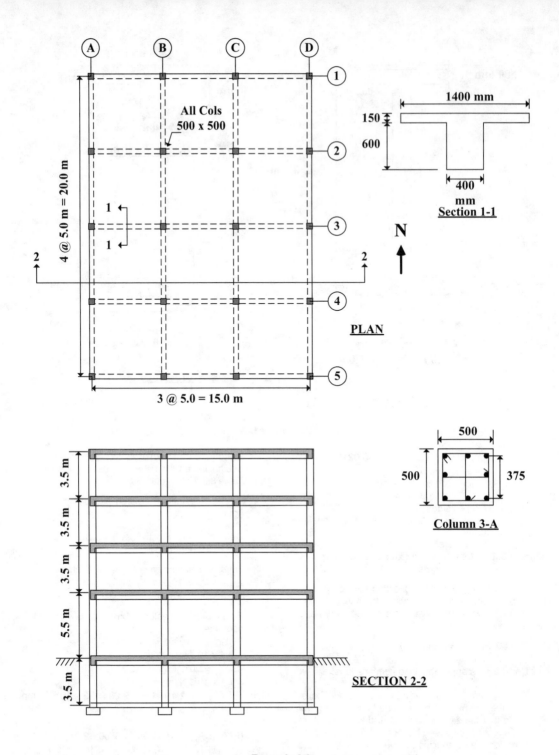

PLAN

All Cols
500 x 500

4 @ 5.0 m = 20.0 m

3 @ 5.0 = 15.0 m

N

1400 mm

150

600

400 mm

Section 1-1

500

500

375

Column 3-A

3.5 m

3.5 m

3.5 m

5.5 m

3.5 m

SECTION 2-2

Example 8.2

$\psi_A = (3.1 \times 10^{10} + 2.0 \times 10^{10}) / (4.8 \times 10^{10} + 4.8 \times 10^{10}) = 0.53$

$\psi_B = \psi_A = 0.53$; from Table 8.3 k = 1.15 (for unbraced frame)

3. Compute critical load P_c from Eq. 8.5, and associated E from Eq. 8.6 or 8.7 :

Note: P_c for all load combinations can be computed to be the same if Eq. 8.7 is used in computing EI, since this expression is independent of β_d. $E_c = 29602$ MPa for $f'_c = 40$ MPa (from Table 8.4)

From Eq. 8.7; EI = $0.25 \, E_c I_g$
$= 0.25 \, (29602)(5.2 \times 10^9) = 3.8 \times 10^{13}$ N·mm^2
$\ell_u = 5500 - 750 = 4750$ mm

i) For exterior columns (columns on lines A and D):

$P_c = \pi^2 \, EI \, / \, (k\ell_u)^2 = \pi^2 \, (3.8 \times 10^{13})/(1.35 \times 4750)^2$
$= 9{,}121 \times 10^3$ N for a sway frame.
$P_c = \pi^2 \, EI \, / \, (k\ell_u)^2 = \pi^2 \, (3.8 \times 10^{13})/(0.78 \times 4750)^2$
$= 27{,}322 \times 10^3$ N for braced columns.
P_c for braced columns may be needed if further magnification of moments is required as per Clause 10.16.4 of CSA A23.3-94 for column 3-A.

ii) For interior columns (columns on lines B and C):

$P_c = \pi^2 \, EI \, / \, (k\ell_u)^2 = \pi^2 \, (3.8 \times 10^{13}) \, / \, (1.15 \times 4750)^2$
$= 12{,}569 \times 10^3$ N for a sway frame.

4. Compute magnified sway moment $\delta_s M_s$:

i) Load Combination I: U = 1.25D + 0.70 (1.5L + 1.5W)

Consider the factored axial loads and bending moments obtained from a first-order frame analysis conducted using the stiffness values given in Table 8.4.

	1.25D+1.05L	1.05W
P_f (kN) – Corner Column:	2130	±49
P_f (kN) – Edge Column:	3047	±67
P_f (kN) – Interior Column:	4772	±16
$(M_f)_{top}$ kN·m – Column 3-A	−204	±114
$(M_f)_{bot}$ kN·m – Column 3-A	−216	±122

Note: Counterclockwise moment at column end is positive.

a) Sway magnification factor δ_s from Eq. 8.12.

$\Sigma P_f = 4 \, (2130 + 49) + 10 \, (3047 + 67) + 6 \, (4772 + 16)$
$= 68584$ kN
From Step 3;
$\Sigma P_c = 10 \, (9121) + 10 \, (12569) = 216900$ kN

$\delta_s = 1 \, / \, [1 - \Sigma P_f \, / \, (\phi_m \Sigma P_c \,)]$
$= 1 \, / \, [1 - 68584 \, / \, (0.75 \times 216900)] = 1.73$
$\delta_s \, M_{1s} = 1.73 \times 114 = 197$ kN·m
$\delta_s \, M_{2s} = 1.73 \times 122 = 211$ kN·m

b) Compute design moments M_1 and M_2 from Eqs. 8.10 and 8.11, and Table 8.7.

$M_1 = M_{1ns} + \delta_s \, M_{1s} = 204 + 197 = 401$ kN·m
$M_2 = M_{2ns} + \delta_s \, M_{2s} = 216 + 211 = 427$ kN·m

c) Check if further magnification of moments are required due to the curvature of the columns between the ends using Eq. 8.14.

$\dfrac{\ell_u}{r} > \dfrac{35}{\sqrt{P_f / \, (f'_c \, A_g)}}$

$P_f = 3047 + 67 = 3114$ kN
$\ell_u/r = 4750 \, / \, (0.3 \times 500)$
$= 31.7 < 35 \, / \sqrt{3114 \times 10^3 /(40 \times (500)^2)} = 62.7$
Therefore, no further magnification is required.

ii) Load Combination II : U = 1.25D + 1.5W

Consider the factored axial loads and bending moments obtained from a first-order frame analysis conducted using the stiffness values given in Table 8.4.

	1.25D	1.50W
P_f (kN) – Corner Column:	1596	±69
P_f (kN) – Edge Column:	2281	±98
P_f (kN) – Interior Column:	3571	±22
$(M_f)_{top}$ kN·m – Column 3-A	−153	±163
$(M_f)_{bot}$ kN·m – Column 3-A	−163	±174

Note: Counterclockwise moment at column end is positive.

a) Sway magnification factor δ_s and magnified sway moments $\delta_s \, M_{1s}$ and $\delta_s \, M_{2s}$

$\Sigma P_f = 4 \, (1596 + 69) + 10 \, (2281 + 98) + 6 \, (3571 + 22) = 52008$ kN
From Step 3;
$\Sigma P_c = 10 \, (9121) + 10 \, (12569) = 216900$ kN

$\delta_s = 1 \, / \, [1 - \Sigma P_f \, / \, (\phi_m \Sigma P_c \,)]$
$= 1 \, / \, [1 - 52008 \, / \, (0.75 \times 216900)] = 1.47$
$\delta_s \, M_{1s} = 1.47 \times 163 = 240$ kN·m
$\delta_s \, M_{2s} = 1.47 \times 174 = 256$ kN·m

b) Compute design moments M_1 and M_2 from Eqs. 8.10 and 8.11, and Table 8.7.

$M_1 = M_{1ns} + \delta_s \, M_{1s} = 153 + 240 = 393$ kN·m
$M_2 = M_{2ns} + \delta_s \, M_{2s} = 163 + 256 = 419$ kN·m

c) Check if further magnification of moments are required due to the curvature of the columns between the ends using Eq. 8.14.

$\dfrac{\ell_u}{r} > \dfrac{35}{\sqrt{P_f / \, (f'_c \, A_g)}}$

$P_f = 2281 + 98 = 2379$ kN
$\ell_u/r = 4750 \, / \, (0.3 \times 500)$
$= 31.7 < 35 \, / \sqrt{2379 \times 10^3 /(40 \times (500)^2)} = 71.8$
Therefore, no further magnification is required.

5. Check the stability of column under gravity loads only (Load Combination III) as per CSA A23.3-94, Clause 10.16.5:

Consider the factored axial loads and bending moments obtained from a first-order frame analysis conducted using the stiffness values given in Table 8.4.

	1.25D	1.50L
P_f (kN) – Corner Column:	1596	765
P_f (kN) – Edge Column:	2281	1096
P_f (kN) – Interior Column:	3571	1715
$(M_f)_{top}$ kN·m – Column 3-A	−153	−73
$(M_f)_{bot}$ kN·m – Column 3-A	−163	−78

Note: Counterclockwise moment at column end is positive.

Compute the sway magnification factor δ_s

$\Sigma P_f = 4\,(1596 + 765) + 10\,(2281 + 1096) +$
$6\,(3571 + 1715) = 74930$ kN
From Step 3;
$\Sigma P_c = 10\,(9121) + 10\,(12569) = 216900$ kN

$\delta_s = 1\,/\,[1 - \Sigma P_f\,/\,(\phi_m \Sigma P_c\,)]$
$\quad = 1\,/\,[1 - 74930\,/\,(0.75 \times 216900)] = 1.85$

$\delta_s = 1.85 < 2.5$ O.K.

6. Design the column for the governing load combination:
Summary of Design Loads

	P_f (kN)	M_f (kN·m)
Load Combination I : 1.25D+0.7(1.5L+1.5W)	3114	427
Load Combination II : 1.25D+1.5W	2379	419
Load Combination III : 1.25D+1.5L	3377	241

Select the interaction diagrams given in Table 7.5.15 from Chapter 7.

For Load Combination I;
$P_f/A_g = 3114 \times 10^3\,/\,(500)^2 = 12.5$ MPa
$M_f/A_g h = 427 \times 10^6\,/\,(500)^3 = 3.4$ MPa
Select $\rho_t = 0.02$. $A_{st} = 0.02\,(500)^2 = 5000$ mm^2. Try #30 bars ($A_{st} = 700$ mm^2);
5000 / 700 = 7.14. Use 8 #30 bars equally distributed on all four faces.

Check the capacity for Load Combination III;
$P_f/A_g = 3377 \times 10^3\,/\,(500)^2 = 13.5$ MPa
$M_f/A_g h = 241 \times 10^6\,/\,(500)^3 = 1.9$ MPa; the point lies inside the interaction diagram, O.K.

Note: For further details of cross-sectional design refer to Chapter 7.

8.6 DESIGN AIDS

Table 8.1   Unsupported Column Length, ℓ_u

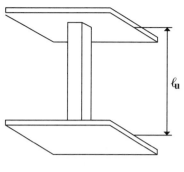

a) Flat Plate

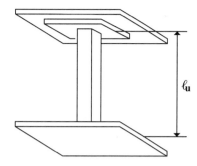

b) Flat Slab

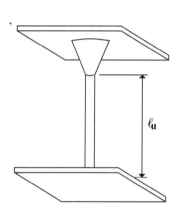

c) Column Capital

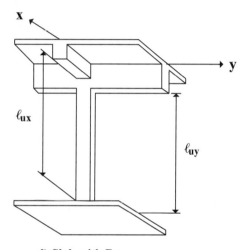

d) Slab with Beams

Table 8.2 Effective Length Factor — Alignment Chart for Columns in Braced Frames

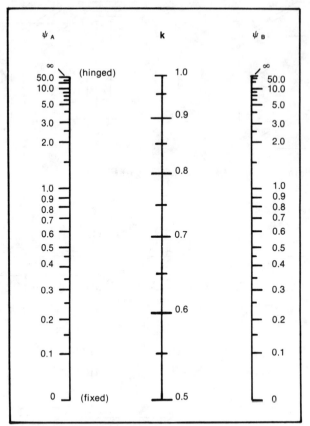

$$\psi_i = \frac{(\Sigma EI/\ell_c)_{\text{columns}}}{(\Sigma EI/\ell)_{\text{beams}}} \quad \text{at end i of column}$$

Table 8.3 Effective Length Factor — Alignment Chart for Columns in Unbraced Frames

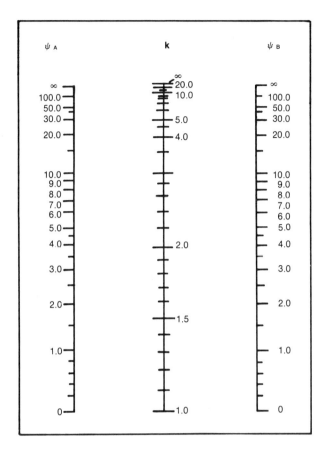

$$\psi_i = \frac{(\Sigma EI/\ell_c)_{columns}}{(\Sigma EI/\ell)_{beams}} \quad \text{at end i of column}$$

Table 8.4 Recommended Flexural Rigidities (EI) for use in First-Order and Second Order Analyses of Frames for Design of Slender Columns

	$E_c I / I_g$ (MPa)							
f'_c (MPa):	20	30	40	50	60	70	80	
E_c (MPa):	23,085	26,621	29,602	32,228	34,602	36,785	38,817	I/I_g
Beams	8,080	9,317	10,361	11,280	12,111	12,875	13,586	0.35
Columns	16,160	18,635	20,721	22,560	24,221	25,750	27,172	0.70
Walls: Uncracked	16,160	18,635	20,721	22,560	24,221	25,750	27,172	0.70
Cracked	8,080	9,317	10,361	11,280	12,111	12,875	13,586	0.35
Flat Plates Flat Slabs:	5,771	6,655	7,400	8,057	8,651	9,196	9,704	0.25

Note: The walls will be analyzed with uncracked flexural rigidities until the analysis indicates cracking based on the modulus of rupture, in which case the analysis will be repeated with cracked rigidities.

The above values will be divided by $(1 + \beta_d)$, when applicable as per CSA A23.3-94.

The above values are applicable to normal-density concretes with $\gamma_c = 2400$ kg/m^3.

CPCA Concrete Design Handbook

Table 8.5 Effective Length Facor "k" for Columns in Braced Frames

TOP			k			
	Hinged		0.81	0.91	0.95	1.00
	Elastic		0.77	0.86	0.90	0.95
	Elastic		0.74	0.83	0.86	0.91
	Stiff		0.67	0.74	0.77	0.81
			Stiff	Elastic	Elastic	Hinged
			BOTTOM			

Table 8.6 Moment of Inertia of Reinforcement About Sectional Centroid

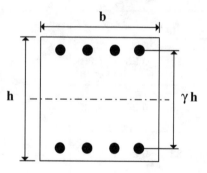

Bars in two end faces

$$I_{st} = 0.25\, \rho_t\, b\, h^3 \gamma^2$$

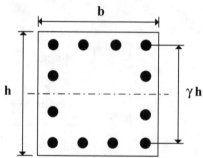

Equal reinforcement on four sides

$$I_{st} = 0.18\, \rho_t\, b\, h^3 \gamma^2$$

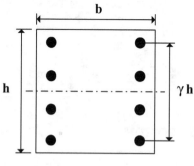

Bars in two side faces

$$I_{st} = 0.17\, \rho_t\, b\, h^3 \gamma^2 \quad \text{(3 bars per face)}$$
$$I_{st} = 0.12\, \rho_t\, b\, h^3 \gamma^2 \quad \text{(6 bars per face)}$$

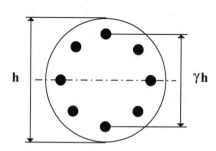

Uniformly distributed reinforcement

$$I_{st} = 0.10\, \rho_t\, h^4 \gamma^2$$

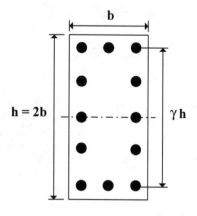

Bars uniformly spaced on all sides

$$I_{st} = 0.13\, \rho_t\, b\, h^3 \gamma^2$$

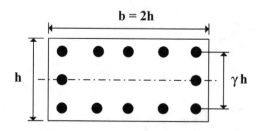

Bars uniformly spaced on all sides

$$I_{st} = 0.22\, \rho_t\, b\, h^3 \gamma^2$$

Note: This table is based on Table 12-1 of MacGregor, J.G., Second Edition, Prentice Hall, Englewood Cliffs, New Jersey, 1992.

Table 8.7 Design Moments in Sway Frames

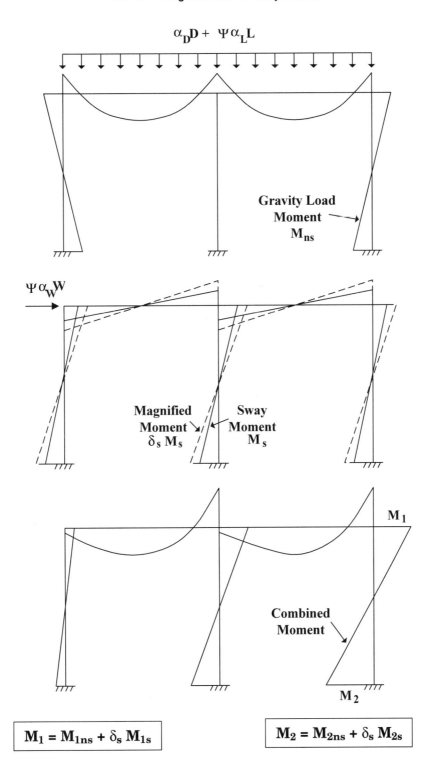

$$M_1 = M_{1ns} + \delta_s M_{1s}$$

$$M_2 = M_{2ns} + \delta_s M_{2s}$$

9

Footings

By Gordon A. Fenton
G. T. Suter

Chapter 9
Footings

9.1 DESIGN PROCEDURE

The design of a footing can be broken down into three general steps;

1) selection of footing type,

2) design of footing size and shape,

3) structural design.

The selection of the type of footing to be used, e.g. spread or pile supported, depends largely on the soil's bearing capacity and settlement properties. A spread footing is usually more economical than a pile supported footing and would be the optimum choice unless the soil is weak or highly deformable. Space limitations may also dictate the use of piles rather than spread footings.

The shape of the footing is primarily governed by such aspects as the type of structural element transmitting the building loads, e.g. walls or columns, the layout and spacing of these elements, and in the case of pile supported footings, the number of piles and the required pile spacing. For walls or closely spaced columns along a line, strip footings are commonly used whereas for a regular array of closely spaced columns, or where differential settlements are to be minimized, a raft or grid foundation may be more appropriate. In many cases it is desirable to tie the footings together with a beam element which may result in the design of a strap footing.

This chapter does not attempt to discuss all the possible types of footings, instead restricting its attention to individual footings under concentric loading. For more complicated footings the interested reader should see, for example, MacGregor [9.4] or Park and Paulay [9.5]. Although the design of more complex systems will be similar in concept to the methods discussed in this chapter, care must be taken with such aspects as soil stress distribution.

Using factored soil or pile bearing capacities, the design of spread footing area or pile configuration is carried out at ultimate limit states. In some cases, the footing size may be influenced by settlement conditions or similar factors which are evaluated under service load conditions. The properties of the supporting soil, such as bearing capacity and settlement parameters, are determined using principles of soil mechanics which do not fall within the scope of this Handbook.

After the size of the footing or pile configuration has been determined, structural design procedures can be applied to evaluate the thickness and reinforcement requirements of the footing. For this purpose, the column or wall load is separated into its dead and live load components and multiplied by the appropriate load factors to obtain the total factored load, P_f. Furthermore, an effective factored soil or pile bearing reaction must be calculated from the factored loads and from the previously established base area or number of piles. The ensuing structural design procedure can be summarized as follows;

1) for pile caps, calculate minimum pile area and minimum column area due to bearing requirements,

2) calculate the minimum footing thickness due to one and two way shear requirements,

3) calculate required reinforcement areas at critical sections,

4) check development length or anchorage requirements and choose bar sizes,

5) distribute reinforcement,

6) for spread footings, check bearing stresses at column-footing interface and determine dowel requirements.

In the following, unless otherwise stated, all Clauses refer to CSA Standard A23.3.

9.2 SPREAD FOOTINGS

9.2.1 Footing Area

The required base area of a spread footing, A_f, is calculated from the supported factored column load, P_f, the factored footing and surcharge pressure, w_f, the factored soil buoyancy pressure (due to displaced soil in buried footings), w_s, and the factored soil bearing capacity, q_r, such that

$$A_f \geq \frac{P_f}{q_r - (w_f - w_s)} \tag{9.1}$$

for concentric vertical loading and a uniform bearing stress. Note that in general the term $(w_f - w_s)$ is negligible, especially for buried footings. Once the footing area has been selected according to Eq. (9.1), the structural design can proceed using an effective factored soil reaction, q_{sr},

$$q_{sr} = \frac{P_f}{A_f} \tag{9.2}$$

9.2.2 Minimum Thickness

It is common practice to design footings in such a way that shear reinforcement will not be necessary. For this reason, the minimum thickness of a footing with flexural reinforcement is generally governed by one or two way shear, although, in some cases, it can be dependent on the compression development length of the continuing column steel or dowels (see Table 9.8). If, for some reason, the shear capacity of the footing is insufficient and the concrete cross-section cannot be enlarged, shear reinforcement may be provided in the same way as for structural slabs.

9.2.2.1 One Way Shear

If the footing base is rectangular or continuous in one direction, its thickness will likely be governed by one way shear, also called beam shear. Tables 9.1 and 9.2 have been provided for this purpose giving the minimum effective footing depth, d, as a function of the footing projection, a_b, beyond the face of the column or wall and the effective factored soil reaction, q_{sr};

$$d = a_b \left[\frac{q_{sr}}{q_{sr} + \psi_d \lambda \phi_c \sqrt{f_c'} \times 1000} \right] \tag{9.3}$$

where q_{sr} is in kN/m^2, f_c' is in MPa and ψ_d is defined according to Clauses 11.3.5.1 and 11.3.5.2 as

$$\psi_d = \frac{260}{1000 + d} \tag{9.4}$$
$$\geq 0.1$$
$$\leq 0.2$$

Note that since ψ_d may depend on d, Eq. (9.3) is solved iteratively when $300 < d < 1600$ mm.

9.2.2.2 Two Way Shear

The effective thickness of square or almost square isolated footings is usually governed by two way or perimeter shear. For a footing of base area A_f in m^2 supporting a column with an aspect ratio, β_c, less than

2.0 and a cross-sectional area, A_c in m^2, Tables 9.3 and 9.4 have been derived from

$$d = 1000 \times \frac{-S + \sqrt{S^2 + 4q_{sr}(A_f - A_c)(2R + q_{sr})}}{2(2R + q_{sr})} \quad (9.5)$$

where

$$R = 2\Omega_d \lambda \varphi_c \sqrt{f_c'} \times 1000 \quad (9.6)$$

$$S = 0.001 \times (h_c + b_c)(R + q_{sr}) \quad (9.7)$$

$$\Omega_d = 0.2 \left(1 + \frac{2}{\beta_c}\right) \quad (9.8)$$

$$\leq 0.2 + \frac{\alpha_s d}{b_o}$$

$$\leq 0.4$$

$$b_o = 2(h_c + b_c + 2d)$$

and h_c and b_c are the column cross-sectional dimensions in mm and d is in mm. The parameter Ω_d is derived from Clause 13.4.4 and α_s is the number of sides of the critical shear section. Note that since Ω_d may depend on d, Eq. (9.5) is generally solved iteratively. Tables 9.3 and 9.4 are given in non-dimensional form in terms of the footing to column area ratio and the ratio d/h_e where $h_e = 1000 \times \sqrt{A_c}$ mm is the effective column dimension for $\beta_c \leq 2.0$. For columns with $\beta_c > 2.0$ or for a more accurate determination of d for a non-square column, Eq. (9.5) should be solved directly.

9.2.3 Flexure

Reinforcement areas required for flexure in a 1 m width of footing are listed in Tables 9.5 and 9.6 as a function of the soil reaction q_{sr} in kN/m^2 and footing projection beyond the face of the column or wall, a_b in m. The effective depth d in mm must be known by the designer, using Tables 9.1 to 9.4, prior to entering Tables 9.5 or 9.6. The tabular values are based on the flexural requirement

$$A_s = \frac{q_{sr} a_b^2 \times 10^6}{\phi_s f_y \left[d + \sqrt{d^2 - \dfrac{q_{sr} a_b^2 \times 1000}{\alpha_1 \phi_c f_c'}}\right]} \quad mm^2/m \quad (9.9)$$

$$\geq 2.0(d + 100) \quad mm^2/m$$

(minimum reinforcement, Clause 7.81)

$$\leq \left(\frac{700}{700 + f_y}\right)\left(\frac{\alpha_1 \beta_1 \phi_c f_c' \, bd}{\phi_s f_y}\right) \quad mm^2/m$$

(maximum reinforcement, Clause 10.5.2)

The minimum reinforcement is computed assuming that the distance between the upper layer of steel and the base of the footing is about 100 mm. The second constraint ensures yield of the steel prior to crushing of the concrete. In these equations both f_y and f_c' are in MPa and the parameters α_1 and β_1 are as defined by Clause 10.1.7;

$$\alpha_1 = 0.85 - 0.0015 f_c' \geq 0.67 \quad (9.10)$$

$$\beta_1 = 0.97 - 0.0025 f_c' \geq 0.67 \quad (9.11)$$

Where numerical values are not shown in the tables, the ductility constraint requirement of Clause 10.5.2 has been violated and an increased effective depth d must be used. For $(q_{sr} \cdot a_b^2)$ values less than those shown on the tables, use minimum reinforcement as specified by Clause 7.8.1.

Note that when the clear span to overall depth ratio ($\approx a_b/d$) is less than 2, Clause 10.7.1 predicts the footing

to act as a deep beam. Although this condition has not been considered in Tables 9.5 and 9.6, it should be checked by the designer in light of the different flexural and increased anchorage requirements of deep beams. For the flexural analysis of deep beams, Park and Paulay[9.5] suggest the use of a reduced lever arm, z, such that

$$z = 0.4(d + M_f/V_f) \quad \text{for } dV_f/M_f \geq 1.0 \quad (9.12)$$

$$z = 1.2 M_f/V_f \quad \text{for } dV_f/M_f \geq 2.0 \quad (9.13)$$

where M_f and V_f are the moment and shear acting at the face of the column. The required steel area is then obtained from

$$A_s = \frac{M_f}{\phi_s f_y z}$$

In the case of deep beam action, additional anchorage requirements apply since the arching action means that the steel stress remains significantly higher than that predicted by the normal flexural model. In lieu of a detailed analysis accounting for both the reduction in steel stress along the bar and development length test results, it is recommended that standard hooks be provided at the outside edge of the footing whenever the spread footing acts as a deep beam.

9.2.4 Development of Tension Reinforcement

When the clear cover to the reinforcement is greater than d_b, where d_b is the nominal bar diameter in mm, and when the clear spacing between bars is greater than $2d_b$, then the development length specified by Clause 12.2.3 may be used. Assuming that only straight bars will be used ending 75 mm from the edge of the footing, then the maximum bar diameter can be found from

$$\max d_b = \frac{\sqrt{f_c'} (a_b - 0.075) \times 1000}{0.45 k_1 k_2 k_3 k_4 f_y} \quad (9.15)$$

where the parameters k_1, k_2, k_3 and k_4 are as specified by Clause 12.2.4. For uncoated bars, normal density concrete, and distance between the reinforcement and base of the footing less than 300 mm, $k_1 = k_2 = k_3 = 1.0$. For No. 20 and smaller bars, $k_4 = 0.8$, otherwise $k_4 = 1.0$. Table 9.7 lists the development lengths required under these conditions for various bar sizes.

9.2.5 Distribution of Reinforcement

According to Clause 15.4.4, a certain percentage of the total reinforcement in the short direction of rectangular spread footings shall be concentrated over a width equal to the length of the short side of the footing or equal to the length of the supported wall or column, whichever is greater. This percentage is $100 \times 2/(\beta+1)$ where β is the ratio of the long to short side of the footing. The remainder of the reinforcement is to be placed outside of this strip.

When it is desirable to space the bars in the short direction uniformly, to expidite field work and minimize the possibility of error, multiply the total calculated reinforcement area in the short direction by $2\beta/(\beta+1)$.

9.2.6 Plain Concrete Spread Footings

In plain or unreinforced concrete footings, the flexural tensile stress in the concrete must not exceed

$$f_t \leq 0.4 \lambda \phi_c \sqrt{f_c'} \quad (9.16)$$

as specified by Clause 22.6.5. Based on flexural tensile stresses, the minimum effective depth of a plain concrete footing can be expressed as a function of its projection, a_b in m, as

$$h_p = K_d a_b \quad (9.17)$$

where

$$K_d = \sqrt{\dfrac{3000 \times q_{sr}}{0.4\lambda\phi_c \sqrt{f'_c}}} \qquad (9.18)$$

and q_{sr} is in kN/m^2. Table 9.9 lists values of K_d for various concrete strengths and soil reactions q_{sr}. Add 50 mm to the required effective footing depth to obtain the total footing thickness, t_f. Plain concrete footings must also be checked for one and two way shear (see Clause 22.6.6).

Example 9.1 — Minimum Thickness of Square Footings

Given:

For the square footing and square column with service loads indicated, select total required thickness for footing of size 2.5 × 2.5 m. Use f'_c = 20 MPa.

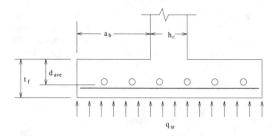

where h_c = 500 mm
P_d = 855 kN (excluding footing weight)
P_ℓ = 540 kN

Calculations and Discussion:

1. Compute factored column loads
   (Clause 8.3)
   $P_f = 1.25P_d + 1.5P_\ell = 1880$ kN

2. Compute factored soil reaction
   (Eq. 9.2)
   $q_{sr} = P_f / A_f = 1880/(2.5)^2 = 300$ kN/m²

3. Compute ratio between footing area and column area
   $A_f / A_c = (2.5)^2/(0.5)^2 = 25$

4. Select minimum d/h_e ratio (two way shear governs)
   (Table 9.3)
   $d/h_e = 0.828$

5. Compute d_{ave}
   for h_e = 500 mm, $d_{ave} = 0.84h_e = 414$ mm

6. Allow at least 95 mm for concrete cover and bar radius (assume $d_b \le 20$ mm)
   (A23.1-94 Clause 12.6.2)
   $t_f = 414 + 95 = 509$ mm
   Use $t_f = 550$ mm

Example 9.2 — Minimum Thickness of Rectangular Footings

Given:

Rectangular footing and rectangular column with factored load of 3500 kN. Determine total required footing

thickness for rectangular footing shown. Use f'_c = 20 MPa.

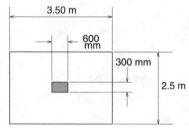

Calculations and Discussion:

1. Compute factored soil reaction, q_{sr}
   (Eq. 9.2)
   $q_{sr} = P_f / A_f = 3500/(3.5 \times 2.5) = 400$ kN/m²

2. Compute maximum overhang distance a_b
   $a_1 = (3.5 - 0.6)/2 = 1.45$ m
   $a_2 = (2.5 - 0.3)/2 = 1.10$ m
   choose $a_b = 1.45$ m

3. Compute minimum depth required by one way shear action for q_{sr} = 400 kN/m²
   (Table 9.1)
   $d \ge 720$ mm

4. Compute minimum average depth required by two way shear action
   $A_f / A_c = (3.5 \times 2.5)/(0.6 \times 0.3) = 49$
   (Table 9.3)
   $d/h_e - 1.56$
   $h_e = \sqrt{A_c} = 420$ mm (conservatively)
   $d \ge 1.56 \times 420 = 655$ mm
   choose $d = 720$ mm (one way shear governs)

5. Add the required cover and allowance for bar diameters to compute the required minimum footing thickness, t_f. Assume No. 25 bars in the long direction.
   (A23.1-94 Clause 12.6.2)
   $t_f = (d) + \dfrac{1}{2}$ (bar dia.) + (cover)
   $= 720 + 12.5 + 75$
   $= 808$ mm
   use $t_f = 850$ mm

Example 9.3 — One Way Footing: Reinforced and Plain

Determine footing depth and reinforcement for the wall footing shown. Also compute required depth for a plain footing. Use a factored soil reaction q_{sr} = 450 kN/m², f'_c = 20 MPa, and f_y = 400 MPa.

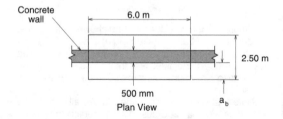

Calculations and Discussion:

1. Determine minimum effective depth required by one way shear for $q_{sr} = 450$ kN/m²

   $a_b = (2.5 - 0.5)/2 = 1.0$ m

   (Table 9.1)

   $d = 490$ mm

2. Determine required A_s

   $a_b/d = 1000/490 = 2.04 > 2$, therefore not a deep beam
   $q_{sr} a_b^2 = 450$ kN

   (Table 9.5)

   $A_s = 1423$ mm²/m width

   $= 8537$ mm²

3. Find maximum bar size that can be developed in distance $a_b - 0.075 = 0.925$ m for $f_y = 400$ MPa,

   (Table 9.7)

   max. $d_b = $ No. 25

   use 29 No. 20 bars in short direction (provided $A_s = 8700$ mm²)

4. Compute total footing depth t_f,

   (A23.1-94 Clause 12.6.2)

   $t_f = (d) + \frac{1}{2}$(bar dia.) + (cover)

   $= 490 + 10 + 75$

   $= 575$ mm

   use $t_f = 600$ mm

   Redesign as an unreinforced footing or structural plain concrete:

5. Find the required minimum depth for $a_b = 1.0$ m, $q_{sr} = 450$ kN/m², $f_c' = 20$ MPa

   (Table 9.9)

   $K_d = 1130$

   (Eq. 9.17)

   $h_p = K_d a_b = 1130$ mm

   $t_f = h_p + 50 = 1180$ mm

use $t_f = 1200$ mm

Note: since $h_p > a_b$ the critical shear plane lies outside the footing. Thus shear capacity is acceptable (Clause 22.6.6).

Example 9.4 — Two Way Square Footing: Minimum Depth and Required Reinforcement

Determine the minimum footing thickness and required reinforcement for the spread footing shown. Assume the footing to be square and use $f_c' = 30$ MPa, $f_y = 400$ MPa, and a factored soil bearing capacity of 625 kN/m². Loading is concentric and vertically applied. The column concrete strength is $f_c' = 40$ MPa. The column is 500 mm square and supports service loads of 3800 kN dead and 725 live.

Calculations and Discussion:

1. Required footing area
   a) factored column load

      $P_f = 1.25(3800) + 1.5(725)$

      $= 5840$ kN

   b) assume footing is to be buried so that $(w_f - w_s)$ is negligible,

   c) required footing area

      (Eq. 9.1)
      $A_f = 5840/625 = 9.34$ m²
      $h_f = b_f = \sqrt{A_f} \approx 3.1$ m

      Provide a 3.1 × 3.1 m square footing ($A_f = 9.61$ m²)

2. Determine minimum footing thickness
   a) one way shear requirement

      $a_b = (3.1 - 0.5)/2 = 1.30$ m
      (Eq. 9.2)
      $q_{sr} = P_f/A_f = 5840/9.61 = 610$ kN/m²
      (Table 9.2)
      $d \geq 716$ mm

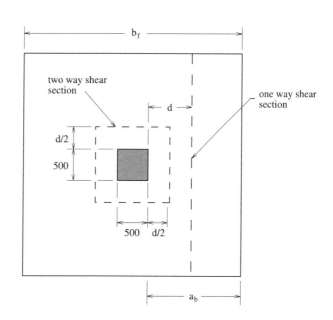

b) two way shear requirement ($h_e = 500$ mm)

$$A_f /A_c = (3.1)^2/(0.5)^2 = 38$$

(Table 9.4)

$$d/h_e = 1.49$$

$$d \geq 1.49(500) = 745 \text{mm}$$

c) dowel development length for No. 25 bars in compression

(Table 9.8)

$$\ell_d = 445 \text{ mm} < 745 \text{ mm, OK}$$

select d = 750 mm

3. Flexural design

check for deep beam action

$a_b/d = 1300/750 = 1.73 < 2$, therefore deep beam action

use Park and Paulay's reduced lever arm[9.5]

$$z = 0.4(d + M_f /V_f) = 0.4(d + a_b/2)$$
$$= 0.4(750 + 1300/2) = 560 \text{ mm}$$
$$A_s = M_f /(\phi_s f_y z) = 0.5a_b^2 q_{sr} b_f /(\phi_s f_y z)$$
$$= 0.5(1.3)^2(610)(3100) \times 1000/(0.85 \times 400 \times 560)$$
$$= 8392 \text{ mm}^2$$

(Clause 7.8.1)

$$\geq 0.002(3100)(750 + 100) = 5270 \text{ mm}^2 \text{ OK}$$

note that the table value gives

$$q_{sr} a_b^2 = (610)(1.3)^2 = 1031 \text{ kN}$$

(Table 9.6)

$$A_s = 2090 \text{ mm}^2/\text{m}$$
$$= 3.1 \times 2090$$
$$= 6480 \text{ mm}^2$$

Provide 17 No. 25 bars each way distributed uniformly (A_s prov. = 8500 mm²)

Anchor bars at outside edge with standard hooks (due to deep beam action)

4. Transfer of force at column base

a) for the footing, the maximum bearing resistance is

$$0.85\phi_c f'_c A_c \sqrt{A_2/A_c}$$
$$\sqrt{A_2/A_c} = \sqrt{3100/500} = 2.5$$
use $\sqrt{A_2/A_c} = 2.0$
thus $(0.85)(0.6)(30)(500^2)(2.0) \times 0.001 = 7650 \text{ kN}$
$7650 \text{ kN} > P_f = 5840 \text{ kN, OK}$

b) for the column, the maximum bearing resistance is

$$0.85\phi_c f'_c A_c = 0.85(0.6)(40)(500^2) \times 0.001$$
$$= 5100 \text{ kN} < P_f$$

must provide dowels for (5840 — 5100) kN

$$A_{sd} = \frac{(5840 - 5100) \times 1000}{(\phi_s f_y)}$$
$$= 2180 \text{ mm}^2$$
$$\geq 0.005(500^2) = 1250 \text{ mm}^2, \text{ OK}$$

provide 6 No. 25 dowels ($A_{sd} = 3000$ mm²)

5. Compute total footing thickness, t_f,

$$t_f = d + d_b + \text{cover} = 750 + 25 + 75$$
$$= 850 \text{ mm}$$

6. Summary

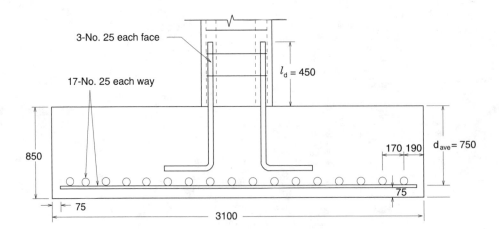

3-No. 25 each face

17-No. 25 each way

$\ell_d = 450$

850

170 190 $d_{ave}= 750$

75

75

3100

Example 9.5 — Two Way Rectangular Footing: Thickness and Reinforcement

Determine the required thickness and reinforcement for the column and footing shown.

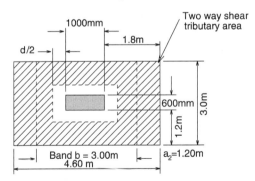

Use f'_c = 20 MPa
f_y = 400 MPa
q_{sr} = 300 kN/m^2

Calculations and Discussion:

1. Minimum d required by one way shear
   for a_b = 1.80 m and q_{sr} = 300 kN/m^2,
   (Table 9.1)
   d ≥ 780 mm

2. Minimum d required by two way shear
   for A_f/A_c = (4.6 × 3.0)/(1.0 × 0.6) = 23
   (Table 9.3)
   d/h_e = 0.78
   for $h_e = \sqrt{A_c}$ = 770 mm   (β_c = 1.67 < 2 OK)
   d ≥ 0.78(770) = 600 mm
   use d = 780 mm

3. Compute A_s required in the long direction
   check for deep beam action

   a_b/d = 1800/780 = 2.3 > 2, therefore normal beam action
   $q_{sr} a_b^2$ = (300)(1.8)^2 = 972 kN
   (Table 9.5)
   A_s = 1918 mm^2/m
   = 3.0 × 1918 = 5754 mm^2
   (Clause 7.8.1)
   ≥ 0.002(3000)(780 + 100) = 5280 mm^2, OK
   (Eq. 9.15)
   max d_b = ($\sqrt{20}$ (1.8 − 0.075) × 1000)/(0.45 × 400)
   = 42.8

   Use 12 No. 25 bars @ 250 mm c/c (provided A_s = 6000 mm^2)

4. Compute A_s required in short direction
   check for deep beam action
   a_b/d = 1200/780 = 1.54 < 2, therefore deep beam action
   use Park and Paulay's reduced lever arm[9.5]

   z = 0.4(d + M_f/V_f) = 0.4(d + $a_b/2$)

= 0.4(780 + 1200/2) = 552 mm
A_s = $M_f/(\phi_s f_y z)$ = 0.5a_b^2 q_{sr} $b_f/(\phi_s f_y z)$
= 0.5(1.2)^2(300)(4600) × 1000/(0.85 × 400 × 552)
= 5294 mm^2
(Clause 7.8.1)
≥ 0.002(4600)(780 + 100) = 8096 mm^2
(Eq. 9.15)
max d_b = ($\sqrt{20}$(1.2 − 0.075) × 1000)/(0.45 × 400)
= 28
Use 17 No. 25 bars (A_s prov = 8500 mm^2)
Anchor bars at outside edge with standard hooks (due to deep beam action)

5. Check short direction bar distribution
   (Clause 15.4.4)
   β = 4.6/3 = 1.53, $\dfrac{2}{\beta + 1}$ = 0.79
   A_{sb} = 0.79(8096) = 6396 mm^2
   Provide 13 No. 25 bars within central 3.0 m bandwidth @ 250 mm c/c
   and 2 No. 25 bars at each end @ 350 mm c/c
   Alternatively provide A_s = $\beta[2/(\beta + 1)](8096)$ = 9792 mm^2
   or 20 No. 25 bars @ 230 mm c/c throughout.

9.3. PILE SUPPORTED FOOTINGS

9.3.1 Structural Design Model

Pile caps are three-dimensional structural elements for which existing code requirements are not clearly defined. In general, pile spacing is such that the plan size of the pile supported footing versus the footing thickness results in deep beam or arching action in the footing. In this case the appropriate design approach involves using either one of a variety of strut and tie models or Park and Paulay's [9.5] reduced lever arm model. After a review of the literature (see, for example, references 9.1 through 9.9), the following five design models were identified as possible candidates;

1) Strut-and-tie model used for reinforcement areas and anchorage requirements only. Effective footing depth is governed by one and two way shear requirements (Clauses 11.3 and 13.4). Pile and column areas are governed by bearing stress requirements of Clause 10.8.

2) Park and Paulay's reduced lever arm model for reinforcement areas with anchorage requirements according to the strut-and-tie model. Effective footing depth is governed by one and two way shear requirements (Clauses 11.3 and 13.4). Pile and column areas are governed by the bearing stress requirements of Clause 10.8.

3) Strut-and-tie model used for reinforcement areas and anchorage requirements. Effective footing depth is governed by one and two way shear requirements (Clauses 11.3 and 13.4) as well as by bearing stress limitations according to Adebar et al. [9.2], [9.9]. Pile and column areas are also governed by the same bearing stress limitations (increased pile and column areas allow decreased effective depths to some extent).

4) Strut-and-tie model used for reinforcement areas, anchorage requirements, effective footing depth and pile and column areas (Clause 11.5).

5) Strut-and-tie model used for reinforcement areas and anchorage requirements only. Effective footing depth is governed by one and two way shear requirements (Clauses 11.3 and 13.4) along with the 'deep beam' shear requirements proposed by CRSI [9.8] and ACI 318-89 [9.7]. Pile and column areas are governed by the bearing stress requirements of Clause 10.8.

The major differences between these models lies in the choice of allowable bearing stresses and the treatment of shear contribution from piles lying within the traditionally defined critical shear section (see Clauses 13.4.3.1 and 13.4.6.1). The strut-and-tie model imposes conditions on the stresses in the compressive struts but does not directly provide a means of computing the minimum effective depth, d, so this is generally selected initially by considering the traditional one and two way shear requirements in all the above models. Model 1 is the simplest model and typically yields the most economical design, however when the footing acts as a deep beam, as all of the pile caps considered here do, the shear provisions of Clauses 11.3 and 13.4 are felt to be unconservative, not adequately predicting the deep beam behaviour. The difference between model 1 and model 2 lies in the approach to finding the required tension reinforcement - model 2 employs a standard flexural model with a reduced lever arm to represent the deep beam arching action. Model 2 also assumes that the reinforcement is distributed across the entire footing width. However, since the effective depth in model 2 is found in the same way as model 1, that is via the traditional one and two way shear requirements, it is felt that model 2 may also be unconservative. Note that model 2 was used to produce the previous edition of this Handbook, and so existing empirical evidence may imply that the designs are in fact not particularly unconservative.

Model 4 tends to yield the most conservative designs, primarily due to the very restrictive bearing stress requirements of Clause 11.5.4.1 which dictate quite large pile and column areas. Also the three-dimensional nodal regions under the column and above the piles are poorly defined by the existing standards of Clause 11.5. Because test results as reported in references 9.1, 9.2, 9.3, 9.6, and 9.9 indicate that ultimate bearing stresses are significantly greater than the stress stipulated by Clause 11.5.4.1, model 4 was not selected as the design model in this Handbook. This does not mean that it is a poor model, just that the admittedly limited test data seem to indicate that it is overly conservative.

Model 5 follows the CRSI Handbook where an attempt was made to explicitly account for deep beam behaviour of pile caps by separately investigating shear stresses in the case where piles lie within the traditionally defined critical shear sections. The approach involves using significantly increased shear capacities on critical sections located at or very near the column face and has been quite a popular method over the years. However, there is some concern that the shear capacities used are rather arbitrary and are not based on formal experimental results. The shear capacities stipulated by ACI 318-89 are about half those suggested by CRSI.

Adebar et al. [9.2] suggest that a maximum bearing stress approach is superior to shear stress calculations on rather arbitrarily prescribed critical sections because it more rationally represents the state of stress in the compressive struts. In model 3, Adebar et al. [9.9] propose a bearing stress limitation which includes the $\sqrt{A_2/A_1}$ factor used also in Clause 10.8.1, giving a limitation which is not as restrictive as that of Clause 11.5.4.1 but also is not as large (typically) as that of Clause 10.8.1 itself. The design approach suggested by Adebar involves checking the traditional one and two way shear requirements (Clauses 11.3 and 13.4) to determine an initial estimate of the required effective depth. Bearing stresses under the column and over the piles are then checked and violations corrected by either increasing the effective depth, increasing the footing plan dimensions, and/or increasing the column or pile areas. Since Adebar verified his proposal against a variety of published test results with reasonable success, model 3 was selected for use in this Handbook. Model 3 leads to more economical designs than does model 4, but still involves allowable bearing stresses typically lower than used in practice currently. Thus the footing depths, minimum column and pile areas, and/or footing plan dimensions reported in the pile cap tables here tend to be larger than reported in the previous edition of this Handbook. The designer should be aware of the fact that test evidence on pile cap design is quite limited, especially for larger numbers of piles, and so the appropriate design model is still a debatable issue. If in doubt, the design can be checked using one or more of the other models.

9.3.2 Use of the Tables

The pile cap tables are used by entering the table at the line where the provided P_f value is less than or equal to the table P_f value and the provided column dimensions are greater than or equal to the table column dimensions h_c and b_c. Read across for

- d the required minimum effective depth in mm
- h_f overall footing dimension in mm measured in the same direction as h_c,
- b_f overall footing dimension measured in the same direction as b_c,
- d_p pile diameter in mm,
- s_p minimum pile center-to-center spacing in mm,
- e_d edge distance (minimum distance between the pile center and the edge of the footing),
- A_{si} required reinforcement area of the ith tie in mm^2.

In all of the tables, the steel reinforcement is assumed to lie in a single layer as ties acting between the piles. The width over which the steel is distributed within each tie is governed by the allowable bar spacing (see Clause A12.5 or CSA Standard A23.1-94), but would normally be chosen so that the tie is somewhat wider than the pile diameter.

The overall footing thickness, t_f, is computed as

$$t_f = d + 1.5d_b + 150 \text{ mm} \tag{9.19}$$

where it is assumed that the distance d is measured from the upper surface of the footing to the centroid of the uppermost layer of steel and d_b is taken as 20 mm when using t_f to compute minimum reinforcement requirements according to Clause 7.8.1.

9.3.3 Pile Configuration

The number of piles, N_p, required to support a given factored column, footing, and surcharge load, $P_f + (W_f - W_s)$, where W_s is the soil buoyancy (due to displaced soil in buried footings) and W_f is the factored footing weight, can be determined from the factored axial pile capacity, Q_f, as

$$N_p = \frac{P_f + (W_f - W_s)}{Q_f} \tag{9.20}$$

if it is assumed that each pile carries an equal portion of the applied load. This assumption has been made for all the pile caps discussed in this Handbook but may be invalid if the load is not concentric or if it is known that the pile cap is relatively flexible or piles have markedly different axial stiffnesses. In the pile cap tables, the factor $(W_f - W_s)$ is assumed to be negligible compared to P_f and so has been ignored.

The shape and size of the footing or pile cap is usually determined on the basis of the required pile spacing. This dimension would normally be specified by the soil engineer to avoid overload of the soil mass under the footing. In the pile cap tables, a pile spacing of three times the pile diameter, center to center, has been assumed.

9.3.4   Pile Diameter

Once the pile cap configuration has been established, the factored column load, P_f, is divided by the number of piles to obtain the effective pile reaction, $Q_{pr} = P_f/N_p$. The pile diameter, d_p, must be computed such that the bearing stress at the top of the pile is less than the stress allowed by Adebar et al.[9.9],

$$f_b \leq \phi_c (0.6 f'_c + 6\alpha\beta\sqrt{f'_c}) \qquad (9.21)$$

where

$$\alpha = 0.33\left(\sqrt{\frac{A_2}{A_1}} - 1\right) \leq 1.0 \qquad (9.22a)$$

$$\beta = 0.33\left(\frac{h_s}{b_s} - 1\right) \leq 1.0 \qquad (9.22b)$$

and the ratio A_2/A_1 is the same as that used in Clause 10.8.1 with $A_1 = A_p$, the pile area. The ratio h_s/b_s is the height to width ratio of the compression strut acting between the pile and the column. In all cases, the pile is assumed to be circular in cross-section so that the pile area is $A_p = 0.25\pi d_p^2$ and

$$\sqrt{\frac{A_2}{A_p}} = 2\frac{e_d}{d_p} \qquad (9.23)$$

whenever $d > 3d_p/4$, where e_d is the minimum distance between the pile center and the edge of the footing. In the pile caps, the edge distance e_d is selected as the greater of 400 mm or $2d_p$, so that the $\sqrt{A_2/A_p}$ factor is never less than 4.0 (giving $\alpha = 1$). Note that this attempt to maximize α sometimes results in quite large edge distances, but the alternative would be quite large pile diameters. It was felt that minimizing the required pile diameter is better than minimizing the edge distance.

Adebar[9.9] suggests that the height to width ratio h_s/b_s for piles may be approximated by d/d_p. Since both d and d_p are unknown at this point in the calculations (the footing dimensions depending on the pile spacing which is assumed to be $3d_p$), the ratio d/d_p is initially approximated as being 2.5 (giving $\beta = 0.5$). The actual bearing stress over the pile must be rechecked once d has been estimated for the footing. If, at this point, $d < 2.5d_p$, then the bearing stress check may fail and d will have to be increased.

Using $\alpha = 1.0$ and β assumed to be 0.5, the bearing force over the pile is limited by

$$Q_{pr} \leq \phi_c (0.6 f'_c + 3\sqrt{f'_c}) A_p \qquad (9.24)$$

from which the minimum pile diameter can be found as

$$d_p \geq \sqrt{\frac{4(Q_{pr} \times 1000)}{\pi\phi_c(0.6f'_c + 3\sqrt{f'_c})}} \text{ mm} \qquad (9.25)$$

for Q_{pr} in kN and f'_c in MPa. Pile diameters listed in the tables have been rounded up to the next higher 50 mm with a minimum of 200 mm. Bearing stresses acting within the pile itself must be checked by the designer.

Note that the pile diameter is chosen here on the basis of allowable bearing stresses over the pile, and not on the basis of loads and pile capacity as provided by the geotechnical engineer. Since this choice also affects the pile spacing and thus the pile cap dimensions, it is admittedly a questionable approach, but is necessary in the absence of a complete geotechnical description of the site (which would lead to much more complicated and extensive tables).

9.3.5   Column Dimensions

The column dimensions, h_c and b_c, shown in the pile cap tables are arranged in 3 groups of two for each factored column load, P_f. Each group of two corresponds to a fixed column aspect ratio, b_c/h_c, and the first element gives the minimum column area required to satisfy Adebar's bearing stress limitations (see Eq. 9.21).

The second element of each of the 3 groups is obtained from the first by incrementing h_c by 200 mm. The column aspect ratios used are as follows; for the square pile caps ($N_p = 4, 5,$ and 9), b_c/h_c was set to 1/1, 3/2, and 2/1. For the non-square pile caps, b_c/h_c was set to 1/1, 3/2, and 2/3. All column dimensions are rounded up to the next closest 10 mm.

For the computation of the allowable column bearing stress, the height to width ratio h_s/b_s is approximated by $2d/h_{eff}$, where $h_{eff} = \sqrt{h_c b_c}$ is an effective column dimension. In that the column dimensions must be known prior to finding d (for one and two way shear calculations), the allowable bearing stress computed using Eq. (9.21) was obtained under the assumption that d = 1500 mm which almost always ensures that $\alpha = 1$ and $\beta = 1$. The column bearing stress is then rechecked after d has been estimated and d is increased if Eq. (9.21) is violated. This generally results in column dimensions which are the minimum allowed by Eq. (9.21), sometimes at the expense of increased effective depths.

Note that no provision has been made in the computation of the minimum column dimensions $h_c \times b_c$ for transfer of load by continuing compression dowels (even though these may be present). This is primarily in acknowledgement of the fact that the strut-and-tie model used here limits the compressive stress in the concrete struts and nodal regions and that the compressive struts will not likely lie along the compression dowels. Bearing stresses acting within the column itself must be checked by the designer. Continuing compression dowels provided to satisfy bearing stress violations in the column itself should also be avoided unless the effect they have on the strut and tie geometry is accounted for in a rational fashion.

9.3.6   Effective Depth

The effective depth, d, listed in the pile cap tables for various combinations of factored column load and column dimensions are derived as the maximum required by;

1) one way shear of footing corner (diagonal shear plane) due to reaction of a single pile, as shown in Figure 9.1 and as required by Clause 13.4.6.2. The resulting required effective depth is limited to being less than that value which would cause the shear section to intersect the column plus 50 mm. One way shear around pile groups has been ignored in the pile cap tables and must be investigated on an individual basis by the designer. Examples of such potential shear sections around pile groups are shown in Figure 9.4.

2) two way shear of footing due to reaction of a single pile located along the side of a footing, as shown in Figure 9.2 and as required by Clause 13.4.2. For

7-pile caps, two way shear at the corners is considered, as shown in Figure 9.3. Two way shear around pile groups is not considered in the pile cap tables and must be checked individually by the designer.

3) one way shear of the entire footing in the worst direction as required by Clauses 13.4.6.1 and 11.3. The critical shear plane is located a distance d from the face of the column and piles lying outside the shear plane contribute to the shear acting on the section. Piles which intersect the shear plane have shear force contributions as stipulated by Clause 15.5.3 (linear interpolation). Piles lying wholly within the shear plane do not contribute to the shear force.

4) two way shear about the column according to Clause 13.4. Contributions of individual piles to the shear force are as specified by Clause 15.5.3 (linear or bilinear interpolation when the critical shear section intersects the pile cross-section).

5) allowable bearing stresses over the piles, see Eq. (9.21), for fixed d_p obtained using approximations discussed above. If the applied bearing stress, Q_{pr}/A_p, exceeds f_b, then d is increased until $f_b \geq Q_{pr}/A_p$.

6) allowable bearing stress under the column, see Eq. (9.21), for fixed column dimensions $h_c \times b_c = A_c$ obtained using approximations discussed above. If the applied bearing stress, P_f/A_c, exceeds f_b, then d is increased until $f_b \geq P_f/A_c$.

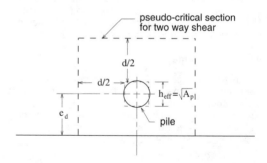

Fig. 9.2   Pseudo-critical section for two way shear of a side pile in a pile cap.

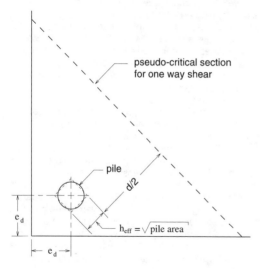

Fig. 9.1   Pseudo-critical section for one way shear of a corner pile in a square cornered pile cap.

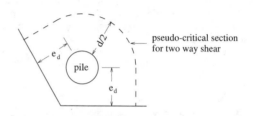

Fig. 9.3   Pseudo-critical section for two way shear of a corner pile in a 7 pile cap.

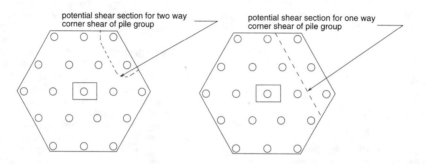

Fig. 9.4   Potential modes of corner shear failure around pile groups not considered in the pile cap tables.

It should also be noted that the effective depths listed in the pile cap tables are the minimums required by shear and bearing considerations and do not necessarily correspond to the optimum design. Often, using increased effective depths results in less tie reinforcement (unless the tie reinforcement is governed by minimum reinforcement requirements of Clause 7.8.1), which in some cases may lead to a more economical design and a better structural element. Since the costs associated with the materials and construction are not considered in this Handbook, the minimum depth criteria is used to establish the tabulated values.

9.3.7 Reinforcement Design

After finding the effective depth according to shear and bearing requirements, the footing is checked to see if it acts as a deep beam. The criterion used is provided by Park and Paulay[9.5]: if $d \cdot V_f/M_f \geq 1.0$ then the footing acts as a deep beam and a strut-and-tie model is used for the reinforcement design; otherwise normal flexural theory is used. All pile caps presented in the tables were found to act as deep beams under this criterion. M_f and V_f are the factored moment and shear force acting at the face of the column (in the direction giving the largest value of V_f/M_f) computed under the assumption that the pile reaction, Q_{pr}, acts at the centroid of the pile.

In the case of normal flexural action, the design of the footing follows very closely the design of spread footings outlined in previous sections. Normal flexural action might be found when the footing is supported on a large number of piles. When the footing acts as a deep beam, the reinforcement must be provided in the form of ties spanning from pile to pile as shown in each pile cap table. This reinforcement acts to tie the truss model together.

Figure 9.5 illustrates the strut-and-tie model used to obtain the required reinforcement areas. The individual compressive struts are assumed to point conservatively at the column 1/4 points for the rectangular or square pile caps (N_p = 2, 4, 5, 6, 8, and 9), that is, at a point 1/2 of the way between the column center and the column face(s) closest to the pile (measured in the two coordinate directions when the pile is located diagonally from the column). For the non-rectangular pile caps (N_p = 3 and 7), the compressive struts are located at the closest point to the pile on the perimeter of a circle of radius min $(h_c, b_c)/4$ centered at the column center. These choices ensure that the force system remains as symmetric as possible, allowing the forces to be computed on the basis of the analysis of a reduced number of struts. The tie reinforcement requirements for the square pile caps (N_p = 4, 5, and 9) will thus differ somewhat in the two coordinate directions when the column is not square. It is suggested that to reduce possible placement errors, the higher tie reinforcement requirement be used in both directions, where appropriate.

For all the pile caps considered, the individual piles have one compressive strut and ties in at most two directions acting over it and the tie forces can be evaluated separately at each pile to satisfy statics. Figure 9.6 shows the truss geometry in a vertical plane along the compressive strut and in plan view. The compressive force in the strut is given by $F_s = (r/d) Q_{pr}$ and the horizontal component is given by

$$F_h = \left(\frac{\ell}{d}\right) Q_{pr} \tag{9.26}$$

For two tie forces acting at horizontal angles θ_1 and θ_2 and F_h acting at the horizontal angle θ_c, the tie forces are given generally by

$$F_{T_1} = F_h \left(\frac{\sin \theta_c - \tan \theta_2 \cos \theta_c}{\sin \theta_1 - \tan \theta_2 \cos \theta_1}\right) \tag{9.27a}$$

$$F_{T_2} = F_h \left(\frac{\sin \theta_c - \tan \theta_1 \cos \theta_c}{\sin \theta_2 - \tan \theta_1 \cos \theta_2}\right) \tag{9.27b}$$

For many of the pile caps, $\theta_1 = 0$ and $\theta_2 = \pi/2$, in which case equations (9.27) reduce to

$$F_{T_1} = F_h \cos \theta_c \tag{9.28a}$$

$$F_{T_2} = F_h \sin \theta_c \tag{9.28b}$$

Once the total tie force F_T has been determined for an individual tie, the required reinforcement area is

$$A_s = \frac{1000 \times F_T}{\phi_s f_y} \ mm^2 \tag{9.29}$$

where F_T is in kN and f_y is in MPa.

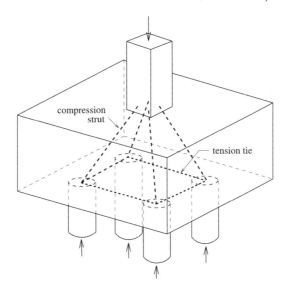

compression strut

tension tie

Fig. 9.5 Strut-and-tie model used to determine required reinforcement.

Elevation in Plane of Compressive Strut   **Plan View**

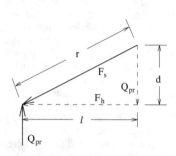
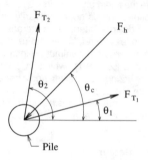

Fig. 9.6   Force diagram for strut-and-tie model at a typical pile.

The total reinforcement area acting in orthogonal coordinate directions is limited to a minimum value of $0.002A_g$, according to Clause 7.8.1. The value of A_g is either $h_f(d + 150 + 30)$ or $b_f(d + 150 + 30)$ depending on the direction being considered, where h_f and b_f are the overall dimensions of the footing and the 30 mm is assumed to approximately account for 1.5 times the bar diameter (d is measured to the centroid of the upper layer of steel). In the case of the 3 and 7 pile caps, where the ties do not necessarily lie along coordinate directions, the components of the total tie steel acting in the orthogonal coordinate directions are checked against the required minimums. For 8-pile caps when minimum reinforcement is required in the long direction, the ratio of A_{s3}/A_{s1} is held the same as computed via the strut-and-tie model with the total steel area adding up to the required minimum. The maximum reinforcement requirements of Clause 10.5.2 are not considered since the flexural model is not being used here.

Test results have shown that the best pile cap designs lie somewhere between the traditional approach where the steel is distributed across the entire footing and the strut-and-tie approach where the steel is concentrated in the ties connecting the piles. Although the strut-and-tie model considered here only addresses the reinforcement in the ties, improved serviceability crack control and limit states behaviour is obtained if a minimum amount of reinforcement is provided in a uniform grid throughout the pile cap along with the primary tie reinforcement. Although no clear guidelines exist on the optimum amount of uniformly distributed steel, it is felt that some fraction of the tie steel can be used for this purpose (the uniformly distributed steel still contributes to the tie strength). Based on this reasoning, it is suggested that some 30% of the tie steel be distributed across the footing in the regions between the ties.

9.3.8   Development of Reinforcement

When the footing acts as a deep beam, as do all the footings in the pile cap tables, then the tie reinforcement must be developed from the inside edge of the pile. Thus the available development length is

$$\text{available } \ell_d = (e_d + d_p/2 - 75) \qquad (9.30)$$

and Table 9.7 can be used to determine the maximum bar size that can be used without a hook (note that Table 9.7 can only be used if clear spacing between bars in the tie is greater than $2d_b$). In general, this limits bar sizes to No. 20 or less. If larger bars are to be used, hooks will often be required at the outer edge of the pile cap.

Example 9.6 — Pile Supported Footing

Design a pile supported footing for a factored column load of 6200 kN with column dimensions $h_c = b_c = 500$ mm. Use $f'_c = 30$ MPa, $f_y = 400$ MPa, and a factored pile resistance of 1300 kN.

Calculations and Discussion:

1. Find number of piles

   estimate $N_p = P_f/Q_f = 6200/1300 = 4.8$

   use $N_p = 5$

2. 5-pile cap dimensions and reinforcement

   (Table 9.13 b)

   for $P_f = 6250 > 6200$ kN, $h_c = b_c = 460 < 500$ mm,

   select

   d = 950 mm (governed by one way shear @ pile)

   $h_f \times b_f = 2480 \times 2480$ mm

   $d_p = 300$ mm

   $s_p = 900$ mm

   $e_d = 600$ mm

   (Clause 7.8.1)

   $A_s = 2802$ mm^2 in each of four ties

   Note: Although the pile cap depth selected is adequate for one and two way shear and bearing, a slight outward deviation in driving piles may increase the shear force on the shear section about the column (because of the shear effect of pile location as defined by Clause 15.5.3). Therefore it may be prudent to select a somewhat deeper pile cap than indicated in the tables and to check pile locations after installation to verify the design. In the current example, since one way shear at the pile governs the value of d, an outward deviation of x in the pile location will result in an increase in d of 2x. Also, since A_s is governed by Clause 7.8.1, an increase in d would necessitate an increase in A_s.

3. Anchorage of reinforcement

   (Eq. 9.30)

   available $\ell_d = e_d + d_p/2 - 75 = 600 + 150 - 75 = 675$ mm

   (Table 9.7)

   choose No. 20 bars ($\ell_d = 526$ mm, OK)

   Use 10 No. 20 bars for each tie (provided $A_s = 3000$ mm^2 per tie)

To provide for additional ductility in the footing, use 7-20M bars @ 60 mm in each tie centered over the piles and 6-20M bars @ 130 mm in each direction distributed in the region between ties.

4. Pile cap thickness

$t_f = d + 1.5d_b + 150 = 950 + 1.5(20) + 150 = 1130$ mm

Use $t_f = 1150$ mm

5. Summary of Design

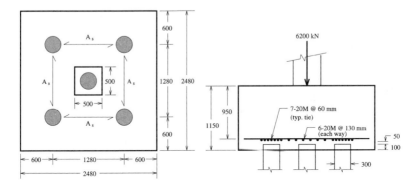

Example 9.7 — Design of 9 Pile Cap

Determine the footing thickness and reinforcement requirements for the symmetric 9 pile footing supporting a rectangular column as shown. Given a factored column load of 9000 kN, use $f'_c = 20$ MPa and $f_y = 400$ MPa.

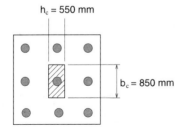

Calculations and Discussion:

1. Determine minimum required effective depth, d

   (Table 9.17a)

   for $P_f = 9000$ kN, $h_c \times b_c = 510 \times 760 <$ provided 550×850,

   select d = 1250 mm (governed by bearing under column)

   See note in Example 9.6

2. Check shear around pile groups

   An inspection of the pile cap configuration indicates that one way corner shear of the three piles in any of the pile cap corners will not occur since the column intersects the critical shear section. Similarly, the two way critical shear section around any two outer piles also intersects the column cross-section so this mode of failure is unlikely. Thus the selected effective depth d = 1250 mm is acceptable.

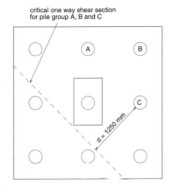

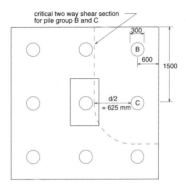

3. Determine required steel areas

due to symmetry, all reinforcement ties support approximately the same load

(Table 9.17a)

for $P_f = 9000$ kN, $h_c \times b_c = 510 \times 760 < 550 \times 850$, select $A_s = 2860$ mm^2 in each tie (governed by Clause 7.8.1)

4. Anchorage of reinforcement

(Eq. 9.30)

available $\ell_d = e_d + d_p/2 - 75 = 600 + 150 - 75 = 675$ mm

(Table 9.7)

choose No. 20 bars ($\ell_d = 644$ mm, OK)

Use 10 No. 20 bars for each tie (provided $A_s = 3000$ mm^2 per tie)

To provide for additional ductility in the footing, use 8-20M bars @ 60 mm for each tie centered over the piles and 3-20M bars @ 120mm distributed between the ties.

5. Pile cap thickness

$t_f = d + 1.5d_b + 150 = 1250 + 1.5(20) + 150 = 1430$ mm

Use $t_f = 1450$ mm

6. Summary of Design

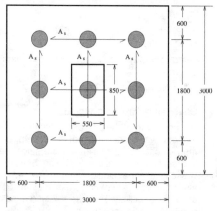

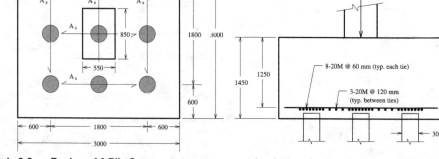

Example 9.8 — Design of 6 Pile Cap

Determine the footing thickness and reinforcement requirements for the rectangular 6 pile footing supporting a rectangular column as shown. Given a factored column load of 7500 kN, use $f'_c = 20$ MPa and $f_y = 400$ MPa.

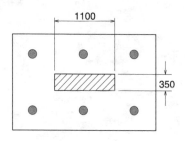

Calculations and Discussion:

A brief look at Table 9.14a indicates that this column does not fit into any of the tabulated values. Thus it must

be designed manually, demonstrating the design methodology, as follows;

1. Compute required pile diameter

$Q_{pr} = P_f/N_p = 7500/6 = 1250$ kN

(Eq. 9.25)

$$d_p \geq \sqrt{\frac{4(1250 \times 10^{3)}}{\pi(0.6)(0.6 \times 20 + 3\sqrt{20})}} = 323 \text{ mm}$$

use $d_p = 350$ mm

2. Pile cap plan geometry

$s_p = 3d_p = 1050$ mm

$e_d = 400$ mm $> 2dp = 700$ mm, use $e_d = 700$ mm

$h_f = 2s_p + 2e_d = 2(1050) + 2(700) = 3500$ mm

$b_f = s_p + 2e_d = 1050 + 2(700) = 2450$ mm

3. Check column bearing stress

$A_c = 1100 \times 350 = 385 \times 10^3$ mm^2

(Clause 10)

if $t_f \geq 600$ mm then $A_2 = 3500 \times 2450 = 8575 \times 10^3$ mm^2

so that $\sqrt{A_2/A_c} = 4.72$

(Eq. 9.22a)

$\alpha = 0.33(4.72 - 1) = 1.23 \leq 1.0$, use $\alpha = 1$

(Eq. 9.22b)

$\beta \approx 0.33(\dfrac{2d}{\sqrt{A_c}} - 1) = 1$ if $d > 1240$ mm

assume $\beta = 1$

(Eq. 9.21)

allowable $f_b = 0.6(0.6(20) + 6\sqrt{20}) = 23.3$ MPa

provided $f_b = (7500 \times 1000)/(350 \times 1100) = 19.5$ MPa < 23.3 MPa, OK

Note: since the column bearing stress must be re-checked again once d has been determined, it is not actually necessary to check it at this point in this example. This step would normally only be performed to estimate the minimum column area, if required.

4. Minimum effective depth from one way shear at corner pile, d_1

(Clause 15.3)

$h_{eff} = \sqrt{A_p} = \sqrt{\pi}d_p/2 = 310$ mm

(Clause 13.4.6.2)

$b_o = 2[\sqrt{2}e_d + 0.5(h_{eff} + d_1)] = 2290 + d_1$

$V_f = 1000 \times Q_{pr} = 1.25 \times 10^6$ N

$V_r = \psi_d \lambda \phi_c \sqrt{f_c'} b_o d_1 = \psi_d (0.6)\sqrt{20}(2290 + d_1) d_1$

$\quad = 2.683\psi_d d_1^2 + 6145\psi_d d_1$

(Clause 11.3.5.2)

$\psi_d = 260/(1000 + d_1)$

$\quad \geq 0.1$

(Clause 11.3.5.1)

$\quad \leq 0.2$

equating $V_r = V_f$ gives

$$d_1 = \frac{-6145\Psi_d + \sqrt{(6145\Psi_d)^2 + 4(2.683\Psi_d)(1.25\times10^6)}}{2(2.683\Psi_d)}$$

$\quad = 1112$ mm, solved iteratively; ($\psi_d = 0.1231$)

check for intersection of diagonal shear plane with column

$d_{crit} = \dfrac{1}{\sqrt{2}}(h_f - h_c + b_f - b_c) - 2\sqrt{2}e_d - h_{eff}$

$\quad = 892$ mm $< d_1 = 1112$ mm

choose $d_1 = d_{crit} + 50 = 942$ mm

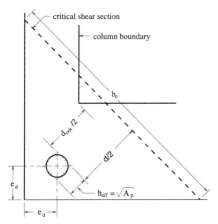

5. Minimum effective depth from two way shear at edge pile, d_2 (see Figure 9.2)

(Clause 13.4.3.1)

$b_o = 2(e_d + h_{eff} + d_2)$

$\quad = 2(700 + 310 + d_2) = 2020 + 2d_2$

(Clause 13.4.4)

$V_r = \Omega_d \lambda \phi_c \sqrt{f_c'} b_o d_2$

$\quad = 5.367\Omega_d d_2^2 + 5420\Omega_d d_2$

(Clause 13.4.4)

$\Omega_d = 0.2(1 + 2/\beta_c) = 0.2(1 + 2) = 0.6$

$\quad \leq 0.2 + \alpha_s d_2/b_o \quad (\alpha_s = 3$ in this case$)$

$\quad \leq 0.4$

equating $V_r = V_f$ gives

$$d_2 = \frac{-5420\Omega_d + \sqrt{(5420\Omega_d)^2 + 4(5.367\Omega_d)(1.25\times10^6)}}{2(5.367\Omega_d)}$$

$\quad = 410$ mm $(\Omega_d = 0.4)$

6. Minimum effective depth from one way shear at column, d_3

check in long direction

(Clause 11.3.2)

$b_o = 2450$ mm

(Clause 11.3.5.2)

$V_r = \psi_d \lambda \phi_c \sqrt{f_c'} b_o d_3 = 6573\psi_d d_3$

$V_f = r(2Q_{pr}) = 2.5 \times 10^6 r$

where r is the fraction of the pile outside the critical shear section;

$r = \dfrac{\frac{1}{2}(h_f - h_c) - d_3 + \frac{1}{2}d_p - e_d}{d_p} = \dfrac{675 - d_3}{350}$

$\quad \leq 1.0$

$\quad \geq 0.0$

equating $V_r = V_f$ gives

$d_3 = \dfrac{V_f}{\Psi_d \lambda \phi_c \sqrt{f_c'} b_o}$

$\quad = 587$ mm

(solved iteratively since both V_f and ψ_d depend on d_3)

check in short direction

(Clause 11.3.2)

$b_o = 3500$ mm

(Clause 11.3.5.2)

$V_r = \psi_d \lambda \phi_c \sqrt{f_c'} b_o d_3 = 9391\psi_d d_3$

$V_f = r(3Q_{pr}) = 3.75 \times 10^6 r$

where r is the fraction of the pile outside the critical shear section;

$r = \dfrac{\frac{1}{2}(b_f - b_c) - d_3 + \frac{1}{2}d_p - e_d}{d_p} = \dfrac{525 - d_3}{350}$

$\quad \leq 1.0$

$\quad \geq 0.0$

since r = 0 for $d_3 = 587$ mm, the long direction governs (shear section is outside piles in short direction)

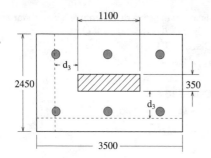

7. Minimum effective depth from two way shear at column, d_4

(Clause 13.4.3.1)

$b_o = 2(h_c + b_c + 2d_4) = 2900 + 4d_4$

$V_r = \Omega_d \lambda \phi_c \sqrt{f_c'} b_o d_4$

$\quad = 2.683\Omega_d (2900 + 4d_4) d_4$

$V_f = r_1 (2Q_{pr}) + (1 - (1 - r_1)(1 - r_2))(4Q_{pr})$

where r_1 is the fraction of piles outside the long edge of the shear section, and r_2 is the fraction of piles outside the short edge of the shear section;

$r_1 = \dfrac{525 - d_4/2}{350} = \dfrac{1050 - d_4}{700}$

$\quad \leq 1.0$

$\quad \geq 0.0$

$r_2 = \dfrac{675 - d_4/2}{350} = \dfrac{1350 - d_4}{700}$

$\quad \leq 1.0$

$\quad \geq 0.0$

equating $V_r = V_f$ and solving iteratively gives

$d_4 = 850$ mm

Check:

$r_1 = 0.28571$

$r_2 = 0.71429$

$V_f = \Big[0.28571(2) + (1 - (1 - 0.28571)$

$\quad (1 - 0.71429)) (4)\Big] (1.25 \times 10^6)$

$\quad = 4.694 \times 10^6$ N

$b_o = 6300$ mm

$\Omega_d = 0.2\left(1 + \dfrac{2}{1100/350}\right) = 0.3273$

$\quad \leq 0.2 + \dfrac{4(850)}{6300} = 0.740$, OK

$\quad \leq 0.4$, OK

$V_r = 2.683(0.3273)(6300)(850) = 4.702 \times 10^6$ N, OK

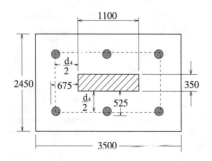

Choose d = max(d_1, d_2, d_3, d_4) = 942 mm

Use d = 950 mm

Note: If all 6 piles are shifted outwards by 50 mm, then d_4 increases by about 65 mm, d_1 increases by 100 mm, and d_3 increases by 50 mm. Due to deviations in pile placement during driving, it may be prudent to select d somewhat greater than the minimum obtained via these calculations and recheck the design after placement of the piles.

8. Recheck column bearing (see step 3)

$t_f > d > 600$ mm, so $\alpha = 1$ as assumed in step 3.

(Eq. 9.22b)

$\beta = 0.33(\dfrac{2(950)}{\sqrt{A_c}} - 1) = 0.68$ (less than 1.0 used in step 3)

(Eq. 9.21)

allowable $f_b = 0.6(0.6(20) + 6(0.68)\sqrt{20}) = 18.2$ MPa

provided $f_b = 19.5$ MPa > 18.2 MPa, so must increase d (assuming column dimensions are fixed)

min $\beta = \dfrac{(19.5/0.6) - 0.6(20)}{6\sqrt{20}} = 0.764$

min d $= \left(\dfrac{0.764}{0.33} + 1\right)\dfrac{\sqrt{A_c}}{2} = 1028$ mm

choose d = 1030 mm

9. Recheck pile bearing

(Eq. 9.22a)

$\alpha = 0.33\left(2\dfrac{e_d}{d_p} - 1\right) = 1.0$

(Eq. 9.22b)

$\beta = 0.33\left(\dfrac{d}{d_p} - 1\right) = 0.33\left(\dfrac{1030}{350} - 1\right) = 0.64$

(Eq. 9.21)

allowable $f_b = 0.6(0.6(20) + 6(0.64)\sqrt{20}) = 17.5$ MPa

provided $f_b = \dfrac{1.25 \times 10^6}{\frac{\pi}{4}(350)^2} = 13.0$ MPa < 17.5 MPa, OK

10. Compute required reinforcement

Check deep beam action:

In long direction, $d V_f / M_f = (1030)(2.5 \times 10^6)/ (1.25 \times 10^9) = 2.06 > 1$

In short direction, $dV_f/M_f = (1030)(3.75 \times 10^6)/ (1.312 \times 10^9) = 2.94 > 1$

therefore footing acts as a deep beam.

Due to symmetry, tie forces only need be computed at the lower left pile (or any corner pile)

(Eq. 9.26)

$F_h = \dfrac{l}{d} Q_{pr} = \dfrac{\sqrt{438^2 + 775^2}}{1030}(1.25 \times 10^6)$

$\quad = \dfrac{890}{1030}(1.25 \times 10^6) = 1.08 \times 10^6$ N

(Eq. 9.28a)

$F_{T_1} = \dfrac{775}{890} F_h = 0.940 \times 10^6$ N

(Eq. 9.28b)

$$F_{T_2} = \frac{438}{890} F_h = 0.532 \times 10^6 \text{ N}$$

$$A_{s_1} = \frac{F_{T_1}}{\phi_s f_y} = \frac{0.940 \times 10^6}{(0.85)(400)} = 2765 \text{ mm}^2$$

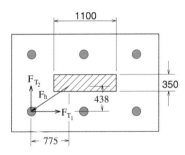

$$A_{s_2} = \frac{F_{T_2}}{\phi_s f_y} = \frac{0.532 \times 10^6}{(0.85)(400)} = 1564 \text{ mm}^2$$

11. Total footing depth (assume 20M bars)

$t_f = d + 1.5d_b + 150 = 1030 + 1.5(20) + 150 = 1210 \text{ mm}$

use $t_f = 1250$ mm

12. Check minimum reinforcement (Clause 7.8.1)

in long direction

$A_{s_{min}} = 0.002(2450)(1250) = 6125 \text{ mm}^2 > 2A_{s_1} = 5530 \text{ mm}^2$

use $A_{s_1} = 6125/2 = 3063 \text{ mm}^2$

in short direction

$A_{s_{min}} = 0.002(3500)(1250) = 8750 \text{ mm}^2 > 3A_{s_2} = 4692 \text{ mm}^2$

use $A_{s_2} = 8750/3 = 2917 \text{ mm}^2$

13. Anchorage requirements

available $\ell_d = e_d + 0.5d_p - 75 = 700 + 175 - 75 = 800$ mm

so, in the long direction, use 11 - 20M bars in each of two ties

(provided $A_s = 3300 \text{ mm}^2$ per tie, required $\ell_d = 644 < 800$ mm, OK)

in the short direction, use 10 - 20M bars in each of three ties

(provided $A_s = 3000 \text{ mm}^2$ per tie)

To provide for additional ductility in the footing, in the long direction use 9 - 20M bars @ 60 mm in each of two ties centered over the piles and 4 - 20M bars @ 120 mm distributed between the ties. In the short direction, use 8 - 20M bars @ 60 mm in each of three ties centered over the piles and 3 - 20M bars @ 160 mm in each of the two regions between ties.

14. Summary of design

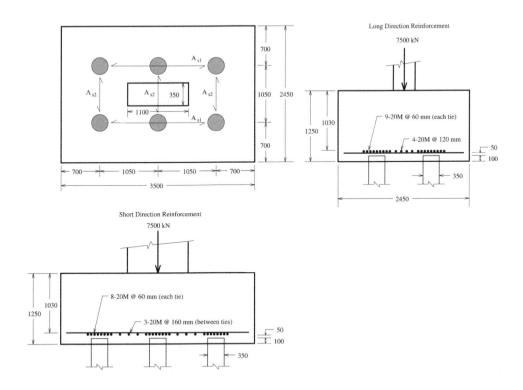

References

9.1 Adebar, P., Kuchma, D., and Collins, M.P., Strut-and-tie models for the design of pile caps: An experimental study, *ACI Structural Journal*, **87**(1), pp. 81—92, 1990.

9.2 Adebar, P., and Zhou, Z., Bearing strength of compressive struts confined by plain concrete, *ACI Structural Journal*, **90**(5), pp. 534—541, 1993.

9.3 Clarke, J.L., Behaviour and design of pile caps with four piles, *Cement and Concrete Association*, 52 Grosvenor Gardens, London, UK, Report No. 42.489, 1973.

9.4 MacGregor, J.G., *Reinforced Concrete: Mechanics and Design*, Second Edition, Prentice Hall, Englewood Cliffs, New Jersey, 1992.

9.5 Park, R., and Paulay, T., *Reinforced Concrete Structures*, Wiley-Interscience Publication, John Wiley and Sons, Toronto, 1975.

9.6 Siao, W.B., Strut-and-tie model for shear behavior in deep beams and pile caps failing in diagonal splitting, *ACI Structural Journal*, **90**(4), pp. 356—363, 1993.

9.7 ACI 318-89 *Building Code Requirements for Reinforced Concrete*, American Concrete Institute, Detroit, Michigan, 1989.

9.8 CRSI Handbook, Concrete Reinforcing Steel Institute, Schaumburg, Illinois, 1982.

9.9 Adebar, P., and Zhou, Z., Design of deep pile caps by strut and tie models, *ACI Structural Journal*, in press, to be published in late 1995 or early 1996.

Table 9.1   Effective depth d required by one-way shear action on spread footings
$f'_c = 20$ MPa

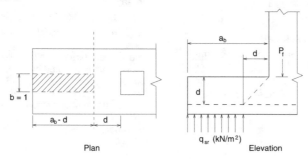

Plan   Elevation

Values of effective depth d in mm

q_{sr} (kN/m²)	a_b (m)														
	0.20	0.40	0.60	0.80	1.00	1.20	1.40	1.60	1.80	2.00	2.20	2.40	2.60	2.80	3.00
100	150	150	150	150	157	188	220	251	283	318	359	401	446	494	543
150	150	150	150	175	218	262	307	362	421	484	550	620	694	773	855
200	150	150	163	217	271	331	401	476	555	639	729	824	924	1030	1141
250	150	150	191	254	321	401	486	578	675	778	888	1003	1123	1249	1381
300	150	150	215	287	371	463	563	668	780	899	1023	1154	1290	1431	1577
350	150	158	237	318	415	519	630	747	872	1002	1138	1281	1428	1579	1735
400	150	171	256	349	455	568	689	816	950	1090	1236	1386	1542	1701	1865
450	150	182	274	376	490	612	740	876	1018	1165	1318	1476	1637	1802	1971
500	150	193	289	401	522	650	786	928	1077	1230	1389	1551	1718	1888	2060
550	150	202	304	423	550	684	826	974	1128	1286	1449	1616	1787	1960	2136
600	150	211	319	443	575	715	862	1014	1172	1335	1502	1672	1846	2022	2200
650	150	219	332	461	598	743	893	1050	1212	1378	1548	1721	1897	2076	2256
700	150	226	345	478	619	767	922	1082	1247	1416	1588	1764	1942	2122	2305
750	150	233	356	493	638	790	947	1110	1278	1449	1624	1801	1981	2163	2347
800	150	239	366	507	655	810	970	1136	1306	1479	1656	1835	2017	2200	2385
850	150	245	376	519	671	828	991	1159	1331	1507	1685	1865	2048	2233	2419
900	150	251	385	531	685	845	1010	1180	1354	1531	1711	1893	2077	2262	2449
950	150	256	393	542	698	860	1028	1199	1375	1553	1734	1917	2102	2289	2477
1000	150	260	400	552	710	874	1044	1217	1394	1573	1755	1940	2125	2313	2501
1100	150	269	414	570	732	900	1072	1248	1427	1609	1793	1979	2166	2355	2545
1200	150	276	426	585	751	921	1096	1274	1455	1639	1824	2012	2200	2390	2581
1300	150	283	437	599	767	940	1117	1297	1480	1665	1852	2040	2229	2420	2612
1400	150	289	446	611	781	956	1135	1317	1501	1687	1875	2064	2255	2446	2639
1500	150	295	455	622	794	971	1151	1334	1519	1707	1896	2086	2277	2469	2662

Notes:

Concrete resistance factor $\phi_c = 0.60$ has been included in table values.

Minimum effective depths have been determined according to;

1) one-way shear requirements (Clauses 11.3.5, 13.4, 15.5)

2) minimum depth requirements (Clause 15.7)

Table 9.2   Effective depth d required by one-way shear action on spread footings
$f_c' = 30$ MPa

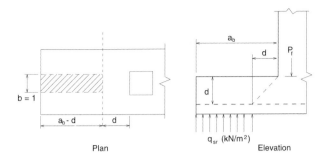

Plan   Elevation

Values of effective depth d in mm

q_{sr} (kN/m²)	a_b (m)														
	0.20	0.40	0.60	0.80	1.00	1.20	1.40	1.60	1.80	2.00	2.20	2.40	2.60	2.80	3.00
100	150	150	150	150	150	158	185	211	238	264	291	321	356	392	430
150	150	150	150	150	186	223	260	297	343	393	445	500	558	620	685
200	150	150	150	187	233	280	333	393	458	526	599	676	758	844	935
250	150	150	165	220	276	337	409	484	565	651	743	840	942	1049	1162
300	150	150	188	251	316	394	478	568	664	765	872	986	1105	1229	1359
350	150	150	208	278	357	446	542	644	752	866	987	1114	1246	1383	1525
400	150	151	227	303	395	494	599	712	831	956	1087	1224	1366	1513	1665
450	150	163	244	329	429	537	651	772	900	1034	1174	1319	1470	1624	1783
500	150	173	259	354	461	576	698	827	962	1103	1250	1402	1558	1719	1883
550	150	182	273	376	489	611	739	875	1017	1164	1317	1474	1636	1801	1969
600	150	191	286	396	516	643	777	918	1065	1218	1375	1537	1703	1872	2043
650	150	199	298	415	539	672	811	957	1109	1266	1427	1592	1761	1933	2108
700	150	206	311	432	561	698	842	992	1148	1308	1473	1641	1813	1988	2165
750	150	213	322	448	581	722	870	1023	1183	1346	1514	1685	1859	2036	2215
800	150	220	333	462	600	744	895	1052	1214	1381	1551	1724	1900	2079	2259
850	150	226	343	476	617	764	919	1078	1243	1411	1584	1759	1937	2117	2299
900	150	231	353	488	632	783	940	1102	1269	1440	1614	1790	1970	2151	2335
950	150	236	361	500	647	800	959	1124	1293	1465	1641	1819	2000	2183	2367
1000	150	241	369	511	660	816	978	1144	1315	1489	1666	1846	2028	2211	2397
1100	150	250	384	531	684	844	1010	1180	1353	1530	1710	1892	2076	2261	2448
1200	150	258	397	548	705	869	1037	1210	1386	1565	1747	1931	2116	2303	2492
1300	150	266	409	563	724	890	1062	1237	1415	1596	1779	1964	2151	2339	2529
1400	150	272	420	577	740	909	1083	1260	1440	1622	1807	1993	2181	2371	2561
1500	150	278	429	589	755	926	1101	1280	1462	1646	1831	2019	2208	2398	2589

Notes:
Concrete resistance factor $\phi_c = 0.60$ has been included in table values.
Minimum effective depths have been determined according to;
1) one-way shear requirements (Clauses 11.3.5, 13.4, 15.5)
2) minimum depth requirements (Clause 15.7)

Table 9.3 **Effective depth d required by two way shear action on spread footings supporting columns with aspect ratios not exceeding 2.0.**
$f'_c = 20$ MPa

A_f = footing area in m^2
A_c = column area in m^2
For circular, polygonal, or rectangular columns with aspect ratios not exceeding 2.0, use $h_e = \sqrt{A_c}$

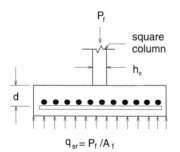

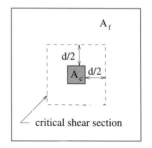

Values of footing to column area ratio, A_f / A_c

q_{sr} (kN/m^2)	d/h$_e$															
	0.5	0.6	0.7	0.8	0.9	1.0	1.1	1.2	1.3	1.4	1.5	1.6	1.7	1.8	1.9	2.0
100	34.4	43.8	54.0	65.1	77.0	89.9	104	118	134	150	167	185	204	224	245	267
150	23.7	30.0	36.9	44.5	52.6	61.2	70.5	80.4	90.9	102	114	126	139	152	166	181
200	18.3	23.2	28.4	34.2	40.3	46.9	54.0	61.5	69.5	77.9	86.7	96.1	106	116	127	138
250	15.1	19.0	23.3	28.0	33.0	38.3	44.1	50.2	56.6	63.5	70.6	78.2	86.1	94.4	103	112
300	13.0	16.3	19.9	23.8	28.1	32.6	37.5	42.6	48.1	53.8	59.9	66.3	73.0	80.0	87.3	94.9
350	11.4	14.3	17.5	20.9	24.6	28.5	32.7	37.2	42.0	47.0	52.2	57.8	63.6	69.7	76.0	82.6
400	10.3	12.9	15.7	18.7	22.0	25.5	29.2	33.2	37.4	41.8	46.5	51.4	56.6	61.9	67.5	73.4
450	9.41	11.7	14.2	17.0	19.9	23.1	26.4	30.0	33.8	37.8	42.0	46.4	51.1	55.9	61.0	66.2
500	8.69	10.8	13.1	15.6	18.3	21.2	24.2	27.5	31.0	34.6	38.4	42.5	46.7	51.1	55.7	60.5
550	8.10	10.1	12.2	14.5	17.0	19.6	22.4	25.4	28.6	32.0	35.5	39.2	43.1	47.2	51.4	55.8
600	7.62	9.43	11.4	13.5	15.8	18.3	20.9	23.7	26.7	29.8	33.1	36.5	40.1	43.9	47.8	51.9
650	7.20	8.90	10.7	12.8	14.9	17.2	19.7	22.3	25.0	28.0	31.0	34.2	37.6	41.1	44.8	48.6
700	6.85	8.45	10.2	12.1	14.1	16.3	18.6	21.0	23.6	26.4	29.2	32.3	35.4	38.8	42.2	45.8
750	6.54	8.06	9.70	11.5	13.4	15.4	17.6	20.0	22.4	25.0	27.7	30.6	33.6	36.7	40.0	43.3
800	6.27	7.71	9.28	11.0	12.8	14.7	16.8	19.0	21.3	23.8	26.4	29.1	31.9	34.9	38.0	41.2
850	6.04	7.41	8.90	10.5	12.2	14.1	16.1	18.2	20.4	22.7	25.2	27.8	30.5	33.3	36.2	39.3
900	5.83	7.14	8.57	10.1	11.8	13.5	15.4	17.4	19.6	21.8	24.1	26.6	29.2	31.9	34.7	37.6
950	5.64	6.90	8.27	9.75	11.3	13.0	14.8	16.8	18.8	20.9	23.2	25.6	28.0	30.6	33.3	36.1
1000	5.47	6.68	8.00	9.42	11.0	12.6	14.3	16.2	18.1	20.2	22.3	24.6	27.0	29.5	32.1	34.8
1100	5.18	6.31	7.53	8.86	10.3	11.8	13.4	15.1	17.0	18.9	20.9	23.0	25.2	27.5	29.9	32.4
1200	4.93	5.99	7.15	8.39	9.73	11.2	12.7	14.3	16.0	17.8	19.7	21.6	23.7	25.9	28.1	30.5
1300	4.73	5.73	6.82	8.00	9.26	10.6	12.0	13.6	15.2	16.9	18.6	20.5	22.4	24.5	26.6	28.8
1400	4.55	5.50	6.54	7.66	8.85	10.1	11.5	12.9	14.5	16.1	17.7	19.5	21.4	23.3	25.3	27.4
1500	4.40	5.31	6.30	7.36	8.50	9.72	11.0	12.4	13.8	15.4	17.0	18.7	20.4	22.3	24.2	26.2

Note:
Concrete resistance factor $\phi_c = 0.60$ has been included in table values. Columns with aspect ratios greater than 2.0 must be considered on an individual basis. Also minimum depth requirements of Clause 15.7 must be checked (d > 150 mm).

Table 9.4 **Effective depth d required by two way shear action on spread footings supporting columns with aspect ratios not exceeding 2.0.**
$f'_c = 30$ MPa

A_f = footing area in m^2
A_c = column area in m^2
For circular, polygonal, or rectangular columns with aspect ratios not exceeding 2.0, use $h_e = \sqrt{A_c}$

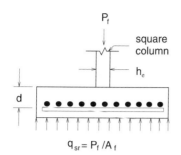

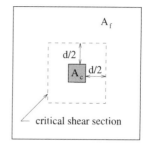

$q_{sr} = P_f / A_f$

Values of footing to column area ratio, A_f / A_c

q_{sr} (kN/m^2)	d/h_e															
	0.5	0.6	0.7	0.8	0.9	1.0	1.1	1.2	1.3	1.4	1.5	1.6	1.7	1.8	1.9	2.0
100	41.7	53.0	65.5	79.0	93.5	109	126	144	163	182	203	225	249	273	298	324
150	28.5	36.2	44.6	53.7	63.6	74.1	85.4	97.4	110	124	138	153	168	185	202	219
200	22.0	27.8	34.2	41.1	48.6	56.6	65.1	74.2	83.9	94.1	105	116	128	140	153	167
250	18.0	22.8	27.9	33.5	39.6	46.1	53.0	60.4	68.2	76.4	85.1	94.3	104	114	124	135
300	15.4	19.4	23.7	28.5	33.6	39.1	44.9	51.1	57.7	64.7	72.0	79.7	87.7	96.2	105	114
350	13.5	17.0	20.8	24.9	29.3	34.0	39.1	44.5	50.2	56.2	62.6	69.3	76.2	83.6	91.2	99.1
400	12.1	15.2	18.5	22.2	26.1	30.3	34.8	39.5	44.6	49.9	55.5	61.4	67.6	74.1	80.8	87.9
450	11.0	13.8	16.8	20.1	23.6	27.4	31.4	35.7	40.2	45.0	50.1	55.4	60.9	66.7	72.8	79.1
500	10.1	12.7	15.4	18.4	21.6	25.0	28.7	32.6	36.7	41.1	45.7	50.5	55.6	60.8	66.4	72.1
550	9.42	11.7	14.3	17.0	20.0	23.1	26.5	30.1	33.9	37.9	42.1	46.5	51.2	56.0	61.1	66.4
600	8.82	11.0	13.3	15.9	18.6	21.5	24.7	28.0	31.5	35.2	39.1	43.2	47.5	52.0	56.7	61.6
650	8.32	10.3	12.5	14.9	17.4	20.2	23.1	26.2	29.5	32.9	36.6	40.4	44.4	48.6	53.0	57.5
700	7.88	9.77	11.8	14.1	16.5	19.0	21.8	24.7	27.7	31.0	34.4	38.0	41.8	45.7	49.8	54.1
750	7.51	9.29	11.2	13.3	15.6	18.0	20.6	23.3	26.3	29.3	32.5	35.9	39.5	43.2	47.0	51.1
800	7.18	8.87	10.7	12.7	14.8	17.1	19.6	22.2	24.9	27.8	30.9	34.1	37.5	41.0	44.6	48.4
850	6.89	8.50	10.3	12.1	14.2	16.4	18.7	21.2	23.8	26.5	29.4	32.5	35.7	39.0	42.5	46.1
900	6.63	8.17	9.84	11.7	13.6	15.7	17.9	20.3	22.8	25.4	28.2	31.1	34.1	37.3	40.6	44.1
950	6.40	7.87	9.48	11.2	13.1	15.1	17.2	19.5	21.8	24.4	27.0	29.8	32.7	35.7	38.9	42.2
1000	6.19	7.61	9.15	10.8	12.6	14.5	16.6	18.7	21.0	23.4	26.0	28.6	31.4	34.3	37.4	40.5
1100	5.84	7.15	8.58	10.1	11.8	13.6	15.5	17.5	19.6	21.8	24.2	26.6	29.2	31.9	34.7	37.7
1200	5.54	6.77	8.10	9.55	11.1	12.8	14.5	16.4	18.4	20.5	22.7	25.0	27.4	29.9	32.6	35.3
1300	5.28	6.44	7.70	9.06	10.5	12.1	13.8	15.5	17.4	19.4	21.4	23.6	25.9	28.2	30.7	33.3
1400	5.07	6.17	7.36	8.65	10.0	11.5	13.1	14.8	16.5	18.4	20.3	22.4	24.5	26.8	29.1	31.5
1500	4.88	5.93	7.06	8.29	9.60	11.0	12.5	14.1	15.8	17.5	19.4	21.3	23.4	25.5	27.7	30.0

Note:
Concrete resistance factor $\phi_c = 0.60$ has been included in table values. Columns with aspect ratios greater than 2.0 must be considered on an individual basis. Also minimum depth requirements of Clause 15.7 must be checked (d > 150 mm).

Table 9.5(a)   Steel areas per 1.0 m width for spread footings.
$f'_c = 20$ MPa, $f_y = 400$ MPa

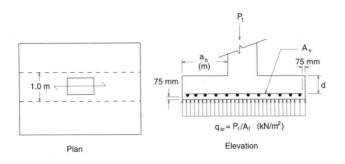

Plan — Elevation

$$q_{sr} = P_f/A_f \quad (kN/m^2)$$

Values of A_s in mm² required in a 1 m width of footing

$q_{sr}a_b^2$ (kN)	|						d (mm)									
	150	175	200	225	250	275	300	325	350	375	400	425	450	475	500	525
50	522	550	600	650	700	750	800	850	900	950	1000	1050	1100	1150	1200	1250
60	635	550	600	650	700	750	800	850	900	950	1000	1050	1100	1150	1200	1250
70	751	627	600	650	700	750	800	850	900	950	1000	1050	1100	1150	1200	1250
80	872	724	622	650	700	750	800	850	900	950	1000	1050	1100	1150	1200	1250
90	997	823	705	650	700	750	800	850	900	950	1000	1050	1100	1150	1200	1250
100	1127	925	789	690	700	750	800	850	900	950	1000	1050	1100	1150	1200	1250
120	1403	1136	962	838	744	750	800	850	900	950	1000	1050	1100	1150	1200	1250
140	1709	1359	1142	990	877	788	800	850	900	950	1000	1050	1100	1150	1200	1250
160	2055	1596	1329	1147	1012	907	823	850	900	950	1000	1050	1100	1150	1200	1250
180	2464	1851	1524	1308	1150	1029	932	853	900	950	1000	1050	1100	1150	1200	1250
200		2128	1729	1474	1292	1153	1043	953	900	950	1000	1050	1100	1150	1200	1250
250			2292	1916	1661	1473	1327	1209	1111	1029	1000	1050	1100	1150	1200	1250
300			2966	2405	2057	1810	1622	1473	1351	1248	1161	1086	1100	1150	1200	1250
350				2961	2486	2167	1930	1746	1596	1472	1368	1277	1199	1150	1200	1250
400				3621	2957	2546	2253	2029	1850	1702	1578	1472	1380	1300	1229	1250
450					3488	2955	2593	2323	2111	1938	1793	1671	1565	1472	1390	1318
500					4107	3400	2953	2630	2381	2180	2013	1873	1752	1647	1554	1472
600						4456	3752	3290	2951	2685	2469	2289	2136	2004	1888	1786
700							4708	4031	3570	3224	2949	2724	2534	2372	2231	2107
800								4892	4255	3804	3457	3179	2948	2752	2584	2436
900									5031	4436	4000	3658	3380	3146	2947	2774
1000										5138	4584	4166	3832	3556	3323	3122
1200											5931	5290	4810	4428	4114	3849
1400												6633	5921	5392	4972	4626
1600													7243	6482	5915	5464
1800														7767	6975	6383
2000															8213	7408
2200																8591

Note:
Steel areas shown are based on flexural and minimum reinforcement requirements (Clause 7.8). Where numerical values are not shown, required steel areas would result in an over-reinforced section - effective depth d must be increased (see Clause 10.5.2).

Table 9.5(b)   Steel areas per 1.0 m width for spread footings.
$f'_c = 20$ MPa, $f_y = 400$ MPa

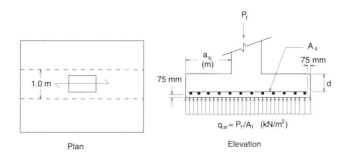

Plan   Elevation

$q_{sr} = P_f / A_f$ (kN/m²)

Values of A_s in mm² required in a 1 m width of footing

$q_{sr}a_b^2$ (kN)	d (mm)															
	550	575	600	625	650	675	700	725	750	775	800	825	850	900	950	1000
400	1300	1350	1400	1450	1500	1550	1600	1650	1700	1750	1800	1850	1900	2000	2100	2200
500	1398	1350	1400	1450	1500	1550	1600	1650	1700	1750	1800	1850	1900	2000	2100	2200
600	1694	1613	1539	1472	1500	1550	1600	1650	1700	1750	1800	1850	1900	2000	2100	2200
700	1997	1899	1810	1730	1657	1590	1600	1650	1700	1750	1800	1850	1900	2000	2100	2200
800	2306	2190	2086	1992	1907	1828	1757	1691	1700	1750	1800	1850	1900	2000	2100	2200
900	2622	2488	2367	2259	2160	2071	1988	1913	1843	1778	1800	1850	1900	2000	2100	2200
1000	2947	2792	2654	2530	2418	2316	2223	2137	2058	1985	1918	1855	1900	2000	2100	2200
1200	3620	3421	3244	3087	2946	2818	2701	2594	2497	2406	2322	2245	2172	2041	2100	2200
1400	4333	4081	3861	3666	3491	3335	3193	3063	2945	2836	2735	2642	2555	2398	2260	2200
1600	5093	4778	4506	4268	4057	3869	3699	3545	3404	3275	3156	3046	2944	2761	2600	2457
1800	5910	5519	5186	4899	4646	4422	4221	4040	3875	3725	3587	3459	3341	3129	2944	2781
2000	6800	6312	5906	5561	5260	4996	4761	4550	4359	4186	4027	3880	3745	3504	3293	3108
2200	7787	7172	6675	6260	5904	5594	5321	5077	4857	4658	4477	4311	4158	3884	3648	3440
2400	8912	8118	7504	7002	6581	6218	5902	5621	5370	5144	4938	4751	4578	4272	4007	3776
2600		9184	8408	7799	7298	6874	6507	6186	5900	5644	5412	5201	5008	4666	4372	4116
2800			9415	8662	8063	7565	7141	6772	6448	6159	5898	5663	5447	5068	4744	4462
3000				9614	8886	8299	7807	7385	7016	6690	6399	6136	5897	5478	5121	4812
3500						10386	9652	9052	8545	8106	7721	7379	7072	6540	6093	5710
4000								10994	10275	9678	9168	8724	8331	7663	7112	6645
4500									12320	11473	10783	10200	9696	8860	8184	7621
5000											12643	11856	11200	10146	9319	8644
5500												13781	12896	11546	10531	9721
6000														13096	11835	10862
6500														14859	13259	12080
7000															14842	13393
7500																14828

Note:
Steel areas shown are based on flexural and minimum reinforcement requirements (Clause 7.8). Where numerical values are not shown, required steel areas would result in an over-reinforced section - effective depth d must be increased (see Clause 10.5.2).

Table 9.6(a) Steel areas per 1.0 m width for spread footings.
$f'_c = 30$ MPa, $f_y = 400$ MPa

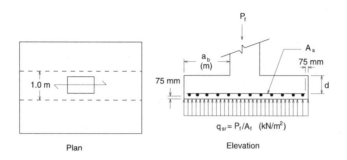

Plan   Elevation

$q_{sr} = P_f/A_f$ (kN/m²)

Values of A_s in mm² required in a 1 m width of footing

$q_{sr}a_b^2$ (kN)	d (mm) 150	175	200	225	250	275	300	325	350	375	400	425	450	475	500	525
50	511	550	600	650	700	750	800	850	900	950	1000	1050	1100	1150	1200	1250
60	618	550	600	650	700	750	800	850	900	950	1000	1050	1100	1150	1200	1250
70	728	613	600	650	700	750	800	850	900	950	1000	1050	1100	1150	1200	1250
80	839	706	610	650	700	750	800	850	900	950	1000	1050	1100	1150	1200	1250
90	953	799	690	650	700	750	800	850	900	950	1000	1050	1100	1150	1200	1250
100	1070	894	770	678	700	750	800	850	900	950	1000	1050	1100	1150	1200	1250
120	1311	1088	933	819	731	750	800	850	900	950	1000	1050	1100	1150	1200	1250
140	1564	1288	1100	963	858	774	800	850	900	950	1000	1050	1100	1150	1200	1250
160	1831	1494	1271	1110	987	889	810	850	900	950	1000	1050	1100	1150	1200	1250
180	2114	1708	1446	1259	1117	1006	915	850	900	950	1000	1050	1100	1150	1200	1250
200	2418	1931	1626	1411	1250	1123	1021	937	900	950	1000	1050	1100	1150	1200	1250
250	3306	2530	2096	1804	1589	1423	1291	1182	1090	1012	1000	1050	1100	1150	1200	1250
300		3213	2604	2217	1942	1732	1567	1431	1319	1223	1141	1070	1100	1150	1200	1250
350		4030	3159	2655	2309	2051	1849	1686	1551	1437	1339	1255	1180	1150	1200	1250
400			3779	3123	2693	2381	2140	1947	1788	1654	1540	1441	1355	1279	1211	1250
450			4493	3627	3097	2723	2438	2213	2029	1875	1744	1630	1532	1445	1367	1298
500				4178	3524	3078	2746	2485	2274	2099	1950	1822	1710	1612	1525	1447
600					4465	3836	3391	3051	2780	2558	2371	2211	2073	1952	1845	1749
700					5578	4676	4083	3648	3308	3033	2804	2610	2443	2298	2169	2055
800						5631	4836	4282	3861	3526	3251	3020	2822	2650	2500	2366
900							5668	4961	4443	4040	3713	3441	3210	3010	2836	2682
1000							6611	5696	5060	4577	4192	3875	3607	3378	3178	3003
1200								7414	6426	5735	5207	4784	4434	4138	3883	3661
1400									8060	7041	6318	5760	5310	4936	4618	4343
1600										8575	7558	6821	6246	5778	5387	5052
1800											8986	7991	7254	6672	6194	5792
2000												9316	8357	7630	7048	6566
2200													9585	8666	7956	7379
2400														9805	8930	8240
2600														11084	9988	9157
2800															11155	10142
3000																11213

Note:
Steel areas shown are based on flexural and minimum reinforcement requirements (Clause 7.8). Where numerical values are not shown, required steel areas would result in an over-reinforced section - effective depth d must be increased (see Clause 10.5.2).

Table 9.6(b)　Steel areas per 1.0 m width for spread footings.
$f'_c = 30$ MPa, $f_y = 400$ MPa

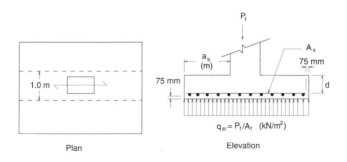

Plan　　　　　　　　　　Elevation

$$q_{sr} = P_f/A_f \quad (kN/m^2)$$

Values of A_s in mm² required in a 1 m width of footing

$q_{sr}a_b^2$ (kN)	d (mm)															
	550	575	600	625	650	675	700	725	750	775	800	825	850	900	950	1000
400	1300	1350	1400	1450	1500	1550	1600	1650	1700	1750	1800	1850	1900	2000	2100	2200
500	1377	1350	1400	1450	1500	1550	1600	1650	1700	1750	1800	1850	1900	2000	2100	2200
600	1663	1586	1515	1451	1500	1550	1600	1650	1700	1750	1800	1850	1900	2000	2100	2200
700	1953	1861	1777	1701	1632	1568	1600	1650	1700	1750	1800	1850	1900	2000	2100	2200
800	2247	2139	2042	1954	1873	1799	1731	1668	1700	1750	1800	1850	1900	2000	2100	2200
900	2545	2421	2310	2209	2117	2033	1955	1883	1816	1754	1800	1850	1900	2000	2100	2200
1000	2847	2707	2581	2467	2363	2268	2181	2100	2025	1955	1891	1850	1900	2000	2100	2200
1200	3465	3290	3133	2992	2863	2745	2638	2538	2447	2361	2282	2208	2139	2014	2100	2200
1400	4102	3889	3699	3528	3373	3232	3103	2984	2874	2773	2679	2591	2509	2360	2229	2200
1600	4762	4506	4280	4077	3894	3727	3576	3437	3308	3190	3080	2978	2883	2710	2558	2422
1800	5445	5143	4877	4639	4426	4233	4057	3897	3749	3613	3487	3370	3261	3064	2889	2735
2000	6156	5802	5492	5217	4971	4749	4548	4365	4197	4042	3899	3767	3643	3420	3224	3050
2200	6897	6485	6126	5810	5529	5277	5049	4842	4652	4478	4317	4169	4030	3781	3562	3368
2400	7673	7194	6782	6421	6102	5817	5560	5327	5115	4921	4741	4576	4422	4146	3903	3689
2600	8489	7934	7461	7051	6690	6370	6082	5822	5586	5370	5172	4988	4819	4514	4248	4012
2800	9352	8709	8167	7702	7296	6937	6616	6327	6066	5827	5608	5407	5220	4886	4595	4338
3000	10272	9523	8903	8376	7919	7518	7162	6843	6554	6292	6052	5831	5627	5263	4946	4667
3500	12918	11785	10903	10181	9572	9048	8590	8183	7819	7491	7192	6920	6669	6224	5839	5502
4000			13223	12211	11392	10707	10120	9607	9154	8749	8384	8052	7749	7214	6756	6356
4500			14577	13443	12535	11779	11134	10572	10076	9633	9234	8872	8238	7698	7231
5000					14596	13608	12789	12091	11484	10949	10472	10043	9297	8668	8128
5500						15670	14611	13736	12991	12345	11776	11268	10396	9668	9049
6000							16664	15545	14622	13837	13157	12557	11540	10703	9996
6500								17579	16411	15448	14630	13920	12735	11774	10971
7000									18418	17213	16218	15372	13989	12887	11977
7500										19184	17952	16934	15311	14047	13018
8000											19881	18633	16713	15260	14096
8500												20515	18213	16534	15217
9000													19834	17880	16385
9500													21611	19312	17608
10000														20847	18894
11000															21702

Note:
Steel areas shown are based on flexural and minimum reinforcement requirements (Clause 7.8). Where numerical values are not shown, required steel areas would result in an over-reinforced section - effective depth d must be increased (see Clause 10.5.2).

Table 9.7 Tension development lengths for deformed reinforcing bars with f_y = 400 MPa according to Clause 12.2.3 (clear spacing greater than $2d_b$).

f_c' (MPa)	Nominal Deformed Reinforcing Bar Size							
	10	15	20	25	30	35	45	55
20	321	483	644	1006	1207	1409	1811	2214
25	300	432	576	900	1080	1260	1620	1980
30	300	395	526	822	986	1150	1479	1807
35	300	365	487	761	913	1065	1369	1673
40	300	342	455	712	854	996	1281	1565

Note:
The modification factor for bar size (k_4) has been included in Table values. See Clause 12.2.4 for other modification factors.

Table 9.8 Compression development lengths for deformed reinforcing bars with f_y = 400 MPa according to Clause 12.3.

f_c' (MPa)	Nominal Deformed Reinforcing Bar Size							
	10	15	20	25	30	35	45	55
20	245	345	420	540	640	765	940	1210
25	215	305	375	485	575	685	840	1085
30	200	280	345	445	525	630	770	995
35	200	280	345	445	525	630	770	995
40	200	280	345	445	525	630	770	995

Note:
The modification factors given by Clause 12.3.3 must be considered individually by the designer.

Table 9.9 Minimum effective thickness of plain footings based on flexural requirements.

$h_p = K_d\, a_b > 200$ mm (effective thickness in mm)
$t_f = h_p + 50$ (total thickness in mm)
a_b = footing projection in m

Values of effective thickness coefficient K_d

q_{sr} (kN/m²)	f_c' (MPa)		
	20	30	40
100	530	480	450
150	650	590	550
200	750	680	630
250	840	760	710
300	920	830	770
350	990	900	840
400	1060	960	890
450	1130	1020	950
500	1190	1070	1000
550	1240	1130	1050
600	1300	1180	1090
650	1350	1220	1140
700	1400	1270	1180
750	1450	1310	1220
800	1500	1360	1260
850	1550	1400	1300
900	1590	1440	1340
950	1630	1480	1370
1000	1680	1520	1410
1100	1760	1590	1480
1200	1840	1660	1540
1300	1910	1730	1610
1400	1980	1790	1670
1500	2050	1860	1730

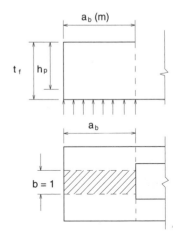

Note:
Concrete resistance factor ϕ_c = 0.60 has been included in the table values. One and two way shear must be checked in accordance with Clause 22.6.6.

CPCA Concrete Design Handbook

Table 9.10(a) Two pile supported footing, $f'_c = 30$ MPa, $f_y = 400$ MPa

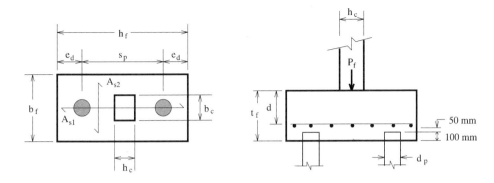

P_f (kN)	h_c (mm)	b_c (mm)	d (mm)	h_f (mm)	b_f (mm)	d_p (mm)	s_p (mm)	e_d (mm)	A_{s1} (mm^2)	A_{s2} (mm^2)
500	200	200	300	1400	800	200	600	400	768[a]	1344[a]
	400	400	300	1400	800	200	600	400	768[a]	1344[a]
	200	300	300	1400	800	200	600	400	768[a]	1344[a]
	400	600	300	1400	800	200	600	400	768[a]	1344[a]
	300	200	300	1400	800	200	600	400	768[a]	1344[a]
	500	330	300	1400	800	200	600	400	768[a]	1344[a]
1000	210	210	420[6]	1750	1000	250	750	500	1200[a]	2100[a]
	410	410	400[5]	1750	1000	250	750	500	1160[a]	2030[a]
	200	300	410[5]	1750	1000	250	750	500	1180[a]	2065[a]
	400	600	400[5]	1750	1000	250	750	500	1160[a]	2030[a]
	300	200	400[5]	1750	1000	250	750	500	1160[a]	2030[a]
	500	330	400[5]	1750	1000	250	750	500	1160[a]	2030[a]
1500	260	260	650[5]	1750	1000	250	750	500	1660[a]	2905[a]
	460	460	640[5]	1750	1000	250	750	500	1640[a]	2870[a]
	230	340	640[5]	1750	1000	250	750	500	1640[a]	2870[a]
	430	650	640[5]	1750	1000	250	750	500	1640[a]	2870[a]
	320	210	640[5]	1750	1000	250	750	500	1640[a]	2870[a]
	520	350	640[5]	1750	1000	250	750	500	1640[a]	2870[a]
2000	300	300	700[5]	2100	1200	300	900	600	2112[a]	3696[a]
	500	500	700[5]	2100	1200	300	900	600	2112[a]	3696[a]
	250	370	700[5]	2100	1200	300	900	600	2112[a]	3696[a]
	450	680	710[5]	2100	1200	300	900	600	2136[a]	3738[a]
	360	240	700[5]	2100	1200	300	900	600	2112[a]	3696[a]
	560	370	700[5]	2100	1200	300	900	600	2112[a]	3696[a]
2500	330	330	750[5]	2450	1400	350	1050	700	2604[a]	4557[a]
	530	530	750[5]	2450	1400	350	1050	700	2604[a]	4557[a]
	270	400	750[5]	2450	1400	350	1050	700	2604[a]	4557[a]
	470	710	740[5]	2450	1400	350	1050	700	2576[a]	4508[a]
	410	270	740[5]	2450	1400	350	1050	700	2576[a]	4508[a]
	610	410	750[5]	2450	1400	350	1050	700	2604[a]	4557[a]
3000	360	360	780[5]	2800	1600	400	1200	800	3072[a]	5376[a]
	560	560	780[5]	2800	1600	400	1200	800	3072[a]	5376[a]
	300	440	780[5]	2800	1600	400	1200	800	3072[a]	5376[a]
	500	750	770[5]	2800	1600	400	1200	800	3040[a]	5320[a]
	440	300	780[5]	2800	1600	400	1200	800	3072[a]	5376[a]
	640	430	770[5]	2800	1600	400	1200	800	3040[a]	5320[a]

[a] steel area governed by Clause 7.8.1
[1] governed by 1-way shear @ pile
[3] governed by 1-way shear @ column
[5] governed by pile bearing stress

[2] governed by 2-way shear @ pile
[4] governed by 2-way shear @ column
[6] governed by column bearing stress

Table 9.10(b) Two pile supported footing, $f'_c = 30$ MPa, $f_y = 400$ MPa

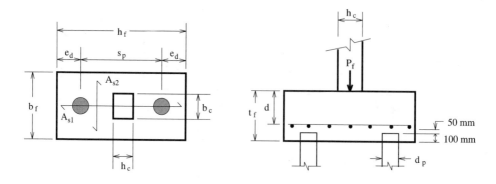

P_f (kN)	h_o (mm)	b_c (mm)	d (mm)	h_f (mm)	b_f (mm)	d_p (mm)	s_p (mm)	e_d (mm)	A_{s1} (mm²)	A_{s2} (mm²)
500	200	200	300	1400	800	200	600	400	768[a]	1344[a]
	400	400	300	1400	800	200	600	400	768[a]	1344[a]
	200	300	300	1400	800	200	600	400	768[a]	1344[a]
	400	600	300	1400	800	200	600	400	768[a]	1344[a]
	300	200	300	1400	800	200	600	400	768[a]	1344[a]
	500	330	300	1400	800	200	600	400	768[a]	1344[a]
1000	200	200	360[5]	1400	800	200	600	400	1021	1512[a]
	400	400	360[5]	1400	800	200	600	400	864[a]	1512[a]
	200	300	360[5]	1400	800	200	600	400	1021	1512[a]
	400	600	360[5]	1400	800	200	600	400	864[a]	1512[a]
	300	200	360[5]	1400	800	200	600	400	919	1512[a]
	500	330	360[5]	1400	800	200	600	400	864[a]	1512[a]
1500	230	230	440[6]	1750	1000	250	750	500	1592	2170[a]
	430	430	440[5]	1750	1000	250	750	500	1341	2170[a]
	200	300	440[5]	1750	1000	250	750	500	1629	2170[a]
	400	600	440[5]	1750	1000	250	750	500	1379	2170[a]
	300	200	430[5]	1750	1000	250	750	500	1539	2135[a]
	500	330	440[5]	1750	1000	250	750	500	1253	2170[a]
2000	270	270	630[5]	1750	1000	250	750	500	1620[a]	2835[a]
	470	470	640[5]	1750	1000	250	750	500	1640[a]	2870[a]
	230	340	630[5]	1750	1000	250	750	500	1620[a]	2835[a]
	430	650	640[5]	1750	1000	250	750	500	1640[a]	2870[a]
	320	210	630[5]	1750	1000	250	750	500	1620[a]	2835[a]
	520	350	640[5]	1750	1000	250	750	500	1640[a]	2870[a]
2500	290	290	630[5]	2100	1200	300	900	600	2203	3402[a]
	490	490	630[5]	2100	1200	300	900	600	1944[a]	3402[a]
	240	360	630[5]	2100	1200	300	900	600	2276	3402[a]
	440	660	640[5]	2100	1200	300	900	600	1968[a]	3444[a]
	360	240	640[5]	2100	1200	300	900	600	2068	3444[a]
	560	370	630[5]	2100	1200	300	900	600	1944[a]	3402[a]
3000	320	320	630[6]	2450	1400	350	1050	700	3116	3969[a]
	520	520	630[5]	2450	1400	350	1050	700	2766	3969[a]
	260	390	630[6]	2450	1400	350	1050	700	3221	3969[a]
	460	690	630[5]	2450	1400	350	1050	700	2871	3969[a]
	390	260	630[6]	2450	1400	350	1050	700	2994	3969[a]
	590	390	630[5]	2450	1400	350	1050	700	2644	3969[a]

[a] steel area governed by Clause 7.8.1
[1] governed by 1-way shear @ pile
[2] governed by 2-way shear @ pile
[3] governed by 1-way shear @ column
[4] governed by 2-way shear @ column
[5] governed by pile bearing stress
[6] governed by column bearing stress

Table 9.11(a) Three pile supported footing, $f'_c = 20$ MPa, $f_y = 400$ MPa

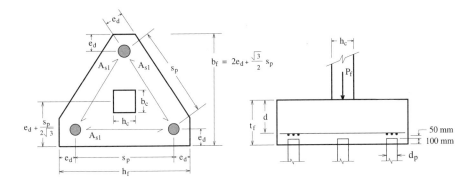

P_f (kN)	h_c (mm)	b_c (mm)	d (mm)	h_f (mm)	b_f (mm)	d_p (mm)	s_p (mm)	e_d (mm)	A_{s1} (mm²)
750	200	200	320[6]	1400	1320	200	600	400	808[a]
	400	400	300	1400	1320	200	600	400	776[a]
	200	300	300	1400	1320	200	600	400	776[a]
	400	600	300	1400	1320	200	600	400	776[a]
	300	200	300	1400	1320	200	600	400	776[a]
	500	330	300	1400	1320	200	600	400	776[a]
1500	260	260	500[6]	1750	1650	250	750	500	1374[a]
	460	460	400[5]	1750	1650	250	750	500	1172[a]
	210	310	510[6]	1750	1650	250	750	500	1394[a]
	410	620	400[5]	1750	1650	250	750	500	1172[a]
	320	210	500[6]	1750	1650	250	750	500	1374[a]
	520	350	400[5]	1750	1650	250	750	500	1172[a]
2250	360	360	730[6]	1750	1650	250	750	500	1839[a]
	560	560	640[5]	1750	1650	250	750	500	1657[a]
	290	430	730[6]	1750	1650	250	750	500	1839[a]
	490	740	640[5]	1750	1650	250	750	500	1657[a]
	450	300	730[6]	1750	1650	250	750	500	1839[a]
	650	430	640[5]	1750	1650	250	750	500	1657[a]
3000	400	400	820[6]	2100	1980	300	900	600	2425[a]
	600	600	700[5]	2100	1980	300	900	600	2134[a]
	330	490	800[6]	2100	1980	300	900	600	2376[a]
	530	800	700[5]	2100	1980	300	900	600	2134[a]
	500	340	830[6]	2100	1980	300	900	600	2449[a]
	700	470	710[5]	2100	1980	300	900	600	2158[a]
3750	440	440	880[6]	2450	2310	350	1050	700	2999[a]
	640	640	750[5]	2450	2310	350	1050	700	2631[a]
	350	520	870[6]	2450	2310	350	1050	700	2970[a]
	550	830	750[5]	2450	2310	350	1050	700	2631[a]
	540	360	900[6]	2450	2310	350	1050	700	3055[a]
	740	490	740[5]	2450	2310	350	1050	700	2603[a]
4500	460	460	920[6]	2800	2640	400	1200	800	3556[a]
	660	660	780[5]	2800	2640	400	1200	800	3104[a]
	370	560	910[6]	2800	2640	400	1200	800	3524[a]
	570	860	780[5]	2800	2640	400	1200	800	3104[a]
	570	380	940[6]	2800	2640	400	1200	800	3621[a]
	770	510	790[6]	2800	2640	400	1200	800	3136[a]

[a] steel area governed by Clause 7.8.1
[1] governed by 1-way shear @ pile
[3] governed by 1-way shear @ column
[5] governed by pile bearing stress

[2] governed by 2-way shear @ pile
[4] governed by 2-way shear @ column
[6] governed by column bearing stress

Table 9.11(b) Three pile supported footing, $f'_c = 30$ MPa, $f_y = 400$ MPa

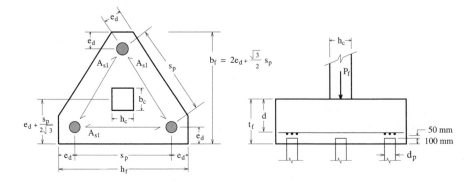

P_f (kN)	h_c (mm)	b_c (mm)	d (mm)	h_f (mm)	b_f (mm)	d_p (mm)	s_p (mm)	e_d (mm)	A_{s1} (mm²)
750	200	200	300	1400	1320	200	600	400	776[a]
	400	400	300	1400	1320	200	600	400	776[a]
	200	300	300	1400	1320	200	600	400	776[a]
	400	600	300	1400	1320	200	600	400	776[a]
	300	200	300	1400	1320	200	600	400	776[a]
	500	330	300	1400	1320	200	600	400	776[a]
1500	240	240	470[6]	1400	1320	200	600	400	1051[a]
	440	440	360[5]	1400	1320	200	600	400	873[a]
	200	300	460[6]	1400	1320	200	600	400	1035[a]
	400	600	360[5]	1400	1320	200	600	400	873[a]
	300	200	470[6]	1400	1320	200	600	400	1051[a]
	500	330	360[5]	1400	1320	200	600	400	873[a]
2250	280	280	570[6]	1750	1650	250	750	500	1516[a]
	480	480	440[5]	1750	1650	250	750	500	1253[a]
	230	340	570[6]	1750	1650	250	750	500	1516[a]
	430	650	440[5]	1750	1650	250	750	500	1253[a]
	350	230	580[6]	1750	1650	250	750	500	1536[a]
	550	370	430[5]	1750	1650	250	750	500	1233[a]
3000	360	360	720[6]	1750	1650	250	750	500	1819[a]
	560	560	640[5]	1750	1650	250	750	500	1657[a]
	290	430	720[6]	1750	1650	250	750	500	1819[a]
	490	740	640[5]	1750	1650	250	750	500	1657[a]
	450	300	740[6]	1750	1650	250	750	500	1859[a]
	650	430	640[5]	1750	1650	250	750	500	1657[a]
3750	380	380	770[6]	2100	1980	300	900	600	2304[a]
	580	580	640[5]	2100	1980	300	900	600	1988[a]
	310	460	760[6]	2100	1980	300	900	600	2279[a]
	510	770	640[5]	2100	1980	300	900	600	1988[a]
	480	320	770[6]	2100	1980	300	900	600	2304[a]
	680	450	630[5]	2100	1980	300	900	600	1964[a]
4500	400	400	800[6]	2450	2310	350	1050	700	2772[a]
	600	600	630[5]	2450	2310	350	1050	700	2292[a]
	330	490	790[6]	2450	2310	350	1050	700	2744[a]
	530	800	620[5]	2450	2310	350	1050	700	2263[a]
	500	330	820[6]	2450	2310	350	1050	700	2829[a]
	700	470	630[5]	2450	2310	350	1050	700	2292[a]

[a] steel area governed by Clause 7.8.1
[1] governed by 1-way shear @ pile
[3] governed by 1-way shear @ column
[5] governed by pile bearing stress

[2] governed by 2-way shear @ pile
[4] governed by 2-way shear @ column
[6] governed by column bearing stress

Table 9.12(a) Four pile supported footing, f'_c = 20 MPa, f_y = 400 MPa

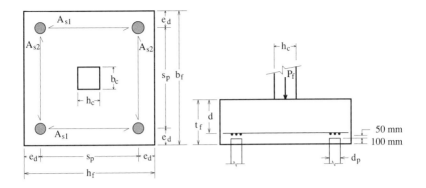

P_f (kN)	h_c (mm)	b_c (mm)	d (mm)	h_f (mm)	b_f (mm)	d_p (mm)	s_p (mm)	e_d (mm)	A_{s1} (mm²)	A_{s2} (mm²)
1000	210	210	430[6]	1400	1400	200	600	400	854[a]	854[a]
	410	410	300	1400	1400	200	600	400	672[a]	672[a]
	200	300	350[6]	1400	1400	200	600	400	742[a]	742[a]
	400	600	300	1400	1400	200	600	400	672[a]	672[a]
	200	400	310[4]	1400	1400	200	600	400	686[a]	686[a]
	400	800	300	1400	1400	200	600	400	672[a]	672[a]
2000	300	300	590[6]	1750	1750	250	750	500	1348[a]	1348[a]
	500	500	410[5]	1750	1750	250	750	500	1033[a]	1033[a]
	240	360	590[6]	1750	1750	250	750	500	1348[a]	1348[a]
	440	660	410[5]	1750	1750	250	750	500	1033[a]	1033[a]
	210	420	600[6]	1750	1750	250	750	500	1365[a]	1365[a]
	410	820	400[5]	1750	1750	250	750	500	1015[a]	1015[a]
3000	360	360	740[6]	1750	1750	250	750	500	1610[a]	1610[a]
	560	560	650[5]	1750	1750	250	750	500	1453[a]	1453[a]
	300	440	730[6]	1750	1750	250	750	500	1593[a]	1593[a]
	500	750	650[5]	1750	1750	250	750	500	1453[a]	1453[a]
	260	510	730[6]	1750	1750	250	750	500	1593[a]	1593[a]
	460	920	640[5]	1750	1750	250	750	500	1435[a]	1435[a]
4000	420	420	830[6]	2100	2100	300	900	600	2121[a]	2121[a]
	620	620	700[5]	2100	2100	300	900	600	1848[a]	1848[a]
	340	510	850[6]	2100	2100	300	900	600	2163[a]	2163[a]
	540	810	700[5]	2100	2100	300	900	600	1848[a]	1848[a]
	300	590	840[6]	2100	2100	300	900	600	2142[a]	2142[a]
	500	1000	710[5]	2100	2100	300	900	600	1869[a]	1869[a]
5000	470	470	920[6]	2450	2450	350	1050	700	2695[a]	2695[a]
	670	670	740[5]	2450	2450	350	1050	700	2254[a]	2254[a]
	380	570	940[6]	2450	2450	350	1050	700	2744[a]	2744[a]
	580	870	750[5]	2450	2450	350	1050	700	2279[a]	2279[a]
	330	660	940[6]	2450	2450	350	1050	700	2744[a]	2744[a]
	530	1060	740[5]	2450	2450	350	1050	700	2254[a]	2254[a]
6000	510	510	1030[6]	2800	2800	400	1200	800	3388[a]	3388[a]
	710	710	780[5]	2800	2800	400	1200	800	2688[a]	2688[a]
	420	630	1010[6]	2800	2800	400	1200	800	3332[a]	3332[a]
	620	930	780[5]	2800	2800	400	1200	800	2688[a]	2688[a]
	360	720	1030[6]	2800	2800	400	1200	800	3388[a]	3388[a]
	560	1120	780[5]	2800	2800	400	1200	800	2688[a]	2688[a]

[a] steel area governed by Clause 7.8.1
[1] governed by 1-way shear @ pile
[3] governed by 1-way shear @ column
[5] governed by pile bearing stress

[2] governed by 2-way shear @ pile
[4] governed by 2-way shear @ column
[6] governed by column bearing stress

Table 9.12(b)   Four pile supported footing, f'_c = 30 MPa, f_y = 400 MPa

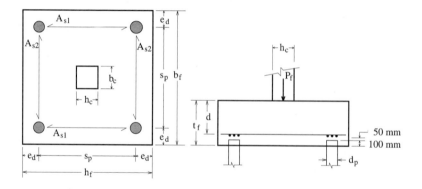

P_f (kN)	h_c (mm)	b_c (mm)	d (mm)	h_f (mm)	b_f (mm)	d_p (mm)	s_p (mm)	e_d (mm)	A_{s1} (mm²)	A_{s2} (mm²)
1000	200	200	330[4]	1400	1400	200	600	400	714[a]	714[a]
	400	400	300	1400	1400	200	600	400	672[a]	672[a]
	200	300	310[4]	1400	1400	200	600	400	686[a]	686[a]
	400	600	300	1400	1400	200	600	400	672[a]	672[a]
	200	400	300	1400	1400	200	600	400	672[a]	672[a]
	400	800	300	1400	1400	200	600	400	672[a]	672[a]
2000	260	260	520[6]	1400	1400	200	600	400	980[a]	980[a]
	460	460	360[5]	1400	1400	200	600	400	756[a]	756[a]
	210	320	520[6]	1400	1400	200	600	400	980[a]	980[a]
	410	620	360[5]	1400	1400	200	600	400	807	756[a]
	200	400	470[6]	1400	1400	200	600	400	910[a]	910[a]
	400	800	360[5]	1400	1400	200	600	400	817	756[a]
3000	320	320	620[6]	1750	1750	250	750	500	1400[a]	1400[a]
	520	520	440[5]	1750	1750	250	750	500	1228	1228
	260	390	620[6]	1750	1750	250	750	500	1400[a]	1400[a]
	460	690	430[5]	1750	1750	250	750	500	1334	1068[a]
	230	450	630[6]	1750	1750	250	750	500	1418[a]	1418[a]
	430	860	430[5]	1750	1750	250	750	500	1372	1068[a]
4000	370	370	720[6]	1750	1750	250	750	500	1575[a]	1575[a]
	570	570	630[5]	1750	1750	250	750	500	1418[a]	1418[a]
	300	450	720[6]	1750	1750	250	750	500	1575[a]	1575[a]
	500	750	630[5]	1750	1750	250	750	500	1418[a]	1418[a]
	260	520	720[6]	1750	1750	250	750	500	1575[a]	1575[a]
	460	920	630[5]	1750	1750	250	750	500	1418[a]	1418[a]
5000	410	410	820[6]	2100	2100	300	900	600	2100[a]	2100[a]
	610	610	630[5]	2100	2100	300	900	600	1736	1736
	330	500	820[6]	2100	2100	300	900	600	2100[a]	2100[a]
	530	800	630[5]	2100	2100	300	900	600	1853	1701[a]
	290	580	810[6]	2100	2100	300	900	600	2079[a]	2079[a]
	490	980	640[5]	2100	2100	300	900	600	1881	1722[a]
6000	450	450	890[6]	2450	2450	350	1050	700	2622[a]	2622[a]
	650	650	630[5]	2450	2450	350	1050	700	2539	2539
	370	550	890 [6]	2450	2450	350	1050	700	2622[a]	2622[a]
	570	860	620[5]	2450	2450	350	1050	700	2722	2206
	320	630	890[6]	2450	2450	350	1050	700	2622[a]	2622[a]
	520	1040	620[5]	2450	2450	350	1050	700	2811	1960[a]

[a] steel area governed by Clause 7.8.1
[1] governed by 1-way shear @ pile
[3] governed by 1-way shear @ column
[5] governed by pile bearing stress
[2] governed by 2-way shear @ pile
[4] governed by 2-way shear @ column
[6] governed by column bearing stress

Table 9.13(a) Five pile supported footing, f'_c = 20 MPa, f_y = 400 MPa

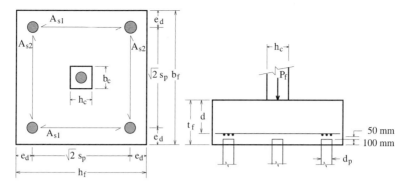

P_f (kN)	h_c (mm)	b_c (mm)	d (mm)	h_f (mm)	b_f (mm)	d_p (mm)	s_p (mm)	e_d (mm)	A_{s1} (mm^2)	A_{s2} (mm^2)
1250	240	240	460[6]	1650	1650	200	600	400	1056[a]	1056[a]
	440	440	300	1650	1650	200	600	400	792[a]	792[a]
	200	300	440[6]	1650	1650	200	600	400	1023[a]	1023[a]
	400	600	300	1650	1650	200	600	400	797	792[a]
	200	400	380[6]	1650	1650	200	600	400	924[a]	924[a]
	400	800	300	1650	1650	200	600	400	797	792[a]
2500	330	330	660[6]	2070	2070	250	750	500	1739[a]	1739[a]
	530	530	510[1]	2070	2070	250	750	500	1428[a]	1428[a]
	270	400	660[6]	2070	2070	250	750	500	1739[a]	1739[a]
	470	710	510[1]	2070	2070	250	750	500	1428[a]	1428[a]
	240	470	650[6]	2070	2070	250	750	500	1718[a]	1718[a]
	440	880	420[4]	2070	2070	250	750	500	1488	1242[a]
3750	410	410	790[6]	2070	2070	250	750	500	2008[a]	2008[a]
	610	610	640[5]	2070	2070	250	750	500	1697[a]	1697[a]
	330	490	810[6]	2070	2070	250	750	500	2049[a]	2049[a]
	530	800	640[5]	2070	2070	250	750	500	1697[a]	1697[a]
	290	570	800[6]	2070	2070	250	750	500	2029[a]	2029[a]
	490	980	650[5]	2070	2070	250	750	500	1718[a]	1718[a]
5000	470	470	930[1]	2480	2480	300	900	600	2753[a]	2753[a]
	670	670	710[5]	2480	2480	300	900	600	2207[a]	2207[a]
	380	570	930[1]	2480	2480	300	900	600	2753[a]	2753[a]
	580	870	710[5]	2480	2480	300	900	600	2207[a]	2207[a]
	330	660	940[6]	2480	2480	300	900	600	2778[a]	2778[a]
	530	1060	710[5]	2480	2480	300	900	600	2207[a]	2207[a]
6250	520	520	1120[1]	2890	2890	350	1050	700	3757[a]	3757[a]
	720	720	830	2890	2890	350	1050	700	2919[a]	2919[a]
	430	640	1100[1]	2890	2890	350	1050	700	3699[a]	3699[a]
	630	950	750[5]	2890	2890	350	1050	700	2880	2688[a]
	370	740	1070[1]	2890	2890	350	1050	700	3613[a]	3613[a]
	570	1140	750[5]	2890	2890	350	1050	700	2953	2688[a]
7500	570	570	1260[1]	3300	3300	400	1200	800	4752[a]	4752[a]
	770	770	1020[1]	3300	3300	400	1200	800	3960[a]	3960[a]
	470	700	1260[1]	3300	3300	400	1200	800	4752[a]	4752[a]
	670	1010	920[1]	3300	3300	400	1200	800	3630[a]	3630[a]
	410	810	1240[1]	3300	3300	400	1200	800	4686[a]	4686[a]
	610	1220	810[1]	3300	3300	400	1200	800	3799	3267[a]

[a] steel area governed by Clause 7.8.1
[1] governed by 1-way shear @ pile
[3] governed by 1-way shear @ column
[5] governed by pile bearing stress
[2] governed by 2-way shear @ pile
[4] governed by 2-way shear @ column
[6] governed by column bearing stress

Table 9.13(b) Five pile supported footing, $f'_c = 30$ MPa, $f_y = 400$ MPa

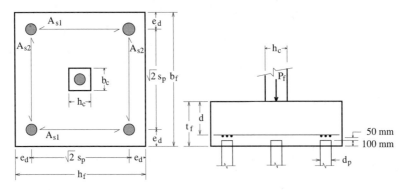

P_f (kN)	h_c (mm)	b_c (mm)	d (mm)	h_f (mm)	b_f (mm)	d_p (mm)	s_p (mm)	e_d (mm)	A_{s1} (mm²)	A_{s2} (mm²)
1250	210	210	390[6]	1650	1650	200	600	400	941[a]	941[a]
	410	410	300	1650	1650	200	600	400	792[a]	792[a]
	200	300	330[4]	1650	1650	200	600	400	842[a]	842[a]
	400	600	300	1650	1650	200	600	400	797	792[a]
	200	400	320[4]	1650	1650	200	600	400	862	825[a]
	400	800	300	1650	1650	200	600	400	797	792[a]
2500	290	290	570[6]	1650	1650	200	600	400	1238[a]	1238[a]
	490	490	390[1]	1650	1650	200	600	400	1141	1141
	240	360	570[6]	1650	1650	200	600	400	1238[a]	1238[a]
	440	660	370[5]	1650	1650	200	600	400	1252	1033
	210	410	570[6]	1650	1650	200	600	400	1238[a]	1238[a]
	410	820	370[5]	1650	1650	200	600	400	1282	908[a]
3750	360	360	700[6]	2070	2070	250	750	500	1822[a]	1822[a]
	560	560	550[1]	2070	2070	250	750	500	1584	1584
	290	430	700[6]	2070	2070	250	750	500	1822[a]	1822[a]
	490	740	480[1]	2070	2070	250	750	500	1896	1608
	250	500	700[6]	2070	2070	250	750	500	1822[a]	1822[a]
	450	900	440[4]	2070	2070	250	750	500	2118	1554
5000	410	410	810[6]	2070	2070	250	750	500	2049[a]	2049[a]
	610	610	630[5]	2070	2070	250	750	500	1786	1786
	330	500	820[6]	2070	2070	250	750	500	2070[a]	2070[a]
	530	800	630[5]	2070	2070	250	750	500	1879	1677[a]
	290	580	810[6]	2070	2070	250	750	500	2049[a]	2049[a]
	490	980	630[5]	2070	2070	250	750	500	1926	1677[a]
6250	460	460	950[1]	2480	2480	300	900	600	2802[a]	2802[a]
	660	660	670[1]	2480	2480	300	900	600	2606	2606
	370	560	940[1]	2480	2480	300	900	600	2778[a]	2778[a]
	570	860	630[5]	2480	2480	300	900	600	2903	2480
	320	640	920[1]	2480	2480	300	900	600	2728[a]	2728[a]
	520	1040	640[5]	2480	2480	300	900	600	2930	2183
7500	500	500	1090[1]	2890	2890	350	1050	700	3670[a]	3670[a]
	700	700	860[1]	2890	2890	350	1050	700	3006[a]	3006[a]
	410	610	1090[1]	2890	2890	350	1050	700	3670[a]	3670[a]
	610	920	770[1]	2890	2890	350	1050	700	3395	2951
	360	710	1090[1]	2890	2890	350	1050	700	3670[a]	3670[a]
	560	1120	670[4]	2890	2890	350	1050	700	3984	3062

[a] steel area governed by Clause 7.8.1
[1] governed by 1-way shear @ pile
[3] governed by 1-way shear @ column
[5] governed by pile bearing stress

[2] governed by 2-way shear @ pile
[4] governed by 2-way shear @ column
[6] governed by column bearing stress

Table 9.14(a) Six pile supported footing, $f'_c = 20$ MPa, $f_y = 400$ MPa

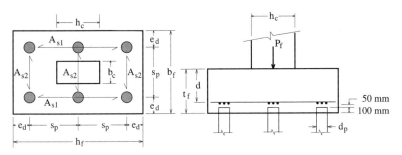

P_f (kN)	h_c (mm)	b_c (mm)	d (mm)	h_f (mm)	b_f (mm)	d_p (mm)	s_p (mm)	e_d (mm)	A_{s1} (mm²)	A_{s2} (mm²)
1500	260	260	510[6]	2000	1400	200	600	400	966[a]	920[a]
	460	460	370[3]	2000	1400	200	600	400	964	733[a]
	210	310	510[6]	2000	1400	200	600	400	966[a]	920[a]
	410	620	390[3]	2000	1400	200	600	400	938	760[a]
	320	210	510[6]	2000	1400	200	600	400	966[a]	920[a]
	520	350	350[4]	2000	1400	200	600	400	987	707[a]
3000	360	360	730[6]	2500	1750	250	750	500	1593[a]	1517[a]
	560	560	510[1]	2500	1750	250	750	500	1759	1150[a]
	300	440	730[6]	2500	1750	250	750	500	1593[a]	1517[a]
	500	750	530[3]	2500	1750	250	750	500	1734	1183[a]
	440	300	730[6]	2500	1750	250	750	500	1593[a]	1517[a]
	640	430	510[1]	2500	1750	250	750	500	1701	1150[a]
4500	450	450	910[6]	2500	1750	250	750	500	1908[a]	1817[a]
	650	650	720[6]	2500	1750	250	750	500	1800	1500[a]
	390	580	940[6]	2500	1750	250	750	500	1960[a]	1867[a]
	590	890	650[5]	2500	1750	250	750	500	2045	1383[a]
	540	360	890[6]	2500	1750	250	750	500	1873[a]	1783[a]
	740	490	740[6]	2500	1750	250	750	500	1684	1533[a]
6000	510	510	1030[6]	3000	2100	300	900	600	2541[a]	2420[a]
	710	710	850[6]	3000	2100	300	900	600	2500	2060[a]
	430	640	1060[6]	3000	2100	300	900	600	2604[a]	2480[a]
	630	950	810[6]	3000	2100	300	900	600	2696	1980[a]
	630	420	1020[6]	3000	2100	300	900	600	2520[a]	2400[a]
	830	550	840[6]	3000	2100	300	900	600	2425	2040[a]
7500	570	570	1140[6]	3500	2450	350	1050	700	3234[a]	3080[a]
	770	770	940[6]	3500	2450	350	1050	700	3354	2613[a]
	470	700	1140[6]	3500	2450	350	1050	700	3234[a]	3080[a]
	670	1010	930[6]	3500	2450	350	1050	700	3489	2590[a]
	700	470	1140[6]	3500	2450	350	1050	700	3234[a]	3080[a]
	900	600	930[6]	3500	2450	350	1050	700	3261	2590[a]
9000	630	630	1260[1]	4000	2800	400	1200	800	4032[a]	3840[a]
	830	830	1070[1]	4000	2800	400	1200	800	4092	3333[a]
	510	760	1260[1]	4000	2800	400	1200	800	4032[a]	3840[a]
	710	1070	1030[6]	4000	2800	400	1200	800	4380	3227[a]
	770	510	1260[1]	4000	2800	400	1200	800	4032[a]	3840[a]
	970	650	1100[1]	4000	2800	400	1200	800	3840	3413[a]

[a] steel area governed by Clause 7.8.1
[1] governed by 1-way shear @ pile
[3] governed by 1-way shear @ column
[5] governed by pile bearing stress
[2] governed by 2-way shear @ pile
[4] governed by 2-way shear @ column
[6] governed by column bearing stress

Table 9.14(b) Six pile supported footing, f'_c = 30 MPa, f_y = 400 MPa

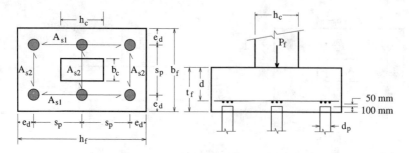

P_f (kN)	h_c (mm)	b_c (mm)	d (mm)	h_f (mm)	b_f (mm)	d_p (mm)	s_p (mm)	e_d (mm)	A_{s1} (mm²)	A_{s2} (mm²)
1500	230	230	440[3]	2000	1400	200	600	400	907	827[a]
	430	430	360[3]	2000	1400	200	600	400	1006	720[a]
	200	300	460[3]	2000	1400	200	600	400	896[a]	853[a]
	400	600	380[3]	2000	1400	200	600	400	967	747[a]
	300	200	420[3]	2000	1400	200	600	400	919	800[a]
	500	330	340[3]	2000	1400	200	600	400	1027	693[a]
3000	320	320	630[6]	2000	1400	200	600	400	1214	1080[a]
	520	520	420[1]	2000	1400	200	600	400	1646	800[a]
	260	390	620[6]	2000	1400	200	600	400	1269	1067[a]
	460	690	410[3]	2000	1400	200	600	400	1740	787[a]
	390	260	620[6]	2000	1400	200	600	400	1192	1067[a]
	590	390	460[1]	2000	1400	200	600	400	1447	853[a]
4500	390	390	760[6]	2500	1750	250	750	500	1894	1567[a]
	590	590	590[1]	2500	1750	250	750	500	2253	1283[a]
	320	480	760[6]	2500	1750	250	750	500	1945	1567[a]
	520	780	530[3]	2500	1750	250	750	500	2580	1183[a]
	480	320	760[6]	2500	1750	250	750	500	1829	1567[a]
	680	450	630[1]	2500	1750	250	750	500	2031	1350[a]
6000	460	460	910[6]	2500	1750	250	750	500	2052	1817[a]
	660	660	640[5]	2500	1750	250	750	500	2688	1367[a]
	390	580	960[6]	2500	1750	250	750	500	1999	1900[a]
	590	890	640[5]	2500	1750	250	750	500	2769	1367[a]
	550	370	890[6]	2500	1750	250	750	500	2024	1783[a]
	750	500	670[6]	2500	1750	250	750	500	2469	1417[a]
7500	500	500	990[1]	3000	2100	300	900	600	2878	2340[a]
	700	700	730[6]	3000	2100	300	900	600	3651	1820[a]
	410	610	1000[6]	3000	2100	300	900	600	2932	2360[a]
	610	920	670[4]	3000	2100	300	900	600	4102	1700[a]
	610	410	1000[6]	3000	2100	300	900	600	2748	2360[a]
	810	540	760[6]	3000	2100	300	900	600	3374	1880[a]
9000	550	550	1090[1]	3500	2450	350	1050	700	3693	2963[a]
	750	750	910[1]	3500	2450	350	1050	700	4181	2543[a]
	450	670	1090[1]	3500	2450	350	1050	700	3795	2963[a]
	650	980	820[1]	3500	2450	350	1050	700	4775	2333[a]
	670	450	1090[1]	3500	2450	350	1050	700	3572	2963[a]
	870	580	950[1]	3500	2450	350	1050	700	3866	2637[a]

[a] steel area governed by Clause 7.8.1
[1] governed by 1-way shear @ pile
[3] governed by 1-way shear @ column
[5] governed by pile bearing stress
[2] governed by 2-way shear @ pile
[4] governed by 2-way shear @ column
[6] governed by column bearing stress

Table 9.15(a) Seven pile supported footing, $f'_c = 20$ MPa, $f_y = 400$ MPa

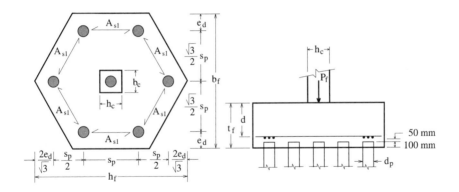

P_f (kN)	h_c (mm)	b_c (mm)	d (mm)	h_f (mm)	b_f (mm)	d_p (mm)	s_p (mm)	e_d (mm)	A_{s1} (mm^2)
1750	280	280	550[6]	2120	1840	200	600	400	1343[a]
	480	480	390[4]	2120	1840	200	600	400	1049[a]
	230	340	550[6]	2120	1840	200	600	400	1343[a]
	430	650	330[4]	2120	1840	200	600	400	1098
	340	230	550[6]	2120	1840	200	600	400	1343[a]
	540	360	410[4]	2120	1840	200	600	400	1086[a]
3500	390	390	790[6]	2660	2300	250	750	500	2231[a]
	590	590	550[4]	2660	2300	250	750	500	1679[a]
	320	480	790[6]	2660	2300	250	750	500	2231[a]
	520	780	470[4]	2660	2300	250	750	500	1941
	480	320	780[6]	2660	2300	250	750	500	2208[a]
	680	450	600[4]	2660	2300	250	750	500	1794[a]
5250	480	480	960[6]	2660	2300	250	750	500	2622[a]
	680	680	770[6]	2660	2300	250	750	500	2185[a]
	390	580	970[6]	2660	2300	250	750	500	2645[a]
	590	890	690[6]	2660	2300	250	750	500	2001[a]
	590	390	960[6]	2660	2300	250	750	500	2622[a]
	790	530	830[6]	2660	2300	250	750	500	2323[a]
7000	550	550	1110[6]	3180	2760	300	900	600	3560[a]
	750	750	890[6]	3180	2760	300	900	600	2953[a]
	450	670	1120[6]	3180	2760	300	900	600	3588[a]
	650	980	820[6]	3180	2760	300	900	600	2760[a]
	680	450	1100[6]	3180	2760	300	900	600	3533[a]
	880	590	950[6]	3180	2760	300	900	600	3119[a]
8750	620	620	1220[6]	3720	3220	350	1050	700	4508[a]
	820	820	990[6]	3720	3220	350	1050	700	3767[a]
	510	760	1220[6]	3720	3220	350	1050	700	4508[a]
	710	1070	900[6]	3720	3220	350	1050	700	3566
	760	510	1230[6]	3720	3220	350	1050	700	4540[a]
	960	640	1050[6]	3720	3220	350	1050	700	3961[a]
10500	680	680	1340[6]	4260	3680	400	1200	800	5594[a]
	880	880	1060[6]	4260	3680	400	1200	800	4563[a]
	550	820	1360[6]	4260	3680	400	1200	800	5667[a]
	750	1130	990[6]	4260	3680	400	1200	800	4514
	830	550	1360[6]	4260	3680	400	1200	800	5667[a]
	1030	690	1100[6]	4260	3680	400	1200	800	4710[a]

[a] steel area governed by Clause 7.8.1
[1] governed by 1-way shear @ pile
[2] governed by 2-way shear @ pile
[3] governed by 1-way shear @ column
[4] governed by 2-way shear @ column
[5] governed by pile bearing stress
[6] governed by column bearing stress

Table 9.15(b)   Seven pile supported footing, f'_c = 30 MPa, f_y = 400 MPa

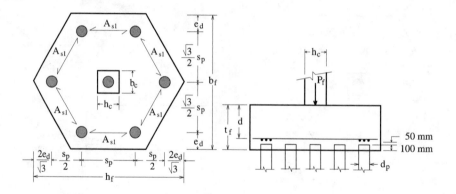

P_f (kN)	h_c (mm)	b_c (mm)	d (mm)	h_f (mm)	b_f (mm)	d_p (mm)	s_p (mm)	e_d (mm)	A_{s1} (mm²)
1750	240	240	490[6]	2120	1840	200	600	400	1233[a]
	440	440	360[4]	2120	1840	200	600	400	1001
	200	300	470[6]	2120	1840	200	600	400	1196[a]
	400	600	320[4]	2120	1840	200	600	400	1149
	300	200	470[6]	2120	1840	200	600	400	1196[a]
	500	330	370[4]	2120	1840	200	600	400	1029
3500	340	340	690[6]	2120	1840	200	600	400	1601[a]
	540	540	450[4]	2120	1840	200	600	400	1520
	280	420	690[6]	2120	1840	200	600	400	1601[a]
	480	720	360[4]	2120	1840	200	600	400	1962
	420	280	690[6]	2120	1840	200	600	400	1601[a]
	620	410	480[4]	2120	1840	200	600	400	1525
5250	420	420	840[6]	2660	2300	250	750	500	2346[a]
	620	620	580[4]	2660	2300	250	750	500	2264
	340	510	850[6]	2660	2300	250	750	500	2369[a]
	540	810	490[4]	2660	2300	250	750	500	2770
	510	340	850[6]	2660	2300	250	750	500	2369[a]
	710	470	630[4]	2660	2300	250	750	500	2216
7000	480	480	980[6]	2660	2300	250	750	500	2668[a]
	680	680	700[6]	2660	2300	250	750	500	2438
	390	590	970[6]	2660	2300	250	750	500	2645[a]
	590	890	630[5]	2660	2300	250	750	500	2814
	590	390	980[6]	2660	2300	250	750	500	2668[a]
	790	530	780[6]	2660	2300	250	750	500	2329
8750	540	540	1080[6]	3180	2760	300	900	600	3478[a]
	740	740	780[6]	3180	2760	300	900	600	3372
	440	660	1070[6]	3180	2760	300	900	600	3450[a]
	640	960	700[6]	3180	2760	300	900	600	3888
	660	440	1070[6]	3180	2760	300	900	600	3450[a]
	860	570	850[6]	3180	2760	300	900	600	3278
10500	590	590	1190[6]	3720	3220	350	1050	700	4411[a]
	790	790	860[4]	3720	3220	350	1050	700	4375
	480	720	1190[6]	3720	3220	350	1050	700	4411[a]
	680	1020	760[4]	3720	3220	350	1050	700	5111
	720	480	1190[6]	3720	3220	350	1050	700	4411[a]
	920	610	920[4]	3720	3220	350	1050	700	4306

[a] steel area governed by Clause 7.8.1
[1] governed by 1-way shear @ pile
[3] governed by 1-way shear @ column
[5] governed by pile bearing stress

[2] governed by 2-way shear @ pile
[4] governed by 2-way shear @ column
[6] governed by column bearing stress

Table 9.16(a)   Eight pile supported footing, $f'_c = 20$ MPa, $f_y = 400$ MPa

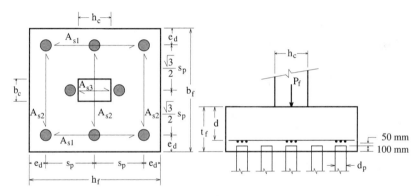

P_f (kN)	h_c (mm)	b_c (mm)	d (mm)	h_f (mm)	b_f (mm)	d_p (mm)	s_p (mm)	e_d (mm)	A_{s1} (mm²)	A_{s2} (mm²)	A_{s3} (mm²)
2000	300	300	590[6]	2000	1840	200	600	400	1167[a]	1027[a]	500[a]
	500	500	390[4]	2000	1840	200	600	400	896	760[a]	330[a]
	240	360	600[6]	2000	1840	200	600	400	1174[a]	1040[a]	522[a]
	440	660	350[3]	2000	1840	200	600	400	1029	746	399
	360	240	600[6]	2000	1840	200	600	400	1190[a]	1040[a]	490[a]
	560	370	410[4]	2000	1840	200	600	400	925[a]	787[a]	322[a]
4000	420	420	830[6]	2500	2300	250	750	500	1921[a]	1683[a]	804[a]
	620	620	550[4]	2500	2300	250	750	500	1591	1324	588
	340	510	840[6]	2500	2300	250	750	500	1926[a]	1700[a]	840[a]
	540	810	510[1]	2500	2300	250	750	500	1773	1290	692
	510	340	850[6]	2500	2300	250	750	500	1976[a]	1717[a]	786[a]
	710	470	590[4]	2500	2300	250	750	500	1510[a]	1327	521
6000	510	510	1020[6]	2500	2300	250	750	500	2302[a]	2000[a]	915[a]
	710	710	800[1]	2500	2300	250	750	500	1922[a]	1633[a]	663[a]
	420	630	1020[6]	2500	2300	250	750	500	2282[a]	2000[a]	955[a]
	620	930	780[6]	2500	2300	250	750	500	1863[a]	1600[a]	689[a]
	630	420	1020[6]	2500	2300	250	750	500	2332[a]	2000[a]	856[a]
	830	550	800[1]	2500	2300	250	750	500	1953[a]	1633[a]	603[a]
8000	590	590	1190[6]	3000	2760	300	900	600	3148[a]	2740[a]	1266[a]
	790	790	970[1]	3000	2760	300	900	600	2690[a]	2300[a]	967[a]
	480	720	1190[6]	3000	2760	300	900	600	3121[a]	2740[a]	1320[a]
	680	1020	960[1]	3000	2760	300	900	600	2640[a]	2280[a]	1013[a]
	720	480	1190[6]	3000	2760	300	900	600	3184[a]	2740[a]	1194[a]
	920	610	970[1]	3000	2760	300	900	600	2726[a]	2300[a]	895[a]
10000	660	660	1320[6]	3500	3220	350	1050	700	4014[a]	3500[a]	1633[a]
	860	860	1120[1]	3500	3220	350	1050	700	3531[a]	3033[a]	1311[a]
	540	810	1320[6]	3500	3220	350	1050	700	3981[a]	3500[a]	1697[a]
	740	1110	1120[1]	3500	3220	350	1050	700	3498[a]	3033[a]	1375[a]
	810	540	1320[6]	3500	3220	350	1050	700	4058[a]	3500[a]	1544[a]
	1010	670	1120[1]	3500	3220	350	1050	700	3575[a]	3033[a]	1222[a]
12000	720	720	1460[6]	4000	3680	400	1200	800	5005[a]	4373[a]	2061[a]
	920	920	1260[1]	4000	3680	400	1200	800	4450[a]	3840[a]	1698[a]
	590	880	1440[6]	4000	3680	400	1200	800	4907[a]	4320[a]	2110[a]
	790	1190	1260[1]	4000	3680	400	1200	800	4413[a]	3840[a]	1772[a]
	880	590	1440[6]	4000	3680	400	1200	800	4993[a]	4320[a]	1936[a]
	1080	720	1260[1]	4000	3680	400	1200	800	4501[a]	3840[a]	1597[a]

[a] steel area governed by Clause 7.8.1
[1] governed by 1-way shear @ pile
[3] governed by 1-way shear @ column
[5] governed by pile bearing stress
[2] governed by 2-way shear @ pile
[4] governed by 2-way shear @ column
[6] governed by column bearing stress

Table 9.16(b) Eight pile supported footing, f'_c = 30 MPa, f_y = 400 MPa

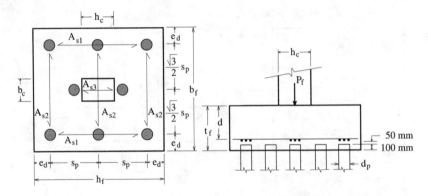

P_f (kN)	h_c (mm)	b_c (mm)	d (mm)	h_f (mm)	b_f (mm)	d_p (mm)	s_p (mm)	e_d (mm)	A_{s1} (mm²)	A_{s2} (mm²)	A_{s3} (mm²)
2000	260	260	510[6]	2000	1840	200	600	400	1041[a]	920[a]	457[a]
	460	460	360[4]	2000	1840	200	600	400	991	827	378
	210	320	510[6]	2000	1840	200	600	400	1036[a]	920[a]	468[a]
	410	620	340[3]	2000	1840	200	600	400	1076	789	427
	320	210	510[6]	2000	1840	200	600	400	1048[a]	920[a]	443[a]
	520	350	360[4]	2000	1840	200	600	400	960	883	347
4000	370	370	710[6]	2000	1840	200	600	400	1360[a]	1187[a]	556[a]
	570	570	490[1]	2000	1840	200	600	400	1373	1133	473
	300	450	730	2000	1840	200	600	400	1379[a]	1213[a]	591[a]
	500	750	490[1]	2000	1840	200	600	400	1426	998	525
	450	300	720[6]	2000	1840	200	600	400	1389[a]	1200[a]	534[a]
	650	430	500[4]	2000	1840	200	600	400	1287	1213	404
6000	450	450	880[6]	2500	2300	250	750	500	2022[a]	1767[a]	832[a]
	650	650	640[1]	2500	2300	250	750	500	2025	1680	732
	370	550	880[6]	2500	2300	250	750	500	2007[a]	1767[a]	862[a]
	570	860	640[1]	2500	2300	250	750	500	2094	1499	801
	550	370	880[6]	2500	2300	250	750	500	2042[a]	1767[a]	792[a]
	750	500	640[1]	2500	2300	250	750	500	1939	1810	646
8000	520	520	1020[6]	2500	2300	250	750	500	2305[a]	2000[a]	911[a]
	720	720	800[1]	2500	2300	250	750	500	2096	1728	717
	420	630	1040[6]	2500	2300	250	750	500	2320[a]	2033[a]	971[a]
	620	930	720[1]	2500	2300	250	750	500	2431	1705	899
	630	420	1040[6]	2500	2300	250	750	500	2371[a]	2033[a]	870[a]
	830	550	840[1]	2500	2300	250	750	500	2032[a]	1794	627
10000	580	580	1150[6]	3000	2760	300	900	600	3054[a]	2660[a]	1234[a]
	780	780	990[1]	3000	2760	300	900	600	2735[a]	2340[a]	989[a]
	470	700	1170[6]	3000	2760	300	900	600	3073[a]	2700[a]	1306[a]
	670	1010	980[1]	3000	2760	300	900	600	2748	2320a	1060[a]
	710	470	1150[6]	3000	2760	300	900	600	3088[a]	2660[a]	1165[a]
	910	610	990[1]	3000	2760	300	900	600	2771[a]	2340[a]	917[a]
12000	630	630	1270[6]	3500	3220	350	1050	700	3872[a]	3383[a]	1594[a]
	830	830	1090[1]	3500	3220	350	1050	700	3441[a]	2963[a]	1297[a]
	520	770	1250[6]	3500	3220	350	1050	700	3791[a]	3337[a]	1628[a]
	720	1080	1090[1]	3500	3220	350	1050	700	3521	2963a	1396[a]
	770	520	1250[6]	3500	3220	350	1050	700	3857[a]	3337[a]	1496[a]
	970	650	1090[1]	3500	3220	350	1050	700	3481[a]	3025	1218

[a] steel area governed by Clause 7.8.1
[1] governed by 1-way shear @ pile
[3] governed by 1-way shear @ column
[5] governed by pile bearing stress

[2] governed by 2-way shear @ pile
[4] governed by 2-way shear @ column
[6] governed by column bearing stress

Table 9.17(a)   Nine pile supported footing, f'_c = 20 MPa, f_y = 400 MPa

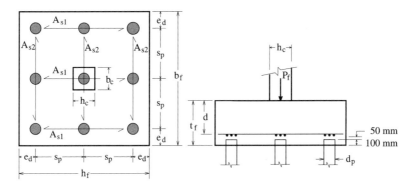

P_f (kN)	h_c (mm)	b_c (mm)	d (mm)	h_f (mm)	b_f (mm)	d_p (mm)	s_p (mm)	e_d (mm)	A_{s1} (mm²)	A_{s2} (mm²)
2250	320	320	610[6]	2000	2000	200	600	400	1053[a]	1053[a]
	520	520	480[4]	2000	2000	200	600	400	880[a]	880[a]
	260	390	620[6]	2000	2000	200	600	400	1067[a]	1067[a]
	460	690	430[4]	2000	2000	200	600	400	829	813[a]
	220	440	640[6]	2000	2000	200	600	400	1093[a]	1093[a]
	420	840	400[4]	2000	2000	200	600	400	910	773[a]
4500	440	440	890[6]	2500	2500	250	750	500	1783[a]	1783[a]
	640	640	670[4]	2500	2500	250	750	500	1417[a]	1417[a]
	360	540	900[6]	2500	2500	250	750	500	1800[a]	1800[a]
	560	840	630[4]	2500	2500	250	750	500	1424	1350[a]
	320	630	880[6]	2500	2500	250	750	500	1767[a]	1767[a]
	520	1040	570[4]	2500	2500	250	750	500	1600	1264
6750	540	540	1090[6]	2500	2500	250	750	500	2117[a]	2117[a]
	740	740	840[6]	2500	2500	250	750	500	1700[a]	1700[a]
	440	660	1090[6]	2500	2500	250	750	500	2117[a]	2117[a]
	640	960	820[6]	2500	2500	250	750	500	1667[a]	1667[a]
	390	770	1070[6]	2500	2500	250	750	500	2083[a]	2083[a]
	590	1180	800[6]	2500	2500	250	750	500	1661	1633[a]
9000	630	630	1240[6]	3000	3000	300	900	600	2840[a]	2840[a]
	830	830	970[1]	3000	3000	300	900	600	2300[a]	2300[a]
	510	760	1250[6]	3000	3000	300	900	600	2860[a]	2860[a]
	710	1070	970[1]	3000	3000	300	900	600	2300[a]	2300[a]
	440	880	1260[6]	3000	3000	300	900	600	2880[a]	2880[a]
	640	1280	970[1]	3000	3000	300	900	600	2300[a]	2300[a]
11250	700	700	1400[6]	3500	3500	350	1050	700	3687[a]	3687[a]
	900	900	1120[1]	3500	3500	350	1050	700	3033[a]	3033[a]
	570	850	1410[6]	3500	3500	350	1050	700	3710[a]	3710[a]
	770	1160	1120[1]	3500	3500	350	1050	700	3033[a]	3033[a]
	500	990	1380[6]	3500	3500	350	1050	700	3640[a]	3640[a]
	700	1400	1120[1]	3500	3500	350	1050	700	3033[a]	3033[a]
13500	780	780	1510[6]	4000	4000	400	1200	800	4507[a]	4507[a]
	980	980	1260[1]	4000	4000	400	1200	800	3840[a]	3840[a]
	640	960	1490[6]	4000	4000	400	1200	800	4453[a]	4453[a]
	840	1260	1260[1]	4000	4000	400	1200	800	3840[a]	3840[a]
	550	1100	1500[6]	4000	4000	400	1200	800	4480[a]	4480[a]
	750	1500	1260[1]	4000	4000	400	1200	800	3840[a]	3840[a]

[a] steel area governed by Clause 7.8.1
[1] governed by 1-way shear @ pile
[3] governed by 1-way shear @ column
[5] governed by pile bearing stress
[2] governed by 2-way shear @ pile
[4] governed by 2-way shear @ column
[6] governed by column bearing stress

Table 9.17(b)   Nine pile supported footing, f'_c = 30 MPa, f_y = 400 MPa

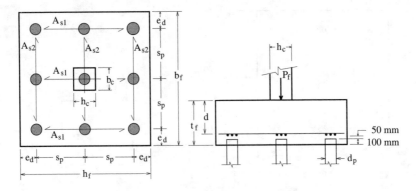

P_f (kN)	h_c (mm)	b_c (mm)	d (mm)	h_f (mm)	b_f (mm)	d_p (mm)	s_p (mm)	e_d (mm)	A_{s1} (mm^2)	A_{s2} (mm^2)
2250	280	280	540[6]	2000	2000	200	600	400	960[a]	960[a]
	480	480	430[4]	2000	2000	200	600	400	821	821
	230	340	540[6]	2000	2000	200	600	400	960[a]	960[a]
	430	650	400[4]	2000	2000	200	600	400	905	804
	200	400	530[6]	2000	2000	200	600	400	947[a]	947[a]
	400	800	380[3]	2000	2000	200	600	400	967	774
4500	390	390	770[6]	2000	2000	200	600	400	1267[a]	1267[a]
	590	590	540[4]	2000	2000	200	600	400	1232	1232
	320	480	760[6]	2000	2000	200	600	400	1253[a]	1253[a]
	520	780	510[4]	2000	2000	200	600	400	1355	1168
	280	550	760[6]	2000	2000	200	600	400	1253[a]	1253[a]
	480	960	490[1]	2000	2000	200	600	400	1441	1080
6750	480	480	930[6]	2500	2500	250	750	500	1850[a]	1850[a]
	680	680	700[4]	2500	2500	250	750	500	1828	1828
	390	580	940[6]	2500	2500	250	750	500	1867[a]	1867[a]
	590	890	680[4]	2500	2500	250	750	500	1954	1711
	340	670	930[6]	2500	2500	250	750	500	1850[a]	1850[a]
	540	1080	640[1]	2500	2500	250	750	500	2120	1654
9000	550	550	1080[6]	2500	2500	250	750	500	2100[a]	2100[a]
	750	750	880[1]	2500	2500	250	750	500	1880	1880
	450	670	1080[6]	2500	2500	250	750	500	2100[a]	2100[a]
	650	980	800[1]	2500	2500	250	750	500	2160	1857
	390	770	1100[6]	2500	2500	250	750	500	2133[a]	2133[a]
	590	1180	700[1]	2500	2500	250	750	500	2532	1912
11250	610	610	1220[6]	3000	3000	300	900	600	2800[a]	2800[a]
	810	810	990[1]	3000	3000	300	900	600	2590	2590
	500	750	1220[6]	3000	3000	300	900	600	2800[a]	2800[a]
	700	1050	990[1]	3000	3000	300	900	600	2692	2367
	430	860	1240[6]	3000	3000	300	900	600	2840[a]	2840[a]
	630	1260	990[1]	3000	3000	300	900	600	2757	2340[a]
13500	670	670	1330[6]	3500	3500	350	1050	700	3523[a]	3523[a]
	870	870	1090[1]	3500	3500	350	1050	700	3370	3370
	550	820	1330[6]	3500	3500	350	1050	700	3523[a]	3523[a]
	750	1130	1090[1]	3500	3500	350	1050	700	3491	3106
	480	950	1320[6]	3500	3500	350	1050	700	3500[a]	3500[a]
	680	1360	1090[1]	3500	3500	350	1050	700	3562	2963[a]

[a] steel area governed by Clause 7.8.1
[1] governed by 1-way shear @ pile
[3] governed by 1-way shear @ column
[5] governed by pile bearing stress

[2] governed by 2-way shear @ pile
[4] governed by 2-way shear @ column
[6] governed by column bearing stress

10

Prestressed Concrete

By Ivan Campbell

Walter Dilger

John Fowler

Chapter 10
Prestressed Concrete

10.1 NOTATION

a = depth of equivalent rectangular compression block

A = area of that part of cross section between flexural tension face and centroid of gross section

A_c = area of concrete cross section

A_{cr} = area of cracked section

A_s = area of tension reinforcement

A_{sb} = area of prestressing steel placed over columns

A_s' = area of compression reinforcement

A_p = area of prestressing tendons in tension zone

A_{tr} = area of uncracked transformed section

A_v = area of shear reinforcement perpendicular to the axis of the member

b = width of compression face member

b_o = perimeter of critical section for slabs

b_v = effective web width

b_w = width of web

c = neutral axis depth

C_r = factored axial load capacity of concrete stress block

C_t = creep coefficient

c_y = neutral axis depth assuming $f_{pr} = f_{py}$

d = effective depth (see Eq. 10.5.13)

d_p = effective depth for prestressing steel

d_s = effective depth for reinforcing steel

d' = distance to centroid of compression steel from extreme compression fibre

d_v = effective shear depth

e = eccentricity of tendon

e_{cr} = eccentricity of tendons in cracked transformed section

e_{tr} = eccentricity of tendons in uncracked transformed section

E_c = modulus of elasticity of concrete

E_p = modulus of elasticity of prestressing tendons

E_s = modulus of elasticity of reinforcement

f_c = concrete stress at level considered

f_c' = specified concrete cylinder strength

f_{ci}' = concrete strength at prestress transfer

f_{cp} = effective prestress at the centroid of the section (see notation in Clause 11)

f_{ns} = steel stress as defined in Equation 10.5.18

f_{pe} = effective stress in prestressing tendons (after losses)

f_{po} = stress in prestressing tendons when the stress in the surrounding concrete is zero

f_{pr} = stress in prestressing tendons at factored resistance

f_{pi} = initial stress in tendon after stressing

f_{pu} = tensile strength of prestressing tendon

f_{py} = yield strength of prestressing tendon

f_{re} = intrinsic relaxation loss in prestressing tendons

f_r = modulus of rupture

f_s = difference in steel stress in the non-prestressed reinforcement as defined by Eq. 10.5.1 or Eq. 10.5.4

f_s = stress in the non-prestressed tension reinforcement at factored resistance

f_s' = stress in compression reinforcement at factored resistance

f_y = specified yield strength of tension reinforcement

f_y' = specified yield strength of compression reinforcement

h = overall depth of member

h_f = depth of compression flange

I_c = moment of inertia of concrete section

I_{cr} = moment of inertia of the cracked section

I_e = effective moment of inertia

I_g = moment of inertia of gross concrete section

I_{tr} = moment of inertia of uncracked transformed section

k = c/d

k_p = factor for type of prestressing steel

k_1 = coefficient (Eq. 10.4.6)

k_y = coefficient for distance of centroid from compression fibre

K_u = coefficient = $M_r/(f_c'bd_p^2)$

ℓ = length of span

ℓ_d = development length

ℓ_e = effective length of tendon as described in Section 10.6.6

ℓ_n – length of clear span (two-way slabs)

ℓ_2 = length of span transverse to ℓ_n

M_{cr} = cracking moment

M_D = moment due to specified dead load

M_{dc} = decompression moment (Eq. 10.4.16)

M_f = moment due to factored loads

M_g = moment due to girder weight

M_L = moment due to specified live load

M_{net} = moment due to net load

M_p = total moment due to prestressing

M_p' = primary moment due to prestressing

M_p'' = secondary moment due to prestressing

M_r = factored moment resistance

M_s = moment due to specified loads

M_{sust} = sustained load moment

n = modular ratio

n_p = E_p/E_c

n_s = E_s/E_c

N = total number of post-tensioning tendons

N_v = equivalent factored axial load caused by shear and torsion

p = coefficient (Eq. 10.5.14)

P = decompression force

$P_{(i)}$ = prestressing force before transfer

P_i = prestressing force after transfer

P_o	=	jacking force
P_r	=	axial load resistance
P_x	=	prestress force at distance x from jacking end
P_e	=	effective prestress force after all losses
P_s	=	force in nonprestressed steel due to time-dependent effects
P_{ro}	=	factored axial load resistance of column with zero eccentricity
P_{rmax}	=	maximum factored load resistance ($= 0.8\ P_{ro}$)
r	=	radius of gyration
s	=	sag of prestressing tendons or, spacing of shear reinforcement
s_1	=	length of critical section (Eq. 10.8.6)
S	=	section modulus for tension fibre
T	=	factored tensile force in a group of bars
t	=	time since prestressing (Eq. 10.4.6)
v_c	=	shear stress resisted by concrete
v_f	=	factored shear stress
v_r	=	shear stress resistance
V_c	=	shear force resisted by concrete
V_{cr}	=	cracking shear resistance
V_f	=	factored shear force
V_p	=	shear resisted by prestressing
V_r	=	factored shear resistance
V_{se}	=	shear due to specified loads
w_{bal}	=	portion of load balanced by prestressing
w_{net}	=	portion of specified load not balanced by prestressing
w_s	=	specified load
x	=	distance from jacking end (m)
x_a	=	length of cable affected by anchorage slip
y_{cr}	=	distance to tension fibre being considered from centroid of cracked section
y_{tr}	=	distance to extreme tension fibre from centroid of uncracked transformed section
z	=	quantity limiting distribution of flexural tension reinforcement
α	=	$M_s/(bd^2)$ (see Eq. 10.5.17)
α	=	angular change of prestressing tendon between jacking end and point x (rad)
α_b	=	b_w/b
α_c	=	creep reduction coefficient determined from Fig. 10.4
α_d	=	coefficient (Eq. 10.8.6)
α_f	=	h_f/d
α_D	=	load factor on dead load
α_L	=	load factor on live load
α_p	=	load factor on prestressing force
α_r	=	relaxation reduction coefficient from Fig. 10.3
α_1	=	ratio of average stress in rectangular compression block to the specified concrete strength
β	=	f_{pi}/f_{pu}
β_1	=	ratio of depth of equivalent rectangular compression block to depth to neutral axis $= a/c$

Δf_c	=	change in concrete stress
Δf_p	=	change in prestress due to creep, shrinkage and relaxation
Δf_s	=	change in stress in reinforcement due to creep and shrinkage
Δ_i	=	initial deflection
ΔL	=	anchor set
Δ_t	=	time-dependent deflection
Δ_i^{su}	=	initial deflection due to sustained load
Δ_t^{su}	=	time-dependent deflection due to sustained load
Δ_i^p	=	initial deflection due to prestressing
Δ_t^p	=	time-dependent deflection due to prestressing
ΔP	=	change in prestressing force (loss)
ΔP_{el}	=	change in prestressing force due to elastic loss
ΔP_{elt}	=	total change in prestressing force due to elastic loss in a post-tensioned member
ΔP_p	=	force in prestressed reinforcement corresponding to f_c due to dead load and effective prestress
ΔP_s	=	force in non-prestressed reinforcement corresponding to f_c due to dead load and effective prestress
ε_{ce}	=	strain in concrete corresponding to a stress of f_{pe} in the steel and zero applied load
ε_p	=	strain at level of prestressed reinforcement
ε_s	=	strain in non-prestressed tension reinforcement
ε_{pe}	=	strain in prestressing steel corresponding to f_{pe}
ε_{sh}	=	shrinkage strain
ε_{total}	=	total strain
ε_s'	=	strain in compression reinforcement
ε_x	=	longitudinal strain in flexural tension chord of the member
ε_y'	=	yield strain of compression reinforcement
ε_1	=	principal tensile strain in cracked concrete due to factored load
θ	=	angle of inclination of diagonal compressive stresses to the longitudinal axis of member
μ	=	coefficient of curvature friction
κ	=	wobble friction coefficient
λ	=	factor to account for low density concrete
ρ	=	reinforcement area ratio
ρ_p	=	A_p/A_c
ρ_s	=	A_s/A_c
ϕ_c	=	resistance factor for concrete
ϕ_s	=	resistance factor for reinforcing bars
ϕ_p	=	resistance factor for prestressing tendons
ω_{pu}	=	reinforcement index
Ω	=	$\Delta f_s/f_{pi}$

10.2 INTRODUCTION

This Chapter of the Handbook provides a summary of the procedures for the design of fully and partially prestressed concrete members in accordance with CSA Standard A23.3, Clause 18.

The design examples which are presented have been selected to provide a broad spectrum of practical cases. Due to the general nature of the examples, it is anticipated that the designer will find them to be useful when clarification of the text is required.

A list of useful references can be found at the conclusion of this chapter. Further information may be obtained from the current edition of the Metric Design Manual for Precast and Prestressed Concrete published by the Canadian Prestressed Concrete Institute, Ottawa, Canada.

Sign Convention

Throughout this Chapter a positive stress in concrete is tensile and a negative stress is compressive.

10.3 PERMISSIBLE CONCRETE STRESSES IN FLEXURAL MEMBERS

10.3.1 General

The limits on permissible stresses in concrete given in Clause 18.4 provide for adequate serviceability but do not ensure adequate strength. Stresses are calculated using specified (unfactored) loads and compared with the given limits.

10.3.2 Permissible Concrete Stresses at Transfer

Clause 18.4.1 provides the limits of tensile and compressive concrete stresses immediately after transfer of the prestress force.

Whereas the tensile stresses may be exceeded, provided bonded reinforcement is added to resist the total tensile force (and developed in accordance with Clause 12), the extreme fibre stress in compression should not exceed $0.6 f'_{ci}$ unless tests or analyses show that performance will not be impaired. Beyond this limit creep increases non-linearly and the camber becomes unpredictable.

In computing the prestress force immediately after transfer allowance should be made for losses due to elastic shortening, shrinkage, relaxation of the tendons, temperature change and the anchorage seating. If the member is post-tensioned additional losses due to friction should be included.

10.3.3 Permissible Concrete Stresses due to Prestress and Specified Loads

Clause 18.4.2 provides the limits for tensile and compressive concrete stresses due to prestress and specified loads when cracking in the precompressed tensile zone is to be avoided. When cracking of the precompressed tensile zone is acceptable, the stress limit given in 18.4.2(c) can be exceeded giving what is said to be a partially prestressed member, which is subject to the additional requirements of Clause 18.4 3. The permissible extreme fibre stress in compression due to total load is $0.6 f'_c$, while that due to sustained loads is $0.45 f'_c$. Exceeding the permissible stress due to sustained loads will cause excessive creep of the concrete and result in undesirably high deflections.

The prestress force should be reduced from the initial force, to allow for all prestress losses, when computing concrete stresses due to prestress and specified loads. Losses from the time of transfer, are influenced by relaxation, creep, shrinkage, non-prestressed reinforcement, composite action and sustained loads, and may be calculated as discussed in Section 10.4. The calculation of permissible stresses is illustrated in Example 10.5.

10.3.4 Section Properties

The section properties (area, moment of inertia, section moduli and location of the section centroid) are calculated using traditional formulae. In addition, consideration must be given to the effect of openings at a particular cross section.

In general, the section properties should be calculated by taking into account the effects of the prestressed and non-prestressed reinforcement. However, in most practical cases the effects of reinforcement are small enough to be negligible. If a substantial quantity of non-prestressed reinforcement is required for a partially prestressed member, all reinforcement should be included when calculating the section properties.

For partially prestressed members (which are assumed to be cracked under application of specified loads), it is recommended that the designer use bilinear moment-deflection relationships to investigate instantaneous deflections. Alternatively, the effective moment of inertia can be calculated in accordance with Clause 9.8.2.3, and the deflection can then be calculated by substituting I_e for I_g in the deflection calculation.

10.3.5 Critical Section for Pretensioned Members

For concrete stresses immediately after transfer, the critical section is usually near the end of the element, although in elements with depressed or draped tendons, the stresses at midspan or at the depressed points may also be critical and should be checked. The critical end stress in pretensioned elements occurs at the point where the prestressing force has been completely transferred to the concrete, usually assumed to be 50 strand diameters from the end. For convenience, it is normal practice to calculate the stress at the end assuming full transfer and, only if necessary, check the stress at the transfer point.

Under uniform specified loads, the critical section in flexure is at mid-span for elements with straight tendons and near 40% of the span length for elements with tendons depressed at the mid-point. For other combinations of specified load and tendon profile, the critical section can be found by analysis.

10.4 PRESTRESS LOSSES AND DEFLECTION

10.4.1 General

The loss of prestress is defined as the difference between the initial prestress and the effective prestress. While the loss of prestress does not significantly affect the strength of a member, it affects the serviceability, namely camber and deflection, the magnitude of the concrete stresses, and the extent of cracking in partially prestressed members. The prestress losses may be divided into instantaneous losses, which occur at the time of application of the prestressing force, and time-dependent losses, which develop after the prestressing force has been applied. In post-tensioned structures the instantaneous losses occur during the post-tensioning operation, as a result of curvature friction and wobble friction, anchor set, and elastic losses caused by sequential stressing of the tendons. In pretensioned members the instantaneous losses are due to the elastic shortening of the concrete only. The loss of prestress due to relaxation of the prestressing steel occurring before prestress transfer needs to be considered when calculating the prestress force being transferred to the concrete.

The time-dependent losses in post-tensioned and pre-tensioned concrete are due to creep and shrinkage of the concrete, and relaxation of the prestressing steel.

10.4.2 Instantaneous Losses

Elastic losses

In pretensioned members the elastic loss corresponds to the elastic strain at the level of the tendon due to the combined effects of prestressing force and the girder weight applied at transfer. The change of force ΔP_{el} in the prestressing steel is accurately determined by the relation

$$\Delta P_{e\ell} = \left[\frac{P_{(i)}}{A_{tr}} + \frac{(P_{(i)}\, e_{tr} + M_g)\, e_{tr}}{I_{tr}} \right] \frac{E_p}{E_c} A_p \quad (10.4.1)$$

where
- $P_{(i)}$ = Prestressing force before transfer (after deducting relaxation losses occurring prior to transfer)
- A_{tr} = Area of uncracked transformed section (including transformed areas of prestressed and nonprestressed reinforcement)
- I_{tr} = Moment of inertia of uncracked transformed section
- e_{tr} = Eccentricity of tendons in uncracked transformed section
- M_g = Moment due to girder weight
- E_p = Modulus of elasticity of prestressing tendons
- E_c = Modulus of elasticity of concrete
- A_p = Area of prestressing tendons in tension zone

It should be noted that the prestressing force acting on the concrete is compressive and therefore is assumed to be negative in Eq. 10.4.1. In addition, eccentricities below the centroid of the section are taken as positive.

In post-tensioned members the overall elastic loss, $\Delta P_{e\ell t}$ is due to sequential stressing of the tendons and is given by

$$\Delta P_{e\ell t} = \frac{N-1}{2N} \Delta P_{e\ell} \quad (10.4.2)$$

where N is the total number of post-tensioning tendons.

Friction losses

The friction loss depends on the type of tendon and the type of duct used for a particular post-tensioning system. Typical values of curvature friction, μ, associated with the intentional curvature of a tendon, and of wobble friction, κ, associated with unintentional curvature of the duct, are listed in Table N18.6 of the Explanatory Notes.

The curvature friction coefficient is a proper friction coefficient, which is a dimensionless quantity, while the wobble friction coefficient is given per metre length.

The force at distance x from the jacking end of the tendon is

$$P_x = P_o e^{-(\mu\alpha + \kappa x)} \quad (10.4.3)$$

where
- P_x = prestress force at distance x from jacking end
- P_o = jacking force
- μ = coefficient of curvature friction
- α = total change in angle between jacking end and point x (in radians)
- κ = wobble friction coefficient (m^{-1})

- x = distance from jacking end to point where loss is desired (in metres).

Anchor set

Anchor set develops at the anchorage when the prestressing force is transferred to the anchorage due to the slip necessary to set the anchor. This results in a decrease of prestress over a certain distance from the anchor. Average values for the anchor set are 8 to 12 mm for Size 13 and Size 15 strands, respectively. The value of the anchor set for a particular post-tensioning system can be provided by the post-tensioning contractor.

The length, x_a, over which the stress in the tendon is affected is

$$x_a = \left[\frac{E_p A_p x_1}{\Delta P_{x_1}} \Delta L \right]^{1/2} \quad (10.4.4)$$

and the reduction in prestress at the anchor is

$$\Delta P = 2 \Delta P_{x_1} \frac{x_a}{x_1} \quad (10.4.5)$$

In Eqs. 10.4.4 and 10.4.5:
- ΔP_{x_1} = prestress loss at distance x_1 from jacking end
- x_1 = arbitrary distance from jacking end; for best results x_1 should be about equal to x_a
- ΔL = anchor set

Care should be taken to ensure that compatible units are used in these equations.

10.4.3 Time-dependent Losses

The time-dependent loss of prestress depends on the magnitude of creep and shrinkage of the concrete, the intrinsic relaxation of the prestressing steel, the concrete stress at the level of the tendon and the section parameters. The intrinsic relaxation is the relaxation obtained from tests under constant strain.

The creep and shrinkage can be predicted with the information provided in Chapter 1, Section 1.2.3 and in Table 1.2.

In lieu of detailed information from the manufacturer, the intrinsic relaxation of prestressing tendons may be predicted as

$$f_{re}(t) = \frac{\log t}{k_1} \left(\frac{f_{pi}}{f_{py}} - 0.55 \right) f_{pi} \quad (10.4.6)$$

In this equation
- $f_{re}(t)$ = intrinsic relaxation at time t (under constant strain)
- f_{pi} = initial stress in tendon after stressing
- f_{py} = 0.85 f_{pu} for stress-relieved wires and strands
- = 0.90 f_{pu} for low-relaxation strands
- f_{pu} = tensile strength of prestressing tendon
- t = time since prestressing (hours)
- k_1 = 10 to 12 for stress-relieved steel
- = 45 for low-relaxation steel

Assuming 50 years as the lifetime of the structure the final value for the intrinsic relaxation of stress-relieved steel (with k_1 = 12) is

$$f_{re} = 0.470 \left(\frac{f_{pi}}{f_{py}} - 0.55\right) f_{pi} \qquad (10.4.7)$$

and for low-relaxation steel is

$$f_{re} = 0.125 \left(\frac{f_{pi}}{f_{py}} - 0.55\right) f_{pi} \qquad (10.4.8)$$

These equations are valid for temperatures up to 20°C. At higher temperatures the relaxation increases (see Fig. 10.2).

The loss of prestress, Δf_p, for a member with one layer of tendons and non-prestressed steel at about the same level can be estimated from the relation

$$\Delta f_p = \frac{n\, f_c\, C_t + \varepsilon_{sh}\, n\, E_c + f_{re}}{1 + n\,(\rho_p + \rho_s)\,(1 + e^2/r^2)\,(1 + 0.8\, C_t)} \qquad (10.4.9)$$

where n = average modular ratio

f_c = concrete stress at level of tendon due to sustained load and initial prestressing force P_i

C_t = creep coefficient

ε_{sh} = shrinkage strain

ρ_p = A_p/A_c

ρ_s = A_s/A_c

A_c = area of concrete cross section

e = eccentricity of tendon

r^2 = I_c/A_c

I_c = moment of inertia of concrete section

The factor 0.8 in the denominator is the value of the so-called aging coefficient (Ref. 10.2) assumed for practical creep calculations. Since the relaxation loss is considerably reduced by the creep and shrinkage of the concrete, the intrinsic loss f_{re} may be replaced by a reduced value $\alpha_r f_{re}$. The coefficient α_r is determined from Fig. 10.3 using the parameters $\beta = f_{pi}/f_{pu}$ and $\Omega = \Delta f_s/f_{pi}$. The stress f_{pi} is the initial stress applied to the tendon, f_{pu} is the tensile strength of the tendon, and Δf_s is the loss of prestress due to creep and shrinkage only.

The value of Δf_s is given by

$$\Delta f_s = \frac{n\, f_c\, C_t + \varepsilon_{sh}\, n\, E_c}{1 + n\,(\rho_p + \rho_s)\,(1 + e^2/r^2)\,(1 + 0.8\, C_t)} \qquad (10.4.10)$$

The value Δf_s is also the time-dependent stress in the non-prestressed steel, the centroid of which is assumed to coincide with that of the prestressing steel. The total reduction in the compression acting on the concrete is

$$\Delta P = \Delta f_p\, A_p + \Delta f_s\, A_s \qquad (10.4.11)$$

Since the stress at the level of the tendon, f_c, is normally compressive, and ε_{sh} and Δf_{re} are always negative, both Δf_p and Δf_s are always negative, resulting in a reduction of the tension in the tendon and an increased compression in the non-prestressed steel (See Examples 10.5 and 10.6.).

If the non-prestressed steel is uniformly distributed throughout the section the term ρ_s in the denominator of Equation 10.4.9 is omitted, and the creep and shrinkage coefficients are multiplied by the creep reduction coefficient α_c depicted in Fig. 10.4 as a function of ρn and the creep coefficient C_t. Thus:

$$\Delta f_p = \frac{n\, f_c\, \alpha_c\, C_t + \varepsilon_{sh}\, \alpha_c\, n\, E_c + f_{re}}{1 + n\, \rho_p\,(1 + e^2/r^2)\,(1 + 0.8\, \alpha_c\, C_t)} \qquad (10.4.12)$$

For detailed treatment of the general case with multiple layers of steel see References 10.1 and 10.2.

10.4.4 Deflections

Two different cases are encountered when computing the deflection of prestressed concrete members namely, uncracked and cracked members. These two cases will be discussed separately.

Uncracked members

The elastic deflections at the time of prestressing are calculated by conventional methods of analysis. The downward deflection due to gravity load is reduced by the upward deflection (camber) due to prestressing. Expressions for computing the camber for the most common tendon profiles are given in Fig. 10.5. Expressions for deflections due to other types of loading are given in Table 1.14.

The initial deflection due to prestressing force is calculated using the initial prestressing force, P_i.

The time-dependent deflections Δ_t^{su} due to sustained loads are obtained by multiplying the initial deflections Δ_i^{su} by the creep coefficient C_t giving

$$\Delta_t^{su} = \Delta_i^{su}\, C_t \qquad (10.4.13)$$

The time-dependent deflections due to prestressing are obtained from the following equation

$$\Delta_t^p = \Delta_i^p \left[C_t - \frac{\Delta P}{P_i}\,(1 + 0.8\, C_t)\right] \qquad (10.4.14)$$

The term $\Delta_i^p C_t$ is the time-dependent deflection assuming that the prestressing force is constant and equal to P_i. The second term in the square bracket is due to the prestress loss ΔP as defined by Eq. 10.4.11. Equation 10.4.14 includes the effect of shrinkage on deflection. The general case with multiple layers of steel is discussed in References 10.1 and 10.2.

The calculation of the deflection due to prestress by using the effective prestress leads to less accurate results, which may, however, still be acceptable considering the uncertainty of the values of creep and shrinkage.

Cracked members

Partially prestressed members are designed so that cracking may be expected under full specified loads. The deflection may be calculated by using an effective moment of inertia of the cracked section or a bilinear moment-curvature diagram. Such a diagram may be established using the information given in Section 10.5, in Fig. 10.7 for rectangular sections and in Figs. 10.8.1 to 10.8.16 for T-beams, or in Table 10.2.

The effective moment of inertia for a cracked prestressed concrete beam is expressed by the relation:

$$I_e = I_{cr} + (I_{tr} - I_{cr}) \left(\frac{M_{cr}}{M_s - M_{dc}}\right)^3 \le I_g \qquad (10.4.15)$$

where M_{cr} = $f_r\, I_{tr}/y_{tr}$ $\qquad (10.4.16)$

M_{dc} = $f_{pd}\, I_{tr}/y_{tr}$ $\qquad (10.4.17)$

In these equations

I_{cr} = moment of inertia of cracked section

I_{tr} = moment of inertia of the uncracked transformed section, or less accurately of the gross section

y_{tr} = distance to extreme tension fibre from centroid of uncracked transformed section

f_{pd} = concrete stress due to effective prestress at the extreme fibre where tensile stresses are caused by applied loads (negative value)

M_s = maximum moment due to specified loads

In continuous structures the average value of I_e has to be established. This is discussed in Chapter 6.

Further details about the calculation of deflections of partially prestressed members are found in Ref. 10.4.

10.5 PARTIALLY PRESTRESSED MEMBERS

In many prestressed concrete structures it is not likely that the full specified load will be applied during the lifetime of the structure. It is therefore possible to design the structural members so that some cracking will occur under full specified load if it should be applied. Under the dead load, however, cracking should normally not occur.

The advantages of partial prestressing are:

— A reduction of camber

— A reduction in prestress force which may allow an increase of the tendon eccentricity

— Reduction of cracking in the end zones of post-tensioned structures

— A reduction in relaxation loss where partial prestressing is achieved by a lower stress in the tendon.

Partial prestressing may be achieved in different ways:

(1) By providing non-prestressed steel in addition to the prestressing tendons. This would normally occur in post-tensioned construction.

(2) By reducing the effective prestress below the maximum allowable stress and relying on the increase in tendon stress after decompression and cracking to resist the increase in moment. This is a useful option in pretensioned construction because of difficulties in placing non-prestressed steel.

In order to assure that the cracks developing in a partially prestressed member are within acceptable limits, crack width criteria similar to those for reinforced concrete have to be satisfied.

For the calculation of the quantity z the same equation (Eq. 10-6 in the Code) as for reinforced concrete members has been adopted. In this equation, the steel stress f_s is the increase in stress in the reinforcing or prestressing steel beyond the state of decompression.

The steel stress increase f_s may be calculated as the stress corresponding to the difference between the moment due to specified loads M_s and the decompression moment M_{dc} according to:

$$f_s = \frac{M_s - M_{dc}}{(A_p + A_s) d} \qquad (10.5.1)$$

The decompression moment M_{dc} is the moment which reduces the compressive stress on the tensile face of a prestressed member to zero. It should be emphasized that the decompression moment does not correspond to the state of decompression of the whole section. Complete decompression requires the removal of the bending moment due to applied loads and the application of the fictitious decompression force, P, to be discussed shortly.

Equation 10.5.1 gives reasonable results for most members, but for members with a small value of ρ it is normally conservative. For this reason a more detailed method of calculating f_s is presented here (see Ref. 10.5).

The rigorous calculation of f_s for a given moment M_s is complicated by the following facts: first, we have to deal with a cracked section subjected to an axial force and a bending moment; second, creep and shrinkage of the concrete put the non-prestressed steel in compression and thus reduce the compression in the precompressed tension fibres. The reference point for the determination of f_s, is zero stress in the concrete section. The following fictitious decompression force would create zero stress throughout the concrete section:

$$P = P_e + \Delta P_p + P_s + \Delta P_s \qquad (10.5.2)$$

where P_e = effective prestress (after all losses)

ΔP_p = $\dfrac{-f_c}{E_c} E_p A_p$

= force in tendons corresponding to the concrete stress f_c at the level of the tendon under dead load and effective prestress

P_s = force in the non-prestressed steel due to time-dependent strain in the non-prestressed steel

ΔP_s = $\dfrac{-f_c}{E_c} E_s A_s$

= force in non-prestressed steel corresponding to the concrete stress f_c at the level of the non-prestressed steel under dead load and effective prestress.

It is to be noted that concrete stress f_c is negative when compressive, and that the forces ΔP_p and ΔP_s are normally small and may be neglected.

The effective prestress $P_e = A_p(f_{pi} - \Delta f_p)$, where f_{pi} is the initial prestress and Δf_p is calculated according to Eq.10.4.9.

The time-dependent force in the nonprestressed steel

$$P_s = A_s \Delta f_s \qquad (10.5.3)$$

where Δf_s is defined by Eq. 10.4.10.

With the decompression force P known, the steel stress under specified load is equal to n times the concrete stress at the level of the steel:

$$f_s = \left(\frac{P}{A_{cr}} + \frac{P e_{cr} + M_s}{I_{cr}} y_{cr}\right) n \qquad (10.5.4)$$

In this equation the terms with subscript "cr" refer to the cracked section. The parameter y_{cr} is the distance of the steel considered from the centroid of the cracked section, and n is the modular ratio for the steel considered (i.e. n_s or n_p).

Cracked section properties

The cracked section properties for a given section are dependent on the decompression force P and the moment M_s due to specified loads.

The calculation of the cracked section properties involves the determination of the neutral axis depth, c, the centroidal depth of the section, y_{cr}, the area, A_{cr}, and the moment of inertia I_{cr}. With the notation and the forces of Fig. 10.6 we have to solve the following cubic equation in c for the general case of a T-section[10.5]

$$\frac{1}{3}Pc^3 - \frac{1}{2}[M_s - P(d_p - c)]bc^2 + [n_s A_s (d_s - c)^2$$

$$+ n_p A_p (d_p - c)^2]P + [n_s A_s (d_s - c) + n_p A_p (d_p - c)]$$

$$\times [M_s - P(d_p - c)] - \frac{1}{3}P(b - b_w)(c - h_f)^3$$

$$+ \frac{1}{2}(b - b_w)(c - h_f)^2 [M_s - P(d_p - c)] = 0$$

$$(10.5.5)$$

The centroidal depth, area and moment of inertia of the cracked section are, respectively:

$$y_{cr} = \frac{\frac{1}{2}(b - b_w)h_f^2 + \frac{1}{2}b_w c^2 + n_s A_s d_s + n_p A_p d_p}{(b - b_w)h_f + b_w c + n_s A_s + n_p A_p} \quad (10.5.6)$$

$$A_{cr} = b_w c + (b - b_w)h_f + n_s A_s + n_p A_p \quad (10.5.7)$$

$$I_{cr} = \frac{1}{12}[h_f^3(b - b_w) + b_w c^3]$$

$$+ [(y_{cr} - \frac{h_f}{2})^2(b - b_w)h_f] + (y_{cr} - \frac{c}{2})^2 b_w c$$

$$+ (d_s - y_{cr})^2 n_s A_s + (d_p - y_{cr})^2 n_p A_p \quad (10.5.8)$$

For rectangular sections $b = b_w$, so that Eqs. 10.5.5 to 10.5.8 simplify to:

$$\frac{1}{3}Pc^3 - \frac{1}{2}[M_s - P(d_p - c)]bc^2 + [n_s A_s (d_s - c)^2$$

$$+ n_p A_p (d_p - c)^2]P + [n_s A_s (d_s - c)$$

$$+ n_p A_p (d_p - c)] \times [M_s - P(d_p - c)] = 0 \quad (10.5.9)$$

$$y_{cr} = \frac{\frac{1}{2}bc^2 + n_s A_s d_s + n_p A_p d_p}{bc + n_s A_s + n_p A_p} \quad (10.5.10)$$

$$A_{cr} = bc + n_s A_s + n_p A_p \quad (10.5.11)$$

$$I_{cr} = \frac{1}{12}bc^3 + (y_{cr} - \frac{c}{2})^2 bc + (d_s - y_{cr})^2 n_s A_s$$

$$+ (d_p - y_{cr})^2 n_p A_p \quad (10.5.12)$$

Assuming $(A_s + A_p)$ to be located at

$$d = \frac{A_s E_s d_s + A_p E_p d_p}{A_s E_s + A_p E_p} \quad (10.5.13)$$

and introducing the parameters

$$k = c/d \qquad \alpha_b = b_w/b$$

$$p = P d_p / M_s \qquad \alpha_f = h_f/d$$

$$n\rho = \frac{A_s E_s + A_p E_p}{E_c bd} \quad (10.5.14)$$

the neutral axis depth coefficients for T-Sections and rectangular sections, respectively, can be expressed by

$$k^3 p - 3k^2(p - 1) - 6n\rho(1 - k) - (1 - \alpha_b)(k - \alpha_f)^2$$

$$\times (kp + 2p\alpha_f - 3p + 3) = 0 \quad (10.5.15)$$

$$k^3 p - 3k^2(p - 1) - 6n\rho(1 - k) = 0 \quad (10.5.16)$$

Knowing k, the section properties can be determined and the steel stress f_s, calculated using Eq. 10.5.4. To facilitate determination of f_s, Figures 10.7 and 10.8.1 to 10.8.16 have been established expressing f_s in the nondimensional form $f_s/(n\alpha)$ as a function of $n\rho$ for different values of p. The term n is the modular ratio and

$$\alpha = \frac{M_s}{bd^2} \quad (10.5.17)$$

If the two steels are not located at the same level, the stress in the non-prestressed steel is:

$$f_{ns} = f_s \frac{d_s - kd}{d(1 - k)} \quad (10.5.18)$$

The use of the design charts is demonstrated in Examples 10.6 and 10.10.

10.6 FACTORED FLEXURAL RESISTANCE

10.6.1 Introduction

The factored flexural resistance of an element must be greater than the moment due to factored load

$$M_r \geq M_f$$

The factored flexural resistance can be determined for any section using procedures which take into account equilibrium and strain compatibility. For many sections a satisfactory approximate solution can be obtained by using the Equations (18-1) and (18-2) to determine the stress in the tendons at factored resistance. Equations 18-1 and 18-2 differ slightly from those used in the CSA Standard A23.3-M84.

Figure 10.1 provides typical stress-strain curves for strand types in common use in Canada, and Figs. 1.3 and 1.4 provide sizes, and properties for strand, wire and deformed prestressing bars.

Typical concrete strengths for prestressed concrete members range from 30 to 50 MPa. Release strengths f_{ci}' will generally be in the range from 20 to 30 MPa.

10.6.2 Analysis of Section Reinforced with Bonded Tendons and Nonprestressed Steel

Provided $f_{pe} > 0.6 f_{py}$ and c/d_p is not greater than 0.5, the stress in the prestressing tendons at factored resistance, f_{pr}, may be found from the approximate equation given in Clause 18.7:

$$f_{pr} = f_{pu}[1 - k_p(c/d_p)] \quad (18-1)$$

where

$$k_p = 2(1.04 - f_{py}/f_{pu})$$

The term k_p accounts for the different shapes of the stress-strain curves for the different types of prestressing steel and values of f_{py}/f_{pu} for typical prestressing steels are given in Clause 18.5 of A23.3.

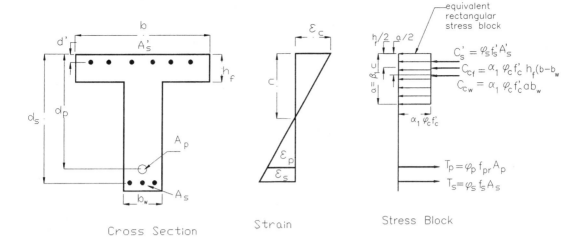

Fig. 10.0

The term c/d_p in Eq. 18-1 may be found from a consideration of the conditions in a section at factored resistance. The above figure shows the strain distribution and related stress block for a T-section containing prestressed and non-prestressed tensile reinforcement, as well as non-prestressed compression reinforcement. Equilibrium of forces in the section requires

$$\phi_s A'_s f'_s + \alpha_1 \phi_c f'_c h_f (b - b_w) + \alpha_1 \phi_c f'_c a b_w$$

$$= \phi_p A_p f_{pr} + \phi_s A_s f_s$$

Substituting for f_{pr} from Eqn. 18-1, setting $a = \beta_1 c$ and rearranging gives

$$\frac{c}{d_p} = \frac{\phi_p A_p f_{pu} + \phi_s A_s f_s - \phi_s A'_s f'_s - \alpha_1 \phi_c f'_c h_f (b - b_w)}{\alpha_1 \phi_c f'_c \beta_1 b_w d_p + \phi_p k_p A_p f_{pu}}$$

The depth of the equivalent rectangular stress block may be found from the above figure in a similar manner and is given by:

$$a = \frac{\phi_p A_p f_{pr} + \phi_s A_s f_s - \phi_s A'_s f'_s - \alpha_1 \phi_c f'_c h_f (b - b_w)}{\alpha_1 \phi_c f'_c b_w}$$

and the factored resistance is

$$M_r = \phi_p A_p f_{pr} (d_p - a/2) + \phi_s A_s f_s (d_s - a/2)$$

$$- \phi_s A'_s f'_s (d' - a/2)$$

$$- \alpha_1 \phi_c f'_c h_f (b - b_w) \left(\frac{h_f}{2} - \frac{a}{2}\right)$$

The stresses f_s and f'_s will generally be equal to f_y and f'_y, respectively. If the strain at the level of the reinforcing steel is less than the yield strain a strain compatibility analysis will be needed to establish these stresses.

The above is the most general formulation. All of the simpler cases can be determined by eliminating the redundant terms. If $a \le h_f$ the section should be treated as a rectangular section for which $b_w = b$.

A step-by-step analysis of a section using both the code equation and strain compatibility to determine f_{pr} is illustrated in Example 10.1. In this example the stress-strain curve for Grade 1860 low-relaxation strand of Fig. 10.1 is used.

10.6.3 Minimum Factored Flexural Resistance

Based on Clause 18.8.1 flexural members (except 2-way slabs) must be designed so that

$$M_r \ge 1.2 M_{cr}$$

unless

$$M_r \ge 1.33 M_f$$

The cracking moment M_{cr} is given by:

$$M_{cr} = -P_e (e + S/A_c) + f_r S$$

where

P_e	=	effective prestress force after losses
e	=	eccentricity of tendon
A_c	=	area of concrete cross section
f_r	=	modulus of rupture = $0.6\lambda\sqrt{f'_c}$ MPa
S	=	section modulus for tension fibre

It should be noted that P_e is a compressive force on the concrete and should be taken as negative in calculating M_{cr}.

10.6.4 Design Tables

Tables 10.1(a) and (b) provide a simple way of quickly estimating the capacity of a given section or establishing the required size of a design section. The tables include the values of k_p for common prestressing steels, as well as α_1 and β_1 for concrete strengths ranging from 30 to 80 MPa.

It should be noted that $\phi_c = 0.60$ has been assumed in Table 10.1(a). However, Clause 16.1.3 permits a value of $\phi_c = 0.65$ to be used for precast elements manufactured in certified plants, and so $\phi_c = 0.65$ has been assumed in Table 10.1(b).

The use of Table 10.1(b) is illustrated in Example 10.4.

10.6.5 Over-Reinforced Sections with Bonded Tendons

It is generally not economical to design over-reinforced beams. These will occur only in rare instances when for some reason more reinforcement than desired must be used.

In over-reinforced sections c/d_p will generally be greater than 0.5 and the approximate equation for f_{pr} cannot be used. However, although the approximate equation can still be used to provide a starting point for an iterative strain-compatibility and equilibrium analysis.

10.6.6 Analysis of Section with Unbonded Tendons

Equation (18-2) differs from that used in CSA Standard A23.3-M84 in that the term $5000/\ell_e$ has been changed to $8000/\ell_e$. This change has been made so that the values of f_{pr} more accurately reflect those obtained from tests.

The approximate equation prescribed by Clause 18.7.2 of the standard is the following:

$$f_{pr} = f_{pe} + \frac{8000}{\ell_e}(d_p - c_y)$$

$$f_{pr} \le f_{py} \tag{18-2}$$

where

$$c_y = \frac{\phi_p A_p f_{py} + \phi_s A_s f_s - \phi_s A'_s f'_s - \alpha_1 \phi_c f'_c h_f (b - b_w)}{\alpha_1 \phi_c \beta_1 f'_c b_w}$$

and ℓ_e = length of tendon between anchors divided by the number of hinges required to develop a failure mechanism in the span under consideration. The definition of ℓ_e is illustrated in Fig. N18.7.2(b) of the Explanatory Notes.

This equation emphasizes the importance of making a realistic assessment of the number of plastic hinges which would have to develop before the particular span under consideration would collapse. For continuous beams where $(d_p - c_y)$ may be different for the positive and negative regions it is reasonable to use the average value.

The analysis of a section with unbonded tendons is illustrated in Examples 10.2 and 10.9.

10.6.7 Prestressed Members Subjected to Flexure and Axial Load

The design of these members is usually carried out by choosing a section and the reinforcing, and then calculating a sufficient number of points on an interaction diagram to establish whether the design is adequate.

The procedure can most easily be illustrated by a sample calculation as indicated in Example 10.3. The easiest approach is to assume a series of neutral axis locations with the strain of 0.0035 at the extreme compression fibre and to then determine the corresponding values of P_r and M_r.

10.7 FACTORED SHEAR RESISTANCE

In the Simplified Method for shear design, the shear resisted by concrete is either controlled by flexure shear cracking, expressed by Eq. (11-8), or by web shear cracking, Eq. (11-10). The shear force due to prestressing is not to be taken into account when using Eq. (11-8). While the effect of prestress is indirectly incorporated in Eq. (11-8) in the term M_{cr}, it enters Eq. (11-10) in two forms, the average effective prestress, f_{cp}, and the shear force due to prestressing, V_p.

The application of the General Method to shear design of reinforced concrete members is explained in detail in Chapter 4. For this reason only the differences between non-prestressed and prestressed concrete members with regard to shear design are discussed here.

First, the shear force due to prestressing, V_p, is included in the shear stress due to applied loads, Eq. (11-21). Second, due to prestressing, the longitudinal strain,

ε_x in the reinforcement is affected by the prestressing force $A_p f_{po}$ in the numerator of Eq. (11-22) and by the term $E_p A_p$ in the denominator of the same equation. The stress f_{po} represents the stress in the prestressing tendons at decompression, which is here defined as the tendon stress when the stress in the sourrounding concrete is zero. In lieu of detailed calculations, f_{po} may be taken as 1.1 times the effective stress f_{pe} in the tendon. As for reinforced concrete ε_x need not be taken as greater than 0.002.

10.8 PRESTRESSED CONCRETE SLABS

10.8.1 General

In Chapter 5 the analysis and design of reinforced concrete slabs is discussed in detail. In this section only those aspects of the design of prestressed slabs which are different from reinforced slabs will be discussed. Only unbonded slabs are considered here. The design of slabs with bonded tendons is similar, except for the calculation of the flexural resistance, where f_{pr} is calculated using Code Eq. (18-1), and for the requirements for bonded steel (see Code Table 18-1).

While the design of reinforced concrete slabs is done only for factored loads, prestressed slabs, if fully prestressed, also have to satisfy the permissible stress criteria of Clause 18.4.2, or if partially prestressed the crack control criteria under specified loads as given in Clause 18.9.3.

10.8.2 One-Way Slabs

The design of a one-way prestressed slab is essentially the design of a wide beam. The only difference is the required amount of transverse nonprestressed steel, which is normally governed by the minimum requirements of Clause 7.8. The thickness of continuous one-way slabs may be taken as $\ell/40$ to $\ell/50$, with the lower value being recommended for partially prestressed slabs.

The analysis of one-way slabs subjected to uniform loading is efficiently done by the load balancing method whereby a certain fraction of the dead load is balanced by the upward load caused by prestressing. For normal live loads about 75 to 85 percent of the dead load needs to be balanced if no cracks are allowed (i.e. satisfying Clause 18.4.2b). For partially prestressed slabs only about 60 percent of the dead load needs to be balanced.

For a parabolic tendon profile, the load balanced by the effective prestress

$$w_{bal} = \frac{8 P_e s}{\ell^2} \tag{10.8.1}$$

where

P_e = effective prestress after all losses (normally per metre width)

s = sag of tendon

ℓ = length of span measured centre-to-centre of supports

The combination of balanced load and prestressing force result in zero flexural stress so that only an axial stress P_e/A_c, is present, where A_c is the cross-sectional area of the slab per metre width. Bending moments are caused only by the net load

$$w_{net} = w_s - w_{bal} \tag{10.8.2}$$

where w_s = specified load (dead load plus live load).

CPCA Concrete Design Handbook

The moments due to w_{net} are determined by established methods of structural analysis.

If the flexural tensile stresses exceed the value permitted in Clause 18.4.2(c), the criteria of Clause 18.13.5 have to be satisfied.

10.8.3 Two-Way Slabs

Slab Thickness

Prestressed slabs can be considerably more slender than non-prestressed slabs. The thickness h may range, between $\ell/40$ to $\ell/50$ with $\ell/45$ being a frequently used value. Because of the smaller thickness, punching shear becomes more critical, particularly at exterior columns. Small capitals or shear reinforcement may be provided to increase the shear resistance locally if it is not desireable to increase the overall slab thickness or to provide an edge beam.

Analysis

One of the major differences between the design of reinforced and prestressed two-way slabs is that only the procedures of Clause 13.9, or more detailed methods of analysis, can be used for the analysis of a prestressed slab. The approach outlined in Clause 13.9.2 was formerly called the "Equivalent Frame Method" and involves non-prismatic modelling of member stiffnesses. The "Prismatic Modelling Method" described in Clause 13.9.3 is simpler as it uses a simple equation for the reduced column stiffness.

Examples 10.9 and 10.10, respectively, illustrate the design of a fully prestressed slab and a partially prestressed slab. The load balancing concept, together with the Prismatic Modelling Method, is used in the analysis. For slabs without rigid beams or supports, 75 to 90 percent of the dead load is balanced by the effective prestress (in each direction). These percentages apply to slabs in which no cracks are expected to develop under full specified load. For partially prestressed slabs it is normally adequate to balance 60 to 70 percent of the slab dead load.

Calculation of Flexural Stress

The flexural stresses are calculated for the moments due to net (unbalanced) loads. The positive and negative moments, determined according to the methods of Clause 13.9 for the full width of the slab strip (width ℓ_2), shall be assigned to column strip according to Clause 18.13.2.1. This clause specifies that 75% of the interior negative moment, 100% of the exterior negative moment and 60% of the positive moment shall be taken by the column strip, unless a more detailed analysis is made. This requirement will assure that the moments due to the load not balanced by prestressing are assessed realistically and that the calculated flexural stresses are realistic values.

The axial stress, however, is more or less uniformly distributed across the width of the panel, particularly at the interior supports (see Clause 18.13.2.2).

If the flexural stress exceeds the value permitted in Clause 18.4.2(c), cracking is expected to occur and the crack control criteria of Clause 18.9.3 have to be satisfied.

Factored Moment

In continuous structural systems prestressing introduces secondary moments. These secondary moments are added to the moments due to factored loads such that

$$M_f = \alpha_D M_D + \alpha_L M_L + \alpha_p M_p'' \qquad (10.8.3)$$

In this equation: α_D and α_L are the load factors for dead load and live load, respectively, M_D and M_L are the moments due to specified dead and live loads, respectively, M_p'' is the secondary moment due to prestressing and α_p is the load factor for secondary moments. According to Clause 18.11 $\alpha_p = 1.0$.

The moments due to factored loads may be determined at the face of the column. The flexural resistance of the cross section is calculated according to Clause 18.7.

Minimum Reinforcement

In prestressed two-way slabs, minimum bonded reinforcement has to be provided in accordance with Clause 18.13.5 and Table 18-1.

Shear

The shear strength of reinforced concrete slabs is discussed in detail in Chapter 5. In prestressed concrete the beneficial effect of the axial stress $f_{cp} = P_e/A_c$ and the vertical component of the prestressing force at the critical section, V_p, increase the shear resistance of the concrete, V_c, considerably. According to Clause 18.13.3.2 the shear stress resistance of the concrete is given by Eq. 18-5 in the Code as:

$$v_c = 0.4\lambda\phi_c\sqrt{f_c'}\,(1 + \frac{\phi_p f_{cp}}{0.4\lambda\phi_c\sqrt{f_c'}})^{1/2} + \frac{\phi_p V_p}{b_o d} \quad (10.8.4)$$

However, the beneficial effect of prestressing can only be counted on if (a) no portion of the column cross section is closer to a discontinuous edge than 4 times the slab thickness, (b) the strength of the slab concrete is not taken greater than 35 MPa and (c) f_{cp} in Eq.10.8.4 shall not exceed 3.5 MPa.

Shear reinforcement consisting of stirrups or headed bars may be used to increase the shear resistance. The design of shear reinforcement consisting of headed bars with anchor plates, referred to in Clause 13.4.7, is discussed in some detail in the following section. The design of this reinforcement is described in detail in References 10.6 and 10.7.

Headed shear reinforcement

When headed shear reinforcement is used, anchor plates having an area of at least 10 times the cross-sectional area of the studs have to be provided.

The design of the headed shear reinforcement is based on a shear stress resistance of the concrete of

$$v_c = 0.3\lambda\phi_c\sqrt{f_c'} \qquad (10.8.5)$$

The required area of headed shear reinforcement of one headed vertical bar along the critical section

$$A_v = \frac{(v_f - v_c)\,s_1\,s}{\phi_s\,f_{yv}} \qquad (10.8.6)$$

where

    s = spacing between rows of rods measured perpendicular to the column face.

    s_1 = length of critical section considered divided by rows of headed bars.

The shear reinforcement shall extend to a distance away from the column face so that the shear stress v_f at a distance $d/2$ from the outermost row of shear reinforcement does not exceed v_c of Eq. 10.8.5. The spacing requirements for the headed shear reinforcement are specified in Clause 13.4.8.6. The upper limit on the shear stress resistance of a slab with headed studs is $0.8\lambda\phi_c\sqrt{f'_c}$.

Normal closed stirrups are only allowed if the slab thickness is at least 300 mm. The design of the shear reinforcement is based on a shear stress resistance of the concrete of

$$v_c = 0.2\lambda\phi_c\sqrt{f'_c} \tag{10.8.7}$$

The design equation for A_v is given by Eq. 10.8.6, and the extension of the shear reinforcement, is the same as for headed shear reinforcement. The upper limit on the shear stress resistance of slabs with stirrups is $0.6\lambda\phi_c\sqrt{f'_c}$.

Structural Integrity

Progressive collapse may develop as a result of a local slab failure caused by punching if there is no mechanism provided to suspend the slab at the point of punching failure. According to Ref. 10.8, an effective mechanism to prevent progressive collapse is the membrane type action provided by draped tendons passing through the columns or reaction areas. In general two tendons in each direction over the column will be sufficient to satisfy the provisions of CSA Standard A23.3 (Clauses 18.13.6.3 and 13.11.5). These requirements are expressed by the following equation (c.f. Eq. 13-19 of the Standard).

$$\Sigma A_{sb} \geq \frac{2 V_{se}}{f_{py}} \tag{10.8.8}$$

where

A_{sb} = area of prestressing steel crossing through one face of the periphery of a column

V_{se} = shear transmitted to column or column capital as defined by Eq. 10.8.9

f_{py} = yield strength of tendon (see Table N18.5 in the Explanatory Notes)

and

$$V_{se} = w_s [\ell_{1a}\,\ell_{2a} - c_1\,c_2] \tag{10.8.9}$$

In this equation

w_s = total specified load but not less than twice the self-weight of the slab

ℓ_{1a} = average length for spans adjacent to a column

ℓ_{2a} = average length of span transverse to ℓ_1

c_1 = size of rectangular or equivalent rectangular, support area of slab

c_2 = size of rectangular or equivalent rectangular support area transverse to c_1

Partial Prestressing

For partially prestressed beams, one-way slabs and two-way slabs on stiff supports, the determination of the parameters needed for the calculation of the stress f_s in Eq. 10-6 of CSA Standard A23.3 is straightforward. For flat slabs and flat plates, these parameters need some discussion.

To determine the necessary parameters it is best to consider a one metre width of the column strip. For this strip the following terms are defined:

M_s: the moment due to specified load equal to 75% of the total negative moment at the face of the column, divided by the width of the column strip.

P, P_e: the decompression force and the effective prestressing force are the total force in the panel (in one direction) divided by the width of the panel, ℓ_2.

A_s: area of the non-prestressed steel in the column strip (in one direction) divided by the width of the column strip.

A_p: total area of the prestressing steel divided by the width of the panel, ℓ_2. If the tendons are unbonded, A_p should not be considered in Eqs. 10.5.13 and 10.5.14

For flat slabs with unbonded tendons, Eq. 10.5.1 simplifies to

$$f_s = \frac{M_{net} - P_e\,(h/6 + e)}{A_s\,d} \tag{10.8.10}$$

where

M_{net} = 75% of the total panel moment due to net load, at face of support, divided by the width of the column strip.

P_e, A_s = as defined above

h = slab thickness

d = effective slab depth.

e = tendon eccentricity

See Example 10.10. Note: M_{net}, P_e and e are positive in Eq. 10.8.10

10.9 COMPOSITE FLEXURAL MEMBERS

The general requirements for composite flexural members are provided in Clause 17 and it is implicit in this clause that both the strength and serviceability limit states have to be satisified.

It is generally considered more economical to place the topping without additional shoring. Hence, the mass of the cast-in-place concrete must be carried by the precast member alone and the strength of the system must be evaluated for both the non-composite and composite sections.

Besides an analysis of the deflections at the various loading stages, serviceability checks should also be carried out considering the time-dependent prestress losses (relaxation, creep and shrinkage) from the time of transfer. As previously discussed, the losses will not significantly affect strength but should be investigated to obtain an assessment of immediate and long-term camber or deflection.

10.10 REFERENCES

10.1 Neville, A M., Dilger, W.H. and Brooks, J.J., "Creep of Plain and Structural Concrete", Longman 1983, 392 pp.

10.2 Dilger, W.H., "Creep Analysis of Prestressed Concrete Members Using Creep-Transformed Section Properties", PCI Journal, Vol. 27, No. 1, Jan.-Feb.1982, pp. 98-118.

10.3 Bazant, Z., "Prediction of Concrete Creep Using Age-Adjusted Effective Modulus Method", ACI Journal 69, 1972, pp. 212-17.

10.4 Branson, D.E. and Trost, H., "Application of the I-Effective Method in Calculating Deflections of Partially Prestressed Members", PCI Journal, Vol. 27, No.5, Sept.-Oct., 1982, pp. 62-77.

10.5 Dilger, W.H., and Suri, K.M., "Steel Stresses in Partially Prestressed Concrete Flexural Members", PCI Journal, Vol. 31, No. 3, May - June, 1986, pp 88-113.

10.6 Dilger, W.H. and Ghali, A., "Shear Reinforcement for Concrete Slabs", ASCE Journal, Vol. 107, No. ST12, Dec. 1981, pp. 2903-2920.

10.7 Ghali, A. and Elgabry, A., "Design of Stud - Shear Reinforcement for Slabs", ACI Structural Journal, V. 87, No. 3, May - June, 1990.

10.8 Mitchell, D. and Cook, W.D., "Preventing Progressive Collapse of Slab Structures", ASCE Journal, Vol.110, No.7, July 1984, pp. 1513-1532.

EXAMPLE 10.1
Flexural Resistance with Bonded Prestressed Steel

Concrete: $f_c' = 40$ MPa, $E_c = 4500 \sqrt{40} = 28,460$ MPa

Section Properties: $A_c = 0.2 \times 0.6 + 0.6 \times 0.2 = 0.240$ m^2

$$y_b = \frac{0.12 \times 0.3 + 0.12 \times 0.7}{0.240} = 0.500 \text{ m}$$

$$e = 0.35 \text{ m}$$

$$I_c = \frac{0.2 \times 0.6^3}{12} + \frac{0.6 \times 0.2^3}{12}$$

$$+ 0.12 \times 0.2^2 + 0.12 \times 0.2^2 = 0.0136 \text{ m}^4$$

$$\beta_1 = 0.97 - 0.0025 f_c' = 0.87 > 0.67$$

$$\alpha_1 = 0.85 - 0.0015 f_c' = 0.79 > 0.67$$

$$k_p = 2(1.04 - 0.9) = 0.28$$

$$\alpha_1 \phi_c f_c' = 0.79 \times 0.6 \times 40 = 18.96$$

$$c/d_p = \frac{\phi_p A_p f_{pu} + \phi_s A_s f_y - \phi_s A_s' f_y' - \alpha_1 \phi_c f_c' h_f (b - b_w)}{\alpha_1 \phi_c f_c' \beta_1 b_w d_p + \phi_p k_p A_p f_{pu}}$$

$$\phi_s A_s f_y = 0.85 \times 2000 \times 10^{-6} \times 400 = 0.680 \text{ MN}$$

$$\phi_s A_s' f_y' = 0.85 \times 800 \times 10^{-6} \times 400 = 0.272 \text{ MN}$$

$$\alpha_1 \phi_c f_c' h_f (b - b_w) = 18.96 \times 0.2 \times 0.4 = 1.517 \text{ MN}$$

$$c/d_p = \frac{0.9 \times 1386 \times 10^{-6} \times 1860 + 0.680 - 0.272 - 1.517}{18.96 \times 0.87 \times 0.2 \times 0.65 + 0.28 \times 2.320}$$

$$= \frac{2.320 - 1.109}{3.299 \times 0.65 + 0.650} = 0.433$$

as $c/d_p \not> 0.5$ Eqn. (18-1) may be used giving

$$f_{pr} = f_{pu} (1 - k_p c/d_p) = 1860 (1 - 0.28 \times 0.433)$$
$$= 1634 \text{ MPa}$$

Although the code equation may be used in this case to compute f_{pr}, the strain compatibility approach in computing f_{pr} is presented for completeness.

Use code equation for the first iteration

$$\phi_p A_p f_{pr} = 0.9 \times 1386 \times 10^{-6} \times 1634 = 2.038 \text{ MN}$$

$$c = \frac{\phi_s A_p f_{pr} + \phi_s A_s f_s - \phi_s A_s' f_s' - \alpha_1 \phi_c f_c' h_f (b - b_w)}{\alpha_1 \phi_c f_c' \beta_1 b_w}$$

$$= \frac{2.038 - 1.109}{3.299} = 0.282 \text{ m}$$

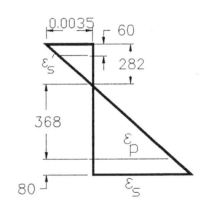

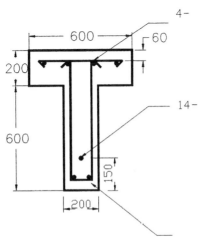

Compression steel:
No. 15 bars, $f_y = 400$ MPa
$A_s' = 4 \times 200 = 800$ mm^2, $d' = 60$ mm

Prestressing steel:
(low relaxation)
Size 13 strands (bonded)
$f_{pu} = 1860$ MPa
$A_p = 14 \times 99 = 1386$ mm^2
$E_p = 190,000$ MPa
$d_p = 650$ mm

Non-prestressed steel:
No. 35 bars, $f_y = 400$ MPa
$A_s = 2 \times 1000 = 2000$ mm^2
$d_s = 730$ mm, $E_s = 200,000$ MPa

$\varepsilon'_s = 0.0035(282-60)/282 = 0.00276$

$\varepsilon'_y = 400/200,000 = 0.0020$

compression steel yields

$\varepsilon_s = 0.0035 \times 448/282 = 0.00556$

tension steel yields

$\varepsilon_p = 0.0035 \times 368/282 = 0.00457$

The prestressing steel has an additional prestrain corresponding to the elastic strain in the steel when the concrete stress is zero at the level of the tendon.

Assume $f_{pe} = 0.6 f_{pu} = 1116$ MPa,

$$f_{ce} = P_e \left(\frac{1}{A_c} + \frac{e^2}{I_c}\right) + \frac{M_D}{I_c} e$$

$$- -1386 \times 10^{-6} \times 1116 \left(\frac{1}{0.240} + \frac{0.35^2}{0.0136}\right)$$

Note that a dead load moment of 500 kN·m has been assumed in computing f_{ce}.

$$= -7.5 \text{ MPa}$$

$$\varepsilon_{ce} = -7.5/28460 = -0.00026$$

$$\varepsilon_{pe} = 0.00587 - (-0.00026) = 0.00613$$

Total strain in prestressing steel = $0.00613 + 0.00457$ = 0.01070

From the stress-strain curve in Fig. 10.1 $f_{pr} = 1735$ MPa

This is higher than the initial estimate of 1634 MPa. The correct value of f_{pr} is bracketed by these values

i.e. $1634 < f_{pr} < 1735$ MPa

Try $f_{pr} = (1634 + 1735)/2 = 1685$ MPa

$$c = \frac{2.038 \times (1685/1634) - 1.109}{3.299} = 0.301 \text{ m}$$

$$\varepsilon_p = 0.0035 \times 348/301 = 0.00405$$

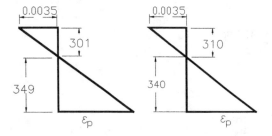

Total strain = $0.00613 + 0.00405 = 0.01018$ and from Fig. 10.1 $f_{pr} = 1710$ MPa

Try $f_{pr} = 1710$ MPa

$$c = \frac{2.038 \times \dfrac{1710}{1634} - 1.109}{3.299}$$

$$= 0.310 \text{ m}$$

$\varepsilon_p = 0.0035 \times 340/310 = 0.000384$

Total strain = $0.00613 + 0.00384 = 0.00997$ and from Fig. 10.1 $f_{pr} = 1710$ MPa. (approx.)

This matches the trial value so that this is the correct solution. Note that the strain compatibility approach gives a higher value of f_{pr} than the code equation.

By inspection it is clear that the strains in the non-prestressed tension and compression steels exceed the yield strains.

$$a/2 = \frac{1}{2} \beta_1 c = \frac{1}{2} \times 0.87 \times 0.310 = 0.135 \text{ m}$$

$$M_r = \phi_p A_p f_{pr}(d_p - a/2) + \phi_s A_s f_y(d - a/2) - \phi_s A'_s f'_y$$

$$\times (d' - a/2) - \alpha_1 \phi_c f'_c h_f (b - b_w) \left(\frac{h_f}{2} - \frac{a}{2}\right)$$

$$\phi_p A_p f_{pr} = 0.9 \times 1386 \times 10^{-6} \times 1710 = 2.133 \text{ MN}$$

$$M_r = 2.133(650 - 135) + 0.68(730 - 135)$$

$$- 0.272(60 - 135) - 1.517(100 - 135)$$

$$M_r = 1576 \text{ kN·m}$$

EXAMPLE 10.2
Flexural Resistance with Unbonded Prestressed Steel

Assume: 10 m span with 400 mm overhangs on each end

$f'_c = 40$ MPa, $\alpha_1 = 0.79$, $\beta_1 = 0.87$

4 – Size 13 low-relaxation strands.

$A_p = 396$ mm^2, $f_{pu} = 1860$ MPa

$d_p = 700$ mm

Assume $f_{pe} = 1100$ MPa

$f_{py} = 0.9 \times 1860 = 1674$ MPa

The centroid of the section is 500 mm from bottom.

The concrete area below the centroid = A = 100,000 mm^2.

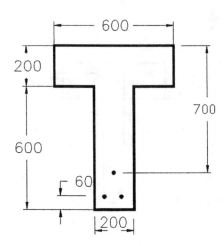

The minimum area of bonded reinforcing (Clause 18.9.1) is $0.004A = 400 \text{ mm}^2$.
Use 2-No. 15 bars.

Assuming that the depth of the stress block is less than 200 mm and that the non-prestressed reinforcement is Grade 400.

$$c_y = \frac{\phi_p A_p f_{py} + \phi_s A_s f_y}{\alpha_1 \phi_c f'_c \beta_1 b}$$

$$= \frac{0.9 \times 396 \times 1674 + 0.85 \times 400 \times 400}{0.79 \times 0.6 \times 40 \times 0.87 \times 600}$$

$$c_y = 74 \text{ mm}$$

For one plastic hinge

$$\ell_e = (10,000 + 2 \times 400)/1.0 = 10800 \text{ mm}$$

$$f_{pr} = f_{pe} + \frac{8000}{10800}(700 - 74)$$

$$f_{pr} = 1100 + 464 = 1564 \text{ MPa} < f_{py}$$

$$M_r = \phi_p A_p f_{pr}(d_p - a/2) + \phi_s A_s f_y(d - a/2)$$

$$a = \frac{\phi_p A_p f_{pr} + \phi_s A_s f_y}{\alpha_1 \phi_c f'_c b}$$

$$= \frac{0.9 \times 396 \times 1564 + 0.85 \times 400 \times 400}{0.79 \times 0.6 \times 40 \times 600}$$

$$a = 61 \text{ mm} < 200 \text{ mm}$$

$$M_r = 0.557(700 - 30.5) + 0.136(740 - 30.5)$$

$$M_r = 372 + 97 = 469 \text{ kN·m}$$

EXAMPLE 10.3
Analysis of Pretensioned Short Column

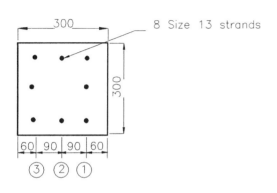

8 Size 13 strands

$$f'_c = 50 \text{ MPa}, \gamma_c = 2400 \text{ kg/m}^3$$

$$E_c = (3300\sqrt{f'_c} + 6900)\left(\frac{\gamma_c}{2300}\right)^{1.5} = 32,230 \text{ MPa}$$

$$\alpha_1 = 0.775, \beta_1 = 0.845, \alpha_1 \phi_c f'_c = 23.25 \text{ MPa}$$

$$A_p = 99 \text{ mm}^2 / \text{strand}$$

$$E_p = 190,000 \text{ MPa}, f_{pe} = 1100 \text{ MPa}$$

Determine prestrain with zero concrete stress

$$\varepsilon_{pe} = 1100/190,000 = 0.00579$$

$$f_c = P/A = \frac{-1100 \times 99 \times 8}{300^2}$$

$$= -9.68 \text{ MPa}$$

$$\varepsilon_{ce} = -9.68/32,230 = -0.00030$$

$$\varepsilon_{pe} - \varepsilon_{ce} = 0.00609$$

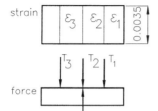

Axial load with zero eccentricity

$$\varepsilon = -0.0035$$

$$\varepsilon_{total} = 0.00609 - 0.0035 = 0.00259$$

$$f_{pr} = 0.00259 \times 190\,000 = 492 \text{ MPa tension}$$

$$C_r = \alpha_1 \phi_c f'_c bc = 23.25 \times 0.3^2$$
$$= 2.093 \text{ MN compression}$$

$$T_1 + T_2 + T_3 = \phi_p A_p f_{pr} = 0.9 \times 8 \times 99 \times 10^{-6} \times 492$$
$$= 0.351 \text{ MN tension}$$

$$P_{ro} = 2.093 - 0.351 = 1.742 \text{ MN compression}$$

$$P_{r(max)} = 0.8 \times 1.742 = 1.394 \text{ MN compression}$$

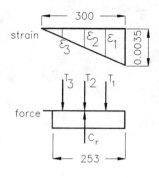

			Consider c = 300 mm, a = 253 mm				
Section	Area mm²	ε_p	ε_{total}	f_{pr} MPa	P_r MN	Moment Arm, mm	M_r KN·m
Conc	76050				+1.768	+23.25	+41.11
1	297	−0.00280	0.00329	625	−0.167	+90	−15.03
2	198	−0.00175	0.00434	825	−0.147	0	0
3	297	−0.00070	0.00539	1024	−0.274	−90	+24.66
					1.180		50.74

$$P_r = 1.180 \text{ MN compression}$$

$$M_r = 50.74 \text{ kN·m}$$

Notes: $\varepsilon_{total} = 0.00609 + \varepsilon_p$

$$P_r = \alpha_1 \phi_c f'_c \ ba - \sum (\phi_p A_p f_{pr})$$

$$M_r = \alpha_1 \phi_c f'_c \ ba \left(\frac{h}{2} - \frac{a}{2}\right) - \sum (\phi_p A_p f_{pr} y)$$

where y = distance from plastic centroid to the force.

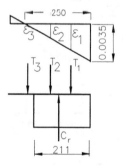

			Consider c = 250 mm, a = 211 mm				
Section	Area	ε_p	ε_{total}	f_{pr}	P_r	Moment Arm	M_r
Conc	76050				+1.473	+44.37	+65.39
1	297	−0.00266	0.00343	652	−0.174	+90	−15.68
2	198	−0.00140	0.00469	891	−0.159	0	0
3	297	−0.00014	0.00595	1130	−0.302	−90	+27.20
					0.838		76.90

P_r = 0.838 MN, M_r = 76.90 kN·m

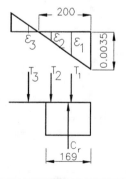

			Consider c = 200 mm, a = 169 mm				
Section	Area	ε_p	ε_{total}	f_{pr}	P_r	Moment Arm	M_r
Conc	50700				+1.179	+65.5	+77.21
1	297	−0.00245	0.00364	692	−0.185	+90	−16.64
2	198	−0.00087	0.00522	991	−0.177	0	0
3	297	0.00070	0.00679	1290	−0.345	−90	+31.03
					0.472		91.61

P_r = 0.472 MN, M_r = 91.61 kN·m

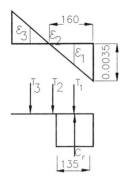

Consider c = 160 mm, a = 135 mm							
Section	Area	ε_p	ε_{total}	f_{pr}	P_r	Moment Arm	M_r
Conc	40560				+0.943	+82.4	+77.70
1	297	−0.00219	+0.00390	741	−0.198	+90	−17.84
2	198	−0.00022	+0.00587	1115	−0.199	0	0
3	297	+0.00175	+0.00784	1490	−0.398	−90	35.84
					0.148		95.70

$P_r = 0.148$ MN, $M_r = 95.70$ kN·m

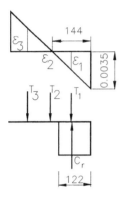

Consider c = 144 mm, a = 122 mm							
Section	Area	ε_p	ε_{total}	f_{pr}	P_r	Moment Arm	M_r
Conc	36504				+0.849	+89.1	+75.67
1	297	−0.00204	0.00405	769	−0.206	+90	−18.50
2	198	0.00015	0.00624	1185	−0.211	0	0
3	297	+0.00233	0.00842	1600	−0.428	−90	+38.50
					+0.004		95.67

$P_r = 0.004$ MN $M_r = 95.67$ kN·m

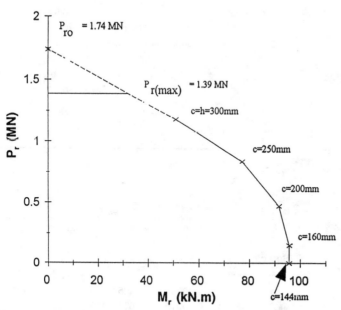

EXAMPLE 10.4
Calculation of A$_p$ and A$_s$ to Resist Factored Loads

Single Tee

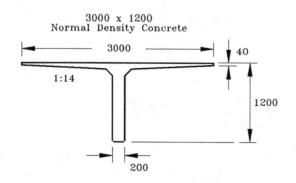

3000 x 1200
Normal Density Concrete

1:14

40

1200

200

Section Properties

A_c = 492,000 mm²
I_c = 66,300 x 10⁶ mm⁴
y_b = 882 mm
y_t = 318 mm
S_b = 75,200 x 10³ mm³
S_t = 208,000 x 10³ mm³
m = 398 kg/m²
w = 3.9 kN/m²
V/S = 60 mm
f'_{ci} = 25 MPa
f'_c = 35 MPa
f_{pu} = 1860 MPa

Given:

Prestressed reinforcement:

All strands to be Grade 1860 low-relaxation and bonded.

A_p = 99 mm²/strand (Size 13 strand)

d_p = 1050 mm

e_c = 1050 – 318 = 732

Non-prestressed reinforcement:

f_y = 400 MPa

A_s = 500 mm²/bar (No. 25)

d_s = 1100 mm

Specified loads:

Dead load = 3.9 kN/m²

Superimposed dead load = 1.5 kN/m²

Live load = 2.0 kN/m²

Span = 27000 mm

Solution:

$$w_f = 3.0 [(1.25 \times 3.9) + (1.25 \times 1.5) + (1.5 \times 2)]$$

$$= 29.25 \text{ kN/m}$$

$$M_f = w_f \ell^2/8 = 29.25 \times 27.0^2/8 = 2665 \text{ kN} \cdot \text{m}$$

$$f_{pr} = f_{pu} (1 - k_p c/d_p)$$

where $k_p = 2(1.04 - f_{py}/f_{pu}) = 0.28$

Assume $a < h_f$ and treat as a rectangular section with A_s and A_p giving

$$c/d_p = \frac{\phi_p A_p f_{pu} + \phi_s A_s f_y}{\alpha_1 \phi_c \beta_1 f'_c b d_p + \phi_p k_p A_p f_{pu}}$$

$$a = \frac{\phi_p A_p f_{pr} + \phi_s A_s f_y}{\alpha_1 \phi_c f'_c b}$$

and $M_r = \phi_p A_p f_{pr} (d_p - a/2) + \phi_s A_s f_y (d - a/2)$

The above equations are valid provided:

$$c/d_p \leq 0.5$$

$$f_{pe} \geq 0.6 f_{py}$$

Now select values of A_s and A_p, and compute f_{pr} and M_r using $\alpha_1 = 0.797$ and $\beta_1 = 0.882$.

The following results were obtained assuming $\phi_c = 0.65$ according to Clause 16.1.3 for elements produced in a certified manufacturing plant.

A_s mm²	No. of strands	A_p mm²	c/d_p	f_{pr} MPa	a mm	M_r kN·m	1.2 M_{cr} kN·m
0	16	1584	0.0518	1833	48	2681	2197
0	18	1782	0.0582	1830	54	3002	2432
1000	14	1386	0.0521	1833	48	2711	1962
1000	16	1584	0.0585	1830	54	3033	2197
2000	12	1188	0.0523	1833	48	2742	1728
2000	14	1386	0.0587	1829	54	3063	1962
3000	12	1188	0.0590	1829	55	3094	1728

Although the effective depth of the compression block, a, is greater than the thickness of the flange at the tip, the precise calculation causes insignificant adjustments to the results.

The results satisfy the basic equations and are all valid solutions with respect to factored flexural resistance since $M_r > M_f$ in each case.

Clause 18.8.1 requires that $M_r \geq 1.2 M_{cr}$, where M_{cr} is the cracking moment based on the modulus of rupture, f_r. At this stage of the design, it is sufficient to make a realistic assessment of the final prestress force, after all losses have occurred. In this example it is assumed that the initial stress in the tendons is 0.75 f_{pu} with losses of 20%.

$$\therefore f_{po} = 0.8 \times 0.75 \times 1860 = 1116 \text{ MPa}$$

and M_{cr} can be calculated from,

$$M_{cr} = (-P/A - Pe/S_b + f_r) S_b$$

where $f_r = 0.6 \lambda \sqrt{f'_c}$ (according to CSA standard A23.3 Eq. 8-8)

Note that P is a compressive force on concrete and should be taken as negative.

Although this design example is concerned with the factored flexural strength of the member, it is customary to design partially prestressed members such that the moment due to sustained loads does not exceed the cracking moment.

The maximum moment due to dead load plus superimposed dead load is 1476 kN·m which is less than M_{cr} for all combinations of A_p and A_s except for the two cases where $A_p = 1188 \text{ mm}^2$ for which $M_{cr} = 1440 \text{ kN} \cdot \text{m}$.

Table 10.1(b) can also be used to determine A_p for a precast member with bonded prestressed reinforcement only.

With $K_u = \dfrac{M_f}{f'_c bd_p^2} = \dfrac{2665 \times 10^6}{35 \times 3000 \times 1050^2} = 0.0230$

from Table 10.1(b) with $k_p = 0.28$ and $f'_c = 35$ MPa:

$$\omega_{pu} = 0.0266$$

$$A_p = \omega_{pu} f'_c b d_p/f_{pu}$$

$$= 0.0266 \times 35 \times 3000 \times 1050/1860$$

$$= 1576 \text{ mm}^2$$

$\therefore$ Provide 16 - Size 13 strands, $A_p = 1584 \text{ mm}^2$

Examples 10.5 and 10.6 investigate the permissible stress requirements of Clauses 18.4.1 and 18.4.2

EXAMPLE 10.5
Calculation of Critical Concrete Stresses to Comply with Clauses 18.4.1 and 18.4.2 (fully prestressed member)

Given:

The data and notation from Example 10.4

Solution:

For an initial estimate of A_p, find A_p required at midspan due to action of all specified loads and assume 20% prestress losses.

Moment due to specified loads

$$M_s = 3.0 (3.9 + 1.5 + 2.0) 27^2/8 = 2023 \text{ kN} \cdot \text{m}$$

In accordance with Clause 18.4.2(c), maximum permissible extreme fibre stress in tension in the precompressed tensile zone (for fully-prestressed member) is $0.5 \lambda \sqrt{f'_c}$ which is 2.96 MPa.

$$\therefore \frac{-P_e}{A_c} + \frac{-P_e e}{S_b} + \frac{M_s}{S_b} \not> 2.96 \text{ MPa}$$

where $A_c = 492,000 \text{ mm}^2$

$e = e_c = 732 \text{ mm}$

$S_b = 75,200 \times 10^3 \text{ mm}^3$

From which, the minimum final prestress force, $P_e = 2035 \text{ kN}$

$\therefore$ Initial prestress force, $P_i = 2035/0.8 = 2543 \text{ kN}$

Initial prestress force/strand $= .75 \times 1860 \times 99 \times 10^{-3}$
$$= 138.1 \text{ kN}$$

∴ Minimum number of Size 13 strands required to satisfy Clause 18.4.2(c) is:

$$2543/138.1 = 18.5 \text{ strands}$$

Hence, initial estimate of minimum number of strands for symmetrical pattern is 20, giving $A_p = 1980 \text{ mm}^2$.

Instantaneous prestress losses:

$$\Delta P_{e\ell} = \left[\frac{P_{(i)}}{A_{tr}} + \frac{(P_{(i)} \, e_{tr} + M_g) \, e_{tr}}{I_{tr}}\right] \frac{E_p}{E_c} A_p \quad \text{(Eq. 10.4.1)}$$

In this example, using low-relaxation steel, $P_{(i)} \approx P_o$ and, because ρ_p is small, the properties of the gross concrete section can be used

$$P_o = 0.75 \times 20 \times 99 \times 1860 \times 10^{-3} = 2762 \text{ kN}$$

$$\Delta P_{e\ell} = \left[\frac{-2762 \times 10^3}{492000} + \frac{(-2762 \times 10^3 \times 732 + 1066 \times 10^6) \times 732}{66300 \times 10^6}\right]$$

$$\times \frac{190000}{26620} \times 1980 \times 10^{-3}$$

$$= -228 \text{ kN } (=8\% \text{ of } P_o)$$

Time-dependent prestress losses:

According to Eqs. (1.9) and (1.10), respectively:

$$\text{Creep Coefficient } C_t = \frac{t^{0.6}}{10 + t^{0.6}} C_u \, Q_{cr}$$

$$\text{Shrinkage } \varepsilon_{sh} = \frac{t}{C_s + t} \, \varepsilon_{shu} \, P_{sh}$$

According to Table 1.2: $Q_{cr} = Q_a Q_h Q_f Q_r Q_s Q_v$

and $P_{sh} = P_c P_h P_f P_r P_s P_v$

The coefficients Q and P are determined for the following assumptions:

	Q	P
Age at loading — 1 day, steam cured	1.00	—
Cement content — 300 kg/m³	—	0.93
Relative Humidity — 60%	0.87	0.80
Ratio of fine to total aggregate — 0.40	0.98	0.86
Volume to surface ratio — 60 mm	0.89	0.89
Slump — 50 mm	0.95	0.97
Air content — 7%	1.09	1.00

With $C_u = 2.35$ and $\varepsilon_{shu} = 780 \times 10^{-6}$ (see Section 1.2.3) we get at time t_∞

$$C_\infty = 2.35 \times 1.00 \times 0.87 \times 0.98 \times 0.89 \times 0.95 \times 1.09 = 1.84$$

$$\varepsilon_{sh\infty} = 780 \times 10^{-6} \times 0.93 \times 0.80 \times 0.86 \times 0.89 \times 0.97 \times 1.00 = 430 \times 10^{-6}$$

Intrinsic relaxation at 20°C after 50 years (Eq. 10.4.7), $f_{re} = 50$ MPa.

Concrete stress at level of tendons due to sustained load and initial prestress

$$P_i = 2762 - 228 = 2534 \text{ kN}$$

$$f_c = \frac{P_i}{A_c} + \frac{(M_{sust} + P_i \, e) \, e}{I_c}$$

$$f_c = -\frac{2534 \times 10^3}{492,000} +$$

$$\frac{((1066 + 410) \, 10^6 - 2534 \times 10^3 \times 732) \, 732}{66300 \times 10^6}$$

$$= -9.33 \text{ MPa}$$

We first determine the loss of prestress due to creep and shrinkage alone to be able to determine the relaxation reduction coefficient α_r according to Fig. 10.3.

$$\rho_p = A_p/A_c = 1980/(492 \times 10^3) = 0.00402,$$

$$n_p = 190000/26620 = 7.14$$

$$r = (I/A)^{1/2} = [66.3 \times 10^9/492 \times 10^3]^{1/2} = 367 \text{ mm}$$

From Eq. (10.4.9)

$$\Delta f_s = \frac{7.14(-9.33) \, 1.84 - 430 \times 10^{-6} \times 190 \times 10^3}{1 + 0.00402 \times 7.14 \left\{ 1 + (\frac{732}{367})^2 (1 + 0.8 \times 1.84) \right\}}$$

$$= -\frac{204.3}{1.31} = -156 \text{ MPa}$$

$$\beta = \frac{f_{pi}}{f_{pu}} = 0.75$$

$$\Omega = 156/(0.75 \times 1860) = 0.12,$$

and from Fig. 10.3 $\alpha_r = 0.72$

Prestress loss, including reduced relaxation,

$$\Delta f_{pr} = -156 - \frac{50 \times 0.72}{1.31} = -183 \text{ MPa}$$

This corresponds to a 13 percent loss of the initial prestress.

Hence, total prestress loss = 8% + 13% = 21%.

Prestress Force:

$$P_i = 0.92 \times 2762 = 2541 \text{ kN}$$

$$P_e = 0.79 \times 2762 = 2182 \text{ kN}$$

Check if deflected strands are required at transfer i.e. determine maximum eccentricity of prestress force at ends of member, e_e, assuming no additional top reinforcement.

For top tension

$$e_{e \, max} = (0.5 \sqrt{f'_{ci}} + P_i \, A_c) \frac{S_t}{P_i}$$

$$= (2.50 + 5.16) \, 81.9 = 627 \text{ mm}$$

For bottom compression

$$e_{e \, max} = (0.6 \, f'_{ci} - P_i/A_c) \frac{S_b}{P_i}$$

$$= (15.00 - 5.16) \, 29.6 = 291 \text{ mm (governs)}$$

Stresses at transfer and at final condition for various sections are given in the following table,

where f_b = concrete stress in bottom fibre and

f_t = concrete stress in top fibre

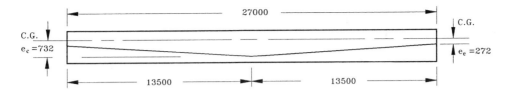

Centroid of Prestressing Force

Load	End at Transfer Prestress = P_i		Midspan at Transfer Prestress = P_i		0.4ℓ at Final Condition Prestress = P_e	
	f_b	f_t	f_b	f_t	f_b	f_t
P_i/A_c or P_e/A_c	−5.16	−5.16	−5.16	−5.16	−4.53	−4.53
P_ie/S or P_ee/S M_g/S M_{sd}/S M_ℓ/S	−9.19	+3.32	−24.73 +14.18	+8.94 −5.13	−18.57 +13.62 +5.24 (+6.98)	+6.71 −4.92 −1.89 (−2.52)
Stresses	−14.35	−1.84	−15.71	−1.35	−4.24 (+2.74)	−4.63 (−7.15)
Allowable	$-0.6f'_{ci}$ −15.00	$-0.6f'_{ci}$ −15.00	$-0.6f'_{ci}$ −15.00	$-0.6f'_{ci}$ −15.00	$+0.5\sqrt{f'_c}$ +2.96	$-0.45f'_c$ $(-0.6f'_c)$ −15.75 (−21.00)
	OK	OK	NG	OK	OK	OK

$$e_e = 272 \text{ mm} \qquad e_c = 732 \text{ mm} \qquad e_{(0.4\ell)} = 640 \text{ mm}$$

Note that Clause 18.4.2 specifies a permissible compressive stress of 0.45 f'_c under sustained loads and 0.6 f'_c under total load. In the above table stress under total load is shown in parenthesis.

Therefore, to satisfy the requirements of Clauses 18.4.1 and 18.4.2, provide 20-Size 13 strands with profile shown, but increase f'_{ci} to 27 MPa in order to accommodate the compressive stress of 15.71 MPa which occurs in the bottom at the mid-span of the member at transfer.

Referring to the results of Example 10.4, the value of A_p to satisfy permissible stresses is greater than that required for factored flexural resistance. This is often the case with prestressed members designed in accordance with Clause 18.4.2(c).

EXAMPLE 10.6
Calculation of Critical Stresses and Crack Widths to Comply with Clause 18.4.3 (partially prestressed member)

Given: The data from Example 10.4 with

$$A_p = 1188 \text{ mm}^2$$
$$A_s = 2000 \text{ mm}^2$$

Solution:

From the results of Example 10.5, it is apparent that if A_p is reduced from 1980 mm² to 1188 mm², the member does not comply with Clause 18.4.2(c) and the member is partially prestressed.

Transformed Section Properties:

$$A_{tr} = (492000 - 1188 - 2000) + (1188 \times \frac{190000}{26620})$$
$$+ (2000 \times \frac{200,000}{26620})$$
$$= 512,300 \text{ mm}^2$$

$$y_{tr} = \frac{(492000 \times 882) + (13026 \times 100) + (7290 \times 150)]}{512300}$$
$$= 852 \text{ mm}$$

$$I_{tr} = 77.7 \times 10^9 \text{ mm}^4$$

Instantaneous prestress losses:

$$\Delta P_{e\ell} = \left[\frac{P_{(i)}}{A_{tr}} + \frac{(P_{(i)} e_{tr} + M_g) e_{tr}}{I_{tr}}\right] \frac{E_p}{E_c} A_p$$

$$P_{(i)} = 0.75 \times 1188 \times 1860 \times 10^{-3} = 1657 \text{ kN}$$

$$e_{tr} = 852 - (1200 - 1050) = 703 \text{ mm}$$

$$\Delta P_{e\ell} = \left[\frac{-1657 \times 10^3}{512300} + \frac{(-1657 \times 10^3 \times 702 + 1066 \times 10^6) 702}{77.7 \times 10^9}\right]$$
$$\times \frac{190000}{26620} \times 1188 \times 10^{-3}$$

$$= -34.8 \text{ kN } (2\%)$$

Time-dependent losses:

The following data were established in Example 10.5 for the time-dependent material properties:

Creep Coefficient $\quad C_\infty = 1.84$

Shrinkage $\qquad \varepsilon_{sh\infty} = 430 \times 10^{-6}$

Intrinsic Relaxation $\quad f_{re} = 50$ MPa

Concrete stress at the tendon level under sustained load (= dead load)

$$f_c = \frac{-1657 \times 10^3}{512300} +$$
$$\frac{((1066 + 410) - 1657\,(0.732))\,732 \times 10^6}{77.7 \times 10^9}$$

$$= -3.23 + 2.48 = -0.75 \text{ MPa}$$

Since both layers of steel have a common centroid the loss of prestress without relaxation is equal to the compressive stress in the nonprestressed steel.

With $\rho_p\, n_p = \dfrac{1188}{492000} \times \dfrac{190000}{26620} = 0.0172$

and $\rho_s\, n_s = \dfrac{2000}{492000} \times \dfrac{200,000}{26620} = 0.0305$

$$\Delta f_s = \frac{7.3\,(-0.75)\,1.84 - 430 \times 10^{-6} \times 190,000}{1 + (0.0172 + 0.0305)\left[\left(1 + (\frac{732}{367})^2\right)(1 + 0.8 \times 1.84)\right]}$$

$$= \frac{-91.8}{1.587} = -57.8 \text{ MPa}$$

Relaxation reduction coefficient:

With $\beta = 0.75$, $\Omega = \dfrac{57.8}{0.75 \times 1860} = 0.041$
we obtain from Fig. 10.3: $\alpha_r = 0.95$

so that the loss, including relaxation, is:

$$\Delta f_{pr} = -57.8 - \frac{50 \times 0.95}{1.587} = -87.7 \text{ MPa (5\%)}$$

The total reduction of the compression on the concrete is

$$\Delta P = (87.7 \times 1188 + 57.8 \times 2000) \times 10^{-3} = 219 \text{ kN}$$

This corresponds to a reduction in compressive stress at the bottom fibre of:

$$\Delta f_c = \frac{219 \times 10^3}{492 \times 10^3} + \frac{219 \times 10^3 \times 732}{66.3 \times 10^9} \times 882$$

$$= 2.58 \text{ MPa}$$

Total prestress loss = 2% + 5% = 7%

Prestress force:

$$P_i = 0.98 \times 1657 = 1624 \text{ kN}$$

$$P_e = 0.93 \times 1657 = 1541 \text{ kN}$$

With deflected strands such that $e_e = 540$ mm and $e_c = 705$ mm, the following concrete stresses are calculated at transfer.

Load	End at Transfer		Midspan at Transfer	
	f_b	f_t	f_b	f_t
$P_{(i)}/A_{tr}$	−3.17	−3.17	−3.17	−3.17
$P_{(i)}e_{tr}/S_{tr}$	−9.08	+3.71	−12.02	+4.91
M_g/S_{tr}			+11.69	−4.77
Stresses	−12.26	+0.54	−3.50	−3.03
	$-0.6f'_{ci}$	$+0.5\sqrt{f'_{ci}}$	$-0.6f'_{ci}$	$-0.6f'_{ci}$
Allowable	−15.00	+2.50	−15.00	−15.00
	OK	OK	OK	OK

In this table f_b and f_t are concrete stresses in bottom and top fibre, respectively.

Hence, concrete stresses at transfer are within the permissible limits of Clause 18.4.1.

Crack Control:

Components of the decompression force P are:

$$P_e = 1541 \text{ kN}$$

$$P_s = \Delta f_s\, A_s = -57.8 \times 2000 \times 10^{-3} = -116 \text{ kN}$$

$$\Delta P_p = \frac{-f_c}{E_c}\, E_p\, A_p = \frac{0.75}{26620}\, 190 \times 10^3 \times 1188 \times 10^{-3}$$

$$= 6.4 \text{ kN}$$

$$\Delta P_s = \frac{-f_c}{E_c}\, E_s\, A_s = \frac{0.75}{26620}\, 200 \times 10^3 \times 2000 \times 10^{-3}$$

$$= 11.3 \text{ kN}$$

$$P = 1541 - 116 + 6.4 + 11.3 = 1443 \text{ kN}$$

It is obvious that the terms ΔP_p and ΔP_a could be neglected.

The following parameters are needed to determine $f_s/(n\alpha)$ from Figure 10.8:

$$d = \frac{A_s\, E_s\, d_s + A_p\, E_p\, d_p}{A_s\, E_s + A_p\, E_p}$$

$$= \frac{2000 \times 200 \times 1100 + 1188 \times 190 \times 1050}{2000 \times 200 + 1188 \times 190} \times \frac{10^3}{10^3}$$

$$= 1082 \text{ mm}$$

$$n\rho = \frac{A_p\, E_p + A_s\, E_s}{E_c\, bd}$$

$$= \frac{1188 \times 190 \times 10^3 + 2000 \times 200 \times 10^3}{26620 \times 3000 \times 1082}$$

$$= 0.00714$$

$$\rho = \frac{Pd_p}{M_s} = \frac{1443 \times 1050 \times 10^3}{(1066 + 410 + 547)\,10^6} = 0.749$$

$$\alpha_b = \frac{b_w}{b} = \frac{200}{3000} = 0.0667$$

$$\alpha_f = \frac{h_f}{d} = \frac{90}{1082} = 0.0832$$

With these values we find by interpolation $f_s/n\alpha = 43$

Steel stress at the level of the centroid of the steel:

$$f_s = 43\,\frac{nM_s}{bd^2} = 43\,\frac{7.5 \times 2023 \times 10^6}{3000 \times 1082^2} = 186 \text{ MPa}$$

Disregarding the bundled prestressing steel for the calculation of A, we find

$$A = \frac{200 \times 2 \times 100}{4} = 10{,}000 \text{ mm}^2$$

Thus

$$z = f_s \sqrt[3]{d_c A} = 186(50 \times 10{,}000)^{1/3} \times 10^{-3} = 14.8$$

For interior exposure (assumed), $z \le 20$ (Clause 18.9.3)
   Hence, 12-Size 13 strands plus 4-No. 25 bars satisfy concrete stresses at transfer and crack control under specified loads.

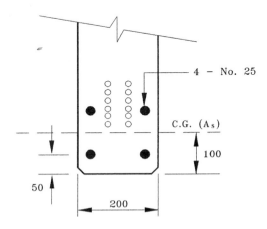

Midspan Detail

EXAMPLE 10.7
Shear Design of a Prestressed Concrete Member — Simplified Method

Given:

The data from Example 10.4

Shear reinforcement (A_v): $f_y = 400$ MPa

Solution:

V_f at centre line of support = $29.25 \times 27.0/2 = 395$ kN

At distance $h/2 = 600$ mm from the face of the support (CL. 11.3.2 (b)), see Fig. 10.7.1.

$V_f = 29.25 [27.0/2 - (0.10 + 0.60)] = 375$ kN

Calculation of V_c and V_{cw} (CL. 11.3.6)

$$V_c = 0.06 \lambda \phi_c \sqrt{f'_c} \, b_w d + \frac{V_f}{M_f} M_{cr}$$

where $0.17 \lambda \phi_c \sqrt{f'_c} \, b_w d \le V_c \le V_{cw}$

$$M_{cr} = (\frac{I_g}{y_t}) (0.6 \lambda \phi_c \sqrt{f'_c} + \phi_p f_{ce})$$

$$V_{cw} = 0.4 \lambda \phi_c \sqrt{f'_c} \, (1 + \frac{\phi_p f_{cp}}{0.4 \lambda \phi_c \sqrt{f'_c}})^{1/2} b_w d + \phi_p V_p$$

In these equations, $d_p \ge 0.8$ h.

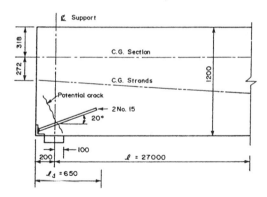

Fig. 10.7.1 Beam end zone

Transfer length = $50 \times 13 = 650$ mm (CL. 11.2.1.2)

Hence, from the end of the member for a distance of 650 mm, f_{cp} will vary from zero to a maximum of

$$P_e/A_c = 2237 \times 10^3 /492000 = 4.55 \text{ MPa}$$

Eccentricity of tendons at centre of member = 732 mm
Eccentricity of tendons at end of member = 272 mm

Tendon drape = 460 mm

At a distance equal to or greater than 650 mm from the end of the member, the component of the effective prestress force in the direction of the applied shear,

$$V_p = 2237 \times 460/13500 = 76 \text{ kN}.$$

The solution to this example will be determined by constructing the V_c, V_{cw} and V_f diagrams.

At the end of the member where f_{cp} and V_p are zero:

$$V_{cw} = (0.4 \times 1.0 \times 0.65\sqrt{35})(200 \times 0.80 \times 1200)10^{-3}$$
$$= 1.54 \times 192 = 295 \text{ kN}$$

At 650 mm from the end,

$$V_{cw} = 1.54 (1 + 0.9 \times \frac{4.55}{1.54})^{1/2}192 + 0.9 \times 76$$

$$= 634 \text{ kN}$$

At distance $x = 650 - 200 = 450$ mm from the centre line of support (see Fig. 10.7.1), $V_f = 382$ kN and

$$M_f = \frac{1}{2} w_f x(\ell - x) = \frac{1}{2} \times 29.25 \times 0.45(27.0 - 0.45)$$
$$= 175 \text{ kN·m}.$$

To calculate M_{cr}, f_{ce} has to be calculated with

$$f_{ce} = P_e (\frac{1}{A_c} + \frac{e \, y_t}{I})$$

where e is the eccentricity at 450 mm to the centre of the support.

$$e = 272 + 460 \frac{450}{13500} = 287 \text{ mm}$$

Thus:

$$f_{ce} = \frac{-2237 \times 10^3}{492000} + \frac{(-2237)10^3 \times 287}{66300 \times 10^6} \times 882$$

$$= -13.09 \, \text{MPa (Compression)}$$

$$M_{cr} = \frac{66300 \times 10^6}{882}(0.6 \times 1.0 \times 0.65\sqrt{35} + 0.9 \times 13.09)$$

$$= 1059 \, \text{kN} \cdot \text{m}$$

$$V_c = 0.06 \times 1.0 \times 0.65\sqrt{35} \times 200 \times 960 \times 10^{-3}$$
$$+ \frac{382}{175} \times 1059$$

$$= 2355 \, \text{kN}$$

But $V_c \leq V_{cw}$, hence $V_c = 634 \, \text{kN}$

The V_c curve is established by selecting four or five points between 650 mm and 10000 mm from the end of the member.
(See Fig. 10.7.2)

Now determine minimum value of V_s (CL. 11.2.8.4):

$$\frac{A_v}{s} = 0.06\sqrt{f_c'}(\frac{b_w}{f_y}) = 0.06\sqrt{35}(\frac{200}{400}) = 0.177 \, \text{mm}^2/\text{mm}$$

For stirrups No. 10 the spacing is

$$s = \frac{2 \times 100}{0.177} = 1130 \, \text{mm}$$

For $v_f = \frac{V_f - \phi_p V_p}{b_w d_v}$

$$= \frac{(375 - 0.9 \times 76) \times 10^3}{200 \times 0.9 \, (0.8 \times 1200)} = 1.77 \, \text{MPa}$$

$$< 0.1\phi_c \, f_c' = 2.27 \, \text{MPa}$$

the maximum spacing is 0.7 d or 600 mm (CL. 11.2.11):

0.7 d = 0.7 × 0.8 × 1200 = 672 mm.

Hence for minimum shear reinforcement, provide No. 10 stirrups at 600 mm. Thus:

$$V_s = \phi_s \, f_y \, A_v \frac{d}{s}$$

$$= 0.85 \times 400 \times 2 \times 100 \times \frac{960}{600} \times 10^{-3} = 109 \, \text{kN}$$

Minimum shear reinforcement is required where $V_f > 0.5 \, V_c + \phi_p \, V_p$ (CL. 11.2.8.1) where $V_c = 0.2 \, \lambda\phi_c\sqrt{f_c'} \, b_w \, d$. With the data given:

$$0.5 \times 0.2 \times 1.0 \times 0.65\sqrt{35} \times 200 \times 960 \times 10^{-3}$$
$$+ 0.9 \times 76 = 142 \, \text{kN}.$$

$V_f = 142 \, \text{kN}$ is reached at distance 142/29.25 = 4.86m from the centre line of the beam (see Fig. 10.7.2). In the rest of the beam, minimum shear reinforcement governs. Additional tension reinforcement near support, (CL. 11.3.8.2)

$$T_r \geq V_f - 0.5 V_s$$

At the inside edge of the bearing area, $V_f = 395 - 0.1 \times 29.25 = 392 \, \text{kN}$ and $V_s = 109 \, \text{kN}$. Thus:

$$T_r \geq 392 - 0.5 \times 109 = 338 \, \text{kN}$$

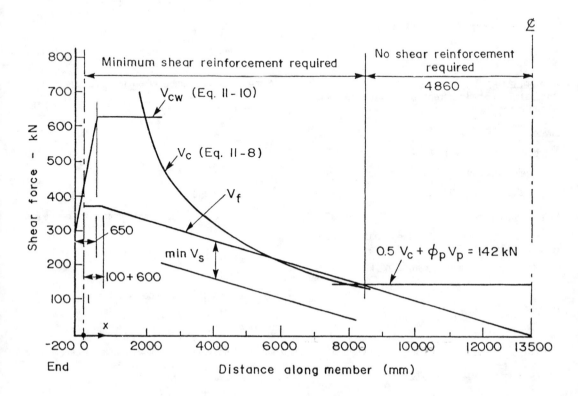

Fig. 10.7.2 Shear design diagram

Assume that four straight strands contribute to the tension at the face of the support at x = 300 mm from the beam end:

$$T_{rp} = A_p f_{pe} \frac{x}{\ell_d} = 4 \times 99 \times 1130 \left(\frac{300}{650}\right)10^{-3} = 206 \text{ kN}.$$

Reinforcement required

$$A_s = \frac{(338 - 206)10^3}{0.85 \times 400} = 388 \text{mm}^2$$

Use 2 No. 15 as shown in Fig. 10.7.1.

EXAMPLE 10.8
Shear Design of Prestressed Concrete Member — General Method

The beam of Example 10.4 is designed for shear.

Data given: h = 1200 mm ; b_w = 200 mm

d = 1050 mm ; w_f = 29.25 kN/m

f_c' = 35 MPa; f_y = 400 MPa

Effective prestress P_e = 2237 kN

Slope of the tendons (732 − 272)/13500 = 0.03407

V_p = 2237 × 0.03407 = 76 kN

1.   Factored Shear Force:

According to Clause 11.4.1, the critical section maybe taken at a distance d_v = 0.9 d = 0.9 × 0.8 h = 0.9 × 0.8 × 1200 = 864 mm from the face of the support. Shear force and moment due to factored load at (864 + 100) = 964 mm from the centreline of the support.

V_f = 29.25 (13.50 − 0.964) = 367 kN.

M_f = 0.5 × 29.25 × 0.964 (27.0 − 0.964) = 367 kN · m

2.   Shear stress ratio

$$\frac{v_f}{\phi_c f_c'} = \frac{V_f - \phi_p V_p}{b_w d_v \phi_c f_c'} = \frac{(367 - 0.9 \times 76)10^3}{200 \times 864 \times 0.65 \times 35} = 0.076$$

3.   Determination of ε_x

According to Eq. 11-22 with $N_f = 0$, $A_s = 0$, $f_{po} = 1.1 f_{pe}$ and $A_p f_{pe} = P_e$

$$\varepsilon_x = \frac{0.5 V_f \cot\theta + \frac{M_f}{d_v} - 1.1 P_e}{E_p A_p}$$

Assuming θ = 30°:

$$\varepsilon_x = \frac{(0.5 \times 367 \times 10^3)\cot 30° + \frac{367 \times 10^6}{864} - 1.1 \times 2237 \times 10^3}{190000 \times 1980}$$

$$= -4.6 \times 10^{-3} < 0$$

4.   Establish β and θ from Fig. 11-1

For $v_f/\phi_c f_c'$ = 0.076, θ = 26.5°

Using this value of θ in the above equation will still result in $\varepsilon_x < 0$.

Thus use θ = 26.5° and β = 0.405.

5.   Shear resistance

$$V_{cg} = 1.3\lambda\phi_c\beta\sqrt{f_c'}b_w d_v$$

= 1.3 × 1.0 × 0.65 × 0.405√35 × 200 × 864 × 10⁻³

= 350 kN

$V_{rg} = V_{cg} + \phi_p V_p = 350 + 0.9 \times 76 = 418 \text{ kN} > V_f$

The calculation of the shear resistance $V_{rg} = V_{cg} + \phi_p V_p$ at different sections is tabulated below:

Distance from support (m)	1.00	2.00	4.00	6.00	8.00	10.00
V_f (kN)	365	336	278	219	161	102
M_f (kN · m)	380	731	1346	1842	2223	2486
d_p	624	658	726	794	862	930
$d_p - a/2$	580	628	669	764	832	900
$d_v = 0.72h$	864	864	864	864	864	864
$v_f / \phi_c f_c'$	0.076	0.068	0.054	0.039	0.024	0.008
$\varepsilon_x (10^{-3})$	-4.5	-3.5	-1.6	-0.3	0.3	1.37
β	0.406	0.406	0.406	0.406	0.290	0.165
θ°	27	27	27	27	28	39
$V_{cg}+\phi_p V_p$ (kN)	418	418	418	418	301	215

(6)   Minimum shear reinforcement $A_{v,min}$

$A_{v,min}$ is required where $V_f > 0.5 V_c + \phi_p V_p = 142$ kN, which occurs at 4.86 m from the centre line of the beam (See Example 10.7).

From the table it is obvious that $V_{rg} = V_{cg} + \phi_p V_p > V_f$ at all sections. As for Example 10.7, the stirrup design is governed by $A_{v,min}$ and is the same as for Example 10.7, namely No.10 stirrups spaced at 600 mm.

EXAMPLE 10.9
Design of Prestressed Concrete Slab

1.   Geometry — (See Fig. 10.9.1)

2.   Materials

Concrete Strength:

Slab f_c' = 30 MPa, f_{ci}' = 25 MPa, α_1 = 0.805, β_1 = 0.895

Column f_c' = 40 MPa

Prestressing Steel:

Low-relaxation strand, 15 mm diameter

f_{pu} = 1860 MPa, f_{py} = 1670 MPa, A_p = 140 mm²

Non-prestressed Steel:

f_y = 400 MPa

3.   Slab Thickness

h = ℓ/45 = 7500/45 = 167 mm, select 170 mm

4.   Loads

Specified Loads

Dead Load;

170 mm slab (170/1000) × 2.4 × 9.81   = 4.00 kN/m²

Partitions: = 1.30 kN/m²

	w_D	=	5.30 kN/m^2
Live Load:	w_L	=	2.40 kN/m^2
	$w_s = w_D + w_L$	=	7.70 kN/m2

$w_L < \dfrac{3}{4} w_D$ — Use full live loads on all spans (CL. 13.9.4.2)

Factored Loads:

$w_{Df} = 1.25 \times 5.30$		=	6.63 kN/m^2
$w_{Lf} = 1.50 \times 2.40$		=	3.60 kN/m^2
	w_f	=	10.23 kN/m^2

5. Cable Profile

Point of maximum eccentricity in span 1 is at $x = \alpha\ell_1$ (See Fig. 10.9.5):

$$\alpha = 1/[1 + (\frac{d_2 - d_3}{d_1 - d_3})^{1/2}] = 1/[1 + (\frac{140 - 30}{85 - 30})^{1/2}]$$

$$- 0.4142$$

Equation of parabola of span 1 (y from bottom of slab in mm, x in m)

$$y = \frac{d_1 - d_3}{(\alpha\ell_1)^2} x^2 + 2 \frac{d_1 - d_3}{\alpha\ell_1} x + d_1$$

$$y = 6.93 \times 10^{-6} x^2 - 0.03905 x + 85$$

at $x = \dfrac{\ell_1}{2} = 3400$: $y = 32$ mm.

Sag in span 1:

$$s_1 = 85 - 32 + \frac{1}{2}(85 - 30) = 80 \text{ mm} = 0.080 \text{ m}$$

An approximate value of $s_1 = 82$ mm is obtained by assuming that the maximum eccentricity occurs at mid span.

6. Load Balancing

Assume that approximately 80 percent of the dead load is balanced by the effective prestressing force

$$w_{bal} = 0.80 \times 5.30 = 4.24 \text{ kN/m}^2$$

Span 1

Required effective prestressing force (per metre)

$$P_e = \frac{w_{bal} \ell_1^2}{8 s_1} = \frac{4.24 \times 6.80^2}{8 \times 0.080} = 306 \text{ kN/m}$$

For full width of panel

$$P_e = 306 \times 7.40 = 2267 \text{ kN}$$

Assuming the effective prestress to be 0.6 f_{pu}, we have per tendon

$$P_e = 0.60 f_{pu} A_p = 0.6 \times 1860 \times 140 \times 10^{-3} = 156 \text{ kN}$$

Number of tendons required

N = 2267/156 = 14.5. Select 15 tendons

Actual balanced load in span 1:

$$w_{bal} = \frac{8 P_e s_1}{\ell_1^2} = \frac{8 \times 15 \times 156 \times 0.080}{6.80^2} = 32.4 \text{ kN/m}$$

Per metre width

$$w_{bal} = 32.4/7.40 = 4.38 \text{ kN/m}^2$$

Unbalanced Load

$$w_{net} = w_s - w_{bal} = 7.70 - 4.38 = 3.32 \text{ kN/m}^2$$

Span 2

Utilizing the maximum possible cable sag $s_2 = 140 - 30 = 110$ mm results in a balanced load (neglecting friction), per meter width

$$w_{bal} = \frac{8 \times 15 \times 156 \times 0.110}{7.4 \times 7.00^2} = 5.68 \text{ kN/m}^2$$

This is too high since it exceeds the dead load. A balanced load $w_{bal} = 4.70$ kN/m^2 is chosen. The sag corresponding to this balanced load is

$$s_2 = \frac{4.70 \times 7.40 \times 7.00^2}{8 \times 15 \times 156} = 0.091 \text{ m (91 mm)}$$

Unbalanced load in span 2

$$w_{net} = 7.70 - 4.70 = 3.00 \text{ kN/m}^2$$

7. Analysis according to Clause 13.9.3 — Prismatic modelling of members

7.1 Section Properties

Slab — Beam:

$$I_s = (1/12) \ell_{2a} h_s^3 = (1/12) 7400 (170)^3$$
$$= 3.03 \times 10^9 \text{ mm}^4$$

Column:

$$I_c = (1/12) 400 (400)^3 = 2.13 \times 10^9 \text{ mm}^4$$

Effective moment of inertia of column (CL. 13.9.3.3)

$$I_{ec} = \psi I_c$$

From Eq. (13-15)

$$\psi = (0.25 + 0.75 \frac{\alpha \ell_{2a}}{\ell_{1a}}) (\frac{\ell_{2a}}{\ell_{1a}})^2, \quad 0.3 \leq \psi \leq 1.0$$

For both spans $\alpha\ell_{2a}/\ell_{1a} = 0$.

Column A:

$$\ell_{2a}/\ell_{1a} = 7400/6800 = 1.088;$$
$$\psi = 0.25 (1.088)^2 = 0.296. \text{ Use } 0.30$$

Column B:

$$\ell_{2a}/\ell_{1a} = 7400/6900 = 1.072;$$
$$\psi = 0.25 (1.072)^2 = 0.287. \text{ Use } 0.30$$

Column C:

$$\ell_{2a}/\ell_{1a} = 7400/7000 = 1.057;$$
$$\psi = 0.25 (1.057)^2 = 0.280. \text{ Use } 0.30$$

Thus: $I_{ec} = 0.30 \times 2.13 \times 10^9 = 0.639 \times 10^9$ mm^4 for all columns.

7.2 Frame Geometry

The dimensions and the moment of inertia used in the frame analysis are shown in Fig. 10.9.7.2.

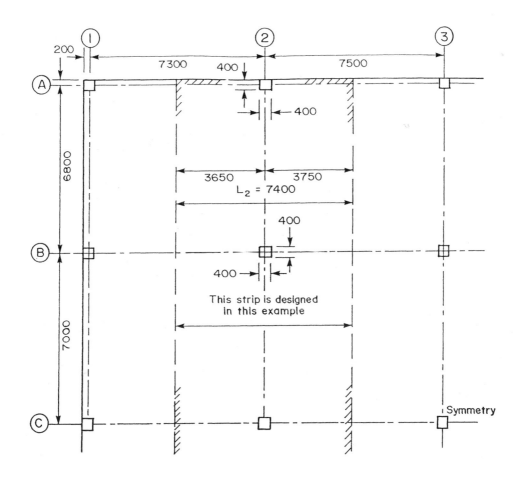

Fig. 10.9.1   Slab geometry

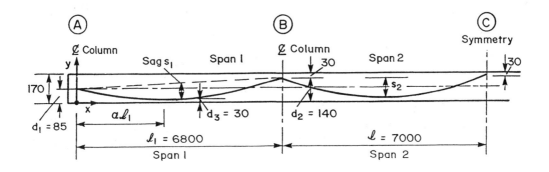

Fig. 10.9.5   Tendon profile

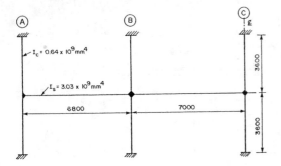

Fig. 10.9.7.2 Frame geometry

7.3 Results of Frame Analysis

The results for the unbalanced (net) loads are shown in Fig. 10.9.7.3 (a).

7.4 Check of Flexural Stresses

Maximum Stress at Face of Column B

Moment at face of column (calculated for slab width ℓ_2 = 7.4 m) due to unbalanced loads is -92.1 kN · m. (See Fig. 10.9.7.3(a)) In the column strip 75 percent of the total moment is resisted (CL. 18.13.2.1). The moment per metre in the column strip at the face of the column is obtained with a width of the column strip

$$\frac{1}{2}(\frac{7.00 + 6.80}{2}) = 3.45m$$

$$M_B = \frac{92.1 \times 0.75}{3.45} = -20.0\,kN\cdot m/m$$

Concrete stress in top fibre

$$f_c = \frac{P_e}{A_c} - \frac{M}{S} = \frac{15(-156)10^3}{7400 \times 170} - \frac{(-20.0)\,6 \times 10^6}{170^2 \times 1000}$$

$$= -1.86 + 4.16 = 2.30\ MPa$$

Permissible $f'_c = 0.5\sqrt{f'_c} = 2.74$ MPa.   OK.

Note: The axial stress is calculated as the average stress over the full width of the slab (CL. 18.13.2.2).

Concrete stress in bottom fibre

$$f_c = -1.86 - 4.16 = -6.02\ MPa < Permissible$$

$$f_c = 0.60\ f'_c$$

$$= 18.0\ MPa\ (Compression).\qquad OK.$$

Mid Span:

Maximum moment in Span 1 from Fig. 10.9.7.3 (a). The positive moment in the column strip is equal to 60% of the total positive moment. Moment per metre (width 3.45 m)

$$M_1 = \frac{64.6 \times 0.60}{3.45} = 11.23\,kN\cdot m/m$$

Bottom fibre stress

$$f_c = -1.86 + \frac{11.23 \times 10^6}{170^2 \times 1000/6}$$

$$= -1.86 + 2.33 = 0.47\ MPa$$

$$< permissible\ f_t = 0.5\ \sqrt{f'_c} = 2.74\ MPa.\qquad OK.$$

Non-prestressed steel not required because $f_c \leq 0.2\sqrt{f'_c} = 1.09$ MPa (Table 18-1).

8.   Factored Flexural Resistance

The factored flexural resistance, M_f, must be at least equal to the bending moment due to factored load, plus the secondary moment due to prestressing:

$$M_f = \alpha_D\,M_D + \alpha_L\,M_L + \alpha_p\,M''_p$$

According to CSA Standard A23.3 Clause 8.3.2.1, α_D = 1.25, α_L = 1.50 and α_p = 1.0.

8.1   Factored Moments

The factored moments due to w_f = 10.23 kN/m² (= 75.7 kN/m) are plotted in Fig. 10.9.7.3(b), together with the secondary moments, M''_p, and the moments at the column faces and in the spans. These moments are summarized in the following table:

Support		A	B$_{left}$	B$_{right}$	C
$\alpha_D M_D + \alpha_L M_L$	kN·m	−144.8	−349.1	−329.8	−298.7
$\alpha_p M''_p$	kN·m	+61.2	+23.8	+19.3	+10.3
M_f	kN·m	−83.6	−325.3	−310.5	−288.4
V_f	kN	221.9	292.8	268.1	261.8
M_f at column face[1]	kN·m	40.7[1]	−268.0	−259.0	−238.0
M_f − span	kN·m		242.0		164.0

[1] At column face $M_f = -83.6 + 221.9 \times 0.2 - \frac{1}{2}(0.2)^2\,75.7$
$= -40.7\ kN\cdot m$

8.2   Factored Flexural Resistance

8.2.1   At interior columns

According to Clause 18.9.1 (Table 18-1)

min $A_s = 0.0006\ h_s\ \ell_n = 0.0006 \times 170 \times 6600 = 673$ mm²

Provide 7— No. 10 bars = 700 mm².

These bars shall be placed within a zone $c_2 + 3h = 400 + 3 \times 170 = 910$ mm at the column (CL. 18.13.5.1).

Stress in unbonded tendon at flexural failure (Eq. 18-2)

$$f_p = f_{se} + \frac{8000}{\ell_e}\,(d_p - c_y)$$

With three hinges necessary to form a mechanism

$$\ell_e = 4 \times 7000/3 = 9330\ mm$$

$$d_p = 140\ mm,\ A_p = 15 \times 140 = 2100\ mm^2$$

$$f_{py} = 1670\ MPa,\ f_y = 400\ MPa$$

$$c_y = \frac{0.9 \times 2100 \times 1670 + 0.85 \times 700 \times 400}{0.805 \times 0.895 \times 0.60 \times 30 \times 7400}$$

$$= 35\ mm$$

$$f_{pr} = 0.6 \times 1860 + (8000/9330)\,(140 - 35)$$

$$= 1206\ MPa$$

$$M_f = \phi_p A_p f_{pr}(d_p - a/2) + \phi_s A_s f_y(d_s - a/2)$$

(a) Moments due to specified loads and prestressing (= unbalanced loads)

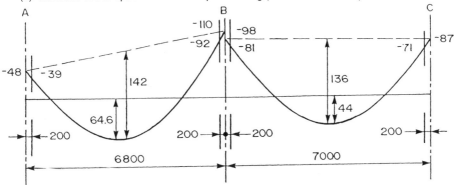

(b) Moments due to factored loads (with and without secondary moments)

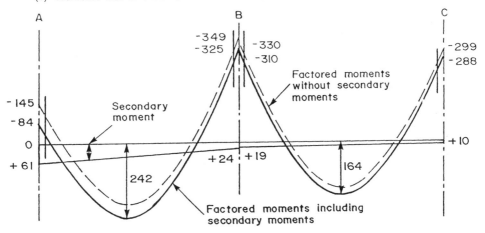

(c) Shear force due to factored loads and secondary moments.

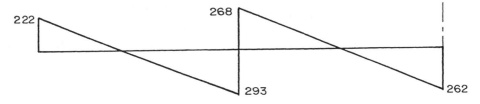

Fig. 10.9.7.3   Moment and shear force diagrams

$$a = \frac{\phi_p \, A_p \, f_{pr} + \phi_s \, A_s \, f_y}{\alpha_1 \, \phi_c \, f'_c \, \ell_2}$$

$$= \frac{0.9 \times 2100 \times 1206 + 0.85 \times 700 \times 400}{0.805 \times 0.60 \times 30 \times 7400}$$

$$= 24 \text{ mm}$$

$$M_f = 0.9 \times 2100 \times 1206(140 - 12) + 0.8 \times 700$$
$$\times \; 400 \; (140 - 12)$$

$$= 322 \times 10^6 \text{ N·mm} = 322 \text{ kN·m} > 268 \text{ kN·m}. \quad \text{OK.}$$

9. Shear Design

9.1 At Exterior Column

9.1.1 Shear Force

Shear due to factored loads on slab and M''_p: = 221.9 kN
Shear due to facade: (Brick + glass, @2.4 kN/m):
= 1.25 x 2.4 x 7.4 = 22.2 kN

Total Shear: V_f = 244.1 kN

The beneficial effect of prestressing on shear resistance cannot be considered (CL. 18.13.3.2 (a)). At exterior columns a portion of the unbalanced moment is transferred to the column by eccentricity of shear.

9.1.2 Section Properties of Critical Section

With d = 130 mm, d/2 = 65 mm (see sketch)

$$A_1 = d(2b_1 + b_2) = 130 \; (\; 2 \times 465 + 530)$$

$$= 190 \times 10^3 \text{ mm}^2$$

$$e_1 = \frac{b_1^2}{2b_1 + b_2} = \frac{465^2}{2 \times 465 + 530} = 148 \text{ mm}$$

$$e_3 = \frac{1}{2} \, (c_1 + d) - e_1 = \frac{1}{2} \, (400 + 130) - 148 = 117 \text{ mm}$$

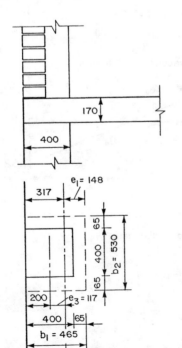

$$J = \frac{1}{6} \, (b_1 d^3 + b_1^3 d) + b_2 d e_1^2 + 2db_1(\frac{1}{2} \, b_1 - e_1)^2$$

$$= \frac{1}{6} \, (465 \times 130^3 + 465^3 \times 130) + 530 \times 130 \times 148^2$$

$$+ \; 2 \times 130 \times 465 \; (\frac{1}{2} \times 530 - 148)^2$$

$$= 5.51 \times 10^9 \text{ mm}^4$$

9.1.3 Moment to be Transferred by Eccentricity of Shear

The moment to be transferred from the slab to the column, M_f, is the unbalanced moment due to factored load to be taken at the centroid of the critical section, i.e., the moment obtained at the column axis, minus the shear times the eccentricity e_3.

$$M_f = - 83.6 + 221.9 \times 0.117 = - 57.6 \text{ kN·m}$$

$$\gamma_v = 1 - \frac{1}{1 + \frac{2}{3}\left(\frac{b_1}{b_2}\right)^{1/2}} = 1 - \frac{1}{1 + \frac{2}{3}\left(\frac{465}{530}\right)^{1/2}} = 0.384$$

(CL. 13.4.5.3)

Maximum shear stress under factored loads:

$$v_f = \frac{V_f}{A} + \frac{\gamma_v \, M_f \, e_1}{J_1}$$

$$= \frac{244.1 \times 10^3}{190 \times 10^3} + \frac{0.384 \times 57.6 \times 10^6 \times 148}{5.51 \times 10^9}$$

$$= 1.28 + 0.59 = 1.87 \text{ MPa}$$

The shear stress resistance (CL. 13.4.4) of concrete is controlled by Eq. 13-6.

$$v_r = v_c = 0.4\lambda\phi_c\sqrt{f'_c} = 0.4 \times 1.0 \times 0.6\sqrt{30}$$

$$= 1.31 \text{MPa} < 1.87 \text{ MPa}$$

Shear reinforcement or shear capital required.

9.1.4 Shear Capital

Critical Section

With h_c = 100 mm and d/2 = 65 mm, the critical section is 165 mm from column face.

$$A = 130 \, (2 \times 565 + 730) = 242 \times 10^3 \text{ mm}^2$$

$$e_1 = \frac{565^2}{2 \times 565 + 730} = 172 \text{mm}$$

$$e_3 = 565 - 400/2 - 172 = 193 \text{ mm}$$

$$J_1 = \frac{1}{6} \, (565 \times 130^3 + 565^3 \times 130) + 730 \times 130 \times 172^2$$

$$+ \; 2 \times 130 \times 565 \, (565/2 - 172)^2$$

$$= 8.72 \times 10^9 \text{ mm}^4$$

Moment at the centroid of critical section:

$$M_f = -83.6 + 221.9 \times 0.193 = -40.8 \text{ kNm}$$

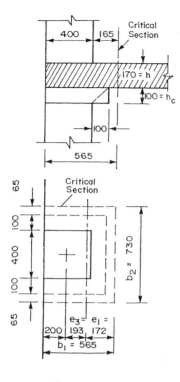

$$\gamma_v = 1 - \frac{1}{1 + \frac{2}{3}\left(\frac{565}{730}\right)^{1/2}} = 0.370$$

Maximum shear stress

$$v_f = \frac{244.1 \times 10^3}{242 \times 10^3} + \frac{0.370 \times 40.8 \times 10^6 \times 172}{8.72 \times 10^9}$$

$$= 1.01 + 0.30 = 1.31 \text{ MPa} \le v_c = 1.31 \text{ MPa. OK.}$$

9.1.5 Design of Shear Reinforcement

The shear stress $v_f = 1.97$ MPa obtained without shear capital is at the upper limit of the allowable value for stirrups, $v_c = 0.6\lambda\phi_c\sqrt{f'_c} = 1.97$ MPa (c.f. CL. 13.4.9.2), but less than the maximum allowable value for headed shear reinforcement $0.8\lambda\phi_c\sqrt{f'_c} = 2.63$ MPa (CL. 13.4.8.2).

Headed Shear Reinforcement

Using shear reinforcement ($f_{vy} = 400$ MPa), which is mechanically anchored at top and bottom (CL. 13.4.8), the shear stress resistance of concrete

$$v_c = 0.3\lambda\phi_c\sqrt{f'_c} = 0.3 \times 1.0 \times 0.6\sqrt{30} = 0.98 \text{ MPa}$$

Using two rows of headed bars along the strip of width $b_2 = 530$ mm, the area of shear reinforcement per unit length of each row is:

$$\frac{A_v}{s} = \frac{(v_f - v_c)b_2}{2 \phi_s f_{vy}} = \frac{(1.97 - 0.98)530}{2 \times 0.85 \times 400} = 0.772 \frac{\text{mm}^2}{\text{mm}}$$

Selecting 9.5 mm diameter headed stirrups ($A_v = 71$ mm²) requires

$$s \le \frac{71}{0.772} = 92 \text{ mm}$$

According to CL. 13.4.8.6, max s = 0.75d = 0.75 × 130 = 98 mm for $v_f \le 0.6 \lambda\phi_c\sqrt{f'_c} = 1.97$ MPa. Select s = 90 mm. The first stirrup is at the smaller of d/4 = 32 mm and s/2 = 98/2 = 49 mm from column face.

The selected bars with area $A_v = 71$ mm² must have an anchor plate area of at least 10 × 71 = 710 mm², corresponding to a head diameter of 30 mm.

The headed shear reinforcement has to extend to a zone where $v_f \le v_c = 0.2\lambda\phi_c\sqrt{f'_c} = 0.66$ MPa. The arrangement of the headed shear reinforcement is shown in Fig. 10.9.9.1.5.

At distance 600 mm from the faces of the column (see Fig. 10.9.9.1.5)

$$A = (3 \times 400 + 2 \times 600\sqrt{2})130 = 376 \times 10^3 \text{ mm}^2$$

$$e_1 = \frac{2 \times 400 \times 800 + 2\sqrt{2} \times 600 \times 300}{3 \times 400 + 2\sqrt{2}\,600} = 397 \text{ mm.}$$

$$e_3 = 1000 - 397 - 400/2 = 403 \text{mm}$$

$$J_1 = \frac{1}{6}(130^3 \times 1000 + 400^3 \times 130)$$

$$+ \frac{2}{3} \times \sqrt{2}\,(397^3 + 203^3) \times 130 + 400 \times 130 \times 397^2$$

$$+ (603 - 400/2)^2 \times 400 \times 130 \times 2$$

$$= 35.5 \times 10^9 \text{ mm}^4$$

Factored moment at $e_3 = 0.403$ m from center line of column

$$M_f = -83.6 + 221.9 \times 0.403 - 10.23 \times 7.4(0.403)^2/2$$

$$= -0.3 \text{ kN} \cdot \text{m}$$

For the critical section outside the shear reinforced zone $b_1 = 1000$ mm, $b_2 = 1600$mm, thus

$$\gamma_v = 1 - \frac{1}{1 + \frac{2}{3}\left(\frac{1000}{1600}\right)^{\frac{1}{2}}} = 0.35$$

$$v_f = \frac{244 \times 10^3}{376 \times 10^3} + \frac{0.3 \times 10^6 \times 0.35\,(397)}{35.5 \times 10^9}$$

$$= 0.65 + 0.001 = 0.65 \text{ MPa} = v_c. \qquad \text{OK.}$$

Normal stirrups:

Normal stirrups are not allowed for this slab since h < 300 mm (CL. 13.4.9.1)

9.2 At Interior Column B

Shear force (see table in Section 8.1)

$$V_f = 292.8 + 268.1 - 10.23 \times 0.53^2 = 558 \text{ kN}$$

Unbalanced moment

$$M_f = 349.1 - 329.8 = 19.3 \text{ kN} \cdot \text{m}$$

Properties of the critical section (see sketch)

$$A = 4 \times 130 \times 530 = 275 \times 10^3 \text{ mm}^2$$

$$J_1 = \frac{1}{6}(130^3 \times 530 + 530^3 \times 130) + 130 \times \frac{530^3}{2}$$

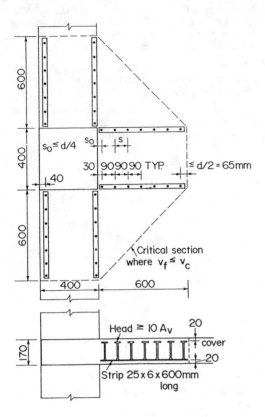

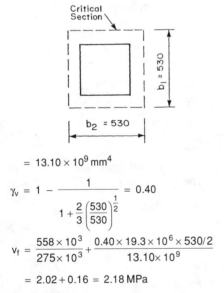

Fig. 10.9.9.1.5 Arrangement of headed reinforcement

$= 13.10 \times 10^9 \text{ mm}^4$

$$\gamma_v = 1 - \cfrac{1}{1 + \cfrac{2}{3}\left(\cfrac{530}{530}\right)^{\frac{1}{2}}} = 0.40$$

$$v_f = \frac{558 \times 10^3}{275 \times 10^3} + \frac{0.40 \times 19.3 \times 10^6 \times 530/2}{13.10 \times 10^9}$$

$= 2.02 + 0.16 = 2.18 \text{ MPa}$

Assuming that 2 tendons cross the critical section in one direction and 4 (bundled) tendons in the other direction, the vertical component of the prestressing force is:

$$V_p = 2(2+4)\, P_e \sin \beta$$

where P_e = effective prestressing force per strand and β = slope of strand at the critical section. It is assumed

that the cable profile over the columns is a cubic parabola over length $\alpha\ell$.

Equation of the cubic parabola for $0 \le x \le \alpha\ell$

$$e(x) = -\frac{s}{\alpha^2 \ell^3}(4 - \delta)\, x^3 - \frac{s}{\alpha \ell^2}[4\alpha - 2(4 - \delta)]\, x^2 + e_A$$

where

s = sag

$$\delta = \frac{e_A - e_B}{s}$$

The other symbols are defined in the sketch.

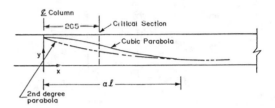

Considering Span 2, $e_A = e_B = -55$ mm, $s = 91$ mm, $\delta = 0$, and assuming $\alpha\ell = 700$ mm, i.e., $\alpha = 0.1$;

$$e(x) = -\frac{91}{0.1^2 \times 7000^3}(4 - 0)\, x^3$$

$$-\frac{91}{0.1 \times 7000^2}[4 \times 0.1 - 2(4 - 0)]\, x^2 - 55$$

$$e(x) = -0.106 \times 10^{-6}\, x^3 + 141 \times 10^{-6}\, x^2 - 55$$

Slope $de(x)/dx$:

$$\beta(x) = -0.318 \times 10^{-6}\, x^2 + 282 \times 10^{-6}\, x$$

At critical section ($x = 265$ mm)

$$\beta = 0.0524$$

Assuming the same slope to apply for all cables we find with

$P_e = 156$ kN per strand:

$$V_p = 2(2+4)\, 156 \times 0.0524 = 98 \text{ kN}$$

Shear resisted by concrete (CSA Standard A23.3 Eq.18-5 with f_{cp} =1.86 MPa

$$v_c = 0.4 \times 1.0 \times 0.6\sqrt{30}\left[1 + \frac{0.9 \times 1.86}{0.4 \times 1.0 \times 0.6 \times \sqrt{30}}\right]^{1/2}$$

$$+ 0.9\frac{98 \times 10^3}{275 \times 10^3}$$

$$= 2.30 \text{ MPa} > 2.18 \text{ MPa.} \qquad\qquad \text{OK.}$$

The limitations for applications of Eq. 18-5 are satisfied (CL.18.13.3.2 (a) to (c)).

10. Structural Integrity

CSA Standard A23.3, Eq. (13-19) has to be satisfied (CL. 13.11.5)

$$\Sigma A_{sb} \ge \frac{2V_{se}}{f_{py}}$$

$$= \frac{2 \times 2 \times 4.00 \times 10^{-3} \times 7400 \times 6900}{0.9 \times 1860}$$

$= 488 \text{ mm}^2 < 8 \times 140 = 1120 \text{ mm}^2$
(2 strands in each direction).

11. Cable Layout

The cable layout is shown in Fig. 10.9.11.

EXAMPLE 10.10
Design of Partially Prestressed Concrete Slab

Example 10.9 is redesigned as a partially prestressed slab

1. Load Balancing

Assuming that about 60% of the dead load is balanced by prestressing $w_{bal} = 0.6 \times 5.30 = 3.18 \text{ kN/m}^2$

Span 1:

$$P_e = \frac{3.18 \times 6.80^2}{8 \times 0.080} = 230 \text{ kN/m}$$

For full width of panel

$P_e = 230 \times 7.40 = 1702$ kN.

Number of tendons N = 1702/156 = 10.9. Select 11 tendons.

Actual:

$w_{bal} = 8 \times 11 \times 156 \times 0.080/(6.80^2)$

$\qquad = 23.7$ kN/m

Per m width: $w_{bal} = 23.7/7.40 = 3.20 \text{ kN/m}^2$

Net Load: $w_{net} = 7.70 - 3.20 = 4.50 \text{ kN/m}^2$

Span 2: Making use of maximum possible sag

$s = 170 - 2 \times 30 = 110$ mm.

$w_{bal} = 8 \times 11 \times 156 \times 0.110/(7.00)^2 = 30.8$ kN/m

Per m width: $w_{bal} = 30.8/7.40 = 4.16 \text{ kN/m}^2$

Net Load: $w_{net} = 7.70 - 4.16 = 3.54 \text{ kN/m}^2$

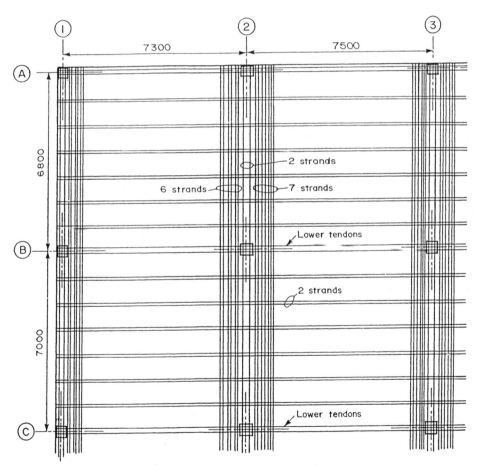

Strand layout: the strands are banded in one direction and in the other direction they are placed in pairs at equal spacing.

Fig. 10.9.11 Cable layout

2. Moments and Stresses
From Frame analysis (see Fig. 10.9.7.2)

$M_{AB} = -66.3$ kN · m

$M_{BA} = -144.4$ kN · m

$M_{BD} = -126.2$ kN · m

$M_{DB} = -97.3$ kN · m

$M_1 = 89.1$ kN · m

$M_2 = 49.0$ kN · m

Moment at face of column B:

$M_{BA} = -120.2$ kN · m

Column Strip:

Negative moment per metre width (CL. 18.13.2.1)

$$M = \frac{-120.2 \times 0.75}{3.45} = -26.1 \text{ kN} \cdot \text{m}$$

Stress in top fibre:

$$f_c = \frac{11(-156)10^3}{170 \times 7400} + \frac{26.1 \times 10^6}{170^2 \times 1000/6}$$

$$= -1.36 + 5.42 = +4.06 \text{ MPa} > 0.5 \sqrt{f'_c}$$

$$= 2.73 \text{ MPa.}$$

The average compressive stress criterion of Clause 18.13.2.3 is satisfied, i.e.,:

$f_{cp} = 1.36$ MPa > 0.8 MPa

Minimum non-prestressed steel required (Table 18-1)

$A_s = 0.00075 \times 170 \times 6600 = 842$ mm^2

It is anticipated that more nonprestressed steel will be required to provide the necessary factored flexural resistance (See 10.4).

Positive moment per meter width of column strip

$M = (89.4 \times 0.6) / 3.45 = 15.5$ kN · m/m

Stress in bottom fibre:

$$f_c = -1.36 + \frac{15.5 \times 10^6}{170^2 \times 1000/6}$$

$$= 1.86 \text{ MPa} < 2.73 \text{ MPa} > 0.2\sqrt{f'_c} = 1.1 \text{ MPa}$$

For steel provided see strength requirements.

Middle Strip:

Moment per metre width in middle strip at face of column

$$M = -\frac{-120.2 \times 0.25}{7.40 - 3.45} = -7.60 \text{ kN·m/m}$$

Top fibre stress

$$f_c = -1.36 - \left[\frac{-7.60 \times 10^6}{170^2 \times 1000/6}\right]$$

$$= 0.22 \text{ MPa} < 2.73 \text{ MPa.}$$ OK.

Positive moment per metre width of middle strip

$M = (89.1 \times 0.40) / 3.95 = 9.02$ kN · m/m

Bottom fibre stress

$$f_c = -1.36 + \left[\frac{9.02 \times 10^6}{170^2 \times 1000/6}\right] = +0.52 < 1.10 \text{ MPa}$$

No additional steel required.

3. Moments due to Factored Loads

The moments due to the factored load $w_f = 10.23$ kN/m^2 are the same as for Example 10.9 but the secondary moements, M''_p are different.

The values are listed below:

Support			A	B_{left}	B_{right}	C
$\alpha_D M_D + \alpha_L M_L$	kN · m		-144.8	-349.1	-329.8	-298.7
$\alpha_p M''_p$	kN.m		$+42.8$	$+24.0$	$+27.6$	$+3.2$
M_f	kN · m		-102.0	-325.1	-302.2	-265.5
V_f	kN		224.6	290.2	262.6	252.1
M_f at column face	kN · m		-58.6	-268.6	-251.2	-216.6
M_f −span	kN · m		231.0		153.3	

4. Factored Flexural Resistance

4.1 At Edge Column

Factored moments at face of column $M_f = -58.6$ kN · m

Assuming 4 tendons to be anchored within a width $(c_2 + 3h_s) = 910$ mm (CL. 13.11.2 and 13.12.2.2)

$A_p = 4 \times 140 = 560$ mm^2

$f_{pr} = 1206$ MPa — see Example 10.9.

Non-prestressed steel: Table 18-1.

$A_s = 0.00075 \times 170 (6800 - 400) = 816$ mm^2

3 No. 15 + 4 No. 10 bars with $A_s = 1000$ mm^2

$$a = \frac{0.9 \times 1206 \times 560 + 0.85 \times 1000 \times 400}{0.805 \times 0.6 \times 30 \times 910}$$

$$= 72 \text{ mm}$$

$$M_r = 0.9 \times 1206 \times 560(85-72/2) + 0.85 \times 1000$$

$$\times 400 (140-72/2)$$

$$= 65.0 \times 10^6 \text{ N·mm} = 65.0 \text{ kN·m} > 58.6 \text{ kN·m}$$
OK.

Note: The 3 No.15 bars are bent into column.

4.2 At Interior Column

Factored moment at face of column: $M_f = -268.6$ kN · m

Factored moment resistance provided by $11 - 15$ mm strands ($A_p = 1540$ mm^2) assuming $f_{pr} = 1200$ MPa:

$M_{rp} = 0.9 \times 1200 \times 1540 (140 - 10) = 216$ kN · m

Estimate of the non-prestressed steel required:

$$A_s = \frac{M_f - M_{rp}}{\phi_s f_y (d - \frac{a}{2})} = \frac{(268.6 - 216) \, 10^6}{0.85 \times 400(140 - 10)}$$

$$= 1180 \text{ mm}^2$$

Provide 12 No. 10 bars with $A_s = 1200$ mm^2.

Check:

$$c_y = \frac{0.9 \times 1670 \times 1540 + 0.85 \times 400 \times 1200}{0.805 \times 0.895 \times 0.6 \times 30 \times 7400} = 28 \text{ mm}$$

$$f_{pr} = 0.6 \times 1860 + \frac{8000}{9330}(140 - 28) = 1212 \text{ MPa}$$

$$a = \frac{0.9 \times 1212 \times 1540 + 0.85 \times 400 \times 1200}{0.805 \times 0.60 \times 30 \times 7400}$$

$$= 20 \text{ mm}$$

$$\begin{aligned} M_r &= [\,0.9 \times 1212 \times 1540\,(140 - 20/2) \\ &\quad + 0.85 \times 400 \times 1200\,(140 - 20/2)]\,10^{-6} \\ &= 271 \text{ kN} \cdot \text{m} > 268.6 \text{ kN} \cdot \text{m}. \end{aligned}$$

Provide 12 No. 10 bars @ 300 mm in column strip.

4.3 Span 1

Positive moment due to factored loads for full width of panel $M_f = 231$ kN $\cdot$ m

Factored moment resistance provided by tendons

$$M_{pr} = 216 \text{ kN} \cdot \text{m}$$

Non-prestressed steel required for strength

$$A_s = \frac{(231-216)\,10^6}{0.85 \times 400\,(140-10)} = 340 \text{ mm}^2$$

Provide 4 No. 10 bars in column strip.

5. Crack Control

According to Eq. 10.8.9 with No. 10 bars @ 300 mm at face of column B:

$$f_s = \frac{M_{net} - P_e\,(h/6 + e)}{A_s\,d}$$

$$= \frac{26.1 \times 10^6 - 232.2 \times 10^3\,(170/6 + 55)}{(100/0.30)\,140}$$

$$= 145 \text{ MPa}$$

$$\begin{aligned} z &= f_s\,(d_c\,A)^{1/3} \\ &= 145\,(30 \times 2 \times 30 \times 300)^{1/3} \\ &= 11800 \text{ N/mm} = 11.8 \text{ kN/mm} \\ &< 20 \text{ kN/mm . OK. (CL. 18.9.3).} \end{aligned}$$

Table 10.1a Flexural Resistance Coefficients, k_u, for Rectangular Elements with Bonded Prestressing Steel Only (Assuming $\phi_c = 0.60$ and $\phi_s = 0.90$)

	k_p = 0.28						k_p = 0.38						k_p = 0.48					
f'_c	30	40	50	60	70	80	30	40	50	60	70	80	30	40	50	60	70	80
α_1	.805	.790	.775	.760	.745	.730	.805	.790	.775	.760	.745	.730	.805	.790	.775	.760	.745	.730
β_1	.895	.870	.845	.820	.795	.770	.895	.870	.845	.820	.795	.770	.895	.870	.845	.820	.795	.770
w_{pu}	k_u						k_u						k_u					
.005	.0045	.0045	.0045	.0045	.0045	.0045	.0045	.0045	.0045	.0045	.0045	.0045	.0045	.0045	.0045	.0045	.0045	.0044
.010	.0089	.0089	.0089	.0089	.0088	.0088	.0089	.0088	.0088	.0088	.0088	.0088	.0088	.0089	.0088	.0088	.0088	.0088
.015	.0132	.0132	.0132	.0132	.0132	.0131	.0133	.0131	.0131	.0131	.0131	.0131	.0131	.0133	.0131	.0131	.0131	.0130
.020	.0175	.0174	.0174	.0174	.0174	.0174	.0177	.0174	.0174	.0173	.0173	.0173	.0173	.0176	.0173	.0173	.0172	.0172
.025	.0217	.0216	.0216	.0216	.0216	.0215	.0221	.0215	.0215	.0215	.0214	.0214	.0215	.0219	.0214	.0213	.0213	.0213
.030	.0258	.0258	.0257	.0257	.0257	.0256	.0264	.0256	.0256	.0255	.0255	.0254	.0255	.0262	.0254	.0253	.0253	.0252
.035	.0299	.0298	.0298	.0297	.0297	.0296	.0307	.0296	.0296	.0295	.0294	.0294	.0295	.0304	.0293	.0293	.0292	.0291
.040	.0339	.0338	.0338	.0337	.0336	.0336	.0349	.0336	.0335	.0334	.0333	.0332	.0334	.0346	.0332	.0331	.0330	.0329
.045	.0379	.0378	.0377	.0376	.0375	.0374	.0391	.0374	.0373	.0372	.0371	.0370	.0372	.0387	.0370	.0369	.0368	.0366
.050	.0417	.0417	.0416	.0415	.0413	.0412	.0433	.0412	.0411	.0410	.0409	.0407	.0410	.0428	.0407	.0406	.0404	.0402
.055	.0456	.0455	.0454	.0452	.0451	.0450	.0474	.0450	.0448	.0447	.0445	.0444	.0446	.0468	.0443	.0442	.0440	.0438
.060	.0494	.0492	.0491	.0489	.0488	.0486	.0516	.0486	.0485	.0483	.0481	.0479	.0483	.0508	.0479	.0477	.0475	.0473
.065	.0531	.0529	.0528	.0526	.0524	.0522	.0556	.0523	.0521	.0519	.0517	.0514	.0518	.0548	.0514	.0512	.0509	.0507
.070	.0567	.0566	.0564	.0562	.0560	.0558	.0597	.0558	.0556	.0554	.0551	.0549	.0553	.0587	.0548	.0546	.0543	.0540
.075	.0603	.0601	.0599	.0597	.0595	.0593	.0637	.0593	.0590	.0588	.0585	.0582	.0587	.0626	.0582	.0579	.0576	.0573
.080	.0639	.0637	.0634	.0632	.0629	.0627	.0677	.0627	.0624	.0622	.0619	.0615	.0621	.0664	.0615	.0611	.0608	.0604
.085	.0674	.0671	.0669	.0666	.0663	.0660	.0717	.0661	.0658	.0655	.0651	.0648	.0654	.0702	.0647	.0643	.0640	.0636
.090	.0708	.0706	.0703	.0700	.0697	.0693	.0756	.0694	.0690	.0687	.0683	.0679	.0686	.0740	.0679	.0675	.0670	.0666
.095	.0742	.0739	.0736	.0733	.0729	.0726	.0795	.0726	.0723	.0719	.0715	.0710	.0718	.0778	.0710	.0705	.0701	.0696
.100	.0776	.0772	.0769	.0765	.0761	.0757	.0834	.0758	.0754	.0750	.0746	.0741	.0749	.0815	.0740	.0735	.0730	.0725
.105	.0808	.0805	.0801	.0797	.0793	.0789	.0873	.0790	.0785	.0781	.0776	.0771	.0780	.0851	.0770	.0765	.0759	.0754
.110	.0841	.0837	.0833	.0829	.0824	.0819	.0911	.0820	.0816	.0811	.0806	.0800	.0810	.0888	.0799	.0794	.0788	.0782
.115	.0873	.0868	.0864	.0859	.0855	.0849	.0949	.0851	.0846	.0840	.0835	.0829	.0839	.0924	.0828	.0822	.0816	.0809
.120	.0904	.0899	.0895	.0890	.0884	.0879	.0986	.0880	.0875	.0869	.0863	.0857	.0868	.0959	.0856	.0850	.0843	.0836
.125	.0935	.0930	.0925	.0920	.0914	.0908	.1024	.0910	.0904	.0898	.0891	.0885	.0897	.0995	.0884	.0877	.0870	.0862
.130	.0965	.0960	.0955	.0949	.0943	.0937	.1061	.0938	.0932	.0926	.0919	.0912	.0924	.1030	.0911	.0904	.0896	.0888
.135	.0995	.0990	.0984	.0978	.0971	.0965	.1098	.0967	.0960	.0953	.0946	.0938	.0952	.1064	.0938	.0930	.0922	.0913
.140	.1024	.1019	.1012	.1006	.0999	.0992	.1134	.0994	.0988	.0980	.0972	.0964	.0979	.1099	.0964	.0956	.0947	.0938
.145	.1053	.1047	.1041	.1034	.1027	.1019	.1171	.1022	.1014	.1007	.0998	.0990	.1005	.1133	.0989	.0981	.0972	.0962
.150	.1082	.1075	.1068	.1061	.1054	.1046	.1207	.1049	.1041	.1033	.1024	.1015	.1031	.1167	.1014	.1005	.0996	.0986
.155	.1110	.1103	.1096	.1088	.1080	.1072	.1243	.1075	.1067	.1058	.1049	.1040	.1057	.1200	.1039	.1030	.1020	.1009
.160	.1138	.1130	.1123	.1115	.1106	.1097	.1278	.1101	.1092	.1083	.1074	.1064	.1082	.1233	.1063	.1053	.1043	.1032
.165	.1165	.1157	.1149	.1141	.1132	.1123	.1314	.1126	.1117	.1108	.1098	.1087	.1107	.1266	.1087	.1077	.1066	.1054
.170	.1191	.1183	.1175	.1166	.1157	.1147	.1349	.1151	.1142	.1132	.1121	.1111	.1131	.1299	.1110	.1100	.1088	.1076
.175	.1218	.1209	.1200	.1191	.1182	.1171	.1383	.1176	.1166	.1156	.1145	.1133	.1155	.1331	.1133	.1122	.1110	.1098
.180	.1244	.1235	.1226	.1216	.1206	.1195	.1418	.1200	.1190	.1179	.1168	.1156	.1178	.1363	.1156	.1144	.1132	.1119
.185	.1269	.1260	.1250	.1240	.1230	.1219	.1452	.1224	.1213	.1202	.1190	.1178	.1201	.1395	.1178	.1165	.1153	.1139
.190	.1294	.1284	.1274	.1264	.1253	.1241	.1487	.1247	.1236	.1224	.1212	.1199	.1223	.1426	.1199	.1187	.1173	.1159
.195	.1319	.1309	.1298	.1287	.1276	.1264	.1520	.1270	.1258	.1246	.1233	.1220	.1245	.1457	.1221	.1207	.1194	.1179
.200	.1343	.1333	.1322	.1310	.1298	.1286	.1554	.1292	.1280	.1268	.1255	.1241	.1267	.1488	.1241	.1228	.1213	.1199

Table 10.1b   Flexural Resistance Coefficients, k_u, for Rectangular Elements with Bonded Prestressing Steel Only (Assuming $\phi_c = 0.65$ and $\phi_s = 0.90$)

	$k_p =$ 0.28						$k_p =$ 0.38						$k_p =$ 0.48					
f'_c	30	40	50	60	70	80	30	40	50	60	70	80	30	40	50	60	70	80
α_1	.805	.790	.775	.760	.745	.730	.805	.790	.775	.760	.745	.730	.805	.790	.775	.760	.745	.730
β_1	.895	.870	.845	.820	.795	.770	.895	.870	.845	.820	.795	.770	.895	.870	.845	.820	.795	.770
w_{pu}	k_u						k_u						k_u					
.005	.0045	.0045	.0045	.0045	.0045	.0045	.0045	.0045	.0045	.0045	.0045	.0045	.0045	.0045	.0045	.0045	.0045	.0045
.010	.0089	.0089	.0089	.0089	.0089	.0089	.0089	.0089	.0088	.0088	.0088	.0088	.0088	.0089	.0088	.0088	.0088	.0088
.015	.0132	.0132	.0132	.0132	.0132	.0132	.0134	.0132	.0132	.0132	.0131	.0131	.0131	.0133	.0131	.0131	.0131	.0131
.020	.0175	.0175	.0175	.0175	.0174	.0174	.0177	.0174	.0174	.0174	.0174	.0173	.0174	.0177	.0173	.0173	.0173	.0173
.025	.0217	.0217	.0217	.0217	.0216	.0216	.0221	.0216	.0216	.0215	.0215	.0215	.0215	.0220	.0215	.0214	.0214	.0214
.030	.0259	.0259	.0258	.0258	.0258	.0257	.0264	.0257	.0257	.0256	.0256	.0255	.0256	.0262	.0255	.0255	.0254	.0254
.035	.0300	.0300	.0299	.0299	.0298	.0298	.0307	.0298	.0297	.0296	.0296	.0295	.0296	.0305	.0295	.0294	.0294	.0293
.040	.0341	.0340	.0339	.0339	.0338	.0337	.0350	.0337	.0337	.0336	.0335	.0334	.0336	.0347	.0334	.0333	.0332	.0331
.045	.0380	.0380	.0379	.0378	.0377	.0377	.0392	.0377	.0376	.0375	.0374	.0373	.0374	.0388	.0372	.0371	.0370	.0369
.050	.0420	.0419	.0418	.0417	.0416	.0415	.0434	.0415	.0414	.0413	.0412	.0410	.0412	.0429	.0410	.0409	.0407	.0406
.055	.0459	.0458	.0457	.0455	.0454	.0453	.0476	.0453	.0452	.0450	.0449	.0447	.0450	.0470	.0447	.0445	.0444	.0442
.060	.0497	.0496	.0494	.0493	.0492	.0490	.0517	.0490	.0489	.0487	.0486	.0484	.0487	.0510	.0483	.0481	.0480	.0477
.065	.0535	.0533	.0532	.0530	.0529	.0527	.0558	.0527	.0525	.0523	.0521	.0519	.0523	.0550	.0519	.0517	.0515	.0512
.070	.0572	.0570	.0569	.0567	.0565	.0563	.0599	.0563	.0561	.0559	.0557	.0554	.0558	.0590	.0554	.0551	.0549	.0546
.075	.0609	.0607	.0605	.0603	.0601	.0598	.0640	.0599	.0596	.0594	.0591	.0589	.0593	.0629	.0588	.0585	.0583	.0580
.080	.0645	.0643	.0641	.0638	.0636	.0633	.0680	.0634	.0631	.0628	.0626	.0623	.0628	.0668	.0622	.0619	.0616	.0612
.085	.0680	.0678	.0676	.0673	.0670	.0668	.0720	.0668	.0665	.0662	.0659	.0656	.0661	.0707	.0655	.0652	.0648	.0644
.090	.0716	.0713	.0710	.0708	.0705	.0701	.0760	.0702	.0699	.0695	.0692	.0688	.0694	.0745	.0688	.0684	.0680	.0676
.095	.0750	.0747	.0744	.0741	.0738	.0735	.0800	.0735	.0732	.0728	.0724	.0720	.0727	.0783	.0719	.0715	.0711	.0706
.100	.0784	.0781	.0778	.0775	.0771	.0767	.0839	.0768	.0764	.0760	.0756	.0752	.0759	.0821	.0751	.0746	.0742	.0737
.105	.0818	.0815	.0811	.0807	.0803	.0799	.0878	.0800	.0796	.0792	.0787	.0782	.0791	.0858	.0782	.0777	.0772	.0766
.110	.0851	.0848	.0844	.0840	.0835	.0831	.0916	.0832	.0827	.0823	.0818	.0813	.0822	.0895	.0812	.0807	.0801	.0795
.115	.0884	.0880	.0876	.0871	.0867	.0862	.0955	.0863	.0858	.0853	.0848	.0842	.0852	.0931	.0842	.0836	.0830	.0824
.120	.0916	.0912	.0907	.0903	.0898	.0893	.0993	.0894	.0889	.0883	.0878	.0872	.0882	.0968	.0871	.0865	.0858	.0852
.125	.0948	.0943	.0939	.0934	.0928	.0923	.1031	.0924	.0919	.0913	.0907	.0900	.0911	.1004	.0899	.0893	.0886	.0879
.130	.0979	.0974	.0969	.0964	.0958	.0952	.1069	.0954	.0948	.0942	.0935	.0928	.0940	.1039	.0928	.0921	.0913	.0906
.135	.1010	.1005	.0999	.0994	.0988	.0981	.1106	.0983	.0977	.0970	.0963	.0956	.0969	.1075	.0955	.0948	.0940	.0932
.140	.1041	.1035	.1029	.1023	.1017	.1010	.1143	.1012	.1005	.0998	.0991	.0983	.0997	.1110	.0982	.0975	.0966	.0958
.145	.1071	.1065	.1058	.1052	.1045	.1038	.1180	.1040	.1033	.1026	.1018	.1010	.1024	.1145	.1009	.1001	.0992	.0983
.150	.1100	.1094	.1087	.1080	.1073	.1066	.1217	.1068	.1061	.1053	.1045	.1036	.1052	.1179	.1035	.1027	.1018	.1008
.155	.1129	.1123	.1116	.1108	.1101	.1093	.1253	.1096	.1088	.1080	.1071	.1062	.1078	.1213	.1061	.1052	.1043	.1032
.160	.1158	.1151	.1144	.1136	.1128	.1120	.1289	.1123	.1114	.1106	.1097	.1087	.1104	.1247	.1087	.1077	.1067	.1056
.165	.1186	.1179	.1171	.1163	.1155	.1146	.1325	.1149	.1141	.1131	.1122	.1112	.1130	.1281	.1111	.1101	.1091	.1080
.170	.1214	.1206	.1198	.1190	.1181	.1172	.1361	.1175	.1166	.1157	.1147	.1136	.1155	.1314	.1136	.1125	.1114	.1103
.175	.1241	.1233	.1225	.1216	.1207	.1197	.1397	.1201	.1192	.1182	.1171	.1160	.1180	.1347	.1160	.1149	.1138	.1126
.180	.1269	.1260	.1251	.1242	.1232	.1222	.1432	.1226	.1216	.1206	.1195	.1184	.1205	.1380	.1184	.1172	.1160	.1148
.185	.1295	.1286	.1277	.1267	.1257	.1247	.1467	.1251	.1241	.1230	.1219	.1207	.1229	.1412	.1207	.1195	.1182	.1169
.190	.1321	.1312	.1303	.1293	.1282	.1271	.1502	.1276	.1265	.1254	.1242	.1230	.1253	.1445	.1230	.1217	.1204	.1191
.195	.1347	.1338	.1328	.1317	.1306	.1295	.1536	.1300	.1289	.1277	.1265	.1252	.1276	.1477	.1252	.1239	.1226	.1212
.200	.1373	.1363	.1352	.1341	.1330	.1318	.1571	.1324	.1312	.1300	.1287	.1274	.1299	.1508	.1274	.1261	.1247	.1232

Table 10.2 **Moment of Inertia of Rectangular Transformed Section**

$$I_{cr}/bd^3 = k^3/3 + n\rho_p(1-k)^2$$

$$k = \sqrt{(n\rho_p)^2 + 2(n\rho_p)} - n\rho_p$$

$$\rho_p = A_p/bd \quad n = E_s/E_c$$

	ρ_p	20	30	40	50	60	70	80
Normal Density Concrete (2400kg/m³)	0.0005	0.0038	0.0033	0.0030	0.0028	0.0026	0.0025	0.0023
	0.001	0.0073	0.0064	0.0058	0.0054	0.0050	0.0047	0.0045
	0.0015	0.0105	0.0092	0.0084	0.0078	0.0073	0.0069	0.0066
	0.002	0.0136	0.0120	0.0109	0.0101	0.0095	0.0090	0.0085
	0.0025	0.0165	0.0146	0.0133	0.0123	0.0116	0.0109	0.0104
	0.003	0.0193	0.0171	0.0156	0.0145	0.0136	0.0129	0.0123
	0.0035	0.0220	0.0195	0.0178	0.0165	0.0155	0.0147	0.0141
	0.004	0.0246	0.0218	0.0200	0.0186	0.0175	0.0166	0.0158
	0.0045	0.0271	0.0241	0.0220	0.0205	0.0193	0.0183	0.0175
	0.005	0.0296	0.0263	0.0241	0.0224	0.0211	0.0201	0.0192
	0.0055	0.0319	0.0285	0.0261	0.0243	0.0229	0.0217	0.0208
	0.006	0.0343	0.0305	0.0280	0.0261	0.0246	0.0234	0.0224
	0.0065	0.0365	0.0326	0.0299	0.0279	0.0263	0.0250	0.0239
	0.007	0.0387	0.0346	0.0318	0.0296	0.0280	0.0266	0.0254
	0.0075	0.0408	0.0365	0.0336	0.0313	0.0296	0.0281	0.0269
	0.008	0.0429	0.0384	0.0353	0.0330	0.0312	0.0297	0.0284
	0.0085	0.0450	0.0403	0.0371	0.0347	0.0327	0.0312	0.0298
	0.009	0.0470	0.0421	0.0388	0.0363	0.0343	0.0326	0.0313
	0.0095	0.0489	0.0439	0.0405	0.0378	0.0358	0.0341	0.0326
	0.01	0.0508	0.0457	0.0421	0.0394	0.0373	0.0355	0.0340
Semi-Low Density Concrete (2000kg/m³)	0.0005	0.0049	0.0043	0.0039	0.0036	0.0034	0.0032	0.0030
	0.001	0.0093	0.0082	0.0075	0.0069	0.0065	0.0061	0.0058
	0.0015	0.0134	0.0118	0.0108	0.0100	0.0093	0.0088	0.0084
	0.002	0.0172	0.0152	0.0139	0.0129	0.0121	0.0114	0.0109
	0.0025	0.0209	0.0185	0.0169	0.0157	0.0147	0.0139	0.0133
	0.003	0.0243	0.0216	0.0197	0.0183	0.0172	0.0164	0.0156
	0.0035	0.0276	0.0245	0.0225	0.0209	0.0197	0.0187	0.0178
	0.004	0.0308	0.0274	0.0251	0.0234	0.0220	0.0209	0.0200
	0.0045	0.0339	0.0302	0.0277	0.0258	0.0243	0.0231	0.0221
	0.005	0.0368	0.0329	0.0302	0.0282	0.0266	0.0252	0.0241
	0.0055	0.0397	0.0355	0.0326	0.0304	0.0287	0.0273	0.0261
	0.006	0.0425	0.0380	0.0349	0.0326	0.0308	0.0293	0.0281
	0.0065	0.0451	0.0405	0.0372	0.0348	0.0329	0.0313	0.0300
	0.007	0.0478	0.0428	0.0395	0.0369	0.0349	0.0332	0.0318
	0.0075	0.0503	0.0452	0.0416	0.0390	0.0368	0.0351	0.0336
	0.008	0.0528	0.0474	0.0438	0.0410	0.0388	0.0369	0.0354
	0.0085	0.0552	0.0497	0.0458	0.0429	0.0406	0.0388	0.0371
	0.009	0.0575	0.0518	0.0479	0.0449	0.0425	0.0405	0.0389
	0.0095	0.0598	0.0539	0.0498	0.0468	0.0443	0.0423	0.0405
	0.01	0.0621	0.0560	0.0518	0.0486	0.0461	0.0440	0.0422

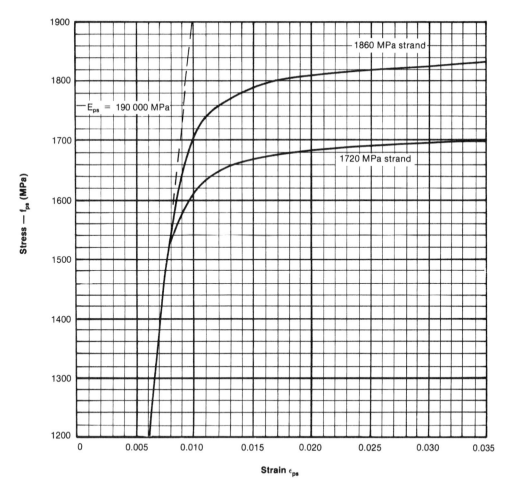

These curves are based on the following equations

For $\epsilon_{ps} \leq 0.008$, $f_{ps} = 190\,000\,\epsilon_{ps}$ (MPa)

Grade 1720 — For $\epsilon_{ps} > 0.008$, $f_{ps} = 1710 - \dfrac{0.400}{\epsilon_{ps} - 0.006} < 0.98\,f_{pu}$ (MPa)

Grade 1860 — For $\epsilon_{ps} > 0.008$, $f_{ps} = 1848 - \dfrac{0.517}{\epsilon_{ps} - 0.0065} < 0.98\,f_{pu}$ (MPa)

The above curves exceed the minimum requirements of CSA Standard G279. The designer should check that the properties of the steel used correspond to the assumed values.

Fig. 10.1   Typical stress-strain curve, 7-wire stress-relieved and low-relaxation prestressing strand

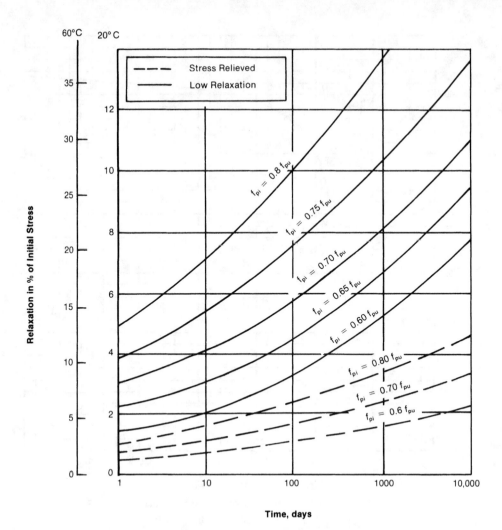

Fig. 10.2 Intrinsic relaxation of stress relieved and low relaxation strand for different levels of initial stress f_{psi} at 20°C and 60°C.

CPCA Concrete Design Handbook

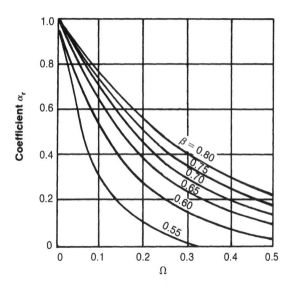

Fig. 10.3 Relaxation reduction coefficient α_r as a function

of $\Omega = \dfrac{\Delta f_s}{f_{pi}}$ for different values of $\beta = \dfrac{f_{pi}}{f_{pu}}$

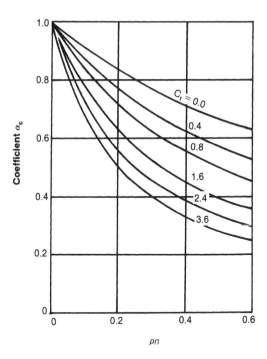

Fig. 10.4 Coefficient α_c as a function of ρn and C_t

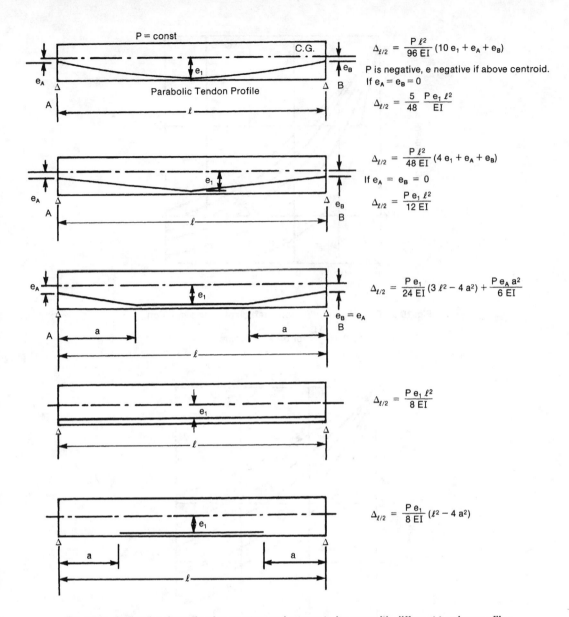

Fig. 10.5 Deflection formulas for prestressed concrete beams with different tendon profiles.

The formulas shown in the figure are:

$$\Delta_{\ell/2} = \frac{P\,\ell^2}{96\,EI}\,(10\,e_1 + e_A + e_B)$$

P is negative, e negative if above centroid.
If $e_A = e_B = 0$

$$\Delta_{\ell/2} = \frac{5}{48}\,\frac{P\,e_1\,\ell^2}{EI}$$

$$\Delta_{\ell/2} = \frac{P\,\ell^2}{48\,EI}\,(4\,e_1 + e_A + e_B)$$

If $e_A = e_B = 0$

$$\Delta_{\ell/2} = \frac{P\,e_1\,\ell^2}{12\,EI}$$

$$\Delta_{\ell/2} = \frac{P\,e_1}{24\,EI}\,(3\,\ell^2 - 4\,a^2) + \frac{P\,e_A\,a^2}{6\,EI}$$

$$\Delta_{\ell/2} = \frac{P\,e_1\,\ell^2}{8\,EI}$$

$$\Delta_{\ell/2} = \frac{P\,e_1}{8\,EI}\,(\ell^2 - 4\,a^2)$$

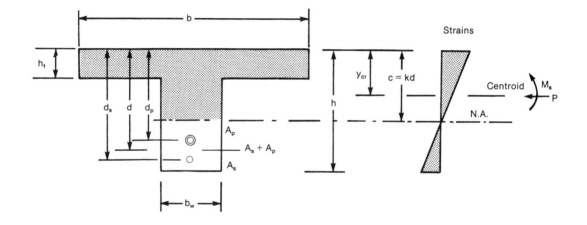

Fig. 10.6   T-Section subjected to M_s and decompression force P

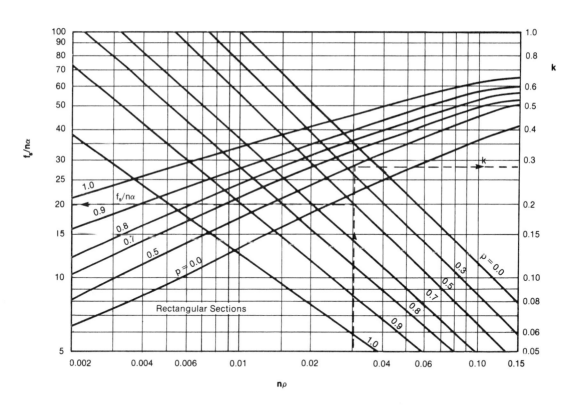

Fig. 10.7 $f_s/n\alpha$ and k versus $n\rho$ for rectangular sections.

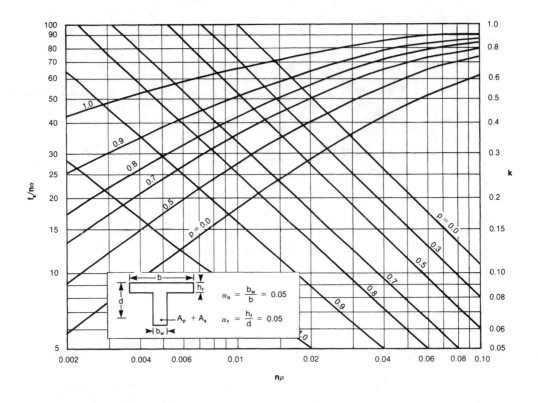

Fig. 10.8.1 $f_s/n\alpha$ and k versus $n\rho$ for T-beams with $\alpha_b = 0.05$ and $\alpha_f = 0.05$.

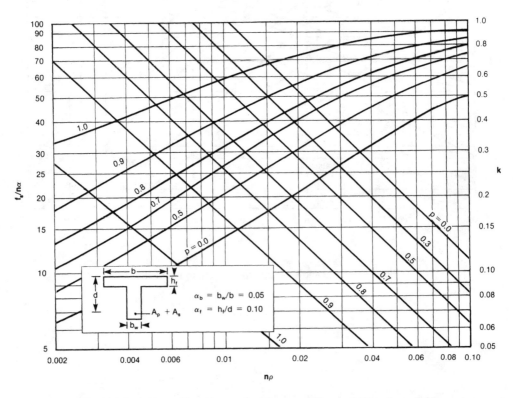

Fig. 10.8.2 $f_s/n\alpha$ and k versus $n\rho$ for T-beams with $\alpha_b = 0.05$ and $\alpha_f = 0.10$.

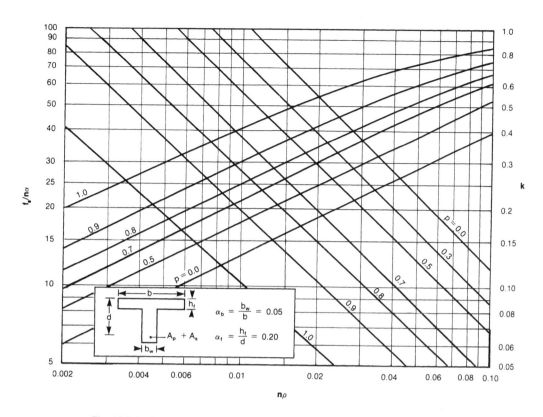

Fig. 10.8.3 $f_s/n\alpha$ and k versus $n\rho$ for T-beams with $\alpha_b = 0.05$ and $\alpha_f = 0.20$.

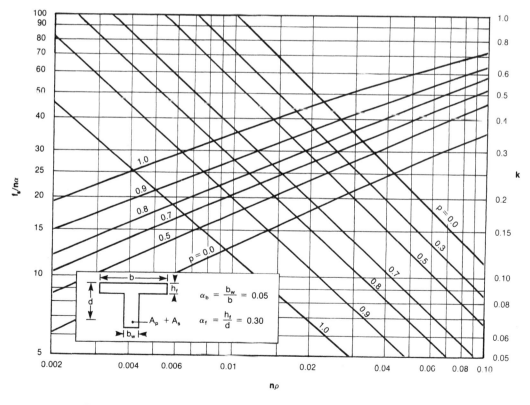

Fig. 10.8.4 $f_s/n\alpha$ and k versus $n\rho$ for T-beams with $\alpha_b = 0.05$ and $\alpha_f = 0.30$.

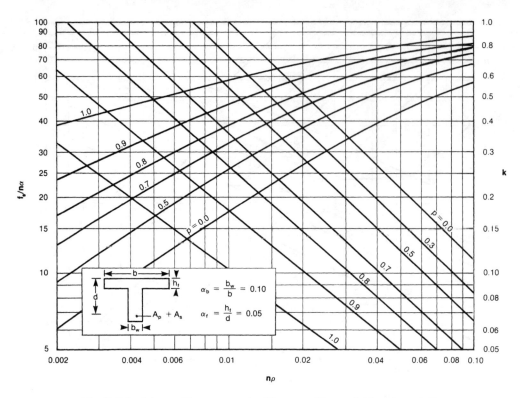

Fig. 10.8.5 $f_s/n\alpha$ and k versus nρ for T-beams with $\alpha_b = 0.10$ and $\alpha_f = 0.05$.

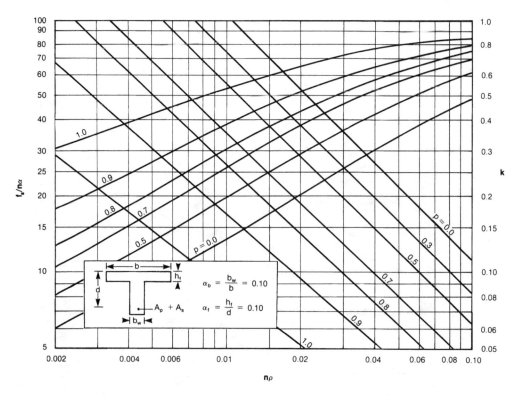

Fig. 10.8.6 $f_s/n\alpha$ and k versus nρ for T-beams with $\alpha_b = 0.10$ and $\alpha_f = 0.10$.

CPCA Concrete Design Handbook

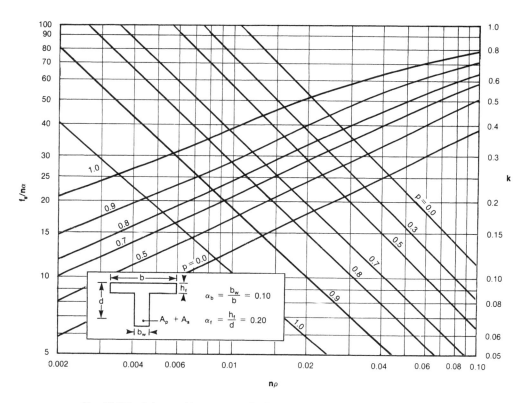

Fig. 10.8.7 $f_s/n\alpha$ and k versus $n\rho$ for T-beams with $\alpha_b = 0.10$ and $\alpha_f = 0.20$.

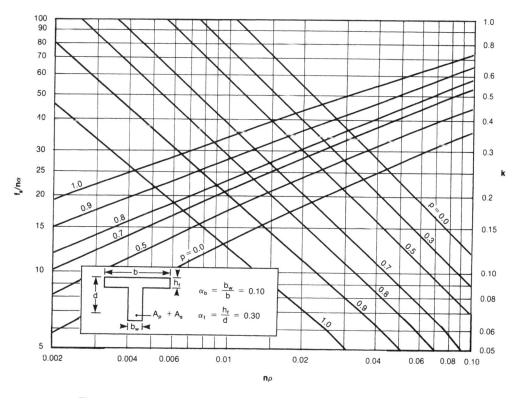

Fig. 10.8.8 $f_s/n\alpha$ and k versus $n\rho$ for T-beams with $\alpha_b = 0.10$ and $\alpha_f = 0.30$.

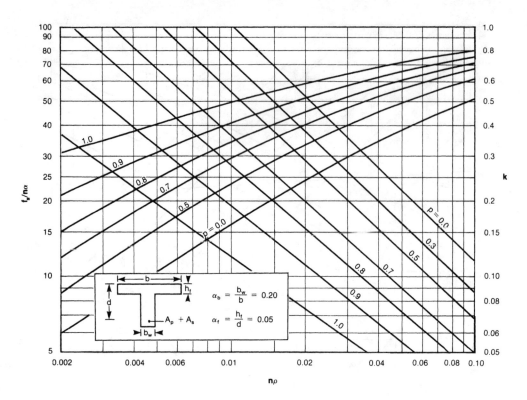

Fig. 10.8.9 $f_s/n\alpha$ and k versus $n\rho$ for T-beams with $\alpha_b = 0.20$ and $\alpha_f = 0.05$.

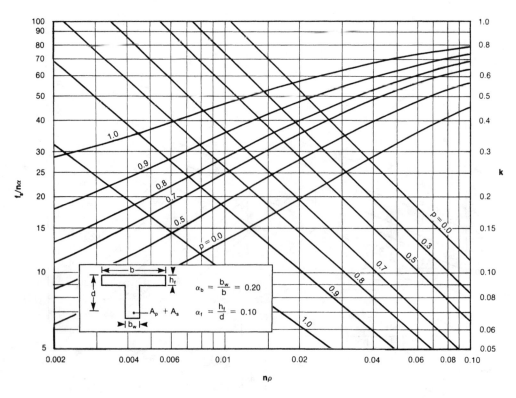

Fig. 10.8.10 $f_s/n\alpha$ and k versus $n\rho$ for T-beams with $\alpha_b = 0.20$ and $\alpha_f = 0.10$.

CPCA Concrete Design Handbook

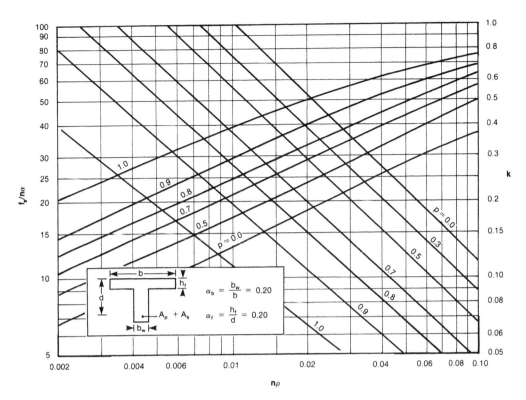

Fig. 10.8.11 $f_s/n\alpha$ and k versus nρ for T-beams with $\alpha_b = 0.20$ and $\alpha_f = 0.20$.

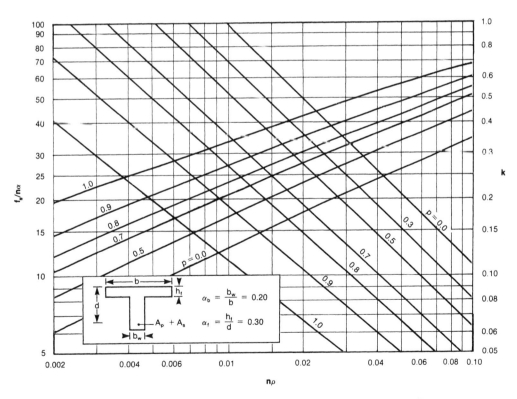

Fig. 10.8.12 $f_s/n\alpha$ and k versus nρ for T-beams with $\alpha_b = 0.20$ and $\alpha_f = 0.30$.

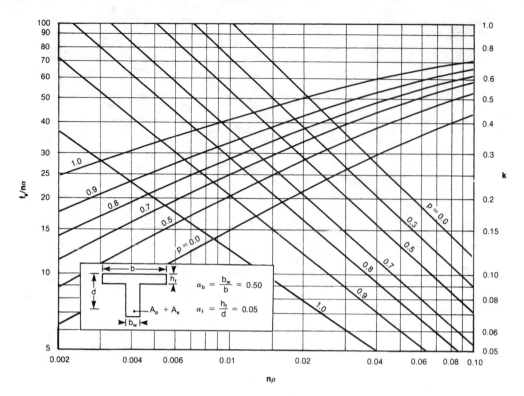

Fig. 10.8.13 $f_s/n\alpha$ and k versus $n\rho$ for T-beams with $\alpha_b = 0.50$ and $\alpha_f = 0.05$.

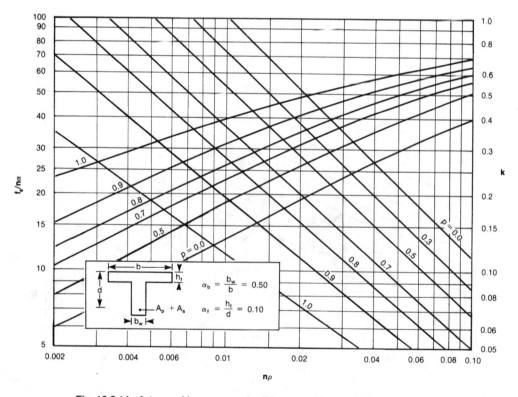

Fig. 10.8.14 $f_s/n\alpha$ and k versus $n\rho$ for T-beams with $\alpha_b = 0.50$ and $\alpha_f = 0.10$.

CPCA Concrete Design Handbook

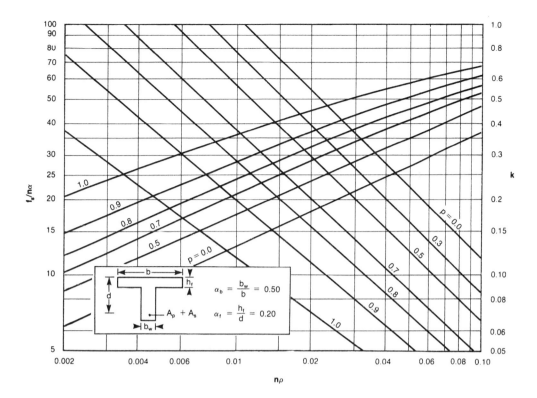

Fig. 10.8.15 $f_s/n\alpha$ and k versus $n\rho$ for T-beams with $\alpha_b = 0.50$ and $\alpha_f = 0.20$.

11

Seismic Design

By Denis Mitchell,
Patrick Paultre and
Michael P. Collins

Chapter 11
Seismic Design

11.1 INTRODUCTION

The National Building Code of Canada (NBC) gives the minimum lateral seismic force, V, for the design of structures as:

$$V = \frac{V_e}{R} U$$

where

V_e = equivalent lateral seismic force representing elastic response

R = force modification factor that reflects the capability of a structure to dissipate energy through inelastic behaviour

U = factor representing level of protection based on experience (U = 0.6)

The equivalent lateral seismic force representing elastic response, V_e is:

$$V_e = vSIFW$$

where

v = zonal velocity ratio

S = seismic response factor

I = seismic importance factor equal to 1.5 for post-disaster buildings, 1.3 for schools and 1.0 for all other buildings

F = foundation factor which varies from 1.0 for buildings founded on rock to 2.0 for buildings founded on very soft and fine-grained soils with depths greater than 15 m

W = dead load plus the following:

  25% of the design snow load

  60% of storage loads

  full contents of tanks

The designer chooses the type of lateral load resisting system and the force modification factor, R. The value of R depends on the ability of the structure to dissipate energy through inelastic response and therefore is a function of the type of lateral load resisting system and the manner in which the structural members are designed and detailed. Table 11.1 provides a guide for the required design and detailing provisions of CSA Standard A23.3 associated with the corresponding R factors.

Table 11.1 Design and Detailing Provisions Required for Different Reinforced Concrete Structural Systems and Different R Factors

Cases in NBC	R	Type of Lateral Load Resisting System	Summary of Design and Detailing Requirements in CSA Standard A23.3 with Applicable Clauses in Brackets
10	4.0	ductile moment-resisting frame	(a) beams capable of significant flexural hinging (21.3 and 21.7) (b) columns properly confined and stronger than the beams (21.4 and 21.7) (c) joints properly confined and capable of transmitting shears from beam hinging (21.6)
11	4.0	ductile coupled wall	(a) at least 66% of base overturning moment resisted by wall must be carried by axial tension and compression in coupled wall resulting from shears in coupling beams (b) wall strength to permit nominal strength of coupling beams to be achieved (21.5.8) (c) ductile coupling beams capable of developing flexural hinging or provide specially detailed diagonal reinforcement (21.5.8)
12	3.5	ductile flexural wall	(a) wall capable of significant flexural hinging without local instability and without shear failure (21.5 and 21.7)
12	3.5	ductile partially coupled wall	(a) wall strength to permit nominal strength of coupling beams to be achieved (21.5.8) (b) ductile coupling beams capable of developing flexural hinging or provide specially detailed diagonal reinforcement (21.5.8)
13	2.0	moment-resisting frame with nominal ductility	(a) beams and columns must satisfy nominal detailing requirements (21.9.2.1-2) (b) beams and columns must have minimum shear strength (21.9.2.3) (c) joints must satisfy nominal detailing requirements and must be capable of transmitting shears from beam hinging (21.9.2.4)
14	2.0	wall with nominal ductility	(a) walls must satisfy dimensional limitations and minimum detailing requirements (21.9.3.1-3) (b) walls must have minimum shear strength (21.9.3.4)
15	1.5	other lateral-force-resisting systems not defined above	(a) beams and columns (10) (b) joints (7.7.3 and 11.8) (c) walls (10 or 14)

11.2 DUCTILITY CONSIDERATIONS

Seismic design is concerned not only with providing the required strength but also with providing minimum levels of ductility and choosing appropriate structural systems. These goals may be achieved by:

(i) choosing structural systems which are as symmetrical as possible in plan and as uniform as possible in elevation;

(ii) designing the primary lateral load resisting structural components so that desirable energy dissipating systems will form (e.g., "weak-beam, strong column" response);

(iii) detailing the energy dissipating regions of the primary lateral load resisting components to

ensure that substantial inelastic deformations can be tolerated without significant loss of strength, and

(iv) ensuring that secondary members which are not part of the lateral load resisting system can maintain their gravity load carrying capacity as they undergo the required lateral deformations.

In the design of ductile members it is necessary to determine the hierarchy of strengths of different members. To ensure that certain hierarchy of strengths are achieved the CSA Standard defines "probable", "nominal" and "factored" resistances. Table 11.2 summarizes the various types of flexural resistances used in the CSA Standard and suggests approximate relationships between these resistances.

Table 11.2   Factored, Nominal and Probable Resistances

Type of flexural resistance	Definition	Where used	Approximate relationships for members subjected to	
			Flexure	Flexure and axial load
M_r = factored flexural resistance	calculated using $\phi_c = 0.60$ and $\phi_s = 0.85$	all members must satisfy $M_r \geq M_f$ 8.1.3		
M_n = nominal flexural resistance	calculated using $\phi_c = 1.00$ and $\phi_s = 1.00$	to ensure columns stronger than beams at a joint $\Sigma M_{rc} \geq 1.1 \Sigma M_{nb}$ 21.4.2.2	$M_n \approx 1.20\, M_r$	
M_p = probable flexural resistance	calculated using $\phi_c = 1.00$ and $\phi_s = 1.25$	to ensure shear capacities exceed shear corresponding to flexural hinging 21.7.2	$M_p \approx 1.47\, M_r$	$M_p \approx 1.57\, M_r$

11.3 LOADING CASES

For loading combinations including earthquake the factored load combinations shall include:

$$1.0D + \gamma(1.0E)$$

and either:

(i) for storage and assembly occupancies:

$$1.0D + \gamma(1.0L + 1.0E)$$

(ii) for all other occupancies:

$$1.0D + \gamma(0.5L + 1.0E)$$

where the importance factor, γ, is taken as 1.0 for all buildings, except where it can be shown that collapse is not likely to cause injury or other serious consequences, where it shall not be less than 0.8.

11.4 DESIGN OF DUCTILE MOMENT-RESISTING FRAMES

To illustrate the procedures involved in designing a ductile moment-resisting frame, a six-storey frame building located in Vancouver is treated. Example 11.1 describes the building, the loading and the structural analysis including torsion and P-Delta effects.

The design of typical beams in this ductile moment-resisting frame building is described in Example 11.2. A typical column is designed in Example 11.3. An interior beam-column joint is designed in Example 11.4.

11.5 DESIGN OF DUCTILE COUPLED WALL AND DUCTILE FLEXURAL WALL STRUCTURE

To illustrate the procedures involved in designing a ductile coupled wall, a coupled wall in a 12-storey reinforced concrete building located in Montreal is described in Examples 11.5, 11.6 and 11.7.

EXAMPLE 11.1 DETERMINATION OF DESIGN FORCES FOR SIX-STOREY DUCTILE MOMENT-RESISTING FRAME BUILDING

The six-storey reinforced concrete frame building shown in Fig. 11.1 is located in Vancouver and is to be designed with R = 4.0.

1. *Description of Building*

The six-storey reinforced concrete office building has 7 – 6 m bays in the N-S direction and 3 bays in the E-W direction which consist of 2 – 9 m office bays and a central 6 m corridor bay.

The interior columns are all 500 × 500 mm while the exterior columns are 450 × 450 mm. The one-way slab floor system consists of a slab 110 mm thick spanning in the E-W direction supported by beams in the N-S direction. The secondary beams supporting the slab are 300 mm wide × 350 mm deep (from top of slab to bottom of beam). The beams of both the N-S and E-W frames are 400 mm wide × 600 mm deep for the first three storeys and 400 × 550 mm for the top three storeys.

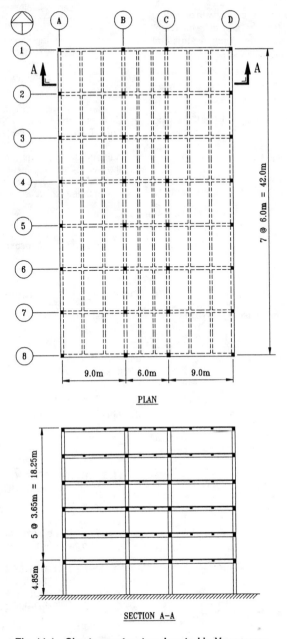

PLAN

SECTION A-A

Fig. 11.1   Six storey structure located in Vancouver

2. *Material Properties*

    Concrete: normal density concrete with
                      $f'_c = 30$ MPa
    Reinforcement: $f_y = 400$ MPa

3. *Gravity and Wind Loadings*

    Floor live load: 2.4 kN /m^2 on typical office floors
                       4.8 kN /m^2 on 6 m wide corridor
                       bay
    Roof load: 2.2 kN /m^2 full snow load
                       1.6 kN /m^2 mechanical services
                       loading in 6 m wide strip over
                       corridor bay
    Dead loads: self-weight of reinforced concrete
                       members calculated at 24 kN /m^3
                       1.0 kN /m^2 partition loading on all
                       floors
                       0.5 kN /m^2 mechanical services
                       loading on all floors
                       0.5 kN /m^2 roof insulation
    Wind loading: 1.84 kN /m^2 net lateral pressure
                       for top 4 storeys
                       1.75 kN /m^2 net lateral pressure
                       for bottom 2 storeys

4. *Seismic loading*

    For this structure located in Vancouver the acceleration-related seismic zone, Z_a, is 4, the velocity-related seismic zone, Z_v, is 4 and the zonal velocity ratio, v, is 0.20.

    The seismic response factor, S, is dependent on the fundamental period, T, of the structure. For this moment-resisting frame structure $T = 0.1N$, where N is the total number of storeys above the exterior grade. Hence for this six-storey structure $T = 0.6$ s. Since $T > 0.50$ s, the seismic response factor is determined as:

$$S = \frac{1.5}{\sqrt{T}} = \frac{1.5}{\sqrt{0.6}} = 1.94$$

Other factors in the base shear equation are:
    I = 1.0 (office building)
    F =1.0 (building founded on rock)

Hence the seismic base shear, V, is:

$$V = \frac{vSIFW}{R} U$$

$$= \frac{0.20 \times 1.94 \times 1.0 \times 1.0W}{4.0} 0.6$$

$$= 0.058 \ W$$

The calculations of the seismic lateral forces at each floor level are summarized in Table 11.3

Table 11.3   Lateral Load Calculations for Each Floor Level

Floor	h_i, m	W_i, kN	h_iW_i, kN·m	F_x, kN	$F_x/8$, kN
roof	23.10	7457	172,257	719.7	90.0
6	19.45	7365	143,258	598.5	74.8
5	15.80	7365	116,374	486.2	60.8
4	12.15	7526	91,445	382.1	47.8
3	8.50	7526	63,974	267.3	33.4
2	4.85	7673	37,212	155.5	19.4
Total	0.00	44,913	624,514	2,609.2	326.2

4. *Analysis Assumptions*

    To determine the member forces the structure was analyzed using a linear elastic plane frame program in the E-W and N-S directions. To make allowances for cracking, member stiffnesses were assumed to be 0.5 of the gross EI for all beams and 0.8 of the gross EI for all columns. The analysis model and lateral forces are illustrated in Fig. 11.2.

    To illustrate the requirements for the design of a ductile moment-resisting frame, components of a typical interior E-W frame will be designed in Examples 11.2, 11.3 and 11.4.

5. *Accounting for Torsional Eccentricity*

    We are analyzing the building for lateral forces in the E-W direction. This building has a symmetrical distribution of masses and stiffness at each floor level and hence the eccentricity, e_x, between the centre of mass and the centre of rigidity is zero. The applied torsional moment, T_x, at each level throughout the building can be found from:

$$T_x = F_x (\pm 0.1 \ D_{nx})$$

where F_x is the lateral force applied at level x and D_{nx} is the plan dimension of the building in direction of the computed eccentricity. The term $0.1D_{nx}F_x$ represents the accidental applied torsional moment at each level. For this structure the applied torsional eccentricity for lateral forces in the E-W direction is $\pm 0.1 \times 42 = \pm 4.2$m.

    The calculations of the additional lateral loads due to torsion are summarized in Table 11.4. The analysis of this structure was carried out using a two-dimensional frame model. In order to account for the torsional moments it is assumed, that for simplicity the torsion will be taken by the frames in the E-W direction. The 8 frames, F1 to F8, in the E-W direction have the same stiffness therefore the shears in these frames induced by torsion will be proportional to their distance from the centre of stiffness. Hence, $F2_{xt} = (15/21)F1_{xt}$, $F3_{xt} = (9/21)F1_{xt}$, $F4_{xt} = (3/21)F1_{xt}$. From statics the shear induced due to torsion in frame 1 at level x is $F1_{xt} = T_x/72$.

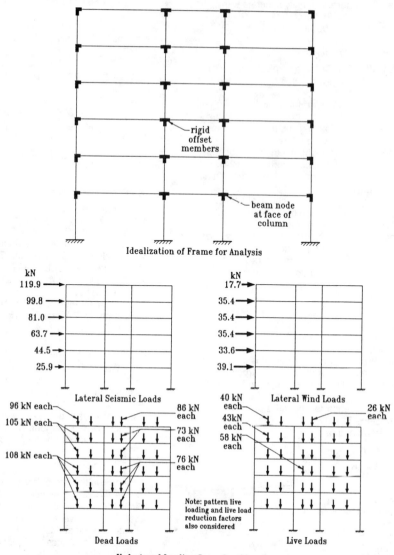

Idealization of Frame for Analysis

Lateral Seismic Loads

kN
119.9 →
99.8 →
81.0 →
63.7 →
44.5 →
25.9 →

Lateral Wind Loads

kN
17.7 →
35.4 →
35.4 →
35.4 →
33.6 →
39.1 →

Dead Loads

96 kN each
105 kN each
108 kN each

86 kN each
73 kN each
76 kN each

Live Loads

40 kN each
43 kN each
58 kN each

26 kN each

Note: pattern live loading and live load reduction factors also considered

Unfactored Loading Cases Considered
in Design of Typical Interior Frame

Fig. 11.2 Unfactored loading cases considered in design of typical interior frame.

Table 11.4   Additional Seismic Forces due to Torsion

Floor	F_x, kN	T_x, kN·m	$F1_{xt}$, kN
Roof	719.7	3002.7	42.0
5	598.5	2513.8	34.9
4	486.2	2042.1	28.4
3	382.1	1604.6	22.3
2	267.3	1122.6	15.6
1	155.5	653.0	9.1
Total	2609.2	10,958.7	152.2

Table 11.5   Design Seismic Lateral Loads on Frame 2

Floor level	Lateral load without torsion $F2_x = F_x/8$, kN	Additional lateral load due to torsion $F2_{xt} = 15/21\ F1_{xt}$, kN	Total lateral load, kN
Roof	90.0	30.0	119.9
6	74.8	24.9	99.8
5	60.8	20.3	81.0
4	47.8	15.9	63.7
3	33.4	11.1	44.5
2	19.4	6.5	25.9
Total	326.2	108.7	434.9

For illustration purposes frame 2 will be designed. This frame, although it has a smaller torsional shear than frame 1, will require more reinforcement than frame 1 because it carries larger dead and live loads. Table 11.5 summarizes the lateral loads taken by frame 2.

It is evident that, even for this symmetrical building, the accidental torsion significantly increases the design forces. For this case, the torsion on frame 2 increases the design shear by about one-third.

7. *Deflections and Drift Ratios*

In seismic design it is necessary to multiply the elastic deflections by R to give realistic values of the anticipated lateral displacements. These increased displacements account for the total anticipated displacements, including the inelastic effects. Furthermore, it is required by the NBCC that sway effects produced by vertical loads acting on the structure in its displayed configuration be taken into account. In order to investigate the influence of P-Delta effects with the inelastic displacements included we will analyze frame 2. This analysis will be carried out using a frame analysis computer program which accounts for second order effects by the addition of the so-called geometric stiffness. In order to carry out this analysis it is necessary to include the vertical loading on the structure. To account for the inelastic displacements the elastic member stiffnesses are reduced by dividing by R = 4.0.

The lateral displacement of the second floor level without P-delta, but accounting for inelastic displacements, is 53 mm. Including P-Delta effects results in an increase in displacement to 65 mm. The roof displacement is 198 mm without P-Delta effects and 227 mm with P-Delta included. The inter-storey drift ratio for the first storey of frame 2 is 65 /4850 = 0.013. Since this is less than the limit of 0.02, this drift is considered acceptable. The exterior frame would have slightly larger drifts due to the effects of torsion.

EXAMPLE 11.2 DESIGN OF BEAM IN A DUCTILE MOMENT-RESISTING FRAME

To illustrate the procedures involved in designing a beam in a ductile moment-resisting frame, a typical first storey interior beam described in Example 11.1 will be designed below. The details of the beam and column framing are given in Fig. 11.3.

1. *Determination of Design Moments*

The moments in the beams resulting from dead load, D, live load, L, and earthquake loading, E, as determined from frame analyses, are in Fig. 11.4. Note that the moments are given at the face of the columns. Since most of the gravity loading in beams AB, BC and CD is introduced at the locations of the secondary beams, the small uniformly distributed loading has been approximated by additional concentrated loads at the secondary beam locations.

Table 11.6 gives the unfactored moments at critical locations and also gives the factored moment combinations which need to be considered.

2. *Moment Redistribution and Moment Envelopes*

Instead of designing each of the critical sections for the maximum factored moments given in Table 11.6, moment redistribution will be used to reduce some of the maximum design moments. Since the beams in a ductile moment-resisting frame structure are designed and detailed to exhibit considerable ductility the maximum redistribution of 20%, permitted by Clause 9.2.4, will be used.

While it is possible to redistribute the earthquake moments[1], care must be exercised to ensure that the total column shears in any one storey remain unchanged after redistribution. A simpler approach is to redistribute only the dead load and live load moments.

In order to reduce the magnitude of the negative moments at locations BA and BC, the dead and 50% of live load support moments are reduced. The moment at BC is reduced by the maximum permitted amount (20%) and the negative moment at BA is reduced by 13.4%. The positive moments are increased by the appropriate amounts. The resulting moments are summarized in Table 11.7.

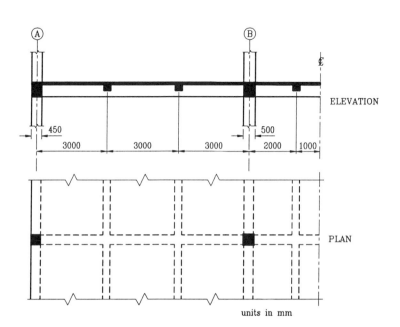

Fig. 11.3 Typical beam and column framing.

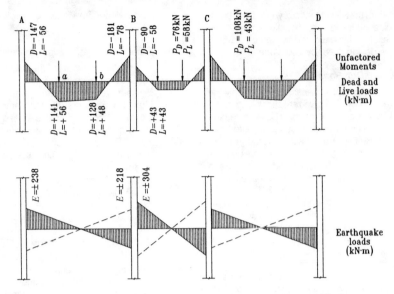

Note: Wind load is not critical.

Fig. 11.4 Loading cases on typical interior beam at second floor level.

Table 11.6   Moments at Critical Locations (kN · m) Before Redistribution

	AB	a	b	BA	BC	c
D	−147	+132	+109	−209	−112	+21
L	−56	+52	+40	−90	−72	+29
E	−238	−90	+71	+218	−304	−111
1.25D+1.5L	−268	+243	+196	−396	−248	+70
1.0D+1.0E	−385	+42	+180	+9	−416	−90
1.0D−1.0E	+91	+222	+38	−427	+192	+132
1.0D+0.5L+1.0E	−413*	+68	+200*	−36	−452*	−75
1.0D+0.5L−1.0E	+63	+248*	+58	−472*	+156	+146*

* controlling load cases

Table 11.7   Moments at Critical Locations (kN · m) After Redistribution

	AB	a	b	BA	BC	c
D	−147	+141	+128	−181	−90	+43
L	−56	+56	+48	−78	−58	+43
E	−238	−90	+71	+218	−304	−111
1.25D+1.5L	−268	+260*	+232*	−343	−200	+118
1.0D+1.0E	−385	+51	+199	+37	−394	−68
1.0D−1.0E	+91	+231	+57	−399	+214	+154
1.0D+0.5L+1.0E	−413*	+79	+223	−2	−423*	−46
1.0D+0.5L−1.0E	+63	+259	+81	−438*	+185	+175*

* controlling load case

CPCA Concrete Design Handbook

3. *Design of Flexural Reinforcement at Critical Sections*

(a) Top bars at column faces

In deciding on the appropriate top reinforcement, note that Clause 21.6.5.6 limits the diameter, d_b, passing through the joint to $\ell_j /24$ for this normal density concrete structure. Thus for this case the maximum diameter of beam bars passing through the interior columns is $500 /24 = 21$ mm. Hence the maximum beam bar size is No. 20.

At column B, a factored moment resistance of at least 438 kN·m is required. Assuming a flexural lever arm of $0.75h = 0.75 \times 0.600 = 0.450$ m. The required area of top bars would be $438 \times 1000 /(0.450 \times 0.85 \times 400) = 2862$ mm^2. Assuming that $4 -$ No. 10 bars in the slab are effective (Clause 21.4.2.2 suggests that slab reinforcement within a distance of $3h_f$ from sides of beam is effective) then 2462 mm^2 of additional reinforcement is required. Note that it is unwise to be too conservative when designing the top reinforcement since beam shears, joint shears, column moments and column shears are all increased if the flexural capacity at the end of the beam is increased.

Let us try an arrangement of $8 -$ No. 20 bars as shown in Fig. 11.5. Keeping in mind that the positive moment resistance of the beam needs to be at least one-half of the negative moment resistance, try using 4 - No. 20 bars on the bottom of the beam.

Accounting for the presence of the compression reinforcement, the depth of compression, c, is found to be 117 mm and the factored negative moment resistance is 442 kN·m. Hence the moment capacity is satisfactory.

The required minimum top and bottom reinforcement, $A_{s,min}$, from Clause 21.3.2.1 is

$A_{s,min} = 1.4\ b_w\ d\ /f_y = 1.4 \times 400 \times 519 /400 = 727$ mm$^2 \leq 1200$ mm^2 O.K.

The maximum reinforcement permitted $= 0.025\ b_w\ d = 0.025 \times 400 \times 519 = 5190$ mm$^2 \geq 2800$ mm^2.

Note that in choosing the arrangement of the beam bars at column faces the following factors must be considered:

(i) the need to restrain the longitudinal bars from buckling by providing lateral restraint in the form of hoops and ties.

(ii) the need to pass the beam bars through the column cage, and

(iii) the need to provide adequate space between top bars to permit placement and vibration of concrete.

Since the magnitudes of the negative moment resistances required at column faces AB, BA and BC are all about the same, we will use the same reinforcing arrangement at these three locations.

(b) Bottom bars for positive moment regions

(i) Span BC:
For span BC, the effective compressive flange width is 1500 mm (see Clause 10.3.3). For $4 -$ No. 20 bars ($A_s =1200$ mm^2), M_r at the column face, accounting for the large amount of top reinforcement, is 248 kN·m which is larger than one half of 442 kN·m (i.e., M_r at column face where $A_s = 2800$ mm^2).

As $4 -$ No. 20 bottom bars are provided at column faces AB, BA and BC, use 4-No. 20 bars in span BC. The positive moment M_r is 217 kN·m in the midspan regions of span BC. As 217 kN·m exceeds 175 kN·m (Table 11.7), 4 - No. 20 bars will be satisfactory.

(ii) Span AB:
For span AB, the effective compressive flange width is 2105 mm (see Clause 10.3.3). For $M_r \geq 260$ kN·m (Table 11.7) try 6-No. 20 bottom bars. The depth of the equivalent rectangular stress block is 20 mm and $M_r = 314$ kN·m (see Fig. 11.6).

4. *Design of Transverse Reinforcement in Beams*

(a) Shear requirements

Determine the shears corresponding to the development of flexural hinging at both ends of the beam. For the chosen reinforcement at the beam ends the probable moment resistances are:

(i) Probable negative moment resistance, M^-_{pr}

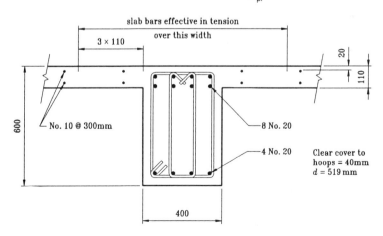

slab bars effective in tension over this width

3×110

20

110

600

No. 10 @ 300mm

8 No. 20

4 No. 20

Clear cover to hoops = 40mm
$d = 519$ mm

400

Fig. 11.5 Beam cross section near column face

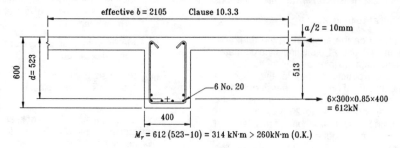

$$M_r = 612\,(523-10) = 314 \text{ kN·m} > 260 \text{kN·m} \ (O.K.)$$

Bottom bars for positive moment regions in span A–B

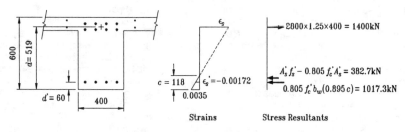

Strains   Stress Resultants

$$M_{pr}^- = 1017.3(519-105/2) + 382.7\,(519-60) = 650\text{kN·m}$$

Probable negative moment resistance M_{pr}^-

Fig. 11.6 Positive and negative moment capacities of beam.

Using a strain compatibility approach to calculate M_{pr}^- results in a depth of compression, $c = 118$ mm, a stress block depth of 106 mm and $M_{pr}^- = 650$ mm (see Fig. 11.6). Note that the probable moment resistance of the beams can be accurately estimated by multiplying M_r by the ratio $1.25/0.85 = 1.47$. In this case M_{pr} would be $442 \times 1.47 = 650$ kN·m. This simple approach is sufficiently accurate for design purposes.

(ii) Probable positive moment resistance, M_{pr}^+

The factored moment resistance at the ends of the beams is 248 kN·m and hence we can estimate the probable moment resistance as $M_{pr}^+ \approx 1.47\ M_r \approx 1.47 \times 248 = 365$ kN·m.

(iii) Determine factored shears

The shear diagrams shown in Fig. 11.7 are drawn for lateral forces acting in the W direction. For lateral forces acting in the E direction the shear diagrams will be "mirror images" of those shown (e.g., the shear at B would be 249 kN).

Using the simplified method of shear design with $V_c = 0$ gives:

$$V_r = V_s = \phi_s\, A_v\, f_y\, d\,/s \quad \text{(Clause 21.7.3.1)}.$$

At the column faces the transverse reinforcement consists of 4 – No. 10 legs, hence $A_v = 400$ mm².

At the ends A and B the required spacing for shear is:

$$s = \frac{0.85 \times 400 \times 400 \times 519}{249 \times 1000} = 283 \text{ mm}$$

At the ends B and C the required spacing for shear is:

$$s = \frac{249}{290} \times 283 = 243 \text{ mm}$$

If 2-legged No. 10 stirrups are used as transverse reinforcement ($A_v = 200$ mm²) the required spacings in the middle third of beams AB and BC are 296 mm and 190 mm, respectively. Hence use spacings of 275 mm and 190 mm, respectively for these regions.

Other shear design requirements:

(i) Maximum shear (Clause 11.3.4)

$$\begin{aligned}
V_s &= 0.8\, \phi_c\, \sqrt{f_c'}\, b_w\, d \\
&= 0.8 \times 0.6\, \sqrt{30} \times 400 \times 519 \times 10^{-3} \\
&= 546 \text{ kN} > 290 \text{ kN}
\end{aligned}$$

(ii) Minimum amount of stirrups (Clause 11.2.8.4):

for 4 stirrup legs:

$$\begin{aligned}
s &\leq \frac{A_v\, f_y}{0.06\, \sqrt{f_c'}\, b_w} \\
&= \frac{400 \times 400}{0.06\, \sqrt{30} \times 400} \\
&= 1217 \text{ mm}
\end{aligned}$$

for 2 stirrup legs:

$$s \leq 608 \text{ mm}$$

(iii) Spacing limits (Clause 11.2.11):

Since $V_f < 0.1\, \phi_c\, f_c'\, b_w\, d$
$$\begin{aligned}
&= 0.1 \times 0.6 \times 30 \times 400 \times 519 \times 10^{-3} \\
&= 374 \text{ kN}
\end{aligned}$$

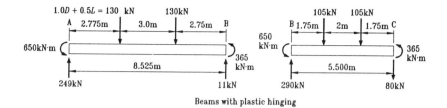

Beams with plastic hinging

Shears corresponding to plastic hinging

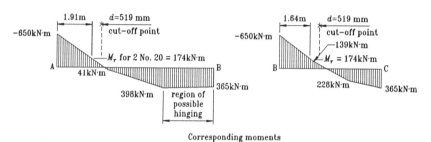

Corresponding moments

Shears and moments due to plastic hinge formation

Fig. 11.7 Determination of shears corresponding to flexural hinging.

then s_{max} = 600 mm or 0.7d = 0.7 × 519 = 363 mm.

Note that near the ends of the beams the stirrup spacing required for shear cannot exceed 243 mm.

(b)   "Anti-buckling and confinement requirements (Clause 21.3.3)

Hoops to prevent buckling of longitudinal bars are required over a length of 2d from the face of the columns. The spacing of the hoops shall not exceed:

(i)   d/4 = 519/4 = 130 mm

(ii) $8d_b$ (smallest bar) = 8 × 20 =160 mm.

(iii) $24d_b$ (hoop) = 24 × 10 = 240 mm

(iv)   300 mm

Note that the 4-legged arrangement of transverse reinforcement satisfies Clause 21.3.3.4. Hence use a spacing of 130 mm for 4-legged hoops over a length of at least 2d = 2 × 519 = 1038 mm.

(c)   Checking extent of plastic hinging

The moment diagrams corresponding to plastic hinging at both ends of beams AB and BC are shown in Fig. 11.7. Hinging can spread along about one-third of the span in beam AB. Since the earthquake loading can reverse, provide the closely spaced hoop reinforcement over the regions from the face of the columns to the locations of the secondary beams.

5.   *Bar Cut-offs*

The locations of bar cut-offs are determined from the moment diagrams corresponding to the formation of plastic hinges at the ends of the beams. The theoretical cut-off location is located at a distance of 1.91 m from the face of the column (see Fig. 11.7). From Clause 12.10.4 it is required to provide an embedment length beyond the theoretical cut-off point of at least d or $12d_b$. Hence the minimum length required is 1910 + d = 1910 + 519 = 2429 mm. Continue the 8 - No. 20 bars a distance of 3 m from the column face such that the bars are terminated in a region of lower shear. In this region of lower shear, since the required shear of 119 kN is less than 2/3 $(V_c + V_s)$ = 2/3 (136.4 + 128.3) = 176 kN, then additional stirrups at the cut-off location are not required (Clause 12.10.5). For span BC, extend the 8 - No. 20 bars a distance of 2.16 m from the face of the column.

6.   *Splice Details*

Flexural reinforcement cannot be spliced within a distance of 2d from the column face nor within a distance d from a potential plastic hinge location (Clause 21.3.2.3). In evaluating cut-off locations, d was taken as 519 mm.

In determining locations of bar cut-offs and splices we will consider the moment diagram corresponding to the formation of hinges at the ends of the beams (see Fig. 11.7). The splices for the top bars will be located in a region of the beam where the bars are predicted to remain in compression. However, as it is required to have a minimum negative and positive moment resistance at the face of the joint (Clause 21.3.2.2) the splice length will be calculated as for a tension splice.

(a) Splicing of the 2-No. 20 "continuous" top bars

The required minimum moment capacity = $0.25 \times 442 = 111$ kN·m. M_r for 2-No. 20 top bars is

1. *Column End-Actions from Analysis*

The column end actions obtained from analysis are summarized in Table 11.8. The earthquake forces given are those for lateral seismic forces acting in the E direction.

Table 11.8 Column End Actions

	P_D kN	P_L kN	P_E kN	M_D kN·m	M_L kN·m	M_E kN·m	V_D kN	V_L kN	V_E kN
1st floor top of column	−1704	−556	+208	−45	−31	+258	+17	+11	+141
1st floor bottom of column	−1704	−556	+208	+26	+18	+341	+17	+11	+141
2nd floor bottom of column	−1598	−486	+151	+52	+35	+220	+25	+17	+147

174 kN·m. Hence for the classification of tension lap splices in accordance with Table 12-2 (A_s provided)/ (A_s required) is about $174/111 = 1.57$. Hence Class B splices are required. The development length ℓ_d from Table 12-1 is:

$$\ell_d = 0.45\, k_1\, k_2\, k_3\, k_4\, \frac{f_y}{\sqrt{f'_c}}\, d_b$$

$$= 0.45 \times 1.3 \times 1 \times 1 \times 0.8\, \frac{400}{\sqrt{30}}\, 20$$

$$= 684 \text{ mm}$$

2. *Factored Axial Loads and Moments*

The column must be designed to resist the appropriate combinations of axial load and moment. From Table 11.8, it is evident that the factored moments at the base of the column will be larger than that at the top.

For the base of the column at the ground floor level the factored axial load and moment combinations are given in Table 11.9.

Table 11.9 Factored Axial Load and Moments at Column Bases

	Case 1 1.25D+1.5L	Case 2 1.0D+1.0E	Case 3 1.0D−1.0E	Case 4 1.0D+0.5L+1.0E	Case 5 1.0D+0.5L−1.0F
P_f kN	−2964	−1496	−1912	−1774	−2190
M_f kN·m	+60	+367	−315	+376	−306

Thus the splice length = $1.3\, \ell_d = 1.3 \times 684 = 890$ mm.

(b) Splicing of the 4 − No. 20 "continuous" bars

The development length for these bottom bars

$$\ell_d = 0.45\, k_1\, k_2\, k_3\, k_4\, \frac{f_y}{\sqrt{f'_c}}\, d_b$$

$$= 0.45 \times 1 \times 1 \times 1 \times 0.8\, \frac{400}{\sqrt{30}}\, 20$$

$$= 526 \text{ mm}$$

Thus the splice length = $1.3\, \ell_d = 1.3 \times 526 = 684$ mm.

The details of the reinforcement in the beam are illustrated in Fig. 11.8.

EXAMPLE 11.3 DESIGN OF COLUMN IN A DUCTILE MOMENT-RESISTING FRAME

To illustrate the procedures involved in designing a column in a ductile moment resisting frame a typical first storey interior column of the building described in Example 11.1 will be designed. A description of the column that will be designed is given in Fig. 11.9.

Note that for this member $A_g f'_c/10 = [(500 \times 500)30/10] \times 10^{-3} = 750$ kN. As P_f exceeds this value, the requirements of Clause 21.4 apply (Clause 21.4.1).

3. *Preliminary Selection of Column Bars*

In selecting the column bars, recall that the diameter of these bars must satisfy the requirements that $d_b \leq \ell_j/24 = 600/24 = 25$ mm (Clause 21.6.5.6). Hence the maximum bar size is No. 25. Try the bar arrangement shown in Fig. 11.10.

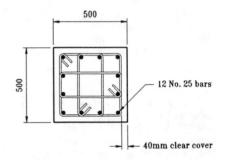

Fig. 11.10 Column reinforcement details.

For this arrangement of reinforcement $A_{st} = 12 \times 500 = 6000$ mm². From Clause 21.4.3.1 the

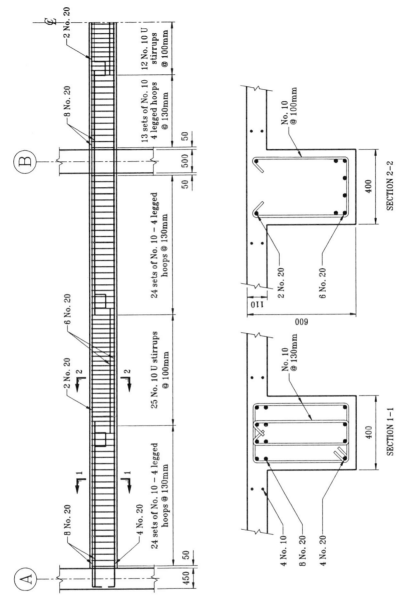

Fig. 11.8 Reinforcement details in beams.

minimum area of longitudinal steel = $0.01 \times 500 \times 500 = 2500$ mm^2 and the maximum area of longitudinal steel outside of lap splice regions (assuming lap splicing with an equal area of steel) = $0.03 \times 500 \times 500 = 7500$ mm^2. Hence this steel arrangement satisfies these requirements.

4. *Checking Column Capacity*

The axial load-moment interaction diagram for the chosen column section is shown in Fig. 11.11. This interaction diagram can be determined by "hand calculations" using the stress block factors of Clause 10.1.7, strain compatibility and a maximum concrete compressive strain of 0.0035 by varying the strain diagram and calculating the corresponding values of P_r and M_r for different strain distribu-

tions. The P-M interaction diagram shown was determined using the computer program "RESPONSE"[2]. In making these predictions the material resistance factors, ϕ_c and ϕ_s, and a realistic stress-strain relationship for the concrete (the "high-strength" curve in the program) with a maximum stress of $0.9f'_c$ (Clause 10.9.2) was used. Several computer runs with different values of axial loads, P_r, were used to determine corresponding values of M_r. It can be seen that the column has adequate capacity to resist the various combinations of P_f and M_f which occur at the base of the column. These values agree very well with those obtained using the "hand calculation" method.

Although the moment capacity of the column exceeds the factored moments at its base this large

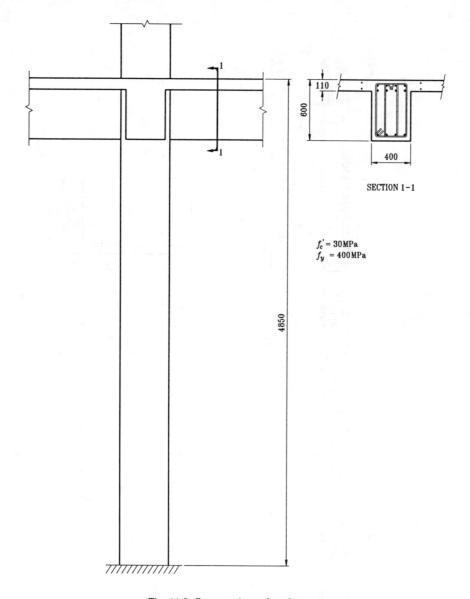

Fig. 11.9 Beam-column framing.

flexural capacity may be needed at the top of the column in order to ensure that the columns are stronger than the beams.

An additional advantage of the apparent excess column capacity is that it makes it possible for the columns to resist the moments caused by frame displacements (P-Delta effect).

5. *"Strong Column - Weak Beam" Requirement*

The flexural capacity of the columns must exceed the flexural capacity of the beams so that

$$\sum M_{rc} \geq 1.1 \sum M_{nb}$$

Hence it is necessary to first determine the nominal resistances of the beams framing into the column.

(a) Nominal negative moment resistance, M_{nb}^-

Note that the nominal resistance, M_{nb}^-, can be approximated by $1.2\,M_r = 1.2 \times 442 = 530$ kN · m. This simple approach is sufficiently accurate for design purposes as can be seen from Fig. 11.12.

(b) Nominal positive moment resistance, M_{nb}^+

$$M_{nb}^+ = 1.2\,M_r = 1.2 \times 248 = 298 \text{ kN} \cdot \text{m}.$$

(c) Determination of $\sum M_{rc}$

To determine $\sum M_{rc}$ for a particular loading case we need to calculate the factored moment resistance of the column above and below the beam-column joint. The lowest flexural resistance will occur at the highest or lowest axial load, that is, load cases 2 and 5 need to be investigated (load case 1 does not involve lateral load). The axial load corresponding to cases 2 and 5 are given in Fig. 11.13 along with the column moment resistances

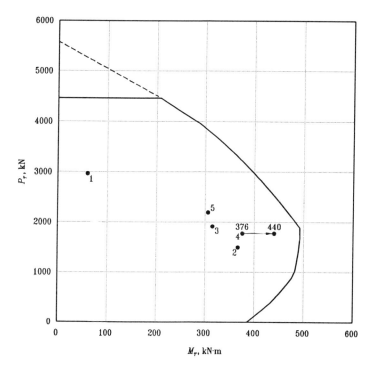

Fig. 11.11 $P_r - M_r$ Interaction diagram for column section.

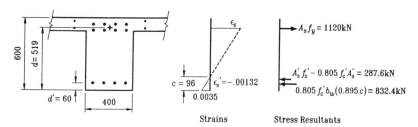

$$M_{nb}^- = 832.6(519-86/2) + 287.6 (519-60) = 528 \text{kN·m}$$

Fig. 11.12 Nominal negative moment resistance, M_{nb}^-, of beam.

corresponding to these axial loads (from the P-M interaction diagram).

Thus the requirement that $\Sigma M_{rc} \geq$ 1.1 ΣM_{nb} is satisfied. Note that for simplicity the above calculations have neglected the influence of the beam and column shears acting at the joint faces.

6. *Checking P-Delta Effect in Columns*

It is required by the NBCC that sway effects produced by vertical loads acting on the structure in its displaced configuration be taken into account in the design of buildings and their structural members. Furthermore, in seismic design it is necessary to multiply the elastic deflections by R to give realistic values of the anticipated lateral displacements. These increased displacements account for the total anticipated displacements including the inelastic effects. In order to investigate the influence of P-Delta effects with the inelastic displacements included we will analyze frame 2. This

analysis will be carried out using a frame analysis computer program which accounts for second order effects by the addition of the so-called geometric stiffness. In order to carry out this analysis it is necessary to include the vertical loading on the structure. To account for the inelastic displacements the elastic member stiffnesses are reduced by dividing by R = 4.0.

Table 11.10 compares the moments in the ground storey columns and the second storey beams of frame 2, under seismic lateral loading with and without the P-Delta effects. The values given are for the loading case of 1.0D + 0.5L + 1.0E. It is important to include all vertical loading, including the curtain wall loads and the column dead loads, which will contribute to P-Delta effects.

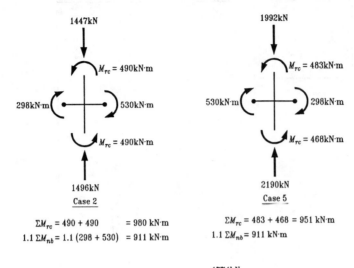

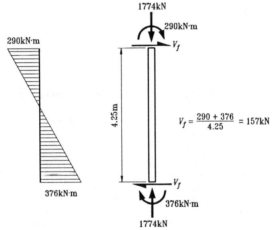

$$V_f = \frac{290 + 376}{4.25} = 157kN$$

Fig. 11.13 Capacity design of columns and factored loads on column.

Table 11.10 Influence of P-Delta on column and beam moments in frame 2

Member	Moment without P-Delta	Moment with P-Delta
Ground storey column 2A	±126 top ±199 bottom	±157 top ±233 bottom
Ground storey column 2B	±258 top ±341 bottom	±318 top ±405 bottom
Second floor beam A-B	±238 left ±218 right	±284 left ±259 right
Second floor beam B-C	±304 left ±304 right	±361 left ±361 right

The P-Delta effect results in an increase in moments of about 19% in the ground storey columns and in the second storey floor beams.

The P-Delta effect for load case 4 is illustrated on the P-M interaction diagram. The column section is adequate to carry additional moments due to the P-Delta effect.

6. *Design of Transverse Reinforcement in Column*

(a) Shear requirements

The column must have a factored shear resistance, V_r, which exceeds the column shear corresponding to the probable moment resistance in the beams and which exceeds the shear forces due to factored loads (Clause 21.7.2.3).

The highest factored shear force acting on the column corresponds to loading case 4 for which the column actions are summarized below. The moment at the top of the column corresponding to the development of the probable moment resistance in the beams may be estimated from:

$$M_{col} = (M_{pr}^+ + M_{pr}^-) \times \frac{(\text{column stiffness})}{\sum(\text{column stiffnesses})}$$

$$= (365 + 650) \times \frac{(1/4.25)}{(1/4.25 + 1/3.05)}$$

$$= 424 \text{ kN} \cdot \text{m}$$

However since we are designing a ground storey column a different approach is required at the

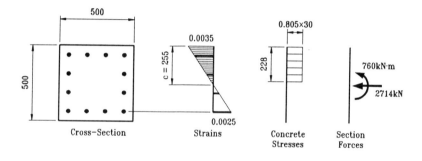

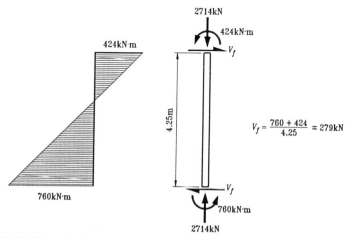

Fig. 11.14 Determination of required shear strength in ground storey column.

base of this column. It is assumed that the column frames into a substructure that is considerably stronger and stiffer than the column and hence the possibility of hinging at the column base must be accounted for. To ensure adequate column shear capacity the moment at the base of the column will be taken as the probable moment resistance corresponding to the balanced loading conditions (i.e., the highest probable moment resistance). The calculations involved in determining this moment resistance are summarized in Fig. 11.14.

This procedure is reasonable because the balanced axial load (2714 kN) is within the range of possible factored axial loads acting on the column.

The column actions which will correspond to the formation of hinges in the beams at the top of the column and the formation of a hinge at the base of the column are given below.

From Clause 21.7.3.1 the shear carried by the concrete is taken as one-half of that calculated using Equation (11-6). Hence:

$$V_c = 0.1 \lambda \, \phi_c \, \sqrt{f_c'} \, b_w \, d$$

$$= 0.1 \times 1 \times 0.6 \sqrt{30} \times 500 \times 437.5 \times 10^{-3}$$

$$= 71.9 \text{ kN}$$

The required V_s is equal to 279 - 71.9 = 207.1 kN. Using 4-legged No. 10 stirrups the required stirrup spacing can be found from Equation (11-11) as:

$$s = \frac{\phi_s \, A_v \, f_y \, d}{V_s}$$

$$= \frac{0.85 \times 400 \times 400 \times 437.5}{207.1 \times 1000}$$

$$= 287 \text{ mm}$$

Since $V_f /(b_w d) = (279 \times 1000)/(500 \times 437.5) = 1.28 < 0.1 \times 0.6 \times 30 = 1.8$ MPa then from Clause 11.2.11, the maximum spacing of the shear reinforcement is $0.7d = 0.7 \times 437.5 = 306$ mm.

In order to satisfy the minimum shear reinforcement requirements of Clause 11.2.8.4, the maximum spacing of the 4-legged No. 10 stirrups is:

$$s = \frac{A_v \, f_y}{0.06 \sqrt{f_c'} \, b_w}$$

$$= \frac{400 \times 400}{0.06 \sqrt{30} \times 500}$$

$$= 973 \text{ mm}$$

Therefore for shear a spacing of 287 mm controls.

(b)   Confinement requirements

Since the column under consideration is at the base of the structure confining reinforcement must be provided over the full height of the column (Clause 21.4.4.7).

From Clause 21.4.4.2, the total cross-sectional area of rectangular hoop reinforcement is:

$$A_{sh} = 0.3 \, s \, h_c \frac{f'_c}{f_{yh}} \left(\frac{A_g}{A_{ch}} - 1 \right)$$

$$= 0.3 \, (s \times 420 \times \frac{30}{400} \, (\frac{500 \times 500}{420 \times 420} - 1)$$

$$= 3.94 \, s$$

but not less than:

$$A_{sh} = 0.09 \, s \, h_c \frac{f'_c}{f_{yh}}$$

$$= 0.09 \times s \times 420 \, \frac{30}{400}$$

$$= 2.84 \, s$$

With 4-legged No. 10 hoops, $A_{sh} = 400 \, mm^2$ and hence s = 101 mm. From Clause 21.4.4.3 the spacing of the hoops shall not exceed:

(i)   h/4 = 500/4 = 125 mm

(ii) 100 mm

(iii) $6d_b = 6 \times 25 = 150$ mm

(iv) $48 \times$ hoop $d_b = 48 \times 10 = 480$ mm

Hence use 4-legged No. 10 hoops at 100 mm centres as shown. The chosen arrangement of hoops and longitudinal reinforcement also satisfies Clauses 21.4.4.4, 21.6.3.2, 7.6.5 and 10.9.2. The details of the first-storey column reinforcement are given in Fig. 11.15.

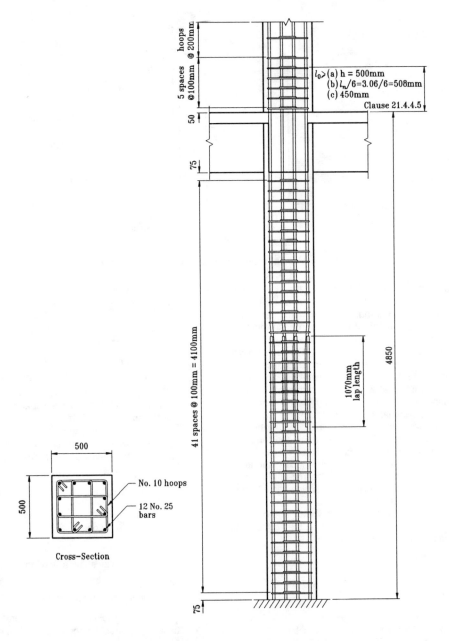

Fig. 11.15 Details of reinforcement in first-storey column.

7. *Splice Details*

We will splice the column bars at mid-height of the column with tension lap splices in accordance with Clause 21.4.3.2. The development length, ℓ_d, can be found from Table 12-1 as:

$$\ell_d = 0.45\, k_1\, k_2\, k_3\, k_4\, \frac{f_y}{\sqrt{f_c'}}\, d_b$$

$$= 0.45 \times 1 \times 1 \times 1 \times 1 \frac{400}{\sqrt{30}}\, 25$$

$$= 822\ \text{mm}$$

Provide a lap length of $1.3\ell_d = 1.3 \times 822 = 1068$ mm (see Fig. 11.15).

EXAMPLE 11.4 DESIGN OF BEAM-COLUMN JOINT IN A DUCTILE MOMENT-RESISTING FRAME

To illustrate the procedures involved in designing a beam-column joint in a ductile moment-resisting frame an interior joint in the structure described in Example 11.1 will be designed. A description of the joint details are given in Fig. 11.16.

1. *Determination of Factored Forces in Joint*

In accordance with Clause 21.6.1.2, assume that the tensile force in the beam reinforcement is $1.25A_s f_y$.

To estimate the corresponding shear, V_{col}, in the column above the joint assume that flexural hinging occurs in the beams at the first and second storey levels. The calculations are summarized in Fig. 11.17.

2. *Check Factored Shear Resistance of Joint*

Since equal depth beams frame into the joint and each covers more than 3/4 of each face of the joint, the joint is considered to be externally confined (Clause 21.6.4.1).

Hence the factored shear resistance of the joint is taken as:

$$V_r = 2.4\, \lambda\, \phi_c\, \sqrt{f_c'}\, A_j$$

$$= 2.4 \times 0.6\, \sqrt{30} \times 500 \times 500 \times 10^{-3}$$

$$= 1972\ \text{kN}$$

As $V_{fb} < 1972$ kN, the shear resistance of the joint is adequate.

3. *Transverse Reinforcement Required in Joint*

As the joint is framed by four equal depth beams which provide confinement, only one-half of the confinement steel required for the column is required through the joint (Clause 21.6.2.2). Hence provide 3 sets of 4-legged No. 10 hoops between the flexural bars in the beams as shown in Fig. 11.18.

4. *Bond of Beam Bars*

As the beam bars pass through the joint their bond characteristics are checked by the requirement that the bar diameters be not greater than $\ell_j/24 = 500/24 = 21$ mm. Since this exceeds the actual bar diameter of 20 mm this requirement is met.

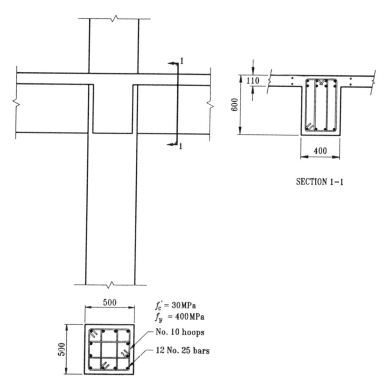

$f_c' = 30\,\text{MPa}$
$f_y = 400\,\text{MPa}$
No. 10 hoops
12 No. 25 bars

SECTION 1–1

Fig. 11.16 Geometry of interior beam-column joint.

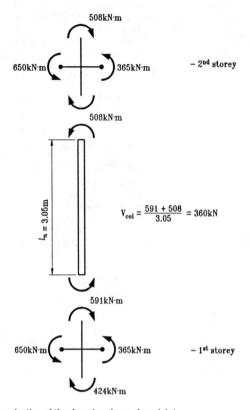

$$V_{col} = \frac{591 + 508}{3.05} = 360kN$$

Determination of the shear in column above joint.

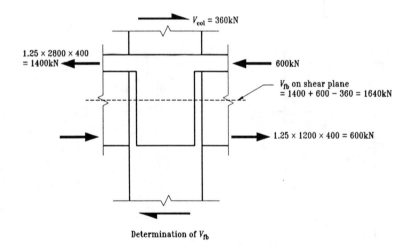

Determination of V_{fb}

Fig. 11.17 Determination of factored shear resistance in joint.

CPCA Concrete Design Handbook

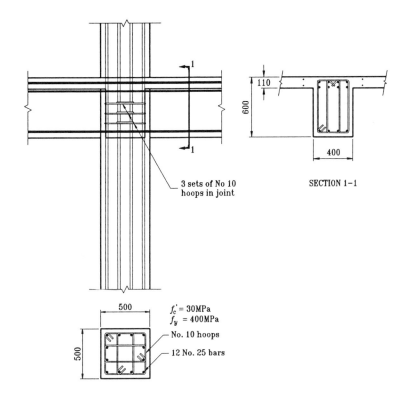

$f'_c = 30 \text{MPa}$
$f_y = 400 \text{MPa}$

3 sets of No 10
hoops in joint

SECTION 1-1

No. 10 hoops

12 No. 25 bars

Fig. 11.18 Details of joint reinforcement.

EXAMPLE 11.5 ANALYSIS OF A DUCTILE CORE-WALL STRUCTURE

The twelve-storey reinforced concrete building shown in Fig. 11.19 is located in Montreal.

1. *Description of Building*

The twelve-storey reinforced concrete office building has a centrally located elevator core. Each floor consists of a 200 mm thick flat plate with 6 m interior spans and 5.5 m end spans. The columns are all 550×550 mm and the thickness of the core wall components is 400 mm. The core wall measures 6.4 m by 8.4 m, outside to outside of the walls. Two 400 mm wide × 600 mm deep coupling beams connect the two C-shaped walls at the ceiling level of each floor. The core walls extend one storey above the roof at the 12th floor level forming an elevator penthouse at the 13th floor level.

2. *Material Properties*

Concrete: normal density concrete with $f'_c = 30$ MPa

Reinforcement: $f_y = 400$ MPa

3. *Gravity and Wind Loadings*

Floor live load: 2.4 kN/m² on typical office floors

4.8 kN/m² on 12 m by 12 m corridor area around core

Roof load: 2.2 kN/m² full snow load

1.6 kN/m² mechanical services loading in 6 m wide strip over corridor bay

Dead loads: self-weight of reinforced concrete members calculated at 24 kN/m³

1.0 kN/m² partition loading on all floors

0.5 kN/m² ceiling and mechanical services loading on all floors

0.5 kN/m² roof insulation

Wind loading: varies from 1.1 to 1.37 kN/m² net lateral pressure over the height of the building

4. *Seismic loading*

For this structure located in Montreal the acceleration-related seismic zone, $Z_a = 4$, the velocity-related seismic zone, $Z_v = 2$ and the zonal velocity ratio, $v = 0.10$.

The seismic response factor, S, is dependent on the fundamental period, T, of the structure. For this core-wall structure, the total height, h_n, has been taken as 45 m and the length of the shear wall, D_s, is 6.4 m in the N-S direction and 8.4 m in the E-W direction. Hence the fundamental period, T, in the N-S direction can be found from:

$$T = \frac{0.09 \, h_n}{\sqrt{D_s}}$$

$$= \frac{0.09 \times 45}{\sqrt{6.4}} = 1.601 \text{ s}$$

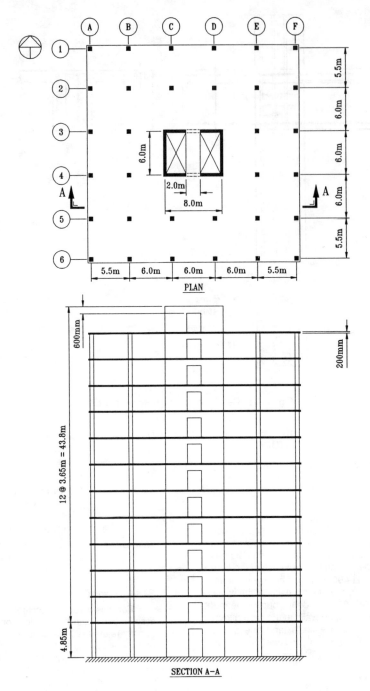

Fig. 11.19 Plan and elevation of twelve-storey office building.

Since T > 0.50s, the seismic response factor is determined as:

$$S = \frac{1.5}{\sqrt{T}}$$

$$= \frac{1.5}{\sqrt{1.601}} = 1.186$$

The fundamental period, T, in the E-W direction is:

$$T = \frac{0.09\,h_n}{\sqrt{D_s}}$$

$$= \frac{0.09 \times 45}{\sqrt{8.4}} = 1.397 \text{ s}$$

Since T > 0.50s, the seismic response factor, in the E-W direction is:

$$S = \frac{1.5}{\sqrt{T}}$$

$$= \frac{1.5}{\sqrt{1.397}} = 1.269$$

Other factors in the base shear equation are:

I = 1.0 (office building)

F = 1.0 (building founded on rock)

For the force modification factor, R, we will assume that the core-wall system will take 100% of the lateral loads. In the N-S direction we will design and detail the walls as ductile flexural walls and hence R = 3.5. In the E-W direction we will design and detail the coupling beams and walls as a ductile partially coupled wall system and hence R = 3.5. Since R is the same in both directions we will use a value of R of 3.5 for the design of the structure.

Hence the seismic base shear, V, in the N-S direction is:

$$V = \frac{v\,S\,I\,F\,W}{R}\,U$$

$$= \frac{0.10 \times 1.186 \times 1.0 \times 1.0\,W}{3.5}\,0.6$$

$$= 0.0203\,W$$

The seismic base shear, V, in the E-W direction is:

$$V = \frac{v\,S\,I\,F\,W}{R}\,U$$

$$= \frac{0.10 \times 1.269 \times 1.0 \times 1.0\,W}{3.5}\,0.6$$

$$= 0.0218\,W$$

The calculations of the seismic lateral forces at each floor level are summarized in Table 11.11. The weight of the penthouse has been included at the roof level. The concentrated force at the top, F_t, is $0.07\,TV \le 0.25\,V$. In the N-S direction F_t = 205.7 kN and in the E-W direction F_t = 192.8 kN.

Table 11.11 Lateral Load Calculations for Each Floor Level

Floor	h_i, m	W_i, kN	h_iW_i, kN·m	N-S F_x, kN	E-W F_x, kN
roof	45.00	8131	365895	469.5	480.6
12	41.35	7455	308264	222.2	242.4
11	37.70	7455	281053	202.6	221.0
10	34.05	7455	253843	183.0	199.6
9	30.40	7455	226632	163.3	178.2
8	26.75	7455	199421	143.7	156.8
7	23.10	7455	172210	124.1	135.4
6	19.45	7455	145000	104.5	114.0
5	15.80	7455	117789	84.9	92.6
4	12.15	7455	90578	65.3	71.2
3	8.50	7455	63368	45.7	49.8
2	4.85	7754	37607	27.1	29.6
Total		90435	2261661	1835.8	1971.5

5. *Analysis Assumptions*

To determine the member forces the structure was analyzed using a linear elastic plane frame program in the E-W and N-S directions. To make allowances for cracking, member stiffnesses were assumed to be 0.2 of the gross EI for all coupling beams and 0.7 of the gross EI for all walls.

The design of the ductile coupled wall system resisting lateral forces in the E-W direction is illustrated in Examples 11.6 and 11.7.

6. *Accounting for Torsional Eccentricity*

This building has a symmetrical distribution of masses and stiffness at each floor level and hence the eccentricity, e_x, between the centre of mass and the centre of rigidity is zero. The applied torsional moment, T_x, at each level throughout the building can be found from:

$$T_x = F_x\,(\pm\,0.1\,D_{nx})$$

where F_x is the lateral force applied at level x and D_{nx} is the plan dimension of the building in the direction of the computed eccentricity. The term $0.1D_{nx}F_x$ represents the accidental applied torsional moment at each level. For this structure the applied torsional eccentricity for lateral forces in either the E-W or N-S direction is $\pm\,0.1 \times 29.75$ = $\pm\,2.975$ m. In addition to the wind pressure, considered to be uniform across the width of the structure, an eccentric wind pressure loading case was also considered.

The structure was analyzed with a 3-D model of the core-wall structure for both wind and seismic loading, with and without eccentricity. In these analyses the participation of the flat plate and columns was neglected.

7. *Design Forces*

The results from the 3-D analyses for both seismic and wind loading are summarized in Tables 11.12, 11.13 and 11.14.

In order to check the degree of coupling provided by the wall system in the E-W direction, the overturning moment carried by axial tension and compression forces in the walls, divided by the total overturning moment is:

$$\frac{T\ell}{M_1 + M_2 + T\ell} = \frac{6008 \times 6.5}{2(12788) + 6.5(6008)}$$

$$= 0.604$$

where

T = axial tension and compression acting at centroid of coupled walls

ℓ = distance between centroids of coupled walls, equal to 6.5 m for this example

The degree of coupling is 60.4%, which is less than the upper limit for ductile partially coupled walls of 66%.

Table 11.12 Results of Seismic Loading Analyses (1.0E)

Storey	E–W Direction (Coupled Wall)				N-S Direction
	Overturning moment, kN·m	Moment in wall $M_1 = M_2$, kN·m	axial load in wall, kN	couple from axial loads, kN·m	Overturning moment, kN·m
penthouse top	0	−990	305	1983	0
penthouse bot	0	−990			0
12 top	0	−2071	637	4140	0
12 bot	1754	−1194			1714
11 top	1754	−2424	1016	6604	1714
11 bot	4393	−1104			4238
10 top	4393	−2501	1446	9399	4238
10 bot	7839	−779			7503
9 top	7839	−2343	1927	12526	7503
9 bot	12013	−256			11435
8 top	12013	−1971	2455	15958	11435
8 bot	16837	441			15963
7 top	16837	−1394	3019	19634	15963
7 bot	22234	1305			21016
6 top	22234	−604	3606	23439	21016
6 bot	28125	2342			26521
5 top	28125	421	4197	27281	26521
5 bot	34433	3575			32408
4 top	34433	1720	4768	30992	32408
4 bot	41078	5042			38605
3 top	41078	3353	5288	34372	38605
3 bot	47983	6805			45041
2 top	47983	5408	5718	37167	45041
2 bot	55070	8952			51643
1 top	55070	8008	6008	39052	51643
1 bot	64630	12788			60547

Table 11.13 Results of Wind Loading Analyses (1.5W)

Storey	N-S and E-W Overturning moment, kN·m	E-W Direction (Coupled Wall) Moment in wall $M_1 = M_2$, kN·m	axial load in wall, kN	couple from axial loads, kN·m
penthouse top	0	−807	248	1612
penthouse bot	0	−807		
12 top	0	−1687	519	3374
12 bot	975	−1200		
11 top	975	−2211	830	5395
11 bot	2753	−1322		
10 top	2753	−2496	1192	7748
10 bot	5327	−1209		
9 top	5327	−2562	1608	10452
9 bot	8687	−882		
8 top	8687	−2413	2079	13513
8 bot	12822	−345		
7 top	12822	−2037	2600	16900
7 bot	17723	+413		
6 top	17723	−1406	3159	20534
6 bot	23376	+1421		
5 top	23376	−470	3741	24317
5 bot	29768	+2725		
4 top	29768	+840	4321	28087
4 bot	36881	+4397		
3 top	36881	+2624	4867	31636
3 bot	44697	+6532		
2 top	44697	+5021	5331	34652
2 bot	53191	+9268		
1 top	53191	+8216	5655	36758
1 bot	65487	+14364		

Table 11.14 Beam Shears Due to Seismic and Wind Loading for E-W Direction

Storey	Seismic Loading (1.0E) beam shear (concentric loading), kN	Seismic Loading (1.0E) beam shear (eccentric loading), kN	Wind Loading (1.5W) beam shear, kN
penthouse	152.3	221.5	124.1
12	166.4	238.9	135.5
11	189.1	264.8	155.5
10	214.9	293.8	180.7
9	240.7	322.4	208.2
8	263.9	347.6	235.6
7	282.3	366.4	260.3
6	293.6	376.4	279.8
5	295.5	374.7	291.0
4	285.4	358.1	290.1
3	259.9	323.0	272.6
2	215.0	264.7	232.5
1	145.2	177.9	161.8
Total	3004.2	3930.2	2827.7

The design forces for both seismic and wind loading are given in Fig. 11.20.

EXAMPLE 11.6 DESIGN OF COUPLING BEAMS IN A DUCTILE PARTIALLY-COUPLED WALL (E-W DIRECTION)

1. *Design Forces for Coupling Beams*

The maximum coupling beam shear, of 376 kN (beam moment of 376 kN·m), occurs at the sixth floor level under seismic loading, including torsional eccentricity. If we use the same coupling beam details over the height of the structure, and if we account for redistribution of moments between the coupling beams, then the minimum flexural resistance required would be 3930.2/13 = 302.3 kN·m. This would require a redistribution of moments in the most heavily loaded coupling beam equal to (376.4 - 302.3)/376.4 = 19.7%, which is less than the maximum permitted redistribution of 20%. It is noted that the factored flexural resistance of 302 kN·m is slightly greater than the maximum factored coupling beam shear under wind loading. Hence design for a moment of 302 kN·m.

Since the design torsions arise only from accidental torsional eccentricity, which can act in either direction, the same coupling design forces and beam details will be used on the north and south sides of the core wall.

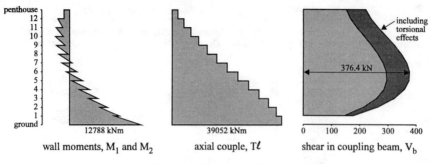

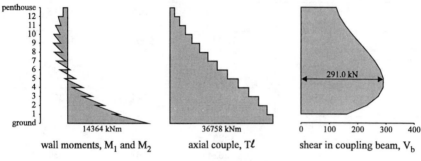

Fig. 11.20 Results of analyses for seismic and wind loading in E-W direction.

2. *Check Stress and Dimensional Limitations of Coupling Beams*

Assume that No. 25 longitudinal bars are used in the beams giving an effective depth, d, of 537.5 mm. Hence, the shear stress from factored load effects is:

$$v_f = \frac{V_f}{b_w d}$$

$$= \frac{302 \times 1000}{400 \times 537.5}$$

$$= 1.405 \text{ MPa}$$

The maximum shear stress permitted, in order that a conventionally reinforced coupling beam be provided (Clause 21.5.8.2), is:

$$v_{max} = 0.1 (\ell_u/d)\sqrt{f_c'}$$

$$= 0.1 \times (2000/537.5) \times \sqrt{30}$$

$$= 2.04 \text{ MPa}$$

Since v_f is less than v_{max}, transverse hoops and longitudinal bars can be used.

3. *Choice of Flexural Reinforcement for Coupling Beams*

Assuming No.10 hoops and No. 25 longitudinal bars are used, the effective depth, d, is 600–40 – 10 – 12.5 = 537.5 mm. Assuming a flexural lever arm of 0.9d gives a required area of flexural reinforcement of $302 \times 1000 / (0.9 \times 0.5375 \times 0.85 \times 400) = 1836 \text{ mm}^2$.

Try an arrangement of 4 - No. 25 bars, top and bottom, as shown in Fig. 11.21. Accounting for the presence of the compression reinforcement, the depth of compression, c, is found to be 82 mm and the factored moment resistance is 334 kN·m.

The required minimum top and bottom reinforcement, $A_{s,min}$, from Clause 21.3.2.1 is

$A_{s,min} = 1.4 b_w d/f_y = 1.4 \times 400 \times 537.5/400 = 752.5 \text{ mm}^2 \le 2000 \text{ mm}^2$ O.K.

Maximum reinforcement permitted

$= 0.025 b_w d = 0.025 \times 400 \times 537.5 = 5375 \text{ mm}^2 \ge 2000 \text{ mm}^2$

4. *Design of Transverse Reinforcement in Coupling Beams*

(a) Shear requirements

Determine shears corresponding to the development of flexural hinging at both ends of the beam. For the chosen reinforcement at the beam ends the probable moment resistances, M_{pr}^- and M_{pr}^+, are both equal to about $1.47 \times 334 = 491$ kN·m. This corresponds to a required shear capacity of 491 kN along the clearspan of each beam.

Using the simplified method of shear design with $V_c = 0$ gives:

$V_r = V_s = \phi_s A_v f_y d/s$ (Clause 21.7.3.1).

Try two sets of hoops, giving 4 – No. 10 legs, hence $A_v = 400 \text{ mm}^2$.

The required spacing of the hoops is:

$$s = \frac{0.85 \times 400 \times 400 \times 537.5}{491 \times 1000}$$

$$= 148.9 \text{ mm}$$

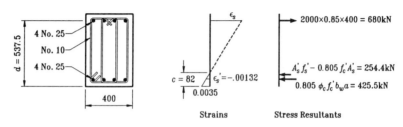

$$M_r = 425.5(537.5 - 73.4/2) + 254.4(537.5 - 62.5) = 334 \text{kN·m}$$

Fig. 11.21 Details of coupling beam reinforcement.

Other shear design requirements:

(i) Maximum shear (Clause 11.3.4)

$$V_s = 0.8 \, \phi_c \, \sqrt{f_c'} \, b_w \, d$$

$$= 0.8 \times 0.6 \, \sqrt{30} \times 400 \times 537.5 \times 10^{-3}$$

$$= 565.2 \text{ kN} > 491 \text{ kN}$$

(ii) Minimum amount of stirrups (Clause 11.2.8.4):
for 4 stirrup legs:

$$s \leq \frac{A_v \, f_y}{0.06 \, \sqrt{f_c'} \, b_w}$$

$$= \frac{400 \times 400}{0.06 \, \sqrt{30} \times 400}$$

$$= 1217 \text{ mm}$$

(iii) Spacing limits (Clause 11.2.11):

Since Design shear $> 0.1 \, \phi_c \, f_c' \, b_w \, d$

$$= 0.1 \times 0.6 \times 30 \times 400 \times 537.5 \times 10^{-3}$$

$$= 387 \text{ kN}$$

then $s_{max} = 300$ mm or $0.35d = 0.35 \times 537.5 = 188$ mm.

Note that the hoop spacing required for shear cannot exceed 149 mm.

(b) "Anti-buckling and confinement requirements (Clause 21.3.3)

Hoops to prevent buckling of longitudinal bars are required over a length of 2d from the face of the walls. Hence, provide this reinforcement over the full clearspan of each beam. The spacing of the hoops shall not exceed:

(i) $d/4 = 537.5/4 = 134$ mm

(ii) $8d_b$ (smallest bar) $= 8 \times 25 = 200$ mm.

(iii) $24d_b$ (hoop) $= 24 \times 10 = 240$ mm, or

(iv) 300 mm

Note that the 4-legged arrangement of transverse reinforcement satisfies Clause 21.3.3.4.

Hence use a spacing of 130 mm for 4-legged hoops over the entire length of the coupling beam.

EXAMPLE 11.7 DESIGN OF DUCTILE PARTIALLY-COUPLED WALL (E-W) AND DUCTILE FLEXURAL WALL (N-S)

1. *Determination of Design Forces in East-West Direction*

The design forces in the walls are determined from a capacity design approach. It is desired that the walls be strong enough that flexural hinging occurs in the coupling beams, which are the primary energy dissipators of the structural system. In order to determine the design forces in the walls, we will consider a "push-over" type of loading on the coupled wall system. It is required that the factored resistance of the walls be at least equal to the moment corresponding to the development of flexural hinging in the beams. We will approximate the nominal moment resistance of the beams as $1.2M_r = 1.2 \times 334 = 401$ kN·m. The shear, V_n, corresponding to flexural hinging in the beams is $(401 \text{ kN·m})/(1.0 \text{ m}) = 401$ kN.

The coupling beam overstrength factor at level x, γ_{hx}, is determined as:

$$\gamma_{hx} = \frac{\Sigma \, V_n}{\Sigma \, V_f}$$

where

ΣV_n = sum of the shears corresponding to the nominal flexural resistance of coupling beams above level x

ΣV_f = sum of factored shears above level x

The overstrength factors and cumulative dead and live loads are shown on Table 11.15. The values of ΣV_f are taken as the wall axial loads given in Table 11.12, since the axial load wall is the sum of the shears in the coupling beams.

Table 11.15 Coupling Beam Overstrength Factors and Dead and Live Loads per Wall

Storey	J_x	$J_x \times M_1$, kN·m	ΣV_f, kN	ΣV_n, kN	γ_{hx}	1.0D, kN	1.0L, kN
penthouse top	1.00	−990	305	802	2.63		
penthouse bot	0.96	−950				939	
12 top	0.96	−1988	637	1604	2.52		
12 bot	0.92	−1098				1695	196
11 top	0.92	−2230	1016	2406	2.37		
11 bot	0.89	−983				2451	394
10 top	0.89	−2226	1446	3208	2.22	3207	
10 bot	0.86	−670					513
9 top	0.86	−2015	1927	4010	2.08		
9 bot	0.84	−215				3963	621
8 top	0.84	−1656	2455	4812	1.96		
8 bot	0.83	366				4719	725
7 top	0.83	−1157	3019	5614	1.86		
7 bot	0.82	1070				5475	825
6 top	0.82	−495	3606	6416	1.78		
6 bot	0.81	1897				6231	924
5 top	0.81	341	4197	7218	1.72		
5 bot	0.80	2860				6987	1020
4 top	0.80	1376	4768	8020	1.68		
4 bot	0.80	4034				7743	1115
3 top	0.80	2682	5288	8822	1.67		
3 bot	0.80	5444				8500	1208
2 top	0.80	4326	5718	9624	1.68		
2 bot	0.80	7162				9256	1301
1 top	0.80	6406	6008	10426	1.74		
1 bot	0.80	11230				9791	1393

In determining the required strengths of the wall, we will use the J-factor to reduce both the wall moment and wall axial loads.

The required moment capacity at the base of each wall is:

$$\gamma_{hx} \times J_x \times M_1 = 1.74 \times 11230 = 19540 \text{ kN·m}$$

The axial force at the base of the "tension wall" corresponding to development of flexural hinges in the coupling beams is:

$$J_x \times \Sigma V_n - 1.0D = 0.80 \times (+10426) - 9791$$
$$= -1450 \text{ kN (compression)}$$

The axial force at the base of the "compression wall" corresponding to development of flexural hinges in the coupling beams is:

$$J_x \times \Sigma V_n + 1.0D + 0.5L = 0.80 \times (-10426) -$$
$$9791 - 0.5(1393) = -18828 \text{ kN (compression)}$$

2. *Design Forces in N-S Direction*

From Tables 11.12 and 11.13, the base moment due to lateral seismic loading is 60547 kN·m or 30 273 kN·m per wall, however when the torsional eccentricity is considered, the most heavily loaded wall must resist a moment of 39 202 kN·m. The base moment due to factored wind loading is 65487 kN·m or 32 743 kN·m per wall. Hence, for flexural design in the N-S direction, the earthquake loading controls.

3. *Design of Base of Wall for Flexure and Axial Load*

(a) Preliminary choice of vertical reinforcement

(i) Minimum area of concentrated reinforcement (Clause 21.5.6.4)

In the 3.2 m long walls in the E-W direction

$A_s \geq 0.002\, b_w\, \ell_w = 0.002 \times 400 \times 3200 = 2560 \text{ mm}^2$

In the 6.4 m long walls in the N-S direction

$A_s \geq 0.002\, b_w\, \ell_w = 0.002 \times 400 \times 6400 = 5120 \text{ mm}^2$

Therefore try 6 – No. 25 bars (A_s = 3000 mm^2) as concentrated reinforcement at one end of the 3.2 m long wall. Try 10 – No. 25 bars (A_s = 5000 mm^2) at the intersection of the two walls resulting in an area within 2% of the required area and a practical reinforcement layout. The reinforcement details are shown in Fig. 11.22.

Outside the plastic hinge regions, only one half of this area of concentrated reinforcement is required.

(ii) Maximum area of concentrated reinforcement (Clause 21.5.4.3)

$A_s \leq 0.06 \times$ area of concentrated reinforcement region.

With the layout of the 6–No. 25 bars as shown in Fig. 11.22, the percentage of steel equals $(6 \times 500)/(400 \times 400) = 0.019$. The 10 – No. 25 bar arrangement results in a reinforcement ratio of $(10 \times 500)/(400 \times 547 5) = 0.023$. Both of these arrangements allow for lap splicing of the reinforcement.

CPCA Concrete Design Handbook

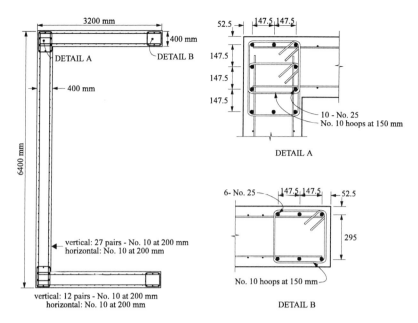

Fig. 11.22 Details of reinforcement in walls.

(iii) Maximum bar diameters (Clause 21.5.4.4)

In the 400 mm thick walls, the maximum diameter of reinforcement is 400/10 = 40 mm.

(iv) Distributed reinforcement (Clause 21.5.5.1)

In the plastic hinge region, s_{max} = 300 mm in each direction. Outside of this region, s_{max} = 450 mm in each direction. The distributed reinforcement ratio must be greater than 0.0025 in each direction.

In the 400 mm thick wall elements, the maximum spacing, assuming two curtains of No. 10 reinforcement is $(2 \times 100)/(0.0025 \times 400)$ = 200 mm. Hence, at the base of the walls, use 2 curtains of No. 10 bars at 200 mm in each direction.

Two curtains of reinforcement must be provided in the N-S direction if the design shear in one wall exceeds:

$$0.2 \lambda \, \phi_c \, \sqrt{f_c'} \, A_{cv} = 0.2 \times 0.6 \times \sqrt{30} \times 400 \times 6400 \times 10^{-3}$$

= 1683 kN

Two curtains of reinforcement must be provided in the E-W direction if the design shear in one wall exceeds:

$$0.2 \lambda \, \phi_c \, \sqrt{f_c'} \, A_{cv} = 0.2 \times 0.6 \times \sqrt{30} \times 2 \times 400 \times$$
$$3200 \times 10^{-3} = 1683 \text{kN}$$

(b) Calculation of M_r at base of walls

Both the computer program RESPONSE[2] and calculations using the stress block factors of Clause 10.1.7, strain compatibility and a maximum concrete compressive strain of 0.0035, were used to determine the factored moment resistances of the walls. In making the predictions using program RESPONSE, the material resistance factors, ϕ_c = 0.60 and ϕ_s = 0.85, together with a compressive stress-strain curve of concrete with a maximum concrete stress of $0.9f_c'$ (Clause 10.9.2) were used. Table 11.16 summarizes the results from these two approaches. As can be seen the two approaches give predicted moments which are in close agreement.

Table 11.16 Predicted Factored Moment Resistances and Depths of Compression per Wall

Load Case	N_r, kN	"RESPONSE" predictions		Calculations using stress block factors	
		M_r, kN m	c, mm	M_r, kN m	c, mm
E-W "tension wall" 1.0E + 1.0D	−1450	19378	664	19412	628
E-W "compression wall" 1.0E + 1.0D 1.0E + 1.0D + 0.5L	−18132 −18828	23786 24291	266 274	23756 24253	249 256
N-S 1.0E + 1.0D	−9791	56983	368	56689	353
N-S 1.0E + 1.0D + 0.5L	−10488	58983	380	58686	367

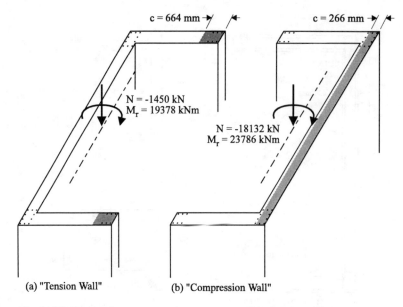

c = 664 mm

c = 266 mm

N = -1450 kN
M_r = 19378 kNm

N = -18132 kN
M_r = 23786 kNm

(a) "Tension Wall"

(b) "Compression Wall"

Fig. 11.23 Factored moment resistances of coupled walls (E-W direction)

The required moment capacity in the E-W direction from analysis is 19540 kN·m per wall. As can be seen from Table 11.16, the tension wall has a factored moment resistance of 19378 kN·m, while the compression wall has a factored moment resistance of 23786 kN·m. Hence a small amount of redistribution from the "tension wall" to the "compression wall" would give the required total capacity at the base of the structure. It is noted that, due to the softening of the "tension wall", considerable redistribution is possible (i.e., up to 30%). Figure 11.23 illustrates the moment resistances for the walls in the E-W direction.

In the N-S direction, the factored moment resistance for both load cases significantly exceeds the required moment of 39 202 kN m per wall (see Fig. 11.24).

(c) Ductility check

We will use the depths of compression calculated above as c_c in checking the ductility requirements of Clause 21.5.7. For all cases c_c is less than the upper limit of $0.55 \ell_w = 0.55 \times 3200 = 1760$ mm for the E-W wall, and $0.55 \times 6400 = 3520$ mm for the N-S wall.

In order to check if special confinement reinforcement is required, it is necessary to determine whether c_c exceeds $0.14\gamma_w\ell_w$. The wall overstrength factor, γ_w, is equal to the ratio of the load corresponding to nominal moment resistance of the wall system to the factored load on the wall system. Hence:

$$\gamma_w = \frac{M_{1n} + M_{2n} + J \Sigma V_n \ell}{J \times M_{overturning}}$$

where

M_{1n} and M_{2n} = nominal flexural resistance of walls 1 and 2, respectively

$M_{overturning}$ = overturning moment

In order to determine the nominal moment resistances of the walls, axial load - moment calculations were carried out with $\phi_c = \phi_s = 1.0$. The resulting wall overstrength factor for the partially coupled wall system is:

$$\gamma_w = \frac{23043 + 26370 + (0.8 \times 10426 \times 6.5)}{0.8 \times 64630}$$

$$= 2.00$$

Hence in the E-W direction, $0.14\gamma_w\ell_w = 0.14 \times 2.00 \times 3200 = 896$ mm. As c_c is less than 896 mm, special confinement reinforcement is not required.

The overstrength factor for one of the ductile flexural walls (N-S direction) is:

$$\gamma_w = \frac{M_n}{J \times M_{overturning}}$$

$$= \frac{62399}{0.8 \times 39\,202}$$

$$= 1.99$$

Hence in the N-S direction, $0.14\gamma_w\ell_w = 0.14 \times 1.99 \times 6400 = 1783$ mm. As c_c is considerably less than 1783 mm, special confinement reinforcement outside of the region of concentrated reinforcement is not required.

(d) Check wall stability

Clause 21.5.3 requires a wall thickness of $\ell_u/10$ in those parts of a wall that, under factored vertical and lateral loads, are more than half way from the neutral axis to the compression face of the wall section.

The 3200 mm long portions of the E-W "tension wall" may be considered as simple rectangular wall elements as shown in Fig. 11.23(a) with a neutral axis depth of 664 mm. Since the neutral axis depth is less than $4b_w = 4 \times 400 - 1600$ mm and Is less than $0.3\ell_w = 0.3 \times 3200 = 960$ mm, the $\ell_u/10$ need not apply (see Clause 21.5.3.4).

CPCA Concrete Design Handbook

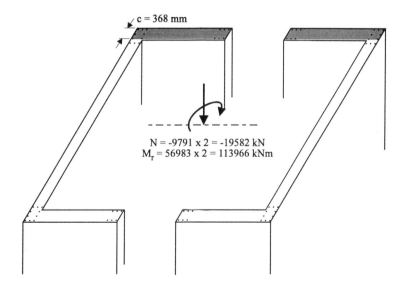

$c = 368$ mm

$N = -9791 \times 2 = -19582$ kN
$M_r = 56983 \times 2 = 113966$ kNm

Fig. 11.24 Factored moment resistance of ductile flexural walls (N-S direction)

For the 6400 mm long portion of the E-W "compression wall", it is noted that $c/2 = 133$ mm, which is less than the wall thickness, and furthermore, the wall is laterally supported at its ends by the 3200 mm wall portions. Hence, this portion of the wall need not have a thickness of $\ell_u/10$ (see Clause 21.5.3.3).

For stability considerations for the wall loaded in the N-S direction, the value of $c/2 = 368/2 = 184$ mm is smaller than the 400 mm thickness of the flanges. Therefore the 400 mm wall dimension is adequate and the width of the flange of 3100, greatly exceeds $\ell_u/10$ (see Clause 21.5.3.3).

Therefore all of the stability requirements are satisfied.

(e) Confinement of concentrated reinforcement

The concentrated reinforcement should be confined as a column in accordance with Clause 7.6 and the ties will be detailed as hoops (Clause 21.5.6.5). In plastic hinge regions, the hoop spacing shall not exceed:

(i) $6d_b = 6 \times 25 = 150$ mm

(ii) $24d_b$ (tie) $= 24 \times 10 = 240$ mm

(iii) one half the wall thickness $= 400/2 = 200$ mm

Hence provide No. 10 hoops at a spacing of 150 mm as shown in Fig. 11.22.

4. *Design for Shear at Base of Walls*

The walls must be designed to resist the shear corresponding to the formation of plastic hinges at their bases (Clause 21.7.2.3).

(a) Determine probable moment resistances of walls

In order to determine the probable moment resistances of the walls, axial load-moment calculations were carried out with $\phi_c = \phi_s = 1.00$ and using an equivalent "yield" strength of steel of $1.25f_y$. In the E-W direction, we only need to determine the probable moment resistance of the "compression wall" subjected to an axial load corresponding to $1.0E + 1.0D + 0.5L$, since it results in the larger resistance. From calculations, the probable moment resistance of the wall, M_{pw}, is 29370 kN m in the E-W direction and 72349 kN m per wall in the N-S direction.

(b) Estimate the design shear at base

It is assumed that earthquake loading causes plastic hinging at the base of the walls. Assuming that the ratio of the shear to moment at the base of a wall remains constant as the moment increases to the probable resistance, the shear at the base as the wall develops a plastic hinge will be:

In the E-W direction:

$$V = \frac{M_{pw}}{M_f} \times V_f$$

$$= \frac{29370}{12788} \times \frac{1971.5}{2}$$

$$= 2264 \text{ kN per wall}$$

In calculating the shear capacity of the wall, in accordance with Clause 21.7.3.2, we will assume an effective shear depth, $d_v = 0.8\ell_w = 0.8 \times 3200 = 2560$ mm. The average vertical strain, ε_v, is:

$$\varepsilon_v = \frac{0.001}{\gamma_w}\left(0.5 - \frac{c_c}{\ell_w}\right)\left(18 + \frac{h_w}{\ell_w}\right)$$

$$= \frac{0.001}{2.00}\left(0.5 - \frac{266}{3200}\right)\left(18 + \frac{48650}{3200}\right)$$

$$= 0.0069$$

The factored shear stress ratio, $v_f/(\phi_c f'_c) = (2264 \times 1000)/(800 \times 2560 \times 0.6 \times 30) = 0.061$. From Table 21-1, the value of β is 0.0891. Hence the factored shear resistance is:

$V_{rg} = V_{cg} + V_{sg}$

$$= 2 \left(1.3 \phi_c \, \beta \sqrt{f_c'} \, b_w \, d_v + \frac{\phi_s \, A_v \, f_y \, d}{s} \right)$$

$$= 2 \left(1.3 \times 0.6 \times 0.0891 \times \sqrt{30} \times 400 \times 2560 + \right.$$

$$\left. \frac{0.85 \times 200 \times 400 \times 2560}{200} \right) \times 10^{-3}$$

$$= 2 \, (389.8 + 870.4)$$

$$= 2520 \text{ kN}$$

Hence the shear strength in the E-W direction is adequate with 2 No. 10 bars at 200 mm spacing.

And in the N-S direction:

The factored shear force on the most heavily loaded wall is 1387 kN. Hence:

$$V = \frac{M_{pw}}{M_f} \times V_f$$

$$= \frac{72 \, 349}{39 \, 202} \times 1387$$

$$= 2560 \text{ kN per wall}$$

In calculating the shear capacity of the wall, in accordance with Clause 21.7.3.2, we will assume an effective shear depth, $d_v = 0.8\ell_w = 0.8 \times 6400 = 5120$ mm. The average vertical strain, ε_v, is:

$$\varepsilon_v = \frac{0.001}{2.58} (0.5 - \frac{380}{6400}) \, (18 + \frac{48650}{6400})$$

$$= 0.0044$$

The factored shear stress ratio, $v_f/(\phi_c f_c') = (2194 \times 1000)/(400 \times 5120 \times 0.6 \times 30) = 0.0595$. From Table 21-1, the value of β is 0.110. Hence the factored shear resistance is:

$$V_{rg} = \left(1.3 \times 0.6 \times 0.110 \times \sqrt{30} \times 400 \times 5120 + \right.$$

$$\left. \frac{0.85 \times 200 \times 400 \times 5120}{200} \right) \times 10^{-3}$$

$$= (962.4 + 1740.8)$$

$$= 2703 \text{ kN}$$

Hence the shear strength in the N-S direction is adequate with 2 No. 10 bars at 200 mm spacing.

Extend the No. 10 horizontal reinforcement a distance of $\ell_d = 300$ mm into the confined core of the region of concentrated reinforcement (see Fig 11.22). Extend this reinforcement into the core as close to the outside surface of the walls as cover will permit.

5. *Determination of Plastic Hinge Region*

As the wall cross sectional dimensions remain constant over the 48.65 m height of the wall and provided that the main flexural reinforcement is appropriately curtailed, only one plastic hinge region will form, near the base of the walls. We will assume that the plastic hinge length at the base of the wall will be governed by the longer, N-S, wall and may be taken as:

(i) $\ell_w = 6.4$ m in the N-S direction

(ii) $\geq h_w/6 = 48.65/6 = 8.1$ m

(iii) $\leq 2\ell_w = 2 \times 6.4 = 12.8$ m

Hence the plastic hinge region can be assumed to cover the first 8.1 m of the height of the wall. Therefore detail the first two storeys as plastic hinge regions.

6. *Changes in Horizontal Distributed Reinforcement Over the Height of the Walls*

The maximum spacing of the 2 – No. 10 horizontal bars, outside of the plastic hinge region is 200 mm, since the minimum reinforcement ratio of 0.0025 must be satisfied. Therefore use 2 No. 10 bars at 200 mm spacing over the entire height of the wall. Note that the shear capacity will be more than adequate since this amount of reinforcement satisfies the shear requirements at the base of the wall.

7. *Changes in Vertical Distributed Reinforcement Over the Height of the Walls*

Once again, the minimum reinforcement ratio of 0.0025 governs the selection of vertical distributed reinforcement. Hence use 2 No. 10 bars at 200 mm spacing over the entire height of the wall.

8. *Changes in Concentrated Vertical Reinforcement Over the Height of the Walls*

The minimum area of concentrated reinforcement which can be used outside the plastic hinge region is $0.001 b_w \ell_w$, that is, one half of the amounts required in the plastic hinge region. At one end of the 3200 mm long wall, the minimum amount of concentrated reinforcement is $0.001 \times 400 \times 3200 = 1280 \text{ mm}^2$. Similarly, the minimum amount of concentrated reinforcement required at the intersection of the wall components is 2560 mm^2.

Note that in deciding on the changes to the concentrated reinforcement over the height of the structure, it is necessary to ensure that the factored moment resistance at each floor level is sufficient to develop the plastic hinging at the base of the structure. This check should be made with due consideration for the effect of lap splices in the reinforcement. An example of the calculations necessary to ensure adequate flexural strength is given in Reference 3.

9. *Checking Sliding Shear Resistance at Construction Joints.*

In accordance with Clause 21.7.3.2, we must check the sliding shear resistance of the construction joints. Since the vertical uniformly distributed reinforcement is constant over the height of the walls, the most critical situation is at the base of the walls. In the E-W direction, the required shear strength is 2264 kN per wall. If the construction joint is intentionally roughened, the factored shear stress resistance from Clause 11.6.2 is:

$$v_r = \phi_c \, (c + \mu \, (\rho_v \, f_y + \frac{N}{A_g}))$$

$$= 0.6 \left(0.50 + 1.0 \left(0.0025 \times 400 + \right. \right.$$

$$\left. \left. \frac{1450 \times 1000}{(800 \times 3200 + 400 \times 5600)} \right) \right)$$

$$= 1.081 \text{ MPa}$$

Hence, the sliding shear resistance is $1.081 \times A_{cv} = 1.081 \times 800 \times 3200 \times 10^{-3} = 2768$ kN.

Since the sliding shear resistance exceeds the shear corresponding to plastic hinging, sliding shear will be prevented.

In the N-S direction, the required shear strength is 2560 kN per wall. If the construction joint is intentionally roughened, the factored shear stress resistance from Clause 11.6.2 is:

$$v_r = 0.6 \left(0.50 + 1.0 \left(0.0025 \times 400 + \right. \right.$$

$$\left. \left. \frac{9791 \times 1000}{(800 \times 3200 + 400 \times 5600)} \right) \right)$$

$$= 2.124 \text{ MPa}$$

Hence, the sliding shear resistance is $2.124 \times A_{cv} = 2.124 \times 400 \times 6400 \times 10^{-3} = 5437$ kN.

Since the sliding shear resistance exceeds the shear corresponding to plastic hinging, sliding shear will be prevented.

11.8 REFERENCES

1. Paulay, T. and Priestley, M.J.N.,"Seismic Design of Reinforced Concrete and Masonry Buildings", John Wiley and Sons, Inc., 1992, 744 p.

2. Collins, M.P. and Mitchell, D., "Prestressed Concrete Structures", Prentice Hall, Englewood Cliffs, NJ, 1991, 766 p.

3. Mitchell, D. and Collins, M.P., "Chapter 11 - Seismic Design", Concrete Design Handbook, Canadian Portland Cement Association, 1985, 31 p.

Anchorage to Concrete

By Richard J. McGrath

Chapter 12
Anchorage
to Concrete

12.1 INTRODUCTION

To aid engineers in the design of cast-in-place, adhesive and grouted anchors, Appendix 'D', Anchorage Systems has been retained in the 1994 edition of the CSA A23.3 Standard. The Appendix 'D' material remains unchanged from the previous edition of the Standard. Chapter 12 illustrates the use of Appendix 'D' in the design of Anchorage Systems which are embedded in concrete and are essential to the structural integrity of the building. Wherever possible the design philosophy of Appendix 'D' is one of ductile failure involving yielding of the steel embedment prior to failure of the concrete. This philosophy is consistent with that of the CSA A23.3 Standard.

A wide variety of cast-in-place and other types of anchorage devices can be used. This Handbook chapter is limited to cast-in-place anchors made of A307 bolts or similar material. Some guidance is given concerning the use of higher strength materials.

12.2 OVERVIEW OF DESIGN PROCESSES

Anchorage systems may fail due to a failure of the steel portion of the system or a failure of the concrete surrounding the anchorage device. Design must consider both types of failures. The concrete may fail due to pulling out a cone of concrete (Clause D4.1); by crushing or spalling adjacent to the anchor head (Clause D4.2); or, when subjected to a force parallel to the surface of the concrete, by bearing, shearing or tearing of the concrete (Clause D4.3). Properly designed reinforcement may be used to increase the strength of the concrete portion of the anchorage system (Clause D4.4). Design requirements for the steel portion are given in Clause D5.

A flow chart illustrating the design process is given in Fig. 12.1. The sections that follow are intended to guide the user through this flow chart.

12.3 DESIGN REQUIREMENTS FOR STEEL COMPONENTS

Typical embedment steels exhibit significant variation in actual yield strength above specified minimums and have widely differing ratios of yield to tensile strength. Therefore in keeping with the Limit States Design approach of the CSA A23.3 Standard, $\phi_s f_{su}$ rather than a factor times f_y, is used to ensure ductile behaviour. For threaded anchor bolts in tension, the net tensile area is conservatively taken as 75% of the gross area. This assumes failure is in the threaded section of the bolt.

12.4 DESIGN REQUIREMENTS FOR CONCRETE

12.4.1 Tensile Load Transfer Mechanism

The development length requirements for deformed reinforcement are dependent on the relationship of the height and spacing of deformation with respect to bar size and the influence of adjacent stressed reinforcement. The development length requirements of Clause 12 of the CSA A23.3 Standard are based on clear side covers and bar spacings typically found in beams and columns where splitting away of the concrete cover occurs to produce bond failure. When a reinforcing bar is used as a tensile stress component embedded into the interior of a concrete mass, the development length requirements of Clause 12 may be conservative. However, these requirements are recommended for the development of reinforcement without mechanical anchorage (head of an anchor bolt or stud) due to a lack of available data necessary to reduce the embedment requirements.

For uniformly sized and spaced bar deformations, the tensile stress in a reinforcing bar varies from a maximum at the surface of the concrete to zero at the embedded end of the bar. A single mechanical anchor at the end of a smooth bar or rod behaves in a different manner to deformed reinforcement. As the tensile load increases, bond failure along the length occurs and the entire tensile load is transferred to the concrete by the anchor head. Unless preceded by failure of the steel, this will produce a conical failure surface in the concrete. Such anchorages must be designed to produce failure in the steel embedment prior to failure in the concrete, if a ductile failure is required under severe overloading (Clause D3.2).

12.4.2 Tension

This section sets forth the method of calculating the design pullout strength of concrete, i.e. direct tensile capacity of an anchorage system where headed anchors are employed. The term "standard anchor bolt" when used in this chapter means a bolt with dimensions conforming to those for Square Head Bolts listed in CSA Standard B18.2.1-1961, Hexagonal Head Bolts listed in CSA Standard B33.1-1961 or ASTM A307 Bolts as described in Table 12.3. An anchor bolt head conforming to Clause D4.2.3(a) will have a total area of 2.5 times the area of the bolt cross section, thereby providing a bearing area between the bold head and concrete of 1.5 times the bolt cross section. A standard nut and washer on a standard anchor bolt will provide sufficient bearing area to fully develop the tensile strength of the bolt if $f_y \le 400$ MPa.

a) Single Anchorages

The tensile strength of concrete is generally accepted to be in the range of 0.5 to 0.6 times the square root of the compressive strength of the concrete (in MPa).

Along the potential pullout failure plane defined by Clause D4.1.2, the principal tensile stress in the concrete is assumed to vary from a maximum at the mechanical anchor head of the steel embedment to zero at the surface of the concrete. For a conical failure surface with a slope of 45°, the average resistance provided by the concrete on the basis of a projected resisting area can be taken as $0.40 \, \phi_c \sqrt{f'_c}$. This value will provide the same overall factor of safety recommended by Cannon, Godfrey and Moreadith (1981) when the ϕ factors required in A23.3-94 are utilized. A reduction factor of $\pi/4$ is then applied to the average concrete stress noted above to account for the difference between the assumed pyramid failure planes versus the actual cone failure surfaces observed in practice to give a value of $0.314 \, \phi_c \sqrt{f'_c}$. The equation in Clause D4.1.1 is conservatively rounded to $0.3 \, \phi_c \sqrt{f'_c}$. Because failure in the concrete is initiated at the outside of the periphery of the mechanical anchor (anchor head), the area of the anchor head does not contribute to the effective stress area and should not be included in this area.

In calculating the tension embedment depth necessary to ensure ductile yielding of the anchorage component the tensile strength of the anchor is equated to the tensile resistance of the potential failure pyramid defined in Clause D4.1.2. For single anchor bolts the embedment depth ℓ_d is thus:

$$0.75 \, \frac{\pi d_a^2}{4} \, \phi_s \, f_{su} = 0.3 \, \phi_c \sqrt{f'_c} \times$$

$$\left[(2\ell_d + 1.58 \, d_a)^2 - \frac{\pi}{4} (1.58 \, d_a)^2 \, \frac{4}{\pi} \right]$$

(Steel Tensile Force) =
(Concrete Stress) $\times$ (Projected Area)
where $\phi_s = 0.85$
$\phi_c = 0.60$

Fig. 12.1:   Design of Anchorage Systems

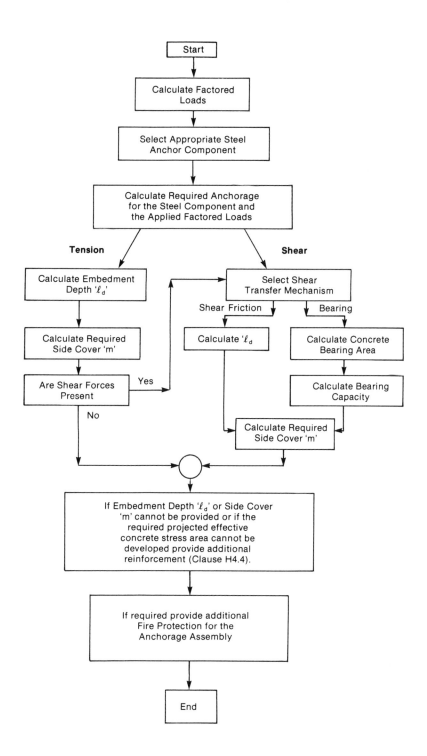

The tension embedment depths (ℓ_d), represented in Table 12.4, are measured from the surface of the concrete to the bearing surface of the anchor head, and are based on threaded anchors having a tensile strength of 690 MPa. This represents the maximum possible tensile strength of A307 bolts. Subtraction of the anchor head area from the effective concrete stress area as required by Clause D4.1.2 has been incorporated into the calculation of ℓ_d used in Table 12.4. The anchor head area, taken as $2.5 \times A_b$ as specified in Clause D4.2.3(a) was multiplied by $4/\pi$ to conform with the modified effective stress pyramid area of Clause D4.1.2. The ℓ_d values of Table 12.4 can be used for anchors with anchor head areas exceeding that of Clause D4.2.3(a) as the resulting increase in the effective concrete stress area will more than offset the increased anchor head area. When using unthreaded anchors or anchors where 100% of the anchor cross section may be expected to fail in tension, the ℓ_d values in Table 12.4 will be multiplied by correction factor $C_A = 1.15$ to provide adequate embedment to ensure ductile failure. An additional factor C_f is to be applied separately or in combination with C_A to modify plotted ℓ_d values for anchor tensile strengths ranging from 400 MPa to 900 MPa.

Caution is advised when using anchors with a yield strength which exceeds 400 MPa since Clause D4.2.2 requires a bolt head or washer area greatly in excess of the 2.5 times the cross sectional area of the bolt that is provided by an A307 bolt head. As an extreme example, if $f_{su} = 900$ MPa and $f'_c = 20$ MPa, the bearing area required is 28 times the bolt area.

Lateral thrust is generated at the head of an anchor loaded in tension by the full load transfer from steel to concrete and must be confined by a minimum side cover at the anchor head. The lateral bursting force is of a magnitude relative to the longitudinal load similar to that of the lateral strain to the longitudinal strain. Cannon, Godfrey and Moreadith (1981) recommend a conservative lateral bursting force of 25% of the tensile load on the anchor for establishing the minimum edge distance to the anchor. Clause D.4.2.1 equates this lateral bursting force to the concrete capacity for a single anchor bolt, stud or bar and provides a side cover calculated by Equation D-1 as:

$$m = d_a \sqrt{\frac{f_{su}}{6 \sqrt{f'_c}}}$$

Table 12.5 represents concrete side cover 'm' in millimetres required by Equation D-1 for threaded anchor bolts with a tensile strength $f_{su} = 690$ MPa. A bolt tensile stress area equal to 75% of the bolt gross area has been used to account for the threaded section of the bolt where tensile failure is assumed to occur. If ductile failure of the gross cross section of the bolt is required, the side cover values in Table 12.5 should be multiplied by the factor $C_A = 1.15$. Where anchors with tensile strengths other than 690 MPa are used, a corresponding C_f factor chosen from the list of factors included with Table 12.3 is to be applied to the side cover value. C_A and C_f factors are used in combination where applicable. When expansion type anchors are used, consideration should be given to increasing the side cover 'm' for tension anchorage because of the significant lateral force required to restrain an expansion factor.

b) **Multiple Anchorages**

When the centre to centre spacing of anchors is less than two times the embedment depth plus one bolt head diameter, Clause D4.1.2 limits the effective stress area to the projected area of the overlapping stress pyramids. This resulting loss of effective tensile stress area can be compensated for by increasing the depth of embedment

(see Example No. 12.2). The projected tensile stress area of the group must be capable of developing the combined strengths of the tensile stress components. For fully developed embedments the concrete dimension parallel to the development length must be of sufficient thickness to meet the nominal shear stress requirements of Clause 11.10 of CSA A23.3 for two-way action.

The allowable stress area for such a situation where concrete depth is limited is illustrated in Fig. 12.2.

The inclination of the failure angle will vary in response to the state of stress in the plane of the concrete structure (e.g. wall or slab) into which the embedment is being anchored and to a lesser extent the depth to which the anchor is embedded. For design purposes, it is generally felt that the selection of a failure plane inclination of 45° is appropriate.

In accordance with the design requirements for group anchors described in Section 12.4.2(b) of this chapter, Table 12.6 provides the designer with the required concrete tensile stress area as a function of the total steel anchor area used in the group anchor. Example No. 12.2 describes the calculation of group anchorage embedment depths.

12.4.3 Shear Load Transfer Mechanism

The strength of anchors subject to shear is not significantly affected by concrete strength unless the anchors are located near an edge or where shell-type expansion anchors which exhibit non-linear load deflection behaviour are used. Clause D4.3.1 provides two methods, bearing and shear friction, for transferring shear forces from the embedment to the concrete. In either case when shear acts towards a free edge, the projected effective concrete tensile stress area defined by Clause D4.3.6 and Fig. D2 or Fig. D3 must not be overstressed unless reinforcement is provided to intercept the potential cracking planes (Clause D4.4 and Fig. D4).

a) **Bearing**

Clause D4.3.2 provides design requirements for the transfer of shear forces through bearing. For anchor bolts, the allowable bearing area 'A' in Equation D-2 will usually equal one quarter of the embedment depth times the diameter of the bolt, except in the case of high strength bolts which may require tensile embedment depths greater than 20 bolt diameters. Clause D4.3.2 also provides design requirements when shear lugs are employed.

A minimum edge distance as illustrated in Figure D2 of Appendix 'D' is required to develop the shear strength of a steel anchor designed using direct bearing to develop the shear. This model is conservative when used for shear lugs, or for anchor bolts or studs designed using the shear friction approach (Clause D4.3.6(c) and Fig. D3). Using the concrete stress defined in Clause D4.3.6 and tensile stress area defined in Clause D4.3.6(a) the shear resistance V provided by edge distance 'm' equals:

$$V = 0.3 \lambda \phi_c \sqrt{(2 \cdot m^2)}$$

where λ is a modification factor defined in Clause 11.2.3.

Table 12.7 shows the shear transferred by direct bearing as a function of bearing area for various concrete strengths. When shear resisted by direct bearing acts towards a free edge, minimum concrete side cover must be provided in accordance with Clause D4.3.6.

b) **Shear Friction**

When shear is to be transferred by shear friction the factored resistance is calculated in accordance with the requirements of Clause D4.3.5 of Appendix 'D'. In

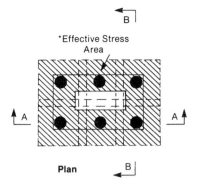

*Effective Stress Area

Plan

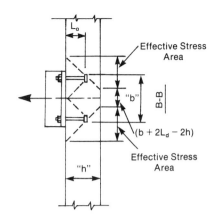

Effective Stress Area

Effective Stress Area

Stress Area Reduction for Limited Depth (A_r)

$$A_r = (a + 2L_d - 2h)(b + 2L_d - 2h)$$

*Reduced by the Total Bearing Area of the Anchor Steel

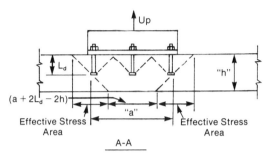

A-A

Fig. 12.2: Stress Area Reduction for Limited Depth A_r

designing for shear friction, it is assumed that the shear force is transmitted from the bolt to the concrete through direct bearing at the surface forming a concrete wedge approximately $\frac{1}{4}$ of the bolt diameter in depth as illustrated in Fig. 12.3. Vertical translation of the wedge is prevented by the clamping force of the anchored base plate. This clamping force on the wedge created by tensile elongation in the anchor increases in direct proportion to the shear as long as the anchor steel remains elastic.

In most instances greater shear resistance can be developed using shear friction with bolted anchorage systems than by using direct bearing of the bolt against the surrounding concrete. For this reason anchorage systems using studs or bolts typically are designed by the shear friction method. Shear resistance through direct bearing is usually used when shear lugs which provide a larger bearing area against the concrete are used in the anchor system.

Using a friction coefficient μ the shear friction strength V of a steel anchor for which concrete side cover must be provided is:

$$V = \mu \pi \frac{d_a^2}{4} \phi_s f_{su}$$

where μ is given in Clause D4.3.5.

By equating Eq. 12.1 and 12.2, the side cover distance, m, can be calculated for load transfer by shear friction. This distance is conservative because the failure pyramid in Fig. D2 has been used in place of that in Fig. D3.

Table 12.9 represents the minimum concrete side cover required when shear acting towards a free edge is resisted by shear friction using threaded steel anchor bolts with $f_{su} = 690$ MPa and $\mu = 0.8$. The table of C_f correction factors provided with Table 12.9 is used to modify the concrete side cover values to accommodate a range of steel tensile strengths and the friction coefficient values of Clause D4.3.5. When unthreaded studs or bars are used, the side cover values in Table 12.9 should be multiplied by correction factor C_A to account for the larger effective steel tensile stress area.

12.4.4 Reinforcement

Clause D4.4 requires the use of reinforcement when minimum side cover or embedment depth requirements cannot be provided. Studies indicate that side covers less than $\frac{1}{3}$ that required by Clause D4.3 for shear cannot be sufficiently reinforced and should not be used. When side covers are less than that required by Clause D4.2 and reinforcement is required to prevent the lateral bursting of concrete around tension anchors, the engineer should rely on accepted practices (Reference 4) for prestressing anchorages and spiral reinforcement as illustrated in Fig. 12.4.

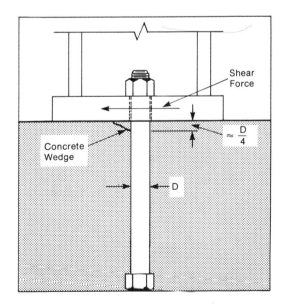

Fig 12.3: Concrete Wedge Due to Shear

12.4.5 Combined Tension and Shear

For bolts, studs and bars the area of embedment steel required by Clause D5.1 for tension and for shear should be additive. The effect of direct tension on an anchorage is a reduction of the clamping force which provides shear transfer resistance by shear friction. By preloading the anchor in the elastic range, this effect can be offset somewhat but there is no difference in effect once the tensile load exceeds the preload. Because the loss of clamping force reduces the shear strength and affects the combined load capacity of the anchor, no less than a straight addition of the areas providing the component strengths is allowed. For bearing shear design, this approach is conservative.

12.5 EFFECT OF ELEVATED TEMPERATURES ON ANCHORAGE SYSTEMS

Anchorage systems that can be weakened by fire and thereby jeopardize the structure's stability should be protected to the same degree as that required for the structural frame. The three main areas of concern when dealing with the effects of elevated temperatures on anchorage systems are

a) fire protection of the exposed portion of the steel embedment;

b) behaviour of grouts and/or adhesives that may be used in the anchorage system; and

c) possible loss of bond or anchorage between the steel embedment and the surrounding concrete or grout.

Table No. 12.8 shows thickness of protection required for structural steel portions of connection details to provide fire resistance ratings of 1 hour to 4 hours. The sprayed mineral fibre referred to in Table No. 12.8 should consist of refined mineral fibres with inorganic binders and water added during the spraying operation. The unit weight of the oven-dry material should be at least 14 pcf. Vermiculite cementitious material also listed in Table No. 12.8 should consist of expanded vermiculite with inorganic binders and water. The unit weight of the oven-dry material should be at least 16 pcf.

Grouts or adhesives containing organic material have been observed to perform poorly at elevated temperatures. Due to the widely varying material properties of epoxy grouts and grouts containing organic material, the designer should have available to him suitable test data on which to base his assessment of the grout's suitability for use in a fire rated anchorage system. If such test data is not available, a testing program should be conducted to establish the material's suitability for its intended use.

References 7 and 8 provide further information on fire ratings and fire protection of concrete and steel connections.

12.6 CORROSION RESISTANT COATINGS

Where corrosion resistant protective coatings have been applied to the steel embedment component of the anchorage system, consideration should be given to the effect of possible debonding between the steel embedment and the surrounding concrete or grout. Where anchorage is provided by mechanical means such as a bolt head, the loss of bond may not reduce the anchor's capacity. For expansion type anchors, however, a loss of bond or friction reduction between the steel embedment and the surrounding concrete could have disastrous effects.

References

1. Guide to the Design of Anchor Bolts and Other Steel Embedments, R.W. Cannon, D.A. Godfrey and F.L. Moreadith, Concrete International, July 1981.
2. Commentary on Guide to the Design of Anchor Bolts and Other Steel Embedments, Concrete International, July 1981.
3. CSA N287.3 Design for Requirements for Concrete Containment Structures for CANDU Nuclear Power Plants.
4. CPCI Metric Design Manual Precast and Prestressed Concrete, Ottawa, 1982.
5. Proposed Addition to Code Requirements for Nuclear Safety Related Concrete Structures (ACI 349-76).
6. CSA A23.3-94 Design of Concrete Structures.
7. PCI Design for Fire Resistance of Precast and Prestressed Concrete, 1977.
8. CPCI Fire Resistance Ratings for Prestressed and Precast Concrete, 1978.

	CSA A23.3 CLAUSE
Example No. 12.1 — Tension (Single Anchor)	

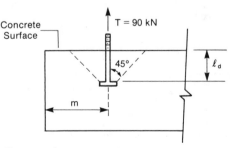

Given:

Factored tensile load = 90 kN
Threaded anchor bolts (A307)
f_{su} = 414 MPa f'_c = 30 MPa

Required:

Design single tension anchor for given tensile load.

Fig. 12.4: Example of Reinforcement to prevent lateral bursting.

(Figure labels: Tension Force; Spiral Reinforcement; Potential Failure Plane)

Solution:

Calculate required area of anchor bolt A_b

From CSA S16.1 Standard or Table 1 unit factored tensile resistance of A307 bolt = 0.5 f_{su} = 208 MPa **H5**

$$A_b = 90 \times 10^3 \, N / (208 \, N/mm^2) = 432 \, mm^2$$

From Table 12.2 select 1 M24 A307 threaded anchor bolt. The bolt size could have been selected directly from Table 12.2.

$$A_b = 452 \, mm^2 > Req'd$$

Calculate anchorage required to ensure ductile failure

Embedment depth: From Table 12.4 for f'_c = 30 MPa **H4.1.1**

and 24 mm diameter bolt with f_{su} = 414 MPa select **H4.1.2**

$$\ell_d = 207 \times C_f = 207 \times .79 = 163 \, mm$$

Side cover for tension:

From Table 12.5 using threaded M24 bolt with f_{su} = 414 MPa, **H4.2**

f'_c = 30 MPa and C_A = 1.0

$$m = 112 \times C_f \times C_A = 112 \times .81 \times 1.0 = 91 \, mm$$

Side cover necessary to ensure development of required effective concrete tensile stress area using ℓ_d = 163 mm:

$$m = 163 + \frac{1.58 \, d_a}{2} \, mm$$

$$= 163 + 19$$

$$= 182 \, mm$$

The actual tensile strengths of anchor bolts often exceed the specified minimum f_{su} values used to calculate their factored resistance. In recognition of this fact, a more conservative design for the embedment and side cover of the above bolt would incorporate a higher f_{su} value, thus preventing an overstrength anchor bolt from producing sudden failure in the concrete.

Potential overstrength in f_{su} is partly addressed in this example by using C_f values for f_{su} = 450 MPa, rather than interpolating for the specified f_{su} = 414 MPa.

CSA A23.3

Example No. 12.2 — Tension (Group Anchor) CLAUSE

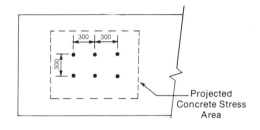

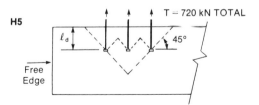

H5

Free Edge

Given:

Factored tensile load = 720 kN
Unthreaded stud anchors
Anchor spacing = 300 mm c/c
f_{su} = 600 MPa; $f_y \leq$ 400 MPa
f'_c = 20 MPa

Required:

Design a grouped anchor system for the given tensile load.

Solution:

Calculate total area of anchor bolt steel required

$$A_b(TOTAL) = 720 \times 10^3 \, N / (\phi f_{su})$$
where ϕ = 0.67 from CSA S16.1 **H5.1**
$$= 1791 mm^2$$

From Table 12.2 select 6 M20 stud anchors

$$A_{b(prov)} = 6 \times 314 \, mm^2$$
$$= 1884 \, mm^2 \text{ Req'd}$$

For the given anchor layout, calculate required embedment depth.

For f'_c = 20 MPa and M20 unthreaded stud anchors with f_{su} = 600 MPa, Table 12.4 gives

$$\ell_d = 193 \, mm \times C_f \times C_A$$
$$= 193 \times 0.93 \times 1.15$$
$$= 207 \, mm$$

The C_f and C_A factors adjust the plotted embedment values in Table 12.4 to suit the f_{su} value and anchor type used in the design.

For an anchor spacing of 300 mm c/c and ℓ_d = 207, the resulting concrete stress pyramids of each anchor will overlap, reducing the net effective area. **H4.1.2**

Select from Table 12.6 the total required effective concrete stress area. For unthreaded anchors of total area 1884 mm^2, f_{su} = 600 MPa and f'_c = 20 MPa, Table 12.6 gives an A_{eff} of:

$$A_{eff} = 1.03 \times 10^6 \, mm^2 \times C_f \times C_A$$
$$= 1.03 \times 10^6 \times .87 \times 1.33$$
$$= 1.19 \times 10^6 \, mm^2$$

In calculating the required ℓ_d for the grouped anchors, a conservative anchor head diameter of 1.58 d_a = 31 mm is used (see section 12.4.2(a)). **D4.2.2.a**

For an anchor spacing of 300 mm and with failure in the concrete initiated at the anchor head periphery:

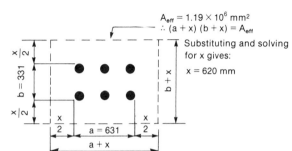

$$A_{eff} = 1.19 \times 10^6 \, mm^2$$
$$\therefore (a + x)(b + x) = A_{eff}$$

Substituting and solving for x gives:
$$x = 620 \, mm$$

The embedment depth required for the anchor arrangement chosen is:

$$\ell_d = x/2 = 620/2 = 310 \, mm$$

A minimum side cover =

$$\ell_d + \frac{\text{anchor head diameter}}{2}$$

should be observed to ensure the development of the projected concrete stress area.

H4.1.2

$$\therefore m = 310 + 1.58\ d_a/2$$
$$= 310 + 1.58(20) / 2$$
$$= 326\ mm$$

Calculate minimum depth of concrete required to ensure tensile concrete area provided is fully effective.

D4.1.2

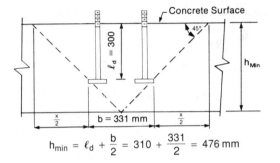

$$h_{min} = \ell_d + \frac{b}{2} = 310 + \frac{331}{2} = 476\ mm$$

CSA A23.3 CLAUSE

Example No. 12.3 — Shear Friction

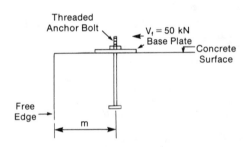

Given:

Factored shear force $V_f = 50$ kN
Threaded anchor $f_{su} = 700$ MPa
$f'_c = 20$ MPa
Free edge condition.

Required:

Using the shear friction concept, design an anchorage system to support the given loading condition above.

Solution:

For base plate bearing condition illustrated above, select friction coefficient $\mu = 0.6$.

D4.3.5

Calculated required A_b:

$$.75\ A_b\ \phi\ f_{su} = V_f/\mu \quad \text{where } \phi = 0.67$$

D4.3.5

$$A_b = \frac{50 \times 10^3\ N}{0.75 \times 0.67 \times 700 \times 0.6\ N/mm^2} = 237\ mm^2$$

From Table 12.2 select 1¾" diameter anchor
$$A_b(prov) = 285\ mm^2 > \text{Req'd}$$

Provide sufficient side cover to prevent concrete failure. For $f_{su} = 700$ MPa, $f'_c = 20$ MPa, $\mu = 0.6$

D4.3.6

and a ¾" (19mm) diameter threaded anchor. Table 12.9 gives:

$$m = 250 \times C_f = 250 \times 0.86 = 215\ mm$$

Provide sufficient embedment depth to develop full anchor capacity. For $f_{su} = 700$, $f'_c = 20$

D4.3.3

and a ¾" (19 mm) diameter threaded anchor bolt, Table 12.4 gives:

$$\ell_d = 183\ mm \times C_f = 183 \times 1.01 = 186\ mm$$

Since $m = 215$ mm $> \ell_d = 186$ mm, no additional reinforcement is required.

D4.4

Determine anchor head (washer) requirements:

D4.2.2

$$f_{su} = 700\ MPa \text{ will likely give } f_y > 400\ MPa$$

∴ provide special washer on the bolt head to limit the bearing stress, ie. calculate the bearing area A_1 needed to satisfy A23.3, Clause 10.15.

$$B_r = 0.85\ \phi_c\ f'_c\ A_1\ \sqrt{A_2/A_1} = 0.75\ A_{bolt}\ \phi_s\ f_{su}$$
$$\not> 2.0 - \text{controls for } A_2 \text{ very large}$$
$$= A_{bolt} + 21.9\ A_{bolt} = 22.9\ A_{bolt}$$

$$\therefore A_1 = \frac{0.75\ A_{bolt} \times 0.85\ f_{su}}{0.85 \times 0.6 \times f'_c \times 2} = \frac{0.625\ A_{bolt}\ f_{su}}{f'_c}$$

$$\therefore A_{TOTAL} \text{ (washer including bolt hole)}$$

$$A_1 = \frac{0.625 \times A_{bolt} \times 700}{20} = 21.9\ A_{bolt}$$

$$d_{WASHER} = \frac{4}{\pi} \sqrt{22.9 \times 285} = 103\ mm$$

$$d_{WASHER} = \frac{103}{19}\ d_a = 5.40\ d_a >> 1.58\ d_a$$
for standard bolt head

CSA A23.3 CLAUSE

Example No. 12.4 — Bearing

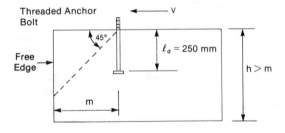

Given:

36 mm diameter anchor bolt
$f_{su} = 400$ MPa
$f'_c = 40$ MPa
Side cover 'm' = 400 mm
Embedment depth $\ell = 250$ mm
Bearing type shear resistance

Required:

Calculate the shear capacity of the above anchor assembly.

Solution:

Bolt factored shear capacity: (assuming no threads in the shear plane)

$$V = 0.6 \frac{\pi d_a^2}{4} \phi f_{su} = 0.6 \times 1018 \times 0.67 \times 400$$
$$= 163.7 \text{ kN} \qquad \text{D5.1}$$

Bolt ultimate shear capacity: **D5**

$$V = 0.6 \frac{\pi d_a^2}{4} \phi_s f_{su} = 1018 \times 0.85 \times 400$$
$$= 346 \text{ kN}$$

This can fail by bearing on the concrete or by pushing out a half cone of concrete in the side cover.

Factored resistance of concrete side cover:

$$V = 0.3 \phi_c \sqrt{f_c'} \times 2m^2 \qquad \text{H4.3.6}$$
$$= 0.3 \times 0.6 \times \sqrt{40} \times 2 \times 400^2$$
$$= 364 \text{ kN}$$

Bearing capacity of anchor assembly on the surrounding concrete

Effective bearing area 'A' equals the smaller of: **H4.3.2**

$$5 d_a^2 \text{ or } \ell_d/4 \times d_a$$
$$= 5 \times 36^2 \text{ mm}^2 \text{ or } 250/4 \times 36 \text{ mm}^2$$
$$= 6480 \text{ mm}^2 \text{ or } 2250 \text{ mm}^2$$

∴ Using 'A' = 2250 mm², f_c' = 40 MPa and f_{su} = 400 MPa, Table 12.7 gives a factored bearing resistance of:

75 kN

The maximum factored shear resistance of the given anchor assembly is governed by the bearing capacity of the surrounding concrete and is equal to:

$$V = 75 \text{ kN}$$

Example No. 12.5 — Combined Tension and Shear

CSA
A23.3
Clause

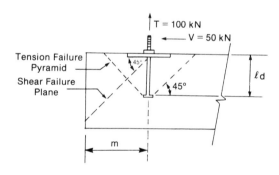

Tension Failure Pyramid

Shear Failure Plane

T = 100 kN
V = 50 kN
ℓ_d
45°
m

Given:

Factored loads — tension T = 100 kN
— shear V = 50 kN

Threaded anchor bolts
f_{su} = 500 MPa
f_c' = 30 MPa
Friction coefficient μ = 0.8

Required:

Design an anchor system for the given factored loads

Solution:

Calculate steel anchor area required:

For tension: ϕ 0.75 $A_{bT} f_{su}$ = T where ϕ = 0.67 **H5.1**

∴ A_{bT} = 100 × 10³ N / (0.67 × .75 × 500)
= 398 mm²

For shear: ϕ 0.75 $A_{bS} f_{su}$ = V/μ **H4.3.3**

∴ A_{bS} = 50 × 10³ N / (0.8 × .67 × .75 × 500)
= 248 mm²

Total bolt area required equals:

$A_b = A_{bT} + A_{bS}$ = 398 + 248 mm²
= 646 mm²

From Table 12.2 select 1 M30 anchor bolt:

$A_{(prov)}$ = 707 mm² > $A_{(req'd)}$ = 646 mm²

Calculate anchorage required:

For an M30 threaded anchor bolt with f_{su} = 500 and f_c' = 30, Table 12.4 gives:

ℓ_d = 260 mm × C_f
= 260 × 0.84
= 218 mm

For a friction coefficient μ = 0.8 and the above anchor, Table 12.9 gives a side cover for shear friction equal to:

m = 358 mm × C_f
= 358 × 0.85
= 304 mm

For the given loading and material properties, use 1 M30 threaded anchor bolt with tension embedment depth:

ℓ_d = 220 mm

and shear side cover equal to:

m = 305 mm

Table 12.1: Unit Factored Shear and Tensile Resistances

	Unit Factored Shear Resistance			
Bolt Grade	Specified Minimum Tensile Strength F_u (MPa)	Threads Excluded 0.40 F_u (MPa)	Threads Intercepted 0.28 F_u (MPa)	Unit Factored Tensile Resistance 0.50 F_u (MPa)
A307*	414	166	117	208

Table 12.2: Factored Shear and Tensile Resistances (kN per bolt)

Bolt Size		Nominal Area A_b (mm^2)	Factored Shear Resistance – Single Shear (kN/bolt)		Factored Tensile Resistance Tr(kN/bolt)
			Threads Excluded 0.40 F$_u$(MPa)	Threads Intercepted††	
Metric*	Imperial		A307	A307	A307
	$\frac{1}{2}$	127	21.0	14.8	26.4
	$\frac{5}{8}$	198	32.9	23.2	41.2
M16		201	33.3	23.5	41.8
	$\frac{3}{4}$	285	47.3	33.4	59.3
M20		314	52.1	36.7	65.3
M22		380	63.0	44.4	79.0
	$\frac{7}{8}$	388	64.4	45.4	80.7
M24		452	75.0	52.9	94.0
	1	507	84.1	59.3	105
M27		573	95.1	67.0	119
	$1\frac{1}{8}$	641	106	74.9	133
M30		707	117	82.7	147
	$1\frac{1}{4}$	792	131	92.6	165
M36		1018	168	119	211
	$1\frac{1}{2}$	1140	189	133	237

* The number following the letter M is the nominal bolt diameter in millimetres.
†† Threads assumed to be intercepted when thickness of part adjacent to nut <10 mm unless special precautions are taken.

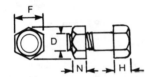
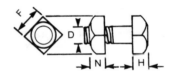

Table 12.3: ASTM Bolts and Nuts Dimensions in Imperial Units

Nominal Diameter of bolt	Regular Square Bolts		Finished Hex Bolts		Minimum Thread Lengths		Regular Square Nuts		Finished Hex Nuts	
	Nominal Width F	Nominal Height H	Basic Width F	Basic Height H	Length Under Head		Nominal Width F	Nominal Height N	Basic Width F	Basic Height N
					6 In. and Under	Over 6 In.				
Inches	Inches	Inches	Inches	Inches	Inches	Inches	Inches	Inches	Inches	Inches
$\frac{1}{4}$	$\frac{3}{8}$	$\frac{11}{64}$	$\frac{7}{16}$	$\frac{5}{32}$	$\frac{3}{4}$	1	$\frac{7}{16}$	$\frac{7}{32}$	$\frac{7}{16}$	$\frac{7}{32}$
$\frac{3}{8}$	$\frac{9}{16}$	$\frac{1}{4}$	$\frac{9}{16}$	$\frac{15}{64}$	1	$1\frac{1}{4}$	$\frac{5}{8}$	$\frac{21}{64}$	$\frac{9}{16}$	$\frac{21}{64}$
$\frac{1}{2}$	$\frac{3}{4}$	$\frac{21}{64}$	$\frac{3}{4}$	$\frac{5}{16}$	$1\frac{1}{4}$	$1\frac{1}{2}$	$\frac{13}{16}$	$\frac{7}{16}$	$\frac{3}{4}$	$\frac{7}{16}$
$\frac{5}{8}$	$\frac{15}{16}$	$\frac{27}{64}$	$\frac{15}{16}$	$\frac{25}{64}$	$1\frac{1}{2}$	$1\frac{3}{4}$	1	$\frac{35}{64}$	$\frac{15}{16}$	$\frac{35}{64}$
$\frac{3}{4}$	$1\frac{1}{8}$	$\frac{1}{2}$	$1\frac{1}{8}$	$\frac{15}{32}$	$1\frac{3}{4}$	2	$1\frac{1}{8}$	$\frac{21}{32}$	$1\frac{1}{8}$	$\frac{41}{64}$
$\frac{7}{8}$	$1\frac{5}{16}$	$\frac{19}{32}$	$1\frac{5}{16}$	$\frac{35}{64}$	2	$2\frac{1}{4}$	$1\frac{5}{16}$	$\frac{49}{64}$	$1\frac{5}{16}$	$\frac{3}{4}$
1	$1\frac{1}{2}$	$\frac{21}{32}$	$1\frac{1}{2}$	$\frac{39}{64}$	$2\frac{1}{4}$	$2\frac{1}{2}$	$1\frac{1}{2}$	$\frac{7}{8}$	$1\frac{1}{2}$	$\frac{55}{64}$
$1\frac{1}{8}$	$1\frac{11}{16}$	$\frac{3}{4}$	$1\frac{11}{16}$	$\frac{11}{16}$	$2\frac{1}{2}$	$2\frac{3}{4}$	$1\frac{11}{16}$	1	$1\frac{11}{16}$	$\frac{31}{32}$
$1\frac{1}{4}$	$1\frac{7}{8}$	$\frac{27}{32}$	$1\frac{7}{8}$	$\frac{25}{32}$	$2\frac{3}{4}$	3	$1\frac{7}{8}$	$1\frac{3}{32}$	$1\frac{7}{8}$	$1\frac{1}{16}$

CPCA Concrete Design Handbook

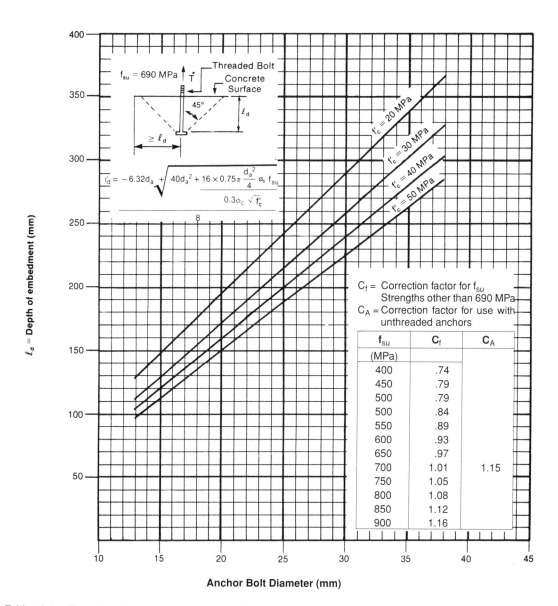

Table 12.4: Threaded Anchor Bolt Embedment Depth

The graph contains the following labeled elements:

- y-axis: ℓ_d = Depth of embedment (mm), ranging from 50 to 400
- x-axis: Anchor Bolt Diameter (mm), ranging from 10 to 45

Inset diagram:
- $f_{su} = 690$ MPa
- Threaded Bolt
- Concrete Surface
- T
- 45°
- ℓ_d
- $\geq \ell_d$

$$\ell_d' = -6.32d_a + \sqrt{\dfrac{40d_a{}^2 + 16 \times 0.75\pi \dfrac{d_a{}^2}{4} \, \phi_s \, f_{su}}{0.3\phi_c \sqrt{f_c'}}}$$

8

Curves labeled: $f_c' = 20$ MPa, $f_c' = 30$ MPa, $f_c' = 40$ MPa, $f_c' = 50$ MPa

C_f = Correction factor for f_{su} Strengths other than 690 MPa
C_A = Correction factor for use with unthreaded anchors

f_{su} (MPa)	C_f	C_A
400	.74	
450	.79	
500	.79	
500	.84	
550	.89	
600	.93	
650	.97	
700	1.01	1.15
750	1.05	
800	1.08	
850	1.12	
900	1.16	

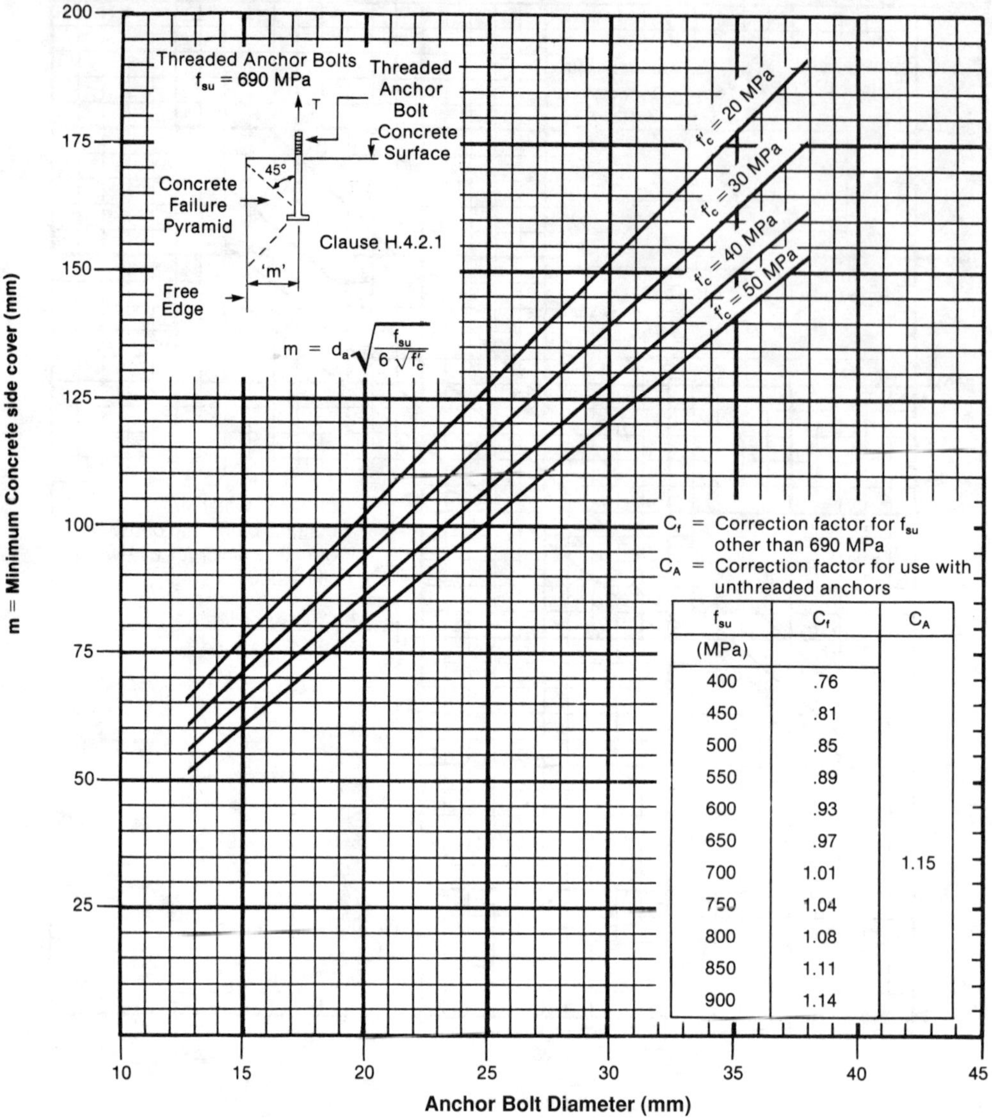
Threaded Anchor Bolts
f_{su} = 690 MPa
T
Threaded Anchor Bolt
Concrete Surface
45°
Concrete Failure Pyramid
Clause H.4.2.1
'm'
Free Edge
$m = d_a \sqrt{\frac{f_{su}}{6\sqrt{f'_c}}}$
f'_c = 20 MPa
f'_c = 30 MPa
f'_c = 40 MPa
f'_c = 50 MPa
C_f = Correction factor for f_{su} other than 690 MPa
C_A = Correction factor for use with unthreaded anchors
m = Minimum Concrete side cover (mm)
Anchor Bolt Diameter (mm)
200
175
150
125
100
75
50
25
10
15
20
25
30
35
40
45

f_{su} (MPa)	C_f	C_A
400	.76	
450	.81	
500	.85	
550	.89	
600	.93	
650	.97	
700	1.01	1.15
750	1.04	
800	1.08	
850	1.11	
900	1.14	

Table 12.5: Minimum Side Cover for Threaded Anchors in Tension

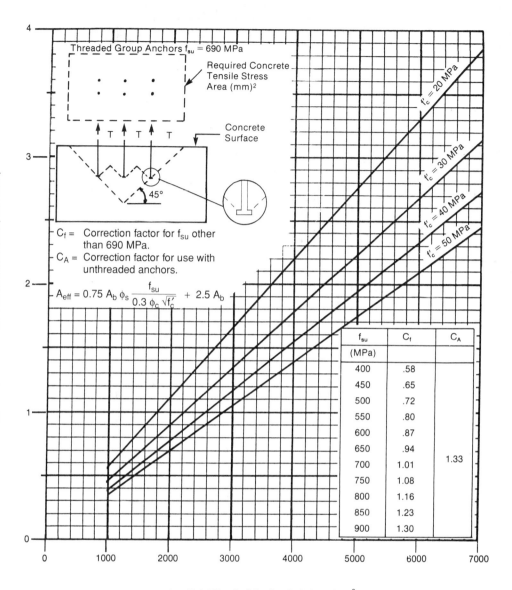

Inside the figure:

Threaded Group Anchors f_{su} = 690 MPa

Required Concrete Tensile Stress Area (mm)^2

Concrete Surface

$45°$

C_f = Correction factor for f_{su} other than 690 MPa.

C_A = Correction factor for use with unthreaded anchors.

$$A_{eff} = 0.75\, A_b\, \phi_s \frac{f_{su}}{0.3\, \phi_c\, \sqrt{f'_c}} + 2.5\, A_b$$

$f'_c = 20$ MPa
$f'_c = 30$ MPa
$f'_c = 40$ MPa
$f'_c = 50$ MPa

f_{su} (MPa)	C_f	C_A
400	.58	
450	.65	
500	.72	
550	.80	
600	.87	
650	.94	
700	1.01	1.33
750	1.08	
800	1.16	
850	1.23	
900	1.30	

Y-axis: A_{eff} — Required Concrete Tensile Stress Area ($\times 10^6$ mm^2)

X-axis: A_b = Total Nominal Anchor Bolt Area (mm^2)

Anchor Bolt Diameter (mm)

Table 12.6: Effective Concrete Tensile Stress Areas for Threaded Group Anchors

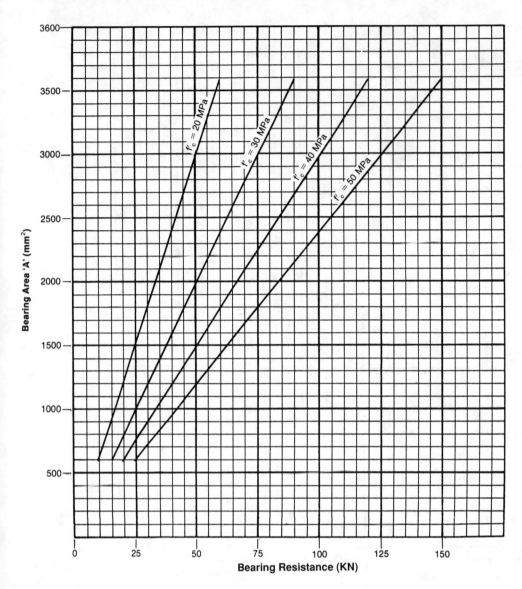

Table 12.7: Bearing Resistance Vs Bearing Area

CPCA Concrete Design Handbook

Table 12.8 Fire Protection of Steel Embedments

	Thickness of Protective Material[1], in., for Fire-Resistance Rating of				
	1hr.	1½	2 hr.	3 hr.	4 hr.
Sprayed mineral fiber					
† = 5/16 in.[2]	1	1¼	1½	2⅜	3⅜
† = 1 1/16 in[2]	½	¾	⅞	1⅛	1⅜
Vermiculite cementitious material					
† = 5/16 in.[2]	1	1¼	1½	2	2⅝
† = 1 1/16 in[2]	½	¾	⅞	1⅛	1⅜
Concrete or dry pack mortar					
b ≦ 8 in.[3]	¾	1¼	1⅝	2⅝	3½
b ≧ 12 in.[3]	¾	1⅛	1¼	1⅝	1⅞
Column 1	2	3	4	5	6

(1) Descriptions of sprayed mineral fiber and vermiculite cementitious materials are given in Section 12.5 of this Handbook.
(2) † = minimum thickness of steel subjected to fire from both sides. Direct interpolation may be used for values of † between $5/16$ and $1 1/16$ in.
(3) b = minimum width of concrete protection. Direct interpolation may be used for values of b between 8 and 12 in.

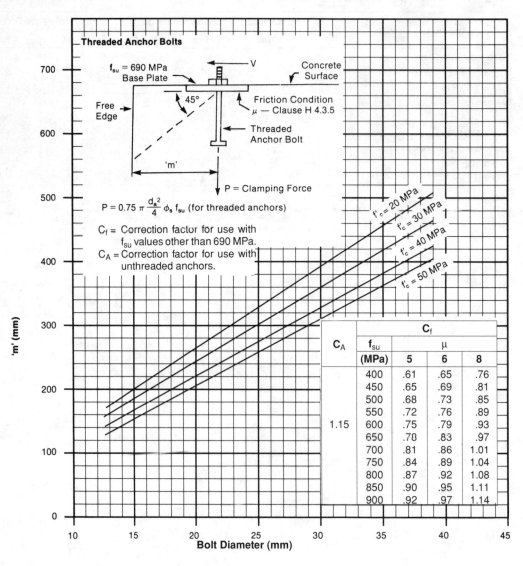

Table 12.9: Required Side Cover for Shear Friction

Tilt-up Concrete Wall Panels

By Gerry Weiler

Chapter 13
Tilt-up Concrete Wall Panels

13.1 INTRODUCTION

Tilt-up concrete buildings have been constructed in Canada for over 30 years. Until recently, Canadian codes have not specifically addressed the design issues.

The latest edition of CSA A23.3-94, Design of Concrete Structures, has dedicated Chapter 23 to the design of tilt-up wall panels. This now provides comprehensive guidelines for dealing with vertical and transverse out-of-plane loading. Further development of this design standard is required in areas including:

a. Connection requirements

b. In-plane shear forces

c. Construction details and tolerances

d. Panel lift design and analysis

13.2 CONCRETE WALL PANEL ANALYSIS METHOD

Tilt-up concrete wall panels are most often used as load bearing wall elements spanning vertically from the floor slab to the roof. Bending moments induced by transverse loads (wind or seismic) are usually significantly greater than those caused by eccentric axial loads. The P-Δ effects due to axial loads will increase these moments. Limit states failure of a slender wall panel is defined as the point where the maximum factored bending moment at or near mid height exceeds the resisting moment of the concrete section.

The maximum bending moment can be separated into two components: (See Figure 13.1)

a. Primary moment due to applied loadings.

b. Secondary moment due to P-Δ deflections.

Primary moments are determined from conventional statics. In most cases, it is the moment at mid height that is of concern since this is where maximum P-Δ deflections and eventual failure will normally occur. See Figure 13.1

The following contributes to the primary moment:

a. Eccentric axial loads.

b. Transverse loads (wind or seismic).

c. Initial out-of-straightness.

d. Panel self weight.

Secondary P-Δ moments are dependent on the bending stiffness of the wall panel. For reinforced concrete, this parameter can be difficult to calculate since it varies with a number of parameters, including:

a. Wall thickness.

b. Concrete compression strength.

c. Concrete tensile strength.

d. Reinforcing steel quantities.

e. Location of reinforcing steel in the wall section.

f. Applied axial load.

The bending properties of a concrete section behave in an elastoplastic manner. Both strength and stiffness will vary with changes in axial compression and flexural bending. In most cases, however, we are only concerned with the condition at ultimate failure where the resisting moment and bending stiffness can be determined by simple calculations.

The parameter K_b is used to define bending stiffness:

$$K_b = \frac{48 \, E_c \, I_{cr}}{5 \, L^2} \qquad (\text{kN-m} / \text{m}) \quad (23\text{-}6)$$

Where:

L = vertical span of wall panel (m)

$E_c = 4500 \, \sqrt{f_c'}$ (MPa) (8-7)

I_{cr} = cracked section stiffness (mm^4)

$$= \frac{bc^3}{3} + \frac{E_s \, A_s \, (d - c)^2}{E_c} \qquad (23\text{-}7)$$

A_s = reinforcing area, mm^2 E_s = 200,000 MPa

d = reinforcing depth, mm b = width of section, mm

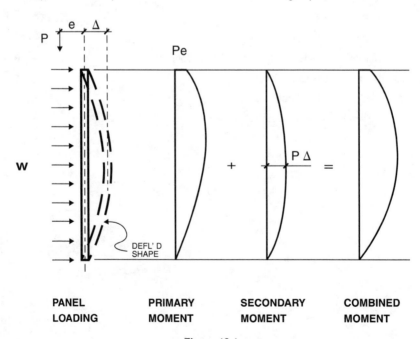

| PANEL | PRIMARY | SECONDARY | COMBINED |
| LOADING | MOMENT | MOMENT | MOMENT |

Figure 13.1

$$a = \frac{A_s \, \phi_s \, f_y}{\alpha_1 \, \phi_c \, f'_c \, b} \qquad c = \frac{a}{\beta_1}$$

$$\alpha_1 = 0.85 - .0015 f'_c \qquad (10\text{-}1)$$

$\alpha_1 = 0.81$ for 25 MPa concrete

$$\beta_1 = 0.97 - 0.0025 f'_c \qquad (10\text{-}2)$$

$\beta_1 = 0.91$ for 25 MPa concrete

Bending stiffness represents the maximum bending moment in the panel divided by the maximum deflection:

$$M_{max} = K_b \, \Delta_{max}$$

At this time it is worthwhile to note that K_b is essentially equivalent to the more familiar critical buckling load:

$$P_{cr} = \frac{\pi^2 \, EI}{L^2}$$

Critical buckling capacity is a by-product of the P-Δ analysis and represents the maximum axial load that can be sustained by a pin ended slender column (or wall) in the absence of any other applied loadings. The factor $\pi^2 = 9.87$ defines a sinusoidal deflected shape due to applied end moments. For a parabolic deflection, as is obtained for a beam subjected to a uniformly distributed load, this factor should be $48/5 = 9.6$. This is considered to be more representative of tilt-up panels.

When combined axial and transverse loadings are applied to a wall panel, the maximum moment can be calculated as follows:

$$M_f = \text{Primary Moment} + \text{Secondary Moment}$$
$$= M_b + P_f \, \Delta$$

Where:

M_b = maximum factored moment due to applied loadings but not including P-Δ effects

$$M_b = \frac{w_f \, L^2}{8} + P_{tf} \frac{e}{2} + (P_{wf} + P_{tf}) \, \Delta_0 \qquad (23\text{-}3)$$

$$P_f = P_{wf} + P_{tf} \qquad (23\text{-}5)$$
$$= \text{factored axial load at mid height}$$

P_{wf} = factored panel weight above mid height

P_{tf} = factored axial load at the top of panel

e = axial load eccentricity at the top of the panel

Δ_0 = initial deflection at panel mid height

Δ = maximum total deflection at mid height
$\quad = M_f \, / \, K_b$

When other forces contribute to the primary moment such as transverse point loads, these should also be included when computing M_b.

The factored moment M_f can now be written in the following form:

$$M_f = M_b + \frac{P_f M_f}{K_b} = M_b \left(\frac{1}{1 - P_f / K_b} \right) = M_b \delta_b \quad (23\text{-}2)$$

$$\delta_b = \frac{1}{1 - P_f / K_b} = \text{moment amplification factor}$$

Alternately, the maximum bending moment may be obtained by iteration of deflection calculations with applied axial load in order to obtain the P-Δ effects. The moment magnifier method, using the amplification factor δ_b, gives the identical result by direct calculation.

For design, it is necessary to apply strength reduction factors to account for material variations and workmanship. The member resistance factor ϕ_m reduces bending stiffness and increases P-Δ magnification:

$$\delta_b = \frac{1}{1 - \frac{P_f}{\phi_m \, K_b}} \qquad (23\text{-}4)$$

where $\phi_m = 0.65$

While this reduction may seem severe, it is considered to be appropriate for tilt-up panel sections. For example, a 140 mm panel with 15M @ 300 mm o/c reinforcing centred in the panel would have a cracked section I_{cr} as follows:

$f'_c = 25$ MPa $\qquad f_y = 400$ MPa
$b = 300$ mm $\qquad h = 140$ mm
$d = 70$ mm $\qquad A_s = 200$ mm^2

$$a = \frac{200 \times 0.85 \times 400}{0.81 \times 0.6 \times 25 \times 300} = 18.7 \text{ mm}$$

$$c = \frac{18.7}{0.91} = 20.5 \text{ mm}$$

$$I_{cr} = \frac{300 \times 20.5^3}{3} + \frac{200000 \times 200 \, (70 - 20.5)^2}{25000}$$

$$= (0.86 + 3.92) \times 10^6 = 4.78 \times 10^6 \text{ mm}^4$$

A reduction of 15% in d or 10.5 mm would result in a decrease in I_{cr}:

$$I_{cr} = 3.30 \times 10^6 \text{ mm}^4$$

$$\text{Reduction} = \frac{3.30}{4.78} = 0.69$$

Deflections at the top of the panel due to roof diaphragm flexibility have little or no effect on a pinned base panel. This is because full lateral support from the roof or floor assembly can almost always be assumed. Additional P-Δ effects resulting from a panel leaning 40 or 50 mm is negligible.

The resisting moment M_r is calculated by conventional methods defined in Chapter 10.

$$M_r = \phi_s \, A_{se} \, f_y \, (d - a/2) \le M_f$$

A modification in the area of reinforcement is used to partially account for the increased bending moment resistance due to applied axial loads.

$$A_{se} = \frac{\phi_s \, A_s \, f_y + P_f}{\phi_s \, f_y} \qquad (23\text{-}9)$$

The axial load at the critical section or panel mid height is used.

The preceding method of analysis for slender wall panels is applicable where the effect of axial load is small relative to lateral load. A limitation in axial load is given in Chapter 23:

$$\frac{P_{wf} + P_{tf}}{A_g} < .09 \, \phi_c \, f'_c \qquad (23\text{-}1)$$

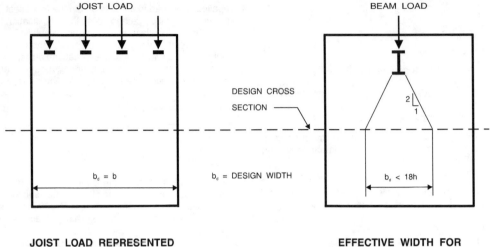

JOIST LOAD   BEAM LOAD

DESIGN CROSS
SECTION

$b_d = b$ b_d = DESIGN WIDTH $b_d < 18h$

JOIST LOAD REPRESENTED   **EFFECTIVE WIDTH FOR**
BY LINE LOAD   **LARGE POINT LOADS**

Figure 13.2

13.3 LOADING CONDITIONS

13.3.1 Lateral Loads

Wind pressures or seismic accelerations are applied to the wall panel as a uniformly distributed lateral load. For exterior walls, lateral load effects will often control the design. NBC 1995 Section 4.1.8 specifies wind pressure as the algebraic difference between external and internal pressure or suction:

$$p = qC_e (C_{pe}C_g + C_\pi C_g)$$

q = 1:30 reference velocity pressure.

$C_{pe}C_g$ = Combined exterior pressure/gust coefficient. Values in the order of +0.75 or –0.55 are often used.

$C_\pi C_g$ = Interior pressure/gust coefficient. A value of ±0.7 is common.

C_e = Exposure factor. A value of 1.0 is used for most low rise buildings.

Seismic accelerations for the design of individual wall panels are based on NBC 1995 Section 4.1.9.1(15) for an S_p factor equal to 1.5. Note that the seismic force required for parts of a building such as wall panels is greater than that required for the overall building. This loading will sometimes exceed wind pressure, particularly for thicker panels.

V_p = 1.5 × v × panel weight

v = zonal velocity ratio

It is recommended that all tilt-up walls, whether interior or exterior, be designed for a minimum lateral pressure of ±0.5 kPa.

13.3.2 Axial Loads

Vertical axial loads from roof or floor joists can often be assumed as a uniformly distributed line load. These should be applied at some eccentricity to the centreline axis of the panel either intentionally or due to bearing irregularities. A minimum load eccentricity of one half the panel thickness is recommended, and to be additive to the effect of lateral pressures. Axial load eccentricities should not be used to reduce the bending moment caused by lateral loading.

Where large concentrated loads are supported directly on the panel, the effective width should be limited as indicated in the Figure 13.2.

13.3.3 Panel Self Weight

The effect of panel self weight must be considered since it represents a significant contribution to P-Δ effects in slender walls. It is sufficient to assume that the weight of panel above mid height acts as an additional concentrated axial load applied at the top with no eccentricity.

13.3.4 Load Combinations

The following load combinations should be considered:

a. 1.25D + 1.5L
b. 1.25D + 1.5W (Wind)
c. 1.0 D + 1.0E (Earthquake)
d. 1.25D + 0.7 (1.5L + 1.5W)
e. 1.0 D + 0.5L + 1.0E

Combination (a) seldom applies except for short panels with large eccentric loads. In many cases, combination (b) controls.

For the common load case of large bending moments due to lateral forces combined with small axial loads, the critical section for bending will occur very near panel mid height. As axial load and top end eccentricity increase, this point will shift upwards.

13.4 CONTINUITY AND END FIXITY

Most tilt-up panels are designed as simply supported vertical beams spanning between the footing and the roof structure. Where a panel is connected to both the floor slab and the footing, some degree of end fixity can be considered. In other cases, a panel may be laterally supported by an intermediate floor resulting in reduced effective panel height and negative moment continuity.

It is difficult to properly analyze this condition and at best only approximate methods are practical. Some of the problems include the following:

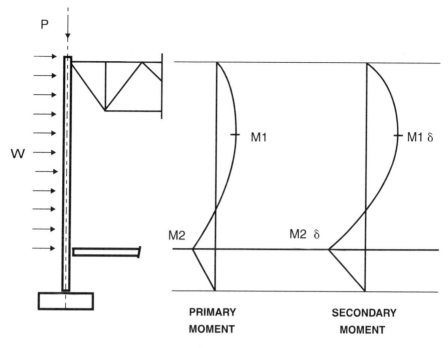

Figure 13.3

a. Deflection at supports, particularly at flexible roof diaphragms will affect the final results.

b. Loadings due to soil pressure below the floor slab may be significant.

c. Lateral restraint provided by footings may be questionable such that full end fixity may not be fully realized.

d. P-Δ calculations for a non-statically determinate element must be obtained by a complex iterative technique that is only practical with computer analysis.

Because of these concerns, it is best to be somewhat conservative in the design approach. One technique involves using a reduced effective panel height coefficient k. A value of k = 0.8 is suitable for an elastic column fixed at one end and pinned at the other. Since concrete stiffness is not uniform and the lower end is seldom completely fixed, k should not be taken as less than 0.90.

An alternative method is based on the assumption that the initial positive mid span moment and negative support moment increase proportionally by the same amount when considering P-Δ magnifications. The primary moments are calculated by conventional elastic methods. Both the positive and negative moments are then increased by the P-Δ moment magnifier. (See Figure 13.3)

13.5 CREEP AND INITIAL DEFLECTIONS

Initial panel out-of-straightness may be the result of uneven casting beds, excessive bending caused by the tilting process, thermal gradients, or uneven shrinkage. Long term creep deflections have not been a significant problem in the history of tilt-up panels. This is likely due to the fact that most loads are transitory. For design, an initial deflection at mid height of L/400 is considered to be adequate.

Deflection at service loads have similarly not been a concern, particularly for warehouse applications where there are few architectural components that could be affected. A limit to service load deflections at panel mid

height of L/100 is considered to be a minimum (23.4.2). Horizontal midheight deflection is given by:

$$\Delta_s = \frac{5 \, M_a \, L^2}{48 \, E_c \, I_e} \tag{23-10}$$

13.6 OPENINGS IN PANELS

The effect of openings for out-of-plane bending in tilt-up panels can be approximated by a simple one dimensional strip analysis that gives sufficient accuracy and economy for most designs.

Where openings occur, the entire lateral and axial load (including self weight) must be distributed to supporting legs or design strips on each side of the opening. The effective width of the strip should be limited to about 12 times the panel thickness in order to avoid localized stress concentrations at the edge of the opening. This limitation is intended primarily as a practical guideline. The tributary width for design can usually be taken as the leg width plus one half the width of adjacent openings. (See Figure 13.4)

For very wide openings, it may be necessary to provide an edge thickening or pilaster to carry the loads at each supporting leg. In addition, a horizontal header may also be required.

13.7 ISOLATED FOOTINGS OR PIER FOUNDATIONS

In many areas of Canada, soil conditions or frost depth requirements dictate the use of pier foundations at panel joint locations only. For design, this has the effect of concentrating the vertical load at the edges of the panel.

In most cases, there is continuous horizontal support provided at the top by the roof deck and at the bottom by ties to the floor slab. Lateral loads can therefore be uniformly distributed across the width of panel.

Vertical loads should effectively be increased at either end as indicated in Figure 13.5. Where the clear panel

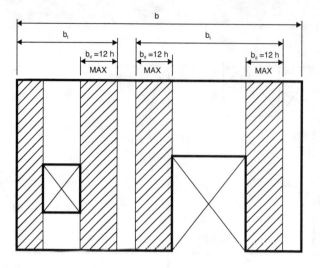

PANEL WITH OPENINGS

b_t = TRIBUTARY WIDTH
b_d = DESIGN WIDTH

Figure 13.4

height is greater than $1\frac{1}{2}$ times the clear distance between footings, the effect of isolated footings can be ignored.

Depending on the width of pier cap and effective bearing area at the bottom of the panel, additional hooked reinforcing or confining ties may be required to prevent localized shear failure.

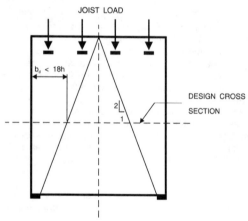

ISOLATED FOOTINGS

Figure 13.5

13.8 STIFFENING PILASTERS

Extra thickenings in the panel or pilasters are sometimes necessary to support heavy vertical loads. They may also be required at the edge of large openings as suggested in section 13.6.

Tilt-up panel pilasters are often reinforced with ties around vertical reinforcing bars. The design, however, may be controlled by bonding, such that confining ties

may not always be required. As a minimum, ties should be used in the vicinity of the point of bearing to ensure that the axial load is distributed into the panel.

13.9 IN-PLANE SHEAR

Design for In-plane shear is distinctly different from the normal out-of-plane bending procedure. It involves forces from roof or floor diaphragms acting parallel to the plane of the panel in true shear wall fashion. In seismic areas, the in-plane shear requirements may control the design of panel reinforcing.

13.9.1 Panel Overturning

Factored roof or floor diaphragm forces are applied to the wall panel resulting in an overturning moment. The point of rotation is usually taken as the outside edge of the panel. It would be slightly more correct to use a point 200 mm to 300 mm inside of this edge to account for concrete spalling at the corner, but this refinement does not usually affect results significantly. Resistance to overturning is obtained from a combination of panel weight, tributary roof or floor loads, panel edge connectors and base tie down anchors.

Overturning Moment $M_{of} \leq$ Resisting Moment M_r

NBC 1995 no longer requires that the dead load used for computing the resisting moment be reduced by 0.85.

13.9.2 Sliding

Resistance to sliding forces can be obtained by a combination of friction to the footing and connections to the floor slab or foundation. For non-seismic shear forces, base friction may be all that is required. Where panels are subjected to in-plane seismic shear forces, a positive connection to the slab or footing with cast-in dowels or welded connectors is recommended.

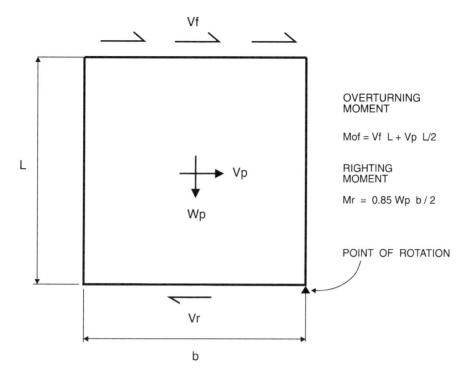

$$M_{of} = V_f \, L + V_p \, L/2$$

OVERTURNING MOMENT

RIGHTING MOMENT

$$M_r = 0.85 \, W_p \, b / 2$$

POINT OF ROTATION

PANEL OVERTURNING RESISTANCE

Figure 13.6

13.9.3 Shear Resistance

Requirements for concrete shear resistance are covered in Chapters 11 and 21. Clause 11.2.8 states that minimum shear reinforcement is to be provided where:

$$V_f \leq 0.5 \, V_c$$

$$V_c = 0.2 \, \phi_c \, \sqrt{f'_c} \, b_w \, d$$

b_w = panel thickness h

Minimum shear reinforcing is given by:

$$A_v = 0.06 \, \phi_c \, \sqrt{f'_c} \, \frac{b_w \, s}{f_y} \qquad (11\text{-}1)$$

This is always less than the minimum requirements for temperature or shrinkage reinforcing specified for walls in Clause 14.3.3 as .002 A_g.

Example:

140 mm panel, 25 MPa concrete, reinf spacing s = 400 mm

Minimum A_v = 0.06 × $\sqrt{25}$ × 140 × 400 / 400 = 42 mm^2

or	= 0.002 × 140 × 400
	= 112 mm^2 (CONTROLS)

Panel shear resistance is given by:

$$V_r = V_c + V_s \qquad (11\text{-}4)$$

$$V_r \leq V_c + 0.8 \, \lambda \, \phi_c \, \sqrt{f'_c} \, h \, d \qquad (11\text{-}5)$$

$$V_c = 0.2 \, \lambda \, \phi_c \, \sqrt{f'_c} \, h \, d \qquad (11\text{-}6)$$

$$V_s = \frac{\phi_s \, A_v \, f_y \, d}{s} \qquad (11\text{-}11)$$

When computing the average shear in a plain, rectangular panel, d can be taken as the overall width of the panel. Alternatively, the interface shear transfer provisions of Clause 11.6 (shear friction) may be used:

$$v_r = \phi_c \, (c + \mu \, \sigma) + \phi_s \, \rho_v \, f_y \, \cos \alpha_f \qquad (11\text{-}32)$$

For tilt-up panels, this expression can be simplified and re-written as:

$$V_r = \phi_c \times 1.00 \text{ MPa} \times h \, d + \frac{1.4 \, \phi_c \, A_v \, f_y \, d}{s}$$

$$= \phi_c \, h \, d + \frac{\phi_s \, A_v \, f_y \, d}{s}$$

13.9.4 Plastic Hinge Formation

The forces specified by NBC 4.1.9 for buildings located in seismic areas represent only a portion of the total energy imparted to a structure. The structural components must therefore be able to resist overstress and deformation without total failure, and contain mechanisms capable of absorbing seismic energy. This property is known as ductility and is defined in NBC 4.1.9 by means of the force modification factor R.

Buildings designed with perimeter tilt-up panel shear walls often employ horizontal roof and floor diaphragms. An R factor equal to 2.0 is considered to be appropriate. In order to qualify for this, the wall panels must conform to Clause 21.9 for members requiring nominal ductility. The provisions for shear walls contained in this chapter were written primarily for cast-in-place concrete and do not completely apply to structural precast concrete com-

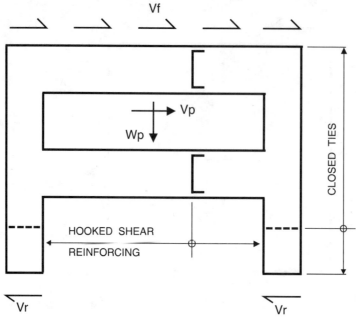

PORTAL FRAME PANEL

Figure 13.7

ponents. It is necessary, therefore, to exercise some degree of interpretation and engineering judgement.

The requirements in Clause 21.9.3.2 for the formation of plastic hinges are difficult to achieve in solid, rectangular tilt-up panels. Ductility mechanisms can be obtained by tie down anchors or panel edge connectors. The value of these devices for energy absorbtion may be limited. Often, the perimeter walls are very stiff and capable of resisting 3 to 4 times the specified code forces such that yielding is unlikely. Much of the energy dissipation in these buildings is expected to occur in the roof or floor diaphragms. The designer should be satisfied that an R = 2.0 is achievable.

Where nominal ductility, in the form of plastic hinging cannot be provided in the wall panels, the design shear resistance in these components should be based on applied seismic loads calculated using an R factor equal to 1.0. In effect, the shear strength of the panels due to in-plane seismic forces should be increased by a factor of 2 in order to ensure that shear failure will not occur.

As an alternative, the entire building could be designed for an R equal to 1.5 whereby the requirements of Chapter 21 need not apply. This will not necessarily provide the most desirable results since yielding of ductile components such as steel roof diaphragms may not occur before failure of other less ductile parts including connections and concrete shear.

Panels with large openings that rely on frame action to resist the seismic shear forces should be designed in accordance with Clause 21.9.2 Frames. Adequate shear resistance must be provided to ensure that flexural yielding or plastic hinging occurs first. Clause 21.9.2.3(b) suggests that shear resistance need not be greater than the shear force obtained using earthquake loads based on R equal to 1.0. Reinforcing details given in this section were originally intended for compact beam and column sections with relatively large ratios of longitudinal reinforcing. Closely spaced ties are required around reinforcing when it is expected to yield in both compression and tension.

Tilt-up wall panel frames will often have deep cross sections such that compression yielding of longitudinal bars is unlikely, even at large deformations. Tie spacing limitations based on longitudinal bar diameters do not necessarily apply. The need for meeting the stirrup spacing requirements specified in 21.9.2.1.2 is a controversial area among designers, particularly item (b) limiting spacing to 8 times the diameter of the smallest longitudinal bar. Header beams in tilt-up panels are generally much stronger than the supporting legs and a stirrup spacing of d/2 is considered to be adequate for most cases.

Since the supporting legs will often develop plastic hinging before the header beams, shear tie spacing should be in accordance with 21.9.2.2. Usually, tie spacing is governed by the panel thickness.

13.9.5 Design Recommendations for In-Plane Seismic Shear

The following criteria is recommended for the design of tilt-up wall panels subjected to in-plane seismic forces:

a. Calculate the design force on the overall building based on R equal to 2.0 where the wall panels are part of the primary load resisting system.

b. Compute panel overturning and sliding forces for R equal to 2.0. Requirements for connections should be based on an R equal to 1.5 where nominal ductility can be assumed. Otherwise, design connections for R equal to 1.0. This is discussed in the next section.

c. Where in-plane bending can occur, provide reinforcing to resist forces based on R equal to 2.0. Details for reinforcing should conform to 21.9.3 for walls or 21.9.2 for frames.

d. Compute concrete shear force V_f based on R equal to 1.0.

Where $V_f > 0.5 V_c$, minimum shear reinforcing should be provided.

The shear resistance V_r of the wall section is given by:

$$V_r = \frac{V_c}{2} + V_s$$

$$V_c = 0.2\, \phi_c\, \sqrt{f'_c}\ h\, d$$

$$V_s = \frac{\phi_s\, A_v\, f_y\, d}{s}$$

e. The minimum area of distributed reinforcing as specified by Clause 21.9.3.3.1 for nominally ductile seismic design is .0025 bd. Clause 23.3.4 allows a relaxation of this requirement when there is adequate strength and ductility. Where $V_f \leq V_c/2$, a minimum area of .0020 Ag is considered to be acceptable. Often, sufficient shear reinforcement would be provided to resist the entire factored shear force, ignoring the contribution of concrete shear.

f. Shear reinforcing in the supporting legs of a frame panel should consist of 10M closed loop ties. Larger bar sizes are impractical in thin concrete sections such as tilt-up panels. A panel thickness of 190 mm is a minimum where tied reinforcing is used. Tie spacing should be limited to the panel thickness or 300 mm where plastic hinging is expected. A maximum tie spacing of d/2 is considered to be adequate when hinging does not occur at seismic force levels calculated on an R equal to 1.0.

g. Stirrup spacing in header beams should consist of 10M hooked bars or closed loop ties. Where plastic hinging is not expected, stirrup spacing should be limited to d/2.

13.10 CONNECTIONS FOR TILT-UP PANELS

Design requirements for connections to tilt-up panels generally follow traditional methods. Connections must be designed to resist forces equal to or greater than the maximum load imposed on the panel component. Connections in panels designed for seismic conditions should typically be stronger and more ductile than those for non-seismic forces.

There are three main categories of connections for tilt-up panels:

13.10.1 Cast-in-place concrete in-fill sections

This type of connection involves casting concrete around reinforcing bars projecting from the panel in order to tie into another building component.

These connections are often very strong and can be used to distribute loads over a greater length. Good ductility can be achieved if the overlapping bars are confined by closed ties, (See Figure 13.8). Cast-in-place connections are used infrequently now due to problems with excessive rigidity and concrete cracking. They also tend to be more expensive than other types of connectors.

13.10.2 Welded embedded metal

Welded embedded metal is the type of connection preferred by most designers and builders due to its relative cost and construction flexibility in various applications. Strength and ductility can vary considerably, depending on the length of embedment and configuration of the anchor.

Steel plates with studs are suitable for shear and tension forces as long as they are located well away from the panel edges (300 mm or more). The lack of sufficient embedment makes these connectors non-ductile. Steel angles or plates with short studs located at the edge of the panel should be avoided entirely. Often concrete

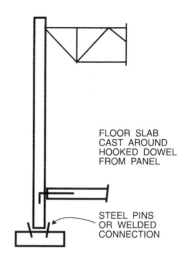

FLOOR SLAB
CAST AROUND
HOOKED DOWEL
FROM PANEL

STEEL PINS
OR WELDED
CONNECTION

**PANEL TO FLOOR SLAB
CONNECTION**

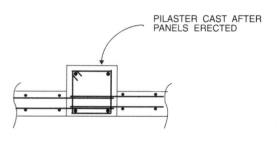

PILASTER CAST AFTER
PANELS ERECTED

**CAST - IN - PLACE
CONNECTION**

Figure 13.8

shrinkage in the panels after welding causes stress build-up that may result in complete failure.

Where possible, embedded metal connections should have deformed bar anchors extending into the concrete panel. These are more expensive to fabricate and install but provide superior strength and performance, particularly for seismic loadings. In general, this type of connector can provide reasonable seismic ductility. Figure 13.9 contains 5 standard connection types that have been used in tilt-up panels. Calculated load capacities are also given.

13.10.3 Drilled-in anchors

Expansion bolts and epoxy anchors are used extensively in tilt-up construction. Their use should be restricted to supporting light loads or for repairs. There is very little ductility compared to cast-in-place or welded deformed bar anchors making them unsuitable where seismic forces or differential foundation movement is expected. Expansion anchors can also cause problems in thin panel sections particularly where edge distance is inadequate.

Power driven fasteners or ram drive pins may be used for light architectural components or light gauge steel stud framing. Design loads should be limited due to the relative unreliability of these fasteners in concrete.

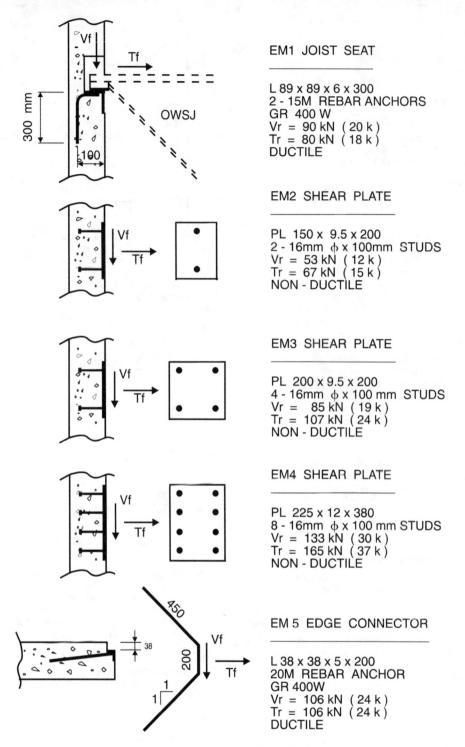

EM1 JOIST SEAT

L 89 x 89 x 6 x 300
2 - 15M REBAR ANCHORS
GR 400 W
Vr = 90 kN (20 k)
Tr = 80 kN (18 k)
DUCTILE

EM2 SHEAR PLATE

PL 150 x 9.5 x 200
2 - 16mm φ x 100mm STUDS
Vr = 53 kN (12 k)
Tr = 67 kN (15 k)
NON - DUCTILE

EM3 SHEAR PLATE

PL 200 x 9.5 x 200
4 - 16mm φ x 100 mm STUDS
Vr =   85 kN (19 k)
Tr = 107 kN (24 k)
NON - DUCTILE

EM4 SHEAR PLATE

PL 225 x 12 x 380
8 - 16mm φ x 100 mm STUDS
Vr = 133 kN (30 k)
Tr = 165 kN (37 k)
NON - DUCTILE

EM 5 EDGE CONNECTOR

L 38 x 38 x 5 x 200
20M REBAR ANCHOR
GR 400W
Vr = 106 kN (24 k)
Tr = 106 kN (24 k)
DUCTILE

Figure 13.9

13.11 SEISMIC DESIGN REQUIREMENTS FOR TILT-UP CONNECTIONS

Tilt-up panel connections should be capable of resisting forces greater than that specified by the NBC Code for the overall structural system. It is recommended that all connections be designed for seismic forces greater than the force on the component. When the building design is based on an R of 2.0, the connection should be designed for a resisting force of:

R = 1.5 for ductile connections (1.33 increase)
R = 1.0 for non-ductile connections (2.0 increase)

NBC Sentence 4.1.9.1(15) for parts of buildings requires connections for walls to be designed for a lateral force V_p equal to $v I S_p W_p$. The S_p factor is given as 2.5 for ductile connections and 15 for non-ductile connections. When this is applied to seismic zone 4 with v equal to 0.20, the factored connection design force would be:

V_p = 0.20 × 2.5 W_p = 0.5 W_p (ductile)
or 0.20 × 15 W_p = 3.0 W_p (non-ductile)

W_p represents the tributary weight (mass) of the element.

The intent of NBC 1995 for ductile connections designed to an Sp factor of 2.5 is to ensure that the body of the connector yields before other parts such as bolts, inserts, welds or dowels. In general, embedded plates with studs are considered to be non-ductile since the concrete is expected to fail before the anchor. A connector with long, deformed bar anchors may qualify as ductile if it can be shown that yielding will occur well before concrete pullout failure. Testing of the EM5 connector, Reference 7, suggests that it has good ductility since it can sustain a large percentage of its peak capacity after several load cycles.

13.12 CONSTRUCTION REQUIREMENTS

13.12.1 Forming and Construction Tolerances

Chapter 23 does not provide specific requirements for tolerances in tilt-up construction. Instead, it refers to the CSA A23.4-94 Standard for precast concrete with a precautionary note that adequate quality control procedures must be carried out. Otherwise, the tolerances are to comply with A23.1.

Quality control of panel forming and reinforcing steel placing for site cast tilt-up concrete panels is usually better than for standard cast-in-place concrete work, but cannot compare with the controlled conditions of a precast concrete plant. Tolerance requirements should therefore be somewhere in between.

The Building and Construction Industry Division of the Department of Labour in Australia has developed a code of practice for tilt-up construction. Their recommended fabrication tolerances are considered to be appropriate:

Length and Height:		Straightness or Skewness:	
Up to 3 m	+0 to –10 mm	Up to 3 m	±10 mm
3 m to 6 m	+0 to –12 mm	3 m to 6 m	±15 mm
Over 6 m	+0 to –15 mm	6 m to 12 m	±20 mm

Thickness:
Overall   ±5 mm

Clear concrete cover over reinforcement in tilt-up panels should be greater than that required by CSA A23.4 for plant cast precast concrete. In general, the following covers have been found to be adequate for tilt-up panels above grade:

Main Reinforcing		Ties and Stirrups	
Outside face of panel	25 mm	Inside or outside face	20 mm
Inside face of panel	20 mm	Edge of panel	40 mm
Edge of panel	50 mm		

13.12.2 Concrete Requirements

Concrete used for tilt-up panels should provide adequate strength for both the in-place condition and for erection requirements. A minimum of 25 MPa compressive strength should be provided. Often, the concrete mix is proportioned for flexural strength requirements as defined by the Modulus of Rupture. This property is important for resisting flexural cracking, particularly during the lifting operation. Depending on what is specified, the resulting compressive strength may be greater than 25 MPa.

Entrained air for freeze/thaw resistance is not normally required where exposed surfaces are primarily vertical and protected with a paint or sealer. Local experience in the performance of non air entrained concrete should be investigated.

The specifications for the concrete mix are usually controlled by requirements for lifting. A minimum compressive strength of 17 MPa is often specified by the lift insert manufacturer in order to ensure that the full load capacity of their product can be achieved. Since this is required in about 7 days, a 28 day design strength of 25 MPa or even 30 MPa is often used. Flyash should be limited to not more than 20% of the total cementing material content since it slows the rate of early strength gain.

In summary, the following concrete specifications are recommended:

28 Day Compressive Strength	30 MPa
28 Day Flexural Strength	4.5 MPa
Exposure Class	None
Maximum Size Aggregate	20 mm
Entrained Air	1-3%

13.12.3 Reinforcing Steel

Standard hard grade 400 MPa reinforcing steel should be specified for tilt-up panels. Intermediate grade 300 MPa or less should be avoided. The main vertical bars should be 15M or 20M, with 10M bars used for horizontal temperature reinforcing or ties. Bars larger than 20M are not recommended for tilt-up panels of thickness less than 240 mm.

13.13 DESIGN FOR LIFTING STRESS

It has been common practice for the panel lift analysis and pick up point locations to be carried out by a separate designer. This is often the supplier of embedded lift inserts or other specialist engineers. Although there is no direct conflict with this split of responsibility, it is important that the building designer has some basic knowledge of the operation and potential limitations.

Panel lift design takes into account the following considerations:

a. Bending stress should be kept low enough to avoid flexural cracking.

b. The lift insert capacity should have a safety factor of at least 2.0 at the time of lift, including an allowance for adhesion and impact. Some Canadian jurisdictions require a safety factor of 2.5.

c. The panel should tilt with at least 10% of the weight at the bottom. It should be balanced to hang level when lifted off the casting bed.

A minimum concrete compressive strength of 17 MPa (2500 psi) is often specified for full lift insert capacity. Concrete flexural strengths of 2.9 MPa (420 psi) are sufficient to prevent panel cracking where computed bending stresses are less than 1.7 MPa (250 psi). Beyond this, reinforcing steel should be provided on the tension face to carry the entire load.

For panels with 2 layers of reinforcing, there is usually sufficient capacity to resist the lifting moments. Reinforcing on each face will greatly increase the resistance to cracking even if allowable concrete flexural stresses are exceeded.

Reinforcing in the middle of the panel will only be effective after the concrete has cracked. It is for this reason that 2 layers are greatly preferred over a single layer. The variation in the total amount of reinforcing steel required in either case may be negligible due to the differences in effective depths used in design.

13.14 DESIGN EXAMPLES

Example 13.1 — Plain Wall Panel

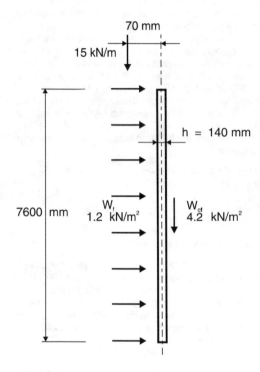

Panel properties:

$\phi_c = 0.6, \phi_s = 0.85, \phi_m = 0.65$

$f'_c = 25$ MPa, $f_y = 400$ MPa

$E_s = 200,000$ MPa

$E_c = 4500\sqrt{25} = 22,500$ MPa

$L = 7600$ mm, $h = 140$ mm, $\Delta_0 = 25$ mm

Loading:

$P_{tf} = 15$ kN/m, ecc = 70 mm

$W_f = 1.2$ kN/m² $W_{cf} = 4.2$ kN/m²

At mid-height:

$P_f = 15 + 4.2 \times 7.6 / 2 = 30.96$ kN/m

For reinforcing on 2 faces:

$A_s = 15M$ @ 400 EF or 500 mm²/m EF

$b = 1000$ mm, $d = 100$ mm

$A_{se} = \dfrac{0.85 \times 500 \times 400 + 30960}{0.85 \times 400} = 591$ mm²/m

$a = \dfrac{591 \times 0.85 \times 400}{0.81 \times 0.6 \times 25 \times 1000} = 16.5$

$c = \dfrac{16.5}{0.91} = 18.2$

$I_{cr} = \dfrac{c^3}{3} + \dfrac{E_s}{E_c} A_{se} (d - c)^2$

$I_{cr} = \dfrac{1000 \times 18.2^3}{3} + \dfrac{200}{22.5} \times 591 (100 - 18.2)^2$

$= 37.2 \times 10^6$ mm⁴/m

$K_b = \dfrac{8 E_c I_{cr}}{5 L^2} = \dfrac{48 \times 22500 \times 37.2 \times 10^6}{5 \times 7600^2 \times 1000}$

$= 139.1$ kN-m/m

$\delta_b = \dfrac{1}{1 - 30.96/(.65 \times 139.1)} = 1.52$

Primary Bending Moment:

$M_h = 1.2 \times 7.6^2 / 8 + 15 \times 0.07 / 2 + 30.96 \times 0.025$

$= 8.66 + 0.53 + 0.77 = 9.96$ kN-m/m

Total Moment:

$M_f = 9.96 \times 1.52 = 15.1$ kN-m/m

Resisting Moment:

$M_f = 0.85 \times 591 \times 400 (100 - 16.5 / 2) / 10^6$

$= 18.4 > 15.1$ kN-m/m

Deflections at service loads:

$W = 0.8$ kN/m² $P = 10$ kN/m $W_c = 3.3$ kN/m²

$I_g = 1000 \times 140^3 / 12 = 229 \times 10^6$ mm⁴

$M_{cr} = \dfrac{f_r I_g}{y_t} = \dfrac{0.6\sqrt{25} \times 229}{140/2} = 9.81$ kN-m/m

$M_a = 0.8 \times 7.6^2 / 8 + 10 \times 0.07 / 2 + 22.7 \times 0.025$

$= 6.69$ kN-m/m

Since $M_{cr} > M_a$, $I_e = I_g = 229 \times 10^6$ mm⁴

$\Delta = \dfrac{5}{48} \times \dfrac{6.69 \times 7.6^2}{22500 \times 229} \times 10^6 = 7.8$ mm

$\dfrac{\Delta}{L} = \dfrac{7.8}{7600} = \dfrac{1}{974}$ O.K.

Summary:

Vertical reinforcing:
    15M @ 400 EF
Horizontal reinforcing: } 6.4 kg/m²
    10M @ 350 Alt Face (AF)

For reinforcing in the center of the panel section:

$A_s = 15M$ @ 200 Ctr or 1000 mm²/m Ctr

$h = 140$ mm, $d = 70$ mm

$A_{se} = \dfrac{0.85 \times 1000 \times 400 + 30960}{0.85 \times 400} = 1091$ mm²/m

$a = \dfrac{1091 \times 0.85 \times 400}{0.81 \times 0.6 \times 25 \times 1000} = 30.53$

$c = \dfrac{30.53}{0.91} = 33.55$

$I_{cr} = \dfrac{1000 \times 33.55^3}{3} + \dfrac{200}{22.5} \times 1091 (70 - 33.55)^2$

$= 25.5 \times 10^6$ mm⁴/m

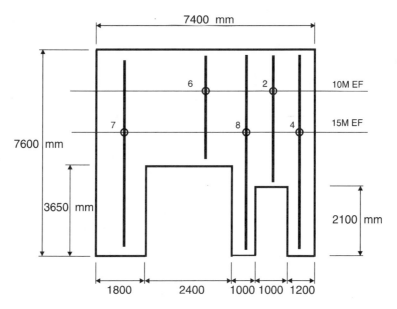

$$h = 140 \text{ mm}$$

(EXAMPLE 13.2)

$K_b = \dfrac{48 \times 22500 \times 25.5 \times 10^6}{5 \times 7600^2 \times 1000} = 95.3 \text{ kN-m/m}$

$\delta_b = 2.00$

$M_f = 9.96 \times 2.00 = 19.9 \text{ kN-m/m}$

$M_r = 0.85 \times 1091 \times 400 \, (70 - 30.53/2)/10^6$
$\quad = 20.3 > 19.9 \text{ kN-m/m}$

Summary:

Vertical reinforcing:
   15M @ 200 Ctr
Horizontal reinforcing: } 6.4 kg/m²
   10M @ 350 Ctr

Example 13.2 — Panel with openings

Panel properties – Refer also to Example 13.1

$L = 7.6 \text{ m}, h = 140 \text{ mm}, d = 100 \text{ mm}$

$A_s = 19 - 15M = 3800 \text{ mm}^2$

Total panel width $= 7400 \text{ mm}$

Effective leg width $= 1800 + 1000 + 1200$
$\qquad\qquad\qquad = 4000 \text{ mm}$

$12h = 12 \times 140 = 1680 \text{ mm}$

∴   Assume each leg carries loads in proportion
    to their tributary areas.

Load Ratio $= \dfrac{7400}{4000} = 1.85$

Effective loads per unit width of supporting legs:

$P_{tf} = 15 \times 1.85 = 27.75 \text{ kN/m}$

$W_f = 1.2 \times 1.85 = 2.22 \text{ kN/m}$

$W_{cf} = 4.2 \times 1.85 = 7.77 \text{ kN/m}$

$P_{wf} = 7.77 \times 7.6/2 = 29.5 \text{ kN/m}$

At mid-height:

$P_f = 27.75 + 29.5 = 57.25 \text{ kN/m}$

$A_s = 19 \times 200 = 3800 \text{ mm}^2$ or $3800/4 = 950 \text{ mm}^2/\text{m}$

$A_{se} = \dfrac{0.85 \times 950 \times 400 + 57250}{0.85 \times 400} = 1118 \text{ mm}^2/\text{m}$

$a = \dfrac{1118 \times 0.85 \times 400}{0.81 \times 25 \times 0.6 \times 1000} = 31.3$

$c = \dfrac{31.3}{0.91} = 34.4$

$I_{cr} = \dfrac{1000 \times 34.4^3}{3} + \dfrac{200}{22.5} \times 1118 \, (100 - 34.4)^2$
$\quad = 56.3 \times 10^6 \text{ mm}^4$

$K_b = \dfrac{48 \times 22500 \times 56.3 \times 10^6}{5 \times 7600^2 \times 1000} = 210.7 \text{ kN-m/m}$

$\delta_b = \dfrac{1}{1 - 57.25/(0.65 \times 210.7)} = 1.72$

Primary Moment:

$M_b = 2.22 \times 7.6^2/8 + 27.75 \times .07/2 + 57.25 \times .025$
$\quad = 16.0 + 1.0 + 1.4 = 18.4 \text{ kN-m/m}$

Total Moment:

$M_f = 18.4 \times 1.72 = 31.6 \text{ kN-m/m}$

Resisting Moment:

$M_r = 0.85 \times 1118 \times 400 \, (100 - 31.3/2)/10^6$
$\quad = 32.1 > 31.6 \text{ kN-m/m}$

∴   19 – 15M EF is adequate

Example 13.3 — Panel Continuous Over Support

Panel properties:

$f'_c = 25 \text{ MPa}, f_y = 400 \text{ MPa}$

$L = 7.0 \text{ m}, h = 140 \text{ mm}, \Delta_0 = 25 \text{ mm}$

Loading:

$P_{tf} = 15 \text{ kN/m}, ecc = 70 \text{ mm}$

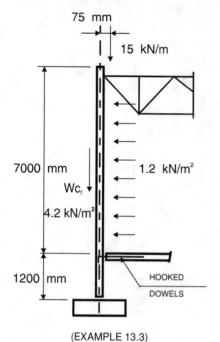

75 mm

15 kN/m

7000 mm

W_{cf}

4.2 kN/m²

1.2 kN/m²

1200 mm

HOOKED
DOWELS

(EXAMPLE 13.3)

W_f = 1.2 kN/m², W_{cf} = 4.2 kN/m²

At mid-height:

P_f = 15 + 4.2 × 7.0 / 2 = 29.7 kN/m

For effective length kL = 1.0 × 7.0 = 7.0 m

A_s = 15M @ 250 mm = 800 mm²/m Ctr

d = 70 mm, b = 1000 mm

A_{se} = 887 mm²/m, K_b = 93.2 kN-m/m

δ_b = 1.96

M_b = 1.2 × 7² / 8 + 15 × .07 / 2 + 29.7 × .025
= 8.6 kN-m/m

M_f = 8.6 × 1.9 = 16.9 kN-m/m

M_r = 17.5 > 16.9 kN-m/m

For effective length kL = 0.9 × 7.0 = 6.3 m

p_{tf} = 28.2 kN/m

A_s = 15M @ 300 mm = 666 mm²/m Ctr

A_{se} = 749 mm²/m, K_b = 102.4 kN-m/m

δ_b = 1.74

M_b = 1.2 × 6.3² / 8 + 15 × 0.07 / 2 + 28.2 × 0.025
= 7.2 kN-m/m

M_f = 7.2 × 1.74 = 12.5 kN-m/m

M_r = 15.1 > 12.5 kN-m/m

Example 13.4 — In-Plane Shear (Seismic) for Multiple Panels

Panel properties:

6 panels @ 6 m each = 36 m

f'_c = 25 MPa, f_y = 400 MPa

L = 7.6 m, b = 6.0 m, h = 140 mm

Panel weight W = 7.6 × 6 × 0.14 × 24 kN/m² = 153 kN

Seismic shear force based on a force modification factor R = 2.0:

V_f = 18 kN/m at the top of the panels

or 18 × 6 × 6 = 648 kN

Roof loads:

D = 1.0 kN/m², L = 2.0/4 = 0.5 kN/m²,
Tributary joist span = 6 m

Overturning Moment:

M_{of} = 648 × 7.6 = 4925 kN-m

Resisting Moment:

Panel M_r = 6 × 153 × 6 / 2 = 2754 kN-m

Roof M_r = (1 + 0.5)6 × 6²/2 × 6 = 972

Connections M_r = 2 × 2 × 106/1.33 × 6 = 1913

Total = 5639 > 4925 kN-m

∴ Provide 2 EM5 panel to panel connection in 2 locations

Base shear:

V_f = 648 kN @ R = 2.0

= 1296 kN @ R = 1.0

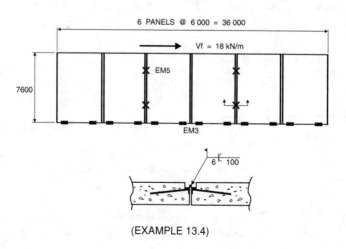

6 PANELS @ 6 000 = 36 000

Vf = 18 kN/m

EM5

7600

EM3

6   100

(EXAMPLE 13.4)

Base Connections 2 EM3 connections per panel @ 85 kN each

$V_r = 2 \times 6 \times 85 = 1020$ kN

Friction $= 6 \times 0.5 \times 153 = 459$

Concrete shear resistance:

Total $= 1479 > 1296$ kN

Concrete shear resistance:

@ R = 1.0

$V_f = 1296$ kN/m

$v_f = \dfrac{1296}{36 \times 140} = 0.257$ MPa

$v_c = 0.6 \times 0.2 \sqrt{25} = 0.6$ MPa

$v_c/2 = 0.3 > .257$ MPa　　　　　　　　　　O.K.

Minimum Reinforcing:

$A_s = .002$ bh $= .002 \times 1000 \times 140 = 280$ mm^2/m

10M @ 350 mm $= 285$ mm^2/m

Example 13.5 — In-Plane Shear for Frame Panel

Seismic shear force (zonal velocity = 0.20, R = 2.0)

$V_f = 12$ kN/m or $12 \times 9.0 = 108$ kN

Panel Properties (see diagram)

Weight $= 24 (9 \times 7.6 - 1.5 \times 7.2 - 3 \times 7.2) \, 0.190$
$= 164$ kN

Overturning Moment

$M_{of} = 108 \times 7.6 = 821$ kN-m

Resisting Moment

Panel $M_r = 164 \times 9/2$ 　　　　　　 $= 738$

Roof $M_r = (1 + 0.5) \, 12/2 \times 9.0^2/2$ 　 $= 364$

　　　　　　　　Total 　　　 1102 kN-m > 821

∴ no panel to panel connections are required

Shear force in each supporting leg:

$V_f = 108 / 2 = 54$ kN

In-plane moment in each leg:

$M_f = 54 \times 3.0 = 162$ kN-m/m

For

h $= 900$ mm, d $= 840$ mm, $A_s = 2$-20M $= 600$ mm^2

$M_r = \dfrac{0.85 \times 600 \times 400}{10^6} \left(840 - \dfrac{0.85 \times 400 \times 600}{2 \times 0.81 \times 25 \times 0.60 \times 190} \right)$

$= 162$ kN-m

$V_f = 54 \times 2 = 108$ kN / leg 　 @ R = 1.0

Concrete shear:

$V_c = 0.6 \times 190 \times 840/1000 = 96$ kN

$V_c/2 = 48$ kN < 108 kN

∴ Provide shear reinforcement – 10M ties

Maximum s $= d/2 = 840/2 = 420$ mm $\rightarrow$ use 400 mm

Minimum $A_v = 0.35 \times 190 \times 400/400 = 66$ mm^2

　　　　or $.0025 \times 190 \times 400 = 190$ mm^2

10M ties, $A_v = 2 \times 100 = 200 > 190$ mm^2

$V_s = 0.85 \times \dfrac{200 \times 400}{400} \times \dfrac{840}{1000} = 143$ kN

$V_r = V_c/2 + V_s = 48 + 143 = 191 > 108$ kN

use 10M ties @190 in plastic hinge region

Connection Design
Roof Connection:

In-plane shear 　 $V_f = 108$ kN for R = 2.0
　　　　　　　　　 $= 144$ kN for R = 1.5
　　　　　　　　　 $= 216$ kN for R = 1.0

5 EM1 connections
　　　　　　$V_r = 5 \times 90$ kN $= 450 > 144$ kN

5 joist seats 　　$V_r = 5 \times 15$ kN $= 75$ kN

1 EM3 plate 　　V_r 　　　　$= \dfrac{85}{160} > 144$ kN

Out-of-plane forces (v = 0.2)

$S_p = 2.5$ 　　　 $T_f = 0.20 \times 2.5 \times 108/2 = 27$ kN

$S_p = 15$ 　　　 $T_f = 0.20 \times 15 \times 108/2 = 162$ kN

5 EM1 connections
　　　　　　$T_r = 5 \times 80 = 400$ kN

Base Connections:

In-plane shear 　 $V_f = 144$ kN for R = 1.5
　　　　　　　　　 $= 216$ kN for R = 1.0

2 EM3 connections
　　　　　　$V_r = 2 \times 85 = 170$ kN

Friction 　　　　 $= 0.5 \times 164 = 82$ kN

Total 　　　　　 $= 252 > 216$ kN

Weld to 2 EM5 connections in the floor slab

　　　　　　$V_r = 2 \times 80 = 160 > 144$ kN

Out-of-plane forces

$S_p = 15$ 　　$T_f = 0.20 \times 15 \times 108/2 = 162$ kN

2 EM3 connections
　　　　　　$T_r = 2 \times 107 = 214 > 162$ kN

REFERENCES

1.　Tilt-up Concrete Structures, Report by ACI Committee 551, June 1992.
2.　Recommended Tilt-up Wall Panel Design, Structural Engineers Association of Southern California, 1979.
3.　Test Report on Slender Walls, Southern California Chapter, American Concrete Institute and Structural Engineers Association of Southern California, 1982.
4.　The Tilt-up Design and Construction Manual, Hugh Brooks, HBA Publications, 1990.
5.　CPCI Metric Design Manual, Precast and Prestressed Concrete, second edition, 1987.
6.　Approximate Methods for Analysis of Tilt-up Concrete Wall Panels, G. Weiler, ACI International, November 1982.
7.　Spencer, R.A., Earthquake Resistant Connections for Low Rise Precast Concrete Buildings, U.S./Japan Seminar on Precast Concrete Construction in Seismic Zones, October 1986, pp 61-81.

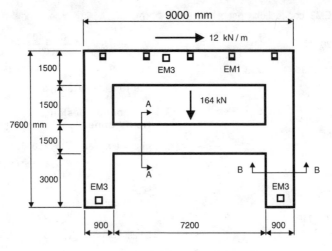

PANEL ELEVATION

9000 mm

12 kN / m

EM3   EM1

164 kN

7600 mm

1500

1500

1500

3000

EM3   EM3

900   7200   900

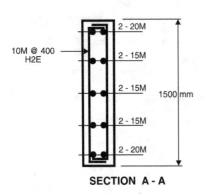

10M @ 400
H2E

2 - 20M

2 - 15M

2 - 15M

2 - 15M

2 - 20M

1500 mm

SECTION A - A

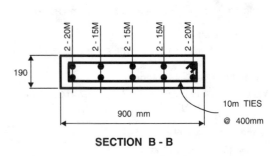

2 - 20M   2 - 15M   2 - 15M   2 - 15M   2 - 20M

190

900 mm

10m TIES
@ 400mm

SECTION B - B

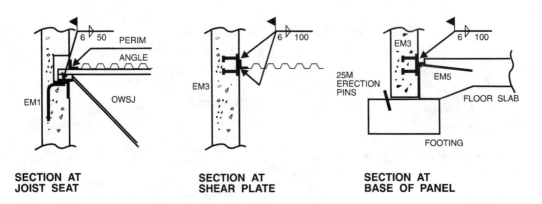

6 50   PERIM
ANGLE

EM1   OWSJ

**SECTION AT
JOIST SEAT**

6 100

EM3

**SECTION AT
SHEAR PLATE**

6 100

EM3

25M
ERECTION
PINS

EM5

FLOOR SLAB

FOOTING

**SECTION AT
BASE OF PANEL**

IN - PLANE SHEAR IN FRAME PANEL

(EXAMPLE 13.5)